Teacher's Edition

CONCEPTS AND CHALLENGES

PHYSICAL ✶ SCIENCE

Fourth Edition

Leonard Bernstein ◆ Martin Schachter ◆ Alan Winkler ◆ Stanley Wolfe

Stanley Wolfe
Project Coordinator

Globe
Fearon

Pearson Learning Group

ISBN: 0-130-23851-1
Printed in the United States of America
3 4 5 6 7 8 9 10 06 05 04 03
1-800-321-3106
www.pearsonlearning.com

Concepts and Challenges, Fourth Edition
Science Textbooks Your Students Will Be Able to Read and Understand

Concepts and Challenges—the complete program proven to make scientific discovery accessible to all learners—now offers you and your students more:

- ✔ Hands-on inquiry
- ✔ Skill-building
- ✔ Teacher support for every lesson

Concepts and Challenges delivers the unique, two-page lesson format that teachers have always relied on to provide the right balance of challenge and accessibility. Now, science teachers have more of what they need:

- ✳ Completely revised Life, Earth, and Physical Science textbooks
- ✳ Full-length labs and hands-on activities in every chapter
- ✳ Special features that build skills and integrate content
- ✳ Point-of-use teacher lesson plans
- ✳ Teaching options for every learning style
- ✳ A separate Laboratory Manual that supports every chapter in the Student Edition
- ✳ Customizable Teacher's Resources on a CD-ROM
- ✳ Laboratory Videos on VHS cassettes
- ✳ A companion Web site that extends and enriches every lesson

CONCEPTS AND CHALLENGES
LIFE SCIENCE
GLOBE FEARON
Pearson Learning Group

CONCEPTS AND CHALLENGES
EARTH SCIENCE
GLOBE FEARON
Pearson Learning Group

CONCEPTS AND CHALLENGES
PHYSICAL SCIENCE

Physical Science **Table of Contents**

The NEW! *Concepts and Challenges* Program

This complete program gives you and your students solutions for success.

Student Edition

The Student Edition provides accessible text that your students will be able to read independently. Every chapter includes investigations, lab activities, integrated science connections, and technology applications. All lessons are presented in the acclaimed two-page format of "concept" and "challenge" that ensures learning and discovery for every student. *See pages vi–xiii.*

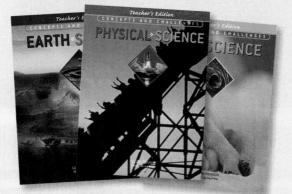

Teacher's Edition

The all-new wraparound Teacher's Edition puts everything you need right at the point of use, including four-step lesson plans, an abundance of teaching options and enhancement activities, and chapter planning pages with information to help you prepare for each chapter. *See pages xiv–xvii.*

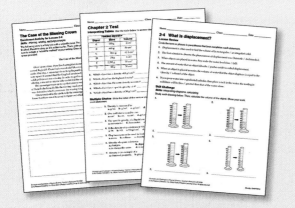

Teacher's Resources CD-ROM

The ultimate teaching resource, the Teacher's Resources CD-ROM supplies a wealth of modifiable lesson review and enrichment worksheets, English and Spanish lesson notes, scoring rubrics, and graphic organizers. It also includes a comprehensive assessment program with chapter tests as well as a diagnostic, a midterm, and a final exam that can be easily customized to meet your needs. *See page xviii.*

Laboratory Videos

New Laboratory Videos, three each for Life Science, Earth Science, and Physical Science, demonstrate selected hands-on activities that appear in the Student Edition and the Lab Manual. You can use the videos as demonstration tools, as previews, or as make-up lessons. *See page xix.*

Laboratory Manual

Revised and redesigned for appeal and ease of use, the new student Laboratory Manual furnishes a full, formal hands-on laboratory program correlated to the text. The Teacher's Laboratory Guide and Answers provides alternate materials, tips for success, safety warnings, and expected outcomes.

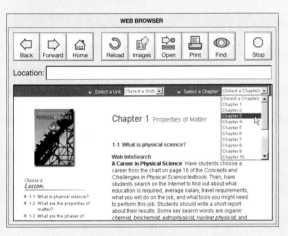

Concepts and Challenges Online

The new edition of our Web site, **www.conceptsandchallenges.com**, brings a highly interactive, free technology to your classroom with activities that extend and enrich every lesson, develop your students' online research skills, and sharpen problem-solving and analysis skills. Use the teacher password to register your class and allow students to post and share their work on The Big Ideas. *See page xix.*

Concepts and Challenges in Science — Program Components

Concepts and Challenges in Life Science

Student Edition	0-130-23857-0
Teacher's Edition	0-130-23858-9
Teacher's Resources CD-ROM	0-130-23859-7
Laboratory Manual	0-130-23850-3
Teacher's Laboratory Guide and Answers	0-130-23861-9
Laboratory Videos	0-130-23972-0

Concepts and Challenges in Earth Science

Student Edition	0-130-23815-5
Teacher's Edition	0-130-23844-9
Teacher's Resources CD-ROM	0-130-23845-7
Laboratory Manual	0-130-23847-3
Teacher's Laboratory Guide and Answers	0-130-23848-1
Laboratory Videos	0-130-23973-9

Concepts and Challenges in Physical Science

Student Edition	0-130-23840-6
Teacher's Edition	0-130-23851-1
Teacher's Resources CD-ROM	0-130-23853-8
Laboratory Manual	0-130-23855-4
Teacher's Laboratory Guide and Answers	0-130-23856-2
Laboratory Videos	0-130-23974-7

FOR MORE INFORMATION:
Call 800-321-3106
Fax 800-393-3156

Two-Page Lessons: A Proven Success

Consistent two-page lesson format provides the right pacing and the right balance of content for the right level of accessibility. This teacher-tested format is a proven success with students.

Investigate Activities help you jump start selected lessons, heighten student interest, and develop inquiry skills.

16-5 What is conduction?

INVESTIGATE

Observing Heat Transfer
HANDS-ON ACTIVITY

1. Half-fill a jar with hot water. Place a wooden spoon, a metal spoon, and a plastic spoon into the jar. Do not allow the spoons to touch each other.
2. After a full minute, touch the handle of each spoon.

THINK ABOUT IT: Did the handles of all three spoons feel the same? If not, how can you explain the difference?

STEP 1

Objectives aid students in goal setting and furnish an important reference point throughout the lesson.

Key Terms identify and define vocabulary words students need to know before beginning the lesson.

Objective

Describe how heat is transferred through solids.

Key Terms

conduction (kuhn-DUK-shuhn)**:** process of heat transfer in solids

conductor: material that conducts heat easily

insulator: material that does not conduct heat easily

Short Reading Passages give students frequent places to pause and check for understanding.

Heat Transfer in Solids A blacksmith hammers a piece of iron to make horseshoes. When a blacksmith places a piece of iron into a flame, the iron gets very hot. The heat energy causes the particles in the iron to bump into each other. After a while, the iron gets hot enough so that it becomes soft. The piece of iron can then be hammered into shape.

Photographs and descriptive captions reinforce student comprehension.

▲ **Figure 16-16** As the iron gets hot, the particles within it bump into each other.

340

Heat is transferred through solids by **conduction.** You learned that heat moves from an object with a higher temperature to an object with a lower temperature. When fast-moving particles in a sample of matter bump into slow-moving particles, heat energy passes from the fast-moving particles to the slow-moving particles. As a piece of iron is heated, heat energy is transferred from the fast-moving particles to the slow-moving particles. The slow-moving particles gain energy and bump into other particles. In this way, heat energy is transferred throughout the sample of matter.

▶ DEFINE: What is conduction?

Conductors of Heat All metals are good conductors of heat. A **conductor** is a material that allows heat to move through it easily. Copper, gold, silver, iron, aluminum, and steel are all good conductors of heat. Copper and silver are two of the best conductors of heat. Heat will travel faster through items made of copper and silver than it will through items made of iron or steel.

▶ IDENTIFY: What substances are good conductors of heat?

Poor Conductors of Heat Many materials are poor conductors of heat. Materials that do not conduct heat easily are called **insulators.** Wood, paper, wax, and air are poor conductors of heat. These materials are insulators.

Insulators prevent heat from moving from place to place. Houses are insulated to keep them warm in winter and cool in summer. To insulate houses, spaces are left between the inside and

Comprehension Questions provide a basis for outlining lessons and make class discussions easy.

outside walls of the house. The spaces are filled with an insulating material. During winter, this insulation helps keep heat from escaping to the outside. During the summer, insulation helps keep heat from getting into the house.

▲ **Figure 16-17** Pots made of copper are good conductors of heat. Handles made of plastic are good insulators.

▶ EXPLAIN: Why are insulators used in houses?

 Real-Life Science

HOME INSULATION

In many parts of the United States, winters are cold and summers are hot. In these parts of the country, houses must be insulated. Home insulation keeps houses warm in winter and cool in summer. Home insulation can help reduce the amount of fuel needed to heat or cool a home. Good insulation can cut fuel use by as much as 50%.

Insulation is needed in those parts of a house where the most heat is usually lost. In most homes, heat loss occurs through the attic floor, the ceiling of an unheated basement, and the side walls. Different types of insulation can be used in these places. For example, blankets of fiberglass can be inserted between beams in floors and ceilings. Liquid plastic foam can be sprayed into the spaces between the inside and outside walls.

▲ **Figure 16-18** Home insulation keeps houses warm in winter and cool in summer.

A number called an R-value is used to grade insulating materials. An insulating material with a high R-value is best at preventing heat loss. Choosing insulation with the highest R-value can greatly reduce fuel costs.

Thinking Critically How does insulation keep a house cool in summer?

CHAPTER 16: Heat **341**

Sample pages from *Concepts and Challenges in Physical Science*, pages 340–341

Checking Concepts questions supply a quick and easy way to review and assess learning at the end of the lesson.

Critical Thinking questions challenge students to use higher order thinking skills.

Challenge Features such as Building Science Skills give students the chance to hone essential skills, such as researching and making models. Other Challenges are Health and Safety Tips, Interpreting Visuals, Web InfoSearch, Building Math Skills, and Designing an Experiment.

Lesson Features such as Real-Life Science provide students with interesting articles and activities that make the lesson content more meaningful. Here, for example, connections are made between concepts covered in the lesson to real-life events and situations. Other features are How Do They Know That?, Science and Technology, People in Science, and Integrating the Sciences.

Standards-Based Activities

Promote Scientific Inquiry

To help you engage students in scientific inquiry, experiments and hands-on activities are built into each chapter. These exercises have been carefully designed to meet the National Science Education Standards for scientific inquiry and discovery. A lesson may have any of the following features:

- **Investigate** heightens student interest and develops inquiry skills.

- **Hands-On Activity** gives students hands-on practice in making observations, interpreting information, thinking critically and logically, and communicating their findings. Students also use basic lab equipment, such as a graduated cylinder or a microscope, to gather, analyze, and interpret data.

- **Designing an Experiment** asks students to plan a method for solving a problem. In the process, they gain valuable experience in clarifying questions, collecting evidence, interpreting data, and generating and critiquing explanations. Use the rubric on the Teacher's Resources CD-ROM to assess it.

- **Web InfoSearch** activities help students sharpen their research and technology skills via the Internet. Web activities relate directly to the lesson content. Use this with *Concepts and Challenges Online*.

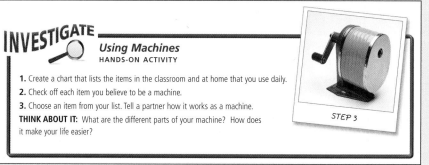

INVESTIGATE
Using Machines
HANDS-ON ACTIVITY

1. Create a chart that lists the items in the classroom and at home that you use daily.
2. Check off each item you believe to be a machine.
3. Choose an item from your list. Tell a partner how it works as a machine.
THINK ABOUT IT: What are the different parts of your machine? How does it make your life easier?

STEP 3

Clipped from page 192

DESIGNING AN EXPERIMENT

Design an experiment to solve the following problem. Include a hypothesis, variables, a procedure, and a data table to be completed.

PROBLEM: Which is more effective in reducing friction between a block of steel and a smooth, flat surface, rollers or a lubricant?

Clipped from page 257

Hands-On Activity
OBSERVING BOILING POINT ELEVATION

You will need three beakers, a thermometer, a heat source, a spoon, distilled water, and salt.

1. Put 100 mL of water in each beaker.
2. Add 5 g of salt to the first beaker and stir.
3. Heat the water in the beaker until it begins to boil. Record the temperature.
4. Add 10 g of salt to the second beaker and stir. Repeat Step 3.
5. Add 20 g of salt to the third beaker and stir. Repeat Step 3.

▲ STEP 3 Heat the water until it begins to boil.

Practicing Your Skills

6. OBSERVE: What was the boiling point of the first solution?
7. OBSERVE: What was the boiling point of the second solution?
8. OBSERVE: What was the boiling point of the third solution?
9. ANALYZE: What is the relationship between the amount of a solute and the boiling point of a solution?

Clipped from page 117

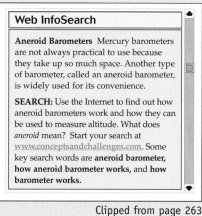

Web InfoSearch

Aneroid Barometers Mercury barometers are not always practical to use because they take up so much space. Another type of barometer, called an aneroid barometer, is widely used for its convenience.

SEARCH: Use the Internet to find out how aneroid barometers work and how they can be used to measure altitude. What does *aneroid* mean? Start your search at www.conceptsandchallenges.com. Some key search words are **aneroid barometer**, **how aneroid barometer works**, and **how barometer works**.

Clipped from page 263

Make Connections to All the Sciences and Other Subjects

To help you make connections to topics in life and earth science, as well as technology, mathematics, social studies, and health, look for the following features in every chapter:

- **Science and Technology** integrates technological applications into the lessons.
- **Building Math Skills** challenges students to use computation and the application of formulas in the context of a lesson.
- **Health and Safety Tips** promotes student awareness of the connections between science and personal health.

- **Building Social Studies Skills** leads students to discover connections between history and science through exercises that reveal the origin of scientific concepts.
- **Integrating the Sciences** uses a high-interest topic as a springboard for connecting different branches of science.

Science and Technology
ELECTRIC POWER PLANTS

Electric power plants provide electricity for large numbers of people. Electric power plants use generators to produce electricity. Instead of a simple loop of wire spinning in the magnetic field of a magnet, these generators use many coils of wire and strong electromagnets. The spinning wires are connected to a turbine. The energy to spin the turbine comes from steam or moving water.

▲ Figure 21-31 Moving water spins turbines in this hydroelectric power plant.

Some generators use the energy from waterfalls to spin the turbine. These generators are known as hydroelectric (hy-droh-ee-LEHK-trihk) plants. Hydroelectric plants are usually built near dams and reservoirs. Hydroelectric plants provide only a limited amount of power in the United States. The high cost to build them and the damage to the environment that they cause are some reasons why hydroelectric power plants are not a major source of electricity.

Thinking Critically Why are hydroelectric power plants usually built near dams and reservoirs?

Clipped from page 473

HEALTH AND SAFETY TIP

Many elements are dangerous to handle. The elements mercury and chlorine are poisonous. Sodium and potassium are explosive when exposed to water. Review the rules for chemical safety in the Handbook on page 14. Make a poster illustrating some chemical safety rules.

Clipped from page 53

BUILDING SOCIAL STUDIES SKILLS

Analyzing A few of the elements in the periodic table are named after countries, states, and planets. Use library resources, encyclopedias, or the Internet to find three of these elements. List their names and the name of the country, state, or planet for which they are named.

Clipped from page 65

BUILDING MATH SKILLS

Calculating Density Use Figure 2-8 to answer the following questions.

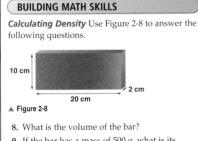

▲ Figure 2-8

8. What is the volume of the bar?
9. If the bar has a mass of 500 g, what is its density? Show your work.
10. How would the density of the bar be different if its mass was 4,520 g? What would the bar be made of?

Clipped from page 37

Integrating Life Science
TOPICS: nervous system, adaptation, predator, prey

ANIMALS THAT USE ELECTRICITY
Electric currents, or impulses, are also found in living things. The nervous system of most organisms uses electric charges. Some organisms, however, have more specialized uses of electricity.

An electric eel can stun or kill its prey with a strong electric charge. The electric eel has special musclelike cells that generate electricity. Eels also use their electric ability for self-defense against predators.

The duck-billed platypus uses electricity to find its food, even in total darkness. Duck-billed platypuses live in streams in Australia. With a special sense that detects electricity, they can find tasty crayfish and other prey, even at night in muddy water. The platypus has a special organ on the end of its soft bill that picks up faint electric signals coming from the muscles of animals swimming nearby.

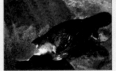
▲ Figure 20-13 An electric eel (top) and a platypus (bottom) both use electricity to survive.

Animals that produce and use electricity are usually found in water habitats. They are not found on land because water can conduct electricity, whereas air is a good insulator.

Thinking Critically Do you think that an electric eel can produce electricity out of water as well as it does in water? Explain your answer.

Clipped from page 437

The Big Idea Integrates Science! NEW!

Connect the science disciplines with this engaging two-page feature in each chapter. Set in a real-world context, The Big Idea helps your students synthesize what they're learning into one big idea.

Topic of integration is clearly identified at the top of the page.

High-interest graphic instantly captures students' attention with colorful illustrations and photos.

Short, easy-to-read article summarizes the science connection.

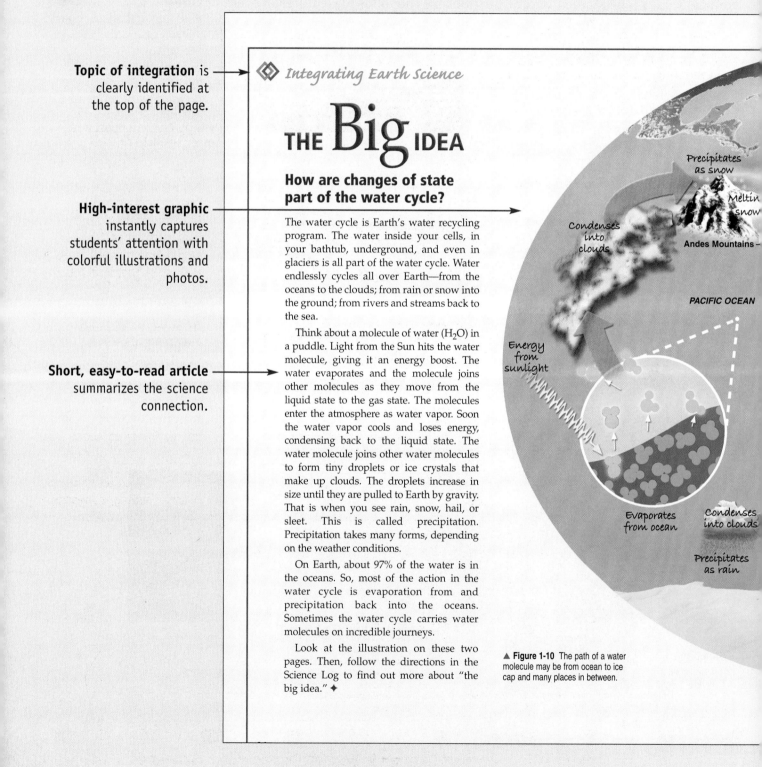

Integrating Earth Science

THE Big IDEA

How are changes of state part of the water cycle?

The water cycle is Earth's water recycling program. The water inside your cells, in your bathtub, underground, and even in glaciers is all part of the water cycle. Water endlessly cycles all over Earth—from the oceans to the clouds; from rain or snow into the ground; from rivers and streams back to the sea.

Think about a molecule of water (H_2O) in a puddle. Light from the Sun hits the water molecule, giving it an energy boost. The water evaporates and the molecule joins other molecules as they move from the liquid state to the gas state. The molecules enter the atmosphere as water vapor. Soon the water vapor cools and loses energy, condensing back to the liquid state. The water molecule joins other water molecules to form tiny droplets or ice crystals that make up clouds. The droplets increase in size until they are pulled to Earth by gravity. That is when you see rain, snow, hail, or sleet. This is called precipitation. Precipitation takes many forms, depending on the weather conditions.

On Earth, about 97% of the water is in the oceans. So, most of the action in the water cycle is evaporation from and precipitation back into the oceans. Sometimes the water cycle carries water molecules on incredible journeys.

Look at the illustration on these two pages. Then, follow the directions in the Science Log to find out more about "the big idea." ✦

Precipitates as snow

Melting snow

Condenses into clouds

Andes Mountains –

PACIFIC OCEAN

Energy from sunlight

Evaporates from ocean

Condenses into clouds

Precipitates as rain

▲ **Figure 1-10** The path of a water molecule may be from ocean to ice cap and many places in between.

The Big Idea Online helps you guide students through researching on the Internet and sharing their data online.

THE BIG IDEA ONLINE

How are changes of state part of the water cycle? Have students research their Science Log Writing Activity at www.conceptsandchallenges.com. You can have students organize their log by completing the Big Idea activity online. Students may post their work in the Online Classroom Database for others to read.

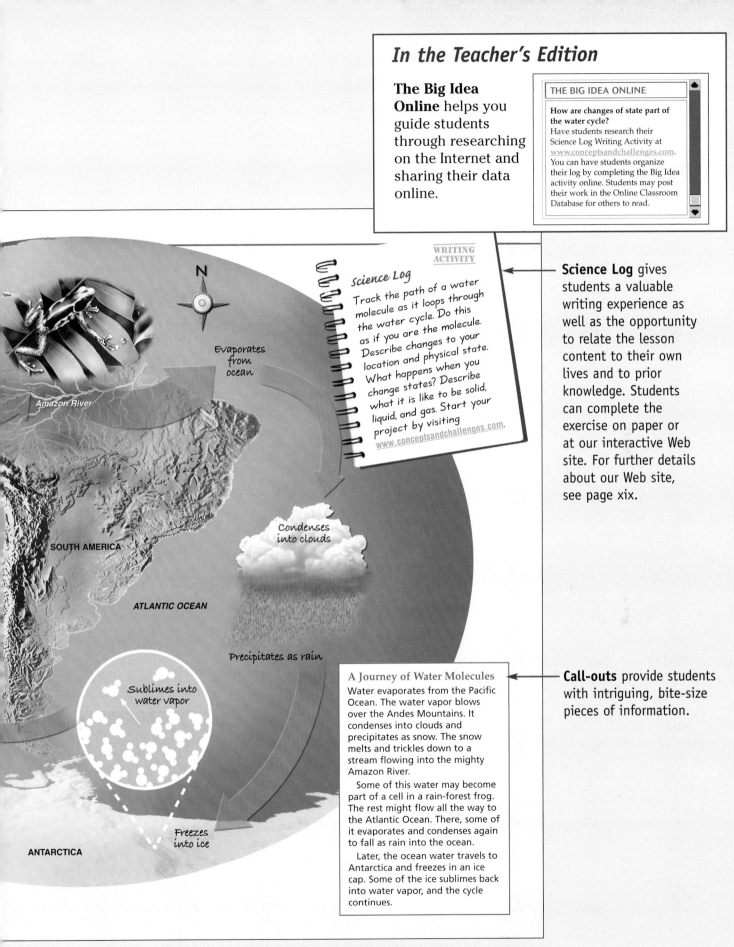

WRITING ACTIVITY

Science Log

Track the path of a water molecule as it loops through the water cycle. Do this as if you are the molecule. Describe changes to your location and physical state. What happens when you change states? Describe what it is like to be solid, liquid, and gas. Start your project by visiting www.conceptsandchallenges.com.

Evaporates from ocean

Amazon River

SOUTH AMERICA

Condenses into clouds

ATLANTIC OCEAN

Precipitates as rain

Sublimes into water vapor

Freezes into ice

ANTARCTICA

Science Log gives students a valuable writing experience as well as the opportunity to relate the lesson content to their own lives and to prior knowledge. Students can complete the exercise on paper or at our interactive Web site. For further details about our Web site, see page xix.

A Journey of Water Molecules

Water evaporates from the Pacific Ocean. The water vapor blows over the Andes Mountains. It condenses into clouds and precipitates as snow. The snow melts and trickles down to a stream flowing into the mighty Amazon River.

Some of this water may become part of a cell in a rain-forest frog. The rest might flow all the way to the Atlantic Ocean. There, some of it evaporates and condenses again to fall as rain into the ocean.

Later, the ocean water travels to Antarctica and freezes in an ice cap. Some of the ice sublimes back into water vapor, and the cycle continues.

Call-outs provide students with intriguing, bite-size pieces of information.

Sample pages from *Concepts and Challenges in Physical Science*, pages 24–25

NEW!

Hands-On Approach in Every Chapter

A stand-alone Lab Activity is built into each chapter of the Student Edition. Directly correlated to chapter content, each easy-to-follow lab helps students apply a systematic approach to the scientific method. See the Teacher's Edition for point-of-use support.

Background reviews relevant chapter concepts to ensure understanding and to set the stage for the activity.

Materials provides an accessible list of what is needed to complete the lab.

Purpose clearly identifies the objective and provides an important reference point for students.

Procedure walks students step by step through the experiment with clear, easy-to-follow instructions.

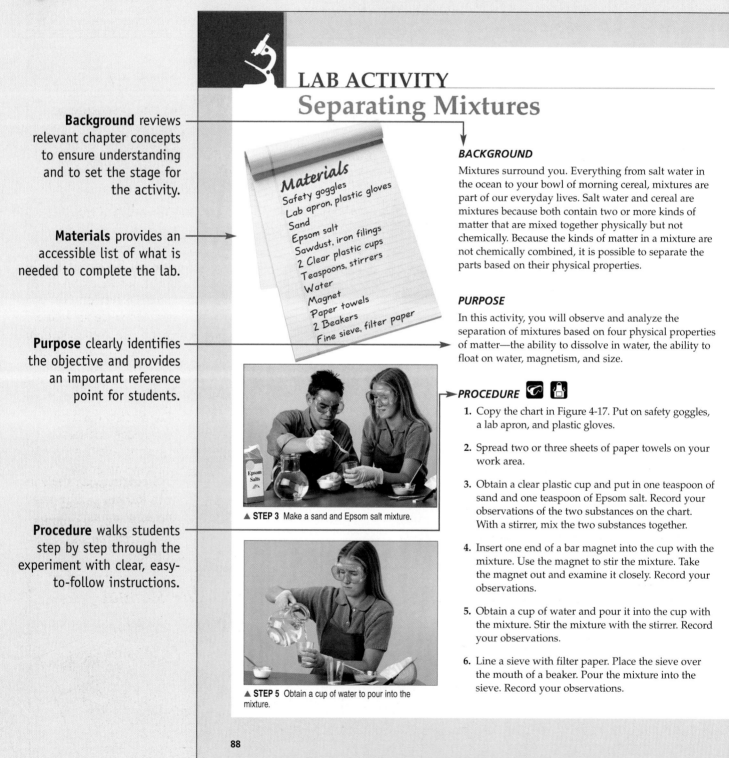

LAB ACTIVITY
Separating Mixtures

Materials
Safety goggles
Lab apron, plastic gloves
Sand
Epsom salt
Sawdust, iron filings
2 Clear plastic cups
Teaspoons, stirrers
Water
Magnet
Paper towels
2 Beakers
Fine sieve, filter paper

▲ STEP 3 Make a sand and Epsom salt mixture.

▲ STEP 5 Obtain a cup of water to pour into the mixture.

88

BACKGROUND

Mixtures surround you. Everything from salt water in the ocean to your bowl of morning cereal, mixtures are part of our everyday lives. Salt water and cereal are mixtures because both contain two or more kinds of matter that are mixed together physically but not chemically. Because the kinds of matter in a mixture are not chemically combined, it is possible to separate the parts based on their physical properties.

PURPOSE

In this activity, you will observe and analyze the separation of mixtures based on four physical properties of matter—the ability to dissolve in water, the ability to float on water, magnetism, and size.

PROCEDURE

1. Copy the chart in Figure 4-17. Put on safety goggles, a lab apron, and plastic gloves.

2. Spread two or three sheets of paper towels on your work area.

3. Obtain a clear plastic cup and put in one teaspoon of sand and one teaspoon of Epsom salt. Record your observations of the two substances on the chart. With a stirrer, mix the two substances together.

4. Insert one end of a bar magnet into the cup with the mixture. Use the magnet to stir the mixture. Take the magnet out and examine it closely. Record your observations.

5. Obtain a cup of water and pour it into the cup with the mixture. Stir the mixture with the stirrer. Record your observations.

6. Line a sieve with filter paper. Place the sieve over the mouth of a beaker. Pour the mixture into the sieve. Record your observations.

Sample pages from *Concepts and Challenges in Physical Science*, pages 88–89

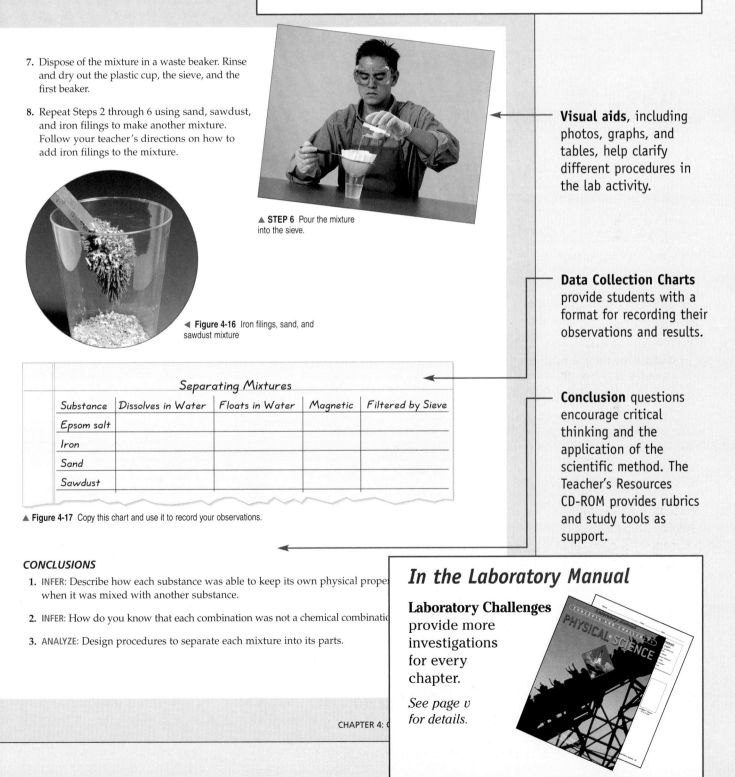

In the Teacher's Edition

Prepare the Lab provides you with everything you need to know to plan your lab.
Set-Up Time indicates the approximate time you should allot for setting up the lab.
Lab Time indicates the approximate time it will take students to complete the lab.

1 *Prepare the Lab*

Separating Mixtures

SET-UP TIME: ⏱   LAB TIME: ⏱

7. Dispose of the mixture in a waste beaker. Rinse and dry out the plastic cup, the sieve, and the first beaker.

8. Repeat Steps 2 through 6 using sand, sawdust, and iron filings to make another mixture. Follow your teacher's directions on how to add iron filings to the mixture.

▲ **STEP 6** Pour the mixture into the sieve.

Visual aids, including photos, graphs, and tables, help clarify different procedures in the lab activity.

◀ **Figure 4-16** Iron filings, sand, and sawdust mixture

Data Collection Charts provide students with a format for recording their observations and results.

Separating Mixtures

Substance	Dissolves in Water	Floats in Water	Magnetic	Filtered by Sieve
Epsom salt				
Iron				
Sand				
Sawdust				

▲ **Figure 4-17** Copy this chart and use it to record your observations.

Conclusion questions encourage critical thinking and the application of the scientific method. The Teacher's Resources CD-ROM provides rubrics and study tools as support.

CONCLUSIONS

1. INFER: Describe how each substance was able to keep its own physical prope[r]
   when it was mixed with another substance.

2. INFER: How do you know that each combination was not a chemical combinatio[n]

3. ANALYZE: Design procedures to separate each mixture into its parts.

In the Laboratory Manual

Laboratory Challenges provide more investigations for every chapter.

See page v for details.

PHYSICAL SCIENCE

Planning Made Easy NEW!

Concepts and Challenges new wraparound lesson plans enable you to customize lessons for diverse learning styles. A consistent four-step lesson plan puts the activities and answers right where you need them!

Step 1 Introduce furnishes tools for setting up the lesson and linking your students' prior knowledge to the lesson content.

Step 2 Teach delivers support for presenting the lesson, including discussion guidelines, ways to accommodate different learning styles, answers to questions on the student pages, and ideas for demonstrations that reinforce the concepts.

Demonstration helps you show students the concepts in a visual and tactile way.

Fast Facts provides in-depth background to support and extend the lesson.

Reading Strategy builds in techniques to help students become more proficient readers.

5-6 (pp. 114–115)

1 Introduce

STUDY HINT Before beginning this lesson, have students study Figure 5-16. Then, have them draw cause-and-effect diagrams for each of the compounds listed. Students can use the Cause-and-Effect Diagram on the Teacher's Resources CD-ROM.

Linking Prior Knowledge Have students review and describe the different states of matter (Lesson 1-3).

2 Teach

Demonstration Before class begins, put 200 mL of distilled water in a beaker. In a second beaker, add 30 g of salt to 200 mL of distilled water and stir until the salt dissolves. Place a thermometer in each beaker and put the beakers in a freezer. Monitor the liquids during class. When the water begins to freeze, remove the beaker and show students that freezing began at 0°C (32°F). Repeat with the salt solution, showing that freezing began at about −5°C (23°F). Tell students that the salt has lowered the freezing point of water, and that this is an example of freezing point depression.
learning styles: visual, auditory

Discussion Provide motivation for this lesson by displaying a bag of rock salt in front of the class. Ask students when rock salt is used. (when snowy, icy conditions exist on sidewalks, driveways, and roads) Then, ask how students think rock salt affects ice. Many students may think that the rock salt causes the ice to melt. Instead, the salt dissolves in the thin film of water that forms when the ice begins to melt. Point out that as the salt dissolves in the thin film of water, the freezing point of water is lowered. Thus, the water is less likely to refreeze. Identify rock salt as one application of freezing point depression.
learning styles: auditory, visual

READING STRATEGY As students read through each section in the lesson, ask them to make a sketch that could be used to explain the information in the section. Tell them to use labels if necessary.

T114 UNIT 2: Types of Matter

5-6 How do solutes affect freezing point?

Objective
Describe how the presence of a solute affects the freezing point of a liquid solvent.

Key Terms
freezing point: temperature at which a liquid changes to a solid

freezing point depression: decrease in the freezing point of a liquid solvent because of the addition of a solute

Freezing Point of Water The temperature at which a liquid changes to a solid is called its **freezing point.** The freezing point of pure water is 0°C. When pure liquid water reaches this temperature, it begins changing to solid ice. When water freezes, its molecules become arranged in a crystal pattern called a lattice.

Salt water does not freeze at 0°C. The particles of salt dissolved in the water interfere with the change from a liquid to a solid. Because salt water contains dissolved salt and other minerals, its freezing point is lower than that of pure water.

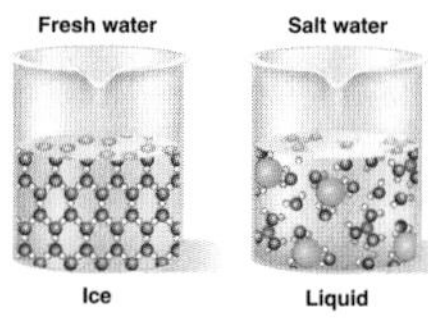

Fresh water   **Salt water**

Ice   **Liquid**

▲ **Figure 5-16** Sodium and chloride ions in salt water lower the freezing point of the water. Crystals cannot form unless the temperature is below 0°C.

DESCRIBE: What happens to liquid water at its freezing point?

Freezing Point Depression The amount of solute dissolved in a solvent affects the freezing point of the solvent. This special property of

114

solutions is called **freezing point depression.** Adding solute lowers the freezing point of the solvent. The greater the amount of dissolved solute, the lower the freezing point of the solvent.

PREDICT: What will happen to the freezing point of water as you add solute to the water?

Melting Danger Away Have you ever sprinkled rock salt or calcium chloride pellets on an icy sidewalk? Ice melters like these lower the freezing point of water. When the ice begins to melt, the chemical compounds dissolve in the water, forming solutions that freeze at a lower temperature than pure water.

Unfortunately, the use of salts for deicing can be hazardous to us and harmful to the environment. The salt residue that remains after the ice has melted can weaken pavement, forming potholes. In addition, chemicals wash off of paved surfaces into storm drains, increasing the salinity, or salt content, of nearby streams and lakes. Look at the differences among ice melters in the table in Figure 5-16.

ICE MELTERS		
Compound	Practical Melting Temperature	Advantages/Disadvantages
Rock salt (NaCl) Sodium chloride	−7° C	Abundant resource; pollutes streams and lakes; corrodes metal
Calcium chloride (CaCl₂)	−20° C	Abundant resource; may cause skin irritation; attacks concrete
Magnesium chloride (MgCl₂)	−15° C	Less toxic to plants and concrete surfaces than rock salts; leaves no powder residue
Calcium magnesium acetate (CMA)	−7° C	Less corrosive to automobiles and roads and less toxic to plants than other salts
Potassium chloride (KCl)	−11° C	Less toxic to plants and surfaces than rock salt; used in fertilizer so overuse may cause plants and grass to burn

▲ **Figure 5-17** The practical melting temperature is the lowest outdoor temperature for which each compound is effective. Below that temperature, the solution will start to freeze.

PREDICT: What effects do you think the use of salts would have on plants and animals in the environment?

Teaching Options

! FAST FACTS   *More on Freezing Point Depression*

Ionic substances are more effective than molecular substances in reducing the freezing point of water. When an ionic substance dissolves in water, it separates into positive and negative ions. For example, sodium chloride (NaCl) separates into positive sodium ions (Na⁺) and negative chloride ions (Cl⁻). The increased number of particles in solution causes more interference with the change from a liquid to a solid, resulting in a larger freezing point depression. A molecular substance such as sugar does not separate into ions when it dissolves, so it produces a smaller freezing point depression. When calcium chloride (CaCl₂) dissolves in water, its ions separate and two negative chloride ions (Cl⁻) enter the solution for every positive calcium ion (Ca²⁺). Therefore, CaCl₂ produces three particles in water solution, and the result is a greater freezing point depression.

Planning Guide

The planning guide in each chapter contains:

✔ A suggested number of days to teach the chapter
✔ Every lesson, Lab Activity, and Big Idea
✔ The National Science Education Standards
✔ Skills and features in each lesson including
  • Building Science Skills
  • Hands-On Activity
✔ Projects and activities, including
  • Chapter Project
  • Cooperative Learning
  • More on the Web

✔ Achieving Science Literacy
  • Reading Strategy
  • Writing Hint
  • Tips for Using Technology
✔ Meeting Individual Needs
  • ESL/ELL Strategy
  • Enrichment Activity
  • Laboratory Video

✔ CHECKING CONCEPTS

1. The _____ of pure water is 0°C.
2. The greater the amount of dissolved solute in a solvent, the _____ the freezing point of the solvent.
3. The freezing point of salt water is _____ than the freezing point of pure water.
4. Lowering the freezing point of a liquid solvent by adding solute is a property called _____.
5. Putting salt on icy roads _____ the freezing point of the melted ice.

THINKING CRITICALLY

6. ANALYZE: Beaker A contains 2 g of sugar dissolved in 100 mL of water. Beaker B contains 10 g of sugar dissolved in 100 mL of water. Which beaker contains the solution with the lower freezing point? Explain your answer.

7. ANALYZE: Beaker C and Beaker D contain 5 g of dissolved copper sulfate. Beaker C contains 100 mL of water while Beaker D contains 250 mL of water. Which beaker contains the solution with the lower freezing point? Explain your answer.

Web InfoSearch

Salt and Ice Cream "I scream, you scream, we all scream for…" Rock salt is not only for deicing sidewalks. It can also be used to reduce the temperature of a container of juice, milk, or cream to make frozen desserts.

SEARCH: Use the Internet to find out about the history of the hand-cranked ice cream freezer. Describe its parts and how it can be used to make ice cream in a short report. Start your search at www.conceptsandchallenges.com. Some key search words are **Nancy Johnson** and **ice cream.**

Integrating Life Science
TOPICS: cold-blooded animals, circulation

FISH WITH ANTIFREEZE

Fish that live in the Arctic Ocean must survive freezing and near-freezing water temperatures. Scientists wondered why these fish did not freeze in such an environment.

By studying fish in the Arctic region of northern Labrador, scientists discovered that the blood of the Arctic fish contained a high concentration of a certain protein. The protein acts like a solute in a solution. The greater the amount of protein in the blood of the fish, the lower the freezing point of the blood.

As a result of this freezing point depression, the fish can survive in the cold Arctic environment. Should the water temperature reach 0°C, the blood of the fish would still be a liquid.

Thinking Critically What helps fish live in such frigid water?

▲ Figure 5-18 These fish can survive in subfreezing conditions.

CHAPTER 5: Solutions **115**

Answers to questions

▶1 DESCRIBE: It changes into a solid.

▶2 PREDICT: It will become lower.

▶3 PREDICT: Possible answer: The salinity of nearby lakes and streams might increase.

3 Assess ◄ — **Step 3 Assess** saves you time by supplying point-of-use answers to every question in the Checking Concepts and Thinking Critically sections.

✔ CHECKING CONCEPT ANSWERS

1. freezing point
2. lower
3. lower
4. freezing point depression
5. lowers

THINKING CRITICALLY ANSWERS

6. ANALYZE: Beaker B; It has more solute. Adding more solute to a solution lowers the freezing point.
7. ANALYZE: Beaker C; There is more solute per volume of solvent in beaker C.

4 Close ◄

Step 4 Close presents activities that challenge students to apply what they have learned in the lesson.

Web InfoSearch

Salt and Ice Cream Have students visit www.conceptsand challenges.com to find out about the history of the hand-cranked ice cream freezer. Have students write a report describing its parts and how it can be used to make ice cream.

Web InfoSearch is a handy reminder that students can find additional information on the day's topic at the program's Web site.

COOPERATIVE LEARNING

Debating the Evidence Have two small groups of volunteers debate whether the benefits of using salts for deicing outweigh the harmful effects. Then, ask students to suggest ways to reduce the harmful effects of deicing salts. **learning styles: linguistic, logical**

• TEACHING RESOURCES •

Teacher's Resources CD-ROM
Lesson Review: Chapter 5, p. 9
Enrichment: Chapter 5, p. 10
Cause-and-Effect Diagram: Study Tools, p. 3

Integrating Life Science
TOPICS: cold-blooded animals, circulation

FISH WITH ANTIFREEZE

Life Science Connection Fish are cold-blooded, which means that their body temperatures change with the temperature of the environment. When the temperature of the water falls below the body temperature of the fish, the fish loses body heat to its surroundings, and it becomes cooler. If the water warms above the body temperature of the fish, heat travels from the water to the fish, and the temperature of the fish rises.

Thinking Critically Answer
The protein in their blood lowers the temperature at which their blood freezes.

CHAPTER 5: Solutions **T115**

Teaching Resources refers you to worksheets and support materials on the CD-ROM that reinforce and enrich the lesson. You'll also find references to relevant lab manual pages and videos.

ONGOING ASSESSMENT

Interpreting a Table Have students rank the compounds in Figure 5-17 in order of decreasing practical melting temperature.

Ongoing Assessment helps you monitor students' comprehension of the topic.

Successful Teaching Strategies

Concepts and Challenges already maximizes comprehension through its extensive visual support, highly focused content, and strong reinforcement of key vocabulary terms. In addition, a wide variety of hands-on activities motivate tactile learners.

Focusing on Reading

The Teacher's Edition provides you with many innovative tools that can be used to successfully teach struggling students.

- **Linking Prior Knowledge** builds on what students know by reminding them of material already covered or their own real-life experiences.

- **Reading Strategy and Writing Hint** help students develop their language arts skills, which can improve their reading and writing in the content area.

- **Demonstration** makes complex concepts come to life for students who have difficulty visualizing these concepts.

- **Reteach** provides innovative ways of presenting lesson concepts so that students do not have to rely on print. Many of these activities also include suggestions for using a variety of graphic organizers, which can be found on the Teacher's Resources CD-ROM.

- **Cooperative Learning** offers activities that encourage students of different abilities and levels of knowledge to share their knowledge and to work together to improve understanding of core content.

Linking Prior Knowledge Write *Metals* and *Nonmetals* on the board. First, ask students to name some metals. Then, ask students to name some nonmetals. List their responses on the board. **learning style: linguistic**

Clipped from page T68

READING STRATEGY Remind students that paraphrasing can help them self-monitor as they read. After you the first paragraph, demonstrate paraphrasing, or restating the mat your own words. Remind students they are unable to paraphrase, the likely need to reread to be sure tha understand what they have read.

Clipped from page T401

WRITING HINT Encourage students to write complete sentences to compare and contrast mixtures and compounds. Remind them of words and phrases that show contrast, such as *on the other hand, but, in contrast,* and so on.

Clipped from page T87

Demonstration Show students the undisturbed glass from the Investigate activity. Ask them to identify the order in which the sand, clay, and pebbles settled. (pebbles, clay, sand) Guide students to recognize that the size of particles determines the rate at which the particles settle. **learning styles: visual, auditory**

Clipped from page T132

RETEACH

Classifying a Mixture Pour a mixture of milk and water into a clear glass container. Darken the classroom and shine a flashlight on the container. Have students explain why this mixture is classified as a suspension. (The light is scattered as it passes through the liquid.) **learning styles: visual, auditory**

Clipped from page T130

COOPERATIVE LEARNING

Making Models Have pairs of students make models of two atoms, one with an oxidation number of 1+ and one with an oxidation number of 1−. Using their models, students can show how the atoms become stable. Students can also use the Valence Electrons chart found on the Teacher's Resources CD-ROM. **learning styles: visual, tactile**

Clipped from page T151

Focusing on ESL/ELL Students

Concepts and Challenges recognizes the need to customize teaching for English-language learners. ESL/ELL Strategies, which appear in each chapter of the Teacher's Edition, provide insights into English vocabulary and increase comprehension of scientific concepts. Specific techniques that are cited in these strategies ensure that learning is taking place. The techniques may also remove potential language barriers for English-language learners at beginning levels of proficiency. The ESL/ELL Strategies help students by:

> **ESL/ELL STRATEGY**
>
> *Pairing Students* English-language learners may have difficulty following the procedure. Pair an English-language learner with an English proficient student during this lab. The English-proficient student can help the English-language learner in carrying out the procedure.

Clipped from page T42

- **Recommending peer tutoring**, which encourages communication with peers and gives students an opportunity to ask questions and receive answers without the pressures of having to perform in front of the whole class.

- **Suggesting simple projects or activities** that reinforce comprehension of scientific concepts.

- **Using cooperative learning** to encourage English-language learners to interact within a group and thereby gain greater comprehension of the content while improving communication skills.

- **Providing vocabulary and linguistic clues** to help them understand and remember scientific terminology.

- **Having students use study tools and graphic organizers** to visually reinforce the comprehension of concepts. For example, a Venn diagram can be used to visually compare and contrast concepts.

- **Using graphic organizers and other study tools** to provide a focus for activities and assessment. Graphic organizers allow students to present complex processes and show what they know using the language skills they do possess. The Teaching Resources box, in the Teacher's Edition, provides references to a complete collection of study tools and graphic organizers. Look for activities and suggestions using any of the pages listed below.

Venn Diagram

Similarities
Differences   Differences

Clipped from Study Tools on CD-ROM

• TEACHING RESOURCES •

Teacher's Resources CD-ROM

Big Idea Planner	Lab Activity Report
Big Idea Science Log Entry	Making Connections
Cause-and-Effect Diagram	Project Sketch
Concept Map	Spider Map
Database Planner	Spreadsheet
Designing An Experiment	Thumbnail Sketch
Fishbone Map	Venn Diagram
Flowchart	Web Page Planner
Folder	Weekly Journal
KWL chart	Writing Activity Outline

Customize With Technology

NEW!

Teacher's Resources CD-ROM ⊙

Modifiable and printable pages make it easy for you to customize materials to meet the needs of students with varied ability levels.

On your **computer screen**, you can easily navigate to the page you want. Then, click on the PRINT button to print out the page as is, or click the MODIFY button to open the page and customize it to meet your needs.

A variety of **chapter support** pages are provided on the CD-ROM, including: Lesson Reviews, Enrichment Activities, Key Term Reviews, English and Spanish Lesson Notes, and Chapter Tests. In addition, Diagnostic, Midterm, and Final Exams provide cumulative assessment, while a wealth of Teaching Tools, Study Tools, and Visuals help you meet individual needs.

Name _____ Class _____ Date _____

1-5 What are physical and chemical changes?

Lesson Review

Decide whether each item describes a physical change or a chemical change. Write *P* to indicate a physical change or *C* to indicate a chemical change in the spaces provided.

_____ 1. melting wax

_____ 2. tarnishing of silver

_____ 3. rusting of a nail

_____ 4. breaking an egg

_____ 5. burning oil

_____ 6. evaporating water

_____ 7. mixing flour and salt

_____ 8. cutting wood into ten pieces

Skill Challenge

Skills: organizing, classifying

Physical properties can be observed without changing the makeup of a substance. Chemical properties describe how a substance will react during a chemical change. Decide whether each example below describes a physical property or a chemical property. Place an *X* in the correct column.

Example	Physical Property	Chemical Property
1. reacts with acid to release hydrogen gas		
2. has a rectangular shape		
3. yellow color		
4. burns in the presence of oxygen		
5. combines with oxygen to form iron oxide		

Name _____ Class _____ Date _____

Chapter 2 Test

Interpreting Tables Use the table below to answer the following questions.

FINDING DENSITY		
Object	**Mass**	**Volume**
A	100 g	2 cm³
B	600 g	50 cm³
C	82.1 g	82.1 cm³
D	24 g	6 cm³
E	7,255 g	55 cm³
F	90 g	30 cm³

1. Which object has a density of 3 g/cm³? _____

2. Which object has the highest density? _____

3. Which object has the same density as water? _____

4. Which object has a specific gravity of 4? _____

5. Which object has a density of 50 g/cm³? _____

Multiple Choice Write the letter of the term o_____ each statement.

_____ 1. Density is measured in
a. g/m.   b. g/m².   c. g/cm².

_____ 2. One milliliter is equal to one
a. cm³.   b. cm.   c. cm².   d. g/

_____ 3. The specific gravity of a liquid ca_____
a. manometer.   b. barometer.

_____ 4. If the density of a substance is 9.8
a. .98.   b. 9.8.   c. 9.8 g/cm³.   d

_____ 5. Displacement can be used to find
a. mass.   b. volume.   c. density

_____ 6. Density of a pure substance
a. changes.   b. depe_____
c. is always the same.   d. is nev_____

_____ 7. Density is an example of a
a. chemical property.   b. physic_____

Concepts and Challenges in Physical Science, Teacher's Resources CD-RO_____
(c) by Pearson Education, Inc./Globe Fearon/Pearson Learning Group. All rig_____

Name _____ Class _____ Date _____

2-4 What is displacement?

Lesson Review

Circle the term or phrase in parentheses that best completes each statement.

1. Displacement is often used to find the volume of (a rectangular / an irregular) solid.

2. The first scientist to observe the phenomenon of displacement was (Aristotle / Archimedes).

3. When objects are placed in water, they make the water level (rise / fall).

4. The amount of water that an object (absorbs / pushes aside) is called displacement.

5. When an object is placed in water, the volume of water that the object displaces is equal to the (density / volume) of the object.

6. If you pour water into a graduated cylinder, then place a rock in the water, the reading in milliliters will be (less / greater) than that of the water alone.

Skill Challenge

Skills: interpreting diagrams, calculating

Study each drawing below. Then, calculate the volume of the object. Show your work.

1.   2.

1. _____   2. _____

3.   4.

3. _____   4. _____

Concepts and Challenges in Physical Science, Teacher's Resources CD-ROM
(c) by Pearson Education, Inc./Globe Fearon/Pearson Learning Group. All rights reserved.   **Density: CHAPTER 2**

Sample pages from *Concepts and Challenges in Physical Science, Teacher's Resources CD-ROM*

Unique Web Support

Concepts and Challenges Online integrates relevant Internet activities to extend and enrich every lesson through our new companion Web site at **www.conceptsandchallenges.com**.

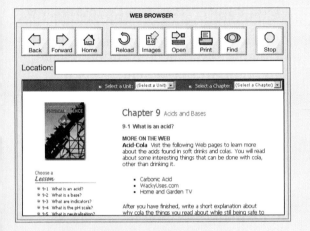

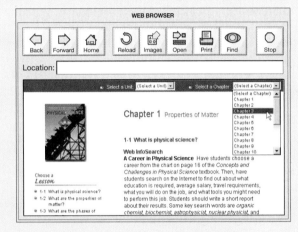

Student's Version provides directions for activities and Web links that will give students experience in using the Internet to research information, analyze science data, and form conclusions about science problems and issues.

Teacher's Version supplies lesson plans, links to other Web sites, assessment plans, and further information and guidance for assisting your students in their online explorations. Register your class so students can post and share their work.
The Teacher Password is **0130239194**.

Versatile Videotapes

Selected hands-on activities on video can be used for lab preparations, demonstrations, or substitutions.

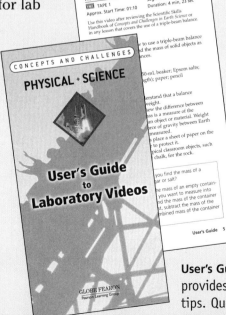

Each laboratory video provides comprehensive step-by-step procedures carried out by real students.

User's Guide to Laboratory Videos provides support and teacher tips. Question/Answer screens encourage drawing conclusions.

Physical Science
Content Standards B Grades 5–8

1. PROPERTIES AND CHANGES OF PROPERTIES IN MATTER

Standard	Chapter Correlation			
a. A substance has characteristic properties, such as density, a boiling point, and solubility, all of which are independent of the amount of the sample. A mixture of substances often can be separated into the original substances using one or more of the characteristic properties. Code: B1a	**Chapter 1** 1-2, 1-5 **Chapter 2** 2-1, 2-2, 2-3, Lab, BI **Chapter 3** 3-1, 3-8, 3-9 **Chapter 4** 4-1, 4-3, 4-4, Lab **Chapter 5** 5-1, 5-2, 5-3, 5-4, 5-5, 5-6, 5-7, 5-8, 5-9, Lab		**Chapter 6** 6-1, 6-2 **Chapter 9** 9-1, 9-2, 9-4, 9-6 **Chapter 10** 10-2 **Chapter 16** 16-3, 16-4, 16-6, 16-8, 16-9, Lab **Chapter 21** 21-1, 21-3	
b. Substances react chemically in characteristic ways with other substances to form new substances (compounds) with different characteristic properties. In chemical reactions, the total mass is conserved. Substances often are placed in categories or groups if they react in similar ways; metals is an example of such a group. Code: B1b	**Chapter 1** 1-5 **Chapter 3** 3-7, 3-8, 3-9, BI **Chapter 4** 4-2, 4-4, 4-5, 4-6 **Chapter 7** 7-1, 7-2, 7-3, 7-4, 7-5, 7-6, Lab, BI **Chapter 8** 8-1, 8-2, 8-4, 8-5, 8-6, 8-7, Lab, BI		**Chapter 9** 9-1, 9-2, 9-3, 9-5, 9-6 **Chapter 10** 10-1, 10-3, 10-4, 10-5, Lab, BI **Chapter 11** 11-1, 11-2, 11-3 **Chapter 20** 20-2, 20-3	
c. Chemical elements do not break down during normal laboratory reactions involving such treatments as heating, exposure to electric current, or reaction with acids. There are more than 100 known elements that combine in a multitude of ways to produce compounds, which account for the living and nonliving substances that we encounter. Code: B1c	**Chapter 1** 1-4 **Chapter 3** 3-1, 3-2, 3-7 **Chapter 4** 4-1, 4-2, 4-7, 4-8, BI **Chapter 7** 7-1, 7-2, 7-3, 7-4, 7-5, 7-6, Lab, BI		**Chapter 8** 8-4, 8-6, 8-7, Lab, BI **Chapter 9** 9-1, 9-2, 9-5, 9-6, Lab, BI **Chapter 10** 10-1, 10-3, BI	

2. MOTION AND FORCES

Standard	Chapter Correlation			
a. The motion of an object can be described by its position, direction of motion, and speed. That motion can be measured and represented on a graph. Code: B2a	**Chapter 12** 12-1, 12-2, 12-6, BI **Chapter 13** 13-1, 13-2, 13-3, 13-4, 13-5, 13-6, Lab, BI **Chapter 14** 14-1		**Chapter 17** 17-1, 17-2, 17-3, 17-4, 17-5, Lab, BI **Chapter 18** 18-1, 18-3 **Chapter 21** 21-8, 21-9, Lab, BI	
b. An object that is not being subjected to a force will continue to move at a constant speed and in a straight line. Code: B2b	**Chapter 12** 12-1, 12-4 ,12-6 **Chapter 13** 13-4			
c. If more than one force acts on an object along a straight line, then the forces will reinforce or cancel one another, depending on their direction and magnitude. Unbalanced forces will cause changes in the speed or direction of an object's motion. Code: B2c	**Chapter 12** 12-1, 12-4, 12-5, 12-6, BI **Chapter 13** 13-2, 13-3, 13-4, 13-5, Lab, BI		**Chapter 15** 15-1, 15-2, 15-3, 15-4, 15-5, Lab, BI **Chapter 20** 20-1	

3. TRANSFER OF ENERGY

Standard	Chapter Correlation	
a. Energy is a property of many substances and is associated with heat, light, electricity, mechanical motion, sound, nuclei, and the nature of a chemical. Energy is transferred in many ways. Code: B3a	**Chapter 1** 1-4, BI **Chapter 3** 3-6 **Chapter 11** 11-3, 11-4 **Chapter 14** 14-1, 14-2, 14-3, 14-4, Lab, BI **Chapter 16** 16-1, 16-2, 16-3, 16-4, 16-5, 16-6, 16-7, Lab **Chapter 17** 17-1, 17-2, 17-3, 17-4, Lab, BI	**Chapter 18** 18-1, 18-2, 18-4, 18-5 **Chapter 19** 19-1, 19-2, 19-3, 19-5, BI **Chapter 20** 20-2, 20-3, 20-4, 20-5, 20-6, 20-7, 20-8, 20-9, Lab, BI **Chapter 21** 21-5, 21-6, 21-7, 21-8, 21-9, Lab, BI
b. Heat moves in predictable ways, flowing from warmer objects to cooler ones, until both reach the same temperature. Code: B3b	**Chapter 16** 16-1, 16-2, 16-3, 16-4, 16-5, 16-6, 16-7, 16-8, Lab	**Chapter 19** BI
c. Light interacts with matter by transmission (including refraction), absorption, or scattering (including reflection). To see an object, light from that object—emitted by or scattered from it—must enter the eye. Code: B3c	**Chapter 6** 6-4, Lab	**Chapter 19** 19-2, 19-3, 19-4, 19-5, 19-6, 19-7, 19-8, 19-9, 19-10, Lab, BI
d. Electrical circuits provide a means of transferring electrical energy when heat, light, sound, and chemical changes are produced. Code: B3d	**Chapter 19** 19-10 **Chapter 20** 20-1, 20-2, 20-3, 20-4, 20-5, 20-6, 20-7, 20-8, 20-9	**Chapter 21** 21-5, 21-6, 21-7, 21-8, 21-9, Lab
e. In most chemical and nuclear reactions, energy is transferred into or out of a system. Heat, light, mechanical motion, or electricity might all be involved in such transfers. Code: B3e	**Chapter 11** 11-4 **Chapter 14** 14-2	**Chapter 19** 19-5 **Chapter 20** 20-2
f. The Sun is a major source of energy for changes on Earth's surface. The Sun loses energy by emitting light. A tiny fraction of that light reaches Earth, transferring energy from the Sun to Earth. The Sun's energy arrives as light with a range of wavelengths, consisting of visible light, infrared, and ultraviolet radiation. Code: B3f	**Chapter 11** 11-4 **Chapter 14** BI **Chapter 16** 16-6, 16-7, BI	**Chapter 19** 19-5, BI **Chapter 21** 21-4

 For a complete correlation to all of the National Standards and correlations to selected states, see the **Teacher's Resources CD-ROM** or visit **www.pearsonlearning.com**.

Physical Science
Materials and Equipment

The following charts provide comprehensive lists of the materials needed to complete all of the Investigates, Hands-On Activities, and Lab Activities in the Student Edition of *Concepts and Challenges Physical Science*. This list assumes that the students are grouped according to the suggestions given in the Teacher's Edition for each activity. For a list of material suppliers, see p. xxvii.

Consumables	Amount*	Investigate	Hands-On Activity	Lab Activity
Aluminum strips	15**		16-8	
Ammonia	1 bottle††	9-2		
Antacid tablets	15** 90**			Ch. 1 Ch. 8
Baking soda	1 large box†		8-1	
Balloons, average size	10† 30	13-6, 20-1	8-1	
Bottles, 2-L plastic, with caps	30		12-7	Ch. 12
Boxes, shoe-box size	60		16-7	
Butter or margarine	1 stick††	9-2		
Cabbage, red	2 heads†		9-3	
Carbon paper	15 sheets**			Ch. 3
Cereal, iron-fortified	1 box**	4-3		
Clay	1 package**	6-2		
Construction paper	1 pad**			Ch. 7
Construction paper, black	60 large sheets		16-7, 17-4	Ch. 6, 19
Construction paper, white	15 sheets**			Ch. 19
Copper sulfate	1 bottle	5-5	8-6	
Corn syrup	300 mL		2-2	
Cups, clear plastic	30**† 15** 45**	5-1 6-2	9-6	Ch. 1, 2, 4, 10
Cups, foam	90**			Ch. 8
Cups, paper	30**	18-2		
Drinking straws, plastic	15 packages**			Ch. 13
Eggs, hard-boiled	30		10-5	
Eggs, raw	15**		6-3	
Epsom salt	1 box			Ch. 4, 5
Filter paper	1 box**			Ch. 4
Food coloring	1 box		2-2	Ch. 16
Gloves, plastic	30 pairs per activity		8-1, 16-8	Ch. 4, 8, 9, 10
Glue or tape	15 packages**			Ch. 7
Glycerine	300 mL		2-2	

* Unless otherwise noted, the amount is for 30 students working individually.
** Amount for 30 students working in pairs
† Amount for 30 students working in groups of three
†† Amount for 30 students working in groups of four (8 groups)

Materials and Equipment *(continued)*

	Amount*	Investigate	Hands-On Activity	Lab Activity
Consumables *(continued)*				
Graph paper	1 pad**			Ch. 7, 11
Graphite (from mechanical pencils)	30 pieces		3-8	
Ice cubes	1 bag		1-5	
Index cards, 4 in. × 6 in.	30†	19-2		
Juice mix, powdered	15 tsp**			Ch. 6
Lemons	30	20-2		
Milk cartons, half-gal size or soda bottles, plastic 2-L size	30		12-9	
Milk, whole	1 pint**			Ch. 6
Modeling clay	1 package		12-9	Ch. 21
Nail polish, clear	3 bottles		10-6	
Nails, galvanized, 12 Penny (D) size	30†			Ch. 10
Nails, ungalvanized, 12 Penny (D) size	60 30† 90		8-6 10-6	Ch. 10
Oak tag, heavy	30 sheets		19-8	
Pepper	1 container**	5-1		
Petroleum jelly	1 large jar		6-5, 10-6	
pH papers	180 strips**			Ch. 9
Plastic bags, small	45**			Ch. 8
Plastic wrap	2 rolls	3-5	16-7	Ch. 10
Rubber cement	1 bottle		19-8	
Rubbing alcohol	150 mL**			Ch. 6
Salt	1 box	5-1	5-7, 16-4	Ch. 5, 10
Samples for acid/base tests (such as milk, fruit juice, shampoo, or liquid soap.)	10 sets† 15 sets**		9-3	Ch. 9
Samples for conductivity tests (such as table salt, sugar, and vinegar.)	30 sets		9-6	
Sand	1 bag**	6-2		Ch. 4
Sandpaper	15 long sheets**		12-4	
Sandpaper, fine	10 sheets†			Ch. 21
Sandwich bags, sealable	1 box**	4-3		
Sawdust	15 tsp**			Ch. 4
Silver nitrate	60 g		8-6	
Soap, liquid	1 large bottle††	9-2		
Soda cans, empty	30	10-3		
Starch	2 packages**		6-1	
String	2 large spools	18-2, 21-2	15-4, 14-5, 15-5	Ch. 13
Sugar, 5-lb size bag	1 bag**	5-9		Ch. 5, 6
Sugar cubes	120 cubes		5-4	
Talcum powder, 22-oz size	1 container		17-4	
Tape, clear cellophane	4 rolls		12-4, 16-7	Ch. 19
Tape, duct, 2 in. × 60 yd. sized roll	1 roll			Ch. 21
Tape, masking, 2 in. × 60 yd. sized roll	2 rolls	21-2		Ch. 14
Teaspoons, plastic	60			Ch. 1, 5
Thread	1 spool**		5-9	
Tissues	1 box**	1-2		
Toothpicks	1 box		4-6	

Materials and Equipment *(continued)*

	Amount*	Investigate	Hands-On Activity	Lab Activity
Consumables *(continued)*				
Tracing paper	15 sheets**			Ch. 20
Vegetable cans, empty	30	10-3		
Vegetable oil	1 L		2-2, 6-1, 6-3	Ch. 6
Vinegar	2 bottles		6-3, 8-1, 10-6	
Vinegar, white	1 L†			Ch. 10
Water, distilled	12 L		5-7, 9-6	
Wax paper	1 roll**			Ch. 1
Wax, paraffin	30 blocks**		16-8	
Non-Consumables				
Balances, pan	30	2-4, 10-3	8-6, 16-4	
Balances, triple-beam	15**			Ch. 1, 2
Ball bearings or glass beads, small	10†			Ch. 14
Bar magnets	60	4-3, 21-2	21-3	Ch. 4
Basins	30		12-9	
Batteries, 1.5-volt	30		3-8, 9-6	
Batteries, 6-volt	30		21-6	
Batteries, D-cell	30	20-5, 20-6, 21-5	21-6	Ch. 21
Beakers, 100 mL glass	90		8-6, 10-6	
Beakers, 250 mL glass	120	5-5	5-4, 5-7, 9-3, 16-4, 16-8	Ch. 4, 5
Bingo chips	600 chips	7-2		
Blocks, wooden	30	15-3	3-8	
Boards, wooden, 2-m long	10†	13-4		
Boards, wooden, 1-m long	15**		15-5	
Bottles or jars, narrow-necked	30		1-5, 8-1	
Bowls, medium mixing	15**	17-5	6-3	
Bowls, small mixing	15**	4-3		
Calculators	15**			Ch. 2, 15
Cardboard, 8.5 in. × 11 in.	15 pieces**		13-1	
Cardboard, small squares	3,000**			Ch. 11
Clocks with second hands	10†			Ch. 17
Coil springs	10†			Ch. 17
Compasses, drawing	15**			Ch. 20
Compasses, magnetic	30	20-2, 21-5	21-3	
Connecting cubes	150 cubes**	8-2		
Containers, deep	10†			Ch. 16
Containers, small, plastic	30		21-3	
Copper strips	60	20-2	8-6, 16-8	
Copper wire	60 25-cm pieces	20-2		
Cords	20†			Ch. 15
Corks	30	17-1	21-3	
Dimes	15**			Ch. 2
Discs, blue	120**	3-5		
Discs, red	120**	3-5		
Egg beaters	15**		6-3	
Eye droppers	15**			Ch. 2, 6, 9

Materials and Equipment *(continued)*

	Amount*	Investigate	Hands-On Activity	Lab Activity
Non-Consumables *(continued)*				
Fabric pieces, silk	15**			Ch. 20
Fabric pieces, wool or nylon	30	20-1		
Film canisters	15**			Ch. 13, 21
Flashlight bulbs & sockets	60	20-6	3-8, 9-6, 20-5	
Flashlights	15**	19-2		Ch. 6, 19
Forceps	10†			Ch. 10
Funnels	15**		8-1	Ch. 6
Glasses, drinking 12-oz size	30	1-2	5-9, 18-1	
Glass slides	120		6-5	
Graduated cylinders, 10 mL	15**		9-3	Ch. 6
Graduated cylinders, 25 mL	15**			Ch. 2
Graduated cylinders, 50 mL	30		2-2	
Graduated cylinders, 100 mL	30	2-4, 5-4, 8-6		Ch. 5, 6, 10
Hammers	30	10-3		
Hand lenses	30	4-3	6-5	
Heat sources	15**		5-7, 9-3	
Hole punch	1	19-2		
Hot plates	15**		16-4, 16-8	Ch. 5
Iron filings	15 tsp**			Ch. 4
Jars, with lids	90**	16-5	6-1	Ch. 6
Lab aprons	30		8-1, 16-8	Ch. 1, 4, 5, 6, 8, 9, 10, 16, 21
Lenses, concave, 10-cm focal length	15**			Ch. 19
Lenses, convex, 10-cm focal length	15**			Ch. 19
Light bulbs	10†	21-5		
Light sources	15**	16-1		
Magnet wire	1 spool			Ch. 21
Magnets, ceramic	10†			Ch. 21
Marbles	30	2-4	13-1	Ch. 3
Marking pens			17-4	Ch. 5, 7, 8, 9, 12
Measuring cups, 1-cup size	15**		6-3, 16-4	
Meter sticks	30	13-4, 15-3	14-5	Ch. 13, 14, 17
Modeling clay, various colors	8 packages	13-4	4-6, 11-4	Ch. 1, 21
Molecular models (made from modeling kits, paper, or modeling clay and toothpicks)	15 sets of 4 different models**	3-1		
Nails, ungalvanized, 12 Penny (D) size	30		21-6	
Newton carts	15**			Ch. 13
Nickels	15**			Ch. 2
Oven mitts	30**			Ch. 5
Pails, plastic or metal, 2-gal size	15**	1-2		
Pans, shallow	45	16-2, 17-1		
Paper clips, metal	5 boxes		3-8, 21-6	Ch. 3, 10
Paper clips, metal, large	1 box			Ch. 21
Paper clips, plastic-coated	1 box			Ch. 10
Pebbles	30 pebbles 30 tsp**	2-4 6-2		
Pen lights	15**	19-7		

Materials and Equipment *(continued)*

Non-Consumables *(continued)*	Amount*	Investigate	Hands-On Activity	Lab Activity
Pennies	150		17-5	Ch. 2, 10
Pens, plastic	15**			Ch. 20
pH charts	15**			Ch. 9
Pie plates, metal	15**			Ch. 20
Pinwheels	15**	16-1		
Pipettes, plastic	10†			Ch. 12
Plates, ceramic, 6-in.	24††	9-2		
Pliers, needle-nose	10†			Ch. 21
Pocket mirrors, round	60		19-8	
Protractors	15**		17-4	
Pulleys	30**		15-4	Ch. 15
Pushpins	30		21-3	
Quarters	30†			Ch. 10
Ribbon	1 spool	17-2		
Ring stands with rings	10†			Ch. 15
Rope	90 m	17-2		
Rubber balls	15**		17-4	
Rubber bands	3 packages**	6-2		Ch. 13
Rubber bands, large	1 package**	13-2		
Rulers, metric	30		12-1, 12-9, 13-1, 13-2, 15-5, 17-4, 18-5	Ch. 7, 12, 15, 18, 19, 20
Safety goggles	30	20-1	3-8, 8-1, 8-6, 16-8	Ch. 1, 4, 5, 6, 8, 9, 10, 12, 16, 17, 21
Sand	1 bag**			Ch. 13
Scissors	30		16-7, 19-8	Ch. 7, 13, 19, 20
Sewing needles	30		21-3	
Shoeboxes	15**			Ch. 11
Sieves, fine	15**			Ch. 4
Sponges, kitchen med. size	24††	9-2		
Spoons, metal	15**	16-5		
Spoons, plastic	15**	16-5		
Spoons, reg. serving size	30		5-4, 5-7, 6-1	
Spoons, silver	30		10-5	
Spoons, wooden	15**	16-5		
Spring scales	30	15-3	12-3, 12-4, 14-5, 15-4,15-5	Ch. 15
Stirrers, glass	180		16-4	Ch. 4, 5, 9
Stopwatches	30		8-6, 13-1	Ch. 8, 17
Strainers	10†		9-3	
Stringed instrument	1	18-6		
Tape measures	15**			Ch. 1
Targets	30**			Ch. 3
Teaspoons	30	5-1, 5-4, 5-5, 5-7, 6-1, 6-2	8-1	Ch. 4, 6
Test tube racks	15**			Ch. 9
	30		18-5	
Test tubes	180		8-6, 18-5	Ch. 9, 16
Thermometers	60		5-7, 16-4, 16-7	Ch. 8
Timers	15**		16-8	

Materials and Equipment (continued)

Non-Consumables (continued)	Amount*	Investigate	Hands-On Activity	Lab Activity
Tongs	15**		16-8	
Toy cars	15	13-4	13-2	
Toy cars, windup	15**	14-3		
Tubing, 3/4 in. clear plastic	8 meters†			Ch. 14
Tuning forks	30		18-1	
Wax pencils	15			Ch. 9, 10
Weights, 1-lb	15**	15-3		
Weights with hooks 0.5 kg	30		12-3	Ch. 15
Wire, copper, uninsulated	2 m		3-8	
Wire cutters	10†			Ch. 21
Wire, insulated	1 roll†			Ch. 12
Wire pieces, insulated, with stripped ends	90 25-cm pieces 60 25-cm pieces 120 25-cm pieces 20 pieces†	20-5 20-6, 21-5	3-8, 9-6 21-6	
Wire ties	30**	3-5		
Zinc strips	30	20-2		

Laboratory Suppliers and Addresses

American Science & Surplus
3605 Howard Street
Skokie, IL 60076
Phone: (847)982-0870
Fax: (800)934-0722
Email: info@sciplus.com
Web: http://www.sciplus.com

Arbor Scientific
P.O. Box 2750
Ann Arbor, MI 48106
Phone: (800)367-6695
Fax: (734)913-6201
Email: mail@arborsci.com
Web: http://www.arborsci.com

Carolina Biological Supply Co.
2700 York Road
Burlington, NC 27215
Phone: (800)334-5551
Fax: (800)222-7112
Email: carolina@carolina.com
Web: http://www.carolina.com

**Connecticut Valley
Biological Supply Co., Inc.**
82 Valley Road, P.O. Box 326
Southhampton, MA 01073
Phone: (800)628-7748
Fax: (800)355-6813
Email: connval@ctvalleybio.com
Web: http://www.ctvalleybio.com

Edmund Scientific
60 Pearce Avenue
Tonawanda, NY 14150
Phone: (800)728-6999
Fax: (800)828-3299
Email: scientifics@edsci.com
Web: http://www.scientificsonline.com

Fisher Science Education
4500 Turnberry
Hanover Park, IL 60133
Phone: (800)955-1177
Fax: (800)955-0740
Email: info@fisheredu.com
Web: http://www.fisheredu.com

Frey Scientific
P.O. Box 8101
100 Paragon Parkway
Mansfield, OH 44903
Phone: (800)225-3739
Fax: (877)256-3739
Email: customercare@freyscientific.com
Web: http://www.freyscientific.com

NASCO - Fort Atkinson
901 Janesville Avenue, P.O. Box 901
Fort Atkinson, WI 53538
Phone: (800)558-9595
Fax: (920)563-8296
Email: custserv@eNASCO.com
Web: http://www.nascofa.com

NASCO - Modesto
4825 Stoddard Road , P.O. Box 3837
Modesto, CA 95352
Phone: (800)558-9595
Fax: (209)545-1669
Email: cusserv@nascomodesto.com
Web: http://www.enasco.com

Nature Watch
5312 Derry Avenue Unit R
Agoura Hills, CA 91301
Phone: (800)228-5816
Fax: (800)228-5814
Email: info@nature-watch.com
Web: http://www.nature-watch.com

Nebraska Scientific
3823 Leavenworth Street
Omaha, NE 68105
Phone: (800)228-7117
Fax: (402)346-2216
Email: staff@nebraskascientific.com
Web: http://www.nebraskascientific.com

Sargent Welch Scientific Company
P.O. Box 5229
Buffalo Grove, IL 60089
Phone: (800)727-4368
Fax: (800)676-2540
Email: sarwel@sargentwelch.com
Web: http://www.sargentwelch.com

Science Kit & Boreal Laboratories
777 East Park Drive
P.O. Box 5003
Tonawanda, NY 14150
Phone: (800)828-7777
Fax: (800)828-3299
Email: sk@sciencekit.com
Web: http://www.sciencekit.com

Southern Scientific, Inc.
83 Euclid Avenue
McKenzie, TN 38201
Phone: (800)748-8735
Fax: (800)770-6265
Email: merchant@southernscientific.com
Web: http://www.southernscientific.com

WARD'S Natural Science Establishment, Inc.
5100 West Henrietta Road
Rochester, NY 14692
Phone: 800-962-2660
Fax: 800-635-8439
Email: customer_service@warsci.com
Web: http://www.wardsci.com

Enhance Your Students' Performance

These additional titles can offer you more choices to help meet the diverse needs of your students and your teaching situation.

Event-Based Science

Engage your students in real-world, interdisciplinary tasks that motivate them to learn more about Physical science. This program incudes books, videos, and a CD-ROM. Students are "hooked" after watching media coverage of a real-life event such as the opening of two new roller coasters. Extend your *Concepts and Challenges* lesson with the following Event-Based Science modules:

Fire!   *First Flight!*
Blackout!   *Thrill Ride!*
Fraud!

Writing in Science

These short, manageable lessons, clear guidelines, and practical applications help students master the writing skills needed in science, including keeping a science journal, taking notes, recording experiments, and writing reports. Because *Concepts and Challenges* is loaded with activities that encourage students to write about science, you'll want to implement *Writing in Science* for further practice.

Science Reading Strategies

Develop the reading strategies already built into *Concepts and Challenges* with *Science Reading Strategies*. This tool enables students to decode, comprehend, and organize science content into main ideas and supporting details. It's certain to boost content literacy, student confidence, and test scores.

Science and Technology: A Rich Heritage

Guide your students in developing a personal understanding of science and technology—from the past, in the present, and into the future. This unique history-based text highlights the critical link between studying science in school and future opportunities to succeed in related careers. You can blend the lessons in this text with the Science and Technology features in *Concepts and Challenges* for lesson enrichment.

PHYSICAL · SCIENCE

Fourth Edition

Leonard Bernstein ◆ Martin Schachter ◆ Alan Winkler ◆ Stanley Wolfe

Stanley Wolfe
Project Coordinator

GLOBE FEARON
Pearson Learning Group

The following people have contributed to the development of this product:

Art and Design: Evelyn Bauer, Susan Brorein, Tracey Gerber, Bernadette Hruby, Carol Marie Kiernan, Mindy Klarman, Judy Mahoney, Karen Mancinelli, Elbaliz Mendez, April Okano, Dan Thomas, Jennifer Visco

Editorial: Stephanie P. Cahill, Gina Dalessio, Nija Dixon, Martha Feehan, Theresa McCarthy, Maurice Sabean, Marilyn Sarch, Maury Solomon, Jeffrey Wickersty, Shirley C. White, S. Adrienn Vegh-Soti

Editorial Services: Thomas Daning, Richetta Lobban

Manufacturing: Mark Cirillo, Tom Dunne

Marketing: Douglas Falk, Stephanie Schuler

Production: Irene Belinsky, Linda Bierniak, Carlos Blas, Karen Edmonds, Cheryl Golding, Leslie Greenberg, Roxanne Knoll, Susan Levine, Cynthia Lynch, Jennifer Murphy, Lisa Svoronos, Susan Tamm

Publishing Operations: Carolyn Coyle

Technology: Jessie Lin, Ellen Strain

About the Cover: Physical science is the study of both physics and chemistry. The roller coaster and the spaceship on the cover illustrate examples of these concepts. The roller coaster represents the study of forces and motion. The spaceship, as it is lifting off, represents the chemistry that goes into creating the right mix of fuels. These concepts are just a few of the many things you will be learning about in this book. What do you think are some other things that you will study in physical science?

ISBN: 0-130-23840-6

Printed in the United States of America

3 4 5 6 7 8 9 10   06 05 04 03

Globe Fearon
Pearson Learning Group

1-800-321-3106
www.pearsonlearning.com

Acknowledgments

Science Consultants

Jonathan Cohen
Science Teacher
Longfellow Arts and Technology
Magnet Middle School
Berkeley, California

Kenneth S. Fink
Liberty Science Center
Jersey City, New Jersey

Laboratory Consultants

Sean Devine
Science Teacher
Ridge High School
Basking Ridge, New Jersey

Vincent Dionisio
Science Teacher
Clifton High School
Clifton, New Jersey

Gregory Vogt, Ph.D.
Associate Professor, Civil Engineering
Colorado State University
Fort Collins, Colorado

Reading Consultant

Sharon Cook
Consultant
Leadership in Literacy

Internet Consultant

Janet M. Gaudino
Seventh Grade Science Teacher
Montgomery Middle School
Skillman, New Jersey

ESL/ELL Consultant

Elizabeth Jimenez
Consultant
Pomona, CA

Content Reviewers

Dr. Vincent Adamo, M.D. (pp. 200, 201)
Parsippany, New Jersey

Ron Asteak (pp. 216, 217)
Bike King Manager
Clinton, New Jersey

Sharon Danielsen (pp. 352, 353)
Site Manager
Darrin Fresh Water Institute
Rensselaer Polytechnic Institute
Troy, New York

Scott Denny (pp. 138,139)
Food Service Manager
Denville, New Jersey

Ivan Dmochowski (Chs. 7–9)
Helen Hay Whitney Postdoctoral Scholar
California Institute of Technology
Pasadena, California

T. Ferbel (Ch. 20)
Professor of Physics
University of Rochester
Rochester, New York

Ernest Freund (Chs. 17–19)
Lecturer
University of California at Santa Barbara
Santa Barbara, California

Paul Heiney (Chs. 9, 12, and 13)
Professor of Physics
University of Pennsylvania
Philadelphia, Pennsylvania

Samuel P. Kounaves (Chs. 4–6)
Professor of Chemistry
Tufts University
Medford, Massachusetts

Dr. Charles Liu (pp. 236, 237, 250, 251)
Astrophysicist
Department of Astrophysics and Hayden
Planetarium
American Museum of Natural History
New York, New York

John Margrave (Chs. 10 and 11)
Department of Chemistry
Rice University
Houston, Texas

Terry Moran (pp. 46, 47, 324, 325)
Moran Research Service
Harvard, Massachusetts

George F. Palladino (Chs. 1 and 2)
Director, Master of Chemistry Education
Department of Chemistry
University of Pennsylvania
Philadelphia, Pennsylvania

Thomas Rauchfuss (Ch. 3)
School of Chemical Sciences
University of Illinois
Urbana, Illinois

Dr. Dirk Schulze-Makuch (pp. 24, 25, 98, 99)
Department of Geological Sciences
University of Texas at El Paso
El Paso, Texas

Dr. Raymond C. Turner (Chs. 14, 15, and 21)
Alumni Distinguished Professor Emeritus of Physics
Department of Physics and Astronomy
Clemson University
Clemson, South Carolina

Todd Woerner (Ch. 16 and pp. 66, 67, 162, 163, 184, 185, 278, 279, 298, 299)
Department of Chemistry
Duke University
Durham, North Carolina

Teacher Reviewers

Leonard GeRue
Hanshaw Middle School
Modesto, California

Charles Sehulster
Science Teacher
Horace Greeley High School
Chappaqua, New York

iv

Contents

Scientific Skills and Investigations Handbooks

UNIT 1 INTRODUCTION TO MATTER

Chapter 1 Properties of Matter

Chapter 2 Density

UNIT **4** EXPLORING THE PERIODIC TABLE

UNIT 5   FORCE, MOTION, AND ENERGY

after 14

after 17

If time after 5

Appendices

Physical Science Features

Hands-On Activities

How Do They Know That?

Integrating the Sciences

Real-Life Science

People in Science

Science and Technology

INVESTIGATE

Web InfoSearch

What are scientific skills?

People are naturally curious. They want to understand the world around them. The field of science would probably not exist if it were not for human curiosity about the natural world.

People also want to be able to make good guesses about the future. They want to know how to use alternative forms of energy. They want to improve technology and communications.

Scientists use many skills to explore the world and gather information about it. These skills are called science process skills. Another name for them is science inquiry skills.

Science process skills allow you to think like a scientist. They help you identify problems and answer questions. Sometimes they help you solve problems. More often, they provide some possible answers and lead to more questions. In this book, you will use a variety of science process skills to understand the facts and theories in physical science.

Science process skills are not only used in science. You compare prices when you shop and you observe what happens to foods when you cook them. You predict what the weather will be by looking at the sky. In fact, science process skills are really everyday life skills that have been adapted for problem solving in science.

1. NAME: What is the name for the skills scientists use to solve problems?

▲ **Figure 1** Scientists use science process skills to understand what makes a nuclear power plant run safely, how robots work in spaces too small for humans, and why communications are better using fiber optics.

Contents

1. Observing and Comparing
2. Classifying Data
3. Modeling and Simulating
4. Measuring
5. Analyzing Data and Communicating Results
6. Making Predictions

Handbook A: Developing Skills
What are scientific skills?

Handbook Overview

In this chapter, students will identify science process skills and learn how to use these skills to help them think like scientists. They will read about the tools used to collect data and how scientists classify data. Students will learn about measurement and how scientists analyze data and communicate their results to other scientists. Finally, students will come to understand the importance of using data to make scientific predictions.

About Figure 1 Science process skills can help scientists understand how to prevent nuclear accidents, such as the one that occurred on April 26, 1986 at the Chernobyl nuclear power plant in the Ukraine. Using science process skills, scientists determine how robots, such as the one shown in the bottom photograph, can be used for tasks that are dangerous or unpleasant for people, including cleaning up nuclear waste, factory assembly, and exploring active volcanoes. Science process skills have also helped scientists develop fiber optics, shown in the top photograph. Fiber optics can be used for viewing inside the human body, for laser surgery, in computer graphics, and other applications.

Answer to question

1. NAME: science process skills or science inquiry skills

Handbook Project
SCIENCE PROCESS SKILLS JOURNAL

MATERIALS: Weekly Journal, pen or pencil

As students read Handbook A, ask them to keep a journal of the science process skills that they use in their daily lives. Students should make journal entries every day for a week and include at least five of the seven skills discussed in this handbook. Encourage students to write about experiences at home in addition to experiences in school. Invite students to share their projects with the class.
learning style: linguistic

Teaching Options

ASSESSMENT PLANNER

For assessment in the Student Edition, see the following pages:
Performance-Based Assessment
Hands-On Activity: pp. 2, 3, 6, 7

• TEACHING RESOURCES •

Teacher's Resources CD-ROM
Weekly Journal: Study Tools, p. 19

Writing Activity Rubric: Teaching Tools, p. 9

Developing Science Skills: Handbook Resources, p. 1

Handbook Key Term Review: Handbook Resources, p. 8

1 Observing and Comparing

STUDY HINT Before beginning this lesson, write the title of each section on the board. Have students copy these titles in their notebooks, using an outline format. As students read each section, they should write notes in their outlines.

Demonstration To introduce the lesson, ask students what it means to observe. Make sure students understand that observing is not limited to what they can see. Then, point to an object, such as a wooden block, and allow students to observe it. You might pass the object around so that students can touch it. Ask them to write their observations and share them with the class.
learning styles: visual, tactile

Discussion As students read the description of each science skill, ask them to identify examples of how they use the skill in their daily lives. Emphasize that these skills are used in all academic disciplines, not only in science.
learning style: auditory

Answers to questions

2 LIST: sight, hearing, touch, smell, and taste

3 COMPARE/CONTRAST: Possible answer: Both are shiny and metallic. Aluminum is lighter (less dense) than silver.

4 INFER: things that are too small for the human eye to see

Hands-On Activity
MAKING OBSERVATIONS

TIME: 15 minutes

PURPOSE: identifying, analyzing

PREPARATION: Gather materials before class, including shoeboxes, rubber bands, and small objects. You can also make several boxes before class and allow students to work in pairs or small groups.

Practicing Your Skills Answers

6. IDENTIFY: the skill of making observations

7. IDENTIFY: the sense of hearing

8. ANALYZE: Possible answer: Both. I used direct observation when I listened to the sounds that the object made in the box. I used indirect observation when I used my past experiences to try to picture what object was in the box.

T2

---

1 Observing and Comparing

Making Observations An important part of solving any problem is observing, or using your senses to find out what is going on around you. The five senses are sight, hearing, touch, smell, and taste. When you look at the properties of an ore or watch an ice cube melt, you are observing. When you observe, you pay close attention to everything that happens around you.

Scientists observe the world in ways that other scientists can repeat. This is a goal of scientific observation. It is expected that when a scientist has made an observation, other people will be able to make the same observation.

2 LIST: What are the five senses?

Comparing and Contrasting Part of observing is comparing and contrasting. When you compare data, you observe the characteristics of several things or events to see how they are alike. When you contrast data, you look for ways that similar things are different from one another.

▲ **Figure 2** Silver and aluminum are alike in many ways. They also have many differences.

3 COMPARE/CONTRAST: How are a bar of aluminum and a bar of silver alike? How are they different?

Using Tools to Observe Sometimes an object is too small or too distant to see with your eyes alone. Often, special tools are needed for making observations. Sometimes scientists use tools to make observations of things like radio waves or X-rays that are outside the range of our senses. Telescopes, spectrometers, microscopes, and magnifying glasses are all examples of tools that help with scientific observations.

▲ **Figure 3** Examining a slide with a magnifying glass

4 INFER: What are some things that scientists might need a microscope to see?

Hands-On Activity
MAKING OBSERVATIONS

You and a partner will need 2 shoeboxes with lids, 2 rubber bands, and several small objects.

1. Place several small objects into the shoebox. Do not let your partner see what you put into the shoebox.
2. Cover the shoebox with the lid. Put a rubber band around the shoebox to keep the lid on.
3. Exchange shoeboxes with your partner.
4. Gently shake, turn, and rattle the shoebox.
5. Try to describe what is in the shoebox without opening it. Write your descriptions on a sheet of paper.

Practicing Your Skills

6. IDENTIFY: What science process skill did you use?

7. IDENTIFY: Which of your senses was most important to you?

8. ANALYZE: Direct observation is seeing something with your eyes or hearing it with your ears. Indirect observation involves using a model or past experience to make a guess about something. Which kind of observation did you use?

2

Teaching Options

• *TEACHING RESOURCES* •

Teacher's Resources CD-ROM
Venn Diagram: Study Tools, p. 10

Writing Activity Outline: Study Tools, pp. 20–21

ESL/ELL STRATEGY

Setting Goals Before reading each section, English-language learners can read the question at the end and set a goal. For the first section, students could set the goal: *I am going to find out about the five senses and how they are used in making observations.*

COOPERATIVE LEARNING

Comparing and Contrasting Practice Students can work with partners to practice the skill of comparing and contrasting. Give pairs of students two objects or pictures of objects to compare and contrast. Give each student a copy of the Venn Diagram on the Teacher's Resources CD-ROM. Have students write similarities between a paper clip and a penny where the circles overlap and write the differences between the two in the individual circles.
learning styles: visual, linguistic

2 Classifying Data

Key Term

data: information you collect when you observe something

Collecting and Classifying Data The information you collect when you observe something is called **data**. The data from an experiment or from observations you have made are first recorded, or written down. Then, they are classified.

When you classify data, you group things together based on how they are alike. This information often comes from making comparisons as you observe. You may classify by size, shape, color, use, or any other important feature. Classifying data helps you recognize and understand the relationships between things. Classification makes studying large groups of things easier. For example, physical scientists use classification to organize different types of elements.

▶ **EXPLAIN:** How can you classify data?

Hands-On Activity

ORGANIZING LIQUIDS

You will need 10 to 15 jars or bottles filled with a variety of liquids.

1. Carefully examine the liquids in the containers. Observe their color, thickness, and composition. Notice what happens when you gently shake the bottle. What happens when you let the liquid settle?
2. Make a system for classifying the liquids.
3. Categorize all the liquids.
4. Write a description of how you would use your classification system to classify a new liquid that you have never seen before.

Practicing Your Skills

5. **ANALYZE:** How did you classify the liquids?
6. **EXPLAIN:** Why is a classification system useful?

3 Modeling and Simulating

Key Terms

model: tool scientists use to represent an object or process

simulation: computer model that usually shows a process

Modeling Sometimes things are too small to see with your eyes alone. Other times, an object is too large to see. You may need a model to help you examine the object. A **model** is a good way to show what a very small or a very large object looks like. A model can have more details than what may be seen with just your eyes. It can be used to represent a process or an object that is hard to explain with words. A model can be a three-dimensional picture, a drawing, a computer image, or a diagram.

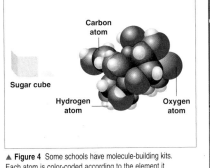

▲ **Figure 4** Some schools have molecule-building kits. Each atom is color-coded according to the element it represents.

▶ **DEFINE:** What is a model?

Simulating A **simulation** is a kind of model that shows a process. It is often done using a computer. You can use a simulation to predict the outcome of an experiment. Scientists use simulations to study everything from chemical reactions to the global climate.

▶ **DEFINE:** What is a simulation?

MORE ON THE WEB

Coming to Your Senses Have students visit www.concepts andchallenges.com to learn more about the five senses. In groups, students will prepare an oral presentation on one of the senses. You may also choose from a number of activities to use with your class.

• TEACHING RESOURCES •

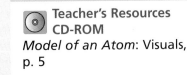 **Teacher's Resources CD-ROM**
Model of an Atom: Visuals, p. 5

2 Classifying Data

✏️ **STUDY HINT** Ask students to write the terms *data* and *classify* on separate lines in their notebooks. As students read, they should write the definitions of these terms.

Discussion Explain to students that classifying is a way to organize information. Have students mention ways that they can classify rocks. (Possible answers include by size, shape, or color.)

Answer to question

▶ **EXPLAIN:** by size, shape, color, use, or any other important feature

Hands-On Activity

ORGANIZING LIQUIDS

TIME: 25 minutes
PURPOSE: analyzing, explaining
PREPARATION: Choose liquids such as dish-soap water, water, vegetable oil, juice, milk, soda, and paint. You might place the liquids in medicine bottles or baby food jars. Make enough sets of liquids so that students can work in small groups to classify.

Practicing Your Skills Answers

5. **ANALYZE:** Possible answers: by color, whether the liquid makes bubbles when shaken, or whether the liquid is thin or thick
6. **EXPLAIN:** Classifying makes studying large groups of things easier.

3 Modeling and Simulating

✏️ **STUDY HINT** Read the Key Terms with students. Encourage students to give examples of models and simulations.

Demonstration Show students a model of an atom. Ask students why a model might be better than a picture when studying certain topics. (A model gives a better idea of the shape and dimensions of an object.)

Answers to questions

▶ **DEFINE:** a tool that scientists use to represent an object

▶ **DEFINE:** a model that shows a process

4 Measuring

Measuring

STUDY HINT Read the Key Terms aloud with students and ask them to give examples of items that might be measured in terms of meters (a running track), grams (a box of cereal), and so on. Have students write the terms in their notebooks and notes or questions that pertain to each term as they read. Allow time for students to share their notes and ask questions.

Discussion Remind students that the inch, foot, and yard are measurements in the English system. Point out that no simple relationship exists among these units. Perform a sample calculation on the board such as changing 60 inches into feet. (5 feet; 12 inches = 1 foot) Then, introduce the metric system. Write 1,500 mm on the board. Show students how this number can be changed to centimeters (150) or meters (1.5) by moving the decimal point to the left.
learning styles: visual, logical/mathematical

Demonstration Show students a metric ruler. Point out centimeter and millimeter divisions. Demonstrate the proper way to measure the lengths of different objects. Show students how objects can be measured in centimeters and in millimeters.
learning style: visual

Answers to questions

8 IDENTIFY: Accept any two of the following systems: the metric, English, and the SI systems.

9 CALCULATE: 300 cm

READING STRATEGY Have students study Figure 5 and remind students that prefixes are word parts that, when added to words, change the meanings of the words. Encourage students to think of other words that they know that include these prefixes, such as *kilogram* and *decimal*. Ask how knowing the meanings of prefixes might help students become better readers.

WRITING HINT Inform students that the units of length can be abbreviated. For example, kilometer can be written as *km* and centimeter can be written as *cm*.

---

4 Measuring

Key Terms
unit: amount used to measure something
meter: basic unit of length or distance
mass: amount of matter in something
gram: basic unit of mass
volume: amount of space an object takes up
liter: basic unit of liquid volume
meniscus: curve at the surface of a liquid
temperature: measure of the amount of heat energy something contains

Two Systems of Measurement When you measure, you compare an unknown value with a known value using standard units. A **unit** is an amount used to measure something. The metric system is an international system of measurement. Examples of metric units are the gram, the kilometer, and the liter. In the United States, the English system and the metric system are both used. Examples of units in the English system are the pound, the foot, and the gallon.

There is also a more modern form of the metric system. This measurement system is called SI. The letters *SI* stand for the French words *Système International.* Many of the units in the SI are the same as those in the metric system.

The metric and SI systems are both based on units of ten. This makes them easy to use. Each unit in these systems is ten times greater than the unit before it. To show a change in the size of a unit, you add a prefix to the unit. The prefix tells you whether the unit is larger or smaller. For example, a centimeter is ten times bigger than a millimeter.

PREFIXES AND THEIR MEANINGS	
kilo-	one thousand (1,000)
hecto-	one hundred (100)
deca-	ten (10)
deci-	one-tenth (1/10)
centi-	one-hundredth (1/100)
milli-	one-thousandth (1/1,000)

◀ **Figure 5**

8 IDENTIFY: What are two measurement systems?

4

Units of Length Length is the distance from one point to another. In the metric system, the basic unit of length or distance is the **meter**. A meter is about the length from a doorknob to the floor. Longer distances, such as the distances between cities, are measured in kilometers. A kilometer is 1,000 meters. Centimeters and millimeters measure shorter distances. A centimeter is 1/100 of a meter. A millimeter is 1/1,000 of a meter. Figure 6 compares common units of length. It also shows the abbreviation for each unit.

SI/METRIC UNITS OF LENGTH	
1,000 millimeters (mm)	1 meter (m)
100 centimeters (cm)	1 meter
10 decimeters (dm)	1 meter
10 millimeters	1 centimeter
1,000 meters	1 kilometer (km)

▲ **Figure 6**

Length can be measured with a meter stick. A meter stick is 1m long and is divided into 100 equal lengths by numbered lines. The distance between each of these lines is equal to 1 cm. Each centimeter is divided into ten equal parts. Each one of these parts is equal to 1 mm.

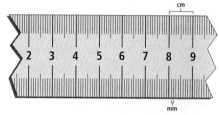

▲ **Figure 7** A meter stick is divided into centimeters and millimeters.

9 CALCULATE: How many centimeters are there in 3 m?

Teaching Options

EXTENDING THE LESSON

Measurements From the Past
Discuss with students some of the measurements that people used in the past. (Alternatively, students could research past units of measurement on their own.) At one time, for example, the distance from a king's nose to his hand equaled 1 yard, and the length of a king's foot equaled 1 foot. Elicit from students why this system of measurement created problems. (Possible answer: The measuring system changed each time a new king was crowned.) Use this discussion to point out the importance of having a standard system of measurement.
learning style: auditory

RETEACH

Metric Unit Practice If students need more practice with metric units, use Figure 6 as the basis for review. Copy the chart by writing each of the units of measurement on separate index cards. Students can work in pairs or small groups to match equivalent measurements. They can check their answers against Figure 6.
learning styles: visual, tactile

Measuring Area Do you know how people find the area of the floor of a room? They measure the length and the width of the room. Then, they multiply the two numbers. You can find the area of any rectangle by multiplying its length by its width. Area is expressed in square units, such as square meters (m^2) or square centimeters (cm^2).

Area = length × width

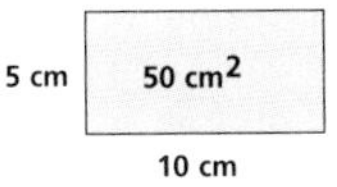

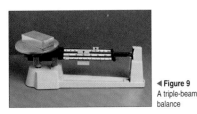

5 cm | 50 cm² | 10 cm

◀ **Figure 8** The area of a rectangle equals length times width.

10▶ CALCULATE: What is the area of a rectangle 12 cm by 6 cm?

Mass and Weight The amount of matter in something is its **mass**. The basic metric unit of mass is called a **gram (g)**. A paper clip has about 1 g of mass. Mass is measured with an instrument called a balance. A balance works like a seesaw. It compares an unknown mass with a known mass.

One kind of balance that is commonly used to measure mass is a triple-beam balance. A triple-beam balance has a pan. The object being measured is placed on the pan. The balance also has three beams. Weights, called riders, are moved along each beam until the object on the pan is balanced. Each rider gives a reading in grams. The mass of the object is equal to the total readings of all three riders.

◀ **Figure 9** A triple-beam balance

Mass and weight are related; however, they are not the same. The weight of an object is a measure of Earth's pull of gravity between Earth and that object. Gravity is the force that pulls objects toward the center of Earth. The strength of the pull of gravity between two objects depends on the distance between the objects and how much mass they each contain. So, the weight of an object changes as its mass changes and as its distance from the center of Earth changes.

11▶ IDENTIFY: What instrument is used to measure mass?

Volume The amount of space an object takes up is its **volume**. You can measure the volume of liquids and solids. Liquid volume is usually measured in **liters**. Soft drinks in the United States often come in 2-liter bottles.

A graduated cylinder is used to measure liquid volume. Graduated cylinders are calibrated, or marked off, at regular intervals. Look at Figure 10. It shows a graduated cylinder. On this graduated cylinder, each small line is equal to 0.05 mL. The longer lines mark off every 0.25 mL up to 5.00 mL. However, every graduated cylinder is not marked in this manner. They come in different sizes up to 2,000 mL with different markings.

Always read the measurement at eye level. If you are using a glass graduated cylinder, you will need to read the mark on the graduated cylinder closest to the bottom of the meniscus. A **meniscus** is the curve at the surface of a liquid. A plastic graduated cylinder does not show a meniscus.

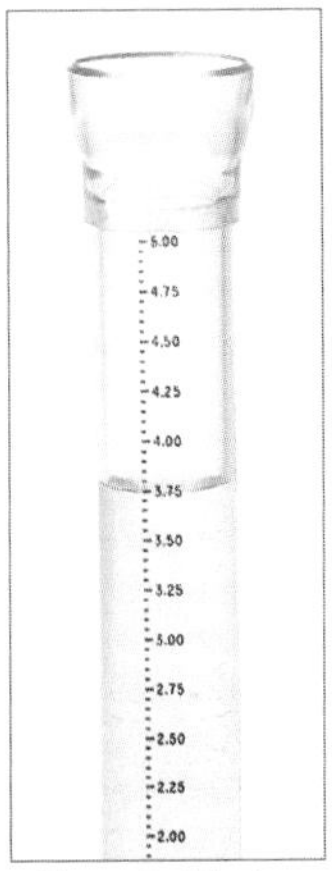

▲ **Figure 10** This glass graduated cylinder shows a meniscus.

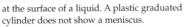

Demonstration Distribute 1-gram masses to the class. Have students lift these masses. Using the 1-gram masses for comparison, challenge students to estimate the mass (in grams) of books, pencils, and other common objects. Demonstrate by using a triple-beam balance to check estimations. **learning styles: visual, tactile**

Demonstration Display a 1-liter flask and explain that its volume is equal to 1,000 cubic cm. Remind students that 1/1,000 of a liter is equal to 1 milliliter and, therefore, 1 mL is equal to 1 cubic cm.

You may also want to demonstrate reading the meniscus to students. Fill a glass graduated cylinder with a liquid. Lower your head until your eye is level with the meniscus. The line closest to the bottom of the meniscus should be recorded as the volume of the liquid. Allow students to observe the meniscus.
learning styles: visual, logical/mathematical

Discussion Introduce the square centimeter and square meter as units of area. Using a meter stick, measure the length and width of the classroom. Then, have students calculate the area of the classroom.
learning styles: auditory, visual

Reinforcement Make sure students understand that mass and weight are not the same measurement. Ask students to describe the difference between mass and weight. (*Mass* is the amount of matter in something, while an object's *weight* is the measure of Earth's pull of gravity between Earth and that object.)

Answers to questions

10▶ CALCULATE: 72 cm²

11▶ IDENTIFY: a balance

COOPERATIVE LEARNING

Volume Displacement Experiment
Ask students how they could estimate the volume of an object if they had the following materials: a graduated cylinder, a cup, some liquid, and an object. Students can work in pairs or small groups to design an experiment. If students need help, lead them to realize that they should measure the volume of the liquid and the object. Then, they should remove the object, remeasure the volume, and subtract to find the difference. If time allows, groups of students can use displacement to approximate the volume of several small objects.
learning styles: tactile, visual

• TEACHING RESOURCES •

Teacher's Resources CD-ROM
Measuring Length and Area: Handbook Resources, p. 2

Measuring Volume: Handbook Resources, p. 4

Laboratory Manual
Lab. Skills Worksheets 1, 2, and 3

Laboratory Videos
Segment 1: How to Use a Triple-Beam Balance

Segment 2: Using Graduated Cylinders

Discussion Use Figure 12 to point out the differences between area and volume. The total area of the cubes at the front of the box is 6 cm², while the volume of the entire box is 12 cm³. Explain to students that area is measured in square units. (Area involves two dimensions—length and width—so it must be measured in square units.) Volume is recorded in cubic units because it involves three dimensions.
learning style: auditory

Answer to question

12 CALCULATE: 12 mL

Hands-On Activity

CALCULATING AREA AND VOLUME

TIME: 15 minutes

PURPOSE: analyzing, calculating

PREPARATION: Gather a variety of boxes and label them with letters so that students can record their measurements. Remind students that volume is measured in cubic units, while area is measured in square units. Draw a table on the board with the columns labeled *Box*, *Length (cm)*, *Width (cm)*, *Height (cm)*, *Volume (cm³)*, and *Surface Area (cm²)*. Ask students to copy the table into their notebooks and use it to record their measurements. Remind students that 1 cubic cm is equal to 1 mL.

COOPERATIVE LEARNING: Students can work in pairs or small groups for this activity.

Practicing Your Skills Answers

4. ANALYZE: Answer will depend on the boxes that are provided for the group.

5. CALCULATE: Answer will depend on the boxes that are provided for the group. Students should calculate the volume of each box and convert their answers to milliliters.

6. ANALYZE: Answer will depend on the boxes that are provided for the group.

Demonstration Demonstrate for students how a thermometer works. Display two beakers, one with ice and one with hot water. Place the thermometer in the ice and leave it until the temperature reading on the thermometer drops. Then, place the thermometer in the hot water and have students observe the liquid in the thermometer. Ask students to explain why the liquid rises in the tube.
learning style: visual

The volume of solid objects is often measured in cubic centimeters. One cubic centimeter equals 1 mL.

Look at Figure 11. Each side of the cube is 1 cm long. The volume of the cube is 1 cubic centimeter (1 cm³). Now, look at the drawing of the box in Figure 12. Its length is 3 cm. Its width is 2 cm. Its height is 2 cm. The volume of the box can be found by multiplying length by width by height. In this case, volume equals 3 × 2 × 2. Therefore, the volume of the box is 12 cm³.

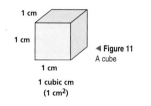

1 cm
1 cm
1 cm
◀ **Figure 11**
A cube
1 cubic cm
(1 cm²)

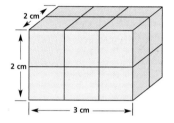

2 cm
2 cm
3 cm

▲ **Figure 12** The volume of a box equals length times width times height.

$$V = l \times w \times h$$

If you have a box that is 10 cm on each side, its volume would be 1,000 cm³. A liter is the same as 1,000 cm³. One liter of liquid will fill the box exactly.

12 CALCULATE: How many milliliters of water would fill a 12-cm³ box?

6

Hands-On Activity

CALCULATING AREA AND VOLUME

You will need 3 boxes of different sizes, paper, and a metric ruler.

1. Measure the length, width, and height of each box in centimeters. Record each measurement in your notes.

2. Calculate the volume of each box. Record each volume in your notes.

3. Find the surface area of each box. Record each area in your notes.

Practicing Your Skills

4. ANALYZE: Which of the three boxes has the largest volume?

5. CALCULATE: How many milliliters of liquid would fill each box?

6. ANALYZE: What is the surface area of the largest box?

Temperature **Temperature** is a measure of the amount of heat energy something contains. An instrument that measures temperature is called a thermometer.

Most thermometers are glass tubes. At the bottom of the tube is a wider part, called the bulb. The bulb is filled with liquid. Liquids that are often used include mercury, colored alcohol, or colored water. When heat is added, the liquid expands, or gets larger. It rises in the glass tube. When heat is taken away, the liquid contracts, or gets smaller. The liquid falls in the tube. On the side of the tube is a series of marks. You read the temperature by looking at the mark on the tube where the liquid stops.

Temperature can be measured on three different scales. These scales are the Fahrenheit (F) scale, the Celsius (C) scale, and the Kelvin (K) scale. The Fahrenheit scale is part of the English system of measurement. The Celsius scale is usually used in science. Almost all scientists, even in the United States, use the Celsius scale. Each unit on the Celsius scale is a degree Celsius (°C). The degree Celsius is the metric unit of temperature. Water freezes at 0°C. It boils at 100°C.

Teaching Options

Scientists working with very low temperatures use the Kelvin scale. The Kelvin scale is part of the SI measurement system. It begins at absolute zero, or 0K. This number indicates, in theory at least, a total lack of heat.

COMPARING TEMPERATURE SCALES

	Kelvin	Fahrenheit	Celsius
Boiling point of water	373K	212°F	100°C
Human body temperature	310K	98.6°F	37°C
Freezing point of water	273K	32°F	0°C
Absolute zero	0K	−459.67°F	−273.15°C

▲ Figure 13

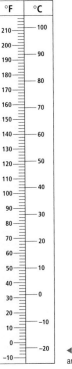

◄ **Figure 14** The Fahrenheit and Celsius scales

13 ▶ NAME: What are the three scales used to measure temperature?

Hands-On Activity
READING A THERMOMETER

You will need safety goggles, lab apron, 2 beakers, a heat source, ice water, a wax pencil, a ruler, and a standard Celsius thermometer.

1. Boil some water in a beaker.
   ⚠CAUTION: Be very careful when working with heat. Place your thermometer in the beaker. Do not let the thermometer touch the sides or bottom of the beaker. Wait until the mercury rises as far as it will go. Record the temperature.

2. Fill a beaker with ice water. Place the unmarked thermometer into this beaker. Wait until the mercury goes as low as it will go. Record the temperature.

▲ **STEP 1** Record the temperature of the boiling water.

Practicing Your Skills

3. IDENTIFY: What is the temperature at which the mercury rose as high as it would go?

4. IDENTIFY: What is the temperature at which the mercury went as low as it would go?

Discussion Using Figure 13, read aloud the temperatures of the items listed under one of the scales. Have students identify the temperature readings on the other two scales. Then, have students refer to Figure 14. Ask: *Which temperature is higher—90°F or 40°C? Which temperature would you most likely find on a winter day in the northern United States—20°F or 20°C?* Have students make up questions and answers of their own.

Answer to question

13 ▶ NAME: Kelvin, Fahrenheit, and Celsius

✎ **WRITING HINT** Inform students that when they write temperatures using the Fahrenheit and Celsius scales, they should include the degree symbol (°). However, when they write temperatures using the Kelvin scale, they should omit the degree symbol.

Hands-On Activity
READING A THERMOMETER

TIME: 15 minutes

PURPOSE: identifying

PREPARATION: Be sure to gather the materials before class. Demonstrate the experiment for students before they begin, emphasizing safety as you boil the water.

SAFETY TIP: Tell students that the most accurate thermometers are filled with mercury. Because mercury is poisonous and can be absorbed through the skin, a person should wear protective gloves to clean up any mercury that spills out of a broken thermometer. Mercury can be cleaned with paper towels. Caution students to handle thermometers carefully and to notify you of any broken thermometers.

COOPERATIVE LEARNING: You can have students work in pairs. Ask them to set up the experiment. Make sure that you check their setups before they begin boiling water. Remind them that they should read the thermometer at eye level to get an accurate reading.

Practicing Your Skills Answers

3. IDENTIFY: 100°C
4. IDENTIFY: 0°C

ESL/ELL STRATEGY

Indicating the Scale Inform students that when temperatures are read and written, the scale is always indicated. The scale has to be indicated because the three temperature scales are different from one another. For example, 0K, 0°C, and 0°F are not the same temperatures. **learning styles: auditory, logical/mathematical**

• TEACHING RESOURCES •

◉ **Teacher's Resources CD-ROM**

Ruler—Inches and Centimeters: Visuals, p. 1

Temperature Scale: Visuals, p. 2

Measuring Temperature: Handbook Resources, p. 5

MORE ON THE WEB

The History of the Metric System Have students visit www.conceptsandchallenges.com to learn about the history of the metric system, including its modern form as the Système Internationale (SI).

5 Analyzing Data and Communicating Results

Discussion Draw students' attention to the table and the graph in Figures 15 and 16. Point out that each graphic organizer shows the same data. Ask students: *Which is easier to use and understand? Why?*

Answers to questions

14 EXPLAIN: They make data easier to compare and interpret.

15 LIST: books, magazines, newspaper articles, Web sites, and graphs

6 Making Predictions

STUDY HINT Ask students to write the Key Terms in their notebooks. After they read the lesson, students can write the definitions in their own words and summarize the lesson in a paragraph.

Demonstration Give a concrete example to help students understand what it means to infer. Place a rock in a paper bag and use it to demonstrate the following narration: *Someone placed an object in this paper bag. I picked up the bag, and it was heavy. I shook the bag, and the item did not move very much. I touched the bag, and I felt something that was round and smooth. I inferred that the object inside was a rock.* Ask students how they can tell that you are inferring and not predicting. Then, encourage them to describe situations where they have both inferred and predicted.

Answer to question

16 CONTRAST: When you infer, you form a conclusion. When you predict, you state ahead of time what you think is going to happen.

Handbook Project Wrap-Up

SCIENCE PROCESS SKILLS JOURNAL

Students can share their journals with the class. You can use the Individual Activity Rubric found on the Teacher's Resources CD-ROM to assess students' projects. Fill in the rubric with the additional information below. For this project, students should have:

- made a journal entry every day.
- included five skills discussed in the handbook.

5 Analyzing Data and Communicating Results

Key Term

communication: sharing information

Analyzing Data When you organize information, you put it in a logical order. In scientific experiments, it is important to organize your data. Data collected during an experiment are not very useful unless they are organized and easy to read. It is also important to organize your data if you plan to share the results of your experiment.

Scientists often organize information visually by using data tables, charts, graphs, and diagrams. By using tables, charts, graphs, and diagrams, scientists can display a lot of information in a small space. They also make it easier to compare and interpret data.

Tables are made up of rows and columns. Columns run up and down. Rows run from left to right. Tables display data in an orderly arrangement, often numerically. For example, reading a table containing the uses of sulfuric acid shows that the largest use of sulfuric acid is in fertilizers. Figure 15 is a table that shows some uses of sulfuric acid.

USES OF SULFURIC ACID	
Product	**Percentage**
Dyes, batteries, paint, explosives	15
Raw materials	15
Fertilizers	60
Petroleum refining	5
Metal processing	5

▲ **Figure 15**

Graphs, such as bar graphs, line graphs, and circle graphs, often use special coloring, shading, or patterns to represent information. Keys indicate what the special markings represent. Line graphs have horizontal (x) and vertical (y) axes to indicate such things as time and quantities.

14 EXPLAIN: How do tables and graphs help you analyze data?

Sharing Results When you talk to a friend, you are communicating, or sharing information. If you write a letter or a report, you are also communicating but in a different way. Scientists communicate all the time. They communicate to share results, information, and opinions. They write books and magazine or newspaper articles. They may also create Web sites about their work. This is called written **communication.**

Graphs are a visual way to communicate. The circle graph in Figure 16 is showing the same information that is shown in Figure 15. The circle graph presents the information in a different way.

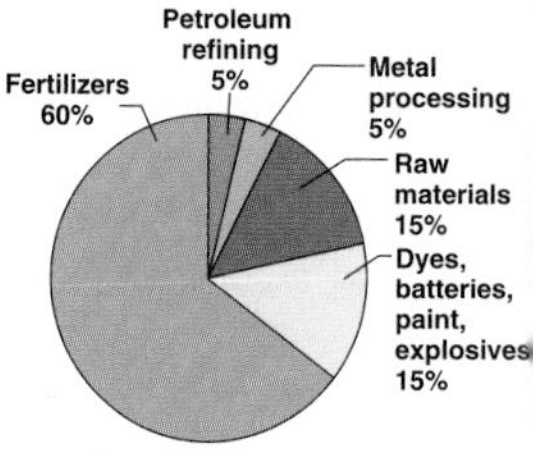

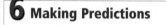

▲ **Figure 16** Circle graphs are a good way to show parts of a whole.

15 LIST: What are some ways to communicate the results of an experiment?

6 Making Predictions

Key Terms

infer: to form a conclusion

predict: to state ahead of time what you think is going to happen

Thinking of Possibilities When you **infer** something, you form a conclusion. This is called making an inference. Your conclusion will usually be based on observations or past experience. You may use logic to form your statement. Your statement might be supported by evidence and perhaps can be tested by an experiment. An inference is not a fact. It is only one possible explanation.

When you **predict,** you state ahead of time what you think will happen. Predictions about future events are based on inferences, evidence, or past experience. The two science process skills of inferring and predicting are very closely related.

16 CONTRAST: What is the difference between inferring and predicting?

8

Teaching Options

EXTENDING THE LESSON

Organizing Data Use classroom data for a table and a graph such as those in Figures 15 and 16. Ask students what their favorite school lunches are. Record responses on the board. Then, lead students as they construct a table and circle graph based on the data.

ONGOING ASSESSMENT

Reading Figures 15 and 16 Have students refer to Figures 15 and 16 to answer these questions: *What percent of sulfuric acid is used to make raw materials?* (15) *What is the largest use of sulfuric acid?* (fertilizers)

• TEACHING RESOURCES •

Teacher's Resources CD-ROM

Graph: Visuals, p. 3

Graph Paper: Visuals, p. 4

Laboratory Manual

Lab. Worksheet 4: Organizing and Analyzing Data, pp. 9–10

Lab. Worksheet 5: Graphing, pp. 11–14

How do you conduct a scientific investigation?

By now, you should have a good understanding of the science process skills. These skills are used to solve many science problems. There is also a basic procedure, or plan, that scientists usually follow when conducting investigations. Some people call this procedure the scientific method.

The scientific method is a series of steps that can serve as a guide to solving problems or answering questions. It uses many of the science process skills you know, such as observing and predicting.

Not all experiments use all of the steps in the scientific method. Some experiments follow all of them, but in a different order. In fact, there is no one right scientific method. Each problem is different. Some problems may require steps that another problem would not. However, most investigations will follow the same basic procedure.

1 DESCRIBE: What is the scientific method?

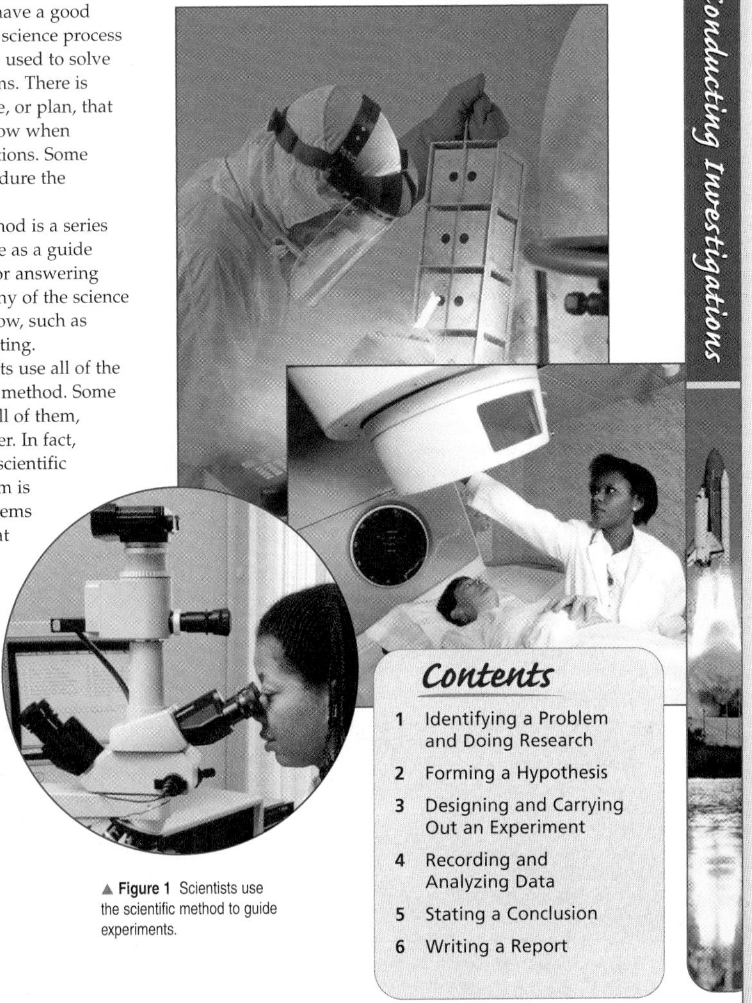

▲ **Figure 1** Scientists use the scientific method to guide experiments.

Contents

1 Identifying a Problem and Doing Research

2 Forming a Hypothesis

3 Designing and Carrying Out an Experiment

4 Recording and Analyzing Data

5 Stating a Conclusion

6 Writing a Report

Handbook B: Conducting Investigations

How do you conduct a scientific investigation?

Handbook Overview

In this part of the handbook, students will identify the steps of the scientific method, learn how to identify a problem, form a hypothesis, design and carry out an experiment, and find out different ways that they can record and analyze data. Students will also learn some basic safety procedures to be followed in the lab.

About Figure 1 Many people, including the ones shown here, use the scientific method in everyday life to help solve problems. The people shown in the photographs are most likely carrying out experiments. Scientists may use all or only parts of the scientific method to solve a problem, depending on the type of problem.

Answer to Question

1 DESCRIBE: a series of steps that can serve as a guide to solving problems or asking questions

Handbook Project

CONDUCTING EXPERIMENTS REFERENCE

MATERIALS (depending upon project chosen): posterboard or paper, markers or crayons, pen and pencil, computer

As students read Handbook B, they should create a resource to use throughout the year when they conduct experiments. Students should clearly record the steps of the scientific process and explain how to complete each of the steps. They might choose to illustrate the steps in a real experiment, such as the one described in this handbook. They should also include a copy of their completed lab report with the important parts highlighted and labeled. Students' resources could be in the form of pamphlets, illustrated posters, or a class Web site. Encourage students to use this resource throughout the year as they conduct and report on scientific experiments. **learning style: linguistic**

ASSESSMENT PLANNER

For assessment in the Student Edition, see the following pages:

Alternative Assessment
Building Skills: pp. 10, 12, 13

Performance-Based Assessment
Hands-On Activity: p. 12

• TEACHING RESOURCES •

Teacher's Resources CD-ROM
Conducting Scientific Investigations: Handbook Resources, p. 6

1 Identifying a Problem and Doing Research

✎ **STUDY HINT** Before beginning the lesson, help students create a flowchart that lists the steps in the scientific method. This flowchart should have space for six steps and some details about each one. After students read this section, they should write the step in their flowcharts. They can continue filling in the chart as they read the rest of Handbook B. Give each student a copy of the Flowchart, found on the Teacher's Resources CD-ROM.

Discussion Discuss with students why they would want to research a science problem before conducting experiments of their own. (Other people may have already investigated the problem. Learning all you can about a topic helps you to focus your research.) Give examples of scientific problems that students can restate as questions to be researched. **learning style: auditory**

Answer to question

▶ **IDENTIFY:** State a problem as a question.

BUILDING SCIENCE SKILLS

Researching Background Information Provide resources for students' research. Remind them that using specific text features, such as the table of contents and index, can help them use their research time more effectively.

2 Forming a Hypothesis

Discussion Discuss with students the difference between a guess, a hypothesis, and a theory. Point out that a hypothesis is based on observations or prior knowledge or experience, while a guess may not have any basis or foundation. A theory is a set of hypotheses that have been tested many times. **learning style: auditory**

Answer to question

▶ **DESCRIBE:** A scientist thinks of possible explanations for a set of observations.

BUILDING SCIENCE SKILLS

Developing a Hypothesis Guide students as they narrow the hypothesis. Suggest possible hypotheses and ask students if these hypotheses are narrow enough to test.

1 Identifying a Problem and Doing Research

Starting an Investigation Scientists often state a problem as a question. This is the first step in a scientific investigation. Most experiments begin by asking a scientific question. That is, they ask a question that can be answered by gathering evidence. This question is the reason for the scientific investigation. It also helps determine how the investigation will proceed.

Have you ever done background research for a science project? When you do this kind of research, you are looking for data that others have already obtained on the same subject. You can gather research by reading books, magazines, and newspapers, and by using the Internet to find out what other scientists have done. Doing research is the first step of gathering evidence for a scientific investigation.

▶ **IDENTIFY:** What is the first step of a scientific investigation?

BUILDING SCIENCE SKILLS

Researching Background Information Suppose you notice that the brown paper towels at school do not seem to soak up as much water as the paper towels used in your home. You wonder which kinds of paper towels absorb, or soak up, the most water. You wonder if there is a connection between the paper towels' thickness and absorbency.

To determine which paper towels are most absorbent, look for information on paper towels in magazines, in books, or on the Internet. Put your findings in a report.

▲ **Figure 2** Testing paper towels for absorbency

2 Forming a Hypothesis

Key Terms

hypothesis: suggested answer to a question or problem

theory: set of hypotheses that have been supported by testing over and over again

Focusing the Investigation Scientists usually state clearly what they expect to find out in an investigation. This is called stating a hypothesis. A **hypothesis** is a suggested answer to a question or a solution to a problem. Stating a hypothesis helps to keep you focused on the problem and helps you decide what to test.

To form their hypotheses, scientists must think of possible explanations for a set of observations or they must suggest possible answers to a scientific question. One of those explanations becomes the hypothesis. In science, a hypothesis must include something that can be tested.

A hypothesis is more than just a guess. It must consider observations, past experiences, and previous knowledge. It is an inference turned into a statement that can be tested. A set of hypotheses that have been supported by testing over and over again by many scientists is called a **theory**. An example is the theory that explains how living things have evolved, or changed, over time.

A hypothesis can take the form of an "if . . . then" statement. A well-worded hypothesis is a guide for how to set up and perform an experiment.

▶ **DESCRIBE:** How does a scientist form a hypothesis?

BUILDING SCIENCE SKILLS

Developing a Hypothesis A hypothesis for an experiment about which paper towels absorb the most water might be stated as follows:

If thicker paper towels soak up more water than thin paper towels, then thickness is an important factor for paper towel absorbency.

However, what do you mean by thicker? Are the paper towels really different? Does color or design make a difference? You need to make your hypothesis specific. Revise the hypothesis above to make it more specific.

Teaching Options

EXTENDING THE LESSON

Identifying Research Resources Have students brainstorm various research resources and list them on the board. Discuss with students what kind of information they would find in each one. A Web site, for example, might give up-to-the-minute information. An encyclopedia is a good source for general information about a topic. Have students make a two-column chart. The first column should be labeled *Research Resource* and the second column should be labeled *Type of Information*. Students can work in pairs to fill in the chart. Allow students to share their charts with the class. **learning styles: visual, linguistic**

ESL/ELL STRATEGY

Making Up If...Then Statements Forming hypotheses for scientific investigations may be difficult for English-language learners. Pair an English-proficient student with an English-language learner to practice forming hypotheses. Student pairs should form hypotheses by using if...then statements. The hypotheses can be very simple statements such as "If there are clouds in the sky, then it will rain." The hypotheses do not have to be true nor will students carry out experiments to support their hypotheses. Allow pairs to share their hypotheses with the class. **learning styles: linguistic, interpersonal**

3 Designing and Carrying Out an Experiment

Key Terms

variable: anything that can affect the outcome of an experiment

constant: something that does not change

controlled experiment: experiment in which all the conditions except one are kept constant

Testing the Hypothesis Scientists need to plan how to test their hypotheses. This means they must design an experiment. The plan must be a step-by-step procedure. It should include a record of any observations made or measurements taken.

All experiments must take variables into account. A **variable** is anything that can affect the outcome of an experiment. Room temperature, amount of sunlight, and water vapor in the air are just some of the many variables that could affect the outcome of an experiment.

4 DEFINE: What is a variable?

Controlling the Experiment One of the variables in an experiment should be what you are testing. This is what you will change during the experiment. All other variables need to remain the same. In this experiment, you will vary the type of paper towel.

A **constant** is something that does not change. If there are no constants in your experiment, you will not be sure why you got the results you did. An experiment in which all the conditions except one are kept constant is called a **controlled experiment.**

Some experiments have two setups. In one setup, called the control, nothing is changed. In the other setup, the variable being tested is changed. Later, the control group can be compared with the other group to provide useful data.

5 EXPLAIN: Explain how a controlled experiment is set up.

Designing the Procedure Suppose you want to design an experiment to determine if a paper towel's thickness affects its absorbency. You decide to do a set of measurements to find out the absorbency of three kinds of paper towels in a controlled environment. You will measure the thickness of the paper towels and then determine how much water each paper towel soaks up to see if your hypothesis is correct.

In designing your experiment, you need to identify the variables. The three kinds of paper towels are all variables that could effect the outcome of your experiment. Everything about testing the effect of thickness on absorbency needs to be the same except the actual thickness of each paper towel.

Finally, you should decide on the data you will collect. How will you measure the thickness of the paper towels? In this case, you might want to record the thickness of each towel, its color, whether it absorbed water, and how much water was absorbed.

The hands-on activity on page 12 is one possible experiment you could have designed. It has one method for measuring the absorbency of the paper towels. Sometimes scientists try to measure the same thing two different ways to be sure the test is accurate. Can you think of another method to measure the absorbency of paper towels?

6 LIST: How do constants and variables affect an experiment?

Handbook B: Conducting Investigations **11**

---

3 Designing and Carrying Out an Experiment

✏ **STUDY HINT** Ask students to write a topic sentence for each of the sections as they read them. They can also write some supporting details about each.

Demonstration Tell students that you are going to test the hypothesis that heavier objects fall through a liquid faster than lighter objects do. Set up a clear container, such as a fish tank, and fill it with a liquid. Drop several objects of different weights from the same place above the liquid. Ask: *What were the constants in your experiment?* (the type of liquid and the height from which the objects were dropped) *What were the variables?* (the weights of the various objects) **learning styles: visual, logical/mathematical**

Discussion Explain that in a controlled experiment, only one variable is tested at a time. Ask students to explain why it is important to have a control in an experiment. (By changing only one variable, scientists can be sure that any differences between the control and the experimental setup were caused by the variable being tested.) **learning style: auditory**

Answers to questions:

4 DEFINE: anything that can affect the outcome of an experiment

5 EXPLAIN: An experiment is set up in which all the conditions except one are kept constant.

6 LIST: The data that you wish to collect determine the variables in the experiment. All the variables except one have to be kept constant to be sure that the desired question is being tested.

✏ **WRITING HINT** Tell students that when they design a procedure, they should write step-by-step directions on how to carry out the experiment. The directions should be numbered and each step should flow logically to the next. The directions should also include a list of all the materials that will be needed to perform the experiment.

COOPERATIVE LEARNING

Designing an Experiment Ask students to work in pairs or small groups to design simple experiments that will test a hypothesis. Students should identify the question for research, state the hypothesis they would test, and tell how they would test it. Be sure that students identify both variables and constants in the experiment.

• TEACHING RESOURCES •

Teacher's Resources CD-ROM

Flowchart: Study Tools, p. 6

Designing an Experiment: Study Tools, p. 14

Designing an Experiment Rubric: Teaching Tools, p. 7

T11

Hands-On Activity
CARRYING OUT AN EXPERIMENT

TIME: 30 minutes

PURPOSE: observing, comparing, explaining, inferring

Practicing Your Skills Answers

6. **OBSERVE:** The amount absorbed by each towel will vary, depending on the towels used.

7. **COMPARE:** The amount absorbed by each towel will vary, depending on the towels used.

8. **EXPLAIN:** Possible answer: I spread the paper towel flat, and I added the water drop by drop. I used the same dropper for each towel, and measured the water accurately each time.

9. **IDENTIFY:** the thickness of the towel

4 Recording and Analyzing Data

STUDY HINT Give each student a copy of the Concept Map on the Teacher's Resources CD-ROM. Have students write the words *Dealing With Data* in the center circle. As students read, they can write different ways of dealing with data on their concept maps.

Discussion Point out to students that collecting data is not the end of an experiment. Once data is collected, it must be organized and analyzed. Ask students to name different ways in which data might be organized. (charts, graphs, tables, and reports) **learning style: auditory**

Answer to question

▶ **LIST:** tables, charts, graphs, summaries, reports

BUILDING SCIENCE SKILLS

Analyzing Data Suggest that students copy the table in Figure 3 into their notebooks and add their own data. Ask students if they can think of any other ways that the data could be organized. Make a list of their suggestions and encourage students to evaluate which methods of organization are best suited to this data. **learning style: visual**

Hands-On Activity
CARRYING OUT AN EXPERIMENT

You will need 3 or more kinds of paper towels, a metric ruler, an eyedropper or pipette (preferably calibrated in millimeters), and water.

1. Get three different kinds of paper towels. To find the thickness of each kind of towel, measure the thickness of five towels and divide the result by five. Set up a data table for the information you gather.

2. Now you are ready to compare the absorbency of the paper towels. Cut the paper towels into squares of equal sizes. Squares that are 10 cm in size are good for testing.

3. Lay a square of paper towel on a tray or other nonabsorbent surface. Add drops of water one at a time until the paper towel has soaked up all the water it can. Record how much water was absorbed. If your eyedropper is not marked in milliliters, you can record your data in "drops." If it is marked, then you should record the milliliters.

4. Test all the paper towel samples the exact same way. Be sure that you only measure the water that is absorbed and that you let each paper towel sample soak up as much water as it will hold.

5. You are now ready to compare your data and see if they support your hypothesis.

Practicing Your Skills

6. **OBSERVE:** What happened in the experiment? How much water did each paper towel sample absorb?

7. **COMPARE:** Which paper towel absorbed the most?

8. **EXPLAIN:** What procedures did you follow to make sure the paper towels were all given a fair and equal test?

9. **IDENTIFY:** What is the variable being tested in this experiment?

12

---

4 Recording and Analyzing Data

Dealing With Data During an experiment, you must keep careful notes about what you observe. For example, you might need to note any special steps you took in setting up the experiment, exactly how you made the drops the same size each time, or the temperature of the water. This is important information that might affect your conclusion.

At the end of an experiment, you will need to study the data to find any patterns. Much of the data you will deal with is written text. You may read a report or a summary of an experiment. However, scientific information is often a set of numbers or facts presented in other, more visual ways. These visual presentations make the information more meaningful and easier to understand. Tables, charts, and graphs, for instance, help you understand a collection of facts on a topic.

After your data have been organized, you need to ask what the data show. Do they support your hypothesis? Do they show something wrong in your experiment? Do you need to gather more data by performing another experiment?

▶ **LIST:** What are some ways to display data?

BUILDING SCIENCE SKILLS

Analyzing Data You made the following notes during your experiment. How would you display this information?

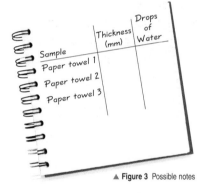

▲ **Figure 3** Possible notes

Teaching Options

• TEACHING RESOURCES •

Teacher's Resources CD-ROM
Concept Map: Study Tools, p. 4

Laboratory Manual
Lab. Worksheet 4: Organizing and Analyzing Data, pp. 13–14

ESL/ELL STRATEGY

Remind students that words like *first*, *next*, *then*, and *later* signal sequence. Sometimes these words show a sequence of events; other times they are implied but not stated directly in the text.

RETEACH

Examining and Displaying Data
Divide students into small groups. Give each group a table, a graph, or a chart to study. Have students examine the data. Ask students if the way that the data is displayed makes it easier to understand the information given. Have each group use the same data in the table, graph, or chart and display the information in another way. Allow groups to share their results. **learning styles: visual, logical/mathematical**

5 Stating a Conclusion

Drawing Conclusions A conclusion is a statement that sums up what you have learned from an experiment. When you draw a conclusion, you need to decide whether the data you collected supported your hypothesis. You may need to repeat an experiment several times before you can draw any conclusions from it. Conclusions often lead you to ask new questions and plan new experiments to answer them.

▶ **8** EXPLAIN: Why might it be necessary to repeat an experiment?

BUILDING SCIENCE SKILLS

Stating a Conclusion Review your hypothesis statement regarding the effect of the thickness of a paper towel on its absorbency. Then, review the data you obtained during your experiment.

- Was your hypothesis correct? Use your observations to support your answer.

- Which paper towel absorbed the most? Was it also the thickest?

▲ **Figure 4** Throughout this program, you may use forms like this one to organize your lab reports.

6 Writing a Report

Communicating Results Scientists keep careful written records of their observations and findings. These records are used to create a lab report. Lab reports are a form of written communication. They explain what happened in the experiment. A good lab report should be written so that anyone reading it can duplicate the experiment. It should contain the following information:

- A title
- A purpose
- Background information
- Your hypothesis
- Materials used
- Your step-by-step procedure
- Your observations
- Your recorded data
- Your analysis of the data
- Your conclusions

Your conclusions should relate back to the questions you asked in the "purpose" section of your report. Also, the report should not have any experimental errors that might have caused unexpected results. For example, did you follow the steps in the correct order? Did an unexpected variable interfere with your results? Was your equipment clean and in good working order? This explanation of possible errors should also be part of your conclusions.

▶ **9** EXPLAIN: Why is it important to explain possible errors in your lab report?

BUILDING SCIENCE SKILLS

Writing a Lab Report Write a lab report to communicate to other scientists your discoveries about the effect of a paper towel's thickness on its water absorbency. Your lab report should include a title, your hypothesis statement, a list of materials you used, the procedure, your observations, and your conclusions. Try to include one table of data in your report.

Handbook B: Conducting Investigations

MORE ON THE WEB

Learning to Write Online
Have students visit www.conceptsandchallenges.com to learn about some Internet resources that can help them write better. Students can use online guides to write paragraphs, essays, and reports. Finally, students can visit an online newspaper written entirely by students.

• *TEACHING RESOURCES* •

Teacher's Resources CD-ROM
Lab Activity Report: Study Tools, pp. 16–17

Laboratory Manual
Lab. Worksheet 6: Writing a Laboratory Report, pp. 19–20

5 Stating a Conclusion

Discussion Although most students think of the word *conclusion* as synonymous with *end*, point out that the conclusion of an experiment may not be the end. An experimenter may find that there is more work to be done if a hypothesis was not proven to be true. **learning style: auditory**

Answer to question

▶ **8** EXPLAIN: The initial results may not lead to a conclusion. An experiment may need to be repeated several times before the conclusions are clear.

BUILDING SCIENCE SKILLS

Stating a Conclusion Ask students to answer the bulleted questions and share their responses in a small group or with the class. Students will probably find that the thickest towels absorbed the most water.

6 Writing a Report

Demonstration Show students examples of lab reports. Point out the parts of the report, which are listed on page 13. Show students that a report could end up in paragraph form, list form, or some other form. Ask students what would happen if various pieces of information were missing. (If the procedure was missing, other scientists could not perform the experiment themselves. If the data were missing, it might be hard to tell if the conclusion was correct.) **learning styles: visual, auditory**

Discussion Review the parts of a report as given in the bulleted list. Discuss with students why each component is necessary for a detailed and organized report. **learning styles: auditory, linguistic**

Answer to question

▶ **9** EXPLAIN: Errors could produce results that were not expected. Those errors could cause the hypothesis to not be proven to be true.

BUILDING SCIENCE SKILLS

Writing a Lab Report Remind students to use the parts of a report listed on page 13. Students could turn the parts on the list into topic heads in their report, such as *title*, *purpose*, *background*, *materials*, and *procedure*.

LAB SAFETY

STUDY HINT As students read each lab safety rule, make sure that they also note the icon to the left of the rule. Getting familiar with the icons will help students recall the proper safety procedure as they do the lab activities. **learning style: visual**

Demonstration Act out or describe for students various situations in the lab that could be dangerous. For example, write "DANGEROUS" on a label and stick it on an empty beaker. Then, pick up the beaker without wearing a lab apron or safety goggles. Ask students to identify the safety precautions that you should have followed. **learning style: visual**

Discussion Read through the safety information with students. Point out the need for lab safety rules, reiterating that students could be injured by not following safety procedures in the lab. As you go through each rule, be sure that students understand the rule and the reasons behind it. **learning style: auditory**

Reinforcement To help students remember the safety rules, have them work with partners or in small groups to make posters that feature safety reminders. Assign one or two rules to each group. Have groups write the rules in their own words and include illustrations. Display students' work around the room as a reminder. **learning style: visual**

Handbook Project Wrap-Up
CONDUCTING EXPERIMENTS REFERENCE

Students can explain their references to the rest of the class. You can use the Individual Activity Rubric found on the Teacher's Resources CD-ROM to assess students' projects. Fill in the rubric with the additional information below. For this project, students should have:

- created a resource reference.
- included a lab report.

LAB SAFETY

Working in a science laboratory can be both exciting and meaningful. However, you must always be aware of safety precautions when carrying out experiments. There are a few basic rules that should be followed in any science laboratory:

- Read all instructions carefully before the start of an experiment. Follow all instructions exactly and in the correct order.

- Check your equipment to make sure it is clean and working properly.

- Never taste, smell, or touch any substance in the lab that you are not told to do so. Never eat or drink anything in the lab. Do not chew gum.

- Never work alone. Tell a teacher at once if an accident occurs.

Experiments that use chemicals or heat can be dangerous. The following list of rules and symbols will help you avoid accidents. There are also rules about what to do if an accident does occur. Here are some rules to remember when working in a lab:

1. Do not use glass that is chipped or metal objects with broken edges. Do not try to clean up broken glassware yourself. Notify your teacher if a piece of glassware is broken.

2. Do not use electrical cords with loose plugs or frayed ends. Do not let electrical cords cross in front of working areas. Do not use electrical equipment near water.

3. Be very careful when using sharp objects such as scissors, knives, or tweezers. Always cut in a direction away from your body.

4. Be careful when you are using a heat source. Use proper equipment, such as tongs or a ringstand, when handling hot objects.

5. Confine loose clothing and hair when working with an open flame. Be sure you know the location of the nearest fire extinguisher. Never reach across an open flame.

6. Be careful when working with poisonous or toxic substances. Never mix chemicals without directions from your teacher. Remove any long jewelry that might hang down and end up in chemicals. Avoid touching your eyes or mouth when working with these chemicals.

7. Use extreme care when working with acids and bases. Never mix acids and bases without direction from your teacher. Never smell anything directly. Use caution when handling chemicals that produce fumes.

8. Wear safety goggles, especially when working with an open flame, chemicals, and any liquids.

9. Wear lab aprons when working with substances of any sort, especially chemicals.

10. Use caution when handling or collecting plants. Some plants can be harmful if they are touched or eaten.

11. Use caution when handling live animals. Some animals can injure you or spread disease. Handle all live animals as humanely as possible.

12. Dispose of all equipment and materials properly. Keep your work area clean at all times.

13. Always wash your hands thoroughly with soap and water after handling chemicals or live organisms.

14. Follow the ⚠ **CAUTION** and safety symbols you see used throughout this book when doing labs or other activities.

14

Teaching Options

ONGOING ASSESSMENT

Reviewing Lab Safety Rules State the rules for students in random order, leaving some as they are but substituting words or rewording others to make them incorrect. Ask students to make a thumbs up sign if the rule is correct or a thumbs down sign if it is not. (Examples of incorrect statements: *You need only safety goggles when working with chemicals* or *It's okay to reach across an open flame if your hair is tied back*.)

• TEACHING RESOURCES •

![CD icon] **Teacher's Resources CD-ROM**
Individual Activity Rubric: Teaching Tools, p. 5

Practicing Lab Safety: Handbook Resources, p. 7

Handbook Key Term Review: Handbook Resources, p. 8

Chapter 1 Properties of Matter

PLANNING GUIDE

◆ **TEACHING THE CHAPTER** This chapter should take approximately 5–8 days to complete instruction and assessment.

	Skills and Features	Projects and Activities	Achieve Science Literacy	Meet Individual Needs
Chapter 1 Opener p. T15	OBSERVE	• Chapter Project		

Lesson 1-1
 	
What is physical science?
pp. T16–T17
	IDENTFY, NAME, ANALYZE
	• Web InfoSearch
	• People in Science
		• Extending the Lesson	• Study Hint
			• Ongoing Assessment
				• ESL/ELL Strategy
				• Reteach
				  CD-ROM
				  Enrichment Activity
				  Concept Map

Lesson 1-2
 	
What are the properties of matter?
pp. T18–T19
 	
Standard: B1a
	OBSERVE, INFER, DEFINE
	• Investigate
	• Building Science Skills
	• How Do They Know That?
		• Extending the Lesson
		• More on the Web
			• Study Hint	• ESL/ELL Strategy
				• Reteach
				  CD-ROM
				  Enrichment Activity
				  Writing Activity
				  Outline

Lesson 1-3
 	
What are the states of matter?
pp. T20–T21
	DEFINE, EXPLAIN, IDENTIFY
	• Web InfoSearch
	• Integrating Earth Science
		• Cooperative Learning	• Study Hint
			• Writing Hint
				• ESL/ELL Strategy
				  CD-ROM
				  Enrichment Activity

Lesson 1-4
 	
How does matter change state?
pp. T22–T23
 	
Standards: B1c, B3a
	INFER, CLASSIFY, EXPLAIN
	• Designing an Experiment
	• Real-Life Science
		• Cooperative Learning
		• More on the Web
		• Lab Challenge
			• Study Hint
			• Reading Strategy
			• Ongoing Assessment
				CD-ROM
				  Enrichment Activity
				  Designing an
				  Experiment
				  Laboratory
				  Video

Big Idea
 	
How are changes of state part of the water cycle?
pp. T24–T25
 	
Standard: B3a
	RESEARCH, COMMUNICATE, ANALYZE
	• Science Log: Writing Activity
		• Big Idea Online
		• Close Activity
			• Tips for Using Technology	CD-ROM
				  Big Idea Planner
				  Flowchart

Planning Guide continues on next page.

Standards: For details on the correlation to National Science Standards see pages *xx–xxi*.

	Skills and Features	Projects and Activities	Achieve Science Literacy	Meet Individual Needs
Lesson 1-5 **What are physical and chemical changes?** pp. T26–T27 Standards: B1a, B1b	CLASSIFY, DEFINE, LIST • Building Science Skills • Hands-On Activity	• Cooperative Learning • More on the Web • Integrating Life Science	• Study Hint	 CD-ROM Flowchart
Lab Activity **Observing Physical and Chemical Changes** pp. T28–T29	ANALYZE, OBSERVE, CLASSIFY • Set-Up Time: 15 min • Lab Time: 30 min	• Integrating Life Science • Lab Skills Worksheets • Extend the Lab Activity	• Tips for Using Technology	• ESL/ELL Strategy CD-ROM Lab Activity Report Database Planner
Chapter 1 Challenges pp. T30–T32	• Chapter Summary • Key Term Challenges • Content Challenges • Concept Challenges	• Chapter Project Wrap-Up	• Study Hint • Preparing Students for Standardized Tests	• ESL/ELL Strategy CD-ROM Chapter Self-Check Weekly Journal

Teacher Notes

_____

_____

_____

_____

_____

_____

_____

_____

_____

_____

_____

Chapter 1 Properties of Matter

▲ **Figure 1-1** Water can exist in any of three states on Earth.

All things are made of some kind of matter. On Earth, most matter exists in one of three states. Matter can change physically from one state to another or it can change chemically. Water is special. It can exist in all three states at the same time under ordinary conditions of temperature and pressure.

► Can you name the different states of matter by identifying them in Figure 1-1?

Contents

Teaching Options

ASSESSMENT PLANNER

For assessment in the Student Edition, see the following pages:

Content Assessment
Checking Concepts: pp. 17, 19, 21, 23, 27
Thinking Critically: pp. 17, 19, 21, 23, 27
Chapter Challenges: pp. 30–32

Alternative Assessment
Building Skills: pp. 19, 27
Web InfoSearch: pp. 17, 21
Science Log: p. 25

Performance-Based Assessment
Hands-On Activity: p. 27
Designing an Experiment: p. 23
Lab Activity: pp. 28–29

• TEACHING RESOURCES •

Teacher's Resources CD-ROM
Lesson Review: Ch. 1, pp. 2, 4, 5, 7, 10
Enrichment: Ch. 1, pp. 3, 6, 8
Key Term Review: Ch. 1, p. 11
Chapter 1 Test: pp. 12–14
Laboratory Manual: pp. 9–10, 19–20, 21–24

Laboratory Video
Segment 3: What Happens During a Phase Change?

Chapter 1
Properties of Matter

Chapter Overview

In this chapter, students will describe the main branches of physical science and identify four basic properties of matter and the four states of matter. They will also describe ways that matter changes state and distinguish between physical and chemical changes in matter.

About Figure 1-1 A vapor is the gaseous form of a substance that is normally a liquid at room temperature. Some vapors are colored, such as violet iodine vapor, and can be seen. Most other vapors, such as water vapor, are colorless and cannot be seen. Clouds are formed from water vapor in the air, but what is seen in a cloud are small ice crystals or drops of liquid water that have condensed from water vapor.

Answer The states of matter are solid, liquid, and gas. Liquid water and many solids, such as ice, can be clearly seen in the figure. Students may state that the fog coming off the water is a gas. However, fog actually consists of small drops of liquid water.

Linking Prior Knowledge

For this chapter, students should recall:

• what they know about solids, liquids, and gases.

• what they know about changes in state, such as melting, freezing, and condensing.

Chapter Project

DEVELOPING A GAME

MATERIALS: posterboard, glue, construction paper

Have students design a game using the Key Terms and their definitions from the chapter. They can use the materials listed or other materials. As they read the chapter, they can add to the game so that it is ready to be played at the end of the chapter. Examples of possible games include a card game, a board game, or a question-and-answer type of game show.
learning styles: tactile, linguistic

1 Introduce

✏️ **STUDY HINT** Before beginning this lesson, read the lesson objective with students. Then, have them review the Key Terms and their definitions.

Linking Prior Knowledge Invite a volunteer to read the lesson title aloud. Ask students to draw upon their reading of the Key Terms to predict how chemistry, physics, and physical science are related.

2 Teach

Discussion Create a concept map with students to help them understand how physical science incorporates chemistry and physics. Draw a rectangle on the board and label it *Physical Science*. Draw two arrows extending from the rectangle to two circles labeled *Chemistry* and *Physics*. Have students connect the specialized fields shown in Figure 1-2 by drawing lines from each circle and labeling each with the appropriate field. Discuss how some specialized fields involve both chemistry and physics. For example, thermodynamics is physics because it is the study of energy conversions that involve heat, but it relates to chemistry because it deals with energy changes that occur during chemical reactions. **learning styles: visual, linguistic**

Demonstration Display objects that operate because of advances in physical science. Possible items include solar powered calculators, computers, CDs, and plastic containers. Discuss how life would be different without such products. Invite volunteers to name other products created through physical science that have had a major impact on their lives.
learning styles: auditory, tactile

Answers to questions

▶ **NAME:** chemistry and physics

▶ **DEFINE:** a person who studies or works in one particular area of a subject

▶ **LIST:** Possible answers: TVs, lasers, holograms, and seat belts

---

1-1 What is physical science?

Objective
Identify and describe the main branches of physical science.

Key Terms
chemistry: branch of science that deals with the study of the structure and the makeup of matter and the changes matter undergoes

physics: branch of science that deals with energy and matter and how they interact

specialization (spehsh-uh-lih-ZAY-shuhn): studying or working in one area of a subject

Studying Physical Science Physical science is one of the major fields of science. It is the study of matter and energy. Everything around you is either matter or energy.

Physical science has two main branches. The two main branches are chemistry and physics. **Chemistry** deals with the study of the structure and the makeup of matter and the changes matter undergoes. **Physics** deals with the study of energy and matter and how they interact.

▶ **NAME:** What are the two main branches of physical science?

Specialization A specialist is a person who studies or works in one particular area of a subject. Working in one area of a subject is called **specialization**. Some of the specialized fields in physical science are listed in Figure 1-2.

▶ **DEFINE:** What is a specialist?

Importance of Physical Science Why study physical science? Physical science is an important part of everyday life. It is difficult to think of anything that does not involve physical science and the discoveries of physical scientists. For example, each year seat belts save thousands of lives. Seat belt technology is based on the laws of motion.

Physical scientists have also discovered how to harness nuclear energy. Using nuclear energy has both problems and benefits. Physical scientists are constantly working to solve the problems related to nuclear energy. Their solutions may someday solve the world's energy problems. Physical scientists are also researching other forms of energy for power. Solar panels, wind farms, and fuel cells are some alternative sources of energy.

The discovery of new materials has resulted in the production of a variety of ceramic tiles, various glass products, and plastics. Our leisure time has benefited through cable and satellite dish TV, lasers,

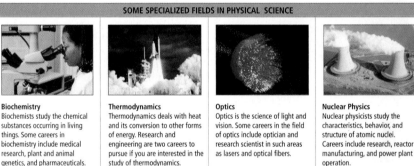

SOME SPECIALIZED FIELDS IN PHYSICAL SCIENCE

Biochemistry
Biochemists study the chemical substances occurring in living things. Some careers in biochemistry include medical research, plant and animal genetics, and pharmaceuticals.

Thermodynamics
Thermodynamics deals with heat and its conversion to other forms of energy. Research and engineering are two careers to pursue if you are interested in the study of thermodynamics.

Optics
Optics is the science of light and vision. Some careers in the field of optics include optician and research scientist in such areas as lasers and optical fibers.

Nuclear Physics
Nuclear physicists study the characteristics, behavior, and structure of atomic nuclei. Careers include research, reactor manufacturing, and power plant operation.

▲ Figure 1-2

16

Teaching Options

EXTENDING THE LESSON

Researching Other Fields in Physical Science Guide students in recognizing that the fields shown in Figure 1-2 are just a few specialized areas of physical science. Explain that astrophysics, organic chemistry, inorganic chemistry, and acoustics are other related fields. Invite students to conduct research to discover the focus of these fields and associated careers. Allow students to share their findings with the class. **learning style: linguistic**

RETEACH

Brainstorming Specialized Fields Have students work in small groups to read the descriptions of the specialized fields of physical science in Figure 1-2. Then, have them brainstorm a list of jobs associated with these fields. As a whole-group activity, compile the groups' lists into a class chart. **learning style: interpersonal**

computers, holograms, and CD and DVD players. Cars and airplanes have been made safer and faster.

Studying matter and how it reacts with other substances has helped create all of these things. We will take a closer look at reactions and interactions of matter and energy as we progress through the book.

3 LIST: What are some of the products that have been created because of the work of physical scientists?

✓ CHECKING CONCEPTS

1. The two main branches of physical science are chemistry and _____.
2. Physical science is the study of matter and _____.
3. A person who works in only one area of a subject is a _____.
4. Physical scientists have helped develop ceramics, plastics, and _____.
5. The harnessing of _____ energy by physical scientists has helped reduce the world's energy problems.

💡 THINKING CRITICALLY

6. ANALYZE: Why do you think the number of specialized fields in physical science has grown during the past few decades?
7. LIST: What are three ways in which physical science is important in your daily life?

Web InfoSearch

A Career in Physical Science If you like science, you may be interested in a career in physical science. Choose a career from Figure 1-2, or a field of science that interests you.

SEARCH: Use the Internet to find out what education is required, what you will do on the job, and what tools you might need to perform this job. Write a short report about your results. Start your search at www.conceptsandchallenges.com. Some key search words are **biochemist** and **nuclear physicist**.

🪐 People in Science
SCIENTIFIC ILLUSTRATOR

Do you like to draw? If so, you may be interested in a career as a scientific illustrator. You can see the work of scientific illustrators on many pages in this book. Scientific illustrators make drawings, diagrams, and sketches to illustrate scientific processes, structures, cycles, or equations, helping people to understand scientific concepts.

Scientific illustrators are employed by publishers of science books and journals or by advertisers. The drawings of scientific illustrators are used in sales brochures, advertisements, and even in this book. In the catalogs of scientific supply houses and pharmaceutical companies, many drawings are used to demonstrate equipment and other supplies.

If you are interested in becoming a scientific illustrator, you need a college degree in graphics or fine arts. Many scientific illustrators also find a background in the sciences helpful in their careers.

Thinking Critically How does the work of a scientific illustrator help people learn science?

▲ **Figure 1-3** Scientific illustrators often use computers as tools.

---

3 Assess

✓ CHECKING CONCEPTS ANSWERS

1. physics
2. energy
3. specialist
4. Possible answers: various glass products, DVD players, lasers, and computers
5. nuclear

💡 THINKING CRITICALLY ANSWERS

6. ANALYZE: Improved tools have created new ways that scientists can study the natural world and have given rise to new careers.
7. LIST: Possible answers: making it easier to complete everyday tasks, helping keep people safe, and providing new forms of entertainment

4 Close

Web InfoSearch

A Career in Physical Science Have students choose a career from Figure 1-2 and search the Internet to find out about this career. Have students find the level of education required and the tools needed to perform the job. Students can write a short report about their results. Have students begin their search at www.conceptsandchallenges.com.

People in Science
SCIENTIFIC ILLUSTRATOR

Real-Life Connection Scientific illustrators use their knowledge of science and their artistic ability to create many types of visuals. Have students look through their textbooks to find examples of illustrations that depict processes, structures, cycles, and equations.

Discussion Ask students how a background in science would help a scientific illustrator. Encourage students to provide reasons for their responses.

Thinking Critically Answer
A scientific illustrator's creations help readers understand scientific concepts.

ONGOING ASSESSMENT

Classifying the Units Have students review the titles of the units in the Table of Contents and classify each unit into its appropriate branch of physical science.

ESL/ELL STRATEGY

Explaining the Word Physical Explain to English-language learners that the word *physical* can mean "of nature and matter" or "of the body." Ask students which definition describes the branch of science known as physical science.

• TEACHING RESOURCES •

Teacher's Resources CD-ROM
Lesson Review: Chapter 1, p. 2
Enrichment: Chapter 1, p. 3
Concept Map: Study Tools, p. 4

1 Introduce

🔍 INVESTIGATE

TIME: 5–10 minutes

PURPOSE: Students will observe that air takes up space.

MATERIALS: glass, tissue, pail, water

PROCEDURE: Have students work in pairs. Make sure that students pull the glass straight out of the water. Explain that after Step 3, each pair should discuss how the tissue feels. **learning styles: tactile, interpersonal**

THINK ABOUT IT: Water did not enter the glass. The tissue remained dry. Air in the glass takes up space.

✏️ **STUDY HINT** Have students copy the title of each section of the lesson in their notebooks. After reading a section, have students list the main ideas under each section title.

2 Teach

Discussion Define matter as anything that has mass and takes up space. Remind students that mass is the amount of matter an object contains, while volume is the amount of space an object takes up. Ask students for examples of matter and point out how each example has mass and takes up space.

Reinforcement Display a flower to the class. Ask students to describe the flower. Record all responses on the board. Then, write *Properties of a Flower* above the list. Explain that properties are characteristics that describe an object. Show students a different type of flower. Point out that, although properties differ from flower to flower, all flowers have certain properties in common. List these properties. Emphasize that just as all flowers share certain properties, all matter shares certain properties, such as mass, volume, weight, and density. **learning styles: visual, auditory**

Answers to questions

▶ **DEFINE:** anything that has mass and takes up space

▶ **DEFINE:** a characteristic used to describe an object

1-2 What are the properties of matter?

INVESTIGATE

Air as Matter
HANDS-ON ACTIVITY

1. Stuff a tissue into the bottom of a glass. Fill a pail with water.
2. Turn the glass upside down; push it straight down into the water.
3. Pull the glass straight out of the water and feel the tissue.
4. Record your observations.

THINK ABOUT IT: Did water enter the glass? How do you know? What does this tell you about air?

STEP 2

Objective
Identify two basic properties of matter.

Key Terms
matter: anything that has mass and takes up space

properties (PRAHP-uhr-teez): characteristics used to describe an object

Matter Look around you. What do all the objects you see around you have in common? They are all made up of matter. **Matter** is anything that has mass and takes up space. Mass is the amount of matter a sample of matter contains. The amount of space the sample takes up is its volume.

Water is matter. A glass filled with water is heavier than an empty glass. The water-filled glass is heavier because water has more mass than the air in the empty container. If you were to keep adding water to a filled glass, the water would overflow. It would overflow because water takes up space, leaving no room in the glass.

Air is matter, too. A balloon filled with air is heavier than a balloon that is not blown up because air has mass. When you blow air into a balloon, the balloon gets larger as air takes up space.

▶ **DEFINE:** What is matter?

Properties of Matter How would you describe an apple? You might say that an apple is red, round, and hard. Color, shape, and hardness are three **properties** of matter. Properties are characteristics used to describe an object.

Mass and volume are two basic properties of matter. Weight and density are also properties that can be used to describe matter. Weight is a measure of the pull of gravity on a sample of matter. Density tells you how much matter is in a unit volume.

▲ **Figure 1-4** Air has mass and takes up space inside of these balloons.

▶ **LIST:** What are the two basic properties of matter?

18

Teaching Options

EXTENDING THE LESSON

Basic Properties Ask students how they would describe an apple. Students might say that an apple is round, red, and hard. Explain to students that not all apples have these properties. Another apple may be round, green, and soft. Explain that some properties are not basic properties. They do not apply to all examples of the object. A basic property of all apples is that they are fruit. Mass and volume are basic properties of matter. Mass is a measure of the amount of matter in an object. Volume is a measure of how much space the object takes up.

RETEACH

Air Is Matter Obtain two identical balloons, a meter stick, and some string. Tie one end of the string around the center of the meterstick. Tie the other end around a stationary object so that the stick is suspended in midair. Hang an identical balloon from either end of the meterstick. The stick will remain balanced. Then, invite a volunteer to blow up one of the balloons. Hang the inflated balloon from one end of the stick and the deflated balloon from the other end. Challenge students to explain how the demonstration proves that air is matter. **learning style: visual**

Studying Matter The study of the structure and the makeup of matter and the changes matter undergoes is called chemistry. Scientists who study matter are called chemists. Chemists study what different substances are made of. They do experiments to learn how different kinds of matter can change and combine. The other branch of physical science is physics. Physicists study the different forms of energy and the ways that energy and matter interact.

▶ **DEFINE:** What is chemistry?

✓ CHECKING CONCEPTS

1. All the objects you see around you are made up of _____.
2. Matter is anything that has mass and takes up _____.
3. Mass is a basic _____ of matter.

4. Weight is a measure of the pull of _____ on an object.
5. The amount of space taken up by matter is its _____.

💡 THINKING CRITICALLY

6. **INFER:** What is the difference between mass and weight?
7. **EXPLAIN:** Why do you think scientists can use the basic properties of matter to help identify an unknown substance?

BUILDING SCIENCE SKILLS

Observing Choose three objects in your home or classroom. Examine each carefully. List four properties of each and the senses you used to help describe each.

How Do They Know That?

MASS IS A PROPERTY OF MATTER

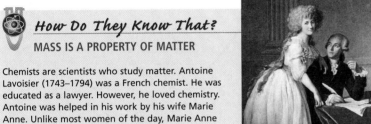

▲ **Figure 1-5** Marie Anne and Antoine Lavoisier working together

Chemists are scientists who study matter. Antoine Lavoisier (1743–1794) was a French chemist. He was educated as a lawyer. However, he loved chemistry. Antoine was helped in his work by his wife Marie Anne. Unlike most women of the day, Marie Anne had received an education in the arts and sciences. This enabled her to work side by side in the lab with her husband.

Before the work of the Lavoisiers, little was known about chemical reactions. For example, it was believed that there were only four elements. People also thought that chemical activities could create mass.

Marie Anne and Antoine showed that these ideas were not true. They explained that mass is not created or lost during a chemical reaction. Before an experiment, Antoine measured all of the materials going into the reaction. After the experiment, he measured the materials produced. He was the first scientist to realize that reactions began and ended with the same amount of mass. He wrote the Law of Conservation of Mass. It states that mass is neither created nor destroyed during a chemical change.

Thinking Critically The burning of wood is a chemical reaction. When wood burns, is mass destroyed?

CHAPTER 1: Properties of Matter **19**

ESL/ELL STRATEGY

Naming Properties Pair an English-language learner with an English-proficient student. Have one partner name an object and the other partner describe the properties of that object.

• TEACHING RESOURCES •

🔘 **Teacher's Resources CD-ROM**

Lesson Review: Chapter 1, p. 4

Enrichment: Chapter 1, p. 8

Writing Activity Outline: Study Tools, pp. 20–21

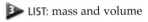

▶ **LIST:** mass and volume

3 Assess

✓ CHECKING CONCEPTS ANSWERS

1. matter
2. space
3. property
4. gravity
5. volume

💡 THINKING CRITICALLY ANSWERS

6. **INFER:** Mass is the amount of matter in an object. Weight is a measure of the pull of gravity on the object.
7. **EXPLAIN:** Possible answer: Scientists can compare the basic properties of an unknown substance with those of known substances.

4 Close

BUILDING SCIENCE SKILLS

Observing Answers will vary based on objects selected. Advise students that it might not be safe to use all five senses to examine each object. Students can use the Writing Activity Outline found on the Teacher's Resources CD-ROM to help them write the properties and senses used to describe each object.

How Do They Know That?

MASS IS A PROPERTY OF MATTER

Discussion Make sure that students understand that, although mass and weight are related, they are not the same property. The weight of an object can change if the gravitational pull is changed. For example, the weight of an object on Earth is greater than the weight of the same object on the Moon. Mass, on the other hand, does not usually change. An object will have the same mass on Earth as it has on the Moon.

Thinking Critically Answer
No; As wood burns, it undergoes a chemical reaction, combining with oxygen in the air. The mass of the products produced is equal to the mass of the wood and oxygen.

1-3 (pp. 20–21)

1 Introduce

✎ **STUDY HINT** Have students write *solids, liquids,* and *gases* in a three-column chart in their notebooks. As they read the lesson, have them write examples for each state of matter.

Linking Prior Knowledge On the board, write *solids, liquids,* and *gases.* Ask students for examples of each state of matter and list them on the board under the correct state.

2 Teach

Discussion Have students study Figure 1-6. Ask them how the call outs are different from one another. (Particles in a solid are packed closely together, particles in a liquid are spread out a little more, and particles in a gas are spread out even farther). Explain to students that particles in a solid constantly vibrate back and forth. Particles in a liquid have more freedom to move. Particles in a gas have a great amount of energy, which keeps them in constant motion.

Demonstration Show students that liquids have a definite volume but lack a definite shape. Pour 100 mL of water from a graduated beaker to a graduated cylinder and then into a plastic bag or balloon. Then, pour the water back into the graduated cylinder. Guide students to recognize that the volume of the water remained the same regardless of the container it was poured into. However, the shape of the water changed according to the container. **learning style: visual**

Answers to questions

▶1 IDENTIFY: four

▶2 DEFINE: a state of matter that has a definite shape and volume

▶3 EXPLAIN: The particles of a liquid can change position to take the shape of the liquid's container.

▶4 DEFINE: a state of matter that has no definite shape or volume

▶5 DEFINE: fourth state of matter made up of small, electrically charged particles

---

1-3 What are the states of matter?

Objective
Identify and describe four states of matter.

Key Terms
state of matter: any of the four physical forms of matter

solid: state of matter with a definite shape and volume

liquid: state of matter with a definite volume but no definite shape

gas: state of matter that has no definite shape or volume

plasma (PLAZ-muh)**:** state of matter made up of electrically charged particles

States of Matter You cool drinks with solid ice cubes. You wash your hands in liquid water. Water that evaporates from puddles after a rainstorm has changed to a gas called water vapor. Ice, liquid water, and water vapor all are made up of particles of water. Different forms of the same substance are called states. A **state of matter** is any one of the four physical forms of matter. The three most familiar states of matter are solid, liquid, and gas. A fourth state, plasma, is found mainly in stars like our Sun.

▶1 IDENTIFY: In how many states can matter exist?

Solids Most of the objects that surround you are made of solids. A **solid** is a state of matter that has a definite shape and volume. In a solid, particles of matter are tightly packed together. The particles cannot change position easily. They can only vibrate, or move back and forth in place.

▶2 DEFINE: What is a solid?

Liquids Milk is a liquid. A **liquid** has a definite volume but no definite shape. Liquids are able to change shape because the particles of a liquid can change position. They can slide past one another. If you pour a liter of milk into different containers, the milk always takes the shape of the container. However, the volume of the milk stays the same. You cannot make a liter of milk fit into a half-liter bottle.

▶3 EXPLAIN: Why can liquids change shape?

Gases A **gas** is a state of matter that has no definite shape or volume. A gas takes the shape of its container. For example, air can take the shape of a basketball, a football, or a bicycle tire. If you fill a balloon with air, the air completely fills the balloon. A container of gas is always completely full. The particles of a gas are in constant motion. They are much farther apart than the particles in solids or liquids. They can move freely to all parts of a container.

▶4 DEFINE: What is a gas?

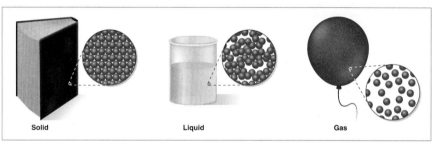

▲ **Figure 1-6** The three most common states of matter are solid, liquid, and gas.

20

Teaching Options

❗ FAST FACTS *More About Plasmas*

Plasmas are made up of free electrons and ions, which are electrically charged particles. Scientists estimate that this fourth state of matter makes up over 99 percent of the universe because the energy-charged environment that sustains plasmas is common in space. Scientists have been able to replicate this unique environment on Earth. Neon signs are actually glass tubes that hold plasmas. When the sign is turned on, electricity flows through the gas-filled tube. The electrical energy causes the atoms in the gas to break into a plasma composed of ions and free electrons. The colorful light given off is actually the plasma's glow.

Another State of Matter Matter can exist in a fourth state called **plasma**. Plasma is rare on Earth, but it is plentiful in other parts of the universe. Plasma has been found in stars, where the temperatures and pressures are very high. Matter in the plasma state is made up of small, electrically charged particles.

Scientists have been able to create plasmas in the laboratory. Such plasmas are relatively cool compared with natural plasmas. This plasma technology has been applied to many things you see everyday, such as flat-screen TVs, street lamps, and fluorescent tubes.

▶ DEFINE: What is plasma?

✔ CHECKING CONCEPTS

1. Plasma exists where _____ and pressure are very high.
2. In what state of matter can particles only vibrate in place?
3. What happens to the shape of a liquid when you pour it into a container?
4. What determines the volume of a gas?
5. What state of matter is air?

💡 THINKING CRITICALLY

6. **EXPLAIN:** What will happen to the particles of a gas if the gas is transferred from a small container to a much larger container?
7. **CLASSIFY:** Classify each of the following substances as a solid, a liquid, or a gas.

   a. Cotton cloth   f. Seltzer
   b. Rain   g. Hydrogen
   c. Carbon dioxide   h. Sugar
   d. Helium   i. Orange juice
   e. Salt   j. Bricks

Web InfoSearch

Plasma As rare as plasma is on Earth, scientists have found ways to make use of it in some interesting ways.

SEARCH: Use the Internet to find out what kinds of products contain plasma. Then, create a chart. Next to each item on your list, include a picture of it. Start your search at www.conceptsandchallenges.com. Some key search words are **plasma** and **digital TV.**

◆ Integrating Earth Science

TOPIC: Earth's layers

EARTH'S MANTLE

The outer layer of Earth is called the crust. The crust is about 5 to 40 km thick, with the thickest part under the mountains. Beneath the crust is the mantle. The mantle is about 2,900 km thick. The upper part of the mantle is solid rock. Below the solid rock, the mantle rock behaves like a very thick liquid, such as molasses. This is because of very high pressure and temperatures. Like all liquids, this rock can flow. The rock also has some properties of a solid. It is in an in-between state of matter called the plastic state. A plastic material is neither a solid nor a liquid; it has properties of both.

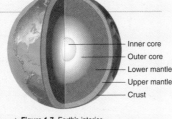
▲ **Figure 1-7** Earth's interior

Inner core
Outer core
Lower mantle
Upper mantle
Crust

Scientists would like to learn more about the plastic material in the mantle. However, they have not been able to drill that far into Earth. What they know has been learned by studying shock waves from earthquakes. Someday, scientists hope to find a way to drill deep enough to reach the mantle. Then, they will be able to study the properties of plastic rock directly.

Thinking Critically What might scientists do with the information they get from the plastic rock?

📝 WRITING HINT
Suggest that students begin composing a written response to a question by turning the question into a statement. For example, the lesson title turned into a statement begins *The states of matter are . . .*

3 Assess

✔ CHECKING CONCEPTS ANSWERS

1. temperature
2. solid
3. It takes the shape of the container.
4. the volume of the container
5. gas

💡 THINKING CRITICALLY ANSWERS

6. **EXPLAIN:** The particles will spread out to completely fill the container.
7. **CLASSIFY:** solid: a, e, h, j; liquid: b, f, i; gas: c, d, g

4 Close

Web InfoSearch

Plasma Have pairs of students search the Internet to identify products that contain plasmas. Students should begin their search at www.conceptsandchallenges.com.

◆ Integrating Earth Science

TOPIC: Earth's layers

EARTH'S MANTLE

Earth-Science Connection Most scientists think that Earth's crust and the solid parts of the mantle are broken into crustal plates. Crustal plates float on the lower part of the mantle. Continents move because these moving plates carry them along.

Discussion Ask students: *If crustal plates cause continents to move, what does this indicate about the location of North America millions of years ago?* Guide students in realizing that the position of the continent likely changed over time.

Thinking Critically Answer
Possible answers: Use the information to create materials similar to plastic rock; determine if plastic rock could be transported to Earth's surface; predict movements of Earth's crust and upper mantle.

COOPERATIVE LEARNING

Modeling Earth Have small groups of students use different colors of modeling clay to create a model of Earth's layers. Tell students to use Figure 1-7 as a guide. **learning style: tactile**

ESL/ELL STRATEGY

States of Matter To help English-language learners reinforce the states of matter, have them draw an illustration of each state and write a caption for each illustration. **learning style: visual**

• TEACHING RESOURCES •

Teacher's Resources CD-ROM
Lesson Review: Chapter 1, p. 5
Enrichment: Chapter 1, p. 6

1 Introduce

STUDY HINT Before beginning this lesson, have students write the lesson title and objective in their notebooks. As students read the lesson, tell them to write sentences that provide information about the objective.

Linking Prior Knowledge Ask students if they are familiar with mothballs. Ask what the purpose of mothballs is. (to repel moths) Inform students that mothballs do not last forever. They get smaller and smaller because they sublime, or change state from a solid directly into a gas. Ask students if they know of any other examples of sublimation. (Snow is one example. It sublimes as well as melts.) **learning style: auditory**

2 Teach

Demonstration Place two pie plates on a windowsill. Pour 50 mL of warm water in each plate. Cover one plate with a clear plastic bag. Have students observe the plates a few hours later. Develop the idea that some of the water in the uncovered plate evaporated into the air. Provide evidence of this by measuring the amount of water left in the plate. Then, explain that some of the water in the covered plate also evaporated. However, when the water vapor struck the plastic covering, condensation occurred. The liquid water fell back into the pie plate. **learning style: visual**

Answers to questions

1 **DESCRIBE:** a change in matter from one state to another

2 **EXPLAIN:** when a liquid has lost enough heat to change into a solid

3 **EXPLAIN:** when gas particles have lost enough heat energy to change into a liquid

4 **DEFINE:** changing of a solid directly to a gas

1-4 How does matter change state?

Objective

Identify ways in which matter can change from one state to another.

Key Terms

freezing: change from a liquid to a solid

melting: change from a solid to a liquid

evaporation (ee-vap-uh-RAY-shuhn): change from a liquid to a gas at the surface of the liquid

condensation (kahn-dehn-SAY-shuhn): change from a gas to a liquid

sublimation: change from a solid directly to a gas

State Changes Matter can change from one state to another. For example, water can change from a solid to a liquid. A change in matter from one state to another is called a change of state. There are four main kinds of changes of state. During a change of state, there is a change in heat energy. A substance either gains or loses heat as it changes from one state to another.

1 **DESCRIBE:** What is a change of state?

Freezing and Melting If you fill an ice cube tray with water and place it in the freezer, the water will change to ice. Water changing into ice is an example of freezing. **Freezing** is a change from a liquid to a solid. Freezing occurs when the temperature of a liquid reaches its freezing point. At its freezing point, a liquid loses enough heat to change to a solid.

▼ **Figure 1-8** Part of this frozen iceberg is melting into the ocean.

When the temperature rises above the freezing point of water, ice changes to a liquid. A change from solid to liquid is called **melting**. Melting occurs when a solid gains enough heat to change into a liquid.

2 **EXPLAIN:** What causes a liquid to freeze?

Evaporation and Condensation Before you go to bed tonight, fill an open plastic container with water. Mark the level of the water. Place the container in a warm, dry place. When you get up tomorrow, see what has happened to the water level. You will find that some of the water has "disappeared." Particles at the surface of the water gained enough heat energy to change into the gas state. **Evaporation** is a change from a liquid to a gas at the surface of the liquid.

You probably have noticed drops of water on your bathroom mirror after taking a hot shower. Hot water from the shower causes the temperature in the bathroom to rise. Some water particles gain enough heat energy to change to water vapor. Water vapor is the gas state of water. Water vapor is invisible. As particles of water vapor hit the cool surface of a mirror, they lose heat energy and change back into liquid water. This process is called condensation. **Condensation** is a change from a gas to a liquid.

3 **EXPLAIN:** What causes condensation?

Sublimation When you fill an ice cube tray with water and place it in the freezer, you have ice cubes in a few hours. If you leave the tray untouched in the freezer for several days, the ice cubes get smaller. This is due to a process called sublimation. **Sublimation** is the changing of a solid directly to a gas, without passing through a liquid state. The temperature at which a solid changes to a gas is its sublimation point. Some other solids that sublime are moth balls (naphthalene), dry ice (CO_2), and iodine.

4 **DEFINE:** What is sublimation?

Teaching Options

COOPERATIVE LEARNING

Changes of State Game Divide students into groups of three or four. Tell students that they have 2 minutes to come up with as many examples of melting as they can. Each group needs to designate one person to make a list of the examples. Do the same for the other changes of state. Make sure that you accurately monitor the time. After students have made all five lists, have groups share their lists with the class. The group that comes up with the most examples wins. **learning styles: interpersonal, linguistic**

ONGOING ASSESSMENT

Making Flowcharts Have students divide a sheet of paper into four parts. Tell them to label the sections *evaporation, condensation, melting,* and *freezing.* Then, have students create a diagram or flowchart that shows how heat is transferred in each process. **learning style: visual**

✓ CHECKING CONCEPTS

1. Melting is a change from a solid to a _____.

2. Water changing into ice is an example of _____.

3. A change in matter from one state to another is called _____.

4. A change from a liquid to a gas at the surface of the liquid is _____.

5. Water vapor changing to liquid water is an example of _____.

6. Dry ice turning into gas is an example of _____.

💡 THINKING CRITICALLY

7. INFER: What happens to the particles of a liquid as the liquid freezes?

8. INFER: What happens to the particles of a liquid as the liquid evaporates?

9. CLASSIFY: Identify the change of state taking place in each of the following situations.
   a. Water droplets form on the inside of your window on a chilly winter night.
   b. A full perfume bottle left open for several days is now half empty.
   c. A block of baking chocolate is heated until it can be poured into a measuring cup.

DESIGNING AN EXPERIMENT

Design an experiment to solve the following problem. Include a hypothesis, variables, a procedure, and a type of data to study.

PROBLEM: How can you identify an unknown material?

Real-Life Science

FOG MACHINES

Dry ice is frozen carbon dioxide, a gas found in the air around us. It looks like regular ice, but it is much colder. The temperature of dry ice is about –78.5°C or –109.3°F. If dry ice comes in contact with your skin, heat is removed from your body so fast that your skin seems to burn! For this reason, dry ice should only be handled with insulated gloves.

Frozen carbon dioxide is called dry ice because it does not melt. It changes directly from a solid to a gas. This process is called sublimation. If you watch a piece of dry ice, it seems to slowly disappear into thin air as it sublimes.

When dry ice is placed in hot water, a fog made of tiny water droplets is produced. Such fogs, produced by a fog machine, can lend a dreamlike or eerie mood to the sets of stage plays, rock concerts, or movies. A dry ice fog machine is made up of a water barrel, a heater, and a fan. Dry ice is placed in a bucket with holes in it. When the bucket is lowered into the barrel of hot water, fog is produced. The fan then blows the fog through the air. The production of fog is stopped by removing the dry ice from the water barrel.

Thinking Critically Where does the water that makes up the fog come from?

▲ Figure 1-9 Dry ice subliming

📖 **READING STRATEGY** Tell students that a passage can be summarized in one statement called the main idea. Suggest that students record the main idea of each passage in this lesson in their notebooks.

3 Assess

✓ CHECKING CONCEPTS ANSWERS

1. liquid
2. freezing
3. a change in state
4. evaporation
5. condensation
6. sublimation

💡 THINKING CRITICALLY ANSWERS

7. INFER: They slow down and can only vibrate in place.
8. INFER: They spread out and move faster.
9. CLASSIFY: **a.** condensation **b.** evaporation **c.** melting

4 Close

DESIGNING AN EXPERIMENT

Use the Designing an Experiment Rubric on the Teacher's Resources CD-ROM to assess students' experiments. Fill in the rubric with the additional information below. For this assignment, students should have:

- developed a step-by-step procedure.
- designed a data table in which to record observations and any quantitative data.

Real-Life Science

FOG MACHINES

Real-Life Connection The use of dry ice is not restricted to the entertainment industry. Transportation companies use dry ice to keep certain food products and medicines cool while in transit. These products, which would be damaged by the melting of regular ice, are packed in dry ice. The gas that forms when the dry ice melts does not affect the products.

Thinking Critically Answer
The water droplets that make up the fog are caused by the condensation of water vapor in the air as it loses heat to the cool carbon dioxide gas.

MORE ON THE WEB

Viewing Natural Condensation Have students use the Internet to learn about different geysers. They can also view images of geyser eruptions. Have students begin their search at www.conceptsandchallenges.com.

• TEACHING RESOURCES •

💿 **Teacher's Resources CD-ROM**
Lesson Review: Chapter 1, p. 7
Enrichment: Chapter 1, p. 8
Designing an Experiment: Study Tools, p. 14

Laboratory Manual
Lab. Challenge: What happens during a change of state? pp. 21–24

📼 **Laboratory Video**
Segment 3: What Happens During a Phase Change?

The Big Idea

(pp. 24–25)

1 Introduce

Objective Students will be able to identify the changes of state a water molecule undergoes as it moves through the water cycle. Students will also be able to explain the processes that cause these changes.

Linking Prior Knowledge Ask students to recall the four states of matter (Lesson 1-3). Have them reflect on the processes that cause matter to change state (Lesson 1-4).

2 Teach

Discussion Remind students that Earth's oceans are comprised of salt water. Explain that when ocean water evaporates, only water molecules become water vapor. The solid salt particles remain in the ocean. Ask students what would happen to Earth's oceans if the water cycle suddenly ceased. Answers might include that all water would eventually end up in the ocean or that all water would eventually evaporate out of oceans. Guide students in recognizing that the continued presence of Earth's oceans actually provides evidence of the constant action of the water cycle.

Use the information in the article and in Fast Facts to help guide students in choosing a topic for their Science Logs.

THE BIG IDEA ONLINE

How are changes of state part of the water cycle?
Have students research their Science Log Writing Activity at www.conceptsandchallenges.com. You can have students organize their log by completing the Big Idea activity online. Students may post their work in the Online Classroom Database for others to read.

Reinforcement Students can also use the Big Idea Planner or Big Idea Science Log Entry found on the Teacher's Resources CD-ROM.

◆ Integrating Earth Science

THE Big IDEA

How are changes of state part of the water cycle?

The water cycle is Earth's water recycling program. The water inside your cells, in your bathtub, underground, and even in glaciers is all part of the water cycle. Water endlessly cycles all over Earth—from the oceans to the clouds; from rain or snow into the ground; from rivers and streams back to the sea.

Think about a molecule of water (H_2O) in a puddle. Light from the Sun hits the water molecule, giving it an energy boost. The water evaporates and the molecule joins other molecules as they move from the liquid state to the gas state. The molecules enter the atmosphere as water vapor. Soon the water vapor cools and loses energy, condensing back to the liquid state. The water molecule joins other water molecules to form tiny droplets or ice crystals that make up clouds. The droplets increase in size until they are pulled to Earth by gravity. That is when you see rain, snow, hail, or sleet. This is called precipitation. Precipitation takes many forms, depending on the weather conditions.

On Earth, about 97% of the water is in the oceans. So, most of the action in the water cycle is evaporation from and precipitation back into the oceans. Sometimes the water cycle carries water molecules on incredible journeys.

Look at the illustration on these two pages. Then, follow the directions in the Science Log to find out more about "the big idea." ✦

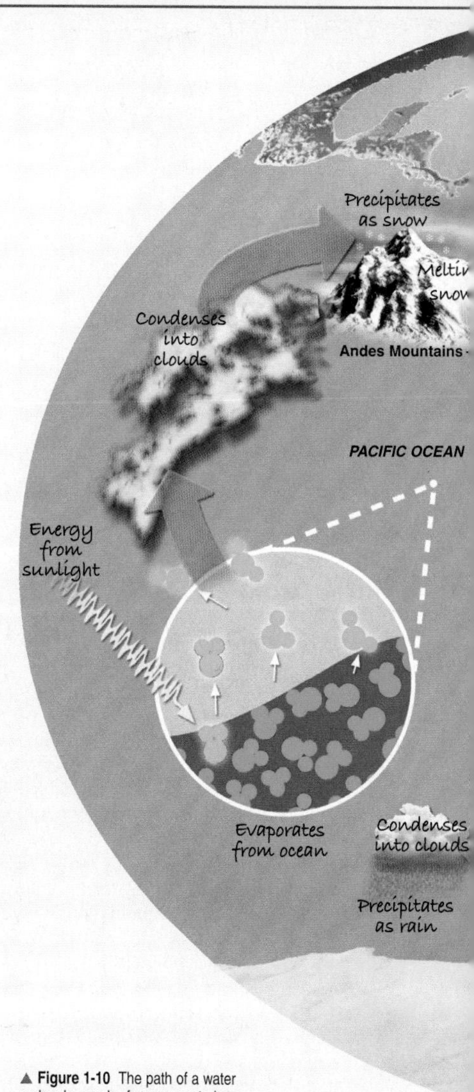

▲ Figure 1-10 The path of a water molecule may be from ocean to ice cap and many places in between.

Precipitates as snow

Melting snow

Condenses into clouds

Andes Mountains

PACIFIC OCEAN

Energy from sunlight

Evaporates from ocean

Condenses into clouds

Precipitates as rain

24

Teaching Options

! FAST FACTS *The Water Cycle*

The water cycle, also called the hydrologic cycle, is the continuous movement of water from sources at Earth's surface into the air and back to Earth's surface. The water cycle has three main processes—evaporation, condensation, and precipitation. During evaporation, water at Earth's surface absorbs energy from the Sun and changes to water vapor. Water vapor is the gaseous state of water. The water vapor rises and cools as it reaches the cooler air above Earth's surface. During condensation, water vapor condenses into droplets of water, which collect to form clouds. When the water droplets become too numerous and too heavy to remain in the air, they fall out of clouds as precipitation. Precipitation can be in the forms of rain, snow, sleet, or hail. The form of precipitation that falls depends upon the temperature of the air from which it falls. Some of the water may fall back into bodies of water and repeat the cycle again. Some of the water may fall onto land and soak into the rocks and soil to become groundwater. At some point, groundwater flows underground into bodies of water.

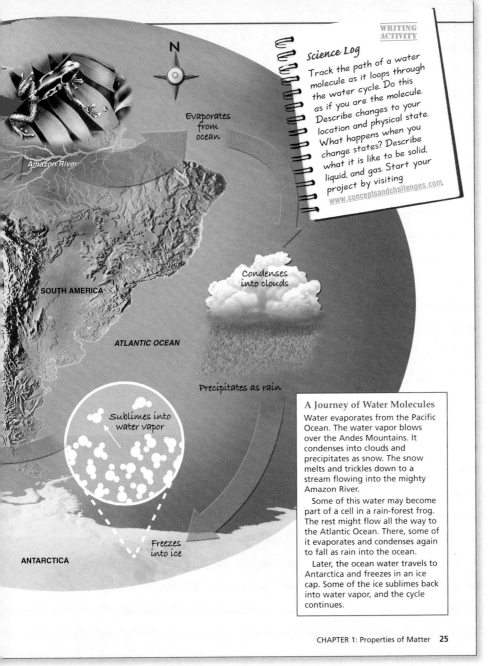

Science Log

Track the path of a water molecule as it loops through the water cycle. Do this as if you are the molecule. Describe changes to your location and physical state. What happens when you change states? Describe what it is like to be solid, liquid, and gas. Start your project by visiting www.conceptsandchallenges.com.

Evaporates from ocean

Amazon River

SOUTH AMERICA

ATLANTIC OCEAN

Condenses into clouds

Precipitates as rain

Sublimes into water vapor

Freezes into ice

ANTARCTICA

A Journey of Water Molecules

Water evaporates from the Pacific Ocean. The water vapor blows over the Andes Mountains. It condenses into clouds and precipitates as snow. The snow melts and trickles down to a stream flowing into the mighty Amazon River.

Some of this water may become part of a cell in a rain-forest frog. The rest might flow all the way to the Atlantic Ocean. There, some of it evaporates and condenses again to fall as rain into the ocean.

Later, the ocean water travels to Antarctica and freezes in an ice cap. Some of the ice sublimes back into water vapor, and the cycle continues.

CHAPTER 1: Properties of Matter **25**

3 Assess

Use the Writing Activity Rubric on the Teacher's Resources CD-ROM to assess students' Science Logs. Fill in the rubric with the additional information below. For this assignment, students should have:

- explained how a water molecule changes state as it moves through the water cycle.
- communicated, in paragraph form, accurate information about the processes that caused these changes.

4 Close

Map It Have small groups of students work together to map the route a water molecule takes as it moves through the water cycle in your state. Groups should begin their maps at a body of water. From there, the water molecule should visit a minimum of four other locations as it changes form. Groups should detail the locations and state of the molecule at each location. Have each group present its completed map to the class.
learning styles: visual, interpersonal

Tips for Using Technology

Presentation Software Have students use presentation software to show the route of a water molecule. Presentation software allows students to use a computer to put text and art together in a slide show. Students can also use presentation software to share their data with the class. Tell students to strive for showing at least four locations of the water molecule. Have students use the Flowchart on the Teacher's Resources CD-ROM to plan their presentation.

• TEACHING RESOURCES •

Teacher's Resources CD-ROM

Big Idea: Chapter 1, p. 9

Big Idea Planner: Study Tools, pp. 11–12

Big Idea Science Log Entry: Study Tools, p. 13

Writing Activity Rubric: Teaching Tools, p. 9

Flowchart: Study Tools, p. 6

1 Introduce

STUDY HINT Before beginning this lesson, have students study Figure 1-11. Ask them to explain how a physical change is different from a chemical change.

Linking Prior Knowledge Ask students to describe changes from one state of matter to another. From the definitions of the Key Terms, have them decide whether these changes are chemical or physical. (They are physical because a change in state does not produce a new substance.)

2 Teach

Discussion Ask students if the evaporation and condensation of water are physical or chemical changes. Stress that during these processes, water changes state but does not become a different type of substance. Therefore, both processes are examples of physical changes. **learning style: auditory**

Demonstration Demonstrate some simple physical and chemical changes. To show a physical change, cut an apple in half or crumple a piece of paper. To demonstrate a chemical change, have students watch the cut apple turn brown as it is exposed to the air or observe the burning of a small piece of the paper. Point out that a chemical change produces new substances. **learning style: visual**

Answers to questions

1 ▸ LIST: Possible answers: state of matter, shape, size, color, and texture

2 ▸ DEFINE: change in the physical properties of a substance that does not produce a new substance

3 ▸ CONTRAST: A chemical change produces new substances. A physical change does not produce new substances.

Reinforcement Ask students to classify each of the following as a physical change or a chemical change: candle melting (physical), cooking an egg (chemical), wood burning in a fireplace (chemical), crushing a sugar cube (physical), silverware tarnishing (chemical).

1-5 What are physical and chemical changes?

Objective
Distinguish between physical and chemical changes in matter.

Key Terms
physical change: change that does not produce new substances

chemical change: change that produces new substances

Physical Properties The states of matter are physical properties. Some other physical properties of matter include shape, size, color, and texture. Physical properties are characteristics that can be observed or measured without changing the makeup of a substance.

1 ▸ LIST: What are some physical properties of matter?

Physical Changes If you cut an apple in half and share it with a friend, it is still an apple. If you change water to ice, it is still water. If you crumple a sheet of paper into a ball, it is still paper. All of these changes are examples of physical changes. A **physical change** does not produce new substances.

▲ **Figure 1-11** The sawing of wood is a physical change. The burning of wood is a chemical change.

26

A physical change involves the physical properties of a material. Cutting an apple in half changes its size. Freezing liquid water changes its state. Crumpling up a sheet of paper changes its size and shape.

2 ▸ DEFINE: What is a physical change?

Chemical Changes If you take a crumpled sheet of paper and smooth it out, you can still write on it. It is still paper. Now, suppose you burn a sheet of paper. When substances burn, they combine with oxygen. Burning is an example of a chemical change. A **chemical change** results in new kinds of matter being formed. When paper burns, ashes, soot, heat, light, and gases are produced. You no longer have paper. Some other examples of chemical changes include the rusting of iron, the digestion of food, and the burning of gasoline in a car engine.

▲ **Figure 1-12** Rusting is an example of a chemical change.

3 ▸ CONTRAST: How is a chemical change different from a physical change?

Teaching Options

✓ CHECKING CONCEPTS

Complete each sentence with the word **physical** *or* **chemical**.

1. Volume and color are examples of _____ properties of matter.
2. State is a _____ property of matter.
3. Changing water to ice is an example of a _____ change.
4. New substances are produced by a _____ change.
5. Iron rusting is an example of a _____ change.
6. Color and shape are _____ properties.

💡 THINKING CRITICALLY

7. ANALYZE: Describe the changes that take place when a match burns. Are these changes physical or chemical?

8. INTERPRET: Mixing vinegar with baking soda produces carbon dioxide and water. Is this a physical change or a chemical change? How do you know?
9. HYPOTHESIZE: You find small pieces of ice instead of ice cubes in the freezer. State how this is possible.

BUILDING SCIENCE SKILLS

Classifying Classify each of the following examples as a physical change or a chemical change. Explain your answers.

a. Match burns
b. Glass breaks
c. Rubber band is stretched
d. Iron rusts
e. Ice melts
f. Sugar cube is crushed

⚛ *Hands-On Activity*
OBSERVING PHYSICAL CHANGES

You will need a bottle or jar with a narrow neck, ice cubes, and hot water.

1. Put a small amount of hot water into a bottle or jar. Place an ice cube over the opening of the bottle so that the ice cube will not fall in.
2. Observe what you see coming from the surface of the hot water.
3. Observe the bottle for a few minutes and note what you see happening near the top of the bottle.
4. Watch for another minute or two. Note if you see anything fall from the top of the bottle.

Practicing Your Skills

5. OBSERVE: **a.** What did you observe coming from the surface of the hot water in Step 2? **b.** What caused this to happen?
6. OBSERVE: **a.** What did you see near the top of the bottle in Step 3? **b.** What caused this to happen?
7. HYPOTHESIZE: **a.** Did you see anything fall inside the bottle in Step 4? **b.** If so, explain what you saw and how it was produced.

▲ **STEP 3** Observe the inside of the bottle.

MORE ON THE WEB

Identifying Physical and Chemical Changes Have students use the Internet to learn more about physical and chemical changes. Students can review what they learn by taking an online quiz. Send students to www.concepts andchallenges.com.

• *TEACHING RESOURCES* •

💿 **Teacher's Resources CD-ROM**
Lesson Review: Chapter 1, p. 10
Flowchart: Study Tools, p. 6

---

3 Assess

✓ CHECKING CONCEPTS ANSWERS

1. physical
2. physical
3. physical
4. chemical
5. chemical
6. physical

💡 THINKING CRITICALLY ANSWERS

7. ANALYZE: Heat, light, gases, soot, and ashes are produced. These are chemical changes.
8. INTERPRET: Chemical change; New substances are produced.
9. HYPOTHESIZE: Possible answers: The ice in larger cubes sublimed, leaving smaller pieces.

4 Close

BUILDING SCIENCE SKILLS ANSWERS

Classifying Physical changes occur in b, c, e, and f because the substances that are changed do not become new substances; chemical changes occur in a and d because new substances are produced.

Hands-On Activity
OBSERVING PHYSICAL CHANGES

TIME: 10–15 minutes
PURPOSE: observing, hypothesizing
SAFETY TIP: Caution students to take care when handling hot water and to immediately clean up any spills.
ALTERNATIVE MATERIALS: A plastic soft-drink bottle can be used in place of the glass bottle or jar.
COOPERATIVE LEARNING: Have pairs of students create a flowchart that details the changes of state that occurred in the activity. **learning styles:** visual, tactile

Practicing Your Skills Answers

5. OBSERVE: **a.** condensed water vapor **b.** The liquid water evaporated.
6. OBSERVE: **a.** water droplets **b.** Water vapor condensed because it cooled.
7. HYPOTHESIZE: **a.** yes **b.** Drops of water, formed by condensation, fell back into the liquid.

Lab Activity

(pp. 28–29)

1 Prepare the Lab

Observing Physical and Chemical Changes

SET-UP TIME: 🕐 **LAB TIME:** 🕐

BACKGROUND: It is important to use the end result of the change to distinguish between a physical change and a chemical change. In a physical change, the substance you start with is the same substance at the end. In a chemical change, an entirely new substance or substances are produced.

PURPOSE: Students will observe and compare physical changes in modeling clay and the chemical changes that occur when water and an antacid tablet are combined. Students will classify the changes as either physical or chemical.

ALTERNATIVE MATERIALS: You may want to provide students with string to measure the circumference of the ball and then have them use the tape measure to determine the string's length. A metric ruler can be used instead of a tape measure.

SCIENCE SKILLS: Students will **observe** and **collect data.** They will **measure** items. They will **infer** which reactions involve physical and chemical changes.

ADVANCE PLANNING: Gather the materials needed for the lab. If the classroom lacks running water, obtain a supply of water in plastic containers. Have an empty bucket on hand for collecting water and the antacid mixture after the experiment.

2 Guide the Lab

PROCEDURE: Divide the class into groups of two or three students. Discuss the procedures. Emphasize the need to work with the clay only on wax paper. Review with students how to operate a triple-beam balance. Discuss data collecting and reporting. Have students make their data charts before starting the experiment. Provide students with a copy of the Lab Activity Report found on the Teacher's Resources CD-ROM on which to record their observations and conclusions.

LAB ACTIVITY
Observing Physical and Chemical Changes

Materials
Safety goggles
Lab apron
Modeling clay
Wax paper
Plastic teaspoon
2 Plastic cups
1 Antacid tablet
Tape measure
Cold water
Triple-beam balance

▲ **STEP 2** Measure the block of clay.

▲ **STEP 4** Mold the clay into any shape.

BACKGROUND

Physical and chemical changes occur everywhere around us. From a scientist's point of view, it is necessary to tell the difference between these two types of changes. A physical change involves a change in what you see but it does not change the identity of the substance. A chemical change alters the identity of a substance and may involve a change in the way a substance looks as well.

PURPOSE

In this activity, you will observe and record data to decide whether the activity involves a physical or a chemical change.

PROCEDURE 🔒 👓

1. Copy the chart in Figure 1-13. Put on safety goggles and a lab apron.

2. Take a block of modeling clay. Measure its dimensions using the tape measure. Record its mass using the triple-beam balance.

3. Shape the clay into a ball and record its mass. Measure the dimensions of the ball with the tape measure.

4. Mold the clay into a shape of your choice. Record its mass and try to measure its dimensions.

5. Put on safety goggles. Take the antacid tablet and place it in a small plastic cup. Measure 2 mL of water into another small plastic cup. Place both cups on the balance and record their combined masses.

6. Crush the antacid tablet and place it back it in the plastic cup. Place the cup with the crushed tablet and the cup with the water on the balance. Record their masses.

28

Teaching Options

Using Antacids to Relieve Indigestion The stomach produces digestive juices. These digestive juices contain hydrochloric acid. This strong acid helps break down food particles. When little food is present in the stomach, hydrochloric acid can build up and cause indigestion. A common remedy for this ailment is drinking an antacid solution, such as the one created in the activity. When the antacid solution reaches the stomach, it neutralizes the excess acid. Eating certain foods can also cause a buildup of acid in the stomach. Encourage students to use reference materials to make a list of foods that have high acid contents.

ESL/ELL STRATEGY

Summarizing Procedures English-language learners may benefit from stating the procedures in their own words. Have students explain the procedures in their own words to English-proficient students.

7. Pour the water into the cup with the crushed tablet. Record your observations. Place the cup with the water-tablet mixture and the empty cup on the balance and record their masses.

8. Clean up your area and dispose of the substances as directed by your teacher.

▲ STEP 7 Pour the water into the cup.

Clay			Antacid Tablet	
Shape	Dimensions	Mass	Materials	Mass
Block			Tablet in cup and water in cup	
Ball			Crushed tablet in cup and water in cup	
Choice			Water in cup and empty cup	

▲ **Figure 1-13** Copy this chart and use it to record your observations.

CONCLUSIONS

1. OBSERVE: How is shaping clay an example of a physical change?

2. ANALYZE: Describe the changes that take place with the antacid tablet. Why does the mixture of the antacid tablet and water have a different mass after the reaction?

3. INFER: Based on your observations of the antacid tablet, what kind of change takes place when it is placed in water? Explain your reasoning.

4. CLASSIFY: Classify each of the following examples as a physical change or a chemical change. Explain your answers.
   a. cutting wood
   b. burning gasoline
   c. crumpling a sheet of paper
   d. wine turning into vinegar over time
   e. milk turning sour

Tips for Using Technology

Databases Have students use database software to record their observations about physical and chemical changes. Databases allow students to enter and edit information, store and organize a lot of information easily, and search for specific information. Databases also allow students to put information in a specific order and to present information by using special layouts. Students can use database software to share their data with the class. Have students use the Database Planner on the Teacher's Resources CD-ROM to plan their databases.

• TEACHING RESOURCES •

Teacher's Resources CD-ROM
Lab Activity Report: Study Tools, pp. 16–17

Laboratory Activity Rubric: Teaching Tools, p. 8

Database Planner: Study Tools, p. 22

Laboratory Manual
Lab. Skills Worksheet 2: Using a Triple-Beam Balance, pp. 7–8

Lab. Skills Worksheet 6: Writing a Laboratory Report, pp. 19–20

TROUBLESHOOTING: Be sure that students crush the antacid tablet into a cup so that they do not lose any of the tablet.

SAFETY TIP: Stress the importance of washing one's hands between working with the clay and the antacid solution. Remind students not to stick their fingers into the solution or taste anything in the lab.

EXPECTED OUTCOME: Students will observe that the mass of the clay remains the same even though the shape changes. They will observe that the mass of the antacid solution becomes less after the reaction.

LAB HINT: Remind students to consider all variables when analyzing the experiment's results.

3 Conclude the Lab

1. OBSERVE: No new substance is formed.
2. ANALYZE: When water is added to the antacid, the solid dissolves and bubbles form. Some mass was lost as gas.
3. INFER: A chemical change occurs because new products are formed.
4. CLASSIFY: **a.** Physical; the wood changes shape but does not become a different substance. **b.** Chemical; the gasoline combines with oxygen to produce new substances. **c.** Physical; the paper changes size, but does not become a different substance. **d.** Chemical; a new substance (vinegar) is produced. **e.** Chemical; a new substance is produced that turns the milk sour.

Use the Laboratory Activity Rubric on the Teacher's Resources CD-ROM to assess students' lab activities. Fill in the rubric with the additional information below. For this activity, students should have:

* performed the activity according to the procedure and filled in the chart with data collected during the activity.

* correctly answered the questions in complete sentences.

4 Extend the Lab

Discuss with students the role of the law of conservation of mass in physical and chemical changes. Guide them in recognizing that in either type of change, matter is neither created nor destroyed. It is rearranged into different types of matter. Challenge groups of students to devise a demonstration that shows the conservation of mass with an antacid solution. (Possible answer: Do the reaction in a sealed plastic bag.) **learning styles: interpersonal, tactile**

Challenges (pp. 30–32)

Chapter Summary

Review Before students begin the Challenges, review the summary with them. If time permits, have students work in pairs. Give each pair of students one summary point to describe in their own words.

STUDY HINT Have students use index cards to create flash cards for each Key Term. Have students write the Key Term on one side of the index card and the definition on the other side. Then, have pairs of students review the Key Terms.

Key Term Challenges

MATCHING

1. state of matter (1-3)
2. chemistry (1-1)
3. condensation (1-4)
4. physical change (1-5)
5. melting (1-4)
6. gas (1-3)
7. specialization (1-1)

FILL IN

8. freezing (1-4)
9. evaporation (1-4)
10. solid (1-3)
11. chemical change (1-5)
12. matter (1-2)
13. properties (1-2)
14. liquid (1-3)
15. physics (1-1)

Chapter Summary

Lesson 1-1
- Physical science has two main branches. They are physics and chemistry. **Chemistry** deals with the study of the structure and makeup of matter and the changes matter undergoes. **Physics** deals with the study of energy and matter and how they interact.

Lesson 1-2
- **Matter** is anything that has mass and takes up space.
- **Properties** are characteristics that describe an object. Mass, volume, weight, and density are four properties of matter.

Lesson 1-3
- A **state of matter** is a physical form of matter. A **solid** is a state of matter with a definite shape and volume.
- A **liquid** is a state of matter with a definite volume but no definite shape.
- A **gas** is a state of matter that has no definite shape or volume.
- **Plasma** is a fourth state of matter that is rare on Earth but plentiful in other parts of the universe.

Lesson 1-4
- Matter can change state.
- **Freezing** is a change from a liquid to a solid.
- **Melting** is a change from a solid to a liquid.
- **Evaporation** is a change from a liquid to a gas at the surface of the liquid.
- **Condensation** is a change from a gas to a liquid.
- **Sublimation** is a change from a solid to a gas.

Lesson 1-5
- Physical properties can be observed or measured without changing the makeup of a substance.
- A **physical change** does not produce any new substances. A **chemical change** produces new substances.

Key Term Challenges

chemical change (p. 26)	physical change (p. 26)
chemistry (p. 16)	physics (p. 16)
condensation (p. 22)	plasma (p. 20)
evaporation (p. 22)	properties (p. 18)
freezing (p. 22)	solid (p. 20)
gas (p. 20)	specialization (p. 16)
liquid (p. 20)	state of matter (p. 20)
matter (p. 18)	sublimation (p. 22)
melting (p. 22)	

MATCHING Write the Key Term from above that best matches each description.

1. solid, liquid, or gas
2. study of the structure and makeup of matter and its changes
3. change from a gas to a liquid
4. change that does not produce a new substance
5. change from a solid to a liquid
6. state of matter that has no definite shape or volume
7. studying or working in only one area of a subject

FILL IN Write the Key Term from above that best completes each statement.

8. Water changing into ice is an example of _____.
9. During _____, liquids gain enough heat energy to change into the gas state.
10. A _____ is a state of matter with a definite shape and volume.
11. New substances are produced during a _____.
12. Anything that has mass and takes up space is _____.
13. Mass and volume are characteristics, or _____, of matter.
14. Milk is an example of a _____.
15. Two branches of physical science are chemistry and _____.

30

Teaching Options

PREPARING STUDENTS FOR STANDARDIZED TESTS

Reading Strategy: Tell students to look for keywords, such as *all*, *not*, or *none*, in multiple-choice questions. This will help them eliminate some incorrect choices.

Writing Strategy: Tell students to pay attention to spelling, grammar, and organization of their thoughts. This will help their audience understand what they are trying to say.

Interpreting Visuals: Remind students to read captions carefully to fully understand what they are seeing.

ESL/ELL STRATEGY

Improving Communications Skills Pair English-language learners with English-proficient students. One partner should make up three questions about the chapter and read them aloud to the other student who should answer the questions. Then, partners should reverse roles. Partners should check each other to make sure that the correct answers were given.

Content Challenges <u>TEST PREP</u>

MULTIPLE CHOICE **Write the letter of the term or phrase that best completes each statement.**

1. Water vapor changes to liquid water in a process called
   a. condensation.
   b. evaporation.
   c. melting.
   d. freezing.

2. The four states of matter are solid, liquid, gas, and
   a. metals.
   b. nonmetals.
   c. plasma.
   d. air.

3. Burning is an example of a
   a. state change.
   b. chemical change.
   c. physical change.
   d. physical property.

4. Particles of matter are tightly packed together in
   a. a solid.
   b. a liquid.
   c. a gas.
   d. a vapor.

5. Four properties of matter are mass, volume, weight, and
   a. distance.
   b. pressure.
   c. density.
   d. size.

6. Sublimation is a process in which a solid changes directly to a
   a. gas.
   b. liquid.
   c. ice.
   d. plasma.

7. Matter is anything that has mass and
   a. changes state.
   b. has color.
   c. takes up space.
   d. energy.

8. Evaporation is an example of a
   a. change of state.
   b. chemical change.
   c. solid changing to a gas.
   d. property of matter.

9. Matter that has no definite shape or volume is
   a. in the nonmetal state.
   b. in the gas state.
   c. in the liquid state.
   d. in the solid state.

10. Freezing is the opposite of
    a. evaporating.
    b. melting.
    c. condensing.
    d. solidifying.

TRUE/FALSE **Write *true* if the statement is true. If the statement is false, change the underlined term to make the statement true.**

11. <u>Weight</u> is a measure of the pull of gravity on an object.

12. When a solid melts, its particles <u>lose</u> heat energy.

13. The particles of a <u>liquid</u> can only vibrate in place.

14. <u>Physical properties</u> can be observed without changing the makeup of a substance.

15. All matter takes up space and has <u>color</u>.

16. Iron rusting is an example of a <u>physical</u> change.

Content Challenges

MULTIPLE CHOICE

1. a (1-4)
2. c (1-3)
3. b (1-5)
4. a (1-3)
5. c (1-2)
6. a (1-4)
7. c (1-2)
8. a (1-4)
9. b (1-3)
10. b (1-4)

TRUE/FALSE

11. true (1-2)
12. false; gain (1-4)
13. false; solid (1-3)
14. true (1-5)
15. false; mass (1-2)
16. false; chemical (1-5)

ALTERNATIVE ASSESSMENT

Relating Information Students may write a Science Log entry comparing the four states of matter and relating how a substance changes state. They should also compare the differences between a physical change and a chemical change and write examples of each.

CUMULATIVE ASSESSMENT

You may wish to administer the pretest examination found on the Teacher's Resources CD-ROM at this point. Distribute copies of the Scantron Sheet, also found on the Teacher's Resources CD-ROM, for students to record their answers.

PORTFOLIO ASSESSMENT

Making Student Portfolios
Portfolio Assessment is designed to evaluate a student's performance over an extended period of time. Students can demonstrate their comprehension of the concepts in this chapter by making a portfolio. The Chapter Self-Check, the Big Idea Planner, and the Weekly Journal are some of the reproducibles on the Teacher's Resources CD-ROM that students can include in their portfolios. You can use the Portfolio Assessment Rubric also found on the Teacher's Resources CD-ROM to assess students' portfolios.

Concept Challenges

WRITTEN RESPONSE

1. **COMPARE:** In a physical change, a physical property or properties of a substance change without new substances forming. In a chemical change, a substance changes to produce a new substance or substances. (1-5)
2. **DESCRIBE:** As the particles of a solid gain heat, they vibrate more rapidly and spread apart, forming a liquid. As the particles of a liquid gain heat, they move more rapidly and spread farther apart, forming a gas. (1-3, 1-4)
3. **INFER:** Heat energy is needed to cause the particles of a liquid to move more rapidly and to enable some particles to become energetic enough to escape from the liquid. (1-4)
4. **RELATE:** Mass is the amount of matter an object contains, while volume is the amount of space the object occupies. (1-2)
5. **ANALYZE:** It is a physical change. (1-5)

INTERPRETING A DIAGRAM (1-3)

6. B
7. A
8. C

Chapter Project Wrap-Up

DEVELOPING A GAME

Students can play their games with one another. You can use the Group Activity Rubric found on the Teacher's Resources CD-ROM to assess students' projects. Fill in the rubric with the additional information below. For this project, students should have:

- created a game that is neat and logical with clear instructions.
- used Key Terms and their correct definitions in the game.

Concept Challenges TEST PREP

WRITTEN RESPONSE Answer each of the following questions in complete sentences.

1. **COMPARE:** What are the differences between physical change and chemical change?
2. **DESCRIBE:** What happens to the particles of a substance as it changes from a solid to a liquid to a gas?
3. **INFER:** Why does evaporation require that heat energy be added to a substance?
4. **RELATE:** What is the relationship between the mass and the volume of an object?
5. **ANALYZE:** Is tearing paper a physical change or a chemical change?

INTERPRETING A DIAGRAM Match the picture of each object to the arrangement of its molecules.

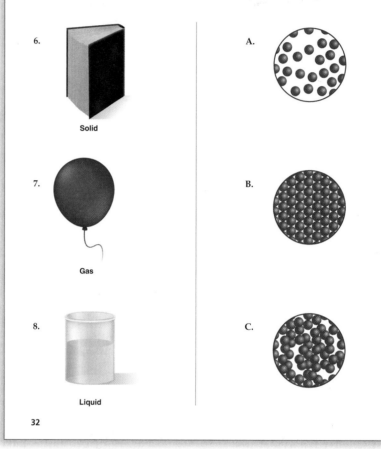

6. Solid

7. Gas

8. Liquid

A.

B.

C.

Teaching Options

• TEACHING RESOURCES •

Teacher's Resources CD-ROM

Key Term Review: Chapter 1, p. 11

Chapter 1 Test: pp. 12–14

Chapter Self-Check: Teaching Tools, p. 11

Big Idea Planner: Study Tools, pp. 11–12

Weekly Journal: Study Tools, p. 19

Portfolio Assessment Rubric: Teaching Tools, p. 10

Group Activity Rubric: Teaching Tools, p. 6

PLANNING GUIDE

◆ **TEACHING THE CHAPTER** This chapter should take approximately 5–8 days to complete instruction and assessment.

	Skills and Features	Projects and Activities	Achieve Science Literacy	Meet Individual Needs
Chapter 2 Opener p. T33	OBSERVE, MODEL	• Chapter Project		
Lesson 2-1 **What is density?** pp. T34–T35 Standard: B1a	IDENTIFY, SEQUENCE, PREDICT • Designing an Experiment • Integrating Earth Science	• Extending the Lesson • More on the Web	• Study Hint • Reading Strategy • Ongoing Assessment	◎ CD-ROM Enrichment Activity Designing an Experiment
Lesson 2-2 **How is density measured?** pp. T36–T37 Standard: B1a	CALCULATE, EXPLAIN, DESCRIBE • Building Math Skills • Hands-On Activity	• Cooperative Learning • More on the Web • Lab Challenge • Lab Skills Worksheets	• Study Hint	• Reteach
Lesson 2-3 **What is specific gravity?** pp. T38–T39 Standard: B1a	RESEARCH, CALCULATE, NAME • Building Science Skills • People in Science	• More on the Web	• Study Hint • Writing Hint • Ongoing Assessment	
Lesson 2-4 **What is displacement?** pp. T40–T41	DEFINE, EXPLAIN, ANALYZE • Investigate • Building Math Skills • Real-Life Science	• Cooperative Learning • Extending the Lesson • More on the Web • Lab Skills Worksheets	• Study Hint • Ongoing Assessment	◎ CD-ROM Enrichment Activity
Lab Activity **Comparing Densities of Coins** pp. T42–T43 Standard: B1a	COMPARE, INFER, ANALYZE • Set-Up Time: 15 min • Lab Time: 45 min	• Lab Skills Worksheets • Extend the Lab Activity	• Tips for Using Technology	• ESL/ELL Strategy ◎ CD-ROM Lab Activity Report Database Planner Graph Paper

Planning Guide continues on next page.

Standards: For details on the correlation to National Science Standards see pages *xx–xxi*.

	Skills and Features	Projects and Activities	Achieve Science Literacy	Meet Individual Needs
Lesson 2-5 **What is buoyancy?** pp. T44–T45	APPLY, STATE, CALCULATE • Health and Safety Tip • Science and Technology	• Extending the Lesson • More on the Web	• Study Hint	• ESL/ELL Strategy CD-ROM Flowchart
Big Idea **How has shipbuilding changed throughout history?** pp. T46–T47 Standard: B1a	RESEARCH, COMMUNICATE, ANALYZE • Science Log: Writing Activity	• Big Idea Online • Close Activity	• Tips for Using Technology	CD-ROM Big Idea Planner
Chapter 2 Challenges pp. T48–T50	• Chapter Summary • Key Term Challenges • Content Challenges • Concept Challenges	• Chapter Project Wrap-Up	• Study Hint • Preparing Students for Standardized Tests	• ESL/ELL Strategy CD-ROM Chapter Self-Check

Teacher Notes

Chapter 2 Density

▲ Figure 2-1 A buoy floats in water.

What would happen if you were to drop an iron nail in the water next to the buoy in Figure 2-1? If you say that the nail would sink, you are correct. Yet, the buoy is also made of iron, and it is floating. Even the added mass of the animals on the buoy does not make it sink. It has to do with the density of the nail and the shape and density of the buoy. All matter has density. By making certain measurements, the density of any sample of matter can be calculated. Knowing the density of a substance can help us identify it.

► How is knowing density helpful in the science lab?

Contents

Teaching Options

ASSESSMENT PLANNER

For assessment in the Student Edition, see the following pages:

Content Assessment
Checking Concepts: pp. 35, 37, 39, 41, 45
Thinking Critically: pp. 35, 37, 39, 41, 45
Chapter Challenges: pp. 48–50

Alternative Assessment
Building Skills: pp. 37, 39, 41
Science Log: p. 47

Performance-Based Assessment
Hands-On Activity: p. 37
Designing an Experiment: p. 35
Lab Activity: pp. 42–43

• TEACHING RESOURCES •

Teacher's Resources CD-ROM
Lesson Review: Ch. 2, pp. 2, 4, 5, 6, 8
Enrichment: Ch. 2, pp. 3, 7
Key Term Review: Ch. 2, p. 10
Chapter 2 Test: pp. 11–12
Laboratory Manual: pp. 5–8, 9–10, 25–28

Chapter 2
Density

Chapter Overview

In this chapter, students will learn about density, a derived property of matter. They will calculate the densities of objects from measurements of mass and volume and explain specific gravity. Students will use displacement to measure the volume of irregularly shaped solids. Finally, students will explain Archimedes' principle in terms of buoyancy and displacement.

About Figure 2-1 A buoy is a floating object anchored in a body of water to warn ship captains of rocks or to mark a channel. Most buoys are equipped with a bell or light.

Answer Possible answer: Knowing density can help people identify substances.

Linking Prior Knowledge

For this chapter, students should recall:
- the physical properties of mass and volume, and their measurements (Lesson 1-2).
- the solid and liquid states of matter (Lesson 1-3).

Chapter Project

MODEL BOATS

MATERIALS: clay, paper, aluminum foil, 3 marbles, glue, paper clips, staples, tape

Divide students into groups of three or four. After students complete Lesson 2-5, each group will design and make a small model boat. The model boat can be any shape or size that the group chooses. The model boat must be able to float in water while holding three marbles. Assign a type of material, such as clay, paper, or aluminum foil, to each group to use to make its model. (More than one group can use the same type of material.) Groups may also use glue, paper clips, staples, and other fasteners to make their models. Allow students time to design and build their models and to test them in large containers of water.
learning styles: tactile, interpersonal

1 *Introduce*

STUDY HINT Before beginning this lesson, have students read the subheads and captions. This will allow them to preview what is to come as well as to focus on the most important ideas in the lesson.

Linking Prior Knowledge Have students review the properties of matter (Lesson 1-2). Ask students: *What is the physical property that describes the quantity of matter?* (mass) *What is the physical property that describes how much space matter occupies?* (volume)

2 *Teach*

Demonstration Using two clear plastic cups with lids, fill one with cotton and the other with sand. Securely place the lid on each cup. Have students visually inspect and then lift each cup. Ask them to compare the sizes of the cups and contrast the heaviness of the cups. Explain to students that the heavier cup contains matter that is more packed or concentrated. Lead students to relate size to volume and weight to mass. Introduce the term *density* as a measure of the mass of matter within a certain volume.
learning styles: visual, tactile

READING STRATEGY Write the following on the board: *Oranges—$1.95 per dozen.* Ask students to discuss the meaning of this sign if they saw it in a grocery store. Lead students to realize that the term *per* means "for each" or "for every." Rewrite the sign as *Oranges—$1.95/doz* and explain its meaning. Ask students to list measurements that contain the term *per*, such as measurements of speed (mile per hour, mi/h; kilometer per hour, km/h) and density (gram per cubic centimeter, g/cm³; gram per milliliter, g/mL).

Answers to questions

▶ **1** DEFINE: mass per unit volume of a substance

▶ **2** IDENTIFY: g/cm³ or grams per cubic centimeter

▶ **3** IDENTIFY: a physical property

2-1 What is density?

Objective
Define density.

Key Term
density (DEHN-suh-tee): mass per unit volume

Density Which do you think is heavier, a kilogram of cotton or a kilogram of iron? You may already know the answer to this riddle. They both weigh the same amount. However, a kilogram of cotton takes up a greater amount of space, or volume. A kilogram of iron is small enough to hold in your hand. A kilogram of iron takes up less space because iron has a much greater density than cotton does. **Density** is the mass per unit volume of a substance. Substances that are very heavy for their volume are called dense substances.

▲ **Figure 2-2** The bale of cotton at the top has a mass of 1 kg. The iron frying pan below it also has a mass of 1 kg.

▶ **1** DEFINE: What is density?

Units of Density You can find the density of a substance by finding the mass of a unit volume of the substance. Units of density include units of

mass and volume. Mass is measured in grams. The volume of solids is measured in cubic centimeters. The volume of liquids can be measured in milliliters. One milliliter is equal to one cubic centimeter. Therefore, the density of any substance can be given in grams per cubic centimeter, or g/cm³. For example, water has a density of 1 g/cm³. One gram of water takes up one cubic centimeter of space. The densities of some common substances are listed in Figure 2-3.

DENSITIES OF SOME COMMON SUBSTANCES	
Substance	**Density (g/cm³)**
Air	0.0013
Alcohol	0.8
Aluminum	2.7
Cork	0.2
Gold	19.3
Iron	7.9
Lead	11.3
Mercury	13.6
Silver	10.5
Steel	7.8
Water	1.0

▲ Figure 2-3

▶ **2** IDENTIFY: In what units is density measured?

Using Density Density is a physical property of matter. Every kind of matter has a density that can be measured. The density of a pure substance is always the same. For example, the density of lead is always 11.3 g/cm³. The density of mercury is always 13.6 g/cm³. Density does not depend on the size or shape of the substance.

Density can be used to help identify different kinds of matter. Suppose two metals look similar. You know that one may be silver and the other aluminum. If you know the density of each sample, you can identify them. The sample with a density of 10.5 g/cm³ is silver. The sample with a density of 2.7 g/cm³ is aluminum.

34

Teaching Options

EXTENDING THE LESSON

Comparing Cotton and Iron Have students look at Figure 2-2 and explain how they know the bale of cotton has a greater volume than the iron skillet. (The bale takes up more space.) Ask: *Which would be more massive (heavier)—a bale of cotton or a bale of iron?* Explain that the density of iron is greater than the density of cotton, that is, the mass of a unit volume of iron is greater than the mass of a unit volume of cotton. **learning styles: visual, logical/mathematical**

QUICK CONVERSIONS		
Substance	**Metric/SI**	**English**
Density of air	0.0013 (g/cm³)	0.00075 (oz/in.³)
Density of aluminum	2.7 (g/cm³)	1.5 (oz/in.³)
Density of cork	0.2 (g/cm³)	0.1 (oz/in.³)
Density of gold	19.3 (g/cm³)	11.1 (oz/in.³)
Density of lead	11.3 (g/cm³)	6.48 (oz/in.³)
Density of water	1.0 (g/cm³)	0.57 (oz/in.³)

▲ **Figure 2-4** Aluminum (left) and silver (right) look alike but have different densities.

▶ IDENTIFY: What kind of property is density?

✔ CHECKING CONCEPTS

1. Density is the _____ per unit volume of a substance.
2. When a substance has a high density, a large mass fits into a _____ volume.
3. The units of _____ are grams per cubic centimeter.
4. Density is a physical _____ of all matter.
5. The density of silver is always _____.

💡 THINKING CRITICALLY

6. **CALCULATE:** What is the density of a metal block that has a mass of 525 g and a volume of 50 cm³?
7. **PREDICT:** How large a container would be needed to hold 800 g of water?
8. **SEQUENCE:** List the following substances in order from lowest density to highest density: iron, gold, steel, water, air, silver, and aluminum.

DESIGNING AN EXPERIMENT

Design an experiment to solve the following problem. Include a hypothesis, variables, a procedure, and a type of data to study.

PROBLEM: How can you determine the density of chalk?

◈ *Integrating Earth Science*

TOPICS: neutron stars, black holes

THE DENSEST OBJECTS IN THE UNIVERSE
What are the densest objects thought to exist? The answer is neutron stars and black holes. Here is how they form. A new star is made mostly of hydrogen. As millions of years pass, the hydrogen fuses and changes into helium. When the hydrogen is used up, the star becomes a red giant or a supergiant.

Supergiants start out with a much greater mass than the mass of our Sun. Such massive stars may blow up in a huge explosion called a supernova. After the explosion, some of the star's matter gets squeezed into a very dense object called a neutron star. The density of a neutron star is enormous. One teaspoon of matter from a neutron star would have a mass of 100 billion tons!

Some supergiants do not become neutron stars. The most massive stars collapse into black holes. A black hole has a density even greater than that of a neutron star. The density of a black hole behaves as if it is infinite. Not even light escapes the strong pull of gravity in a black hole.

Thinking Critically Explain the meaning of the name "black hole."

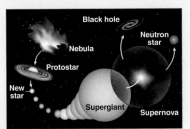

▲ **Figure 2-5** Stages in the life of a star

---

3 Assess

✔ CHECKING CONCEPTS ANSWERS

1. mass
2. small
3. density
4. property
5. 10.5 g/cm³

💡 THINKING CRITICALLY ANSWERS

6. **CALCULATE:** 10.5 g/cm³
7. **PREDICT:** 800 mL (or 800 cm³)
8. **SEQUENCE:** air, water, aluminum, steel, iron, silver, gold

---

4 Close

DESIGNING AN EXPERIMENT

Use the Designing an Experiment Rubric on the Teacher's Resources CD-ROM to assess students' experiments. Fill in the rubric with the additional information below. For this assignment, students should have:

- developed a procedure to determine the density of chalk.
- included a hypothesis and variables in the experiment's design.

◈ *Integrating Earth Science*

TOPICS: neutron stars, black holes

THE DENSEST OBJECTS IN THE UNIVERSE

Astronomy Connection Much of the information about objects in the universe has been learned by using telescopes. One kind of telescope, called an X-ray telescope, can be used to detect black holes. An X-ray telescope uses mirrorlike polished surfaces to collect high-energy electromagnetic radiation from distant objects. As a black hole pulls nearby interstellar matter into it, the matter accelerates and emits high-energy electromagnetic radiation. This radiation can be detected by X-ray telescopes.

Thinking Critically Answer
The term *black* is used to describe a black hole because a black hole does not give off light.

• *TEACHING RESOURCES* •

🔘 **Teacher's Resources CD-ROM**
Lesson Review: Chapter 2, p. 2
Enrichment: Chapter 2, p. 3
Designing an Experiment: Study Tools, p. 14
Designing an Experiment Rubric: Teaching Tools, p. 7

ONGOING ASSESSMENT

Understanding Density Ask students: *If you had a kilogram of water and a kilogram of lead, which would feel heavier?* (neither) *Which has the greater density?* (lead) *How do you know?* (Lead has a greater mass per unit volume.)

1 Introduce

✎ **STUDY HINT** Have students write the lesson title and objective in their notebooks. As students read this lesson, tell them to write the sentence or sentences that provide the information that meets the objective.

Linking Prior Knowledge Ask students to recall the two physical properties of matter needed to determine density. Explain to students that mass and volume are part of the mathematical equation for finding density.

2 Teach

Discussion Inform students that density is a property that can be calculated. Remind them that density is mass per unit volume. If you know the mass and volume of a sample of matter, then you can calculate its density. The formula for density is mass divided by volume. **learning styles: auditory, logical/mathematical**

Demonstration Using a balance and a graduated cylinder, show students how to find the density of water by demonstrating each of the bulleted steps under the section Density of a Liquid. If using a glass graduate, remind students that they should read the meniscus (curved surface) when finding the volume of a liquid. Refer to the Skills Handbook at the front of the Student Edition. **learning style: visual**

Reinforcement Give students several practice problems for calculating density. Make sure that they use the correct units when solving the problems. **learning style: logical/mathematical**

Answers to questions

▶ **IDENTIFY:** mass and volume

▶ **EXPLAIN:** because a volume of 1 milliliter is equal to a volume of 1 cubic centimeter

▶ **DESCRIBE:** Measure its dimensions (length, width, and height) and multiply all three measurements to find the volume.

2-2 How is density measured?

Objective
Explain how to find the density of a solid or a liquid.

Finding Density To find the density of a material, you must measure both mass and volume. You can find density by dividing the mass by the volume. Remember that mass is measured in grams. Volume is measured in cubic centimeters or milliliters, so density is expressed in grams per cubic centimeter or grams per milliliter.

▶ **IDENTIFY:** What measurements must you make before you can calculate the density of a material?

Density of a Liquid You can find the density of a liquid using a graduated cylinder and a balance.

- Find the mass of the graduated cylinder. Record your measurement.
- Pour some of the liquid you want to measure into the graduated cylinder. Write down the volume of the liquid.
- Place the graduated cylinder with the liquid on the balance. Record the mass.
- Find the mass of the liquid by subtracting the mass of the empty graduated cylinder from the mass of the graduated cylinder with the liquid.

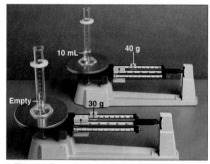

▲ **Figure 2-6** The empty graduated cylinder has a mass of 30 g. With the liquid the mass is 40 g, so the water has a mass of 10 g.

36

Now you are ready to calculate the density of the liquid. Look at the example shown. The mass of the liquid is 10 g. The volume is 10 mL. To find the liquid's density, divide its mass by its volume.

> density = mass ÷ volume
> density = 10 g ÷ 10 mL
> density = 1 g/mL

Notice that in this example, density is expressed in grams per milliliter. One milliliter is equal in volume to one cubic centimeter. The density of a liquid can be measured in grams per milliliter or grams per cubic centimeter.

▶ **EXPLAIN:** Why can density be measured either in grams per cubic centimeter or in grams per milliliter?

Density of a Solid You can find the density of any solid if you know its mass and its volume. You can use a balance to find the mass of a solid. You can find the volume of a rectangular solid by multiplying its length by its width by its height. Look at the aluminum bar in Figure 2-7. Its mass is equal to 270 g. Its volume is equal to 10 cm × 5 cm × 2 cm, or 100 cm³. To find the density of the aluminum bar, divide its mass by its volume.

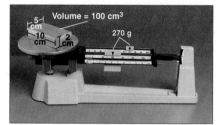

▲ **Figure 2-7** An aluminum bar of volume 100 cm³ has a mass of 270 g.

> density = mass ÷ volume
> density = 270 g ÷ 100 cm³
> density = 2.7 g/cm³

▶ **DESCRIBE:** How can you find the volume of a rectangular solid?

Teaching Options

RETEACH

Finding the Density of a Liquid Place a graduated cylinder containing 25 mL of ethanol or a similar alcohol on one pan of a double-pan balance. Place an identical empty graduated cylinder and two 10-g masses on the other pan. A slight turn of the adjustment screw will level the pans. Ask students to determine the volume of the liquid (25 mL), its mass (20 g), and its density (20 g/25 mL = 0.8 g/mL). Have students use Figure 2-3 on page 34 to identify the liquid as alcohol. **learning styles: visual, logical/mathematical**

COOPERATIVE LEARNING

Measuring the Mass and Volume of a Liquid Supply pairs of students with a graduated cylinder, a pan balance, and a beaker containing 50 mL of water. Ask students to devise a procedure to measure the mass of 10 mL, 25 mL, and 50 mL of water. After approving the procedures, have students measure the mass and volume of each sample and use the measurements to calculate the density of water for the three samples. **learning styles: visual, tactile**

CHAPTER 2: Density 37

✔ CHECKING CONCEPTS

1. What measurements must be known in order to find the density of a substance?
2. What are the units of density for a liquid?
3. What equipment do you need to find the density of a liquid?
4. What three measurements must you make when finding the density of a liquid?
5. How can you find the density of a solid with a regular shape?

💡 THINKING CRITICALLY

6. CALCULATE: If 5 mL of a liquid has a mass of 10 g, what is the density of the liquid?
7. EXPLAIN: When finding the density of a liquid, why must you first find the mass of the container holding the liquid?

BUILDING MATH SKILLS

Calculating Density Use Figure 2-8 to answer the following questions.

▲ Figure 2-8

8. What is the volume of the bar?
9. If the bar has a mass of 500 g, what is its density? Show your work.
10. How would the density of the bar be different if its mass was 4,520 g? What would the bar be made of?

Hands-On Activity

COMPARING DENSITIES OF LIQUIDS

You will need a graduated cylinder, food coloring, water, corn syrup, vegetable oil, and glycerine.

1. Color the water and glycerine differently, so you can tell them apart.
2. One at a time, slowly pour about 10mL each of the water, corn syrup, vegetable oil, and glycerine into the graduated cylinder.
3. Observe the liquids as they form separate layers.
4. Make a sketch showing the order in which the liquids have settled in the graduated cylinder.

Practicing Your Skills

5. HYPOTHESIZE: Why do you think the liquids separate into layers?
6. INFER: Which liquid is the most dense? Which liquid is the least dense?
7. SEQUENCE: List the four liquids in order from least to most dense.

▲ STEP 3 Observe how the liquids separate.

MORE ON THE WEB

Measuring Density Have students use the Internet to calculate the mass and volume of differently shaped objects on a virtual scale and virtual graduated cylinder. Then, have students complete an online worksheet. Send students to www.conceptsandchallenges.com.

• TEACHING RESOURCES •

Teacher's Resources CD-ROM
Lesson Review: Chapter 2, p. 4

Laboratory Manual
Lab. Skills Worksheet 1: Using a Graduated Cylinder, pp. 5–6

Lab. Skills Worksheet 2: Using a Triple-Beam Balance, pp. 7–8

Lab. Challenge: How can you find the density of a substance? pp. 25–28

---

3 Assess

✔ CHECKING CONCEPTS ANSWERS

1. mass and volume
2. g/mL (grams per milliliter) or g/cm^3 (grams per cubic centimeter)
3. balance and graduated cylinder
4. mass of empty graduated cylinder, volume of liquid, and mass of cylinder with liquid
5. Measure its mass and calculate its volume. Then, divide the mass of the object by its volume.

💡 THINKING CRITICALLY ANSWERS

6. CALCULATE: 2 g/mL
7. EXPLAIN: If you know the mass of the container holding the liquid, then you can subtract that mass from the combined mass of the container with the liquid to get the mass of the liquid alone.

4 Close

BUILDING MATH SKILLS ANSWERS

Calculating Density

8. $400 \ cm^3$
9. $500 \ g / 400 \ cm^3 = 1.25 \ g/cm^3$
10. $4{,}520 \ g / 400 \ cm^3 = 11.3 \ g/cm^3$; The bar would be made of lead. (See Figure 2-3 on page T34.)

Hands-On Activity

COMPARING DENSITIES OF LIQUIDS

TIME: 10–15 minutes

PURPOSE: observing, modeling, inferring, classifying

ALTERNATIVE MATERIALS: You can use other liquids as long as they do not mix with each other.

DISCUSSION: Explain to students that since liquids are matter, they have density. All liquids, however, do not have the same density. Inform students that this activity will show them how the densities of different liquids allow them to form separate layers. The densest liquid will form the bottom layer, and the least-dense liquid will form the top layer.

Practicing Your Skills Answers

5. HYPOTHESIZE: because the liquids have different densities
6. INFER: corn syrup; vegetable oil
7. SEQUENCE: vegetable oil, water, glycerine, corn syrup

1 Introduce

STUDY HINT Before beginning this lesson, have students study Figure 2-10. Ask students to identify in which liquid the device is floating higher, and why it floats higher.

Linking Prior Knowledge Have students recall the unit of density (g/cm³) and the density of water (1 g/cm³) (Lesson 2-1).

2 Teach

Demonstration Fill one beaker about three-quarters full of water and another beaker about three-quarters full of super-concentrated salt water. Pour some sand in the bottom of a test tube and fill the tube about two-thirds full of water. Cap the test tube or insert a cork into its mouth. Carefully place the test tube vertically in the beaker filled with water so that the tube floats. Have students observe the height of the test tube above the water. Remove the test tube and place it in the beaker containing salt water. Have students repeat the observation. Explain that the test tube floated higher in the salt water because salt water is denser than water.
learning style: visual

Answers to questions

1 DEFINE: the density of a substance compared with the density of water

2 EXPLAIN: the specific gravity of the liquid in which the hydrometer is floating

3 NAME: identifying substances, checking the chemical purity of substances, checking the quality of products, and testing for sugar or protein in blood and urine

WRITING HINT One of the Key Terms from this lesson, *hydrometer,* ends in *-meter,* a word part that means "instrument for measuring." Ask students to write a list of other words that end in *-meter* and to explain their definitions. (Possible answers: thermometer, speedometer, and pedometer)

2-3 What is specific gravity?

Objective
Explain what is meant by specific gravity.

Key Terms
specific (spuh-SIF-ik) **gravity:** density of a substance compared with the density of water

hydrometer (hy-DRAHM-uht-uhr): device used to measure specific gravity

Specific Gravity **Specific gravity** is the density of a substance compared with the density of water. It is often useful to compare the density of a substance with the density of water. Water is used as the standard for comparison because its density is 1 g/cm³. You can find the specific gravity of a substance by dividing its density by the density of water.

Suppose you want to find the specific gravity of copper. The density of copper is 8.9 g/cm³. The density of water is 1 g/cm³. To find the specific gravity of copper, divide the density of copper by the density of water. The specific gravity of copper is 8.9. Notice that specific gravity has no units. When you divide like units, the units cancel each other out. The specific gravities of some common substances are listed in Figure 2-9.

SPECIFIC GRAVITIES	
Substance	**Specific Gravity**
Aluminum	2.7
Corn syrup	1.38
Diamond	3.5
Gasoline	0.7
Glycerine	1.26
Gold	19.3
Ice	0.92
Marble	2.7
Rubber	1.34
Water	1.00

▲ Figure 2-9

1 DEFINE: What is specific gravity?

38

Measuring Specific Gravity The specific gravity of a liquid can be measured with a device called a **hydrometer**. When a hydrometer is placed in a liquid, it floats. The higher the specific gravity of a liquid, the higher the hydrometer will float. You can tell the specific gravity of the liquid by reading the marking at the surface of the liquid.

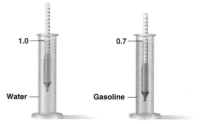

▲ Figure 2-10 Water has a specific gravity of 1.00. Gasoline has a specific gravity of 0.7.

2 EXPLAIN: What determines the height at which a hydrometer floats in a liquid?

Uses of Specific Gravity Specific gravity has many practical uses. It can be used to identify pure substances, because each substance has a particular specific gravity. Hydrometers are used in clinical laboratory tests to find the specific gravity of blood and of urine. Lab technicians look for signs of increased glucose (sugar) or protein. Dehydration, a loss of fluid in the system, is also detected by specific gravity.

▲ Figure 2-11 A hydrometer can test the specific gravity of any liquid.

Teaching Options

! FAST FACTS *Specific Gravity*

From experience, you can predict that a cork stopper will float in water and that an iron washer will sink. This prediction illustrates that a material floats in a liquid that has a greater density and sinks in a liquid that has a lesser density.

You can use specific gravity to predict if a uniform solid or liquid sample of a material will float in water because the specific gravity of a material is a measure of the density of the material compared to the density of water. A material that has a specific gravity less than 1.0 will float in water. A material that has a specific gravity greater than 1.0 will sink in water. Since the specific gravities of gasoline and glycerine are 0.7 and 1.26, respectively, you can predict that gasoline will float in water and that water will float in glycerine.

The specific gravities of gases are sometimes calculated relative to the density of air. A gas that has a specific gravity less than 1.0, such as carbon monoxide, which has a specific gravity of 0.97, rises in air. On the other hand, the vapor from dry ice, which is carbon dioxide, falls in air because its specific gravity is 1.53.

Specific gravity can also be used to check the chemical purity of substances. Industries use specific gravity to check the quality of many of their products. For example, specific gravity is used to check the amount of cane sugar in a solution. It also is used to check the purity of milk.

3 NAME: What are some uses of specific gravity?

CHECKING CONCEPTS

1. Specific gravity compares the density of a substance with the density of _____.
2. Specific gravity has no _____ because the density units cancel each other out.
3. A hydrometer is a device that can be used to measure the specific gravity of a _____.
4. The _____ at which the hydrometer floats depends on the specific gravity of the liquid.
5. The purity of milk can be checked by using _____.

THINKING CRITICALLY

6. PREDICT: In which liquid would a hydrometer float lower, gasoline or corn syrup? Explain.
7. CALCULATE: Silver has a density of 10.5 g/cm³. What is the specific gravity of silver?
8. EXPLAIN: Why does specific gravity have no units?

BUILDING SCIENCE SKILLS

Researching In a brief report, explain whether specific gravity could be useful in each of the following situations.

a. Determining the purity of vegetable oil
b. Determining whether a rock is real gold or fool's gold
c. Separating corn oil from corn syrup
d. Determining whether gasoline has been contaminated with water

People in Science
MINERALOGIST

Minerals are natural substances found in soil and rock. Many products are made from minerals. For example, quartz is a mineral that is used to make timing devices in watches. Sulfur is a mineral that is used to make medicines.

Minerals must be mined, or taken from the earth. When a mineral deposit is found, a mining company needs to know how much of the mineral is present and what form the mineral is in. Mineralogists find answers to these questions. They take samples from a mineral deposit. They then study the specific gravity of the mineral to identify it and to determine its purity.

Mineralogists are employed by private industry, research laboratories, and the government. To be a mineralogist, a person needs a college degree. Many mineralogists also have advanced degrees. If you are interested in this career, you should have a good background in science and mathematics.

Thinking Critically For what part of this job would you need math skills?

▲ **Figure 2-12** This mineralogist is studying a limestone deposit.

CHAPTER 2: Density **39**

3 Assess

CHECKING CONCEPTS ANSWERS

1. water
2. units
3. liquid
4. height
5. specific gravity

THINKING CRITICALLY ANSWERS

6. PREDICT: Gasoline; A hydrometer will float lower in gasoline because gasoline has a lower specific gravity than corn syrup.
7. CALCULATE: 10.5
8. EXPLAIN: When the unit g/cm³ is divided by the unit g/cm³, the units cancel each other out.

4 Close

BUILDING SCIENCE SKILLS

Researching Check students' reports. In each situation, specific gravity can be useful.

People in Science
MINERALOGIST

Real-Life Connection In many locations around the world, hobbyists can still pan for traces of gold in mineral-rich streams and rivers. The technique, used by prospectors in the California and Alaska gold rushes, utilizes gold's high specific gravity.

To isolate gold and gold-containing materials, dry samples are mixed in a pan with water from a gently moving stream. Soluble materials dissolve in the water and are removed as the water is discarded into the stream. Additional water is added, and the pan is agitated. Dense materials, such as gold, fall to the bottom, while the water carries away materials with lower densities. After the procedure is repeated several more times, the contents of the pan are placed on paper to dry. The dried solids are then inspected for gold.

Thinking Critically Answer
Possible answers: making surveying measurements, calculating areas and volumes of deposits, predicting yields, and determining densities and specific gravities of samples

MORE ON THE WEB

Modeling a Hydrometer
Divide students into small groups. Have each group complete an online activity on building a hydrometer at www.conceptsandchallenges.com.

• TEACHING RESOURCES •

Teacher's Resources CD-ROM
Lesson Review: Chapter 2, p. 5

ONGOING ASSESSMENT

Organizing Specific Gravities Have students list the substances in Figure 2-9 in order from lowest to highest specific gravity. Then, have them determine which substances will float in water.

1 *Introduce*

🔍 INVESTIGATE

TIME: 15 minutes

PURPOSE: Students will find the volume of a pebble and a marble.

MATERIALS: small stone, marble, pan balance, 100-mL graduated cylinder

PROCEDURE: After Step 3, have students subtract the original volume reading of the water from the volume reading of the submerged stone and water. Explain that the result is the volume of the stone. Similarly, in Step 4, have them subtract the volume reading of the submerged stone and water from the volume reading of the submerged marble, submerged stone, and water. This result is the volume of the marble. **learning styles: visual, logical/mathematical**

THINK ABOUT IT: Accept all reasonable measurements for the volumes of the stone and marble; No, it depends only on the object's volume. Possible answer: The mass of an object has no effect on displacement.

📝 **STUDY HINT** Before beginning this lesson, have students study Figure 2-15. Ask them to explain the illustrations.

Linking Prior Knowledge Ask students to recall the properties of solids and liquids (Lesson 1-3). Have them identify several properties that make a liquid material different from a solid material. (A liquid takes the shape of its container and can flow.)

2 *Teach*

Demonstration Show students a rock and glass half full of water. Ask them to predict what will happen to the rock if it is placed in the water and what will happen to the height of water in the glass. Then, have students observe that the rock sinks and that the height of the water rises. Ask them to determine which of their predictions were correct. Ask what happened to the volume of water in the glass when the rock was placed in it. Lead them to realize that the volume of the water did not change. Ask students to think about why the water rose. Discuss all responses and then define and discuss displacement.
learning styles: visual, logical/mathematical

2-4 What is displacement?

🔍 INVESTIGATE

Measuring Displacement
HANDS-ON ACTIVITY

STEP 1

1. Use a balance to find the masses of a small stone and a marble. Record your measurements in a data table.
2. Fill a 100-mL graduated cylinder with water to the 50-mL mark.
3. Gently place the stone in the water. Notice how much the water level rises. This increase is equal to the volume of water displaced. Record the change in volume of the water in your data table.
4. Repeat Step 3 with the marble.

THINK ABOUT IT: What is the volume of the stone? Of the marble? Does the amount of water displaced by an object depend on its mass? How do you know?

Objectives
Define displacement. Find the volume of an irregular solid.

Key Term
displacement (dihs-PLAYS-muhnt)**:** the replacement, or pushing aside, of a volume of water, or any fluid, by an object

Displacement About 2,000 years ago, a Greek scientist named Archimedes (ahr-kuh-MEE-deez) made an interesting observation. He stepped into a bathtub full of water and noticed that the water level rose. When he sat down, some of the water spilled over the edge of the tub.

What Archimedes observed occurs whenever an object is placed in water. When objects are placed in water, they make the water level rise. The water level rises because water is pushed out of the way by the object. This replacement of a volume of water by an object is called **displacement**.

▲ **Figure 2-13** Archimedes

▶ **DEFINE:** What is displacement?

40

Displacement and Volume When an object is placed completely under water, the volume of the water that the object displaces is equal to the volume of the object. Many objects, such as rocks, do not have a regular shape. You can use displacement to find the volume of an irregularly shaped object, as shown in Figure 2-14.

The stone displaces the water

▲ **Figure 2-14** When a stone is lowered into a can of water, it displaces a volume of water equal to its own volume.

A simple way to find the volume of an irregularly shaped object is to pour some water into a graduated cylinder or a beaker that is marked to show volume. Record the volume of the water. Then, carefully place the object in the container of water. Record the new reading. The volume of the object is equal to the difference in the two volume readings.

For example, if a rock displaces 5 mL of water, the volume of the rock is 5 mL. This is shown in Figure 2-15.

Teaching Options

EXTENDING THE LESSON

Researching Archimedes
Archimedes was a Greek mathematician and inventor who is credited with many discoveries and inventions. Archimedes described the laws of the lever and pulley, as well as how to find volume by displacement. He was the first to accurately compute the volumes of spheres, cylinders, and other geometric shapes. Have students find out more about the life and work of Archimedes. Tell students to summarize their findings in a written report.
learning style: auditory

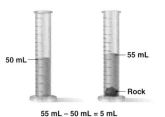

55 mL − 50 mL = 5 mL
Volume of rock = 5 mL

▲ **Figure 2-15** This rock displaced 5 mL of water. It has a volume of 5 mL.

 EXPLAIN: How can you find the volume of an irregularly shaped object?

✓ CHECKING CONCEPTS

1. If an object displaces 50 mL of water, the object's _____ is 50 mL.
2. When an object is placed in water, the water level _____.
3. The amount of water pushed aside by an object is called _____.

4. A rock is an _____ shaped object.
5. The _____ of an irregular object is equal to the volume of water it displaces.

💡 THINKING CRITICALLY

6. ANALYZE: Does the amount of water displaced by an object depend on the object's mass? Explain your answer.
7. EXPLAIN: Why is displacement useful in finding the density of an irregularly shaped object?

📋 BUILDING MATH SKILLS

Finding Volume Use displacement to find the volume of the following objects. Assume each has been placed in a graduated cylinder containing 50 mL of water.

a. A marble: new reading, 54 mL
b. A lead weight: new reading, 71 mL
c. A paper clip: new reading, 50.5 mL

Real-Life Science

PREVENTING SPILL-OVER

Have you ever made an ice cream soda? Did some, if not most, of the liquid wind up on the table after you put in the ice cream?

What happens when you fill a glass with a beverage, then try to put ice in the glass?

In order to prevent this displacement and the mess it causes, you must first place the ice in the glass, then add the liquid. This prevents spill-over.

In the bathroom, both the sink and tub have a feature built in to prevent accidental overflow. Do you know what that might be? If you fill the tub too high and then get into the water, you would cause a small flood without this feature. Pools and decorative fountains use the same principle to prevent overflow.

Thinking Critically How does placing the solid in the glass first prevent displacement?

▲ **Figure 2-16** Displacement can cause spill-over if you're not careful.

Answers to questions

 DEFINE: the pushing aside of a volume of water by an object

2 EXPLAIN: Submerge the object in water and measure the amount of water that it displaces.

3 Assess

✓ CHECKING CONCEPTS ANSWERS

1. volume
2. rises
3. displacement
4. irregularly
5. volume

💡 THINKING CRITICALLY ANSWERS

6. ANALYZE: No, displacement of water by an object is a result of the object's volume, not its mass.
7. EXPLAIN: To find density, you need to know volume. You can find the volume of an irregularly shaped object by using displacement.

4 Close

📋 BUILDING MATH SKILLS ANSWERS

Finding Volume

a. 4 mL
b. 21 mL
c. 0.5 mL

Real-Life Science

PREVENTING SPILL-OVER

Background Displacement of one material by another material illustrates the property of matter called impenetrability. No two particles of matter can occupy the same space simultaneously.

Discussion Have students look at Figure 2-16 and explain what happened when the ice cube was placed in the beverage. (The ice cube displaced some water, causing the water to overflow the glass.) Ask them what will happen if the ice cube is removed. (The water level will fall.)

Thinking Critically Answer
The solid in the glass displaces the liquid as the liquid is added. As a result, you can fill the glass up to the top.

MORE ON THE WEB

Learning about Displacement Boats Have students visit www.conceptsandchallenges.com to learn about displacement boats and how they work. Students should write a report about their findings.

ONGOING ASSESSMENT

Measuring Displacement Have students write a short procedure describing how they could use water displacement to find the volume of an object that sinks.

• TEACHING RESOURCES •

💿 **Teacher's Resources CD-ROM**
Lesson Review: Chapter 2, p. 6
Enrichment: Chapter 2, p. 7
Laboratory Manual
Lab. Skills Worksheet 1: Using a Graduated Cylinder, pp. 5–8
Lab. Skills Worksheet 2: Using a Triple-Beam Balance, pp. 9–10

Lab Activity

(pp. 42–43)

1 Prepare the Lab

Comparing Densities of Coins

SET-UP TIME: 🕐 **LAB TIME:** 🕑

BACKGROUND: The density of a penny or group of pennies is the same because density is a measure of the material from which the penny is made and not a property of the penny. Because density is a ratio of the mass of a material to the volume the material takes up, this ratio remains the same for one or many items as long as each is made of the same material.

PURPOSE: Students will predict the ranked densities of a penny, a nickel, and a dime and then calculate the densities of the coins from mass and volume measurements to confirm their predictions.

ALTERNATIVE MATERIALS: Any set of uniform metallic objects, such as washers, sinkers, or nuts, can be used to verify that the density of the material in one or more identical objects is the same.

SCIENCE SKILLS: Students will **observe**, **predict,** and **measure** properties of mass, volume, and density in the experiment and then **organize data, communicate results,** and **compare** properties.

2 Guide the Lab

PROCEDURE: Divide the class into pairs. Discuss the procedure. Have students make data charts similar to Figure 2-18 before starting the experiment. Provide students with a copy of the Lab Activity Report found on the Teacher's Resources CD-ROM for students to record their observations and conclusions.

TROUBLESHOOTING: Emphasize that students must keep the inside walls of the cylinder above the water level dry because any water droplets encountered by the water as it rises when the coins are placed in it will increase the displacement reading.

EXPECTED OUTCOME: Students should observe measurable readings of mass and displacement. After calculating densities, they should observe that the density of the material in one, five, or ten pennies is about the same.

LAB ACTIVITY
Comparing Densities of Coins

Materials
Safety goggles, triple-beam balance, 25-mL graduated cylinder, calculator, 10 pennies, 10 nickels, 10 dimes, water, eyedropper, plastic cup, paper towels

▲ STEP 3 Fill the graduated cylinder to exactly 10 mL.

▲ Figure 2-17 The water level should be at 10 mL.

BACKGROUND
You have just learned that matter has two basic properties. They are mass, which is the amount of material in an object, and volume, the amount of space that an object takes up. Dividing the mass of an object by its volume gives the density of the object, another property of matter. We will be finding the density of various coins using the displacement method.

PURPOSE
In this activity, you will observe and predict the density of the materials that make up pennies, nickels, and dimes using the displacement method. To do this, you will use 10 of each coin so that the measurements are easy to make.

PROCEDURE 🔒 🔾

1. Copy the chart in Figure 2-18.

2. Predict whether or not the densities of the coins will be different from each other. On what do you base your prediction?

3. Using the eyedropper, put exactly 10 mL of water into the 25-mL graduated cylinder as shown in Figure 2-17.

4. Find the mass of 10 pennies on the triple-beam balance and record it in the chart.

5. Carefully lower the pennies into the graduated cylinder. The water level should go up. Measure and record the new volume of the water.

6. Subtract 10 from the new volume of water to find the volume of the coins. Record this in the chart.

42

Teaching Options

❗ FAST FACTS

Copper in Coins

Pennies minted since 1982 are made of an alloy of zinc and copper coated with copper. Dimes minted after 1964 consist of a core of pure copper with a copper and nickel coating. If you observe a dime on edge, you can identify its three distinct layers: copper core, copper coating, and nickel coating.

\multicolumn{3}{c}{DENSITIES OF COMMON COINAGE METALS}		
Metal	**Metric/SI Density**	**English Density**
Copper	8.92 g/cm³	5.12 oz/in.³
Nickel	8.91 g/cm³	5.11 oz/in.³
Zinc	7.14 g/cm³	4.10 oz/in.³

ESL/ELL STRATEGY

Pairing Students English-language learners may have difficulty following the procedure. Pair an English-language learner with an English proficient student during this lab. The English-proficient student can help the English-language learner in carrying out the procedure.

▲ **STEP 4** Find the mass of 10 pennies.

▲ **STEP 8** Record the volume of water when 10 dimes are added to 10 mL of water.

7. Now find the masses of 10 nickels and 10 dimes. Record the masses in the chart.

8. Repeat steps 4–6 for the 10 nickels and 10 dimes. Record the results in your chart.

Experiment	Mass (g)	Volume of Water (mL)	New Volume of Water (mL)	Volume of Coins (mL)	Density of Coins (g/mL)
10 pennies		10			
10 nickels		10			
10 dimes		10			

▲ **Figure 2-18** Copy this chart and use it to record your observations.

CONCLUSIONS

1. CALCULATE: Find the density of each coin. Divide the mass of coins by the volume of coins. Complete the chart.

2. COMPARE: How does your prediction compare with the actual results?

3. INFER: Which has a greater density, 10 pennies or 10 nickels? Explain why.

4. INFER: Which has a greater density, 10 pennies or 10 dimes? Explain why.

5. APPLY: How would you find the density of a quarter? Explain your reasoning.

Tips for Using Technology

Databases Have students use database software to record the densities of the coins. Databases allow students to enter and edit information, store and organize a lot of information easily, and search for specific information. Students can use database software to share their data with the class. Remind students to enter information into the file carefully. Have students use the Database Planner on the Teacher's Resources CD-ROM to plan their databases.

• TEACHING RESOURCES •

Teacher's Resources CD-ROM
Lab Activity Report: Study Tools, pp. 16–17
Laboratory Activity Rubric: Teaching Tools, p. 8
Database Planner: Study Tools, p. 22
Graph Paper: Visuals, p. 4
Laboratory Manual
Lab. Skills Worksheet 1: Using a Graduated Cylinder, pp. 5–8; *Lab. Skills Worksheet 2*: Using a Triple-Beam Balance, pp. 9–10

LAB HINT: Have students look at Figure 2-17. If using glass graduates, remind students to record the calibration line on the graduated cylinder closest to the bottom of the meniscus (curved surface) of the water as the volume of water measurement.

Because older pennies are slightly less dense, be sure to use pennies minted after 1982, to be sure the results match those given here.

3 Conclude the Lab

1. **OBSERVE:** The approximate densities of the coins are: penny, 6.9 g/mL; nickel, 8.3 g/mL; dime, 7.6 g/mL.
2. **COMPARE:** Answers will vary. Accept all reasonable answers.
3. **INFER:** Possible answer: The density of 10 pennies is less than the density of 10 nickels because the materials in pennies are less dense than the materials in nickels.
4. **INFER:** Possible answer: The density of ten pennies is less than the density of 10 dimes because the materials in pennies are less dense than the materials in dimes.
5. **APPLY:** Possible answer: Find the mass and volume of several quarters. Then divide the value of the mass by the value of the volume to find the density of the materials used to make a quarter.

Use the Laboratory Activity Rubric on the Teacher's Resources CD-ROM to assess students' lab activities. Fill in the rubric with the additional information below. For this activity, students should have:

• performed the activity according to the procedure and filled in the chart with data collected during the activity.

• answered the questions correctly and in complete sentences.

4 Extend the Lab

Have students graph the mass and volume data for one, five, and ten pennies by plotting the volumes of the pennies on the horizontal axis and their corresponding masses on the vertical axis. Students should observe that the three points and the origin (0 mL, 0 g) fall along a straight line. The straight line indicates that the composition of one, five, and ten pennies is the same.

1 Introduce

STUDY HINT Have students study Figure 2-19. Have them write a step-by-step procedure that goes with the figure. Students can use the Flowchart found on the Teacher's Resources CD-ROM.

Linking Prior Knowledge Have students discuss their experiences with trying to float while swimming. Ask students if they have ever used a floating device, such as an inflatable raft. Ask what happened when they first tried to get on the raft. (At first, it sagged or sank a bit, but then it floated.)

2 Teach

Demonstration Loop two identical rubber bands over a pencil held horizontally by a student. Attach identical weights to the rubber bands, using paper clips bent into S-shapes. Have students observe the similar lengths of the rubber bands. Place a glass of water beneath one of the weights and raise the glass so that the weight is completely submerged but not touching the sides or bottom of the glass. Have students compare the lengths of the rubber bands. Lead students to infer that the shortened rubber band indicates that the submerged weight is pulling down with less force on its rubber band than the weight that is not submerged. Allow individual students to push upward on the weight that is suspended in air until the rubber bands are the same lengths. Tell students that the force with which they are pushing up on the weight suspended in air is the same size as the force with which the water is pushing up on the submerged weight. Introduce the terms *buoyancy* and *buoyant force*. **learning styles: visual, tactile**

Answers to questions

STATE: The weight lost by an object in water is equal to the weight of the water that the object displaces.

DEFINE: the tendency of an object to float in a fluid

APPLY: 6 N

RECOGNIZE: when the weight of the displaced water equals the object's weight

---

2-5 What is buoyancy?

Objective
Explain Archimedes' principle in terms of buoyancy and displacement.

Key Terms
buoyancy (BOI-uhn-see): tendency of an object to float in a fluid
newton: SI unit of force

Archimedes' Principle When Archimedes stepped into a bathtub, he observed the water level rising. As he sat down, he also noticed that his body seemed to feel lighter. Archimedes hypothesized that the rising of the water in the tub and his feeling of weight loss must be related. Upon further investigation, he found that the weight "lost" by an object in water is equal to the weight of the water displaced by the object. This is called Archimedes' principle.

▶ **STATE:** What does Archimedes' principle state?

Buoyancy When an object is placed in water, it seems to weigh less than it does in air. The water exerts an upward force on the object. This upward force opposes the downward pull of gravity on the object, thus decreasing its weight. This upward force is responsible for buoyancy. **Buoyancy** is the tendency of an object to float in a fluid. Fluids are gases, such as air, or liquids, such as water.

You can observe buoyancy in action when you watch a person or a boat float on the surface of water. You can experience buoyancy yourself by standing in the shallow end of a swimming pool and lifting your leg. Your leg will seem very light. Your leg feels light because the buoyant force of the water is helping to hold up your leg.

▶ **DEFINE:** What is buoyancy?

44

Buoyancy and Archimedes' Principle Archimedes' principle states that the amount of weight lost by an object in water is equal to the weight of the water that the object displaces. Buoyancy is related to displacement. The buoyant, or upward, force on an object in water is equal to the weight of the water that the object displaces. Look at Figure 2-19. The weight of the rock is shown in newtons (N). The **newton** is the SI unit of force. One kilogram equals 9.8N. If a rock weighing 4N displaces an amount of water weighing 1N, the buoyant force on the rock is 1N. The rock's weight in the water is 4N − 1N, or 3N.

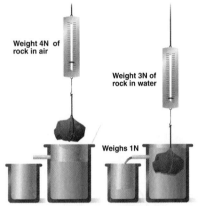

Weight 4N of rock in air

Weight 3N of rock in water

Weighs 1N

▲ **Figure 2-19** The weight lost by the rock when placed in water equals the weight of water displaced by the rock.

▶ **APPLY:** If a buoyant force of 6 N acts on a block placed in water, what is the weight of the water that the block displaces?

Teaching Options

! FAST FACTS

Displaced Water, Buoyant Force, and Floating

A partially submerged object, such as a cork, floats on the surface of water because its weight in water is zero. Similarly, a submerged object, such as a hovering fish, floats beneath the surface because its weight in water is also zero. In both cases, the weight of the volume of water the object displaces equals the weight of the object in air. A sunken object has a submerged weight, which caused the object to sink. The submerged weight of an object equals the weight of the object in air minus the weight of the water it displaces.

EXTENDING THE LESSON

Studying Balloons Tie a paper clip bent in an S-shape to the string of a helium balloon. Add paper clips to the hook until the balloon remains suspended just beneath the ceiling. Explain that the balloon floats because there is an upward force on the balloon equal in size to the combined weights of the empty balloon, helium, string, and paper clips. Have students apply Archimedes' principle to identify the upward force on the balloon as a buoyant force that is equal to the weight of the volume of air that the balloon displaces.

Floating Buoyancy explains why an object sinks or floats. Suppose that an object displaces enough water so that the weight of the displaced water is equal to its own weight. Then, the buoyant force on the object will be equal to the object's weight. As a result, the weight of the object in water is zero. The object floats. An object sinks if its weight is greater than the buoyant force.

▶ 4 **RECOGNIZE:** When will an object float in water?

✔ CHECKING CONCEPTS

1. Buoyancy is the _____ force exerted by a gas or a liquid.

2. The buoyant force on an object is equal to the weight of the water it _____.

3. When the buoyant force on an object is equal to or greater than its weight, the object _____.

4. Buoyancy decreases the downward pull of _____ on an object.

5. Archimedes' principle states the amount of weight lost by an object in water equals the _____ of the displaced water.

THINKING CRITICALLY

6. **CALCULATE: a.** A metal block is 20 cm long, 10 cm high, and 5 cm wide. If submerged in water, how much water will the block displace? **b.** If the density of water is 1 g/cm³, what will be the buoyant force on the block?

7. **EXPLAIN:** How are displacement and buoyant force related?

HEALTH AND SAFETY TIP

Always wear a life jacket if you go sailing or canoeing. If you fall into the water, the air in the jacket will decrease your overall density and help you to float, even if you cannot swim. Visit a local swimming pool. Ask the swimming instructor to describe how people are taught to float.

Science and Technology

SUBMARINE BALLAST

Submarines are specialized ships that travel on or under the surface of water. This is possible because the buoyancy of a submarine can be changed. Submarines have special containers called ballast tanks. Ballast tanks can be filled with either air or water, helping them float or sink.

Submarines are made of steel and other heavy materials. But, when a submarine's ballast tanks are full of air, the average density of the whole ship is less than the density of water. So, the buoyant force of water makes the submarine float.

To dive, the ballast tanks are flooded with water. This added weight makes the average density of the ship greater than the density of water. The buoyant force no longer supports the ship, and it sinks. To resurface, compressed air forces water out of the tanks. This action makes the submarine lighter again.

Thinking Critically What might happen if a ballast tank were to leak?

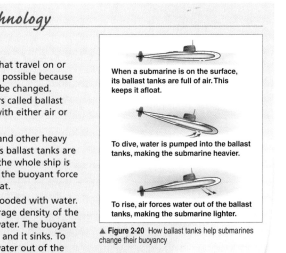

When a submarine is on the surface, its ballast tanks are full of air. This keeps it afloat.

To dive, water is pumped into the ballast tanks, making the submarine heavier.

To rise, air forces water out of the ballast tanks, making the submarine lighter.

▲ **Figure 2-20** How ballast tanks help submarines change their buoyancy

---

3 Assess

✔ CHECKING CONCEPTS ANSWERS

1. upward
2. displaces
3. floats
4. gravity
5. weight

THINKING CRITICALLY ANSWERS

6. **CALCULATE: a.** 1,000 cm³ or 1,000 mL (1L) **b.** 9.8 N

7. **EXPLAIN:** The weight of the liquid displaced by an object is equal to the buoyant force on the object.

4 Close

HEALTH AND SAFETY TIP

Point out that wearing a life jacket slightly increases the wearer's weight. The bulk of the jacket also causes a partially submerged wearer to displace a larger volume of water. The increased displacement increases the buoyant force on the person.
learning styles: auditory, logical/mathematical

Science and Technology

SUBMARINE BALLAST

Technology Connection A submerged submarine has a constant buoyant force on it because the volume of water it displaces remains the same. The size of the force equals the weight of the water the submarine displaces. A submerged submarine dives when it has *negative buoyancy,* that is, when its weight is greater than the buoyant force. To achieve negative buoyancy, the submarine pumps water into its ballast tanks, making the submarine's weight greater than the buoyant force. *Positive buoyancy,* when the weight of the submarine is less than the buoyant force, allows the submarine to rise. To achieve positive buoyancy, water is pushed out of the tanks by compressed air. As a result, the submarine's weight becomes less than the buoyant force.

Thinking Critically Answer
Possible answer: Compressed air would have to be used to remove the excess water so that the submarine could remain on the surface of the water or stay submerged at a constant depth.

MORE ON THE WEB

The Buoyancy Game Show
Have students use the Internet to participate in a game show style quiz about buoyancy. Have students take the quiz three times and write their best score. Send students to www.conceptsandchallenges.com for more details.

• TEACHING RESOURCES •

Teacher's Resources
CD-ROM
Lesson Review: Chapter 2, p. 8
Flowchart: Study Tools, p. 6

ESL/ELL STRATEGY

***Relating* Buoyancy** Inform students that the Spanish word *boyar* means "to float." Ask students to relate this word to *buoyancy.* (the tendency of an object to float)

The Big Idea

(pp. 46–47)

1 Introduce

Objective Students will be able to describe a voyage on a historic or modern ship of their choice. They will investigate how to build and navigate the ship and provide provisions for their voyage.

Linking Prior Knowledge Have students recall the concept of displacement (Lesson 2-4) and Archimedes' principle (Lesson 2-5).

2 Teach

Discussion Using a rectangular fish tank and a model ship, demonstrate the relationship between Archimedes' principle, buoyant force, and flotation. On the side of the tank, mark the water level before and after placing the model in the tank. Calculate the volume of water displaced by the ship. Ask students what the weight of this volume of water represents. (the buoyant force on the model)

Use the information in the article and the captions to help guide students in choosing a ship and voyage for their Science Logs. **learning styles: visual, logical/mathematical**

THE BIG IDEA ONLINE

How has shipbuilding changed throughout history? Have students research their Science Log Writing Activity at www.conceptsandchallenges.com. You can have students organize their log by completing the Big Idea activity online. Students may post their work in the Online Classroom Database for others to read.

Reinforcement Students can also use the Big Idea Planner or Big Idea Science Log Entry found on the Teacher's Resources CD-ROM.

◆ *Integrating Social Studies*

THE Big IDEA

How has shipbuilding changed throughout history?

How do you build a boat that will float? A boat floats when the weight of the water it displaces is equal to the weight of the boat itself. The more water the boat displaces, the greater the load it can carry.

Buoyancy is the tendency for an object to float in a fluid. Humans have made buoyant watercraft for ages. One ancient design is a raft built with a low-density material, like reeds or bamboo. A raft displaces water and remains buoyant, even though water may flow all around and through the raft. The first people of Australia probably arrived there from Asia

Bamboo Rafts, Circa B.C. 38,000

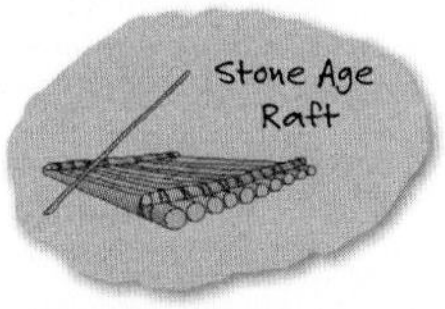

Stone Age Raft

We can only guess what the boats looked like. However, there is strong evidence that the first people of New Guinea and Australia arrived in those countries on bamboo rafts 30,000 to 40,000 years ago.

Tree Trunk Canoes, Circa B.C. 1000

Around 1000 B.C., Polynesian sailors began to travel to the remote islands of the western Pacific. Their boats were made from hollowed tree trunks and planks lashed together with coconut fibers. The outrigger design gives stability. Double outrigger sailing canoes can make long ocean voyages.

Pacific Sailing Canoe

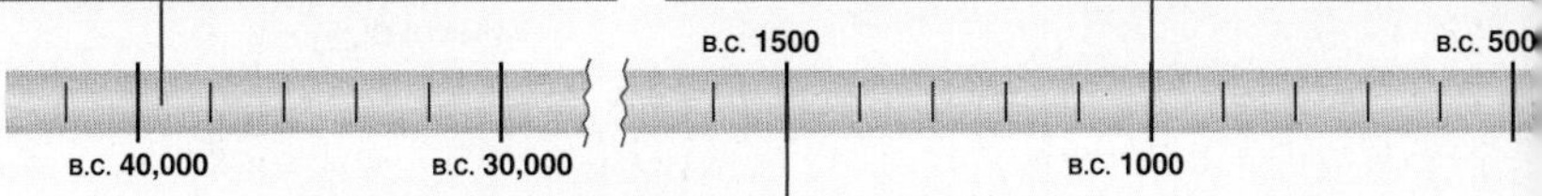

B.C. 1500   B.C. 500

B.C. 40,000   B.C. 30,000   B.C. 1000

Reed Rafts, B.C. 1500

Egyptian Raft

Pharaohs were buried with models of the boats that were used in Egypt in ancient times.

▲ **Figure 2-21** Shipbuilding throughout history

46

Teaching Options

! FAST FACTS Ship Displacements

There are a variety of ways to describe a ship's size, displacement, and weight. A common measurement of a merchant ship is its deadweight tonnage. This measurement indicates the total cargo weight that the ship can carry. The deadweight tonnage is the difference between the full-load displacement (the weight of the ship filled with cargo, crew, provisions, and fuel) and the lightweight displacement (the weight of the empty ship). The full-load displacement is found by calculating the displacement of the hull submerged to its load line (the maximum depth that the hull can be submerged when fully loaded) and then calculating the weight of this volume of water. In a similar manner, the lightweight displacement is found by calculating the displacement of the submerged part of the empty ship's hull and then calculating the weight of this volume of water.

by floating on bamboo rafts. Ancient Egyptians used reed bundles to float on the Nile.

Another boat design is the watertight hull. A boat with a watertight hull encloses an air space that displaces water, giving buoyancy. The hull can be made of a material much more dense than water, like steel, iron, or even concrete. If the hull springs a leak, the air space in the boat fills with water and the boat begins to sink.

Look at the timeline to compare boat designs throughout history. Then, follow the directions in the Science Log to find out more about "the big idea." ✦

WRITING ACTIVITY

Science Log

Plan a voyage on one of these crafts. How would you build your boat? Where would you go? What provisions would you bring? How would you navigate? Write a story about your voyage. To learn more about replicating ancient boats, start your project at www.conceptsandchallenges.com.

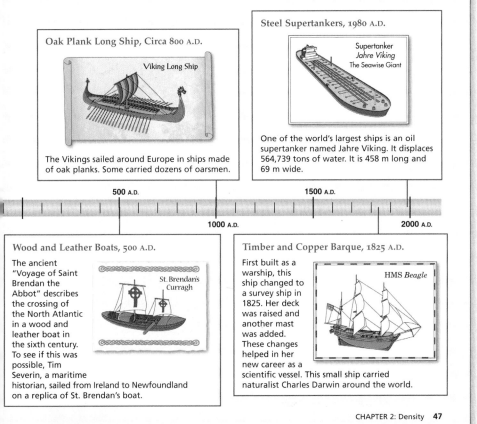

Oak Plank Long Ship, Circa 800 A.D.

Viking Long Ship

The Vikings sailed around Europe in ships made of oak planks. Some carried dozens of oarsmen.

Steel Supertankers, 1980 A.D.

Supertanker *Jahre Viking* The Seawise Giant

One of the world's largest ships is an oil supertanker named Jahre Viking. It displaces 564,739 tons of water. It is 458 m long and 69 m wide.

500 A.D.   1000 A.D.   1500 A.D.   2000 A.D.

Wood and Leather Boats, 500 A.D.

St. Brendan's Curragh

The ancient "Voyage of Saint Brendan the Abbot" describes the crossing of the North Atlantic in a wood and leather boat in the sixth century. To see if this was possible, Tim Severin, a maritime historian, sailed from Ireland to Newfoundland on a replica of St. Brendan's boat.

Timber and Copper Barque, 1825 A.D.

HMS *Beagle*

First built as a warship, this ship changed to a survey ship in 1825. Her deck was raised and another mast was added. These changes helped in her new career as a scientific vessel. This small ship carried naturalist Charles Darwin around the world.

CHAPTER 2: Density   47

Tips for Using Technology

Presenting Voyages Have students use presentation software to present to the class their plan for a voyage. Presentation software allows them to use a computer to put text and art together in a slide show. They can use a scanner to incorporate their own art in their slide show. Students can then print out their slide show and use it as a handout for others to follow during their presentation. Students can also use presentation software to share their data with the class. Tell them to create a separate slide to show the results of each observation.

• TEACHING RESOURCES •

Teacher's Resources CD-ROM

Big Idea: Chapter 2, p. 9

Big Idea Planner: Study Tools, pp. 11–12

Big Idea Science Log Entry: Study Tools, p. 13

Writing Activity Rubric: Teaching Tools, p. 9

3 Assess

Use the Writing Activity Rubric on the Teacher's Resources CD-ROM to assess students' Science Logs. Fill in the rubric with the additional information below. For this assignment, students should have:

- described a plan to make a voyage on a ship they chose, including how the ship will be built, navigated, and stocked with provisions.
- communicated, in paragraph form, accurate descriptions of shipbuilding and navigating techniques.

4 Close

Comparing Ship Sizes On a long piece of wrapping paper, draw a rectangle 2.29 m × 0.35 m. Label the rectangle *Jahre Viking*. Attach the paper to the wall. Explain to students that the rectangle represents the outline of the ship drawn to a scale of 5 mm:1 m. Have students research the dimensions of the ship that they chose and draw its outline to scale on a colored piece of paper. Have students label the outline and attach it to the outline of the *Jahre Viking*. Assign a more modern ship, such as the RMS *Queen Elizabeth II,* to any student who initially chose the *Jahre Viking*.

QUICK CONVERSIONS		
Jahre Viking's Dimensions	Metric/SI	English
Length	458 m	1,500 ft
Width	69 m	230 ft
Displacement	512 million kg	565,000 t

Challenges (pp. 48–50)

Chapter Summary

Review Before students begin the Challenges, review the summary with them. You might read the sentences aloud, omitting the boldface words and asking students to supply the omitted words. You could also provide two alternative words from which students can choose.

STUDY HINT Have students use index cards to create flash cards for each Key Term on one side of the index card and the definition on the other side. Then, have students work in pairs to review the Key Terms.

Key Term Challenges

MATCHING

1. hydrometer (2-3)
2. buoyancy (2-5)
3. specific gravity (2-3)
4. displacement (2-4)
5. density (2-1)

FILL IN

6. displacement (2-4)
7. hydrometer (2-3)
8. density (2-1)
9. buoyancy (2-5)
10. specific gravity (2-3)
11. newton (2-5)
12. specific gravity (2-3)

Chapter Summary

Lesson 2-1
- **Density** is the mass per unit volume of a substance.
- Density is measured in grams per cubic centimeter, or g/cm³.
- Density is a basic property of all matter.
- Density can be used to identify different substances.

Lesson 2-2
- Density is equal to mass divided by volume.
- The density of a liquid can be measured in grams per milliliter or grams per cubic centimeter.
- To find the density of a solid with a regular shape, measure its mass and find its volume by multiplying its length by its width by its height.

Lesson 2-3
- **Specific gravity** is the density of a substance compared with the density of water. Specific gravity has no units.
- A **hydrometer** is a device used to measure the specific gravity of a liquid.

Lesson 2-4
- Archimedes observed that when an object is placed in water, it causes the water level to rise.
- The amount of water that an object replaces is called **displacement**.
- The volume of water that an object displaces is equal to the volume of the object.
- The volume of an irregularly shaped solid can be found by measuring how much water the object displaces.

Lesson 2-5
- Archimedes' principle states that the loss of weight of an object in water is equal to the weight of the water that the object displaces.
- **Buoyancy** is the tendency of an object to float in a fluid.
- The buoyant force on an object is equal to the weight of the water that the object displaces.
- An object floats if the weight of the water it displaces is greater than its own weight.

Key Term Challenges

buoyancy (p. 44)
density (p. 34)
displacement (p. 40)
hydrometer (p. 38)
newton (p. 44)
specific gravity (p. 38)

MATCHING Write the Key Term from above that best matches each description.

1. device used to measure specific gravity
2. tendency of an object to float in a fluid
3. density of a substance compared with the density of water
4. amount of water an object replaces
5. mass per unit volume

FILL IN Write the Key Term from above that best completes each statement.

6. To find the volume of an irregular solid, measure its _____.
7. A _____ floats high in a liquid with a high specific gravity.
8. The _____ of a substance tells the amount of mass in a certain volume.
9. A ship can float in water because of _____.
10. If the _____ of a substance is greater than 1.0, the substance is more dense than water.
11. The SI unit of force is _____.
12. If you know the density of a substance, you can easily find its _____.

48

Teaching Options

PREPARING STUDENTS FOR STANDARDIZED TESTS

Reading Strategy: Explain to students that all parts of a true/false statement must be true for the statement to be true. Tell students to look for words that make the statement true or false. These words provide clues.

Writing Strategy: Tell students to write neatly. Neatness may improve the reader's perception of the answer.

Interpreting Visuals: Remind students to read the title of a table before reading its contents. Then, they should carefully read each column and row head to understand what items and characteristics are being compared. Tell students to pay close attention to any units given in the heads.

ESL/ELL STRATEGY

Defining Key Terms Have partners write definitions for ten Key Terms on a sheet of paper. Have partners exchange papers and identify the Key Terms on each other's paper.

Content Challenges TEST PREP

MULTIPLE CHOICE Write the letter of the term or phrase that best completes each statement.

1. Density is measured in
   a. milliliters per cubic centimeter.
   b. cubic centimeters per gram.
   c. grams per cubic centimeter.
   d. milliliters per gram.

2. Density is a basic physical property of
   a. gases.
   b. all matter.
   c. solids.
   d. liquids.

3. A hydrometer is used to measure
   a. mass.
   b. volume.
   c. length.
   d. specific gravity.

4. Archimedes discovered that objects weigh less when they
   a. have a larger volume.
   b. are placed in water.
   c. are suspended in air.
   d. are irregularly shaped.

5. The weight of the water that a floating object displaces is equal to the object's
   a. mass.
   b. weight.
   c. volume.
   d. density.

6. If the buoyant force on an object is equal to the object's weight, then the object will
   a. sink.
   b. float.
   c. become less dense.
   d. increase in mass.

7. If the buoyant force on an object is equal to the object's weight, then the weight of the object in water is
   a. 10.
   b. 100.
   c. zero.
   d. its own weight.

8. One milliliter is equal to one
   a. gram.
   b. cubic centimeter.
   c. meter.
   d. centimeter.

9. To find the density of a substance, you must measure
   a. mass and length.
   b. mass and weight.
   c. mass and volume.
   d. mass and buoyancy.

10. If a rock displaces 50 mL, the volume of the rock is
    a. 50 cm.
    b. 50 g/cm^3.
    c. 5 mL.
    d. 50 cm^3.

TRUE/FALSE Write *true* if the statement is true. If the statement is false, change the underlined term to make the statement true.

11. Specific gravity compares the density of a substance to the <u>weight</u> of water.

12. Units of <u>density</u> include units of mass and volume.

13. <u>Displacement</u> is a force exerted upward by a gas or a liquid.

14. When an object is placed in water, it will lose all or some of its <u>mass</u>.

15. The buoyant force on an object is equal to the <u>volume</u> of the water it displaces.

Content Challenges

MULTIPLE CHOICE

1. c (2-1)
2. b (2-1)
3. d (2-3)
4. b (2-5)
5. b (2-5)
6. b (2-5)
7. c (2-5)
8. b (2-1)
9. c (2-2)
10. d (2-4)

TRUE/FALSE

11. false; density (2-3)
12. true (2-1)
13. false; Buoyancy (2-5)
14. false; weight (2-5)
15. false; weight (2-5)

ALTERNATIVE ASSESSMENT

Modeling Buoyancy On the board, draw a diagram showing an object, such as a cork, floating on the surface of water; an object floating at a submerged level, such as a hovering fish; and a sunken object, such as a rock. Have students copy this diagram onto a sheet of paper. Then, have them draw arrows to represent the direction of the weight in air of each object and the direction of the buoyant force in each situation. Have students circle the situations in which the weight in air and buoyant force are equal in size. (cork and hovering fish) Ask students what the cork and hovering fish would weigh underwater. (zero)

PORTFOLIO ASSESSMENT

Making Student Portfolios Portfolio Assessment is designed to evaluate a student's performance over an extended period of time. It also provides an opportunity for students who are generally not good test-takers to demonstrate their learning in another way. Encourage students to select their own work to include in their portfolios, such as the experiment that they designed to find the density of chalk in Lesson 2-1. You can use the Portfolio Assessment Rubric found on the Teacher's Resources CD-ROM to assess students' portfolios.

Concept Challenges

WRITTEN RESPONSE

1. **EXPLAIN:** The density of wood is less than the density of iron. (2-1)
2. **ANALYZE:** Measure the specific gravity of each object. Marble and plastic have different specific gravities. (2-3)
3. **EXPLAIN:** A volume of 1 milliliter is equal to a volume of 1 cubic centimeter. (2-1)
4. **RELATE:** The numerical value of a substance's density is equal to its specific gravity. (2-3)
5. **RELATE:** The buoyant force on an object is equal to the weight of the water the object displaces. (2-5)
6. **INFER:** The density of the object is less than or equal to the density of water. (2-5)

INTERPRETING A TABLE (2-3)

7. **NAME:** 19.3
8. **INTERPRET:** diamond
9. **NAME:** Possible answers: gasoline and ice
10. **PREDICT:** A layer of water will float on top of the corn syrup.
11. **ANALYZE:** a kilogram of rubber
12. **ANALYZE:** Glycerine; The specific gravity of glycerine is greater than the specific gravity of gasoline.

Chapter Project Wrap-Up

MODEL BOATS

Students can show their model boats to the class. They can explain how they made their models and also describe the process that they went through to make a model that would float with three marbles in it. Finally, students can prove that their models do float by placing them in a large container of water. You can use the Group Activity Rubric found on the Teacher's Resources CD-ROM to assess students' projects. Fill in the rubric with the additional information below. For this project, groups should have:

- built a model boat from the material assigned to the group.
- built a model boat that floats in water with three marbles in it.

Concept Challenges TEST PREP

WRITTEN RESPONSE Answer each of the following questions in complete sentences.

1. **EXPLAIN:** Why is 1 cm³ of wood lighter than 1 cm³ of iron?
2. **ANALYZE:** Suppose two objects look alike, but one is made of marble and the other is made of plastic. How could you use specific gravity to identify the objects?
3. **EXPLAIN:** Why is it possible to measure the volume of a solid in milliliters?
4. **RELATE:** What is the relationship between the density of a substance and its specific gravity?
5. **RELATE:** What is the relationship between the buoyant force on an object and the amount of water that the object displaces?
6. **INFER:** What do you know about the density of an object that floats in water?

INTERPRETING A TABLE Use Figure 2-22 to answer the following questions.

7. **NAME:** What is the specific gravity of gold?
8. **INTERPRET:** Which substance has a higher specific gravity, diamond or glycerine?
9. **NAME:** What are two substances that will float in water?
10. **PREDICT:** What will happen if water and corn syrup are mixed together?
11. **ANALYZE:** Which will take up a greater volume, a kilogram of lead or a kilogram of rubber?
12. **ANALYZE:** Will a hydrometer float higher in glycerine or in gasoline? Explain.

SPECIFIC GRAVITIES	
Substance	Specific Gravity
Aluminum	2.7
Corn syrup	1.38
Diamond	3.5
Gasoline	0.7
Glycerine	1.26
Gold	19.3
Ice	0.92
Marble	2.7
Rubber	1.34
Water	1.00

▲ Figure 2-22

Teaching Options

• TEACHING RESOURCES •

Teacher's Resources CD-ROM

Key Term Review: Chapter 2, p. 10

Chapter 2 Test: pp. 11–12

Portfolio Assessment Rubric: Teaching Tools, p. 10

Group Activity Rubric: Teaching Tools, p. 6

Chapter Self-Check: Teaching Tools, p. 11

PLANNING GUIDE

◆ **TEACHING THE CHAPTER** This chapter should take approximately 10–13 days to complete instruction and assessment.

	Skills and Features	Projects and Activities	Achieve Science Literacy	Meet Individual Needs
Chapter 3 Opener p. T51	MODEL	• Chapter Project		
Lesson 3-1 **What are elements?** pp. T52–T53 Standards: B1a, B1c	CLASSIFY, COMPARE, NAME • Investigate • Health and Safety Tip • People in Science	• More on the Web	• Study Hint • Ongoing Assessment	• Reteach
Lesson 3-2 **What are atoms?** pp. T54–T55 Standard: B1c	COMPARE, INFER, LIST • Web Infosearch • Science and Technology	• Cooperative Learning • Extending the Lesson	• Study Hint • Writing Hint	• Reteach
Lesson 3-3 **What are the parts of an atom?** pp. T56–T57	CONTRAST, IDENTIFY, LOCATE • How Do They Know That?	• Cooperative Learning • More on the Web	• Study Hint • Writing Hint • Ongoing Assessment	• ESL/ELL Strategy
Lesson 3-4 **What is an atomic number?** pp. T58–T59	IDENTIFY, NAME, EXPLAIN • Interpreting Visuals • People in Science	• More on the Web • Extending the Lesson	• Study Hint • Reading Strategy • Ongoing Assessment	• Reteach CD-ROM Model of an Atom Writing Activity Outline
Lesson 3-5 **What is an atomic mass?** pp. T60–T61	ANALYZE, INFER, DEFINE • Investigate • Building Math Skills • People in Science	• More on the Web	• Study Hint • Ongoing Assessment	• Reteach CD-ROM Model of an Atom
Lesson 3-6 **How are electrons arranged in an atom?** pp. T62–T63 Standard: B3a	ANALYZE, DESCRIBE, PREDICT • Hands-On Activity	• Cooperative Learning • More on the Web	• Study Hint • Reading Strategy • Ongoing Assessment	• Reteach CD-ROM Concept Map Model of an Atom

Planning Guide continues on next page.

Standards: For details on the correlation to National Science Standards see pages *xx–xxi*.

	Skills and Features	Projects and Activities	Achieve Science Literacy	Meet Individual Needs
Lesson 3-7 **What is the periodic table?** pp. T64–T65 Standards: B1b, B1c	HYPOTHESIZE, INFER, EXPLAIN • Interpreting Visuals • Building Social Studies Skills	• Extending the Lesson • More on the Web	• Study Hint • Ongoing Assessment	CD-ROM Enrichment Activity
Big Idea **What is the Periodic Table of Elements?** pp. T66–T67 Standard: B1b	RESEARCH, COMMUNICATE, ANALYZE • Science Log: Writing Activity	• Big Idea Online • Close Activity	• Tips for Using Technology	CD-ROM Big Idea Planner Flowchart
Lesson 3-8 **What are metals and nonmetals?** pp. T68–T69 Standards: B1a, B1b	COMPARE, RELATE, DESCRIBE • Designing an Experiment • Hands-On Activity	• More on the Web • Cooperative Learning • Lab Challenge	• Study Hint • Ongoing Assessment	• Reteach CD-ROM Designing an Experiment
Lesson 3-9 **What are the halogens and the noble gases?** pp. T70–T71 Standards: B1a, B1b	EXPLAIN, LIST, DEFINE • Building Language Arts Skills • Real-Life Science	• Integrating Life Science • More on the Web	• Study Hint • Reading Strategy • Ongoing Assessment	
Lesson 3-10 **What are isotopes?** pp. T72–T73	ANALYZE, EXPLAIN, IDENTIFY • Interpreting Visuals • Integrating Life Science	• Cooperative Learning • Integrating Earth Science • More on the Web	• Study Hint • Reading Strategy • Ongoing Assessment	CD-ROM Enrichment Activity Model of an Atom
Lab Activity **Investigating the Modern Model of the Atom** pp. T74–T75	COMPARE, MODEL, INFER • Set-Up Time: 10 min • Lab Time: 30 min	• Cooperative Learning • Extend the Lab Activity	• Tips for Using Technology	• ESL/ELL Strategy CD-ROM Lab Activity Report Database Planner Target
Chapter 3 Challenges pp. T76–T78	• Chapter Summary • Key Term Challenges • Content Challenges • Concept Challenges	• Chapter Project Wrap-Up • Unit Challenge Online	• Study Hint • Preparing Students for Standardized Tests	• ESL/ELL Strategy CD-ROM Chapter Self-Check Concept Map

Chapter 3 Elements and Atoms

▲ Figure 3-1 Bars of gold

Gold is one of the few things that can be found on Earth in pure form. If you could cut a bar of gold into smaller pieces, you would find that the smallest piece that could be identified as gold is one atom of gold. This atom is made up of even smaller parts. These very tiny parts are not gold. They can be found in all forms of matter. However, it is difficult to see them. Special tools are needed in order to study these small pieces of matter.

▶Why is it difficult to study small pieces of matter?

Contents

UNIT 1: Introduction to Matter   **51**

Teaching Options

Chapter 3
Elements and Atoms

Chapter Overview

In this chapter, students will learn about elements and atoms. Students will trace the history of the development of the different models of atomic structure. They will explain the structure of atoms, atomic number, atomic mass, and isotopes. Students will also describe the development of the Periodic Table of Elements and use it to identify metals, nonmetals, halogens, and noble gases.

About Figure 3-1 Gold is one of only a few elements that is found uncombined in nature. Most elements are found in compounds formed when elements react with other substances. Gold is a shiny, yellow metal with useful properties, such as a relatively low melting point, malleability, shiny luster, and ductility.

Answer Possible answer: They are too small to be seen without powerful tools.

Linking Prior Knowledge

For this chapter, students should recall:
- the definition of matter (Lesson 1-2).
- the four phases of matter (Lesson 1-3).
- the difference between physical and chemical changes in matter (Lesson 1-5).

Chapter Project

MODELS OF ATOMS AND THEIR PARTS

MATERIALS: sheet of white paper, sheets of 4 different colors of paper, scissors, 4 envelopes, colored markers, glue

As students read the chapter, they will use colored circles to make models of the atoms that they read about. Have students cut out large circles to represent atoms and small circles to represent electrons, protons, and neutrons. Students should use different-colored paper for each type of circle. Have students put the different circles into separate envelopes. Students can then make models by gluing the circles on a sheet of white paper. Invite students to share their models with the class.
learning styles: visual, tactile

CHAPTER 3: Elements and Atoms   **T51**

1 Introduce

◯ INVESTIGATE

TIME: 10–15 minutes

PURPOSE: Students will use models of different matter to demonstrate that matter can be made up of smaller pieces.

MATERIALS: sheet of paper; 4 different models of matter labeled A, B, C, D. To make models, use molecular model kits, paper circles glued to white paper, or modeling clay and toothpicks. Model A should be two red circles connected to each other. The other models can be anything as long as they are made from different-colored circles or spheres.

PROCEDURE: Have students copy the chart onto a sheet of paper. Give pairs of students the models of different matter. Have students examine the models and notice how each one is made up of smaller, different-colored pieces. After 5 minutes, have students fill in their charts.

THINK ABOUT IT: There are four models of matter. Model A has two pieces. The number of pieces in models B, C, and D depends on the models that students are given.

✎ **STUDY HINT** Have students write the Key Term and its definition in their notebooks. As students read the lesson, have them write examples of elements.

Linking Prior Knowledge Before beginning this lesson, have students review the definition of matter (Lesson 1-2) and the four states of matter (Lesson 1-3). Ask students to define matter and list the four states of matter. (anything that has mass and takes up space; solid, liquid, gas, plasma)

2 Teach

Discussion Ask students to name some elements that they are familiar with. List everything they name on the board. Ask students what makes these substances elements. (They cannot be chemically broken down into simpler substances.) After the lesson, have students go over the list of elements and cross off the ones that are incorrect. If possible, tell students what elements make up the incorrect responses.

3-1 What are elements?

INVESTIGATE ◯ Observing Matter
HANDS-ON ACTIVITY

1. Copy the chart onto a sheet of paper. Your teacher will give you different models of matter. Examine each model. Notice how each one is made up of smaller, different-colored pieces.

2. Fill in the chart. The first line has been completed for you.

THINK ABOUT IT: How many models of matter are there? How many smaller pieces are there in each type of matter?

Observing Matter	
Model of Matter	What is it made of?
A	●●
B	
C	
D	

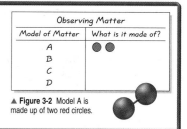

▲ **Figure 3-2** Model A is made up of two red circles.

Objective

Identify elements as substances that cannot be chemically broken down into simpler substances.

Key Term

element (EHL-uh-muhnt): substance that cannot be chemically broken down into simpler substances

Elements Most of the objects around you are made up of combinations of different kinds of matter. For example, the concrete in a sidewalk is made up of different types of matter—gravel, sand, cement, and water. However, even gravel, sand, cement, and water are made from other types of matter. But these types of matter, called elements, are different. **Elements** are substances that cannot be chemically broken down into simpler substances. All of the matter that you can observe on Earth is made up of elements or combinations of elements.

▷1 **DEFINE:** What is an element?

The Known Elements There are more than 100 known elements. Most of the first ninety-two elements are found in nature. The rest of the elements have been made by scientists under special laboratory conditions.

Most elements are solids at room temperature. Some examples that you may be familiar with are iron, zinc, lead, silver, gold, calcium, sodium, nickel, and copper.

A few elements, such as mercury and bromine, are liquids at room temperature. Other elements, such as oxygen, hydrogen, helium, and neon, are gases at room temperature.

▲ **Figure 3-3** At room temperature, copper (left) is a solid, mercury (center) is a liquid, and neon (right) is a gas.

▷2 **IDENTIFY:** How many elements are found in nature?

Elements and Matter All matter is made up of elements. Some types of matter are made up of only one element. An iron nail may contain only the element iron. Aluminum foil may be made up of only the element aluminum. Pure gold and pure silver are also made up of only one element.

There are some types of matter that are made up of more than one element. Water is made up of hydrogen and oxygen. Table salt is made up of sodium and chlorine.

52

Teaching Options

❗ FAST FACTS

What makes up matter?

Long ago, Aristotle and other people thought that all matter was made of combinations of four basic substances: earth, air, water, and fire. Hundreds of years ago, chemists known as alchemists thought that they could change one kind of matter into another, such as lead into gold. Scientists now know that earth, air, water, and fire are not elements, and that nonradioactive elements stay the same element under ordinary conditions.

RETEACH

Identifying Elements in Substances Display a glass of water, a sugar cube, and some salt. Point to each substance and ask students to identify it. Then, ask students what elements make up water, sugar, and salt. Have students refer to their text if necessary. **learning styles: visual, linguistic**

In a laboratory, a chemist can break down this kind of matter. For example, sugar can be broken down into the elements that make it up—carbon, hydrogen, and oxygen. These elements cannot be chemically broken down into simpler substances.

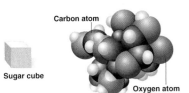

Carbon atom

Sugar cube

Oxygen atom

Hydrogen atom

▲ **Figure 3-4** Sugar can be broken down into the elements that make it up.

3 NAME: What three elements make up sugar?

✓ CHECKING CONCEPTS

1. An _____ is a substance that cannot be chemically broken down into simpler substances.

2. Mercury is a _____ at room temperature.

3. There are more than _____ known elements.

4. Most of the known elements are _____ at room temperature.

5. An example of a substance made up of more than one element is _____.

THINKING CRITICALLY

6. **COMPARE:** Mercury and oxygen are elements. Explain one way in which they differ from each other.

7. **CLASSIFY:** Which of the following substances are elements?
   a. Gold   c. Mercury
   b. Hydrogen   d. Sugar

HEALTH AND SAFETY TIP

Many elements are dangerous to handle. The elements mercury and chlorine are poisonous. Sodium and potassium are explosive when exposed to water. Review the rules for chemical safety in the Handbook on page 14. Make a poster illustrating some chemical safety rules.

 People in Science

MARIE CURIE (1867–1934)

Marie Sklodowska Curie was a Polish chemist. She worked and taught in Paris at the School of Physics and Chemistry and at the Sorbonne, the University of Paris. While teaching in Paris, she met the French scientist Pierre Curie, who became her husband.

Marie and Pierre Curie worked together. They became interested in radioactive (ray-dee-oh-AK-tihv) elements. Radioactive elements give off a form of energy known as radiation (ray-dee-AY-shuhn). Two years after radioactivity was first discovered in the element uranium, the Curies discovered the radioactive elements polonium and radium. In 1903, the Curies were awarded a Nobel Prize in physics.

After the death of her husband in 1906, Marie Curie continued to study radioactive elements. In 1911, she was awarded a Nobel Prize in chemistry. Marie Curie is the only person ever to receive two Nobel Prizes in science.

Thinking Critically Why do you think Marie Curie was an important scientist?

▲ **Figure 3-5** Marie Curie studied radioactive elements.

Demonstration Bring in samples of solid elements, such as iron, tin, lead, silver, aluminum, and copper, for students to observe. If possible, show students a mercury thermometer as an example of an element that is a liquid. Point out that elements in the air, such as oxygen and nitrogen, are gases.
learning styles: visual, tactile

Answers to questions

1 DEFINE: a substance that cannot be chemically broken down into simpler substances

2 IDENTIFY: most of the first 92

3 NAME: carbon, hydrogen, and oxygen

3 Assess

✓ CHECKING CONCEPTS ANSWERS

1. element
2. liquid
3. 100
4. solids
5. Possible answers: water, table salt, or sugar

THINKING CRITICALLY ANSWERS

6. **COMPARE:** Possible answer: At room temperature, mercury is a liquid and oxygen is a gas.

7. **CLASSIFY: a.** Gold, **b.** Hydrogen, **c.** Mercury

4 Close

HEALTH AND SAFETY TIP

Most materials in a laboratory can be used safely if proper precautions are taken. Allow students to present their posters to the class. **learning style: visual**

People in Science

MARIE CURIE (1867–1934)

Real-Life Connection Radioactive elements have many practical uses. Radioactivity is used to sterilize food and drugs, to fight cancer, to find the causes of disease, and to study chemical and biological reactions.

Thinking Critically Answer
Possible answers: She was awarded two Nobel Prizes, and she helped discover two radioactive elements.

MORE ON THE WEB

Learning About Elements
Students can view online movies about some elements. Then, students can write a short report on three elements of their choice. Send students to www.conceptsandchallenges.com.

• TEACHING RESOURCES •

Teacher's Resources CD-ROM
Lesson Review: Chapter 3, p. 2

ONGOING ASSESSMENT

Naming Elements Ask students: *Name an element that is a liquid at room temperature.* (mercury or bromine) *Name an element that is a gas at room temperature.* (Possible answers: neon, oxygen, or hydrogen) *What elements can water be broken down into?* (hydrogen and oxygen)

1 Introduce

STUDY HINT Before beginning this lesson, have students write the lesson title and objectives in their notebooks. As students read the lesson, tell them to write the information that supports the objectives.

Linking Prior Knowledge Ask students what they think the relationship is between elements and atoms. Students should understand that an atom is the smallest part of an element and that an object made up of an element, such as aluminum, is made up of atoms of aluminum.

2 Teach

Discussion Ask students what they think makes up matter. Discuss students' responses. Point out that both scientists mentioned in this lesson—Democritus and Dalton—proposed theories about what makes up matter. Emphasize that many parts of their theories have not been proven to be correct, but that they started other people thinking about what matter is made up of.

Demonstration Use clay, plastic-foam balls, or paper circles to demonstrate the different parts of Dalton's atomic theory. Model how the atoms of two or more elements can join together to form compounds. Form a molecule of water with two hydrogen atoms connected to one oxygen atom. **learning style: visual**

Answers to questions

1 INFER: There would be a piece so small that it could not be cut any more. Then, you would have an atom of the element.

2 STATE: "cannot be divided"

3 LIST: All elements are composed of atoms. Atoms cannot be divided or destroyed. Atoms of the same element are exactly alike. Atoms of different elements are different from each other. The atoms of two or more elements can join together to form types of matter called compounds.

4 NAME: scanning tunneling microscope

3-2 What are atoms?

Objectives

Identify an atom as the smallest part of an element that can be identified as that element. List the main parts of Dalton's atomic theory.

Key Term

atom: smallest part of an element that can be identified as that element

Atoms The element silicon cannot be broken down into a simpler type of matter. But what would happen if you took a piece of silicon and cut it into smaller and smaller pieces? There would be a piece of silicon so small that it could not be further divided. This smallest piece of the element silicon is called an atom. An **atom** is the smallest part of an element that can be identified as that element.

1 INFER: What would happen if you cut a piece of an element into smaller and smaller pieces?

Democritus The first person to suggest the idea of atoms was the Greek philosopher Democritus (dih-MAHK-ruh-tuhs). More than 2,400 years ago, Democritus asked whether it is possible to divide a sample of matter forever into smaller and smaller pieces. After much observation, he came to the conclusion that it is not possible to divide matter forever. At some point, a smallest piece of matter would be reached. Democritus named this smallest piece of matter an atom. The word *atom* comes from a Greek word that means "cannot be divided."

Democritus and his students did not know what atoms looked liked. They did not know what scientists today know about atoms. However, they hypothesized that atoms were small, hard particles that were all made out of the same material but were of different shapes and sizes. They also thought that atoms were infinite in number, that they were always moving, and that they could be joined together.

2 STATE: What does the word *atom* mean?

54

Dalton's Atomic Theory In the early 1800s, an English chemist named John Dalton performed some experiments. He investigated properties of gases. His observations led him to believe that gases are made of individual particles. These individual particles are very similar to the idea of the atom proposed by Democritus. The results of his experiments and other observations about matter led Dalton to state an atomic theory of matter. The main parts of Dalton's atomic theory of matter are as follows:

- All elements are composed of atoms. Atoms cannot be divided or destroyed.
- Atoms of the same element are exactly alike.
- Atoms of different elements are different from each other.
- The atoms of two or more elements can join together to form types of matter called compounds.

Like Democritus, Dalton had some ideas about atoms that scientists no longer agree with. However, Dalton's atomic theory was the beginning of the modern theory of atoms.

▲ Figure 3-6 John Dalton

3 LIST: What are the main parts of Dalton's atomic theory of matter?

Teaching Options

EXTENDING THE LESSON

More of Dalton's Work In addition to his atomic theory of matter, John Dalton also formulated the law of partial pressures for gases. This law states that with an ideal gas, the total pressure of a gas mixture in a container equals the sum of the pressures each gas would exert alone. Have interested students learn more about the law of partial pressures for gases and make a poster that explains this law. Ask volunteers to present their posters to the class.
learning styles: logical/mathematical, visual

RETEACH

Differences Between Democritus and Dalton Inform students that Democritus and Dalton differed in the ways in which they formed their models. Democritus based his models on observations that were nonexperimental. Dalton, on the other hand, investigated and performed experiments that led to the development of his atomic theory. Have students discuss the importance of experimentation in testing hypotheses.

Images of Atoms Atoms are extremely small. As small as they are, a special tool, called a scanning tunneling microscope (STM), can capture images of them. Figure 3-7 shows an image captured by an STM.

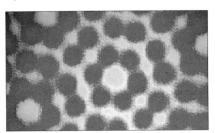

▲ **Figure 3-7** An image of silicon atoms produced by an STM

NAME: What is an STM?

✓ CHECKING CONCEPTS

1. What is an atom?
2. Who was the first person to use the word *atom*?

3. Whose investigation on properties of gases led him to propose an atomic theory of matter?
4. What is the name of the tool that can capture images of an atom?

💡 THINKING CRITICALLY

5. **COMPARE:** How are the ideas of Democritus and Dalton similar? How are they different?
6. **INFER:** How can an STM help prove Dalton's theory?

Web InfoSearch

Scanning Tunneling Microscopes STMs can take images of atoms.

SEARCH: Use the Internet to find out about the inventors of this type of microscope. Start your search at www.conceptsandchallenges.com. Some key search words are **Heinrich Rohrer** and **Gerd Karl Binnig**.

▲ **Figure 3-8** In Batavia, Illinois, a particle accelerator lies under the circular outline.

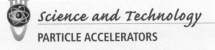

Science and Technology

PARTICLE ACCELERATORS

A particle accelerator is a device used to increase the energy of electrically charged particles. At very high speeds, these charged particles smash into atoms and break them apart. Then, scientists can study the pieces that are left after the collision.

Scientists use particle accelerators to study the forces that hold matter together. The machines speed up particles and race them around and around giant, usually circular, tracks. Many accelerators have one group of particles moving in one direction and another group moving in the other direction. When the particles are traveling fast enough, they are made to crash into each other. From their work with accelerators, scientists have been able to learn more about the parts that atoms are made of.

Particle accelerators are among the largest instruments ever built. In Batavia, Illinois, a particle accelerator is built around a 6.4-km circular track. A particle accelerator in Switzerland is build in a circular underground tunnel that is 27 km wide.

Thinking Critically Why do you think particle accelerators are so large?

---

3 Assess

✓ CHECKING CONCEPTS ANSWERS

1. the smallest part of an element that can be identified as that element
2. Democritus
3. John Dalton
4. scanning tunneling microscope (STM)

💡 THINKING CRITICALLY ANSWERS

5. **COMPARE:** Possible answer: Both believed that atoms are the smallest parts of matter and that atoms can join together. Dalton's ideas were based on experiments and were more specific.
6. **INFER:** Possible answer: by allowing scientists to see images of different elements and compounds

📖 **WRITING HINT** Encourage students to write complete sentences to compare and contrast the ideas of Dalton and Democritus. Remind them of words that show contrast, such as *on the other hand, but, in contrast*, and so on.

4 Close

Web InfoSearch

Scanning Tunneling Microscopes Have pairs of students use the Internet to find out about the inventors of this type of microscope. Students should begin their search at www.conceptsandchallenges.com.

Science and Technology

PARTICLE ACCELERATORS

Background There are two types of particle accelerators. In a linear accelerator, particles are accelerated in a straight line. In a doughnut-shaped accelerator called a cyclotron, particles travel in a circle.

Discussion Ask students what scientists can learn about atoms by using particle accelerators. (They can learn about the forces that hold matter together and more about the composition of atoms.)

Thinking Critically Answer
Possible answer: Particles must accelerate over great distances to attain enough speed and energy to break apart when they strike other high-energy particles.

QUICK CONVERSIONS		
Particle Accelerator	**Metric/SI**	**English**
Batavia (length of track)	6.4 km	3.8 mi
Switzerland (width of tunnel)	27 km	16 mi

• TEACHING RESOURCES •

💿 **Teacher's Resources CD-ROM**
Lesson Review: Chapter 3, p. 3

COOPERATIVE LEARNING

Presenting Dalton's Theory Have two volunteers work together to describe the four main parts of Dalton's atomic theory of matter to the rest of the class.
learning styles: linguistic, auditory

1 Introduce

✏️ **STUDY HINT** Have students compare Figures 3-9, 3-10, 3-11, and 3-12. Ask students how the models differ from one another.

Linking Prior Knowledge Ask students to recall the symbol that represents something that is positive (+) and the symbol that represents something that is negative (−). Inform students that positive and negative objects can attract each other and that they can also cancel each other out. **learning styles: visual, linguistic**

2 Teach

Discussion Using the four models on pages 56 and 57, discuss the similarities and differences among the models. Make sure that students understand that models change as scientists learn more about atoms. Lead students to the realization that new information about atoms usually comes from advances in technology. These advances include high-tech tools and equipment such as scanning tunneling microscopes and particle accelerators. **learning styles: visual, auditory**

Demonstration If possible, use a model of the solar system to demonstrate the planets orbiting the Sun. Compare the Sun to the nucleus of an atom and the planets to electrons orbiting the nucleus. Ask students what the planets' orbits can be compared to in an atom. (energy levels) **learning styles: visual, auditory**

Reinforcement Draw a timeline on the board summarizing the development of the different atomic models. Include the dates and brief descriptions of Thomson's model, Rutherford's model, Bohr's model, and the modern atomic model. Have students copy the timeline in their notebooks. **learning style: visual**

Answers to questions

▶1 STATE: in the center, or core, of an atom

▶2 IDENTIFY: negatively charged particles (electrons)

▶3 DESCRIBE: An atom contains positively charged particles in a central nucleus but is mostly empty space.

3-3 What are the parts of an atom?

Objective
Identify the three basic parts of an atom.

Key Terms
nucleus: center, or core, of an atom
proton: particle that has a positive charge
neutron: particle that has no charge
electron: particle that has a negative charge

Structure of an Atom According to the modern atomic theory, an atom has a center, or core, called the **nucleus**. In the nucleus are protons and neutrons. A **proton** is a particle that has a positive charge (+). A **neutron** is a particle that does not have any charge. Surrounding the nucleus is a cloud of very tiny particles called electrons. An **electron** is a particle that has a negative charge (−). The negative charge on an electron is exactly equal to the positive charge on a proton.

▶1 STATE: Where is the nucleus found?

Thomson's Model The first scientist to suggest that an atom contains smaller particles was J. J. Thomson of England. In 1897, Thomson passed an electric current through a gas. He found that the gas gave off rays made up of negatively charged particles. Today, these particles are known as electrons. Because atoms are neutral, Thomson reasoned that there must also be positively charged particles inside an atom. Thomson hypothesized that an atom was made up of a positively charged material with negatively charged particles scattered evenly throughout.

Negatively charged material

Positively charged material

▲ Figure 3-9 Thomson's model of an atom

▶2 IDENTIFY: What type of particle did Thomson discover in an atom?

Rutherford's Model In 1911, a British scientist named Ernest Rutherford performed an experiment to test Thomson's atomic model. Rutherford discovered that an atom is mostly empty space. He concluded that the positively charged particles are contained in a small central core called the nucleus. He also concluded that the negatively charged particles were attracted to the positively charged particles found in the nucleus. This attraction holds the negatively charged particles in the atom.

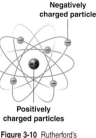

Negatively charged particle

Positively charged particles

▲ Figure 3-10 Rutherford's model of an atom

▶3 DESCRIBE: What did Rutherford discover about an atom?

Bohr's Model Rutherford's model of the atom was useful but it did not explain the arrangement of electrons. In 1913, Danish scientist Niels Bohr proposed that the electrons in an atom are found in different energy levels. Each energy level is at a certain distance from the nucleus. Electrons in different energy levels move around the nucleus in different orbits, much as the planets move in orbits around the Sun. Bohr's model explains simple atoms such as oxygen well, but it does not explain more complex atoms.

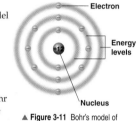

Electron

Energy levels

Nucleus

▲ Figure 3-11 Bohr's model of an atom

▶4 LOCATE: Where did Bohr say that electrons are found in an atom?

Teaching Options

COOPERATIVE LEARNING

Demonstrating Atomic Models
Divide the class into four groups. Ask one group to use colored circles to make a model showing Thomson's atomic model. Ask one group to show Rutherford's atomic model, another group to show Bohr's atomic model, and the last group to show the modern atomic model. Groups should use the colored circles that they made for the Chapter Project. After students complete their models, have a student from each group demonstrate and describe the group's model to the rest of the class. **learning styles: tactile, interpersonal**

ESL/ELL STRATEGY

Using Visuals and Leveled Questions Draw a simple atom. Be sure to include the charges for the protons and electrons. Label the diagram *atom*. Draw arrows to the nucleus, the protons, the neutrons, and the electrons. Make sure that you identify all four components as the basic parts of an atom. Point to different parts of the atom and ask: *Is this a proton? What part of the atom is this? How many neutrons are there? Which particle is positive?*

Modern Model The modern atomic model is based on the works of Thomson, Rutherford, Bohr, and other scientists who have studied the nature of atoms. According to the modern model, the location of the electrons in an atom cannot be known. Therefore, the modern model of the atom does not show any paths that electrons could be found in. Instead, energy levels are used to predict the place where an electron is most likely to be found outside of the nucleus. This area is called the electron cloud. The modern model also identifies the nucleus as containing protons and neutrons.

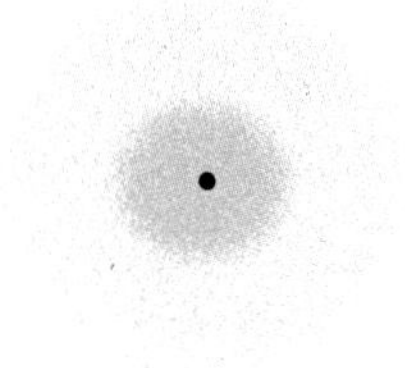

◀ **Figure 3-12** Modern model of an atom

▶ **EXPLAIN:** What is the electron cloud?

How Do They Know That?
QUARKS AND LEPTONS

In recent years, scientists have discovered that protons and neutrons are made up of even smaller particles. Based on experiments using particle accelerators, scientists have identified two groups of subatomic particles. All matter is made up of these particles. These groups of particles are known as quarks and leptons. The word *quark* was first used as the name of a subatomic particle by American physicist Murray Gell-Mann. The word *lepton* comes from a Greek word that means "small" or "thin."

Quarks make up protons, neutrons, and other particles found in the nucleus of an atom. There are six types of quarks and six types of leptons. Electrons are a type of lepton. Electrons are not believed to be made up of smaller particles. The basic particles in an atom are made up of combinations of two or three different quarks or one lepton.

Thinking Critically What is the relationship between an electron and a lepton?

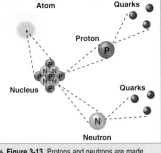

▲ **Figure 3-13** Protons and neutrons are made up of quarks.

✔ CHECKING CONCEPTS

1. What are electrons?
2. Where are protons found in an atom?
3. What are the particles in an atom that do not have any charge called?
4. Who first suggested that atoms are made up of smaller particles?
5. Who discovered that an atom is mostly empty space?
6. Who proposed the idea that electrons are found in different energy levels around the nucleus?

💡 THINKING CRITICALLY

7. **CONTRAST:** How did Rutherford's model of the atom differ from Thomson's model?
8. **EXPLAIN:** According to the modern atomic model, where are protons, neutrons, and electrons found?

---

4 ▶ **LOCATE:** in energy levels in different orbits around the nucleus

5 ▶ **EXPLAIN:** the place where an electron is most likely to be found outside the nucleus

✏ **WRITING HINT** Suggest that students write answers in complete sentences. This helps improve the quality of their writing.

3 Assess

✔ CHECKING CONCEPTS ANSWERS

1. particles in an atom that have a negative charge
2. in the nucleus
3. neutrons
4. J. J. Thomson
5. Ernest Rutherford
6. Niels Bohr

💡 THINKING CRITICALLY ANSWERS

7. **CONTRAST:** Rutherford's model had positively charged particles in the nucleus and negatively charged particles outside the nucleus. Thomson's model had positively charged and negatively charged particles scattered evenly throughout the atom.
8. **EXPLAIN:** Protons and neutrons are found in the nucleus. Electrons are found outside the nucleus in the electron cloud.

4 Close

How Do They Know That?
QUARKS AND LEPTONS

Discussion Have pairs of students compare the modern atomic model to what scientists have discovered about quarks and leptons. Discuss students' findings and point out that new discoveries about quarks and leptons support the modern atomic model.

Thinking Critically Answer
Electrons are a type of lepton.

MORE ON THE WEB

Modeling Atoms Have groups of students complete an online activity to build their own atom. Be sure to preview this online activity to prepare for your class. Have students visit www.conceptsandchallenges.com for more details.

• TEACHING RESOURCES •

💿 **Teacher's Resources CD-ROM**
Lesson Review: Chapter 3, p. 4
Model of an Atom: Visuals, p. 5

ONGOING ASSESSMENT

Ordering Atomic Parts By Size Write the following terms on the board: *atom, electron, nucleus,* and *proton.* Have students list these terms from largest to smallest.

1 Introduce

STUDY HINT Before beginning this lesson, write the title of each section in the lesson on the board. Have students copy these titles in their notebooks, using an outline format. As students read each section, they should write the information that supports each title. Students can also use the Writing Activity Outline found on the Teacher's Resources CD-ROM.

Linking Prior Knowledge Ask students what the purpose of taking fingerprints is. (Fingerprints identify a person because each person's fingerprints are unique.) Explain to students how a person's fingerprint compares to an element's atomic number. Each element has a unique atomic number that represents the number of protons in an atom of the element. learning styles: visual, tactile

2 Teach

Discussion Using the models of nuclei in Figure 3-14, discuss the relationship between the number of protons in an atom of an element and the element's atomic number. Define atomic number as the number of protons in the nucleus of an atom. Explain that no two elements have the same atomic number. Be sure that students understand that the number of electrons in a neutral atom is equal to the number of protons because the overall charge on the atom is zero. learning styles: visual, auditory

Demonstration Use paper circles to make models of the protons in the nuclei of hydrogen, carbon, and oxygen atoms. Ask students to explain how to find the number of protons in each element. Then, ask students how many electrons each of the nuclei would have orbiting it. (the same as the number of protons) Add the electrons to the models. learning styles: visual, tactile

Reinforcement Make sure students understand that, under normal conditions, atoms are neutral. The number of protons and the number of electrons are equal so that their charges cancel each other out. learning style: auditory

3-4 What is an atomic number?

Objective
Explain what is meant by the atomic number of an element.

Key Term
atomic number: number of protons in the nucleus of an atom

Elements and Atomic Number The atoms of different elements have different numbers of protons. You have learned that protons are particles that have a positive charge (+) and are found within the nucleus of an atom. The number of protons found in the nucleus of an atom is called the **atomic number**. Each element has a different atomic number because the atoms of each element have a different number of protons in their nuclei.

The element with the smallest atomic number is hydrogen. Hydrogen has an atomic number of 1. This means that an atom of hydrogen has only one proton in its nucleus. Oxygen has an atomic number of 8 because there are 8 protons in the nucleus of an atom of oxygen. Gold has an atomic number of 79. There are 79 protons in an atom of gold. Figure 3-15 lists the atomic numbers of some common elements. Figure 3-14 shows the nuclei of the elements helium, beryllium, and neon. You can see that the number of protons in the nuclei of each element is the same as the atomic number of each element.

ATOMIC NUMBERS OF SOME ELEMENTS	
Element	**Atomic number**
Hydrogen	1
Helium	2
Carbon	6
Nitrogen	7
Oxygen	8
Sodium	11
Aluminum	13
Sulfur	16
Chlorine	17
Calcium	20
Iron	26
Copper	29
Silver	47
Gold	79
Lead	82

▲ Figure 3-15

▶ **DEFINE:** What is an atomic number?

Importance of Atomic Number Your fingerprint is very important because it identifies you. No other person can have the same fingerprint as yours. The atomic number of an element is very important because it identifies that element. No two elements have the same atomic number. In fact, the number of protons in the nucleus of an atom tells you what that element is.

▶ **EXPLAIN:** Why is the atomic number of an element important?

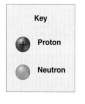

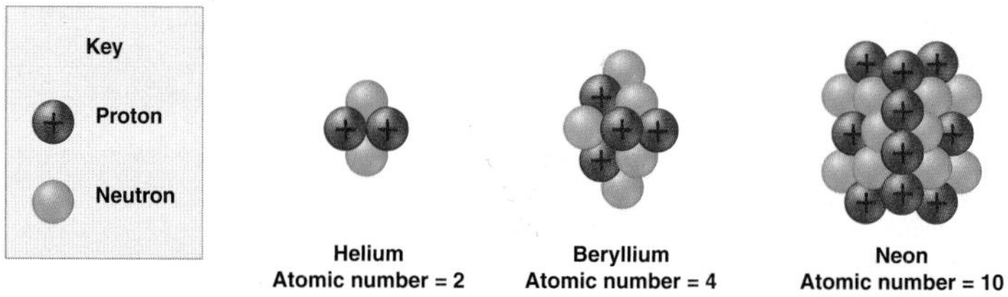

Key
⊕ Proton
○ Neutron

Helium
Atomic number = 2

Beryllium
Atomic number = 4

Neon
Atomic number = 10

▲ **Figure 3-14** The nuclei of helium, beryllium, and neon

58

Teaching Options

RETEACH

Using a Diagram On the board, draw the three nuclei in Figure 3-14. Use different-colored chalk to show the neutrons and the protons. Have students observe the diagrams and state the atomic number of each element. Then, ask students how many electrons each atom has. Make sure that students understand that an atom has the same number of electrons and protons. learning style: visual

EXTENDING THE LESSON

Interpreting Figure 3-15 Have students make a three-column chart. The columns should be labeled *Element, Number of Protons,* and *Number of Electrons.* Select elements from Figure 3-15 and read them aloud. Have students list the elements in the first column of the chart and then have them refer to Figure 3-15 to fill in the two other columns. learning styles: auditory, logical/mathematical

Atomic Number and Electrons If you know the atomic number of an element, you also know the number of electrons in an atom of that element. They are both the same number. They are the same because an atom has neither a positive nor a negative charge. It is neutral. In order for an atom to be neutral, the positive charges of the protons and the negative charges of the electrons must cancel each other out. So the number of electrons must be the same as the number of protons.

▶ CALCULATE: How many electrons are there in an atom of an element with an atomic number of 14?

✓ CHECKING CONCEPTS

1. The atomic number is the number of _____ in the nucleus of an atom.
2. Every _____ has its own atomic number.
3. The element with the smallest atomic number is _____.

4. No two elements have the same _____.
5. The number of protons in an atom is equal to the number of _____ in the atom.

💡 THINKING CRITICALLY

6. ANALYZE: If an atom has an atomic number of 12, how many electrons does the atom have?
7. EXPLAIN: How can knowing the atomic number of an atom help you to identify the element?

INTERPRETING VISUALS

Use Figure 3-15 to answer the following questions.

8. IDENTIFY: What is the atomic number of calcium?
9. IDENTIFY: How many protons are there in an atom of copper?
10. NAME: What element has an atomic number of 13?
11. IDENTIFY: How many electrons are there in an atom of aluminum?

⚛ *People in Science*

CHIEN-SHIUNG WU (1912–1997)

Chien-Shiung Wu was born in Liu Ho, China. She was a theoretical physicist. Chien-Shiung Wu came to America in 1936 to study for a doctorate in physics. She received her Ph.D. from the University of California at Berkeley. During World War II, she taught physics at Smith College and at Princeton University. After the war, she went to Columbia University to do research in nuclear physics. She became a professor of physics at Columbia in 1957.

▲ **Figure 3-16** Chien-Shiung Wu studied beta decay.

Chien-Shiung Wu's area of specialization was beta decay. In beta decay, the nucleus of an atom gives off electrons. This causes the atom to change into another element. Chien-Shiung Wu made many important contributions to scientists' present knowledge of the atom. Her experiments on beta decay confirmed a theory proposed by two other scientists. These scientists, Tsung Dao Lee and Chen Ning Yang, later won a Nobel Prize for their theory. Chien-Shiung Wu was the first woman to receive the Comstock Prize from the National Academy of Sciences.

Thinking Critically How did Chien-Shiung Wu's work contribute to the work of other scientists?

Answers to questions

▶ DEFINE: the number of protons in the nucleus of an atom

▶ EXPLAIN: It identifies the element.

▶ CALCULATE: 14

📖 **READING STRATEGY** Have students look at Figure 3-14 on page 58. Have them use the visual to help them understand the caption. As students read each element's name in the caption, they should locate the corresponding model of the atom.

3 *Assess*

✓ CHECKING CONCEPTS ANSWERS

1. protons
2. element
3. hydrogen
4. atomic number
5. electrons

💡 **THINKING CRITICALLY ANSWERS**

6. ANALYZE: 12
7. EXPLAIN: It is the only element with that atomic number.

INTERPRETING VISUALS ANSWERS

8. IDENTIFY: 20
9. IDENTIFY: 29
10. NAME: aluminum
11. IDENTIFY: 13

4 *Close*

People in Science

CHIEN-SHIUNG WU (1912–1997)

Background Beta decay may confuse students, since the nucleus of an atom does not contain electrons. Tell students that protons and neutrons can transform into other particles under certain conditions. During one type of beta decay, a neutron decays or transforms into a proton, an electron, and an antineutrino. The electron is released from the nucleus.

Thinking Critically Answer
Possible answer: Her work confirmed a theory proposed by two other scientists and contributed to scientific knowledge of the atom.

MORE ON THE WEB

All About Atoms Have students use an interactive presentation to learn more about atoms. Students can browse a list of elements organized by atomic number by visiting www.conceptsandchallenges.com.

ONGOING ASSESSMENT

Determining Atomic Number Have students explain which parts in the nuclei in Figure 3-14 determine each atom's atomic number.
learning style: visual

• *TEACHING RESOURCES* •

💿 **Teacher's Resources CD-ROM**
Lesson Review: Chapter 3, p. 5
Writing Activity Outline: Study Tools, pp. 20–21
Model of an Atom: Visuals, p. 5

1 Introduce

INVESTIGATE

TIME: 10–15 minutes

PURPOSE: Students will make a model of a nucleus.

MATERIALS: 8 red disks, 8 blue disks, 2 small pieces of plastic wrap, 2 wire-ties

PROCEDURE: Have pairs of students make the models of the two nuclei. Each pair should make a nucleus with two red and two blue disks and a nucleus with six red and six blue disks.
learning styles: tactile, interpersonal

THINK ABOUT IT: One color of disks represents the protons. The other color of disks represents the neutrons. The total number of disks inside each bag represents the number of protons and neutrons in the nucleus of each atom.

STUDY HINT
Before beginning this lesson, have students study Figure 3-17. Ask students how they think mass number is calculated.

Linking Prior Knowledge Review two ways that students have learned to identify a specific element. (the element's name and atomic number)

2 Teach

Discussion Explain atomic mass unit, average atomic mass, and mass number to students. Also, explain that, even though the number of protons, or atomic number, never changes, the number of neutrons in the atoms of an element can be different. (See Lesson 3-10 on isotopes.) The different number of neutrons causes the atomic mass to change. Therefore, an average of the different atomic masses for an element is used. To help students understand the very small mass of an electron, ask them how many electrons it would take to equal the mass of one proton or one neutron. (1,836)
learning style: logical/mathematical

Demonstration Using different-colored marbles or disks to represent protons and neutrons, demonstrate how to find the number of neutrons in an atom, given its mass number and atomic number.
learning style: visual

3-5 What is an atomic mass?

INVESTIGATE

Making a Model of a Nucleus
HANDS-ON ACTIVITY

1. Obtain colored disks, plastic wrap, and wire-ties from your teacher. Place two red disks and two blue disks in the center of a small piece of plastic wrap. Use a wire-tie to wrap the plastic around the disks.
2. Wrap and tie six red disks and six blue disks using another piece of plastic wrap.
3. Count the total number of disks inside each bag.

THINK ABOUT IT: If each "bundle" represents the nucleus of an atom, what does each colored disk represent? What does the total number of disks inside each bag represent?

STEP 1

Objective
Explain how to find the atomic mass and the mass number of an atom.

Key Terms
atomic mass: total mass of the protons and neutrons in an atom, measured in atomic mass units (amu)

mass number: number of protons and neutrons in the nucleus of an atom

Atomic Mass Unit Imagine trying to measure the mass of something so small that you cannot see it. Well, scientists do just that when they measure the mass of an atom. The mass of an atom is very small. It is not easy to measure the mass of an atom in grams. So, in order to measure the mass of an atom, scientists have developed a special unit. This unit is called the atomic mass unit, or amu.

One amu is equal to the mass of one proton. Neutrons and protons have almost the same mass. Therefore, one amu is also equal to the mass of one neutron. The mass of an electron is equal to $1/1,836$ amu. Because electrons are so small, only the masses of protons and neutrons are used to find the mass of an atom.

▶ **INFER:** What is the mass, in amu, of an atom with one proton and two neutrons?

Atomic Mass The total mass of the protons and neutrons in an atom is called the **atomic mass**. Atomic mass is measured in atomic mass units (amu). Because the atoms of an element can have different numbers of neutrons, scientists often give the average atomic mass for an element.

▶ **DEFINE:** What is an atomic mass?

Mass Number The total number of protons and neutrons in an atom is called the **mass number**. You can find the mass number for any element. The mass number can be found by rounding the average atomic mass to the nearest whole number. For example, the average atomic mass of lithium is 6.941 amu. The mass number of lithium is 7 (6.941 rounds to 7).

AVERAGE ATOMIC MASS AND MASS NUMBER		
Element	Average atomic mass	Mass number
Hydrogen	1.008	1
Helium	4.003	4
Carbon	12.011	12
Oxygen	15.999	16

▲ **Figure 3-17** To find the mass number, round the average atomic mass to the nearest whole number.

▶ **DEFINE:** What is mass number?

Teaching Options

! FAST FACTS Antimatter Exists

Science fiction stories often include antimatter. For every type of particle that students have read about, an antimatter particle or antiparticle really does exist. There are antiprotons, antielectrons, antiquarks, and so on. These antiparticles have the same mass as their counterparts, but they have opposite charges if their counterparts are charged. For example, an antiproton has the same mass as a proton, but an antiproton has a negative charge. If a matter particle and an antimatter particle collide, they destroy each other, and all their mass changes to energy. Fortunately, there seems to be much more matter than antimatter in the universe. Scientists are still asking questions and looking for answers about antimatter. **learning style: auditory**

Finding Neutrons If you know the atomic number and the mass number of an element, then you can find the number of neutrons in an atom of the most common form of that element. You can use the following formula:

mass number − atomic number = number of neutrons

Look at Figure 3-18 to find the number of neutrons in an atom of lithium.

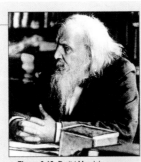

Nucleus of lithium

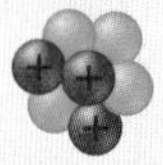

Mass number = 7
Atomic number = 3

Mass number	−	Atomic number	=	Number of neutrons
7	−	3	=	4

▲ **Figure 3-18** You can find the number of neutrons in an atom of the most common form of lithium.

4 ANALYZE: How many neutrons are in the nucleus of an atom of carbon?

✓ CHECKING CONCEPTS

1. The mass of a neutron is the same as the mass of a __________.
2. Because they are so small, __________ are not counted when measuring the mass of an atom.
3. The __________ is the unit used by scientists to measure the mass of an atom.
4. The mass number tells the total number of __________ and neutrons in the nucleus of an atom.

THINKING CRITICALLY

5. ANALYZE: Explain why the mass number of an element can never be less than the atomic number of that element.
6. INFER: Why is the mass of an electron not added to the atomic mass of an atom?

BUILDING MATH SKILLS

Calculating The atomic number of element x is 30 and the mass number is 65. Find the number of protons, neutrons, and electrons in an atom of element x.

People in Science

DMITRI MENDELEEV (1834–1907)

▲ **Figure 3-19** Dmitri Mendeleev

Dmitri Mendeleev (men-duh-LAY-uhf) was a Russian chemist. He was a professor of chemistry at St. Petersburg University in Russia. He is best known for developing the first table of elements organized according to properties.

Mendeleev wrote a book called *Principles of Chemistry.* For this book, Mendeleev collected thousands of facts about the 63 elements that were known at that time. He tried to find a way to organize this information. He thought that a certain pattern, or order, of the elements must exist.

Mendeleev decided to test his hypothesis. He wrote the name of each element and the properties of that element on a card. Then, he tried different arrangements of the cards for the 63 elements. When he arranged the cards in order of increasing atomic mass, the elements fell into groups with similar properties.

Thinking Critically Why do you think it was important to Mendeleev to organize his information into a table?

MORE ON THE WEB

Calculating Neutrons in Atoms Have students take a short online quiz on calculating the number of neutrons in a given atom. Send students to www.conceptsandchallenges.com for more details.

• TEACHING RESOURCES •

Teacher's Resources CD-ROM
Lesson Review: Chapter 3, p. 6
Model of an Atom: Visuals, p. 5

ONGOING ASSESSMENT

Explaining Atomic Differences Ask a volunteer to explain how atomic number, mass number, and average atomic mass differ.

Answers to questions

1 **INFER:** 3 amu

2 **DEFINE:** the total mass of the protons and neutrons in an atom, expressed in amu

3 **DEFINE:** the total number of protons and neutrons in an atom

4 **ANALYZE:** 6 (Refer to Figure 3-15 on page 58 for the atomic number of carbon.)

3 *Assess*

✓ CHECKING CONCEPTS ANSWERS

1. proton
2. electrons
3. atomic mass unit, or amu
4. protons

THINKING CRITICALLY ANSWERS

5. **ANALYZE:** The mass number includes the number of protons (atomic number). If neutrons are present, the number of neutrons is added to the number of protons.
6. **INFER:** It is too small to be significant.

4 *Close*

BUILDING MATH SKILLS ANSWERS

Calculating Element x has 30 protons. To find the number of neutrons, subtract the atomic number of 30 from the mass number of 65 to find that element x has 35 neutrons. An atom has the same number of electrons as protons, so element x has 30 electrons.

People in Science

DMITRI MENDELEEV (1834–1907)

Technology Connection Today's scientists have particle accelerators and other tools to help them study atoms. Mendeleev did not have this technology. In fact, electrons, protons, and almost half of the elements known today had not yet been discovered.

Discussion Ask students how scientists make discoveries. (Possible answers: They make observations, form hypotheses, test hypotheses, draw conclusions, and retest their hypotheses.)

Thinking Critically Answer Possible answer: Maybe he wanted to prove that a pattern, or order, of the elements existed.

1 Introduce

STUDY HINT Before beginning this lesson, have students create a word web or concept map in their notebooks. The main topic should be *energy levels*. As students read the lesson, they can add arms to their webs on which they record supporting information. **learning style: visual**

Linking Prior Knowledge Students are probably familiar with the planets in our solar system following paths around the Sun. Electrons move around the nucleus of an atom but do not follow a definite path. Discuss some differences in the paths of planets and the paths of electrons. (Planets stay in their orbits, and the positions in the orbits are known. The exact paths and positions of electrons are not known.)

2 Teach

Discussion Draw the diagram in Figure 3-20 on the board. Explain to students that energy levels are found inside the electron cloud. Emphasize that an energy level is the place where an electron is most likely to be at any time. **learning styles: visual, auditory**

Demonstration Draw a circle on the board to represent the nucleus of an atom of sulfur. Tell students that sulfur has an atomic number of 16 and, therefore, has 16 protons. Ask students how many electrons sulfur has. (16) Draw three energy levels around sulfur's nucleus. Have students describe where sulfur's electrons are most likely to be found. Fill in the electrons around the atom. The drawing should have two electrons in the first energy level, eight electrons in the second energy level, and six electrons in the third energy level. **learning styles: visual, linguistic**

Answers to questions

1 DESCRIBE: the area in an atom where electrons are likely to be found

2 PREDICT: two in the first energy level and four in the second energy level

3 ANALYZE: gaining or losing energy

3-6 How are electrons arranged in an atom?

Objective
Describe how the electrons in an atom are arranged in energy levels.

Key Term
energy level: place in an electron cloud where an electron is most likely to be found

The Electron Cloud For many years, scientists thought that electrons moved around the nucleus of an atom in much the same way as the planets orbit the Sun. Scientists now know that it is not possible to predict the exact path of an electron. You have learned that the area in an atom where electrons are likely to be found is called the electron cloud. Scientists use the word *cloud* because they know that they cannot predict the exact location of electrons nor the speed at which electrons move at any given time.

1 DESCRIBE: What is an electron cloud?

Energy Levels According to the modern atomic theory, electrons are arranged in energy levels around the nucleus of an atom. An **energy level** is the place in the electron cloud where an electron is most likely to be found. Each energy level is a different distance from the nucleus. The lowest, or first, energy level is closest to the nucleus. Electrons with more energy are found in energy levels farther away from the nucleus.

Each energy level can hold only a certain number of electrons. The first energy level can hold only two electrons. The second energy level can hold up to eight electrons. The third energy level can hold up to 18 electrons. The fourth energy level can hold up to 32 electrons. For the elements with atomic numbers between 1 and 20, the electrons in an atom of an element fill up the energy levels in order, beginning with the lowest.

An atom of helium has two electrons. These two electrons fill the first energy level. An atom of lithium has three electrons. Two of these electrons fill the first energy level. The third electron occupies the second energy level. An atom of chlorine has 17 electrons. Two electrons fill the first energy level, eight electrons fill the second level, and seven electrons occupy the third level.

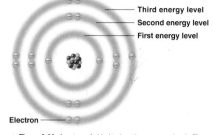

▲ **Figure 3-20** An atom of chlorine has three energy levels. The first two energy levels are completely filled. Seven electrons occupy the third energy level.

2 PREDICT: Where would you expect to find the six electrons in an atom of carbon?

Changing Energy Levels Adding energy to an atom or removing energy from an atom can cause the electrons in the atom to move from one energy level to another. If an electron gains enough energy, it jumps to a higher energy level. When this happens, the atom is in an "excited" state.

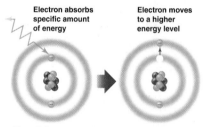

▲ **Figure 3-21** In an "excited" state, an electron jumps to a higher energy level.

Teaching Options

COOPERATIVE LEARNING

Demonstrating Energy Levels
Have a pair of students work on stairs to demonstrate what happens when an electron gains or loses energy. Ask one student to explain while the other student demonstrates for the class. The explanation should include that being on a step is like an electron being in an energy level. Moving up a step is like an electron moving to a higher level; moving down a step is like an electron moving to a lower level. When electrons change levels, they must gain or lose just the right amount of energy. (A student cannot move half a step.)

RETEACH

Making a Table of Energy Levels
Have students make a table with two columns. Tell them to list the four energy levels in the first column and the number of electrons needed to fill the energy levels in the second column. The title of their tables should be *Energy Levels and Electrons*. **learning style: visual**

If an electron in an excited atom loses enough energy, it drops back to a lower energy level. As it drops back, the electron gives off energy, often in the form of light.

Electron loses specific amount of energy

Electron moves to a lower energy level

▲ **Figure 3-22** When an electron in an excited state loses energy, it drops to a lower energy level.

 ANALYZE: What causes an electron to change energy levels?

1. An energy level is the place in the electron cloud where an _____ is most likely to be found in an atom.
2. The _____ energy level is located closest to the nucleus of an atom.
3. The second energy level can hold up to _____ electrons.
4. An electron will drop to a lower energy level when it _____ energy.

💡 **THINKING CRITICALLY**

5. **ANALYZE:** The atoms of a certain element have the first and second energy levels completely filled with electrons. What is the atomic number of this element? Explain how you know this.

Hands-On Activity

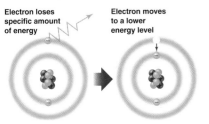

MAKING ELECTRON DOT DIAGRAMS

You will need element symbol cards, a periodic table, and a felt-tip marker.

1. An electron dot diagram is a simple way to show how the electrons in the outermost energy level of an atom are arranged. Look at the electron dot diagrams for the elements carbon, atomic number 6, and nitrogen, atomic number 7 in Figure 3-23.
2. Obtain three element symbol cards from your teacher. Notice how the element on each card has a symbol along with its atomic number.
3. Use the diagrams for carbon and nitrogen to help you make electron dot diagrams of each of your elements.

Practicing Your Skills

4. **EXPLAIN:** Why do you need to know the atomic number of an element to complete an electron dot diagram?
5. **OBSERVE:** What pattern do you notice in the way the electron dots are arranged around the symbol?

▲ **Figure 3-23**
Electron dot diagrams for carbon and nitrogen

📖 **READING STRATEGY** Ask students why scientists use the word *cloud* to describe the location of electrons in an atom. Have students compare an electron cloud with clouds in the sky.

3 Assess

✔ **CHECKING CONCEPTS ANSWERS**

1. electron
2. first
3. eight
4. loses

💡 **THINKING CRITICALLY ANSWER**

5. **ANALYZE:** 10; The first energy level is filled by two electrons, and the second energy level is filled by eight electrons.

4 Close

Hands-On Activity

MAKING ELECTRON DOT DIAGRAMS

TIME: 10–15 minutes

PURPOSE: explaining, observing

ALTERNATIVE MATERIALS: You can write the elements (the ones with atomic numbers between 1 and 20), including their atomic numbers and chemical symbols, on the board instead of using symbol cards. Inform students that the chemical symbols are just a shortened way of writing the name of the element and that they will learn more about chemical symbols in the next lesson.

ADVANCED PLANNING: Before class, prepare sets of index cards for elements 1–20 or write the information on the board.

TROUBLESHOOTING: In order to find the number of electrons in the outermost energy level of their atoms, students should draw a diagram of each atom. They should fill in the energy levels with the appropriate number of electrons.

Practicing Your Skills Answers

4. **EXPLAIN:** The atomic number is the number of protons in the nucleus, which is the same as the number of electrons outside the nucleus.
5. **OBSERVE:** Possible answer: The dots are arranged singly or in pairs on each side of the symbol.

MORE ON THE WEB

Orbitals Have students use the Internet to find out about orbitals. Some key search words are **Thompson atomic model, Bohr atomic model,** and **modern quantum mechanical model.** Have students begin their search at www.conceptsandchallenges.com.

ONGOING ASSESSMENT

Modeling Atoms Have students use their colored circles to model atoms of helium, nitrogen, and carbon to show their understanding of electrons in energy levels.

• TEACHING RESOURCES •

💿 **Teacher's Resources CD-ROM**

Lesson Review: Chapter 3, p. 7

Concept Map: Study Tools, p. 4

Model of an Atom: Visuals, p. 5

1 Introduce

STUDY HINT Before beginning this lesson, read the lesson objective with students. Then, have students read the Key Terms and their definitions.

Linking Prior Knowledge Have students review physical and chemical changes (Lesson 1-5). Tell students that an element's properties determine what physical and chemical changes it undergoes. Elements are organized in the periodic table according to their properties.

2 Teach

Discussion Describe the development of the Periodic Table of Elements. Have students compare Mendeleev's periodic table shown in Figure 3-24 with the modern periodic table shown in Figure 3-25. Inform students that Figure 3-25 is an abbreviated version of the periodic table. A complete table can be found on pages 66 and 67. Emphasize that the modern periodic table is arranged by atomic number, whereas Mendeleev's table was arranged by atomic mass. **learning style: visual**

Demonstration To help students understand the meaning of *periodic* and arranging things based on a certain pattern, show students a calendar. Point out that the days of the week repeat in a regular pattern. Mendeleev arranged elements with similar properties in columns in a chart, just as the same days in a week are listed in columns in a calendar.
learning styles: visual, logical/mathematical

Answers to questions

1 DEFINE: a shortened way of writing the name of an element

2 EXPLAIN: Chemical symbols are usually written as one or two letters. The first letter is capitalized. Any second letter is lowercase.

3 DESCRIBE: Possible answer: Elements with similar properties were listed in the same column in the table.

4 COMPARE: It is arranged in order of increasing atomic number instead of increasing atomic mass.

3-7 What is the periodic table?

Objective

Trace the development of the modern periodic table of elements.

Key Terms

chemical symbol: shortened way of writing the name of an element

periodic (pihr-ee-AHD-ihk): repeating pattern

group: vertical column of elements in the periodic table

period: horizontal row of elements in the periodic table

Shortened Names For many years, scientists had to spell out the names of all the known elements. However, in the early 1800s, a Swedish scientist named Jons Jakob Berzelius (buhr-ZEE-lee-uhs) created a new system of representing elements. This system uses letters called chemical symbols. **Chemical symbols** are a shortened way of writing the names of elements.

1 DEFINE: What is a chemical symbol?

Chemical Symbols Chemical symbols are created from the name of each element. There are usually one or two letters in a chemical symbol. The first letter of a chemical symbol is always capitalized. If there is a second letter, it is written using the lowercase. For example, Ne is the chemical symbol for neon. Some chemical symbols come from the Latin name for the element. The Latin name for lead is *plumbum*. The chemical symbol is Pb. Some elements have three letters in their chemical symbols. These chemical symbols are temporary until scientists come to an agreement on their permanent names.

2 EXPLAIN: How are chemical symbols written?

Arranging Elements By the 1800s, scientists had discovered many elements. They began to search for ways to organize these elements. In 1869, a Russian chemist named Dmitri Mendeleev listed the elements in order of increasing atomic mass.

64

Mendeleev noticed that elements with similar properties occurred periodically. The word **periodic** means "to repeat in a certain pattern." Based on the pattern he observed, Mendeleev arranged the elements in rows in a chart. Elements with similar properties were in the same column of his chart, one under the other. Mendeleev's chart was the first periodic table of elements. Figure 3-24 shows what Mendeleev's periodic table looked like.

			Ti = 50	Zr = 90	? = 180	
			V = 51	Nb = 94	Ta = 182	
			Cr = 52	Mo = 96	W = 186	
			Mn = 55	Rh = 104, 4	Pt = 197,	
			Fe = 56	Rn = 104, 4	Ir = 198	
			Ni = Co = 59	Pd = 106, 6	Os = 199	
H = 1			Cu = 63, 4	Ag = 108	Hg = 200	
	Be = 9,4	Mg = 24	Zn = 65, 2	Cd = 112	Au = 197	
	B = 11	Al = 27, 4	? = 68	Ur = 116	Bi = 210	
	C = 12	Si = 28	? = 70	Sn = 118	Ti = 204	
	N = 14	P = 31	As = 75	Sb = 122	Pb = 207	
	O = 16	S = 32	Se = 79, 4	Te = 128?		
	F = 19	Cl = 35, 5	Br = 80	J = 127		
Li = 7	Na = 23	K = 39	Rb = 85, 4	Cs = 133		
		Ca = 40	Sr = 87, 6	Ba = 137		
		? = 45	Ce = 92			
		?Er = 56	La = 94			
		?Yt = 60	Di = 95			
		?In = 75, 6	Th = 118?			

▲ **Figure 3-24** Mendeleev's periodic table

3 DESCRIBE: How were elements arranged in Mendeleev's periodic table?

The Modern Periodic Table Mendeleev's periodic table was useful, but it had some problems. Some elements did not have properties similar to the other elements in the same column. The discovery of atomic numbers, which occurred about 50 years after Mendeleev's table was developed, led to a new table. By arranging the elements in order of increasing atomic number instead of increasing atomic mass, all the elements in the same column had similar properties. This new arrangement is known as the modern periodic table of elements.

4 COMPARE: How is the modern periodic table different from Mendeleev's periodic table?

Teaching Options

EXTENDING THE LESSON

Comparing Elements in a Group Elements in a group have similar physical and chemical properties because they have the same number of electrons in their outermost energy levels. These outer electrons determine how easily an element undergoes chemical reactions. Group 1 elements are the most reactive and undergo chemical reactions easily and quickly. The elements in Group 11 are much less reactive than the elements in Group 1. Group 11 elements, such as copper, silver, and gold, are durable metals that do not corrode easily. These properties make them useful for coins and jewelry. Elements in Group 18 are the most stable elements. Have students look at the Periodic Table of Elements on pages 66 and 67 and list two elements from the same group and one element from a different group. Ask students which two of the three elements have the most similar properties. For example, ask students if barium or iron has properties that are the most similar to those of calcium. (barium) Give students as much practice as possible finding elements in groups. **learning styles: auditory, logical/mathematical**

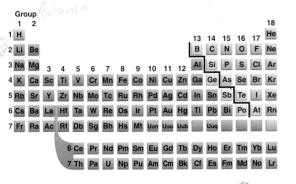

Group /column

Group 1	2											13	14	15	16	17	18
H																	He
Li	Be											B	C	N	O	F	Ne
Na	Mg	3	4	5	6	7	8	9	10	11	12	Al	Si	P	S	Cl	Ar
K	Ca	Sc	Ti	V	Cr	Mn	Fe	Co	Ni	Cu	Zn	Ga	Ge	As	Se	Br	Kr
Rb	Sr	Y	Zr	Nb	Mo	Tc	Ru	Rh	Pd	Ag	Cd	In	Sn	Sb	Te	I	Xe
Cs	Ba	La	Hf	Ta	W	Re	Os	Ir	Pt	Au	Hg	Tl	Pb	Bi	Po	At	Rn
Fr	Ra	Ac	Rf	Db	Sg	Bh	Hs	Mt	Uun	Uuu	Uub		Uuq				

6	Ce	Pr	Nd	Pm	Sm	Eu	Gd	Tb	Dy	Ho	Er	Tm	Yb	Lu
7	Th	Pa	U	Np	Pu	Am	Cm	Bk	Cf	Es	Fm	Md	No	Lr

◀ **Figure 3-25** A simple version of the modern Periodic Table of Elements

Groups and Periods Look at the periodic table in Figure 3-25. Notice that there are 18 columns. These columns are called **groups**, or families. Elements that are in the same group have similar physical and chemical properties. For example, lithium (Li), sodium (Na), and potassium (K) are all solids that react explosively with water. Elements in the same group also have the same number of electrons in their outermost energy levels.

The table also has seven rows. Each row is called a **period**. You can see that Period 1 has only two elements, hydrogen and helium. The elements in a period do not have similar properties. In fact, the properties of each element in a period change greatly as you move from left to right. However, there is a pattern in a period. Part of the pattern is that each period starts with an element that is a solid and ends with an element that is a gas. The first period is the only exception. Elements in the same period also have the same number of energy levels.

5 ▸ **COMPARE:** How is a group different from a period?

✓ CHECKING CONCEPTS

1. How is the first letter of a chemical symbol written?
2. How are the elements arranged in the modern periodic table?
3. What are the horizontal rows of the periodic table called?
4. How are elements in the same group similar?
5. Which scientist developed the first periodic table?

💡 THINKING CRITICALLY

6. **INFER:** Why would a scientist use Berzelius's system of representing elements?
7. **HYPOTHESIZE:** The symbol for carbon is C. The symbol for cobalt is Co. Why do you think a second letter was added to the chemical symbol of some elements? Why is the second letter written in the lowercase?

INTERPRETING VISUALS

Use Figure 3-25 to answer the following questions.

8. **IDENTIFY:** The first element in Group 17 is fluorine. What is its chemical symbol?
9. **INFER:** What group do boron (B) and thallium (Tl) belong to?
10. **NAME:** Name at least one element in Period 2.
11. **EXPLAIN:** Do you think calcium (Ca) and magnesium (Mg) have similar properties? Explain.
12. **IDENTIFY:** What group do copper (Cu) and gold (Au) belong to?
13. **IDENTIFY:** What period does iron (Fe) belong to?

BUILDING SOCIAL STUDIES SKILLS

Analyzing A few of the elements in the periodic table are named after countries, states, and planets. Use library resources, encyclopedias, or the Internet to find three of these elements. List their names and the name of the country, state, or planet for which they are named.

CHAPTER 3: Elements and Atoms **65**

---

5 ▸ **COMPARE:** Possible answer: A group is a column in the periodic table, and a period is a row.

3 Assess

✓ CHECKING CONCEPTS ANSWERS

1. as a capital letter
2. in order of increasing atomic number
3. periods
4. They have similar physical and chemical properties, and the same number of electrons in their outermost energy levels.
5. Dmitri Mendeleev

💡 THINKING CRITICALLY ANSWERS

6. **INFER:** Possible answer: Symbols are shorter to write, and they are a universal language that all scientists understand.
7. **HYPOTHESIZE:** A second letter is added so that elements whose names start with the same letter have different symbols. The second letter is lowercase to avoid confusion. For example, C and O are symbols for carbon and oxygen. Co is the chemical symbol for cobalt.

INTERPRETING VISUALS ANSWERS

8. **IDENTIFY:** F
9. **INFER:** 13
10. **NAME:** Possible answers may include any of the following: lithium, beryllium, boron, carbon, nitrogen, oxygen, fluorine, and neon.
11. **EXPLAIN:** Yes; They are in the same group, and elements in the same group have similar physical and chemical properties.
12. **IDENTIFY:** 11
13. **IDENTIFY:** 4

4 Close

BUILDING SOCIAL STUDIES SKILLS

Analyzing Have students find the names and symbols of elements in the periodic table on pages 66 and 67. Students can start their search for elements named after a country, state, or planet at www.conceptsandchallenges.com. Some of the countries, states, and planets include Poland (Po), France (Fr), California (Cf), Pluto (Pu), and Uranus (U).

ONGOING ASSESSMENT

Reading the Periodic Table Ask students: *What is the chemical symbol for lithium?* (Li) *What group is it in?* (Group I) *What period is it in?* (Period 2)

The Big Idea

(pp. 66–67)

1 Introduce

Objective Students will be able to use the Periodic Table of Elements to identify an element's name, symbol, atomic number, atomic mass, state of matter, group, and period. Students can also identify synthetic elements and classify an element as a metal, a metalloid, or a nonmetal. Students will write the elements that are familiar to them in their Science Logs. Then, students will research the kinds of elements that are in the objects they use every day and write their findings in their Science Logs.

Linking Prior Knowledge Have students recall what they learned about matter and elements (Lesson 3-1). Ask students what elements they already know make up some objects around them. List these elements on the board. Have students look through the periodic table to find the periods and the groups that these elements belong to.

2 Teach

Discussion After students have read the article, ask them what information about an element can be learned from the periodic table. List students' responses on the board. (atomic number; chemical symbol; element's name; average atomic mass; group; period; state of matter; if it is a metal, metalloid, or nonmetal; if it is a synthetic element) Then, name an element and ask a volunteer to tell the class about the element. Give students as much practice as possible giving information about the elements that you name.
learning styles: visual, auditory

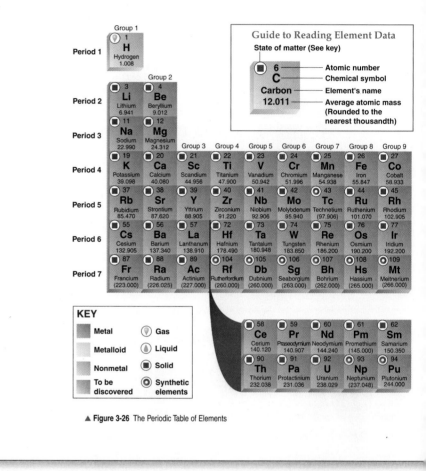

◆ *Integrating Physical, Earth, and Life Science*

THE Big IDEA

What is the Periodic Table of Elements?

A great deal of information about the atoms that make up elements is presented in a chart called the Periodic Table of Elements. Every known element, including synthetic elements (elements made in a laboratory) is listed in the table. Information about each element, such as its name, chemical symbol, atomic number, and average atomic mass, is listed. Each element is arranged in the table in order of increasing atomic number.

▲ **Figure 3-26** The Periodic Table of Elements

66

Teaching Options

! FAST FACTS *Two Rows Do Not Fit in Periodic Table*

Two rows of elements are placed below the periodic table because there is not enough space for them in their periods. The first of the two rows starts with Cerium (atomic number 58) and ends with Lutetium (atomic number 71). This row fits in period 6 between Lanthanum (atomic number 57) and Hafnium (atomic number 72). Elements 58 through 71 have similar properties. They are metals, and they combine well with nonmetals. The second of the two rows starts with Thorium (atomic number 90) and ends with Lawrencium (atomic number 103). This row fits in period 7 between Actinium (atomic number 89) and Rutherfordium (atomic number 104). The first three elements in this row are found in nature. All the other elements in this row do not occur in nature but are made synthetically. **learning styles: auditory, visual**

The elements that are arranged in vertical columns, called groups, have similar properties. The elements that are arranged in horizontal rows, called periods, have the same number of energy levels in each of their atoms. If more elements are discovered, they, too, will be listed in the table. The periodic table can also be used to help explain how elements combine to form every kind of matter in the universe. Elements are studied in all three major fields of science.

Look at the periodic table on these two pages. Then, follow the directions in the Science Log to find out more about "the big idea."✦

Science Log

Look at the periodic table. Which elements are you familiar with? In your science log, research and write about the kinds of elements that are in the objects that you use every day. Start your search at www.conceptsandchallenges.com.

8 -outer shell

3 4 5 6 7

					Group 18
					◉ 2 **He** Helium 4.003

Group 13	Group 14	Group 15	Group 16	Group 17	
▪ 5 **B** Boron 10.811	◉ 6 **C** Carbon 12.011	◉ 7 **N** Nitrogen 14.007	◉ 8 **O** Oxygen 15.999	◉ 9 **F** Fluorine 18.998	◉ 10 **Ne** Neon 20.183
▪ 13 **Al** Aluminum 26.982	▪ 14 **Si** Silicon 28.086	◉ 15 **P** Phosphorus 30.974	◉ 16 **S** Sulfur 32.064	◉ 17 **Cl** Chlorine 35.453	◉ 18 **Ar** Argon 39.948

Group 10	Group 11	Group 12					
▪ 28 **Ni** Nickel 58.710	◉ 29 **Cu** Copper 63.540	◉ 30 **Zn** Zinc 65.370	◉ 31 **Ga** Gallium 69.720	▪ 32 **Ge** Germanium 72.590	◉ 33 **As** Arsenic 74.922	▪ 34 **Se** Selenium 78.960	◉ 35 **Br** Bromine 79.909
▪ 46 **Pd** Palladium 106.400	◉ 47 **Ag** Silver 107.870	◉ 48 **Cd** Cadmium 112.400	◉ 49 **In** Indium 114.820	◉ 50 **Sn** Tin 118.690	▪ 51 **Sb** Antimony 121.750	▪ 52 **Te** Tellurium 127.600	◉ 53 **I** Iodine 126.904
▪ 78 **Pt** Platinum 195.090	◉ 79 **Au** Gold 196.967	◉ 80 **Hg** Mercury 200.590	◉ 81 **Tl** Thallium 204.370	◉ 82 **Pb** Lead 207.200	▪ 83 **Bi** Bismuth 208.980	▪ 84 **Po** Polonium (209.000)	◉ 85 **At** Astatine (210.000)
◉ 110 **Uun** Ununnilium (269)	◉ 111 **Uuu** Unununium (272)	◉ 112 **Uub** Ununbium (272)		◉ 114 **Uuq** Ununquadium (285)			

(Xe 54, Xenon 131.300; Kr 36, Krypton 83.800; Rn 86, Radon (222.000) in Group 18 column)

▪ 63 **Eu** Europium 151.960	▪ 64 **Gd** Gadolinium 157.250	▪ 65 **Tb** Terbium 158.924	▪ 66 **Dy** Dysprosium 162.500	▪ 67 **Ho** Holmium 164.930	▪ 68 **Er** Erbium 167.260	▪ 69 **Tm** Thulium 168.934	▪ 70 **Yb** Ytterbium 173.040	▪ 71 **Lu** Lutetium 174.970
◉ 95 **Am** Americium (243.000)	◉ 96 **Cm** Curium (247.000)	◉ 97 **Bk** Berkelium (247.000)	◉ 98 **Cf** Californium (251.000)	◉ 99 **Es** Einsteinium (254.000)	◉ 100 **Fm** Fermium (257.000)	◉ 101 **Md** Mendelevium (258.000)	◉ 102 **No** Nobelium (259.000)	◉ 103 **Lr** Lawrencium (260.000)

Atomic masses in parentheses are of the most common form of the atom.

Tips for Using Technology

Presentation Software Have students use presentation software to present their findings on elements that are in everyday objects. Presentation software allows students to use a computer to put text and art together in a slide show. They can use a scanner to incorporate their own art in their slide show. Students can then print their slide show and use it as a handout for others to follow during their presentation. Have students use the Flowchart on the Teacher's Resources CD-ROM to plan their presentations.

• TEACHING RESOURCES •

Teacher's Resources CD-ROM

Big Idea: Chapter 3, p. 11

Big Idea Planner: Study Tools, pp. 11–12

Big Idea Science Log Entry: Study Tools, p. 13

Individual Activity Rubric: Teaching Tools, p. 5

Flowchart: Study Tools, p. 6

Use the information presented on the Periodic Table of Elements to help guide students in choosing a topic for their Science Logs.

THE BIG IDEA ONLINE

What is the Periodic Table of Elements? Have students research their Science Log Writing Activity at www.conceptsandchallenges.com. You can have students organize their log by completing the Big Idea activity online. Students may post their work in the Online Classroom Database for others to read.

Reinforcement Students can also use the Big Idea Planner or Big Idea Science Log Entry found on the Teacher's Resources CD-ROM.

3 Assess

Use the Individual Activity Rubric on the Teacher's Resources CD-ROM to assess students' Science Logs. Fill in the rubric with the additional information below. For this assignment, students should have:

- listed familiar elements.
- communicated accurate information about the elements that make up everyday objects.

4 Close

Making a Collage Have pairs of students make a collage of everyday objects. The picture of each object should have call outs for the elements that make up the object. Each call out should include a drawing of the element's square in the Periodic Table of Elements. Have students present their collages to the class.
learning styles: tactile, visual

3-8 (pp. 68-69)

1 Introduce

✐ **STUDY HINT** Before beginning this lesson, read each Key Term aloud so that students can hear its pronunciation.

Linking Prior Knowledge Write *Metals* and *Nonmetals* on the board. First, ask students to name some metals. Then, ask students to name some nonmetals. List their responses on the board. **learning style: linguistic**

2 Teach

Discussion Refer students to the periodic table on pages 66 and 67. Have them locate the dark zigzag line that separates metals from nonmetals. Then, describe the properties of metals, such as shiny luster, malleability, ductility, and conductivity. Point out that nonmetals, such as oxygen and sulfur, do not have these properties. **learning styles: visual, auditory**

Answers to questions

▶1 NAME: metals and nonmetals

▶2 LIST: Possible answers may include any three of the following: luster, ductility, malleability, conduction of electricity, and conduction of heat.

▶3 RELATE: They do not have luster.

3 Assess

✓ CHECKING CONCEPTS ANSWERS

1. nonmetals
2. malleable
3. ductile
4. metals
5. poor
6. phosphorus

💡 THINKING CRITICALLY ANSWERS

7. IDENTIFY: Metals are ductile and are good conductors of electricity.
8. INFER: malleability
9. CLASSIFY: **a.** metal, **b.** nonmetal, **c.** nonmetal, **d.** metal, **e.** nonmetal, **f.** metal, **g.** metal, **h.** nonmetal

---

3-8 What are metals and nonmetals?

Objective

Identify the properties of metals and nonmetals.

Key Terms

metal: element that has the property of shiny luster, ductility, and malleability

luster (LUS-tuhr)**:** the way a material reflects light

malleable (MAL-ee-uh-buhl)**:** able to be hammered into different shapes

ductile (DUK-tuhl)**:** able to be drawn into thin wires

nonmetal: element that lacks most of the properties of a metal

Metals and Nonmetals If you look at the periodic table, you will see a dark zigzag line running from the top of Group 13 to the bottom of Group 16. This line separates two different types of elements. The elements to the left of the line, with the exception of hydrogen, are metals. The elements to the right of the line are nonmetals.

▶1 NAME: What are two different types of elements?

Properties of Metals **Metals** are elements that have the properties of shiny luster, ductility, and malleability. All metals, except mercury, are solids at room temperature. Mercury is a liquid. The properties of metals are as follows:

- Some metals are shiny. A gold ring is shiny. The way a material reflects light is called its **luster**.

- Most metals are **malleable**. They can be hammered into thin sheets and different shapes. Aluminum can be hammered into a thin sheet and into the shape of a pot or pan.

- Metals are **ductile**. They can be made into thin wires. Most of the wires in electrical appliances are made of metals.

- Some metals allow electricity to flow through them easily. These metals are good conductors of electricity. Electricity flows easily through wires made of copper.

68

- Most metals are good conductors of heat. They allow heat to flow easily through them. This is the reason why radiators, pots, pans, and irons are made of metals.

◀ **Figure 3-27** Metals can be hammered into different shapes.

▶2 LIST: What are three properties of metals?

Properties of Nonmetals Elements that lack most of the properties of a metal are called **nonmetals**, so they look dull. Most solid nonmetals are brittle. They are easily broken. They cannot be pounded into different shapes or pulled into thin wires. Nonmetals are poor conductors of electricity and heat. Nonmetallic elements may exist at room temperature as solids, liquids, or gases.

Nonmetals are very useful elements. For example, phosphorus is used in matches. Sulfur is used to make rubber. Nonmetals are also important to all living things in other ways. The nonmetals nitrogen and oxygen are found in the air that we breathe. Nitrogen helps organisms to make proteins. Most organisms need oxygen to breathe.

▲ **Figure 3-28** Matches and rubber are made from nonmetals.

▶3 RELATE: Why do nonmetals look dull?

Teaching Options

RETEACH

Reviewing Nonmetals Show students some samples of nonmetals. Refer to hydrogen, oxygen, and nitrogen in the air. If possible, show them sulfur and iodine in covered containers. Remind students that nonmetals are solids or gases at room temperature, except for bromine, which is a liquid. Elicit that nonmetals do not have a shiny luster, cannot be hammered into different shapes, and cannot be drawn into a wire. Review the terms *luster, malleable,* and *ductile.* Inform students that luster can be shiny or dull. **learning style: auditory**

COOPERATIVE LEARNING

Comparing Properties in a Chart Have students work in pairs to construct charts comparing the properties of metals and nonmetals. Make sure that students include specific examples. Allow students to present their charts to the class. **learning styles: visual, interpersonal**

✔ CHECKING CONCEPTS

1. Elements to the right of the zigzag line in the periodic table are _____.
2. Metals can be hammered into thin sheets because they are _____.
3. It is possible to make copper wire because copper is _____.
4. Most _____ are good conductors of heat.
5. Nonmetals are _____ conductors of heat and electricity.
6. The nonmetal _____ is used in matches.

💡 THINKING CRITICALLY

7. **IDENTIFY:** What two properties of metals make them useful materials for the electrical wiring in your home?

8. **INFER:** What property of metals allows a jeweler to hammer a piece of silver to make jewelry?
9. **CLASSIFY:** Use the periodic table on pages 66 and 67 to identify the following elements as metals or nonmetals.

   a. Zinc   e. Selenium
   b. Sulfur   f. Magnesium
   c. Xenon   g. Platinum
   d. Potassium   h. Phosphorus

DESIGNING AN EXPERIMENT

Design an experiment to solve the following problem. Include a hypothesis, variables, a procedure, and a type of data to study.

PROBLEM: Element *x* is an unidentified element. Is it a metal or a nonmetal?

Hands-On Activity

COMPARING METALS AND NONMETALS

You will need safety goggles, an electrical conductivity tester, a 5- to 6-cm piece of uninsulated copper wire, graphite from a mechanical pencil, a paper clip, and a small block of wood.

1. Compare a piece of uninsulated copper wire to a piece of graphite from a mechanical pencil. Note the luster of both samples.
2. Put on safety goggles. Check for ductility. Bend the copper wire, the piece of graphite, a paper clip, and a block of wood as far as possible. Note changes in each of the samples.
3. Check for electrical conductivity. Touch the free ends of the wires in the electrical conductivity tester to each other. Make sure that the light bulb goes on. Next touch the ends of the wires to the ends of the uninsulated copper wire. Observe any changes to the light bulb. Do the same for the paper clip, the graphite, and the block of wood. Note any changes to the light bulb.

Practicing Your Skills

4. **COMPARE:** What are the properties of the copper wire compared to the properties of the graphite from the mechanical pencil?
5. **DESCRIBE:** Which of the four samples conducted electricity? How do you know?

▲ **STEP 3** Observe any changes to the light bulb.

CHAPTER 3: Elements and Atoms   **69**

ONGOING ASSESSMENT

Explaining Why Gold Is a Metal
Ask students: *According to the properties of metals, why is gold considered a metal?* (It has luster, is ductile, and can conduct electricity and heat well.)

• TEACHING RESOURCES •

Teacher's Resources CD-ROM
Lesson Review: Chapter 3, p. 12

Designing an Experiment: Study Tools, p. 14

Designing an Experiment Rubric: Teaching Tools, p. 7

Laboratory Manual
Lab. Challenge: How can you tell the difference between a metal and a nonmetal? pp. 29–32

---

4 Close

DESIGNING AN EXPERIMENT

Use the Designing an Experiment Rubric on the Teacher's Resources CD-ROM to assess students' experiments. Fill in the rubric with the additional information below. For this assignment, students should have:

- mentioned a characteristic of a metal or a nonmetal in forming the hypothesis.
- included, in the procedure, using a sample of a metal and a nonmetal to compare with element *x*.

Hands-On Activity

COMPARING METALS AND NONMETALS

TIME: 15 minutes

PURPOSE: comparing, observing

SAFETY TIP: Caution students not to touch the uninsulated wire when the circuit is closed. Also caution students to make sure that the circuit is open when they are not testing materials.

MATERIALS: Make electrical conductivity testers ahead of time. For each tester, you will need a 1.5-V dry-cell battery, a flashlight bulb and socket, and three lengths (about 25 cm each) of insulated wire with the ends stripped. To assemble each tester, place the bulb into the socket and turn it until the bulb is secure. Use one piece of wire to connect one terminal of the battery to one screw of the socket. Connect one end of a second piece of wire to the other terminal of the battery. Leave the other end of this wire free. Take a third piece of wire and connect one end of it to the other screw of the socket. The end of this piece of wire should also be free. If the two free ends of wire touch, the bulb should light. Students will test the conductivity of materials by placing the materials between the two free ends of wire. Make sure that students know that graphite is made from the element carbon and not from the element lead.

Practicing Your Skills Answers

4. **COMPARE:** The copper wire is shiny, but the graphite is not. The copper wire bent without breaking, but the graphite broke. The copper wire conducted electricity, but the graphite did not conduct electricity well. (Graphite may conduct electricity.)
5. **DESCRIBE:** The copper wire and the paper clip conducted electricity because the light bulb lit up brightly.

CHAPTER 3: Elements and Atoms   **T69**

1 Introduce

✏️ **STUDY HINT** Have students use the objectives and Key Terms information to locate the halogens and the noble gases in the periodic table on pages 66 and 67.

Linking Prior Knowledge Have students look at Groups 17 and 18 in the periodic table. Tell students that they are familiar with the uses of at least one halogen and one noble gas. Fluorine is a halogen found in toothpastes, some mouthwashes, and some city water supplies. Ask students why flourine is added to these materials. (It helps prevent tooth decay.) Ask students when they last saw a balloon float and what made it float. (helium) Tell them that helium is one of the noble gases.

2 Teach

Discussion Have students identify the elements in Group 17. Tell students that these elements are halogens. They have similar chemical properties but differ in physical properties throughout the group. Have students identify the elements in Group 18. Tell students that these elements are the noble gases. They have similar properties and atomic structure.
learning styles: visual, auditory

Answers to questions

▶1 **LIST:** fluorine, chlorine, bromine, iodine, and astatine

▶2 **DEFINE:** one of six elements in Group 18 of the periodic table

▶3 **LIST:** helium, neon, argon, krypton, xenon, and radon

▶4 **EXPLAIN:** to fill balloons

📖 **READING STRATEGY** Have students list the halogens. Students should notice that the names of all six elements end in *-ine*. Inform students that one of the uses of this suffix is to identify the names of the elements in the halogen group.

3-9 What are the halogens and the noble gases?

Objectives

Locate the halogens and the `noble gases on the periodic table. Identify the properties of the halogens and the noble gases.

Key Terms

halogens: elements that make up Group 17 in the periodic table

noble gases: elements that make up Group 18 in the periodic table

The Halogens Group 17 in the periodic table contains the five elements that make up the **halogens**. These elements, fluorine, chlorine, bromine, iodine, and astatine, have a similar atomic structure. The halogens can vary their physical states from solid to gas at room temperature. They can also change color when changing state. For example, bromine is a red-brown liquid that becomes a red gas at room temperature. Iodine is a gray-black solid that can become a blue-violet gas.

The halogens can also be quite dangerous. However, when they combine with other elements, they can form matter that is very useful. For example, chlorine combines with sodium to form table salt. Fluorine combines with other elements to form products that prevent tooth decay. Matter made with iodine can be used to help prevent infections in wounds. Figure 3-29 lists the halogens.

HALOGENS		
Element	Symbol	Uses
Fluorine	Fl	Prevents tooth decay
Chlorine	Cl	Purifies water
Bromine	Br	Used in photographic film
Iodine	I	Prevents infection
Astatine	At	Used in halogen lights

▲ **Figure 3-29** The halogens can be found in Group 17 in the periodic table.

▶1 **LIST:** Name the five halogens.

70

The Noble Gases Look at Group 18 of the periodic table on page 67. What do the elements in Group 18 have in common? The six elements in the last group of the periodic table are gases. They are called the **noble gases**. All of these elements have similar properties and atomic structure.

In the past, these elements were also called inert gases. The word *inert* means "inactive." At one time, these elements were thought to occur naturally as pure substances. Pure substances that occur naturally do not interact with other substances. However, scientists have discovered that noble gases can be forced to combine with other elements, such as fluorine.

▶2 **DEFINE:** What is a noble gas?

Familiar Noble Gases The six noble gases are helium, neon, argon, krypton, xenon, and radon. The names of some of the noble gases may be familiar to you. You have probably heard of helium and neon. If you have heard of kryptonite, krypton is not related to it. In fact, kryptonite, which is mentioned in fictional tales, is not a real substance. All the noble gases are found in small amounts in Earth's atmosphere. Of all the noble gases, argon is the most plentiful. It makes up about 1% of the atmosphere. The names and chemical symbols of the six noble gases are listed in Figure 3-30.

NOBLE GASES		
Element	Symbol	Uses
Helium	He	Fills balloons
Neon	Ne	Lighting
Argon	Ar	Lighting
Krypton	Kr	Lighting
Xenon	Xe	Lighting
Radon	Rn	None

▲ **Figure 3-30** The noble gases can be found in Group 18 in the periodic table.

▶3 **LIST:** Name the six noble gases.

Teaching Options

💠 INTEGRATING LIFE SCIENCE

Adding Chlorine to Water People need a constant supply of pure drinking water. The water may come from rivers, lakes, reservoirs, or underground sources. In many areas, this water contains bacteria and other disease-causing organisms that would be harmful to people's health. In most communities, chlorine is added to the water before it is sent to homes. The chlorine kills organisms that can make people sick. Chlorine is also added to water in swimming pools for the same reason. Have students find out and report on whether the drinking water in their homes has been chlorinated. Emphasize that if it has not been chlorinated, it is not necessarily unsafe to drink.
learning styles: auditory, linguistic

Uses of Noble Gases Most of the noble gases have many important uses. Neon is used in lights because it gives off a bright red glow when electricity passes through it. By mixing neon with other gases, different colors can be produced. Helium is used to fill balloons and xenon is used in photographic lamps.

▲ **Figure 3-31** Neon is used in lights.

▶ EXPLAIN: What is helium used for?

Real-Life Science

BLIMPS

Have you ever looked up into the sky and seen a blimp passing by? A blimp is a type of airship that is lifted into the air by the noble gas helium. Helium not only lifts a blimp high into the sky, it also gives a blimp its shape. The baglike body of a blimp, called the envelope, does not have structure unless helium fills it.

Helium is used to lift blimps because helium is lighter than air and it will not burn in air. At one time, hydrogen gas was used to fill airships. Hydrogen is lighter than helium. However, on May 6, 1937, the largest airship ever built, the Hindenburg, burst into flames over Lakehurst, New Jersey. Since hydrogen was used to lift and fill the Hindenburg, it was no longer considered safe to use.

Today, blimps are used to advertise certain products, and to transport photographic equipment to film special events. In some countries, they are used in military operations.

Thinking Critically Hydrogen is lighter than helium. Why is hydrogen not used to lift blimps instead of helium?

▲ **Figure 3-32** Blimps are airships that are filled with the noble gas helium.

✓ CHECKING CONCEPTS

1. Where are the halogens located in the periodic table?
2. Where are the noble gases located in the periodic table?
3. What is the meaning of inert?
4. Which noble gas makes up about 1% of Earth's atmosphere?

💡 THINKING CRITICALLY

5. STATE: Why were noble gases once called inert gases?
6. ANALYZE: Why do you think neon is used in signs?

BUILDING LANGUAGE ARTS SKILLS

Researching Noble gases are so named because of nobles. Look up the word *noble* in a dictionary, an encyclopedia, or on the Internet. Find out how noble gases are related to nobles.

---

3 Assess

✓ CHECKING CONCEPTS ANSWERS

1. Group 17
2. Group 18
3. inactive
4. argon

💡 THINKING CRITICALLY ANSWERS

5. STATE: They were thought to occur naturally as pure substances, meaning that they do not interact with other substances.
6. ANALYZE: Possible answer: It gives off a bright red glow when electricity passes through it.

4 Close

BUILDING LANGUAGE ARTS SKILLS

Researching Answers will vary but might include the following: Historically, nobles were the titled class in society, and they did not interact much with other people. Because they do not frequently interact with other elements, Group 18 elements are called noble gases.

Real-Life Science

BLIMPS

Real-Life Connection The Hindenburg was a huge airship that could carry passengers across the ocean. It was about 245 meters (804 feet) long and could hold 190 million liters (about 6.7 million cubic feet) of hydrogen. For over 60 years after the Hindenburg disaster, most people believed that the fire was caused when electrical charges in the air ignited the hydrogen and caused it to explode. Recent studies have led to a different conclusion. The skin that covered the Hindenburg was coated with a highly flammable substance. Also, the skin was attached to the airship in a way that allowed electrical charges from the air to build up on its surface. When enough of a charge built up, it discharged and caused the skin to ignite. The conclusion is that hydrogen did not ignite and cause the fire, but the flammable skin covering the Hindenburg did.

Thinking Critically Answer
Helium will not burn in air, but hydrogen is explosive in air.

MORE ON THE WEB

Learning About the Dangers of Radon Have students find out what they can to do to test for radon and prevent radon from being a problem by visiting www.conceptsandchallenges.com.

• TEACHING RESOURCES •

💿 **Teacher's Resources CD-ROM**
Lesson Review: Chapter 3, p. 13

ONGOING ASSESSMENT

Identifying Groups 17 and 18 Have students point out the noble gases and halogens in the Periodic Table of Elements. **learning style: visual**

3-10 (pp.72–73)

1 Introduce

✏️ **STUDY HINT** Before beginning this lesson, have students study Figure 3-33. Ask them to compare the three nuclei of hydrogen.

Linking Prior Knowledge Have students review what they learned about neutrons and average atomic mass (Lesson 3-5).

2 Teach

Discussion Inform students that there are several isotopes of carbon that can be found in nature. The most abundant isotope is carbon-12 and has an atomic mass of 12.000 amu. The second-most abundant isotope, carbon-13, has an atomic mass of 13.003 amu. The difference in the atomic masses is a result of the extra neutron in the carbon-13 atom. This difference in atomic masses is the reason the average atomic mass for carbon is 12.011 amu. Since there are several isotopes of carbon with different atomic masses, an average of all atomic masses is taken. However, this average is a weighted average because it takes into account the fact that carbon-12 is far more abundant than all of the other isotopes.

Answers to questions

▶ **STATE:** a different number of neutrons in the nuclei

▶ **DEFINE:** an atom of an element with the same number of protons as the other atoms but a different number of neutrons

▶ **EXPLAIN:** an average of the atomic masses of all the isotopes of that element

▶ **LIST:** protium, deuterium, and tritium

📖 **READING STRATEGY** Tell students that the prefix *iso-* means "equal." Suggest that students use a dictionary to find words that begin with *iso-*. (isobar, isotherm, isometric) Students should read their definitions and look for the words *equal* or *same*. The word *isotope* comes from two Greek words, meaning "same" and "place." Isotopes of an element are all found in the same place in the periodic table.
learning style: linguistic

3-10 What are isotopes?

Objectives

Explain what an isotope of an element is.
Compare the three isotopes of hydrogen.

Key Term

isotope (EYE-suh-tohp)**:** atom of an element with the same number of protons as the other atoms but a different number of neutrons

Different Atomic Masses The atomic number of an element never changes. All atoms of the same element have the same number of protons in their nuclei. However, all atoms of the same element may not have the same number of neutrons in their nuclei. This means that atoms of the same element can have different atomic masses. The difference in atomic mass is caused by a different number of neutrons in the nuclei of the atoms of an element.

▶ **STATE:** What causes atoms of the same element to have different atomic masses?

Isotopes Atoms of the same element that have different atomic masses are called isotopes. **Isotopes** are atoms of an element that have the same number of protons as the other atoms of the element but a different number of neutrons in their nuclei.

Although the number of neutrons in the atoms of an element may be different, atoms are always identified by the number of protons. For example, there are several isotopes of the element copper. One of the isotopes has 36 neutrons in the nuclei of its atoms. Another isotope has 34 neutrons in the nuclei of its atoms. Because both of these isotopes have 29 protons in the nuclei of their atoms, they are both atoms of the element copper.

▶ **DEFINE:** What is an isotope?

Atomic Mass The atomic mass for each element can be found in the periodic table. The atomic mass given for each element is actually an average of the atomic masses of all the isotopes of that element. This explains why an element's atomic mass is not a whole number.

▶ **EXPLAIN:** What does the atomic mass for each element actually represent?

Isotopes of Common Elements Hydrogen has three isotopes. The three isotopes of hydrogen are known as protium (PROHT-ee-uhm), deuterium (doo-TIR-ee-uhm), and tritium (TRIHT-ee-uhm). These isotopes of hydrogen are also called hydrogen-1 (H-1), hydrogen-2 (H-2), and hydrogen-3 (H-3). The numbers 1, 2, and 3 represent the mass numbers of each of the isotopes. An atom of protium (H-1) has only one proton and no neutrons in its nucleus. An atom of deuterium (H-2) has one proton and one neutron. An atom of tritium (H-3) has one proton and two neutrons.

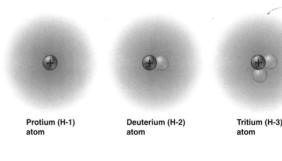

Protium (H-1) atom　　**Deuterium (H-2) atom**　　**Tritium (H-3) atom**

◀ **Figure 3-33**
The three isotopes of hydrogen

72

Teaching Options

◈ INTEGRATING EARTH SCIENCE

Energy From Isotopes Isotopes of hydrogen are involved in the fusion reactions that occur in the Sun. In the Sun, deuterium and tritium nuclei fuse to form helium. A neutron and energy are released by the reaction. Scientists are still researching fusion as an alternative energy source. Have interested students find out some of the difficulties that scientists are having with developing and using nuclear fusion. (It must be done at such high temperatures that no current materials can contain it.)

COOPERATIVE LEARNING

Making a Poster of Isotopes Have pairs of students make a poster, using the colored circles that they prepared for the Chapter Project to model the two isotopes of boron: boron-10 and boron-11. Have students label each isotope. Ask a volunteer to explain what makes both atoms isotopes of boron. Ask another volunteer to explain what makes the isotopes different from each other.
learning styles: visual, interpersonal

All elements have two or more isotopes. Carbon-12 and carbon-14 are two isotopes of the element carbon. These isotopes are also written as C-12 and C-14. Boron-10 (B-10) and boron-11 (B-11) are isotopes of the element boron. Two important isotopes of uranium are uranium-235 (U-235) and uranium-238 (U-238).

4 ▶ LIST: What are the three isotopes of hydrogen called?

✓ CHECKING CONCEPTS

1. What causes some atoms of the same element to have different atomic masses?
2. In the periodic table, where can the atomic mass of an element be found?
3. What identifies an atom of an element?
4. How many neutrons are there in an atom of protium? Deuterium? Tritium?

💡 THINKING CRITICALLY

5. **EXPLAIN:** Why is the atomic mass of an element not a whole number?

6. **CALCULATE:** The atomic number of carbon is 6. How many protons and neutrons are there in an atom of carbon-12? Of carbon-14?

7. **ANALYZE:** The mass number of oxygen is 16. Its atomic mass is 15.999. The atomic number of oxygen is 8. Which of the following statements about the isotopes of oxygen are true? Why?

   a. All of the isotopes have eight neutrons.
   b. All of the isotopes have eight neutrons or more.
   c. Some of the isotopes have fewer than eight neutrons.
   d. All of the isotopes have fewer than eight neutrons.

INTERPRETING VISUALS

Use Figure 3-33 to answer the following questions.

8. **ANALYZE:** Which isotope contains two neutrons in its nucleus?
9. **IDENTIFY:** Which atom has the largest nucleus?
10. **INFER:** What is the atomic number of each isotope?
11. **INFER:** Which isotope has the smallest atomic mass?

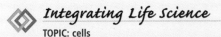

Integrating Life Science

TOPIC: cells

KILLING CANCER CELLS

The human body is made up of trillions of cells. Cells divide and organize themselves to keep the body healthy. They can also replace themselves to promote repair. Cancer occurs when cells cannot control their growth and development. Cancer cells divide, multiply, and spread. These cells can also invade organs. As they invade organs, they damage healthy cells and send out substances that weaken the body.

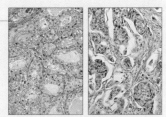

▲ **Figure 3-34** Healthy cells (left) and cancerous cells (right)

Research scientists have uncovered different ways to treat different types of cancer. Radiation therapy is one method. One type of radiation therapy uses radioactive isotopes to kill cancer cells. This type of treatment places radioactive isotopes close to the cancer cells. The high-energy rays from the isotopes attack the cancer cells. Some radioactive isotopes used in this type of therapy are radium-223, gallium-67, iodine-123, and fluorine-18.

Thinking Critically How are radioactive isotopes used to treat certain types of cancer?

CHAPTER 3: Elements and Atoms **73**

---

3 Assess

✓ CHECKING CONCEPTS ANSWERS

1. They have a different number of neutrons.
2. underneath the element's name
3. the number of protons in its nucleus
4. 0; 1; 2

💡 THINKING CRITICALLY ANSWERS

5. **EXPLAIN:** because it is an average of the atomic masses of all the isotopes of that element
6. **CALCULATE:** 6; 8
7. **ANALYZE: c;** Oxygen has 8 protons. The mass number is the number of protons and neutrons, so oxygen usually has 8 neutrons (16 − 8). Because the atomic mass is less than 16, some isotopes of oxygen have fewer than 8 neutrons.

INTERPRETING VISUALS ANSWERS

8. **ANALYZE:** tritium (H-3)
9. **IDENTIFY:** tritium (H-3)
10. **INFER:** 1
11. **INFER:** protium (H-1)

---

4 Close

Integrating Life Science

TOPIC: cells

KILLING CANCER CELLS

Life-Science Connection Although radioactive isotopes are used to treat cancer, some forms of radiation at certain levels can cause cancer. The amount of radiation a person receives while having X-rays and other medical tests involving radiation is carefully controlled. Under controlled conditions, radiation can be used safely.

Discussion Ask students if they have ever had any X-rays taken of their bodies. Ask these students if they noticed whether or not precautions were taken. (The person getting the X-ray has to wear protective clothing, such as a heavy lead apron. The technician should have left the room.) Ask students why precautions have to be followed when taking X-rays. (to protect the body from radiation and to limit the amount of the body exposed to X-rays)

Thinking Critically Answer
The radioactive isotopes are placed close to the cancer cells and give off high-energy rays that attack the cancer cells.

MORE ON THE WEB

Using Isotopes Have students use the Internet to learn about carbon-14 dating. They can visit www.conceptsandchallenges.com for more details.

ONGOING ASSESSMENT

Identifying Atoms and Isotopes Ask students: *What identifies the atoms of an element—the number of protons or the number of neutrons?* (the number of protons) *What does it mean if you have two atoms that have the same number of protons but a different number of neutrons?* (You have isostopes of one element.)

• *TEACHING RESOURCES* •

💿 **Teacher's Resources CD-ROM**
Lesson Review: Chapter 3, p. 14
Enrichment: Chapter 3, p. 15
Model of an Atom: Visuals, p. 5

Lab Activity

(pp. 74–75)

1 Prepare the Lab

Investigating the Modern Model
of the Atom

SET UP TIME: ⏱ **LAB TIME:** 🕐

BACKGROUND: The energy levels in the electron cloud of an atom serve as probable locations of the electrons in the atom. It is impossible to know exactly where an electron in an atom is at any particular time.

PURPOSE: Students will use marks left by the repeated dropping of a marble to investigate and model the electron cloud in the modern theory of the atom.

SCIENCE SKILLS: Students will **observe** and **collect data** as they investigate the atom. They will use their data to **model** the electron cloud of an atom and **infer** how this modeling might help explain the modern theory of the atom.

2 Guide the Lab

PROCEDURE: When students switch roles, have them make sure that the target and chair are in the same location. Discuss data collection and have students copy the data chart before beginning the activity. Provide students with a copy of the Lab Activity Report found on the Teacher's Resources CD-ROM for students to record their observations and conclusions.
learning styles: visual, kinesthetic

TROUBLESHOOTING: Be sure students understand that each mark left behind by the marble represents one possible position of the electron. Observe students and make sure that they are letting the marble drop straight down and not throwing it or changing its direction in any way. Remind students that no electrons are found in the nucleus of an atom (the center of the target).

LAB ACTIVITY
Investigating the Modern Model of the Atom

Materials
2 Sheets of white paper
2 Sheets of carbon paper
Drawing compass
Cardboard
Thumbtack or push pin
Marble

▲ **Figure 3-35** Paper targets

BACKGROUND

Over the past 100 years, the model of the atom has gone through several changes. Our current understanding is that protons and neutrons are found in the atom's center, the nucleus. The electrons are found in an electron cloud. An electron cloud shows the different locations in which an electron can be found. The cloud surrounds the nucleus of an atom.

PURPOSE

In this activity, you will use a target as a model to investigate the nucleus and the electron cloud of an atom according to the modern theory of the atom.

PROCEDURE

1. Copy the chart in Figure 3-36.

2. Work with a partner. Place 2 sheets of carbon paper side by side shiny-side up on a flat surface. Cover each sheet of carbon paper with a sheet of white paper.

3. Use a drawing compass to draw a circle with a diameter of 20 cm on each sheet of white paper. These circles will be your "targets."

4. Place one target with its sheet of carbon paper on a piece of cardboard. Insert a thumbtack or push pin into the center of the target.

Trial	Observations
#1	
#2	

▲ **Figure 3-36** Copy this chart and use it to record your observations.

74

Teaching Options

COOPERATIVE LEARNING

Studying Classroom Data After students have observed all the targets, have students work in their groups to study the results. Ask a volunteer from each group to tell the class how the group's results compare to the classroom results. Make sure that students understand that a group's results may be different from the classroom results. Using classroom results greatly increases the number of trials, and by doing so increases the validity of the observations. Ask volunteers to explain how the models they made represent the modern model of the atom.
learning styles: auditory, interpersonal

ESL/ELL STRATEGY

Filling in Data Charts When filling in a data chart, it may be helpful for English-language learners to add illustrations as well as describe their observations.

5. Carefully stand on a chair. While holding a marble in one hand, extend your arm so that it is about 2 m above the floor. Have your partner position the target directly below the marble.

6. Drop the marble on the target. Have your partner catch the marble on the first bounce and return it to you. Repeat this step 50 times.

7. Remove the target from the cardboard and turn over the sheet of white paper. Describe the pattern of dots for Trial #1 on your chart.

8. Switch roles with your partner for Trial #2. Using a new target, repeat steps 4 through 7.

▲ STEP 4 Drop the marble on the target.

▲ STEP 5 Spots on the target show where the marble was dropped.

CONCLUSIONS

1. MODEL: What do the marks made by the marble-drops on the target represent?

2. INFER: What does the thumbtack in the center of the target represent? What is indicated by the fact that no marks were found in the center of the model?

3. COMPARE: Do you expect the other groups to get the same pattern? Explain your answer.

4. INFER: How might this experiment help to illustrate the modern theory of an atom?

5. ANALYZE: The atomic model proposed by Niels Bohr states that electrons are found in energy levels much like planets moving in orbits around the Sun. How is the electron cloud different from the orbits of planets moving around the Sun?

Tips for Using Technology

Databases Have students use database software to record their observations. Databases allow students to enter and edit information, store and organize a lot of information easily, and search for specific information. Databases also allow students to arrange information by putting it in a specific order and to present information by using special layouts. Have students use the Database Planner on the Teacher's Resources CD-ROM to plan their databases.

• TEACHING RESOURCES •

Teacher's Resources CD-ROM
Lab Activity Report: Study Tools, pp. 16–17
Laboratory Activity Rubric: Teaching Tools, p. 8
Database Planner: Study Tools, p. 22

SAFETY TIP: Tell students to be careful while standing on the chair and dropping the marbles.

EXPECTED OUTCOME: Students should observe a pattern of marks within the circle, with no marks in the center of the circle. The patterns for the two trials will be different.

LAB HINT: It may be helpful to create a display of all the targets to show the variety of patterns produced.

3 Conclude the Lab

1. MODEL: Each mark on the target represents the possible location of an electron in an electron cloud.
2. INFER: The thumbtack represents the nucleus of the atom. The lack of marks in the center of the model indicates that electrons are not present in the nucleus of an atom.
3. COMPARE: Possible answer: Yes, because each group followed the same procedure and performed multiple trials.
4. INFER: Even though there were many marks on the target, most of the target remained empty space, like an atom. Although it was not possible to predict exactly where the marble would land, there was an area of probability, like electrons in the electron cloud.
5. ANALYZE: The position of an electron is not known, but the position of a planet is. A planet stays in a predictable orbit, but an electron does not.

Use the Laboratory Activity Rubric on the Teacher's Resources CD-ROM to assess students' lab activities. Fill in the rubric with the additional information below. For this activity, students should have:

- performed the activity according to the procedure and filled in the chart with data collected during the activity.

- correctly answered the questions in complete sentences.

4 Extend the Lab

Place an electric fan in the front of the classroom. Place a sticker of a different color on each blade. Turn on the fan and have students observe. Ask them where each blade is. Students will notice that the blades are filling all the space in the fan, but they are moving so quickly that you cannot tell where a particular blade is located at any time. Ask students to explain how an operating fan is like electrons in an electron cloud.

Challenges (pp. 76–78)

Chapter Summary

Review Before students begin the Challenges, review the summary with them. If time permits, have students work in pairs. Give each pair of students one summary point to describe in their own words.

✎ **STUDY HINT** Have students write a paragraph using the Key Terms correctly. Encourage them to use more than one Key Term in a sentence. Then, have them exchange and read each other's paragraphs. **learning style: linguistic**

Key Term Challenges

MATCHING

1. mass number (3-5)
2. electron (3-3)
3. atomic number (3-4)
4. atom (3-2)
5. neutron (3-3)
6. isotope (3-10)

FILL IN

7. noble gases (3-9)
8. periodic (3-7)
9. nucleus (3-3)
10. elements (3-1)
11. energy level (3-6)
12. groups (3-7)

Chapter Summary

Lesson 3-1
• **Elements** are substances that cannot be chemically broken down into simpler substances.

Lesson 3-2
• An **atom** is the smallest part of an element that can be identified as that element.

Lesson 3-3
• Atoms are made up of **protons**, **neutrons**, and **electrons**.

Lesson 3-4
• The **atomic number** of an element is the number of protons in the nucleus of an atom of that element.

Lesson 3-5
• The total mass of the protons and neutrons in an atom is the **atomic mass** of that atom.
• The **mass number** of an element is equal to the number of protons and neutrons in the nucleus of an atom of that element.

Lesson 3-6
• Electrons are arranged in **energy levels** around the nucleus of an atom.

Lesson 3-7
• In the modern periodic table, elements are arranged in order of increasing atomic number.

Lesson 3-8
• A zigzag line on the periodic table separates the **metals** from the **nonmetals**.

Lesson 3-9
• The **halogens** are the five elements in Group 17 in the periodic table.
• The **noble gases** are the six elements in Group 18 in the periodic table.

Lesson 3-10
• Atoms of the same element that have different numbers of neutrons are called **isotopes**.

76

Key Term Challenges

atom (p. 54)	luster (p. 68)
atomic mass (p. 60)	malleable (p. 68)
atomic number (p. 58)	mass number (p. 60)
chemical symbol (p. 64)	metal (p. 68)
ductile (p. 68)	neutron (p. 56)
electron (p. 56)	noble gases (p. 70)
element (p. 52)	nonmetal (p. 68)
energy level (p. 62)	nucleus (p. 56)
group (p. 64)	period (p. 64)
halogens (p. 70)	periodic (p. 64)
isotope (p. 72)	proton (p. 56)

MATCHING Write the Key Term from above that best matches each description.

1. number of protons and neutrons in the nucleus of an atom
2. particle in an atom that has a negative charge
3. number of protons in the nucleus of an atom
4. smallest part of an element that can be identified as that element
5. particle in the nucleus of an atom that does not have any charge
6. has the same number of protons but a different number of neutrons

FILL IN Write the Key Term from above that best completes each statement.

7. The _____ are found in Group 18 of the periodic table.
8. A repeating pattern is _____.
9. The center, or core, of an atom is called the _____.
10. There are more than 100 known _____.
11. An _____ is the place in the electron cloud where electrons are most likely to be found.
12. There are 18 columns or _____ on the periodic table.

Teaching Options

PREPARING STUDENTS FOR STANDARDIZED TESTS

Reading Strategy: Tell students to identify the key words in the question and then locate those words in the paragraph. This will help them quickly find the information they need to answer the question.

Writing Strategy: Have students check their writing to ensure that their total number of responses matches the total number of questions.

Interpreting Visuals: Remind students to examine all of the visuals that pertain to a particular question or set of questions.

ESL/ELL STRATEGY

Word Bank Have students create a word bank of Key Terms from this list. Suggest that students classify related words into groups, such as *ductile*, *malleable*, and *luster*. This can be done by scanning the lessons to see which terms were presented in each lesson.

Content Challenges TEST PREP

MULTIPLE CHOICE **Write the letter of the term or phrase that best completes each statement.**

1. In the early 1800s, an atomic theory of matter was developed by
   a. Democritus.
   b. Dalton.
   c. Rutherford.
   d. Thomson.

2. The first scientist to suggest that atoms contain smaller particles was
   a. Thomson.
   b. Rutherford.
   c. Bohr.
   d. Dalton.

3. Rutherford pictured atoms as being made mostly of
   a. empty space.
   b. positively charged material.
   c. electrons.
   d. the nucleus.

4. Rutherford's model of the atom included
   a. a small central core.
   b. a positive material filled with electrons.
   c. energy levels for electrons.
   d. neutrons.

5. Niels Bohr proposed that electrons
   a. orbit the nucleus.
   b. are inside the nucleus.
   c. do not exist.
   d. cannot be located exactly in an atom.

6. If an electron gains enough energy,
   a. it jumps to a higher energy level.
   b. it falls to a lower energy level.
   c. it gives off light.
   d. it falls into the nucleus.

7. The atomic number of an atom is equal to
   a. the number of protons and neutrons.
   b. the number of electrons and neutrons.
   c. the number of protons.
   d. the number of protons and electrons.

8. The letters *amu* stand for
   a. atomic measuring unit.
   b. alternate mass unit.
   c. atomic mass unit.
   d. atomic matter unit.

9. Tritium is an
   a. electron energy level.
   b. isotope of hydrogen.
   c. element with atomic number 102.
   d. isotope of carbon.

10. Argon and krypton are
    a. metals.
    b. protons.
    c. neutrons.
    d. noble gases.

TRUE/FALSE **Write *true* if the statement is true. If the statement is false, change the underlined term to make the statement true.**

11. An isotope of an element has the same number of protons but a different number of <u>electrons</u>.

12. The second energy level can hold <u>eight</u> electrons.

13. Scientists <u>can</u> predict the exact location of an electron in an atom.

14. The number of protons and <u>electrons</u> in a neutral atom must be equal.

Content Challenges

MULTIPLE CHOICE

1. b (3-2)
2. a (3-3)
3. a (3-3)
4. a (3-3)
5. a (3-3)
6. a (3-6)
7. c (3-4)
8. c (3-5)
9. b (3-10)
10. d (3-9)

TRUE/FALSE

11. false; neutrons (3-10)
12. true (3-6)
13. false; cannot (3-3, 3-6)
14. true (3-4)

ALTERNATIVE ASSESSMENT

Element Bulletin Board Divide the class into four groups. Have each group choose a different element and prepare a bulletin board or other display about the element. Be sure that the display includes the element's name, chemical symbol, discovery, atomic number, atomic mass, state of matter, location in the periodic table, properties, and uses.
learning styles: interpersonal, visual

PORTFOLIO ASSESSMENT

Making Student Portfolios Portfolio Assessment provides an opportunity for students who are generally not good test-takers to demonstrate their learning in another way. Students can demonstrate their comprehension of the concepts in this chapter by making a portfolio. The Concept Map, the Big Idea Planner, and the Chapter Self-Check are some of the reproducibles on the Teacher's Resources CD-ROM that they can include in their portfolios. You can use the Portfolio Assessment Rubric also found on the Teacher's Resources CD-ROM to assess students' portfolios.

Concept Challenges

WRITTEN RESPONSE

1. **EXPLAIN:** He performed experiments investigating the properties of gases and made observations. (3-2)
2. **COMPARE:** They all thought elements were composed of atoms. Thomson and Rutherford both concluded that atoms were made up of positively and negatively charged parts. Thomson hypothesized that an atom was made up of positively charged material with negatively charged particles scattered evenly throughout. Rutherford discovered that an atom is mostly empty space with a central core, or nucleus, that contains positively charged particles. (3-2, 3-3)
3. **ANALYZE:** An element's mass number is always a whole number because it is the sum of the number of protons and neutrons in the nucleus of an atom. The same element's atomic mass is not a whole number because it is an average of the total mass of protons and neutrons in all the isotopes of the element. (3-5)
4. **PREDICT:** An atom of nitrogen has five electrons in its second energy level. (3-6)
5. **COMPARE:** Possible answer: Metals have the properties of luster, ductility, and malleability. Nonmetals do not have these properties. (3-8)

INTERPRETING A DIAGRAM (3-6)

6. 17
7. 2
8. 17
9. 35
10. chlorine

Chapter Project Wrap-Up

MODELS OF ATOMS AND THEIR PARTS

Have students assemble their models on posterboard. Students' projects can be exhibited around the classroom. Students can present their models to the class or move around the room to study other students' models. You can use the Individual Activity Rubric found on the Teacher's Resources CD-ROM to assess students' projects. Fill in the rubric with the additional information below. For this project, students should have:

- accurately labeled models of the atoms that they read about.
- organized a logical and neat overall presentation.

Concept Challenges TEST PREP

WRITTEN RESPONSE Answer each of the following questions in complete sentences.

1. **EXPLAIN:** How did Dalton come to the conclusion that matter is made up of atoms?
2. **COMPARE:** In what ways did Dalton, Thomson, and Rutherford have similar ideas about atoms? In what ways did their ideas differ?
3. **ANALYZE:** Why is the atomic mass of an element not a whole number, whereas the mass number is always a whole number?
4. **PREDICT:** How many electrons would be found in the second energy level of an atom of nitrogen, which has an atomic number of 7?
5. **COMPARE:** How are metals different from nonmetals?

INTERPRETING A DIAGRAM Use Figure 3-37 to answer the following questions.

6. How many electrons are in an atom of element *x*?
7. How many electrons are in the first energy level in an atom of element *x*?
8. How many protons are in an atom of element *x*?
9. If there are 18 neutrons in an atom of element *x*, what is the mass number of an atom of element *x*?
10. Use the periodic table on pages 66 and 67 to identify element *x*.

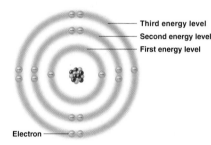

▲ **Figure 3-37** Element *x*

78

Teaching Options

UNIT CHALLENGE ONLINE

Know Your Elements Send students to www.conceptsand challenges.com. Have them complete the online activity for Unit 4. Students will research elements and assemble their findings in a wall-sized display organized like the periodic table. Students will write riddles about an element for other students to solve. Have students post their results on the Online Classroom Database.

• TEACHING RESOURCES •

Teacher's Resources CD-ROM

Key Term Review: Chapter 3, p. 16

Chapter 3 Test: pp. 17–19

Concept Map: Study Tools, p. 4

The Big Idea Planner: Study Tools, p. 11–12

Chapter Self-Check: Teaching Tools, p. 11

Portfolio Assessment Rubric: Teaching Tools, p. 10

Individual Activity Rubric: Teaching Tools, p. 5

PLANNING GUIDE

◆ **TEACHING THE CHAPTER** This chapter should take approximately 8–11 days to complete instruction and assessment.

	Skills and Features	Projects and Activities	Achieve Science Literacy	Meet Individual Needs
Chapter 4 Opener p. T79	IDENTIFY	• Chapter Project		
Lesson 4-1 **What are three types of matter?** pp. T80–T81 Standards: B1a, B1c	ANALYZE, HYPOTHESIZE, IDENTIFY • Investigate • Web Infosearch • People in Science	• Cooperative Learning	• Study Hint • Ongoing Assessment	• Reteach ⊙ CD-ROM Venn Diagram
Lesson 4-2 **What is a compound?** pp. T82–T83 Standards: B1b, B1c	CONTRAST, EXPLAIN, NAME • Health and Safety Tip	• Cooperative Learning • More on the Web	• Study Hint • Reading Strategy	• Reteach ⊙ CD-ROM Concept Map
Lesson 4-3 **What is a mixture?** pp. T84–T85 Standard: B1a	CLASSIFY, EXPLAIN, CONTRAST • Investigate • Designing an Experiment • Real-Life Science	• More on the Web	• Study Hint	⊙ CD-ROM KWL chart Designing an Experiment
Lesson 4-4 **How are mixtures and compounds different?** pp. T86–T87 Standards: B1a, B1b	COMPARE, EXPLAIN, INFER • Integrating Earth Science	• Extending the Lesson • More on the Web	• Study Hint • Writing Hint	• ESL/ELL Strategy • Reteach
Lab Activity **Separating Mixtures** pp. T88–T89 Standard: B1a	INFER, ANALYZE, IDENTIFY • Set-Up Time: 10 min • Lab Time: 30 min	• Integrating the Sciences • Extend the Lab Activity • Lab Skills Worksheet	• Tips for Using Technology	⊙ CD-ROM Lab Activity Report Spreadsheet
Lesson 4-5 **What is an ionic bond?** pp. T90–T91 Standard: B1b	DEFINE, INFER, MODEL • Building Science Skills • How Do They Know That?	• Cooperative Learning • Extending the Lesson • More on the Web	• Study Hint • Ongoing Assessment	⊙ CD-ROM Enrichment Activity Crystal Shapes

Planning Guide continues on next page.

Standards: For details on the correlation to National Science Standards see pages *xx–xxi*.

Compounds and Mixtures *(Planning Guide continued)*

	Skills and Features	Projects and Activities	Achieve Science Literacy	Meet Individual Needs
Lesson 4-6 **What is a covalent bond?** pp. T92–T93 Standard: B1b	CLASSIFY, COMPARE, IDENTIFY • Hands-On Activity	• Extending the Lesson • More on the Web • Lab Challenge	• Study Hint • Reading Strategy • Ongoing Assessment	• ESL/ELL Strategy CD-ROM Writing Activity Outline Venn Diagram
Lesson 4-7 **What is an organic compound?** pp. T94– T95 Standard: B1c	DEFINE, IDENTIFY, EXPLAIN • Interpreting Visuals • Science and Technology	• Extending the Lesson • More on the Web • Integrating Chemistry	• Study Hint • Ongoing Assessment	CD-ROM Enrichment Activity
Lesson 4-8 **What organic compounds are needed by living things?** pp. T96– T97 Standard: B1c	DESCRIBE, RELATE, ORGANIZE • Building Science Skills • Real-Life Science	• Extending the Lesson • More on the Web	• Study Hint • Writing Hint	• ESL/ELL Strategy
Big Idea **What organisms produce poisonous compounds?** pp. T98– T99 Standard: B1c	RESEARCH, COMMUNICATE, ANALYZE • Science Log: Writing Activity	• Big Idea Online • Close Activity	• Tips for Using Technology	CD-ROM Big Idea Planner
Chapter 4 Challenges pp. T100–T102	• Chapter Summary • Key Term Challenges • Content Challenges • Concept Challenges	• Chapter Project Wrap-Up	• Study Hint • Preparing Students for Standardized Tests	• ESL/ELL Strategy CD-ROM Chapter Self-Check Venn Diagram

Teacher Notes

Chapter 4 Compounds and Mixtures

▲ Figure 4-1 Mount Rushmore, South Dakota

Can you recognize the four faces carved in Figure 4-1? The faces are those of George Washington, Thomas Jefferson, Theodore Roosevelt, and Abraham Lincoln—four American presidents. The memorial is carved out of granite. Granite is a hard rock that is actually made up of other types of matter. Granite keeps the properties of the different types of matter that it is made up of.

▶Why do you think the memorial is carved out of granite?

Contents

Chapter 4
Compounds and Mixtures

Chapter Overview

In this chapter, students will learn that matter can be classified into three main types: elements, compounds, and mixtures. They will explain the ways in which mixtures and compounds are different. Students will also differentiate between ionic and covalent bonds and learn that organic compounds contain carbon. Finally, they will describe the organic compounds that sustain living organisms.

About Figure 4-1 Each carved face on Mount Rushmore is about 20 m (60 ft) tall. The bluff into which the faces are carved is made entirely of granite. Granite, which is usually whitish or gray with dark speckles, is a mixture of three main minerals: feldspar, quartz, and mica. Granite is an important building stone. It has greater strength than limestone or marble.

Answer Granite is strong, so the carvings will hold their shape and not crumble. The monument will last for a long time.

Linking Prior Knowledge

For this chapter, students should recall:
- the properties of matter (Lesson 1-2).
- the definition of elements (Lesson 3-1).
- the parts of an atom (Lesson 3-3).

Chapter Project

ELEMENTS, COMPOUNDS, AND MIXTURES CROSSWORD PUZZLE

MATERIALS: paper, pencils

Divide students into pairs. After reading the chapter, pairs will create their own crossword puzzles. They can use the Key Terms and concepts that they learned in the chapter as clues and answers in their puzzles. Allow pairs to solve the puzzles of the other pairs. You may also wish to make copies of all the puzzles to use as studying tools.

Teaching Options

ASSESSMENT PLANNER

For assessment in the Student Edition, see the following pages:

Content Assessment
Checking Concepts: pp. 81, 83, 85, 87, 91, 93, 95, 97
Thinking Critically: pp. 81, 83, 85, 87, 91, 93, 95, 97
Chapter Challenges: pp. 100–102

Alternative Assessment
Building Skills: pp. 91, 97
Web InfoSearch: p. 81
Science Log: p. 99

Performance-Based Assessment
Hands-On Activity: p. 93
Designing an Experiment: p. 85
Lab Activity: pp. 88–89

• TEACHING RESOURCES •

Teacher's Resources CD-ROM
Lesson Review: Ch. 4, pp. 2, 3, 4, 5, 6, 8, 9, 12
Enrichment: Ch. 4, pp. 7, 10, 11
Key Term Review: Ch. 4, p. 14
Chapter 4 Test: pp. 15–17
Laboratory Manual: pp. 13–14, 33–36

1 Introduce

🔍 INVESTIGATE

TIME: 10–15 minutes

PURPOSE: Students will classify different types of matter as either elements or not elements.

MATERIALS: paper, pencils, various types of matter to classify (See Procedure for examples.)

PROCEDURE: Gather materials for students to classify. For "Not Elements," you could include items such as salt, sugar, a rock, or a glass full of water. For "Elements," you might use items such as an aluminum can, gold foil, or a copper wire. You could also include pictures of elements such as silver and gold. Have students work in pairs. Allow students to refer to the periodic table on pages 66 and 67. For samples of substances, have students analyze both the container and the contents of the container.
learning styles: visual, tactile

THINK ABOUT IT: The objects that are not elements are made of combinations of elements.

📝 **STUDY HINT** Ask volunteers to read the Key Terms aloud. Then, invite students to restate the definitions of *element, compound,* and *mixture* in their own words.

Linking Prior Knowledge Have students recall what they learned about matter (Lesson 1-2) and elements (Lesson 3-1).

2 Teach

Demonstration Create a mixture of sugar and cinnamon. Show students how the amount of each substance can be varied, but the result is still a mixture.
learning styles: visual, auditory

Answers to questions

1. LIST: Possible answer: by one characteristic, such as size, shape, or color

2. IDENTIFY: elements, compounds, and mixtures

3. DEFINE: A substance is any element or compound.

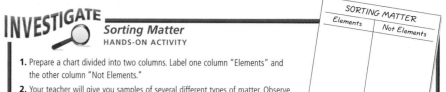

4-1 What are three types of matter?

INVESTIGATE **Sorting Matter**
HANDS-ON ACTIVITY

1. Prepare a chart divided into two columns. Label one column "Elements" and the other column "Not Elements."
2. Your teacher will give you samples of several different types of matter. Observe each type of matter.
3. Write the name of each type of matter in one of the two columns. Refer to the periodic table on pages 66 and 67 to help you identify which ones are elements.

THINK ABOUT IT: What do you think the objects that are not elements are made of?

▲ Figure 4-2

Objective
Describe similarities and differences among elements, compounds, and mixtures.

Key Terms
element: substance that cannot be chemically broken down into simpler substances

compound: substance made up of two or more elements that are chemically combined

mixture: two or more substances that have been physically combined

substance: any element or compound

Organizing Matter You may have items that you like to collect, such as rocks, stamps, sea glass, or baseball cards. If you do, you may sort your collection based on different or similar characteristics, such as size, shape, date, or team. Kinds of matter can be sorted, too. Just like you might sort your collection based on one characteristic, matter can be organized, or classified, into three groups based on the makeup of the matter.

▶ **LIST:** What are some of the ways to organize a collection?

Elements, Compounds, and Mixtures Matter can be classified into three main types—elements, compounds, and mixtures. You have learned that an **element** is made up of only one kind of atom. For example, pure gold is always made up of

atoms that contain 79 protons. A **compound** is made up of atoms of two or more elements that are chemically combined. The elements in a given compound are always combined in a fixed ratio. For example, every particle of the compound baking soda is made up of one atom of sodium, one atom of hydrogen, one atom of carbon, and three atoms of oxygen.

A **mixture** is made up of two or more kinds of matter that are physically combined, or mixed together. The kinds of matter in a mixture can be present in any amounts. A mixture of sugar and cinnamon can contain any amount of sugar and any amount of cinnamon.

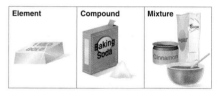

▲ Figure 4-3 Examples of the three main types of matter

▶ **IDENTIFY:** What are the three main types of matter?

Substances Elements and compounds share a similar characteristic. Every sample of an element has the same exact properties as every other sample. Similarly, all samples of a given compound have the same exact properties as every other sample of that compound. For example, the

Teaching Options

COOPERATIVE LEARNING

Playing a Game In three corners of the room, place a sign, one each for *element, compound,* and *mixture.* Give pairs of students an object or a picture. Pairs can confer to decide whether they have an element, a compound, or a mixture and then go to the appropriate corner of the room. Once there, they can check their answers with classmates. Repeat with additional pictures.
learning styles: visual, kinesthetic

ONGOING ASSESSMENT

Drawing a Venn Diagram Draw a Venn diagram on the board or use the Venn diagram reproducible on the Teacher's Resources CD-ROM. Label the circles *compound* and *mixture.* Have students supply details to show how compounds and mixtures are alike and how they are different. **learning styles: visual, linguistic**

copper used to make a teakettle will have the same properties as the copper used to make an electric wire. A sample of pure sugar, a compound used to sweeten coffee, will be identical to a sample of pure sugar used to make candy. Because they share this characteristic, elements and compounds are classified as substances. A **substance** is any element or compound.

▷ DEFINE: What is a substance?

✓ CHECKING CONCEPTS

1. Matter is classified into three groups based on the _____ of the matter.
2. An _____ is made up of only one kind of atom.
3. A _____ is made up of atoms of different elements that are chemically combined.
4. The elements in a given compound are always combined in a _____ ratio.
5. A _____ is made up of two or more different kinds of matter that are physically combined.
6. The amounts of the different kinds of matter in a _____ can vary.
7. A _____ is any element or compound.

THINKING CRITICALLY

8. ANALYZE: A sample of matter is made up of three different atoms that are chemically combined. What type of matter is it? How do you know?
9. HYPOTHESIZE: A substance is made up of two atoms of oxygen. Is it an element or a compound? How do you know?

Web InfoSearch

Properties Substances can be recognized by their physical and chemical properties. These properties can be labeled as *extensive properties* and *intensive properties*. Extensive properties include weight and mass. Intensive properties include melting point and boiling point.

SEARCH: Use the Internet to find out more about these types of properties. List other intensive and extensive properties. Start your search at www.conceptsandchallenges.com. Some key search words are **intensive properties** and **extensive properties.**

People in Science

ROBERT BOYLE (1627–1691)

The Irish-born scientist Robert Boyle was the first scientist to establish the scientific method of experimentation to test hypotheses. He questioned the early belief that materials were made up of four elements—earth, air, fire, and water. He believed that the basic elements of matter were "corpuscles." These corpuscles, or particles, could be found in various types and sizes, and could arrange themselves into groups called mixtures and compounds. Robert Boyle also showed that the properties of a compound are different from those of the particles that it is made up of.

Robert Boyle contributed a vast amount of knowledge to the scientific world. His work with gases and pressure led to Boyle's law. He is also credited with the invention of the match.

▲ **Figure 4-4** Robert Boyle

Thinking Critically Robert Boyle believed that the basic elements of matter were corpuscles. What would a modern scientist call these basic elements of matter?

3 Assess

✓ CHECKING CONCEPTS ANSWERS

1. makeup
2. element
3. compound
4. fixed
5. mixture
6. mixture
7. substance

THINKING CRITICALLY ANSWERS

8. ANALYZE: The sample is a compound. It is more than one element, and the elements are chemically combined, not just mixed.
9. HYPOTHESIZE: It is an element. It is made of only one type of atom.

4 Close

Web InfoSearch

Properties Have students use the Internet to find out more about the extensive properties and intensive properties of substances. Have students begin their search at www.conceptsandchallenges.com.

People in Science

ROBERT BOYLE (1627–1691)

Interdisciplinary Connection Before Robert Boyle, the field of chemistry was considered mystical. For hundreds of years, alchemists performed experiments in their attempts to change common metals into precious metals. Alchemy was not completely founded in science, but it did lead to the sciences of medicine and chemistry. Boyle helped chemistry become an experimental science for studying the composition of substances.

Discussion Ask students: *Which of Boyle's ideas about the makeup of materials are still thought to be scientifically accurate today?* (Matter can be arranged into mixtures and compounds; the properties of a compound are different from those of the substances from which it is made.)

Thinking Critically Answer
Modern scientists would call them atoms.

RETEACH

Understanding Elements and Compounds Students can use their knowledge of color to help them understand the difference between elements and compounds. Ask students to explain how the color green is made with paints. They will remember that green is a mixture of yellow and blue. Remind students that there are some colors, such as yellow, that are not created by mixing, but are instead pure colors. These colors can be compared to elements. Other colors, such as green, are created when colors are mixed together. These colors can be compared to compounds.

• TEACHING RESOURCES •

💿 **Teacher's Resources CD-ROM**
Lesson Review: Chapter 4, p. 2
Venn Diagram: Study Tools, p. 10

1 Introduce

STUDY HINT Before beginning this lesson, have students scan the lesson to look for unfamiliar words. Have students work in pairs or small groups to define each of the words on their lists.

Linking Prior Knowledge Ask students to compare elements, compounds, and mixtures. Students should name examples of each and explain why the example is an element, a compound, or a mixture.

2 Teach

Demonstration Heat a small sample of sugar in a test tube. Be sure to follow laboratory safety procedures, such as wearing safety goggles and an apron. Ask students to observe what happens as the sugar is heated. They should notice that the sugar turns into a liquid and then into a black solid. Point out that the black solid is carbon. The compound sugar is much different from its parts: carbon, oxygen, and hydrogen. **learning style: visual**

Discussion Ask students to suppose that they are using a recipe to make cookies. The recipe calls for salt. Have students look at Figure 4-6. Sodium is a metal, and chlorine is a poisonous gas. (Make sure that students understand that sodium is the substance that is glowing and not the liquid, which is water.) Ask students if they would put sodium chloride in the batter. Inform students that another name for salt is sodium chloride. However, the compound salt is very different from the two elements—sodium and chlorine—that make it up. **learning style: visual**

Answers to questions

1 EXPLAIN: a substance made up of two or more elements that are chemically combined

2 NAME: calcium, carbon, and oxygen

3 CONTRAST: Sodium is an active metal; chlorine is a yellow, poisonous gas; and sodium chloride, or salt, is a relatively harmless substance that can be eaten.

4-2 What is a compound?

Objectives

Explain that a compound is made up of two or more elements. Describe how chemical bonds form new substances.

Key Terms

molecule: smallest part of a substance that has all the properties of that substance

chemical bond: force of attraction that holds atoms together

Combining Elements An element can combine with other elements to form a new substance called a compound. A compound is a substance made up of two or more elements that are chemically combined. For example, hydrogen and oxygen are elements. They are both gases with very different properties at room temperature. When these two elements chemically combine, they can form two different compounds that are liquids at room temperature. You are familiar with one of these compounds. It is water. The other compound is hydrogen peroxide, a substance used to clean cuts.

1 EXPLAIN: What is a compound?

Common Compounds Sugar is a compound. It is made of carbon, hydrogen, and oxygen. Table salt is a compound, too. It is made of the elements sodium and chlorine. You may be familiar with some of the compounds listed in Figure 4-5.

SOME COMMON COMPOUNDS	
Compound	Elements
Sand	Silicon, oxygen
Hydrogen peroxide	Hydrogen, oxygen
Chalk	Calcium, carbon, oxygen
Rust	Iron, oxygen

▲ Figure 4-5

2 NAME: What elements are in chalk?

82

Properties of Compounds The properties of a compound are very different from the properties of the elements that make it up. Some elements that make up a compound may be dangerous. But a compound formed from these elements may be relatively harmless. For example, sodium is a very active metal. Chlorine is a yellow, poisonous gas. When combined, these elements make up the compound sodium chloride, or table salt.

▲ **Figure 4-6** The active metal sodium (left) chemically combines with the poisonous gas chlorine (right) to form table salt.

3 CONTRAST: What are the properties of sodium, chlorine, and sodium chloride?

Molecules Most compounds are made of molecules. A **molecule** is the smallest part of a substance that has all the properties of that substance. A molecule can be a single atom or may be made up of a great many atoms. For example, a molecule of iron is a single iron atom. A molecule of sucrose, a type of sugar, is made up of 45 atoms.

Silicon dioxide is a compound found in sand. It is made of the elements silicon and oxygen. One molecule of silicon dioxide is made from one atom of silicon and two atoms of oxygen. A single molecule of silicon dioxide has all the properties of silicon dioxide. Just as all the atoms of an element are alike, all the molecules of a compound are alike.

4 DEFINE: What is a molecule?

Teaching Options

RETEACH

Modeling Molecules Use interlocking building blocks to create a model of water. Blue blocks can represent hydrogen, and white blocks can represent oxygen. Make one molecule with two blue blocks and one white block and say: *This is a water molecule. The blue blocks represent the two atoms of hydrogen and the white block represents the one atom of oxygen.* You may wish to model other molecules for students to observe. **learning style: visual**

COOPERATIVE LEARNING

Illustrating Compounds Students can find or draw pictures of items that contain the compounds in Figure 4-5. The class can then create a large Compound Web, with the drawings or illustrations organized in sections of the web. Students can also use the Concept Map found on the Teacher's Resources CD-ROM.

Breaking Down Compounds A compound is formed as a result of a chemical change. The elements in a compound combine by forming chemical bonds between the atoms. A **chemical bond** is the force of attraction that holds atoms in a molecule together. Atoms bond together to form molecules. When bonding occurs, a new substance with its own properties is formed.

A chemical change can also cause the molecules that make up a compound to break down into simpler substances. In order to break the molecules down, the chemical bonds holding the atoms together have to be broken. Heating a compound is one way to break it down. When sugar is heated, it melts. If the melted sugar is heated long enough, hydrogen and oxygen enter the air in the form of water vapor. Finally, only a black solid remains. This solid is the element carbon. So, heating sugar can cause it to break down into water, containing hydrogen and oxygen, and carbon. These are the elements that make up sugar.

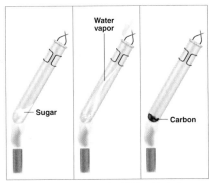

▲ **Figure 4-7** Heating sugar can break it down into simpler substances.

Another way to break down a compound is by using electricity. Scientists working in laboratories can obtain hydrogen gas and oxygen gas by passing electricity through a sample of slightly acidic water.

▶5 EXPLAIN: How can a compound be broken down into the elements that make it up?

✔ **CHECKING CONCEPTS**

1. A compound is made up of two or more _____.

2. The compound _____ is made up of the elements hydrogen, oxygen, and carbon.

3. The properties of a compound are _____ from the properties of the elements that form it.

4. A _____ is the smallest part of a substance that has all the properties of that substance.

5. A compound is formed as a result of a _____.

6. A _____ is the force of attraction that holds atoms together.

7. Using heat and electricity can _____ a compound into the elements that make up the compound.

THINKING CRITICALLY

8. INFER: A recipe calls for a cup of sugar to be heated slowly over a low flame. What could happen if the sugar is heated slowly over a high flame?

9. HYPOTHESIZE: When an unknown solid is heated, two different gases and a liquid are formed. Is the solid a compound or an element? How do you know?

10. ANALYZE: How is a molecule different from an atom?

HEALTH AND SAFETY TIP

The compound carbon monoxide is a deadly gas. It is difficult to detect because it is odorless and colorless. Carbon monoxide can be produced by the incomplete burning of fuels in cars and in heating furnaces. If it is inhaled in small amounts, it can cause people to feel sleepy. If it is inhaled in large amounts, it can cause death. Why do you think having a carbon monoxide detector in your home is a good idea?

◀4 DEFINE: the smallest part of a substance that has all the properties of that substance

◀5 EXPLAIN: by using heat or electricity to break chemical bonds

📖 READING STRATEGY Ask students to think about the definition of a compound word and to give some examples. Tell them to think about that definition as they read about compound substances in this lesson.

3 Assess

✔ **CHECKING CONCEPTS ANSWERS**

1. elements
2. sugar
3. different
4. molecule
5. chemical change
6. chemical bond
7. break down

THINKING CRITICALLY ANSWERS

8. INFER: The sugar could break down into carbon, hydrogen, and oxygen.

9. HYPOTHESIZE: The solid is a compound. Heating caused the solid to break down into several parts with different properties.

10. ANALYZE: A molecule is the smallest part of a substance that has all the properties of that substance. A molecule may be only one atom, but most molecules are made up of two or more atoms.

4 Close

HEALTH AND SAFETY TIP

Carbon monoxide is an important fuel in industry. The carbon in the fuel makes it valuable as a heating agent. In the air, however, it can be poisonous. As little as 1/1000 of 1 percent of carbon monoxide in the air can cause symptoms of poisoning, such as headaches, nausea, and fatigue. In urban areas, carbon monoxide from automobile emissions is a major source of pollution. A carbon monoxide detector can alert people when dangerous levels of the gas are present in their homes.

MORE ON THE WEB

Identifying Compounds Have students use the Internet to learn more about elements and compounds. Then, have them take an online quiz. Have students visit www.concepts andchallenges.com for more details.

• **TEACHING RESOURCES** •

💿 **Teacher's Resources CD-ROM**
Lesson Review: Chapter 4, p. 3

Concept Map: Study Tools, p. 4

1 Introduce

🔍 INVESTIGATE

TIME: 15 minutes

PURPOSE: Students will separate iron particles from crushed fortified cereal flakes, using a bar magnet.

MATERIALS: 1/2 cup of iron-fortified cereal, plastic sealable sandwich bag, bowl, water, bar magnet, sheet of white paper, hand lens

PROCEDURE: Have students work in pairs. Demonstrate how to squeeze the air out of the bag. Explain that the cereal should be crushed very fine. If students need help answering the question, have them look at the information on the cereal box for ingredients that would be attracted to a magnet.

THINK ABOUT IT: Little black flakes; They came from the cereal. **learning styles: visual, tactile**

✏️ **STUDY HINT** Have students form questions based on the headings from each section of the lesson and answer those questions as they read.

Linking Prior Knowledge Ask students to create KWL charts in their notebooks. You can use the KWL Chart on the Teacher's Resources CD-ROM. In the K column, students should list what they already know about mixtures. In the W column, they should write questions that reflect what they want to know. In the L column, they should list what they learn as they read.

2 Teach

Demonstration Make a mixture of salt water. Ask students to examine the mixture. They should notice that the salt is impossible to see. Then, heat the mixture so that the water evaporates. Guide students to realize that the evaporation of the water separates the mixture. **learning style: visual**

Answers to questions

▶ **CONTRAST:** You cannot see the individual parts of salt or water in a salt-water mixture. In a salad, each part is clearly visible.

▶ **INFER:** They have not been chemically changed.

▶ **EXPLAIN:** Use filtration or evaporation.

4-3 What is a mixture?

INVESTIGATE

Separating a Mixture
HANDS-ON ACTIVITY

STEP 3

1. Place one-half cup of iron-fortified cereal into a plastic sandwich bag. Squeeze as much air out of the bag as you can. Seal the plastic bag.

2. Use your hands to crush the cereal into a fine powder. Then, pour the cereal into a bowl. Add enough water to the bowl to completely cover the cereal.

3. Cover one end of a magnet with plastic wrap and use it to stir the mixture for at least 10 minutes. Remove the magnet and let the liquid on the magnet drain back into the bowl.

4. Hold the magnet over a sheet of white paper. Use a hand lens to observe the particles on the end of the magnet.

THINK ABOUT IT: What did you observe on the end of the magnet? Where did the matter come from?

Objective
Describe the physical properties of a mixture.

Mixtures Cut up some tomatoes, lettuce, onions, and green peppers. Put the pieces in a bowl and stir them together. What do you have? Some people would say that you have a salad. A scientist might say that you have a mixture. You have learned that a mixture is made up of two or more substances that are physically combined. Each part of a mixture keeps its own properties.

Not all mixtures are as easy to identify. If you put some salt in a glass of water and stir, you would have a mixture of salt and water. But this mixture is different from the salad mixture. You cannot see the individual parts of salt or water.

▶ **CONTRAST:** What is the difference between a salad mixture and a salt-water mixture?

Kinds of Mixtures The kinds of matter in a mixture can be present in varying amounts. The discussion above describes the two basic types of mixtures—evenly mixed and unevenly mixed. The mixture of salt and water is evenly mixed. You cannot see the individual particles of salt or water. The salt is still salt, and the water is still water. However, they are so evenly mixed that every part of this mixture is exactly the same as every other part. A drop taken from the top of the mixture will be identical to a drop taken from the bottom.

84

The salad is unevenly mixed. One part of the salad may have more tomato while another part has more green pepper. Each part of the mixture keeps its own properties. A tomato is still red and tastes like a tomato.

▲ **Figure 4-8** A salad is a mixture. Each part of the mixture keeps its own properties.

▶ **INFER:** Why do the different kinds of matter in a mixture keep their own properties?

Separating a Mixture The properties of the different kinds of matter in a mixture can be used to separate the mixture. Because the parts of a mixture are not chemically combined, they can be separated by physical means. For example, each of the different vegetables could be picked out of the salad by hand.

Teaching Options

❗ FAST FACTS *The Need for Iron in Diets*

The absorption of iron in the human body is very important. Iron carries oxygen in the blood, and it also helps to form new red blood cells. Iron deficiency, or the lack of iron, in a person can lead to a condition called anemia. Anemia can make a person feel tired, weak, and unable to concentrate. In children, iron deficiency can affect behavior and development.

Many different types of food contain iron. Iron from meat sources is better absorbed than iron found in plant sources. The consumption of meat, however, is lacking in some diets. Consequently, some foods, such as cereals, are fortified with iron. "Iron dust" is added to cereals, usually in the form of iron sulfate or reduced ferrous iron.

A physical property of water is that it evaporates when it is heated. So, if you heat a mixture of salt and water, the water will evaporate and the salt will be left behind. The mixture will be separated. Some mixtures can be separated by filtering. If a mixture of sand and water is poured into a filter, the water will pass through. The sand will be trapped by the filter.

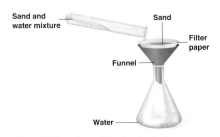
Sand and water mixture
Sand
Filter paper
Funnel
Water

▲ **Figure 4-9** Separating a mixture of sand and water

▶ EXPLAIN: How can you separate a mixture of sand and water?

✓ **CHECKING CONCEPTS**

1. Salt water is an example of a _____.
2. The substances in a mixture are _____ combined.

3. The substances in a mixture can be present in _____ amount.
4. The substances in a mixture always keep their own _____.
5. The substances in a mixture can be _____ by using the physical properties of the substances.
6. A mixture of _____ and water can be separated by filtering the mixture.

💡 **THINKING CRITICALLY**

7. HYPOTHESIZE: Will freezing a mixture of salt and water separate the two substances? Explain your answer.
8. CLASSIFY: A teaspoon of instant coffee is placed in a cup of boiling water. Is this a mixture or a compound? Explain your answer.

DESIGNING AN EXPERIMENT

Design an experiment to solve the following problem. Include a hypothesis, variables, a procedure, and a type of data to study.

PROBLEM: You have a mixture of sand, water, and gravel. How can you separate this mixture into its different parts?

Real-Life Science

MIXTURES THAT YOU CAN EAT

Have you ever gone camping or hiking and taken some trail mix with you? As the name of this snack tells you, trail mix is a mixture. You can see the individual bits of dried fruits and nuts. You could pick out the individual parts with your fingers if you wanted to.

Think about some of the other foods that you eat every day. Many of these foods are mixtures. Rice and beans, vegetable soup, ice cream—all are mixtures.

Thinking Critically If you were to make trail mix, do you have to follow the recipe exactly?

ENERGY TRAIL MIX
1 c. dried apricots
2 c. raisins
½ c. dry roasted peanuts
½ c. almonds
½ c. pineapple chunks
½ c. banana chips or coconut chips
Combine ingredients; mix well. Store in an airtight container. Makes 1¾ quarts.

▲ **Figure 4-10** Recipe for trail mix

MORE ON THE WEB

Understanding Types of Mixtures Have students use the Internet to learn more about unevenly mixed (heterogeneous) and evenly mixed (homogeneous) mixtures. Then, have students take a short online quiz as a review. Visit www.conceptsandchallenges.com for more details.

• TEACHING RESOURCES •

💿 **Teacher's Resources CD-ROM**
Lesson Review: Chapter 4, p. 4
Designing an Experiment: Study Tools, p. 14
Designing an Experiment Rubric: Teaching Tools, p. 7
KWL Chart: Study Tools, p. 7

---

3 Assess

✓ **CHECKING CONCEPTS ANSWERS**

1. mixture
2. physically
3. varying
4. properties
5. separated
6. sand

💡 **THINKING CRITICALLY ANSWERS**

7. HYPOTHESIZE: No; Salt particles will be embedded in the ice that forms when the water freezes.
8. CLASSIFY: It is a mixture. The coffee and the water are physically combined, not chemically combined.

DESIGNING AN EXPERIMENT

Use the Designing an Experiment Rubric on the Teacher's Resources CD-ROM to assess students' experiments. Fill in the rubric with the additional information below. For this assignment, students should have:

• suggested filtering the mixture or evaporating the water to separate the water from the sand and gravel.

• suggested using a sieve to separate the sand from the gravel.

4 Close

Real-Life Science
MIXTURES THAT YOU CAN EAT

Interdisciplinary Connection Tell students that if they have ever made bread, then they have actually made both a mixture and a compound. Among the substances in wheat flour are two compounds called glutenin and gliadin. When the flour is mixed with water to form dough, these two compounds combine with the water to make a third compound, gluten. Gluten is an elastic protein that gives bread its spongy texture.

Discussion Ask students to name some mixtures that they eat. Point out that almost every recipe yields a mixture.

Thinking Critically Answer
No, but adding too much or too little of one ingredient could change the taste or texture of the final product.

1 Introduce

STUDY HINT Have students write the lesson title and objective in their notebooks. As students read the lesson, have them contrast mixtures and compounds and write their findings in their notebooks.

Linking Prior Knowledge Ask students to recall what they have already learned about mixtures and compounds. As students volunteer ideas about the properties of each, write their ideas on the board. Then, have students look for additional items to add to the list as they read.

2 Teach

Demonstration Show students mixtures of two substances in varying proportions. Point out that a mixture does not have a definite chemical composition. Although each mixture has the same substances, the mixtures are not exactly the same. Allow students to use the substances to create different mixtures of their own. Ask students how these mixtures would be different if they were compounds. (The compounds would have the same proportions of substances. Compounds would be chemically combined instead of physically combined.) **learning styles: visual, tactile**

Discussion Introduce the lesson by reviewing the definitions of *compound* and *mixture*. Ask students to name some simple compounds (water, sugar, salt) and some common mixtures (rocks, salt water, trail mix). Refer students to Figures 4-11 and 4-12. Ask them how iron and sulfur are being combined in Figure 4-11. (by physically mixing them) Ask students to contrast Figures 4-11 and 4-12. (In Figure 4-12, the items are being chemically combined instead of physically combined, as in Figure 4-11. Figure 4-12 shows a compound being made.)
learning styles: visual, auditory

Answers to questions

INFER: Physically combine the two substances.

EXPLAIN: The atoms of the two elements combine chemically to create a compound.

4-4 How are mixtures and compounds different?

Objective
Contrast the properties of mixtures with the properties of compounds.

Making a Mixture The different kinds of matter in a mixture are physically combined. A fruit salad is a mixture of different kinds of fruit. You can make a mixture of iron filings and sulfur by mixing the two substances together.

Iron filings are magnetic slivers of gray metal. Sulfur is a nonmetallic yellow powder. Just like each piece of fruit in a salad keeps its properties, each substance in the iron-sulfur mixture will keep its own properties. You would be able to see the grains of yellow powder and slivers of gray metal in a mixture of these two substances.

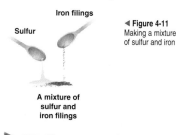

Iron filings

Sulfur

◀ **Figure 4-11**
Making a mixture of sulfur and iron

A mixture of sulfur and iron filings

INFER: How can you make a mixture of iron filings and sulfur?

Making a Compound A compound is made up of two or more elements. It is formed as a result of a chemical change. The elements in a compound combine by forming chemical bonds between the atoms of the elements. For example, molecules of sugar are formed as a result of a chemical change. Atoms of hydrogen form chemical bonds with atoms of oxygen and atoms of carbon to produce molecules of sugar.

Not only can iron and sulfur be physically combined to make a mixture, they can also be chemically combined to form a compound. This compound is called iron sulfide. Iron sulfide forms when a mixture of iron filings and sulfur is heated. The atoms of the two elements will combine to form chemical bonds with each other. The compound iron sulfide will be produced. Like all compounds, the properties of iron sulfide are different from the properties of the elements that make it up.

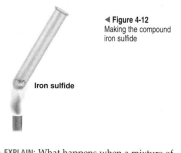

◀ **Figure 4-12**
Making the compound iron sulfide

Iron sulfide

EXPLAIN: What happens when a mixture of iron filings and sulfur is heated?

Comparing Mixtures and Compounds Mixtures and compounds are different in several ways. A mixture of iron and sulfur does not have a definite chemical composition. The mixture might contain equal parts of each element. Or, it might have twice as much of one element as the other. Each substance in a mixture of iron and sulfur keeps its own properties. A mixture of iron and sulfur can be separated by physical means. For example, a magnet can be used to attract the iron.

The compound iron sulfide always has a definite chemical composition. Every molecule of iron sulfide contains one atom of iron and one atom of sulfur.

Teaching Options

EXTENDING THE LESSON

Separating Substances Students can use paper chromatography to study the different pigments in plant material. Gather plant samples such as spinach leaves and blades of grass. Crush them and place them in separate test tubes. Cover the plant matter with acetone (nail polish remover). After the tubes have soaked for a day, place a strip from a paper coffee filter into each test tube. Let the paper absorb the solvent for a day. Take the strips out of the test tubes and lay them on paper towels. Allow students to examine the separated pigments.

RETEACH

Sorting by Properties Write the properties of compounds and mixtures on index cards, one property per card. You could also include names of various compounds and mixtures on the cards. Hold up each card and ask a volunteer to read it aloud. Then, write the words *compounds* and *mixtures* on two separate sections of the board. Distribute cards to pairs of students. Students can work together to decide whether the words on the cards describe compounds, mixtures, or both. They can tape the cards near the appropriate words on the board.
learning styles: visual, tactile

When elements combine chemically, each element loses its properties. The iron and sulfur in iron sulfide cannot be separated by physical means. Figure 4-13 lists some differences between mixtures and compounds.

COMPARING MIXTURES AND COMPOUNDS	
Mixtures	Compounds
Made of two or more substances physically combined	Made of two or more substances chemically combined
Substances keep their own properties	Substances lose their own properties
Can be separated by physical means	Can be separated only by chemical means
Have no definite chemical composition	Have a definite chemical composition

▲ **Figure 4-13** Differences between mixtures and compounds

③ CONTRAST: How are mixtures and compounds different?

✔ CHECKING CONCEPTS

1. The elements in a _____ are chemically combined.
2. Each kind of matter in a _____ keeps its own properties.
3. A _____ does not have a definite chemical composition.
4. A _____ cannot be separated by physical means.

💡 THINKING CRITICALLY

5. **INFER:** When a certain poisonous gas is combined with a chemically active metal, a fine white powdery substance results. The new substance is neither poisonous nor chemically active. Is the powder a mixture or a compound? How do you know?
6. **COMPARE:** Water is a compound. Salt water is a mixture. List the differences between water and salt water.

Integrating Earth Science

TOPICS: rocks, minerals

CLASSIFYING ROCKS

Like other types of matter, rocks can be classified as elements, compounds, or mixtures. Some rocks are actually made of pure elements. For example, copper and gold are elements that can be found in nearly pure form. However, rocks that are mixtures of different compounds are more common than are rocks made of pure elements.

Some compounds that can be found in certain rocks include quartz, mica, and feldspar. Quartz is a hard, cloudy-looking rock that is actually a compound made up of silicon and oxygen. One form of mica is a black compound made up of the elements potassium, aluminum, silicon, oxygen, and hydrogen. Feldspar is a milky-white or pink compound that can be made up of aluminum, silicon, sodium, potassium or calcium and oxygen. A mixture of these three compounds can be found in a type of rock called granite. Granite is a hard rock with big grains of quartz, mica, and feldspar.

Thinking Critically How would you classify granite?

▲ **Figure 4-14** Granite is a mixture.

▲ **Figure 4-15** Mica can be found in granite.

CHAPTER 4: Compounds and Mixtures **87**

---

③ CONTRAST: Mixtures are formed and separated physically. Their components keep their own properties. Mixtures have no definite chemical composition. Compounds are formed and separated chemically. The substances lose their properties. Compounds have definite chemical compositions.

✎ **WRITING HINT** Encourage students to write complete sentences to compare and contrast mixtures and compounds. Remind them of words and phrases that show contrast, such as *on the other hand, but, in contrast,* and so on.

3 Assess

✔ CHECKING CONCEPTS ANSWERS

1. compound
2. mixture
3. mixture
4. compound

💡 THINKING CRITICALLY ANSWERS

5. **INFER:** It is a compound. The substances did not retain their properties when they were combined.
6. **COMPARE:** Water is made of two substances that are chemically combined. These substances lose their own properties. Salt water is made of substances that are physically combined. These substances keep their own properties.

4 Close

Integrating Earth Science

TOPICS: rocks, minerals

CLASSIFYING ROCKS

Discussion Consider bringing rocks to class for students to examine and classify. Ask them to explain how they classified the rocks as elements, compounds, or mixtures. Students may want to bring their own rocks or rock collections to share and classify. Refer to Figure 4-1 at the beginning of the chapter. You may want to provide additional photographs of Mount Rushmore.

Thinking Critically Answer
Granite is a mixture of different compounds.

MORE ON THE WEB

Understanding the Difference
Have students visit www.conceptsandchallenges.com to review the difference between compounds and mixtures. Then, have students take the online quiz.

ESL/ELL STRATEGY

Defining Composition Explain that the word *composition* means "something that is put together by combining parts." From this definition, have students define *chemical composition*.

• TEACHING RESOURCES •

💿 **Teacher's Resources CD-ROM**
Lesson Review: Chapter 4, p. 5

Lab Activity

(pp. 88–89)

1 Prepare the Lab

Separating Mixtures

SET-UP TIME: ⏱ **LAB TIME:** 🕐

BACKGROUND: Because items in mixtures are combined physically rather than chemically, they can be separated based on physical properties, such as magnetism, ability to float, ability to dissolve, and size.

PURPOSE: Students will observe and analyze various substances on the basis of their ability to dissolve in water, ability to float on water, magnetism, and size.

ALTERNATIVE MATERIALS: If you do not have access to running water in your classroom, bring water in plastic milk bottles. Water can be at room temperature for the experiments.

SCIENCE SKILLS: Students will **observe** and **collect data** as they experiment. They will **communicate** their findings in chart form. They will use their findings to **infer** properties of mixtures and substances and to **design an experiment** of their own.

ADVANCE PLANNING: Gather the materials you need for the lab. Have on hand an empty bucket or other container to collect water after the experiment.

2 Guide the Lab

PROCEDURE: Divide the class into pairs or groups of three. Discuss the procedure, and have students make their data charts before they begin the experiment. Be sure that students understand the meanings of *dissolves* and *floats*. Show students how to add iron filings to the mixture by pouring a small amount of filings onto a small folded piece of paper. Then, pour the filings into the mixture from the piece of paper. Prompt students to write concise yet detailed observations in their charts. Model a sample observation if necessary. Provide students with a copy of the Lab Activity Report found on the Teacher's Resources CD-ROM for students to record their observations and conclusions.

TROUBLESHOOTING: Remind students to stir mixtures carefully so that materials do not spill over the sides of the cup.

LAB ACTIVITY
Separating Mixtures

Materials
- Safety goggles
- Lab apron, plastic gloves
- Sand
- Epsom salt
- Sawdust, iron filings
- 2 Clear plastic cups
- Teaspoons, stirrers
- Water
- Magnet
- Plastic wrap
- Paper towels
- 2 Beakers
- Fine sieve, filter paper

▲ **STEP 3** Make a sand and Epsom salt mixture.

▲ **STEP 5** Obtain a cup of water to pour into the mixture.

BACKGROUND

Mixtures surround you. Everything from salt water in the ocean to your bowl of morning cereal, mixtures are part of our everyday lives. Salt water and cereal are mixtures because both contain two or more kinds of matter that are mixed together physically but not chemically. Because the kinds of matter in a mixture are not chemically combined, it is possible to separate the parts based on their physical properties.

PURPOSE

In this activity, you will observe and analyze the separation of mixtures based on four physical properties of matter—the ability to dissolve in water, the ability to float on water, magnetism, and size.

PROCEDURE 🔍 🧤

1. Copy the chart in Figure 4-17. Put on safety goggles, a lab apron, and plastic gloves.

2. Spread two or three sheets of paper towels on your work area.

3. Obtain a clear plastic cup and put in one teaspoon of sand and one teaspoon of Epsom salt. Record your observations of the two substances on the chart. With a stirrer, mix the two substances together.

4. Cover one end of a bar magnet with plastic wrap and insert it into the cup with the mixture. Use the magnet to stir the mixture. Take the magnet out and examine it closely. Record your observations.

5. Obtain a cup of water and pour it into the cup with the mixture. Stir the mixture with the stirrer. Record your observations.

6. Line a sieve with filter paper. Place the sieve over the mouth of a beaker. Pour the mixture into the sieve. Record your observations.

Teaching Options

◈ INTEGRATING THE SCIENCES

Earth Science Many rocks are mixtures of different elements and minerals. Students can examine rock samples and discuss ways in which these rocks could be separated into their components. Show students photographs of gold miners using sieves to separate gold from sand and dirt.

Chemistry In many ways, the principles used in cooking are similar to those of chemistry. Food scientists have been able to make many different types of prepared foods available to millions of people around the world. By analyzing the sense of smell and taste, scientists can combine seasonings to improve the flavor of foods. The seasoning blends are mixtures because they are combinations of herbs and spices that can still be identified in the blend.

Technology Many types of machines help scientists separate mixtures. A centrifuge, for example, is a device that can separate substances of different densities. By spinning a mixture rapidly, a centrifuge can drain water from a wet solid. Medical labs use centrifuges to separate blood cells from whole blood, and dairy farmers use centrifuges to separate cream from milk. Sugar manufacturers use centrifuges to separate sugar from molasses.

7. Dispose of the mixture in a waste beaker. Rinse and dry out the plastic cup, the sieve, and the first beaker.

8. Repeat Steps 2 through 6 using sand, sawdust, and iron filings to make another mixture. Follow your teacher's directions on how to add iron filings to the mixture.

▲ **STEP 6** Pour the mixture into the sieve.

◀ **Figure 4-16** Iron filings, sand, and sawdust mixture

Separating Mixtures				
Substance	Dissolves in Water	Floats in Water	Magnetic	Filtered by Sieve
Epsom salt				
Iron				
Sand				
Sawdust				

▲ **Figure 4-17** Copy this chart and use it to record your observations.

CONCLUSIONS

1. INFER: Describe how each substance was able to keep its own physical properties when it was mixed with another substance.

2. INFER: How do you know that each combination was not a chemical combination?

3. ANALYZE: Design procedures to separate each mixture into its parts.

Tips for Using Technology

Spreadsheets Have students use spreadsheet software to record their observations. Spreadsheets are tables that display data such as numbers, text, dates, or a combination of all three. Students can use spreadsheets to make calculations, analyze numerical data, make graphs and charts of their data, and present their data to the class. Have students use the Spreadsheet on the Teacher's Resources CD-ROM to plan their spreadsheets.

• TEACHING RESOURCES •

Teacher's Resources CD-ROM
Lab Activity Report: Study Tools, pp. 16–17

Laboratory Activity Rubric: Teaching Tools, p. 8

Spreadsheet: Study Tools, p. 23

Laboratory Manual
Lab. Skills Worksheet 4: Organizing and Analyzing Data, pp. 13–14

SAFETY TIP: Caution students not to get any of the materials in their eyes. They should not rub their eyes or take off the safety goggles during the experiment. Be sure that soap and water or hand-washing towels are available. Remind students not to drink the mixtures or hold the cups near their mouths.

EXPECTED OUTCOME: Students should notice that Epsom salt dissolves in water and that sawdust floats in water. Iron filings are the only magnetic material. If the sieve is fine enough, iron filings, sand, and sawdust could all be filtered from the water.

3 Conclude the Lab

1. INFER: The Epsom salt dissolved in the water. The iron was attracted to the magnet. The sand was filtered by the filter paper. The sawdust floated in the water.

2. INFER: The substances all kept their original properties and were separated by physical means.

3. ANALYZE: Mixture 1 (sand, Epsom salt, and water): use filter paper to separate the sand from the Epsom salt and water; separate the water from the Epsom salt by evaporation. Mixture 2 (sand, sawdust, iron filings, and water): use a magnet to separate the iron filings from the water, sand, and sawdust; skim off the floating sawdust; use filter paper to separate the sand from the water.

Use the Laboratory Activity Rubric on the Teacher's Resources CD-ROM to assess students' lab activities. Fill in the rubric with the additional information below. For this activity, students should have:

- performed the activity according to the procedure and filled in the chart with data collected during the activity.

- correctly answered the questions in complete sentences.

4 Extend the Lab

Discuss with students how they would separate mixtures of the various substances. Ask: *How would you separate Epsom salt from iron filings?* (Use a magnet.) *Epsom salt from sawdust?* (Add water to the mixture, filter the sawdust from the water, and then evaporate or boil off the water.)

Ask students to devise a plan to separate a mixture of all four substances. Have them create a flowchart to show the various steps and the outcome of each step.

1 Introduce

STUDY HINT Before beginning this lesson, read the list of Key Terms aloud so that students can hear the pronunciation of each word. Ask students to repeat the words after you.

Linking Prior Knowledge Before beginning this lesson, have students recall what they have already learned about atoms (Lesson 3-3). Ask students: *What parts can be found in an atom?* (a nucleus, protons, neutrons, and electrons) *Why are atoms neutral?* (The number of protons is equal to the number of electrons.)

2 Teach

Demonstration Draw a picture of an atom on the board, labeling the nucleus, protons, neutrons, and electrons. Then, label the charges. Electrons have a negative charge; protons have a positive charge; and neutrons are neutral. Students should notice that the charges balance. Inform students that atoms tend to become stable by completing their outermost energy level. To do this, an atom may gain, lose, or share electrons with another atom.
learning style: visual

Discussion Describe how ions and ionic bonds form, using sodium chloride as an example. Have students study Figure 4-18, which shows the formation of an ionic bond. Ask students which atom loses an electron and which atom gains an electron. (Sodium loses an electron; chlorine gains one.) **learning styles: visual, auditory**

Reinforcement To help students visualize how ions bond together, place several students in a small group representing an atom. One student can be a neutron, while the others are electrons and protons. (You might have group members hold cards with the letters *N*, *E*, and *P* to help students visualize.) Make sure that there are equal numbers of electrons and protons. Prompt an observer to explain why this atom is stable. Take away an electron and ask students what the group represents. (a positive ion) Volunteers can create another ion that would form an ionic bond with the group. **learning styles: visual, kinesthetic**

4-5 What is an ionic bond?

Objective
Describe how atoms form ionic bonds.

Key Terms
valence electron: electron in the outermost energy level of an atom
ion: atom with an electrical charge
ionic bond: bond formed between atoms that have gained or lost electrons

Valence Electrons The formation of chemical bonds is a process involving valence electrons. A **valence electron** is an electron in the outermost energy level of an atom. Except for the elements hydrogen and helium, the outermost energy level of an atom can hold a maximum of eight electrons. An atom with eight electrons in its outermost energy level is very stable.

Atoms of all elements have valence electrons. Atoms with fewer than eight valence electrons tend to form bonds with other atoms. Atoms can give electrons, receive electrons, or share electrons with other atoms to reach the stable number of eight valence electrons.

▶ **DEFINE:** What are valence electrons?

Neutral Atoms All matter is made up of atoms. Every atom is made up of smaller particles called protons, neutrons, and electrons. A proton has a positive charge. An electron has a negative charge. A neutron has no charge.

In an atom, the number of protons and the number of electrons are the same. Because the charges are balanced, all atoms are neutral.

▶ **EXPLAIN:** Why are atoms neutral?

Charged Atoms When forming chemical bonds, the atoms of nonmetals tend to gain electrons while the atoms of metals tend to lose electrons. When the number of electrons in an atom is different from the number of protons, the atom becomes electrically charged. An atom with an electrical charge is called an **ion**.

If a neutral atom gains electrons, it becomes a negative ion. It is a negative ion because there are now more electrons than there are protons. Electrons have a negative charge. If a neutral atom loses electrons, it becomes a positive ion. There are more protons than there are electrons.

▶ **COMPARE:** Does a negative ion have more protons or more electrons?

Ionic Bonds In compounds, particles of matter are held together by chemical bonds. A bond that forms when one atom gains one or more electrons from another atom is called an **ionic bond**. The atom that gains electrons becomes a negative ion. The atom that loses electrons becomes a positive ion. The two ions have opposite electrical charges. As a result, they are attracted to each other. This force of attraction holds atoms together in an ionic bond.

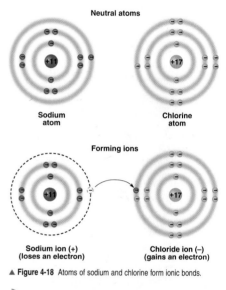

Neutral atoms

Sodium atom   Chlorine atom

Forming ions

Sodium ion (+)   Chloride ion (–)
(loses an electron)   (gains an electron)

▲ **Figure 4-18** Atoms of sodium and chlorine form ionic bonds.

▶ **EXPLAIN:** How does an ionic bond form?

90

Teaching Options

COOPERATIVE LEARNING

Modeling Sodium Chloride
Using Figure 4-18 as a guide, students can work together to create models of sodium chloride. They can draw colored circles to show the neutrons, protons, and electrons and the way in which sodium ions and chloride ions bond to form sodium chloride.
learning styles: visual, tactile

EXTENDING THE LESSON

Modeling Crystal Shapes Remind students that one property of an ionic bond is the formation of crystals. Ask students to research the six basic crystal systems. Then, have students use toothpicks and marshmallows or gumdrops to create three-dimensional models of the crystal shapes.
learning styles: visual, tactile

Ionic Compounds Compounds whose atoms are held together by ionic bonds are called ionic compounds. Ionic compounds are not made up of molecules. Instead, they are made up of one or more positive ions and one or more negative ions. Because the atoms are held together by ionic bonds, ionic compounds have similar properties. One of these properties is crystal shape. A crystal is a solid that contains atoms arranged in a regular pattern. Many ionic compounds, such as sodium chloride, form crystals. Ionic compounds also have high melting points and they are conductors of electricity when they are melted.

▶ IDENTIFY: What is a crystal?

✔ CHECKING CONCEPTS

1. Electrons have a _____ electrical charge.
2. When an atom loses electrons, it becomes a _____ ion.
3. An _____ forms when one atom takes an electron from another atom.
4. Particles with opposite electrical charges _____ each other.

5. An ionic compound is not made up of _____.
6. A _____ is a solid that contains atoms arranged in a regular pattern.

🔍 THINKING CRITICALLY

7. INFER: Could an atom ever lose an electron without another atom gaining the electron? Explain.
8. ANALYZE: Why are ionic compounds not made of molecules?

BUILDING SCIENCE SKILLS

Modeling Crystal A crystal is a solid that contains atoms arranged in a regular pattern. The pattern of atoms forms a crystal lattice. The shape of a crystal is determined by its crystal lattice. Table salt, or sodium chloride, is an example of a crystal. Research the type of crystal lattice found in table salt. Draw a diagram of the crystal lattice of sodium chloride and display it to the class. Label the sodium ions and chloride ions in the lattice.

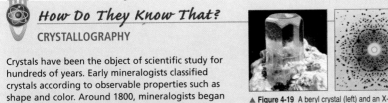

How Do They Know That?
CRYSTALLOGRAPHY

Crystals have been the object of scientific study for hundreds of years. Early mineralogists classified crystals according to observable properties such as shape and color. Around 1800, mineralogists began measuring the angles found on a crystal's surface. The mineralogists thought that the size of a crystal's angles was related to the type of substances that make up the crystal. However, they had no way of looking at the internal structure of a crystal.

In 1895, X-rays were discovered. Using X-rays, scientists could examine the structure of crystals. They discovered that crystal angles are caused by common structural patterns inside the crystal. As a result of X-ray crystallography, scientists were able to identify six basic crystal systems. The names of these crystal systems are cubic, tetragonal, orthorhombic, monoclinic, hexagonal/trigonal, and triclinic.

Thinking Critically How do you think the names of the crystal systems are related to their shapes? Use a reference to find out.

▲ **Figure 4-19** A beryl crystal (left) and an X-ray of beryl (right)

Answers to questions

▶ **1** DEFINE: the electrons in the outermost energy level of an atom

▶ **2** EXPLAIN: The electrical charges of the protons and electrons are balanced.

▶ **3** COMPARE: more electrons

▶ **4** EXPLAIN: It forms when one atom gains one or more electrons from another atom.

▶ **5** IDENTIFY: a solid that contains atoms arranged in a regular pattern

3 *Assess*

✔ CHECKING CONCEPTS ANSWERS

1. negative
2. positive
3. ionic bond
4. attract
5. molecules
6. crystal

🔍 THINKING CRITICALLY ANSWERS

7. INFER: No; For an atom to lose an electron, there must be another atom to attract the electron.
8. ANALYZE: Ionic compounds are made of ions that have positive and negative electrical charges. Molecules do not have a charge.

BUILDING SCIENCE SKILLS ANSWER

Modeling Crystal Students should notice that the crystals are cubic.

4 *Close*

How Do They Know That?
CRYSTALLOGRAPHY

Discussion Ask: *How did early scientists classify crystals?* (by their shape, color, and angles found on the surface)

Ask students how the discovery of X-rays changed crystallography. (Once X-rays were discovered, scientists could examine the structure of crystals. Before then, scientists had no way of seeing the insides of crystals.)

Thinking Critically Answer
All of the names contain a root related to shape. *Cubic*, for example, describes a cube; *tetragonal* includes the prefix *tetra-*, which means "four."

ONGOING ASSESSMENT

Interpreting Diagrams Ask students to explain what is happening in Figure 4-18, using the terms *ion* and *ionic bond*.

• *TEACHING RESOURCES* •

 Teacher's Resources CD-ROM
Lesson Review: Chapter 4, p. 6
Enrichment: Chapter 4, p. 7
Crystal Shapes: Visuals, p. 7

1 Introduce

STUDY HINT Before beginning this lesson, write the title of each section in the lesson on the board. Have students copy these titles in their notebooks in outline format. As students read each section, they should write important details about each main topic. Students can also use the Writing Activity Outline found on the Teacher's Resources CD-ROM.

Linking Prior Knowledge Ask students to recall what they know about the way in which ions form bonds. Prompt them to mention that, in an ionic bond, electrons are given and taken away. Tell them that in other types of bonds—covalent bonds—electrons are shared.

2 Teach

Demonstration On the board, draw a variety of electron dot diagrams showing covalent bonds. For example, you may wish to draw electron dot diagrams for HF, HCl, NH_3, or CH_4. Be sure that students understand that atoms may complete their outermost energy levels by sharing electrons. Show how covalent bonding completes the outermost energy levels. Alternatively, you could draw electron dot diagrams for a few of these compounds and then have students complete the diagrams for additional compounds.
learning style: visual

Discussion Obtain a ball-and-stick molecular model kit to show covalent bonding to students. Help students compare and contrast Figures 4-20 and 4-22. Point out that a water molecule is shown in each figure. The molecules are simply represented in different ways. Show students that the electron dots represent covalent bonds in a water molecule.
learning style: visual

READING STRATEGY Tell students that each section can be summarized by one sentence. Have students use their outlines to craft a main-idea statement for each section.

4-6 What is a covalent bond?

Objective
Describe how atoms combine in covalent bonds.

Key Term
covalent bond: bond formed when atoms share electrons

Outermost Energy Levels In most atoms, the outermost energy level is not completely filled. The outermost energy level does not contain the maximum number of valence electrons that it can hold. In order to complete their outermost energy levels, atoms gain, lose, or share electrons. These electrons come from other atoms that also have incomplete outermost energy levels.

Ionic bonds form when one atom gains one or more electrons from another atom. The result is an ionic compound. Elements can also form compounds when their atoms share electrons to form a molecule. This type of bonding is called a **covalent bond.**

▶ IDENTIFY: How can atoms complete their outermost energy levels?

Covalent Compounds Compounds whose atoms share electrons in covalent bonds are called covalent compounds. The shared electrons are in the outermost energy levels of all the atoms in a molecule of the covalent compound.

Water is an example of a covalent compound. A water molecule has covalent bonds between an atom of oxygen and two atoms of hydrogen. The oxygen atom has six electrons in its outermost energy level. It needs two more electrons to completely fill this energy level. A hydrogen atom has one electron in its one and only energy level. This energy level is complete when it has two electrons. So, a hydrogen atom needs only one more electron to fill its outermost energy level. Figure 4-20 shows the covalent bonds in a molecule of water. Notice how two atoms of hydrogen form covalent bonds with one atom of oxygen to form the water molecule.

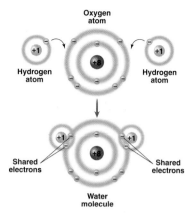

▲ **Figure 4-20** A molecule of water has covalent bonds between the atoms of hydrogen and the atom of oxygen.

▶ CLASSIFY: Is water an ionic compound or a covalent compound?

Comparing Ionic and Covalent Compounds Covalent compounds are formed differently from ionic compounds. Atoms joined by a covalent bond do not lose or gain electrons. So, they do not become positively or negatively charged. They do not become ions. The atoms remain neutral. Figure 4-21 lists the main points to know about ionic compounds and covalent compounds.

COMPARING IONIC AND COVALENT COMPOUNDS	
Ionic Compounds	**Covalent Compounds**
Atoms complete their outermost energy levels.	Atoms complete their outermost energy levels.
Electrons are lost and gained.	Electrons are shared.
Atoms form ions.	Atoms remain neutral.

▲ **Figure 4-21** Ionic compounds and covalent compounds act differently.

▶ COMPARE: How are covalent compounds different from ionic compounds?

Teaching Options

EXTENDING THE LESSON

Exploring Word Meaning To help students remember that in a covalent bond, atoms share electrons, have them look up the meaning of the prefix *co-* in a dictionary. ("together with" or "joined") Ask them how the prefix relates to the meaning of the term *covalent*. (Two atoms join together to share electrons.)
learning style: linguistic

ONGOING ASSESSMENT

Comparing and Contrasting Ask students to contribute details to a Venn diagram comparing and contrasting ionic and covalent compounds. Students can also use the Venn Diagram found on the Teacher's Resources CD-ROM and details from Figure 4-21.

Electron Dot Diagrams Electron dot diagrams include the symbols of the elements in a compound and the arrangement of the valence electrons for each element. These diagrams can be used to show the positive and negative ions in an ionic compound. They can also be used to show a molecule of a covalent compound. Figure 4-22 shows the electron dot diagrams for sodium chloride and water.

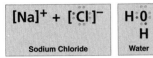

▲ Figure 4-22 Electron dot diagrams for an ionic compound (left) and a covalent compound (right)

 INFER: What do electron dot diagrams show?

✓ CHECKING CONCEPTS

1. In most atoms, the _____ energy level is not completely filled.
2. In a covalent bond, electrons are _____.

3. Water is an example of a _____ compound.
4. In a covalent compound, the atoms join together to form a _____.
5. In a covalent compound, the atoms remain _____.
6. Diagrams that show the symbol of the elements in a compound and the arrangement of the electrons for each element are called _____.

💡 THINKING CRITICALLY

7. **HYPOTHESIZE:** A carbon atom has four valence electrons in its outermost energy level. An oxygen atom has six valence electrons. Hypothesize about the type of bonding that will take place between carbon and oxygen.

Hands-On Activity

MAKING A MOLECULAR MODEL

You will need white and red modeling clay, and toothpicks.

1. Using the red clay, make four round balls that are the same size.
2. Make one round ball of white clay that is the same size as the red balls.
3. Use toothpicks to connect each of the four red balls to the white ball. Space the red balls equally around the white ball. You have just made a model of a methane molecule. A molecule of methane contains four hydrogen atoms joined to one carbon atom.

▲ STEP 3 Make a model of a methane molecule.

Practicing Your Skills

4. **OBSERVE:** What element is represented by the red balls?
5. **OBSERVE:** What element is represented by the white ball?
6. **ANALYZE:** What type of bond joins the atoms?
7. **ANALYZE:** Do the atoms in a methane molecule have an electrical charge? Why or why not?

Answers to questions

▶1 **IDENTIFY:** by gaining, losing, or sharing electrons

▶2 **CLASSIFY:** covalent

▶3 **COMPARE:** In an ionic compound, electrons are lost and gained, and the atoms form ions. In a covalent compound, electrons are shared, and the atoms remain neutral.

▶4 **INFER:** the symbols of the elements in a compound and the arrangement of the valence electrons for each element

---

3 Assess

✓ CHECKING CONCEPTS ANSWERS

1. outermost
2. shared
3. covalent
4. molecule
5. neutral
6. electron dot diagrams

💡 THINKING CRITICALLY ANSWER

7. **HYPOTHESIZE:** Each atom needs eight electrons to complete its outermost energy level. One carbon atom can form a covalent bond with two oxygen atoms.

---

4 Close

Hands-On Activity

MAKING A MOLECULAR MODEL

TIME: 10–15 minutes

PURPOSE: modeling, observing

ALTERNATIVE MATERIALS: Students can use gumdrops or painted plastic-foam balls instead of clay to complete this activity.

Practicing Your Skills Answers

4. **OBSERVE:** hydrogen
5. **OBSERVE:** carbon
6. **ANALYZE:** covalent bonds
7. **ANALYZE:** No; They are neutral because the electrons are shared and the atoms complete their outermost energy levels.

MORE ON THE WEB

Electron Dot Diagrams Have students visit www.concepts andchallenges.com to review drawing electron dot diagrams for ionic and covalent bonds.

ESL/ELL STRATEGY

Defining a Prefix Tell English-language learners that the prefix *co-* means "together." A covalent bond joins atoms together to form a compound. Ask students for other examples of words that contain the prefix *co-*. (copilot, coauthor, cohort)

• TEACHING RESOURCES •

💿 **Teacher's Resources CD-ROM**
Lesson Review: Chapter 4, p. 8
Writing Activity Outline: Study Tools, pp. 20–21
Venn Diagram: Study Tools, p. 10

Laboratory Manual
Lab. Challenge: How are ionic and covalent compounds different? pp. 33–36

1 Introduce

STUDY HINT Before beginning this lesson, have students read the captions and art labels that appear in the lesson. This will allow them to preview what is to come as well as focus them on the most important ideas in the lesson.

Linking Prior Knowledge Ask students to recall facts that they learned about covalent bonds and molecules (Lesson 4-6).

2 Teach

Demonstration Allow students to observe a wide variety of organic compounds, such as wool, wood, and alcohol. Point out that all the items are organic compounds. *Organic* means "of living organisms." Define an organic compound as a compound that contains carbon. However, certain substances such as carbon dioxide, carbon monoxide, and calcium carbonate (found in limestone), contain carbon but are not considered organic compounds. Tell students that the study of organic compounds is called organic chemistry. **learning styles: visual, auditory**

Discussion Explain to students that carbon is unique in its ability to form very strong covalent bonds with other carbon atoms, while, at the same time, being able to form strong bonds with atoms of other elements. This property, more than any other, accounts for the existence of the field called organic chemistry. Refer students to Figure 4-23, pointing out the single, double, and triple bonds. Be sure that students understand that the double and triple bonds are between the two atoms of carbon. **learning styles: visual, auditory**

Answers to questions

1 DEFINE: a compound containing carbon

2 IDENTIFY: the study of organic compounds

3 IDENTIFY: Possible answer: a molecular model that uses straight lines to show bonds

4 LIST: foam drinking cups, garden hoses, milk containers, and automobile parts

---

4-7 What is an organic compound?

Objective
Identify some organic compounds.

Key Terms
organic compound: compound containing carbon
organic chemistry: study of organic compounds
structural formula: molecular model that uses straight lines to indicate bonds
polymers: large molecules that are formed by many smaller molecules

Classifying Compounds Scientists classify compounds based on which ones contain the element carbon and which ones do not. The compounds that contain carbon are called **organic compounds.** The compounds that do not usually contain carbon are called inorganic compounds. An example of an organic compound is sugar, which is made up of carbon, hydrogen, and oxygen. An example of an inorganic compound is water. Water is made up of oxygen and hydrogen.

At one time, scientists thought that only living things contained organic compounds. Today, scientists know that some nonliving substances, such as plastics, contain organic compounds. Also, the compounds carbon dioxide and carbon monoxide are classified as inorganic compounds even though they do contain carbon.

1 DEFINE: What is an organic compound?

Organic Chemistry About 95% of all known substances are organic compounds. Because so many of the compounds around us are organic compounds, the study of these substances has been given its own special branch of science called **organic chemistry.**

Scientists studying organic chemistry have learned that a molecule of an organic compound can contain large numbers of atoms. This can happen because a carbon atom has four electrons in its outermost energy level. As a result, a carbon atom can form covalent bonds with up to four other atoms. A carbon atom can form three

94

different kinds of covalent bonds—a single bond, a double bond, and a triple bond.

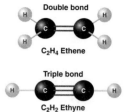

Single bond

In a single bond, a carbon atom shares one pair of electrons with another atom.

C_2H_6 Ethane

Double bond

In a double bond, two pairs of electrons are shared between atoms.

C_2H_4 Ethene

Triple bond

In a triple bond, three pairs of electrons are shared between atoms.

C_2H_2 Ethyne

▲ **Figure 4-23** Three types of covalent bonds allow many different organic compounds to be formed.

2 IDENTIFY: What is organic chemistry?

Structural Formulas When carbon atoms join together, they can form many different atomic structures. The atoms can join in a straight chain or a branched chain, or curve around in a ring. These arrangements of atoms can be shown in a structural formula. A **structural formula** is a molecular model that uses straight lines to show bonds. Structural formulas are frequently used to represent organic compounds. Figure 4-24 shows the structural formulas of some organic compounds.

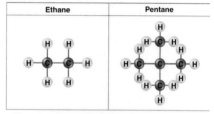

Ethane	Pentane

▲ **Figure 4-24** Structural formulas

3 IDENTIFY: What is a structural formula?

Teaching Options

◈ INTEGRATING CHEMISTRY

Pharmacist Pharmacists use chemistry in their jobs. Some pharmacists prepare medications. Other pharmacists work for companies that make medicines. Many pharmacists work with chemists in laboratories developing new or improved drugs. To become a pharmacist, a person needs a college degree in pharmacy and may need to pass an examination, followed by a one-year internship. Consider inviting a pharmacist to class to speak with students. Ask the pharmacist to describe how chemistry plays a part in pharmacy.

EXTENDING THE LESSON

Exploring Hydrocarbons
Hydrocarbons whose molecules contain a single bond between carbon atoms are called alkanes. Hydrocarbons with a double bond between carbon atoms are called alkenes. Those with a triple bond are called alkynes. Students may be familiar with octane, which is an alkane used in gasoline. Invite students to find out more about hydrocarbons and their practical applications. Students may want to create collages that depict items containing hydrocarbons. **learning styles: visual, auditory**

Polymers Organic compounds can join together to form very large molecules. These molecules can contain thousands or even millions of atoms. Very large molecules that are formed by many smaller molecules are called **polymers.** The smaller molecules that make up polymers are called monomers.

You may be familiar with some polymers, such as silk, nylon and wool. Many kinds of polymers are used to make materials that we use every day. Some products made from polymers include foam drinking cups, garden hoses, milk containers, and automobile parts.

4 LIST: Name some products made from polymers.

✓ CHECKING CONCEPTS

1. All organic compounds contain the element _____.

2. A carbon atom can form covalent bonds with up to _____ other atoms.

Science and Technology

ISOMERS

A structural formula can show you that a certain kind of organic compound can have different arrangements. Two or more compounds that have the same chemical makeup but different structures are called **isomers.** For example, Figure 4-25 shows the two structural formulas for the compound butane. Each isomer has four carbon atoms and ten hydrogen atoms in each of its molecules. However, the atoms of each isomer are arranged differently. One isomer is a straight chain and the other isomer is a branched chain. Because each molecule has a different arrangement, each compound has different physical and chemical properties.

Organic compounds that have a large number of carbon atoms may have many isomers. In general, as the number of carbon atoms increases, the number of isomers will also increase.

Thinking Critically Why do you think the number of isomers increases when the number of carbon atoms increases?

3. In a _____ bond, two pairs of electrons are shared between atoms.

4. The study of organic compounds is called _____.

5. A _____ shows the arrangement of atoms in a molecule of an organic compound.

6. Very large molecules made up of many smaller molecules are called _____.

💡 THINKING CRITICALLY

7. INFER: An atom of hydrogen contains one electron in its one energy level. Could a hydrogen atom form a triple bond with another atom? Explain your answer.

8. EXPLAIN: Why are there more organic compounds than inorganic compounds?

INTERPRETING VISUALS

Use Figure 4-24 to help you answer the following questions.

9. What is the chemical formula of ethane?

10. What is the chemical formula of pentane?

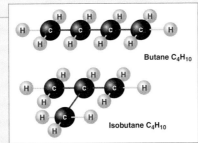

▲ **Figure 4-25** Butane (top) and isobutane (bottom) are isomers.

Butane C_4H_{10}

Isobutane C_4H_{10}

Reinforcement Some students may need help understanding structural formulas. Choose one of the compounds from Figure 4-24 and draw the electron dot diagram for it on the board. Show students that each line in the structural diagram is represented by two dots in the electron dot diagram. Guide students as they draw an electron dot diagram for the other compound shown. **learning style: visual**

3 Assess

✓ CHECKING CONCEPTS ANSWERS

1. carbon
2. four
3. double
4. organic chemistry
5. structural formula
6. polymers

💡 THINKING CRITICALLY ANSWERS

7. INFER: No; A hydrogen atom does not have enough electrons to share in a triple bond.
8. EXPLAIN: Possible answer: Because carbon has four valence electrons, it can form covalent bonds with up to four other atoms. Therefore, there can be many compounds that contain carbon.

INTERPRETING VISUALS ANSWERS

9. C_2H_6
10. C_5H_{12}

4 Close

Science and Technology

ISOMERS

Interdisciplinary Connection Point out to students that the isomers in Figure 4-25 have the same numbers of carbon and hydrogen atoms and the same chemical formulas. Students can count the atoms to prove that the isomers have the same number of atoms.

Thinking Critically Answer
There are more possible ways that the atoms can be arranged in branched chains.

MORE ON THE WEB

Reviewing Organic Compounds Have students use the Internet to review organic compounds. Then, have students take the online quizzes assigned at www.conceptsandchallenges.com.

ONGOING ASSESSMENT

Studying Figure 4-25 Have students study Figure 4-25. Ask: *What are these two molecular models called?* (structural formulas) *How are these two models similar? How are they different?* (They have the same number and kinds of atoms. The atoms are arranged differently in each model.)

• TEACHING RESOURCES •

💿 **Teacher's Resources CD-ROM**
Lesson Review: Chapter 4, p. 9
Enrichment: Chapter 4, pp. 10–11

1 Introduce

✏️ **STUDY HINT** Before beginning the lesson, have students read the Key Terms and give an example for each term.

Linking Prior Knowledge Review the definition of *organic compound* with students. (a compound that contains carbon) Ask students if they are familiar with the Food Guide Pyramid. Ask them if they have seen it printed on the labels of food items such as cereal boxes. Ask students if they understand what the pyramid stands for.

2 Teach

Demonstration Show students that many foods contain organic compounds. Lipids, fats or oils, are found in many different foods. Show students foods such as potato chips and peanut butter. Place the foods on a piece of paper towel and blot. Students will see that the oil that came out of the foods is absorbed by the towel.
learning style: visual

Discussion Discuss with students the importance of vitamins and minerals for living things. Vitamins are organic nutrients that are needed for the body to function normally. Minerals are inorganic nutrients. List the different vitamins and minerals on the board. Give examples of foods that are sources of different vitamins and minerals. **learning style: auditory**

Answers to questions

▸1 **IDENTIFY:** They get these compounds from the foods that they eat.

▸2 **EXPLAIN:** They are the body's main source of energy.

▸3 **DESCRIBE:** Lipids provide an organism with energy and act as a stored energy supply.

▸4 **RELATE:** Amino acids join in long chains to form proteins.

▸5 **DESCRIBE:** carbon, oxygen, hydrogen, nitrogen, and phosphorus

---

4-8 What organic compounds are needed by living things?

Objective
Identify organic compounds needed by living things.

Key Terms
carbohydrates (kahr-boh-HY-drayts): sugars and starches

lipids: fats and oils

proteins: compounds used to build and repair body tissues

amino acids: building blocks of proteins

nucleic acids: compounds made up of carbon, oxygen, hydrogen, nitrogen, and phosphorus

Needs of Living Things All living things need certain organic compounds to stay alive. An organism gets the organic compounds it needs from its food. Most foods are made up of carbohydrates, lipids, and proteins.

▸1 **IDENTIFY:** How do organisms obtain the organic compounds they need?

Carbohydrates The organic compounds that are made up of carbon, hydrogen, and oxygen are called carbohydrates. Sugars and starches are **carbohydrates**. These organic compounds are the body's main source of energy. Foods such as cereals, grains, pasta, vegetables, and fruits are good sources of carbohydrates.

▸2 **EXPLAIN:** Why do all living things need carbohydrates?

Lipids The organic compounds that are made up mostly of carbon and hydrogen are called lipids. Fats and oils are **lipids**. These compounds are another energy source for the body. Lipids can be stored in the body for use at a later time. For this reason, lipids are often called the body's stored energy supply. Foods such as butter, meat, cheese, and nuts are good sources of lipids.

▲ **Figure 4-26** Sources of lipids

Cholesterol is a kind of lipid. Animal fat contains cholesterol. Eating too many foods high in certain kinds of cholesterol can be harmful to the body. Excess amounts of cholesterol may form fatty deposits on the walls of blood vessels. These fatty deposits can interfere with the flow of blood through the body.

▸3 **DESCRIBE:** Why do living things need lipids?

Proteins Organic compounds that are used to build and repair the body are called **proteins**. Proteins are made up of substances called **amino acids**. Amino acids contain carbon, hydrogen, oxygen, and nitrogen. Amino acids join together in long chains to form proteins. For this reason, amino acids are called the building blocks of proteins. Meat, milk, fish, eggs, and beans are good sources of protein. Foods such as fish and soybeans provide the body with most of the amino acids it needs.

▲ **Figure 4-27** Sources of amino acids and proteins

▸4 **RELATE:** What is the relationship between amino acids and proteins?

Nucleic Acids Other organic compounds that your body needs are called nucleic acids. **Nucleic acids** are made up of carbon, oxygen, hydrogen,

---

Teaching Options

EXTENDING THE LESSON

Examining Nutritional Information Ask students to examine the nutritional information listed on various food packages in their homes. They might bring in nutritional information to share in small groups. Students can identify examples of carbohydrates, lipids, and proteins that are found in various foods. **learning styles: visual, tactile**

ESL/ELL STRATEGY

Listing Examples of Organic Compounds Have students make a five-column chart. Each column should be labeled *carbohydrates*, *lipids*, *proteins*, *amino acids*, or *nucleic acids*. Have students list examples for each type of organic compound. Students can also draw pictures to illustrate their examples.
learning styles: linguistic, visual

nitrogen, and phosphorus. There are two types of nucleic acids, deoxyribonucleic acid (DNA) and ribonucleic acid (RNA). These organic compounds are made up of very large molecules. Each molecule is a type of polymer made up of chains of smaller molecules joined together. You have probably heard of DNA. It contains the information about the characteristics that you have inherited and it also controls the activities of the cells in your body.

▲ Figure 4-28 Section of a DNA molecule

 **DESCRIBE:** What elements are nucleic acids made up of?

✓ CHECKING CONCEPTS

1. An organism gets the organic compounds it needs from its _____.
2. Organic compounds made up of carbon, hydrogen, and oxygen are called _____.
3. Sugars and starches are _____.
4. Fats and oils are _____.
5. Organic compounds used to build and repair body parts are called _____.
6. The organic compounds that control the activities in body cells are called _____.

💡 THINKING CRITICALLY

7. **INFER:** Why do many long-distance runners eat a meal of pasta before running a race?

BUILDING SCIENCE SKILLS

Organizing Information Make a table with the following headings: *Carbohydrates, Lipids,* and *Proteins.* Under each heading, identify five types of foods that you enjoy eating which contain that type of organic compound.

Real-Life Science

FOOD PYRAMID

To keep your body healthy you should eat a balanced diet. One way to get a balanced diet is to follow the Food Guide Pyramid.

The pyramid shows the six food groups that provide important organic compounds. It also tells how much food you should eat from each group every day. The bottom row of the pyramid is the bread, cereal, rice, and pasta group. These foods contain carbohydrates. The second row of the pyramid contains the vegetable group and the fruit group. The foods in these groups contain carbohydrates and other substances your body needs. The third level contains the milk, yogurt, and cheese group and the meat, poultry, fish, dry beans, eggs, and nuts group. These two groups contain proteins. The group at the top of the pyramid is the fats, oils, and sweets group. Foods from this group should be eaten in small amounts.

Thinking Critically How does the food pyramid tell you how much food you should eat from each group?

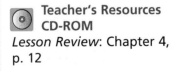

▲ Figure 4-29 The Food Guide Pyramid

MORE ON THE WEB

Using the Food Guide Pyramid
Have students use an online Food Guide Pyramid to learn more about balanced diets. Then, have students create a chart listing a day's meals. Students should include in their charts information about the number of servings and food groups. Have students visit www.conceptsandchallenges.com for more details.

• *TEACHING RESOURCES* •

Teacher's Resources CD-ROM
Lesson Review: Chapter 4, p. 12

WRITING HINT Students are probably familiar with the term *cholesterol* as it relates to health. Have students write their own definitions for this term. Encourage them to research cholesterol and add what they learn to their definitions.

3 Assess

✓ CHECKING CONCEPTS ANSWERS

1. food
2. carbohydrates
3. carbohydrates
4. lipids
5. proteins
6. nucleic acids

💡 THINKING CRITICALLY ANSWER

7. **INFER:** Pasta is a good source of carbohydrates, which are the body's main source of energy.

BUILDING SCIENCE SKILLS

Organizing Information Check students' tables for a logical organization of food types.

4 Close

Real-Life Science

FOOD PYRAMID

Real-Life Connection The pyramid represents a balanced diet. The pyramidal shape indicates the proportion in which each food group should be eaten compared to the other food groups. For example, fats and oils are at the very top. Therefore, these types of foods should be eaten sparingly. On the other hand, more servings of the bread, cereal, and pasta group should be eaten because this group makes up the base of the pyramid.

Discussion Ask students to name some of the foods found in each group. You might have students work in small groups to plan a menu for a day that follows the daily recommendations of the Food Guide Pyramid.

Thinking Critically Answer
The food pyramid recommends a number of servings from each food group.

The Big Idea

(pp. 98–99)

1 Introduce

Objective Students will plan a research trip to look for useful molecules in plants and animals. They will identify the practical uses of these molecules.

Linking Prior Knowledge Ask students to recall the information about compounds that they learned in Lessons 4-2 and 4-4. Then, have them recall what they learned about organic compounds in Lessons 4-7 and 4-8. Prompt them to remember that organic compounds are found in living things. Explain to students that some organic compounds are harmful to people.

2 Teach

Discussion After students have read the article and the captions about the cinchona plant, poison dart frog, saw scaled viper, and strychnos vine, encourage them to use reference materials to find out about other toxins that may be used in beneficial ways. Encourage students to consider how they would collect those toxins in a safe way and where they would find those toxins.

Use the information in the article, the captions, and Fast Facts to help guide students in choosing a topic for their Science Logs.

THE BIG IDEA ONLINE

What organisms produce poisonous compounds? Have students research their Science Log Writing Activity at www.conceptsandchallenges.com. You can have students organize their log by completing the Big Idea activity online. Students may post their work in the Online Classroom Database for others to read.

Reinforcement Students can also use the Big Idea Planner or Big Idea Science Log Entry found on the Teacher's Resources CD-ROM.

THE Big IDEA

What organisms produce poisonous compounds?

Your bones and your organs are very different in chemical structure. Yet, they are all made up of molecules. It takes thousands of different molecules to make up one cell and even more to make up a whole human. Many molecules in living things are complex. We can learn a lot by studying the variety of molecules in Earth's living things.

The cells in all organisms can make different kinds of molecules. Some of these molecules make compounds that help organisms to grow, to fight germs, and to make new cells when old cells die. Some organisms can even make molecules that form poisonous substances.

Poisons from living things are called toxins. Animals and plants that produce toxins are very successful at defending themselves against predators. These organisms can also pass on their ability to make the toxic substances to future generations. Over millions of years, some organisms have evolved to produce very strong toxins.

Some organisms that can produce toxins include the strychnos (STRIHK-nohs) vine, the cinchona (sihn-KOH-nuh) plant, many kinds of snakes, and some tropical frogs.

Look at the photographs of the organisms that appear on these two pages. Read about the poisons that they produce. Find out how some of their poisons can be used in medicines that help treat certain diseases. Then, follow the directions in the Science Log. Go on your own adventure to find other organisms that produce special molecules. ✦

Cinchona Plant
The cinchona plant is grown in countries in South America, India, and parts of Africa. The bark of this poisonous tree is used to make a medicine for the fever caused by the disease malaria. Taking too much of the medicine may, however, lead to coma and death.

98

Teaching Options

! FAST FACTS *Other Sources of Toxins*

Ciguatera (sihg-wuh-TER-uh) is a type of food poisoning that comes from tropical fish. The fish eat algae, which are not toxic to them. However, when a person eats a fish that has high levels of the algae in its system, the toxins in the algae can cause muscular and digestive problems.

Other types of algae can make shellfish poisonous. Creatures such as clams, oysters, and scallops eat algae in plankton. These planktonic algae may contain up to 20 different toxins that can make humans ill when they eat the shellfish.

Eating certain parts of the pufferfish can be deadly. While most of the pufferfish meat is safe, eating the skin can cause a very quick and violent death. The same toxin in the pufferfish can also be found in some newts, crabs, frogs, angelfish, and octopuses.

There are other very common sources of toxins. Raw or undercooked kidney beans contain a toxin that can cause severe digestive problems in just a few hours. Honey made from the nectar of rhododendrons can cause people to become dizzy, weak, and nauseated, although most other types of honey are safe.

Poison Dart Frog

The poison dart frog is a colorful rain-forest frog. It produces strong toxins in its skin. These toxins can cause paralysis and eventually death if absorbed into the bloodstream of other animals. The frogs' bright color warns predators not to eat it.

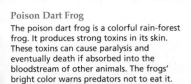

WRITING ACTIVITY

science Log

Sometimes biochemists travel the world looking for useful molecules in exotic organisms. In your science log, plan a research trip. In what part of the world would you look for useful molecules in plants and animals? What are some uses of these molecules? Start your search at www.conceptsandchallenges.com.

Saw Scaled Viper

The saw scaled viper is usually found in very dry desert regions. It makes a highly poisonous toxin. A bite from this snake causes its victim to bleed to death. Medical researchers have studied this toxin to help them make a drug that prevents blood clots in patients at risk for heart attacks.

Strychnos Vine

The strychnos vine makes toxic molecules in its bark. Native peoples of South America use it to make a poison used in hunting called curari. A medicine that helps treat rabies has been made from this poison.

CHAPTER 4: Compounds and Mixtures **99**

---

3 Assess

Use the Writing Activity Rubric on the Teacher's Resources CD-ROM to assess students' Science Logs. Fill in the rubric with the additional information below. For this assignment, students should have:

- planned a research trip to look for useful molecules in plants and animals, and indicated where the trip would take place.
- described some uses of the molecules.

4 Close

Creating an Advertisement Have students create advertisements for helpful products made from poisonous compounds. Advertisements should show how these compounds are beneficial and include persuasive language that will entice readers to use these products. Remind students to use catchy words, phrases, and visuals that pop out at readers.

Tips for Using Technology

Word Processing Software
Have students use word processing software to write about their research trip. A simple word processing program allows them to do basic tasks such as entering and editing text. A more complex word processing program allows students to make tables, draw pictures, do math, and make graphs. Students can print out their word processing documents to share with the class.

• TEACHING RESOURCES •

Teacher's Resources CD-ROM
Big Idea: Chapter 4, p. 13
Big Idea Planner: Study Tools, pp. 11–12
Big Idea Science Log Entry: Study Tools, p. 13
Writing Activity Rubric: Teaching Tools, p. 9

Challenges (pp. 100–102)

Chapter Summary

Review Before students begin the Challenges, review the summary with them. If time permits, have students work in pairs. Give each pair of students one summary point to describe in their own words.

✎ **STUDY HINT** Have students use the material on these pages to write questions and answers. They can write the questions on one side of index cards and the answers on the other side. Then, they can use the cards to quiz each other on the chapter concepts. Alternatively, you can collect the cards and use them to play a class review game.

Key Terms Challenges

MATCHING

1. substance (4-1)
2. organic chemistry (4-7)
3. organic compound (4-7)
4. covalent bond (4-6)
5. lipids (4-8)
6. carbohydrates (4-8)

FILL IN

7. mixture (4-3)
8. ion (4-5)
9. chemical bond (4-2)
10. polymers (4-7)

Chapter Summary

Lesson 4-1
- The three types of matter are **elements**, **compounds**, and **mixtures**.

Lesson 4-2
- A **compound** is a substance made up of two or more elements that are chemically combined.
- Compounds are formed as a result of a chemical change.

Lesson 4-3
- A **mixture** contains two or more substances that have been physically combined.
- The substances in a mixture keep their original properties.

Lesson 4-4
- Mixtures differ from compounds in several ways.

Lesson 4-5
- When an atom gains or loses electrons, it becomes an **ion**.
- An **ionic bond** forms between atoms that gain or lose electrons.

Lesson 4-6
- A **covalent bond** forms when atoms share electrons.

Lesson 4-7
- **Organic compounds** contain the element carbon and can form many different structures.

Lesson 4-8
- Organic compounds needed by living things include **carbohydrates**, **lipids**, **proteins**, and **nucleic acids**.

100

Key Term Challenges

amino acids (p. 96)
carbohydrates (p. 96)
chemical bond (p. 82)
compound (p. 80)
covalent bond (p. 92)
element (p. 80)
ion (p. 90)
ionic bond (p. 90)
lipids (p. 96)
mixture (p. 80)
molecule (p. 82)
nucleic acids (p. 96)
organic chemistry (p. 94)
organic compound (p. 94)
polymer (p. 94)
proteins (p. 96)
structural formula (p. 94)
substance (p. 80)
valence electron (p. 90)

MATCHING Write the Key Term from above that best matches each description.

1. any element or compound
2. study of organic compounds
3. compounds containing carbon
4. bond formed when atoms share electrons
5. fats and oils
6. sugars and starches

FILL IN Write the Key Term from above that best completes each statement.

7. Salt water is an example of a _____.
8. An atom with an electrical charge is called an _____.
9. The force of attraction that holds atoms together is a _____.
10. Very large molecules that are made of a chain of many smaller molecules are called _____.

Teaching Options

PREPARING STUDENTS FOR STANDARDIZED TESTS

Reading Strategy: Tell students to look for key words such as *all*, *not*, or *none* in multiple-choice questions. This will help them eliminate some incorrect choices.

Writing Strategy: Tell students to proofread their writing for mistakes in spelling, grammar, and organization. Remind them that using details will make their answers clearer.

Interpreting Visuals: Remind students to think carefully about what a visual is presenting. Ask them to look at the structure of a graphic organizer or the content of other types of visuals before drawing conclusions.

ESL/ELL STRATEGY

Definitions To help students learn new vocabulary words, have them write each unfamiliar word, such as *lipids* and *polymer*, on one side of an index card. Then, pair English-proficient students with English-language learners to write the definition for the unfamiliar word on the other side of the index card to use as flash cards to study for tests.

Content Challenges <u>TEST PREP</u>

MULTIPLE CHOICE **Write the letter of the term or phrase that best completes each statement.**

1. The compound formed when hydrogen and oxygen combine chemically is
   a. salt.
   b. water.
   c. sugar.
   d. sand.

2. Compounds are formed as a result of
   a. evaporation.
   b. filtration.
   c. a physical change.
   d. a chemical change.

3. A molecule is the smallest part of
   a. a crystal.
   b. a substance.
   c. an atom.
   d. compounds.

4. A salt and water mixture can be separated by
   a. hand.
   b. filtering.
   c. melting.
   d. evaporating.

5. The compound iron sulfide can be formed by
   a. heating.
   b. filtering.
   c. evaporating.
   d. mixing.

6. A molecular model of an organic compound is called a
   a. molecular formula.
   b. compound structure.
   c. structural formula.
   d. compound formula.

7. A covalent bond is formed when atoms
   a. trade electrons.
   b. gain electrons.
   c. lose electrons.
   d. share electrons.

8. In an ionic bond, two atoms form
   a. ions.
   b. protons.
   c. neutrons.
   d. electrons.

9. All organic compounds contain
   a. hydrogen.
   b. oxygen.
   c. nitrogen.
   d. carbon.

10. The building blocks of protein are
    a. carbohydrates.
    b. molecules.
    c. ions.
    d. amino acids.

TRUE/FALSE **Write** *true* **if the statement is true. If the statement is false, change the underlined term to make the statement true.**

11. The three main groups of <u>substances</u> are elements, compounds, and mixtures.

12. The substances in a mixture have not been <u>chemically</u> combined.

13. You can <u>physically</u> separate a mixture of sand and water.

14. A <u>compound</u> is made up of two or more elements.

15. An <u>ionic</u> bond is formed between two atoms that have gained or lost electrons.

16. <u>Nucleic acids</u> control the activities of a cell.

CHAPTER 4: Compounds and Mixtures **101**

Content Challenges

MULTIPLE CHOICE

1. b (4-2)
2. d (4-2)
3. b (4-2)
4. d (4-3)
5. a (4-4)
6. c (4-7)
7. d (4-6)
8. a (4-5)
9. d (4-7)
10. d (4-8)

TRUE/FALSE

11. false; matter (4-1)
12. true (4-3, 4-4)
13. true (4-3)
14. true (4-2)
15. true (4-5)
16. true (4-8)

ALTERNATIVE ASSESSMENT

Relating Information Students may write a Science Log entry comparing and contrasting mixtures and compounds. In their logs, they should also explain what organic compounds are and how those compounds impact our daily lives. Students may also include an explanation of the Food Guide Pyramid.

PORTFOLIO ASSESSMENT

Making Student Portfolios Portfolio Assessment provides an opportunity for students who are generally not good test-takers to demonstrate their learning in another way. Students can demonstrate their comprehension of the concepts in this chapter by making a portfolio. The Chapter Self-Check, the Venn Diagram, and the Big Idea Planner are some of the reproducibles on the Teacher's Resources CD-ROM that they can include in their portfolios. You can use the Portfolio Assessment Rubric also found on the Teacher's Resources CD-ROM to assess students' portfolios.

CHAPTER 4: Compounds and Mixtures **T101**

Concept Challenges

WRITTEN RESPONSE

1. **DESCRIBE:** Possible answers:
   a. Mixing warm water with the sand and sugar will cause the sugar to dissolve. The water can be poured through a filter, leaving just the sand. The water can then be evaporated, leaving the sugar. (4-3)
   b. The mixture can be boiled. The water will evaporate, leaving the sugar behind. (4-3)
   c. A magnet will attract the iron filings, leaving the sawdust. (4-3)
   d. Nickels and dimes can be separated by hand. (4-3)
2. **COMPARE:** Students should list the points included in Figure 4-21. (4-6)
3. **EXPLAIN:** Sodium is an active metal. Chlorine is a poisonous gas. Sodium chloride is neither a metal nor a poisonous gas. It is a relatively harmless, white crystal. (4-2)
4. **PREDICT:** Since carbohydrates provide the human body with energy, getting too few carbohydrates might cause a person not to have enough energy. A person might feel weak or tired. (4-8)
5. **ANALYZE:** It has four electrons that it can share with many different atoms. (4-7)

INTERPRETING A DIAGRAM

6. a covalent compound (4-6)
7. 6 (4-5)
8. 8; 1 (4-6)
9. 2 (4-6)
10. covalent (4-6)

Chapter Project Wrap-Up

ELEMENTS, COMPOUNDS, AND MIXTURES CROSSWORD PUZZLE

Pairs of students can exchange their puzzles with each other. You can make copies of a sample puzzle, distribute them, and solve the puzzle with the entire class. You can use the Group Activity Rubric found on the Teacher's Resources CD-ROM to assess students' projects. Fill in the rubric with the additional information below. For this project, students should have:

- created a crossword puzzle using Key Terms and concepts from the chapter.
- a neat and logical overall presentation of the crossword puzzle.

Concept Challenges TEST PREP

WRITTEN RESPONSE Answer each of the following questions in complete sentences.

1. **DESCRIBE:** Describe a method of separating each of the following mixtures:
   a. sand and sugar
   b. sugar and water
   c. sawdust and iron filings
   d. nickels and dimes
2. **COMPARE:** How are ionic and covalent compounds the same? How are they different?
3. **EXPLAIN:** How are the properties of table salt different from the properties of the elements that make it up?
4. **PREDICT:** What might happen if you did not get enough carbohydrates in your diet? Explain your answer.
5. **ANALYZE:** Why can carbon form so many different kinds of compounds?

INTERPRETING A DIAGRAM Use Figure 4-30 to answer the following questions.

6. What kind of compound is formed in Diagram B?
7. How many electrons are there in the outermost energy level of a neutral oxygen atom?
8. How many protons are there in a neutral oxygen atom? In a neutral hydrogen atom?
9. How many electrons does an atom of oxygen need in order to complete its outermost energy level?
10. What kind of bonds are being formed?

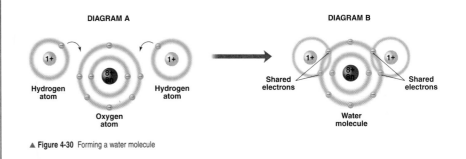

▲ **Figure 4-30** Forming a water molecule

Teaching Options

• TEACHING RESOURCES •

Teacher's Resources CD-ROM

Key Term Review: Chapter 4, p. 14

Chapter 4 Test: pp. 15–17

Group Activity Rubric: Teaching Tools, p. 6

Chapter Self-Check: Teaching Tools, p. 11

Venn Diagram: Study Tools, p. 10

Big Idea Planner: Study Tools, pp. 11–12

Portfolio Assessment Rubric: Teaching Tools, p. 10

PLANNING GUIDE

◆ **TEACHING THE CHAPTER** This chapter should take approximately 9–12 days to complete instruction and assessment.

	Skills and Features	Projects and Activities	Achieve Science Literacy	Meet Individual Needs
Chapter 5 Opener p. T103	IDENTIFY	• Chapter Project		
Lesson 5-1 **What is a solution?** pp. T104–T105 Standard: B1a	CLASSIFY, ANALYZE, DEFINE • Investigate • Web Infosearch • People in Science	• Cooperative Learning	• Study Hint • Ongoing Assessment	
Lesson 5-2 **What are the parts of a solution?** pp. T106–T107 Standard: B1a	CLASSIFY, INFER, ANALYZE • Designing an Experiment • Integrating Earth Science	• More on the Web • Extending the Lesson	• Study Hint	• ESL/ELL Strategy ◎ CD-ROM Designing an Experiment
Lesson 5-3 **Why is water a good solvent?** pp. T108–T109 Standard: B1a	EXPLAIN, HYPOTHESIZE, COMPARE • Web Infosearch	• Cooperative Learning • Extending the Lesson	• Study Hint • Writing Hint • Ongoing Assessment	
Lesson 5-4 **How can you change the rate at which substances dissolve?** pp. T110–T111 Standard: B1a	ANALYZE, INFER, RELATE • Designing an Experiment • Hands-On Activity	• More on the Web • Integrating Environmental Science • Lab Challenge	• Study Hint	• Reteach ◎ CD-ROM Enrichment Activity Designing an Experiment
Lesson 5-5 **What is the concentration of a solution?** pp. T112–T113 Standard: B1a	COMPARE, ANALYZE, HYPOTHESIZE • Investigate • Interpreting Visuals	• More on the Web • Cooperative Learning	• Study Hint • Reading Strategy	• Reteach ◎ CD-ROM Enrichment Activity Concept Map 📼 Laboratory Video
Lesson 5-6 **How do solutes affect freezing point?** pp. T114–T115 Standard: B1a	DESCRIBE, PREDICT, ANALYZE • Web Infosearch • Integrating Life Science	• Cooperative Learning	• Study Hint • Reading Strategy • Ongoing Assessment	◎ CD-ROM Enrichment Activity Cause-and-Effect Diagram

Planning Guide continues on next page.

Standards: For details on the correlation to National Science Standards see pages *xx–xxi*.

	Skills and Features	Projects and Activities	Achieve Science Literacy	Meet Individual Needs
Lesson 5-7 How do solutes affect boiling point? pp. T116–T117 Standard: B1a	DESCRIBE, ANALYZE, DEFINE • Designing an Experiment • Hands-On Activity	• More on the Web • Lab Skills Worksheet	• Study Hint	• Reteach CD-ROM Graph Paper Designing an Experiment Laboratory Video
Lesson 5-8 How can solutions be separated? pp. T118–T119 Standard: B1a	INFER, DEFINE, RESEARCH • Building Science Skills • Science and Technology	• More on the Web • Integrating Earth Science • Cooperative Learning	• Study Hint	
Lab Activity Making Supersaturated Solutions pp. T120–T121 Standard: B1a	OBSERVE, INFER, ANALYZE • Set-Up Time: 10 min • Lab Time: 30 min	• Lab Skills Worksheet • Extend the Lab Activity	• Tips for Using Technology	• ESL/ELL Strategy CD-ROM Lab Activity Report Database Planner
Lesson 5-9 How are crystals formed? pp. T122–T123 Standard: B1a	ORGANIZE, DEFINE, INFER • Building Science Skills • Hands-On Activity	• More on the Web • Extending the Lesson	• Study Hint • Ongoing Assessment	• Reteach CD-ROM Crystal Shapes
Big Idea How are crystals formed on Earth? pp. T124–T125	RESEARCH, COMMUNICATE, ANALYZE • Science Log: Writing Activity	• Big Idea Online • Close Activity	• Tips for Using Technology	• ESL/ELL Strategy CD-ROM Big Idea Planner
Chapter 5 Challenges pp. T126–T128	• Chapter Summary • Key Term Challenges • Content Challenges • Concept Challenges	• Chapter Project Wrap-Up	• Study Hint • Preparing Students for Standardized Tests	• ESL/ELL Strategy CD-ROM Chapter Self-Check Weekly Journal

Chapter **5** Solutions

▲ **Figure 5-1** A surfer is riding the "saltwater solution."

Surfers travel the world looking for the "perfect wave." In our culture, the ocean is important to us for many things. It supplies us with entertainment, food, travel, and shipping. More than three-fourths of Earth is covered by water. About 97% of that is ocean. Ocean water is the largest solution we know of. It contains many salts and minerals.

▶ What makes the ocean's water so important to us?

Contents

Chapter **5**
Solutions

Chapter Overview

In this chapter, students will learn about the properties of solutions, explain why water is a good solvent, and explain how to change the rate at which a substance dissolves. Students will also learn about the concentration of a solution, describe how a solution can be separated, and describe how crystals form.

About Figure 5-1 Ocean water is a solution in which many salts and other minerals are dissolved in water. The most abundant salt in ocean water is sodium chloride, or table salt. Other salts include chlorides and sulfates of magnesium, potassium, and calcium. Every mineral found on land also is found in ocean water. Desalination plants produce fresh water for human use by removing dissolved salts from ocean water. Many of the other minerals could be removed from ocean water, but the process is too expensive.

Answer Possible answer: It provides us with food, entertainment, shipping, and travel.

Linking Prior Knowledge

For this chapter, students should recall:

- the states of matter (Lesson 1-3).
- how matter changes state (Lesson 1-4).
- the physical properties of a mixture (Lesson 4-3).

Chapter Project

SOLUTIONS GUESSING GAME

MATERIALS: paper, pencil

Students will think of ten solutions that they use such as chocolate milk or lemonade. For each solution, they will create five clues to describe the solution or its use. One of the clues must name the solute and the solvent. Other clues can be based on solution type or solubility or insolubility of the solute. At the end of the chapter, students can play a guessing game to name one another's solutions.

learning style: linguistic

Teaching Options

ASSESSMENT PLANNER

For assessment in the Student Edition, see the following pages:

Content Assessment
Checking Concepts: pp. 105, 107, 109, 111, 113, 115, 117, 119, 123
Thinking Critically: pp. 105, 107, 109, 111, 113, 115, 117, 119, 123
Interpreting Visuals: p. 113
Chapter Challenges: pp. 126–128

Alternative Assessment
Building Skills: pp. 119, 123
Web InfoSearch: pp. 105, 109, 115
Science Log: p. 125

Performance-Based Assessment
Hands-On Activity: pp. 111, 117, 123
Designing an Experiment: pp. 107, 111, 117
Lab Activity: pp. 120–121

• TEACHING RESOURCES •

◉ **Teacher's Resources CD-ROM**
Lesson Review: Ch. 5, pp. 2, 3, 4, 5, 6, 9, 11, 12, 13

Enrichment: Ch. 5, pp. 7, 8, 10

Key Term Review: Ch. 5, p. 15

Chapter 5 Test: pp. 16–18

Laboratory Manual: pp. 5–8, 15–18, 37–40

▭ **Laboratory Videos**
Segment 5: Making a Supersaturated Solution

Segment 6: Observing Boiling Point Elevation

1 Introduce

🔍 INVESTIGATE

TIME: 5–10 minutes

PURPOSE: Students will make two mixtures and determine which is a solution.

MATERIALS: 2 clear plastic cups, 2 teaspoons, pepper, salt, water

PROCEDURE: Have students work in pairs and discuss their observations after stirring both mixtures.

THINK ABOUT IT: The pepper did not dissolve, while the salt did. Salt water is a solution because the salt dissolved.

✎ STUDY HINT Before beginning this lesson, have students scan each paragraph and record the solutions in their notebooks. As students read the lesson, they can classify the type of solution each one is.

Linking Prior Knowledge Before beginning this lesson, have students recall the states of matter (Lesson 1-3).

2 Teach

Demonstration In a beaker, mix equal parts of water and vegetable oil and stir the mixture. In a second beaker, mix equal parts of vegetable oil and mineral oil and stir. Explain to students that the water and vegetable oil do not mix evenly, so they do not form a solution. The vegetable oil and mineral oil do mix evenly, so they form a liquid solution. **learning style: visual**

Discussion Display different types of solutions, such as alcohol in water and club soda. Point out that these solutions are examples of liquid solutions. Show students a stainless steel spoon, and tell them that stainless steel is an example of a solid solution, which contains iron and other elements, such as chromium, carbon, and usually nickel. Explain to students that the air we breathe is not pure air. Pure air is a solution of gases that do not contain any pollutants. Then, refer students to Figure 5-3 to see examples of other types of solutions. **learning styles: visual, auditory**

5-1 What is a solution?

🔍 INVESTIGATE Identifying a Solution
HANDS-ON ACTIVITY

STEP 1

1. Put 50 mL of water into a clear plastic cup. Add 1 tsp of pepper and stir.
2. Put the same amount of water in a second cup, and add 1 tsp of salt. Stir.
3. Compare the two mixtures.

THINK ABOUT IT: What differences do you observe? Can you infer which mixture is a solution? On what do you base your inference?

Objective

Describe the characteristics of a solution.

Key Terms

dissolve (dih-ZAHLV): go into solution

solution: mixture in which the particles of one substance are evenly mixed with the particles of another substance

Salt and Water What would happen if you added some sand to a test tube of water? The sand would settle to the bottom of the test tube. Suppose you then added some salt to another test tube of water. The salt seems to disappear in the water. The salt is still in the water, but you cannot see it. The salt has dissolved in the water. When a substance **dissolves**, it goes into solution. The sand did not dissolve in the water.

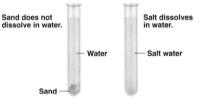

Sand does not dissolve in water.

Salt dissolves in water.

— Water

— Salt water

Sand

▲ **Figure 5-2** One test tube holds a solution. The other does not.

▶ **EXPLAIN:** Why does salt seem to disappear in water?

Solutions A mixture of salt and water is an example of a solution. A **solution** is a mixture in which the particles (molecules or ions) of one substance are evenly mixed with the particles of another substance. In a saltwater solution, sodium ions and chlorine ions are evenly mixed with molecules of water.

▶ **DEFINE:** What is a solution?

Types of Solutions Liquid solutions are formed when solids, liquids, or gases dissolve in liquids. Salt water is a liquid solution. A liquid solution may also be formed when a gas dissolves in a liquid. Club soda is a solution of the gas carbon dioxide dissolved in water. Liquids may dissolve in other liquids.

Solutions can also be formed when different substances dissolve in solids and gases. Figure 5-3 shows some examples of different kinds of solutions.

TYPES OF SOLUTIONS		
Substance	**Dissoved in**	**Examples**
Liquid	Liquid	Antifreeze (ethylene glycol) in water
	Gas	Water droplets in air (fog)
	Solid	Ether in rubber
Gas	Liquid	Club soda (CO_2 in water)
	Gas	Air (O_2 and other gases in N_2)
	Solid	Hydrogen in palladium
Solid	Liquid	Salt in water (ocean)
	Gas	Iodine vapor in air
	Solid	Brass (zinc in copper)

▲ **Figure 5-3**

▶ **LIST:** What are the different types of solutions?

104

Teaching Options

‼ FAST FACTS *A Gaseous Solution*

The air that we breathe is a solution of gases. It consists mostly of nitrogen (78 percent) and oxygen (21 percent). The remaining 1 percent is mostly argon, but also present are minute amounts of carbon dioxide, neon, krypton, xenon, and other gases. The amount of water vapor in the air varies from nearly 0 to about 4 percent, depending on the temperature and the relative humidity.

Carbon dioxide (CO_2) makes up less than 0.1 percent of the atmosphere, but despite its low concentration, it is believed to have a major effect on climate. The amount of carbon dioxide in the atmosphere is increasing because it is produced by the burning of fossil fuels such as oil, coal, and natural gas. The increasing carbon dioxide concentration may contribute to global warming.

Ozone is another important gas that is present in very low concentrations. An ozone molecule is made of three oxygen atoms (O_3). Near Earth's surface, ozone is a dangerous pollutant. High in the atmosphere, ozone forms a layer that prevents harmful solar radiation from reaching Earth's surface.

Other Solutions Tap water, the water you use every day, is not pure water. It is a solution. Most tap water contains dissolved compounds of iron and compounds of calcium. Tap water may also contain dissolved chemicals, such as chlorine, that have been added to make the water safe to drink. Pure air is a solution of gases, mainly nitrogen and oxygen, evenly mixed together.

 ANALYZE: Why is pure air called a solution?

✓ CHECKING CONCEPTS

1. Solutions are formed when substances _____ in other substances.
2. Salt water is a solution formed when a _____ dissolves in a liquid.
3. A mixture in which one substance is evenly mixed with another substance is called a _____.
4. Club soda is an example of a solution formed when a _____ dissolves in a liquid.
5. Pure air is a solution of gases, such as _____ and _____.

💡 THINKING CRITICALLY

6. **CLASSIFY:** Which of the following mixtures are solutions?
   a. sugar and water   e. sea water
   b. brass   f. salt and pepper
   c. club soda   g. sand and water
   d. flour and salt   h. air

7. **ANALYZE:** For each of the mixtures you classified as solutions in question 6, identify the type of solution formed.

Web InfoSearch

Hard Water Because tap water is not pure water, it does not freeze at exactly 0°C. Instead, it freezes at a lower temperature. Tap water containing high concentrations of dissolved salts of calcium, iron, and magnesium is called hard water. This is because the salts make it hard for soap to form a lather with the water.

SEARCH: Find out how these solutes are added to your tap water. Start your search at www.conceptsandchallenges.com. Some key search words are **tap water**, **hard water**, and **water solutes**.

⚛ *People in Science*

ANALYTICAL CHEMIST

Do you enjoy studying science and mathematics? Can you make careful, precise measurements? Are you determined to find the answer to a problem? If so, you may enjoy a career as an analytical chemist. Analytical chemists analyze the chemical composition of substances. They perform experiments to identify characteristics of the substances and to find out what will happen when different substances are combined.

▲ **Figure 5-4** Dr. Sherman K. W. Fung

Most analytical chemists work in laboratories. Dr. Sherman K. W. Fung is such a chemist. He founded and directed the Bio-Sciences Division of SGS Hong Kong Limited, a testing, inspection, and verification organization. Currently, he serves as chief operating officer of the Institute of Chinese Medicine in Hong Kong, China.

To become an analytical chemist, you need a college degree in chemistry. Dr. Fung studied at the University of London and Oxford University.

Thinking Critically Why is it important to be precise and detailed in this line of work?

Answers to questions

1 **EXPLAIN:** It dissolves in the water.

2 **DEFINE:** a mixture in which the particles of one substance are evenly mixed with the particles of another substance

3 **LIST:** liquid solution, gas solution, solid solution

4 **ANALYZE:** Pure air contains different gases that are evenly mixed together.

3 Assess

✓ CHECKING CONCEPTS ANSWERS

1. dissolve
2. solid
3. solution
4. gas
5. nitrogen, oxygen

💡 THINKING CRITICALLY ANSWERS

6. **CLASSIFY:** a, b, c, e, h
7. **ANALYZE:** liquid, solid, liquid, liquid, gas

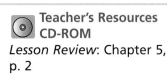

4 Close

Web InfoSearch

Hard Water Have students use the Internet to find out how the solutes that create hard water are added to their tap water. Some key search words are **tap water** and **hard water.** Have students begin their search at www.conceptsandchallenges.com.

COOPERATIVE LEARNING

Identifying Solids That Dissolve Have students work in pairs to make a list of five solids that will dissolve in water. Then, use suggestions from students to write a class list of these solids on the board.

ONGOING ASSESSMENT

Giving Examples of Solutions Make a three-column chart on the board. The heads of the columns should be *Liquid Solutions*, *Gas Solutions*, and *Solid Solutions*. Have volunteers fill in the columns.

• TEACHING RESOURCES •

💿 **Teacher's Resources CD-ROM**
Lesson Review: Chapter 5, p. 2

People in Science

ANALYTICAL CHEMIST

Real-Life Connection The different kinds of work analytical chemists do impact our lives. They work in a broad range of industries, including the food and pharmaceutical industries. For example, you could find them analyzing traces of pesticides in milk or analyzing impurities in medicines.

Thinking Critically Answer
Possible answer: An analytical chemist must be precise and detailed to accurately determine the chemical composition and properties of various substances.

1 Introduce

📝 **STUDY HINT** Before beginning this lesson, have students write the Key Terms in their notebooks. As students read the lesson, they should give an example for each Key Term.

Linking Prior Knowledge Ask students to recall some ingredients in their favorite soft drink. (Possible answers: water or carbonated water, sugar, aspartame, and caffeine.) Explain to students that water is the solvent in the soft drink, and the other substances are solutes.

2 Teach

Demonstration Have students observe the following mixtures: sugar and water, iron filings and water, sulfur and water. Explain that not all substances dissolve in water. Substances that dissolve in water are soluble in water. Substances that do not dissolve in water are insoluble in water. **learning styles: visual, auditory**

Discussion Point out that in a solution the substance that dissolves is called the solute and the substance in which the solute dissolves is called the solvent. Then, prepare a solution of sugar and water. Ask students to identify the solute and solvent of the solution. (solute: sugar; solvent: water) **learning styles: auditory, visual**

Answers to questions

▶ **CONTRAST:** The solute dissolves in the solvent, which is usually present in the greater amount.

▶ **PREDICT:** The substance will dissolve in the water to form a solution.

▶ **ANALYZE:** It may be soluble in one solvent but insoluble in a different solvent.

Reinforcement Be sure that students understand that substances are soluble or insoluble only in terms of another substance. You can demonstrate this concept by adding salt to a beaker containing water and to another beaker containing vegetable oil. Stir the mixtures. Salt dissolves in water but not in vegetable oil. **learning style: visual**

5-2 What are the parts of a solution?

Objective
Identify the parts of a solution.

Key Terms
solute (SAHL-yoot): substance that is dissolved in a solvent

solvent: substance in which a solute dissolves

soluble (SAHL-yoo-buhl): able to dissolve

solubility: maximum amount of a substance that will dissolve in a given quantity of a solvent at a given temperature

insoluble (in-SAHL-yoo-buhl): not able to dissolve

▲ **Figure 5-5** Potassium permanganate dissolves slowly in water. After a few minutes, the solution becomes pink.

Parts of a Solution All solutions are made when one substance dissolves in another substance. A solution of salt and water forms when salt dissolves in water. The part of a solution that dissolves is called the **solute.** Salt is the solute in a solution of salt and water. The part of the solution in which a solute dissolves is called the **solvent.** This substance is usually present in the greater amount, so water is the solvent in a saltwater solution. In pure air, nitrogen is present in the greatest amount of three gases; it is the solvent. Oxygen and argon are the solutes.

 CONTRAST: What is the difference between a solute and a solvent?

Soluble Substances In many solutions, the solute becomes invisible. For example, when sugar dissolves in water, the solution looks like plain water. When some substances dissolve, they produce a colored solution. Look at Figure 5-5 at the top of the next column. The picture on the left shows a crystal of potassium permanganate just after it has been placed in a test tube containing water. The picture on the right shows the same test tube a few minutes later. The crystal has begun to dissolve. If the test tube is allowed to sit long enough, or if the mixture is stirred, the entire solution will be a uniform pink color.

Some substances are more **soluble**, able to dissolve, than other substances. The **solubility** of a substance tells you how much of that substance will dissolve in 100 g of solvent at a given temperature. For example, about 38 g of sodium chloride will dissolve in 100 g of water at 20°C. If you add more than 38 g of sodium chloride to this solution, the excess will not dissolve. It will sink to the bottom of the solution.

▶ **PREDICT:** What will happen when a substance that is soluble in water is mixed with water?

Insoluble Substances Many substances do not dissolve in water. A granite statue does not dissolve in rainwater. Sand does not dissolve in ocean water. A drinking glass does not dissolve when you pour water into it. All of these materials are said to be **insoluble,** or not able to dissolve, in water. A substance that will not dissolve in a given solvent, such as water, is said to be insoluble in that solvent.

You may have heard the saying "water and oil don't mix." This saying means that oil is not soluble in water. If you add oil to a glass of water, the oil will float in a separate layer on top of the water. Even if you stir or shake the mixture, no dissolving will take place. Instead, you will get a mixture like the one shown in Figure 5-6 on the next page. In a short time, this mixture will again separate into its two layers.

Teaching Options

ESL/ELL STRATEGY

Reversing Meanings of Adjectives Have students review the definitions of the words *soluble* and *insoluble* in this lesson. (*soluble*: "able to dissolve"; *insoluble*: "not able to dissolve") Tell students that *in-* is a prefix that means "not." When added to an adjective, it reverses the adjective's meaning. Group students to brainstorm pairs of words that work with this prefix, but caution them that there are other prefixes used for the same purpose (such as *un-* and *non-*) and *in-* does not work in every case. **learning styles: auditory, linguistic**

EXTENDING THE LESSON

Identifying Solutes and Solvents Explain to students that a metal alloy is a solution in which a solid is dissolved in another solid. Tell them that sterling silver is a metal alloy that is 92.5 percent silver and 7.5 percent copper. Ask students which metal is the solute and which is the solvent in this alloy. Lead students to conclude that silver is present in the greater amount, so it is the solvent, while copper is the solute. **learning styles: auditory, logical/mathematical**

▲ Figure 5-6 Oil droplets do not dissolve in water.

A substance may dissolve in one solvent but not in another solvent. For example, sugar will dissolve in water but will not dissolve in vegetable oil. So, sugar can be described as being soluble in water and insoluble in vegetable oil. The chemical makeup of a solvent determines whether another substance is soluble or insoluble in that solvent.

▶ ANALYZE: How can a substance be both soluble and insoluble?

1. Salt is the _____ in a saltwater solution.
2. In air, _____ is the solvent.
3. The substance in which a solute dissolves is called a _____.
4. Sugar is _____ in water.
5. In a solution of sugar and water, water is the _____.

💡 THINKING CRITICALLY

6. CLASSIFY: Instant coffee is a solution formed from powdered coffee and hot water. Identify the solute and the solvent in this solution.
7. INFER: Is wood soluble in water? How do you know?

DESIGNING AN EXPERIMENT

Design an experiment to solve the following problem. Include a hypothesis, variables, a procedure, and a type of data to study.

PROBLEM: Identify the solute and solvent in iced tea.

◈ **Integrating Earth Science**

TOPIC: chemical weathering

AN ACIDIC SOLUTION

Weathering is the breaking down of rocks and minerals by natural forces, such as wind and water. In mechanical weathering, rocks are broken down by the action of wind, water, or ice. In chemical weathering, substances in water cause substances in the rock to dissolve. This action weakens the structure of the rock. The rock is then more easily broken apart by mechanical weathering.

A common type of chemical weathering takes place when carbon dioxide from the air dissolves in rainwater. A solution called carbonic acid forms. When this weak acid seeps into rocks, it dissolves the limestone in the rocks. The dissolved limestone is carried away by the rainwater. As a result, cracks are left in the rocks. Over time, as the rocks are struck by wind or moving water, they will easily crumble.

▲ Figure 5-7 Carbonic acid has dissolved the features of this limestone face.

Thinking Critically What is the difference between chemical and mechanical weathering?

3 Assess

✓ CHECKING CONCEPTS ANSWERS

1. solute
2. nitrogen
3. solvent
4. soluble
5. solvent

💡 THINKING CRITICALLY ANSWERS

6. CLASSIFY: solute: powdered coffee; solvent: hot water
7. INFER: No; Wood floats on water. It does not mix evenly with water.

4 Close

DESIGNING AN EXPERIMENT

Use the Designing an Experiment Rubric on the Teacher's Resources CD-ROM to assess students' experiments. Fill in the rubric with the additional information below. For this assignment, students should have:

- mentioned what makes up a solution in forming the hypothesis.
- in the procedure, stirred the solute (powdered tea) in the solvent (water) to make a solution (instant tea).

◈ **Integrating Earth Science**

TOPIC: chemical weathering

AN ACIDIC SOLUTION

Earth-Science Connection The chemical weathering described in this feature is a result of the action of carbonic acid on limestone. Carbonic acid is a weak acid. However, atmospheric pollution can create stronger acids. When fossil fuels are burned, sulfur oxides and nitrogen oxides are released into the atmosphere. These oxides can combine with moisture in clouds to form dilute solutions of strong acids such as sulfuric acid and nitric acid. The dilute acids fall to Earth as acid rain, causing harmful effects on plant and animal life, and hastening the weathering of stone buildings and sculptures. Historic buildings such as the Parthenon in Greece have been damaged by acid rain.

Thinking Critically Answer
In chemical weathering, substances in water cause substances in rock to dissolve. In mechanical weathering, rocks are broken down by the action of wind, water, or ice.

1 Introduce

STUDY HINT Before beginning this lesson, have students study Figures 5-9 and 5-10. Have them compare the illustrations in both figures. Ask students how the illustrations are similar. (In all the illustrations, water molecules attract solute particles.) **learning styles: logical/mathematical, auditory**

Linking Prior Knowledge Have students recall how atoms combine in ionic bonds and covalent bonds (Lessons 4-5 and 4-6). **learning style: linguistic**

2 Teach

Demonstration You can demonstrate the polarity of water by rubbing a balloon against your hair, which will cause the balloon to become negatively charged as electrons move from your hair to the balloon. Hold the balloon near a thin stream of water. The stream of water will be bent as the balloon attracts the positive end of the water molecules.
learning style: visual

Discussion Use Figures 5-9 and 5-10 to discuss how molecular solutions form and how ionic solutions form. Explain that in both cases, the force of attraction between solvent particles and solute particles causes the solute to dissolve to form a solution.
learning styles: visual, auditory

Reinforcement Make sure students understand that when sugar is dissolved in water, the structure of the sugar crystals breaks apart. Have students study Figure 5-9. The first illustration shows molecules of sugar close together, as in a crystal. The second illustration shows how the crystal breaks apart due to the attraction between the water molecules and the sugar molecules. The third illustration shows how the crystal has broken apart into individual sugar molecules that are spread evenly throughout the solution.
learning style: visual

5-3 Why is water a good solvent?

Objective
Explain why water is sometimes called the universal solvent.

Key Term
polar molecule: molecule in which one end has a positive charge and the other end has a negative charge

Water Molecules Water molecules are polar. A **polar molecule** is a molecule in which one end has a positive charge and the other end has a negative charge. A water molecule is made up of two atoms of hydrogen joined to one atom of oxygen. The hydrogen end of a water molecule has a positive charge. The oxygen end of a water molecule has a negative charge.

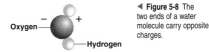

Oxygen — Hydrogen

◀ **Figure 5-8** The two ends of a water molecule carry opposite charges.

Water is sometimes called the universal solvent. This is because many types of substances dissolve in water. The electrical charges associated with the polar molecules of water help to dissolve different kinds of substances.

▶ **EXPLAIN:** Why is a water molecule called a polar molecule?

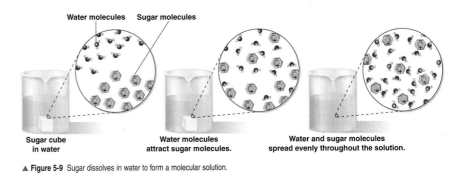

Water molecules   Sugar molecules

Sugar cube in water | Water molecules attract sugar molecules. | Water and sugar molecules spread evenly throughout the solution.

▲ **Figure 5-9** Sugar dissolves in water to form a molecular solution.

108

Molecular Solutions The charged ends of a water molecule help separate particles of a solute and spread them throughout the water. Figure 5-9 shows what happens when you place a sugar cube in a glass of water. The ends of the polar water molecules attract the molecules in the sugar cube. Each sugar molecule is pulled to a water molecule. As the sugar dissolves, sugar molecules are evenly mixed throughout the water. This is a molecular solution.

▶ **DESCRIBE:** What happens to the sugar molecules when sugar is placed in water?

Force of Attraction Molecular solutions form when the force of attraction between the solute molecules and the solvent molecules is greater than the forces of attraction holding the molecules of the solute together. A sugar crystal gets its shape from the force of attraction between sugar molecules. The sugar molecules will break away from the sugar crystal only if they are pulled by a greater force of attraction. This is also true of other types of solutes.

▶ **PREDICT:** What will happen if the force of attraction holding solute particles together is greater than the force of attraction between solute and solvent?

Teaching Options

Ionic Solutions Ionic compounds are made up of charged particles—positive ions and negative ions. These particles are held together by the force of attraction created by their opposite charges.

When an ionic compound such as sodium chloride—table salt—is added to water, these ions are attracted by the charged ends of the polar molecules of water. In time, the water molecules surround the ions and separate them, as shown in Figure 5-9. The salt dissolves completely, forming an ionic solution.

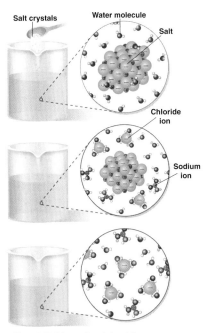

Salt crystals
Water molecule
Salt
Chloride ion
Sodium ion

▲ **Figure 5-10** Salt water is an ionic solution.

4 COMPARE: How are molecular solutions similar to ionic solutions? How are they different?

✓ CHECKING CONCEPTS

1. Water is a _____ molecule.
2. Water is sometimes called the _____ solvent.
3. The hydrogen end of a water molecule has a _____ electrical charge.
4. The force of attraction between water molecules and sugar molecules is _____ than the force of attraction between the sugar molecules.
5. Solutions form when the force of attraction between the solute and the solvent is greater than the force of attraction between the particles of the _____.

💡 THINKING CRITICALLY

6. INFER: A substance put in a glass of water does not dissolve. What does this tell you about the force of attraction between the particles of this substance?
7. HYPOTHESIZE: Will a teaspoon of water dissolve in a glass of water? Explain. (Hint: Review the definitions of *dissolve* and *solution* from Lesson 5-1.)

Web InfoSearch

Water Purification Chemist Drinking water has to be treated before it reaches your home. A water purification process begins after the water is analyzed. Various tests are performed on the water to find out what chemicals it contains. Based on the results of the tests, chemicals that should be removed from or added to the water to make it suitable for drinking are identified. Most of this work is done in the laboratories of purification plants.

SEARCH: Use the Internet to find out more about water purification chemists. Then create a poster. Start your search at www.conceptsandchallenges.com. Some key search words are **water purification, chemist,** and **purification chemistry.**

Answers to questions

1 EXPLAIN: One end has a positive charge, and the other end has a negative charge.

2 DESCRIBE: The sugar molecules are attracted by the water molecules, and the sugar molecules separate.

3 PREDICT: The solute will not dissolve.

4 COMPARE: Both form as a result of attraction between solute and solvent particles. In a molecular solution, the solute particles are neutral molecules. In an ionic solution, the solute particles are positive ions and negative ions.

✏️ **WRITING HINT** Suggest that students write answers to questions in complete sentences. This helps improve the quality of their thinking as well as their writing.

3 Assess

✓ CHECKING CONCEPTS ANSWERS

1. polar
2. universal
3. positive
4. greater
5. solute

💡 THINKING CRITICALLY ANSWERS

6. INFER: The force of attraction between the particles of the substance is greater than the force of attraction between those particles and water.
7. HYPOTHESIZE: No; A solution is formed when one substance dissolves in another substance.

4 Close

Web InfoSearch

Water Purification Chemist Drinking water has to be treated before it reaches your home. Have students use the Internet to find out about water purification chemists. Some key search words are **water purification, water purification chemist,** and **purification chemistry.** Have students begin their search at www.conceptsandchallenges.com.

EXTENDING THE LESSON

Identifying the Stronger Attraction for Electrons A polar molecule results from a covalent bond in which there is an unequal sharing of electrons. Show students a model of a water molecule, and ask them whether a hydrogen atom or an oxygen atom has a stronger attraction for electrons. Guide students to the conclusion that oxygen has a stronger attraction for electrons in a water molecule. The oxygen atom, therefore, has a partial negative charge and the hydrogen atoms have a partial positive charge.
learning style: visual

• TEACHING RESOURCES •

💿 **Teacher's Resources CD-ROM**
Lesson Review: Chapter 5, p. 4

1 Introduce

✏️ **STUDY HINT** Have students write the objective in their notebooks. As students read this lesson, tell them to write the information that meets the objective.

Linking Prior Knowledge Ask students to describe how they would make a glass of lemonade using a powdered lemonade mix. They will probably say that they would add the lemonade mix to a glass of water and then stir the mixture. Ask why students would stir the mixture. (to dissolve the powder faster) Tell students that in this lesson they will learn about ways to speed up the rate of dissolving.

2 Teach

Discussion Show students a few medium-sized crystals of rock salt. Then, show them an equal mass of table salt granules. Tell students that the crystals and granules are the same substance—sodium chloride. Ask students whether the rock salt crystals or the table salt granules will dissolve faster in water. Then, add the rock salt to a beaker of water and the table salt to another beaker of water and stir both mixtures. The table salt should dissolve first. Explain to students that the total surface area of all of the table salt granules is greater than the surface area of the rock salt crystals, so the table salt dissolves faster in water.
learning styles: visual, auditory

Answers to questions

▶ **INFER:** Stirring causes the sugar molecules to leave the crystal more rapidly.

▶ **RELATE:** As the temperature of the liquid increases, the rate at which most solids dissolve also increases.

▶ **PREDICT:** powdered sugar

▶ **HYPOTHESIZE:** Possible answer: As the pressure on a gas increases, its molecules move closer together and its concentration increases. This situation allows more gas particles to dissolve in the solvent.

▶ **RELATE:** polar compounds and ionic compounds

5-4 How can you change the rate at which substances dissolve?

Objective
Describe four ways to speed up the rate of dissolving.

Stirring Solutions form when a solute dissolves in a solvent. The rate at which a solid solute dissolves can be changed. Certain factors can speed up the rate at which a solute dissolves. Stirring a solution will make the solute dissolve faster. If you put a cube of sugar into a glass of water, it will eventually dissolve. However, stirring the water will cause the sugar to dissolve faster. Stirring the water causes the sugar molecules to leave the crystals more rapidly.

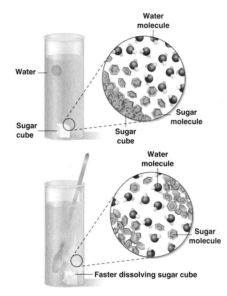

▲ **Figure 5-11** Stirring (bottom) causes sugar to dissolve faster.

▶ **INFER:** Why does stirring make a sugar cube dissolve faster in water?

110

Temperature The temperature of a liquid solvent affects the rate at which a solid solute dissolves. A cube of sugar dissolves faster in hot water than in an equal amount of cold water. Heat increases the motion of water molecules. This increased energy helps to separate sugar molecules more quickly. As the temperature of a liquid solvent increases, the rate at which a solid solute dissolves also increases.

Some gases, such as oxygen and carbon dioxide, are soluble in water. Increasing the temperature of a liquid solvent has the opposite effect on gaseous solutes than it does on solid solutes. As the temperature of the solvent increases, the dissolving rate of a gaseous solute decreases.

▶ **RELATE:** What is the relationship between the temperature of a liquid solvent and the rate at which a solid dissolves in it?

Surface Area The size of the particles of a solid solute also affects the rate at which it dissolves. The smaller the size of the solute particles, the faster the solute dissolves. A crushed sugar cube dissolves faster in water than does a solid sugar cube placed in an equal amount of water at the same temperature. As the size of the solute particles decreases, the rate at which the solute dissolves increases.

▶ **PREDICT:** Which would dissolve faster in the same amount of water at the same temperature, a sugar cube or powdered sugar?

Pressure The solubility of most gases is affected by pressure. When pressure is increased, more gas can dissolve. For example, when you open a bottle or can containing a carbonated soft drink, you hear the gas escaping. This is because carbon dioxide is added under high pressure. However, pressure has little affect on the dissolving of solids or liquids.

▶ **HYPOTHESIZE:** Why do you think more gas can dissolve when pressure is increased?

Teaching Options

◈ INTEGRATING ENVIRONMENTAL SCIENCE

Controlling and Monitoring Thermal Pollution Most students probably think of *water pollution* as contamination of water by one or more chemicals. Explain that a less familiar form of water pollution is *thermal pollution*. Large quantities of water are used for cooling in electric power plants and industrial manufacturing facilities. The water is first pumped from its source, such as a river or lake, and then circulates through the equipment in the industrial facility, absorbing excess heat and helping to maintain a safe operating temperature. The heated water may then return directly to the body of water from which it originated. The resulting increase in water temperature can be harmful to plant and animal species that cannot tolerate significant temperature changes. In addition, the temperature increase reduces the solubility of oxygen in water. Fish and other forms of aquatic life need dissolved oxygen, so an increase in water temperature accompanied by a decrease in the amount of dissolved oxygen can threaten their survival. Thermal pollution must be monitored and controlled to limit its impact on aquatic life. Have students make a poster that shows how thermal pollution affects aquatic life around a power plant or an industrial facility.
learning styles: auditory, tactile

Types of Solvents You have learned that water molecules are polar. Water, then, is a polar solvent. Polar solvents such as water will dissolve compounds made up of polar molecules and compounds that separate into ions. However, polar solvents will not dissolve compounds made up of nonpolar molecules, such as oils and fats. These substances will, however, dissolve in nonpolar solvents, such as benzene. A good way to remember this "rule" is "like dissolves like."

▷ RELATE: What type of compounds will water dissolve?

✓ CHECKING CONCEPTS

1. Stirring a solvent _____ the rate at which a solute dissolves in it.
2. Sugar dissolves more slowly in _____ water than in hot water.
3. The smaller the size of the solute particles, the _____ the rate of dissolving.
4. As the _____ of a solvent increases, the rate at which a solid solute dissolves also increases.

Hands-On Activity

CHANGING THE RATE AT WHICH A SUBSTANCE DISSOLVES

You will need four beakers, a graduated cylinder, water, a spoon, and four sugar cubes.

1. Put 100 mL of water in each beaker.
2. Place one sugar cube in each of the first two beakers. Stir the water in the first beaker with a spoon. Leave the second beaker untouched. Compare the results.
3. Use a spoon to crush a sugar cube. Carefully drop the crushed sugar into the third beaker. Place one sugar cube in the fourth beaker. Stir both mixtures and compare the results.

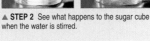
▲ STEP 2 See what happens to the sugar cube when the water is stirred.

Practicing Your Skills

4. OBSERVE: What effect did stirring have on the dissolving rate of the sugar cube?
5. OBSERVE: What effect did crushing the sugar cube have on the rate of dissolving?
6. HYPOTHESIZE: How could you find the fastest way to dissolve a sugar cube in 100 mL of water?

💡 THINKING CRITICALLY

5. INFER: Why are most types of instant coffee made in powdered form?
6. ANALYZE: Explain how each of the following will make a solid solute dissolve faster.
   a. Grind the solute into small pieces.
   b. Place the solvent in a blender.
   c. Heat the solvent.

DESIGNING AN EXPERIMENT

Design an experiment to solve the following problem. Include a hypothesis, variables, a procedure, and a type of data to study.

PROBLEM: How does changing each of these factors affect the rate at which 5 g of sugar will dissolve in 100 mL of water?

a. stirring
b. temperature
c. surface area

---

3 Assess

✓ CHECKING CONCEPTS ANSWERS

1. increases
2. cold
3. greater
4. temperature

💡 THINKING CRITICALLY ANSWERS

5. INFER: Smaller particles dissolve faster than larger particles.
6. ANALYZE: **a.** Decreasing particle size increases the rate of dissolving.
   b. Stirring and decreasing particle size of the solute increase the rate of dissolving.
   c. Increasing the temperature increases the rate of dissolving.

4 Close

DESIGNING AN EXPERIMENT

Use the Designing an Experiment Rubric on the Teacher's Resources CD-ROM to assess students' experiments. Fill in the rubric with the additional information below. For this assignment, students should have:

- mentioned, in forming the hypothesis, three factors that affect the rate at which a solid solute dissolves.
- in the procedure, during different trials, dissolved 5 g of sugar in 100 mL of water while stirring the mixture, changed the temperature of the water, and changed the size of the sugar particles.

Hands-On Activity

CHANGING THE RATE AT WHICH A SUBSTANCE DISSOLVES

TIME: 15–20 minutes

PURPOSE: comparing, analyzing

ALTERNATIVE MATERIALS: Clear plastic cups can be used in place of beakers.

Practicing Your Skills Answers

4. OBSERVE: Stirring increased the rate of dissolving.
5. OBSERVE: Crushing increased the rate of dissolving.
6. HYPOTHESIZE: Possible answer: Measure the dissolving time under various conditions (stirred or not, crushed or not, hot or cold water), alone and in various combinations.

MORE ON THE WEB

More on Dissolving Rates
Have students visit www.conceptsandchallenges.com to take an online quiz on dissolving rates.

RETEACH

Demonstrating the Effect of Temperature on Dissolving Rate
Place a spoonful of sugar into each of two beakers, one containing hot water and the other containing cold water. Stir the beakers simultaneously until the solute completely dissolves in one of the beakers. Students will observe that sugar dissolves faster in hot water. **learning style: visual**

• TEACHING RESOURCES •

🔘 **Teacher's Resources CD-ROM**
Lesson Review: Chapter 5, p. 5
Enrichment: Chapter 5, pp. 7, 8
Designing an Experiment Rubric: Teaching Tools, p. 7
Designing an Experiment: Study Tools, p. 14

Laboratory Manual
Lab. Challenge: What factors affect how fast a substance dissolves? pp. 37–40

1 Introduce

🔍 INVESTIGATE

TIME: 5–10 minutes

PURPOSE: Students will make two mixtures and determine which one contains more solute.

MATERIALS: 2 clear plastic cups or beakers, 2 teaspoons, copper sulfate

PROCEDURE: Have the decision-making partner explain his or her choice to the other partner.

THINK ABOUT IT: One mixture was darker than the other. The darker mixture contained more solute.

✍️ **STUDY HINT** Before beginning this lesson, have students draw a concept map. The main concept would be *Solutions* and its definition. The supporting concepts would be types of solutions that students would fill in and define as they read the lesson. Students can use the Concept Map on the Teacher's Resources CD-ROM.

Linking Prior Knowledge Some students might be familiar with the terms *saturated* and *unsaturated* as they relate to fats. Saturated fats are organic compounds that generally are solids at room temperature. Unsaturated fats are liquids at room temperature. In saturated fats, all of the carbon atoms are joined by single bonds. In unsaturated fats, some of the carbon atoms are joined by double bonds. Be sure that students understand that the terms *saturated* and *unsaturated* have different meanings when applied to fats than when applied to solutions.

2 Teach

Demonstrate Place 1 g, 2 g, and 3 g of copper sulfate into three separate test tubes. Add 15 mL of water to each and stopper the test tubes. Shake the tubes until the copper sulfate dissolves. Display the three test tubes in order of increasing concentration. Point to the first two test tubes and ask: *Which solution is more concentrated?* (test tube 2) Point to test tubes 2 and 3. Ask: *Which solution is more concentrated?* (test tube 3) *Which is more dilute?* (test tube 2) Discuss that the same test tube can be labeled *concentrated* or *dilute*, depending on the concentration of the solution to which it is compared. **learning style: visual**

5-5 What is the concentration of a solution?

INVESTIGATE

🔍 Observing Concentrations
HANDS-ON ACTIVITY

1. Working with a partner, add 100 mL of water to each of two clear plastic glasses.
2. Have one partner face away from the work area. The other partner adds 1/2 tsp of copper sulfate to the water in one glass and 1 tsp of copper sulfate to the water in the other glass and stirs both mixtures.
3. Have the first partner turn and study the two solutions. Ask this student to choose which mixture contains the greater amount of solute.

THINK ABOUT IT: How did the two mixtures differ in appearance? How did this difference help to indicate which solution contained more solute?

STEP 3

Objective
Differentiate between saturated and unsaturated solutions.

Key Terms

dilute solution: solution containing a small amount of solute compared with the amount of solvent present

concentrated solution: solution containing a large amount of solute compared with the amount of solvent present

unsaturated solution: solution containing less solute than it can hold at a given temperature

saturated solution: solution containing all the solute it can hold at a given temperature

supersaturated solution: solution containing more solute than it can normally hold at a given temperature

Dilute and Concentrated Solutions The terms *dilute* and *concentrated* are used to describe the relative amounts of solute and solvent present in a solution. Figure 5-12 shows the appearance of three different concentrations of copper sulfate in 100 mL of water at the same temperature.

As the illustration shows, a **dilute solution** is one containing a small amount of solute compared with the amount of solvent present. Dilute solutions are weak. A **concentrated solution** is one containing a large amount of solute compared with the amount of solvent present. Concentrated solutions are strong.

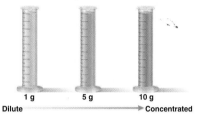

Dilute ——————→ Concentrated

1 g   5 g   10 g

▲ **Figure 5-12** Different concentrations of copper sulfate

▶ **COMPARE:** What is the difference between a dilute solution and a concentrated solution?

Unsaturated Solutions If you were to add 1 g of the compound copper sulfate to 100 mL of water at 20°C, the copper sulfate would quickly dissolve. In fact, quite a bit more copper sulfate could dissolve in that much water at that temperature. This copper sulfate solution is unsaturated. An **unsaturated solution** contains less dissolved solute than it can hold at a given temperature.

112

Teaching Options

RETEACH

Comparing Saturated and Unsaturated Solutions Adding several grams of solute at a time, slowly dissolve enough potassium nitrate in 100 mL of water to make a saturated solution. Solute that is not dissolved will remain on the bottom after vigorous stirring. While preparing the solution, explain that a solution in which more solute can be dissolved is called an unsaturated solution. Define a saturated solution as one that contains all the solute it can hold at a given temperature. Then, heat the saturated solution of potassium nitrate. Stirring the heated solution will cause the solute at the bottom of the beaker to dissolve. Dissolve a small amount of additional solute in the heated solution. Point out that the solution is no longer saturated because heating the solution causes it to become unsaturated as the solubility of potassium nitrate increases.

learning styles: visual, auditory

100 mL

1 g CuSO₄

◀ **Figure 5-13**
Unsaturated solution
of copper sulfate

2> ANALYZE: When is a solution unsaturated?

Saturated Solutions There is a limit to the amount of solute a given amount of solvent can hold at a specific temperature. If you continued to add copper sulfate to the solution described above, the solution would become saturated. A **saturated solution** contains all of the solute it can hold at a given temperature. If you added more copper sulfate to the saturated solution, it would not dissolve. It would settle out of the solution.

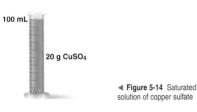
100 mL

20 g CuSO₄

◀ **Figure 5-14** Saturated
solution of copper sulfate

3> HYPOTHESIZE: If you were preparing a solution, how could you tell when it became saturated?

Supersaturated Solutions The temperature of a solvent determines the amount of solute it can dissolve. As the temperature of a solvent increases, so does the amount of a given solute it can hold. For example, 100 mL of water at 20°C can hold about 14 g of copper sulfate. The same amount of water at 80°C can hold about five times as much copper sulfate.

Suppose you have a saturated solution of copper sulfate at 50°C. The solution contains as much solute as it can hold at that temperature. What will happen if the solution is allowed to cool? At the lower temperature, the solution will be holding *more* solute than it could normally hold at that temperature. Such a solution is said to be **supersaturated**.

4> INFER: What happens to a solution that enables it to hold more solute than it normally would?

✔ CHECKING CONCEPTS

1. A _____ solution contains a small amount of dissolved solute.
2. A _____ solution contains a large amount of dissolved solute.
3. An unsaturated solution contains less _____ than it can hold at a given temperature.
4. A solution that contains all the solute it can hold at a given temperature is called a _____ solution.
5. When saturated solutions are _____, they usually become unsaturated.

💡 THINKING CRITICALLY

6. **HYPOTHESIZE:** Is a can of frozen juice a concentrated or a dilute solution? Explain.
7. **PREDICT:** Suppose the directions on a can of frozen juice state that it should be mixed with three cans of water. What type of solution would you make if you added five cans of water? Explain.

INTERPRETING VISUALS

The graph in Figure 5-15 shows the solubility of ammonia, NH₃, and potassium chloride, KCl, at different temperatures. Use the graph to answer the questions.

8. **ANALYZE:** How much more KCl will dissolve in 100mL of water at 100°C than at 0°C?
9. **INFER:** Is NH₃ a gas or a solid? How do you know?

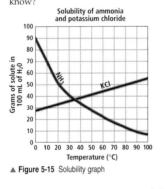
**Solubility of ammonia
and potassium chloride**

Grams of solute in
100 mL of H₂O

NH₃

KCl

Temperature (°C)

▲ **Figure 5-15** Solubility graph

CHAPTER 5: Solutions   **113**

📖 **READING STRATEGY** As students read through the lesson, have them find sentences in the text that contain the Key Terms. Next, have them copy each sentence exactly as it appears. Finally, have students write an original sentence for each Key Term.

Answers to questions

1> **COMPARE:** A dilute solution has a small amount of solute, while a concentrated solution has a large amount of solute.

2> **ANALYZE:** when it contains less solute than it can hold at a given temperature

3> **HYPOTHESIZE:** Some solute would remain undissolved after the solution became saturated.

4> **INFER:** The solution was probably heated and then cooled.

3 Assess

✔ CHECKING CONCEPTS ANSWERS

1. dilute
2. concentrated
3. solute
4. saturated
5. heated

💡 THINKING CRITICALLY ANSWERS

6. **HYPOTHESIZE:** Concentrated solution; Water must be added to dilute the solution.
7. **PREDICT:** A more dilute solution; Adding more water makes the solution weaker.

INTERPRETING VISUALS ANSWERS

8. **ANALYZE:** about 25 grams
9. **INFER:** a gas, because as the temperature rises, less of it dissolves

4 Close

Real-Life Connection Tell students that many products used at home are concentrated solutions that become dilute when a solvent is added. Ask students to think of products found in their homes that are concentrated solutions and list them on the board. (Possible answers: liquid detergent, vinegar, and bleach) Have students describe what must be done to dilute the products. **learning styles: auditory, visual**

COOPERATIVE LEARNING

Explaining Diagrams Have students explain Figure 5-15 to other students.

• TEACHING RESOURCES •

💿 **Teacher's Resources CD-ROM**
Lesson Review: Chapter 5, p. 6
Enrichment: Chapter 5, pp. 7, 8
Concept Map: Study Tools, p. 4

📼 **Laboratory Video**
Segment 5: Making a Supersaturated Solution

1 Introduce

STUDY HINT Before beginning this lesson, have students study Figure 5-16. Then, have them draw cause-and-effect diagrams for each of the compounds listed. Students can use the Cause-and-Effect Diagram on the Teacher's Resources CD-ROM.

Linking Prior Knowledge Have students review and describe the different states of matter (Lesson 1-3).

2 Teach

Demonstration Before class begins, put 200 mL of distilled water in a beaker. In a second beaker, add 30 g of salt to 200 mL of distilled water and stir until the salt dissolves. Place a thermometer in each beaker and put the beakers in a freezer. Monitor the liquids during class. When the water begins to freeze, remove the beaker and show students that freezing began at 0°C (32°F). Repeat with the salt solution, showing that freezing began at about −5°C (23°F). Tell students that the salt has lowered the freezing point of water, and that this is an example of freezing point depression.
learning styles: visual, auditory

Discussion Provide motivation for this lesson by displaying a bag of rock salt in front of the class. Ask students when rock salt is used. (when snowy, icy conditions exist on sidewalks, driveways, and roads) Then, ask how students think rock salt affects ice. Many students may think that the rock salt causes the ice to melt. Instead, the salt dissolves in the thin film of water that forms when the ice begins to melt. Point out that as the salt dissolves in the thin film of water, the freezing point of water is lowered. Thus, the water is less likely to refreeze. Identify rock salt as one application of freezing point depression.
learning styles: auditory, visual

READING STRATEGY As students read through each section in the lesson, ask them to make a sketch that could be used to explain the information in the section. Tell them to use labels if necessary.

5-6 How do solutes affect freezing point?

Objective
Describe how the presence of a solute affects the freezing point of a liquid solvent.

Key Terms
freezing point: temperature at which a liquid changes to a solid

freezing point depression: decrease in the freezing point of a liquid solvent because of the addition of a solute

Freezing Point of Water The temperature at which a liquid changes to a solid is called its **freezing point.** The freezing point of pure water is 0°C. When pure liquid water reaches this temperature, it begins changing to solid ice. When water freezes, its molecules become arranged in a crystal pattern called a lattice.

Salt water does not freeze at 0°C. The particles of salt dissolved in the water interfere with the change from a liquid to a solid. Because salt water contains dissolved salt and other minerals, its freezing point is lower than that of pure water.

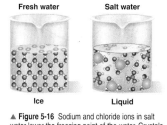

▲ **Figure 5-16** Sodium and chloride ions in salt water lower the freezing point of the water. Crystals cannot form unless the temperature is below 0°C.

▶ **DESCRIBE:** What happens to liquid water at its freezing point?

Freezing Point Depression The amount of solute dissolved in a solvent affects the freezing point of the solvent. This special property of

114

solutions is called **freezing point depression.** Adding solute lowers the freezing point of the solvent. The greater the amount of dissolved solute, the lower the freezing point of the solvent.

▶ **PREDICT:** What will happen to the freezing point of water as you add solute to the water?

Melting Danger Away Have you ever sprinkled rock salt or calcium chloride pellets on an icy sidewalk? Ice melters like these lower the freezing point of water. When the ice begins to melt, the chemical compounds dissolve in the water, forming solutions that freeze at a lower temperature than pure water.

Unfortunately, the use of salts for deicing can be hazardous to us and harmful to the environment. The salt residue that remains after the ice has melted can weaken pavement, forming potholes. In addition, chemicals wash off of paved surfaces into storm drains, increasing the salinity, or salt content, of nearby streams and lakes. Look at the differences among ice melters in the table in Figure 5-16.

ICE MELTERS

Compound	Practical Melting Temperature	Advantages/Disadvantages
Rock salt (NaCl) Sodium chloride	−7° C	Abundant resource; pollutes streams and lakes; corrodes metal
Calcium chloride (CaCl₂)	−20° C	Abundant resource; may cause skin irritation; attacks concrete
Magnesium chloride (MgCl₂)	−15° C	Less toxic to plants and concrete surfaces than rock salts; leaves no powder residue
Calcium magnesium acetate (CMA)	−7° C	Less corrosive to automobiles and roads and less toxic to plants than other salts
Potassium chloride (KCl)	−11° C	Less toxic to plants and surfaces than rock salt; used in fertilizer so overuse may cause plants and grass to burn

▲ **Figure 5-17** The practical melting temperature is the lowest outdoor temperature for which each compound is effective. Below that temperature, the solution will start to freeze.

▶ **PREDICT:** What effects do you think the use of salts would have on plants and animals in the environment?

Teaching Options

! FAST FACTS *More on Freezing Point Depression*

Ionic substances are more effective than molecular substances in reducing the freezing point of water. When an ionic substance dissolves in water, it separates into positive and negative ions. For example, sodium chloride (NaCl) separates into positive sodium ions (Na^+) and negative chloride ions (Cl^-). The increased number of particles in solution causes more interference with the change from a liquid to a solid, resulting in a larger freezing point depression. A molecular substance such as sugar does not separate into ions when it dissolves, so it produces a smaller freezing point depression. When calcium chloride (CaCl₂) dissolves in water, its ions separate and two negative chloride ions (Cl^-) enter the solution for every positive calcium ion (Ca^{2+}). Therefore, CaCl₂ produces three particles in water solution, and the result is a greater freezing point depression.

1. The _____ of pure water is 0°C.

2. The greater the amount of dissolved solute in a solvent, the _____ the freezing point of the solvent.

3. The freezing point of salt water is _____ than the freezing point of pure water.

4. Lowering the freezing point of a liquid solvent by adding solute is a property called _____.

5. Putting salt on icy roads _____ the freezing point of the melted ice.

THINKING CRITICALLY

6. ANALYZE: Beaker A contains 2 g of sugar dissolved in 100 mL of water. Beaker B contains 10 g of sugar dissolved in 100 mL of water. Which beaker contains the solution with the lower freezing point? Explain your answer.

7. ANALYZE: Beaker C and Beaker D each contain 5 g of dissolved copper sulfate. Beaker C contains 100 mL of water while Beaker D contains 250 mL of water. Which beaker contains the solution with the lower freezing point? Explain your answer.

Web InfoSearch

Salt and Ice Cream "I scream, you scream, we all scream for…" Rock salt is not only for deicing sidewalks. It can also be used to reduce the temperature of a container of juice, milk, or cream to make frozen desserts.

SEARCH: Use the Internet to find out about the history of the hand-cranked ice cream freezer. Describe its parts and how it can be used to make ice cream in a short report. Start your search at www.conceptsandchallenges.com. Some key search words are **Nancy Johnson** and **ice cream.**

Integrating Life Science

TOPICS: cold-blooded animals, circulation

FISH WITH ANTIFREEZE

Fish that live in the Arctic Ocean must survive freezing and near-freezing water temperatures. Scientists wondered why these fish did not freeze in such an environment.

By studying fish in the Arctic region of northern Labrador, scientists discovered that the blood of the Arctic fish contained a high concentration of a certain protein. This antifreeze (AFP) protein acts like a solute in a solution. The greater the amount of protein in the blood of the fish, the lower the freezing point of the blood.

As a result of this freezing point depression, the fish can survive in the cold Arctic environment. Should the water temperature reach 0°C, the blood of the fish would still be a liquid.

Thinking Critically What helps fish live in such frigid water?

▲ Figure 5-18 These fish can survive in subfreezing conditions.

Answers to questions

▶1 DESCRIBE: It changes into a solid.

▶2 PREDICT: It will become lower.

▶3 PREDICT: Possible answer: The salinity of nearby lakes and streams might increase.

3 Assess

✔ CHECKING CONCEPT ANSWERS

1. freezing point
2. lower
3. lower
4. freezing point depression
5. lowers

THINKING CRITICALLY ANSWERS

6. ANALYZE: Beaker B; It has more solute. Adding more solute to a solution lowers the freezing point.

7. ANALYZE: Beaker C; There is more solute per volume of solvent in beaker C.

4 Close

Web InfoSearch

Salt and Ice Cream Students can learn about the history of the hand-cranked ice cream freezer at 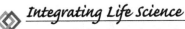www.conceptsandchallenges.com. Have students write a report describing the freezer's parts and how it can be used to make ice cream.

Integrating Life Science

TOPICS: cold-blooded animals, circulation

FISH WITH ANTIFREEZE

Life-Science Connection Fish are cold-blooded, which means that their body temperatures change with the temperature of the environment. When the temperature of the water falls below the body temperature of the fish, the fish loses body heat to its surroundings, and it becomes cooler. If the water warms above the body temperature of the fish, heat travels from the water to the fish, and the temperature of the fish rises.

Thinking Critically Answer
The protein in their blood lowers the temperature at which their blood freezes.

COOPERATIVE LEARNING

Debating the Evidence Have two small groups of volunteers debate whether the benefits of using salts for deicing outweigh the harmful effects. Then, ask students to suggest ways to reduce the harmful effects of deicing salts.
learning style: linguistic

ONGOING ASSESSMENT

Interpreting a Table Have students rank the compounds in Figure 5-17 in order of decreasing practical melting temperature.

• TEACHING RESOURCES •

Teacher's Resources CD-ROM
Lesson Review: Chapter 5, p. 9
Enrichment: Chapter 5, p. 10
Cause-and-Effect Diagram: Study Tools, p. 3

1 Introduce

✎ **STUDY HINT** Before beginning this lesson, have students study Figure 5-19. Then, have them make a graph that shows how increasing the amount of solute increases the boiling point of water. The axes should be labeled *Temperature (°C)* and *Amount of Solute (g)*.

Linking Prior Knowledge Ask students to recall the ways in which matter can change from one state to another (Lesson 1-4).

2 Teach

Demonstration Pour 100 mL of distilled water into each of two beakers. Dissolve 25 g of salt in one of the beakers. Put a thermometer into each beaker. Then, heat the beakers until the solutions boil. Have students note that the presence of salt raises the boiling point of water. Identify this property as boiling point elevation.
learning style: visual

Discussion Bring a bottle of antifreeze to class. Ask students what clue the prefix *anti-* in the word *antifreeze* gives about the reason for putting antifreeze in cars. (*anti-* means "against," so *antifreeze* means "against freeze") Tell students that people use antifreeze to prevent a car's engine from overheating as well as to prevent it from freezing. Ask students how they think antifreeze works. Accept all responses and write them on the board. Tell students that they will know which of their ideas are correct after they read this lesson.
learning style: linguistic

Answers to questions

▸1 **DESCRIBE:** The liquid water changes to steam.

▸2 **DEFINE:** raising the boiling point of a liquid solvent by adding a solute

▸3 **DESCRIBE:** raising the boiling point and lowering the freezing point of water

---

5-7 How do solutes affect boiling point?

Objective

Describe how a solute affects the boiling point of a solution.

Key Terms

boiling point: temperature at which a liquid changes to a gas

boiling point elevation: increase in the boiling point of a liquid solvent because of the addition of a solute

Boiling Point of Water When water is heated, its temperature rises. The temperature at which a liquid changes to a gas is called its **boiling point.** The boiling point of pure water at sea level is 100°C, at which point water changes to steam. Adding heat to boiling water does not raise its temperature.

Salt water does not boil at 100°C. This is because salt water contains dissolved salt particles. The particles of salt dissolved in the water interfere with the change from a liquid to a gas. The temperature of salt water must be higher than 100°C before the water will boil.

▸1 **DESCRIBE:** What happens when the temperature of pure water reaches 100°C?

Boiling Point Elevation The boiling point of a liquid solvent is increased by adding a solute. This property of all solutions is called **boiling point elevation.** As the amount of solute in the solvent increases, the boiling point of the solvent also increases. For example, a solution of sugar and water does not boil at the same temperature as pure water because of boiling point elevation. Figure 5-19 lists some normal boiling points.

BOILING POINTS OF DIFFERENT SOLUTIONS	
Substance	Normal Boiling Point
Distilled water (at sea level)	100°C
Sea water	101°C
Vinegar	118°C
Ethyl alcohol	78.5°C
Acetone	56°C

▲ Figure 5-20

▸2 **DEFINE:** What is boiling point elevation?

Keep That Engine Running Whenever the engine of a car is running, large amounts of heat are produced. A coolant is used to protect the engine from this heat. A coolant must also be able to remain liquid at low temperatures. The most common coolant is a solution of water and another liquid, usually ethylene glycol.

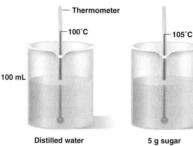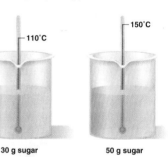

▲ Figure 5-19 The boiling point of a solution increases as more solute is added.

116

Teaching Options

RETEACH

Comparing the Boiling Points of Sugar Water and Salt Water The presence of salt or sugar in water raises the boiling point of pure water. Ask students which one raises the boiling point higher. Fill two beakers with 200 mL of distilled water. Add 1 tablespoon of salt to one beaker and 1 tablespoon of sugar to the other beaker. Heat both solutions. Have students note the temperature of both solutions as they boil. Students should observe that the salt water solution boils at a higher temperature. **learning style: visual**

QUICK CONVERSIONS		
	Boiling Point	
Substance	**Metric/SI**	**English**
Distilled water	100°C	212°F
Seawater	101°C	214°F
Vinegar	118°C	244°F
Ethyl alcohol	78.5°C	173.3°F
Acetone	56°C	133°F

Ethylene glycol freezes at –13°C and boils at 197°C. Although it is commonly called antifreeze, this compound could also be called antiboil because it lowers the freezing point of water and elevates its boiling point. In recent years, new antifreeze products have been developed. These products contain materials that are less toxic and safer for the environment than is ethylene glycol.

▶ DESCRIBE: What two important functions does an engine coolant have?

✓ CHECKING CONCEPTS

1. The _____ of pure water is 100°C.
2. The boiling point of salt water is _____ than the boiling point of pure water.
3. As the amount of solute in a solution increases, the boiling point of the solution _____.
4. Raising the boiling point of a liquid solvent by adding solute is called _____.

💡 THINKING CRITICALLY

5. ANALYZE: Solution A contains 5 g of sugar dissolved in 100 mL of water. Solution B contains 20 g of sugar dissolved in 100 mL of water. Which solution has the higher boiling point? Explain your answer.
6. ANALYZE: Two beakers each contain 12 g of salt dissolved in water. Beaker A contains 200 mL of water and Beaker B contains 100 mL of water. Which solution has the higher boiling point? Explain your answer.

DESIGNING AN EXPERIMENT

Design an experiment to solve the following problem. Include a hypothesis, variables, a procedure, and a type of data to study.

PROBLEM: How does the addition of salt to water affect the time it takes to boil an egg?

⚛ *Hands-On Activity*

OBSERVING BOILING POINT ELEVATION

You will need three beakers, a thermometer, a heat source, a spoon, distilled water, and salt.

1. Put 100 mL of water in each beaker.
2. Add 5 g of salt to the first beaker and stir.
3. Heat the water in the beaker until it begins to boil. Record the temperature.
4. Add 10 g of salt to the second beaker and stir. Repeat Step 3.
5. Add 20 g of salt to the third beaker and stir. Repeat Step 3.

▲ STEP 3 Heat the water until it begins to boil.

Practicing Your Skills

6. OBSERVE: What was the boiling point of the first solution?
7. OBSERVE: What was the boiling point of the second solution?
8. OBSERVE: What was the boiling point of the third solution?
9. ANALYZE: What is the relationship between the amount of a solute and the boiling point of a solution?

CHAPTER 5: Solutions 117

---

3 *Assess*

✓ CHECKING CONCEPTS ANSWERS

1. boiling point
2. higher
3. increases
4. boiling point elevation

💡 THINKING CRITICALLY ANSWERS

5. ANALYZE: Solution B; The solution with more solute has the higher boiling point.
6. ANALYZE: Beaker B; There is more solute per volume of solvent in beaker B.

4 *Close*

DESIGNING AN EXPERIMENT

Use the Designing an Experiment Rubric on the Teacher's Resources CD-ROM to assess students' experiments. Fill in the rubric with the additional information below. For this assignment, students should have:

• in forming the hypothesis, mentioned how adding salt to water changes the boiling point of water.
• in the procedure, included timing how long it takes to boil an egg in pure water and in salt water.

Hands-On Activity

OBSERVING BOILING POINT ELEVATION

TIME: 15–30 minutes

PURPOSE: observing, comparing, measuring

SAFETY TIP: Caution students to work carefully when using a heating source and stirring hot solutions. Be sure that students wear safety goggles.

COOPERATIVE LEARNING: Have students work in pairs.

Practicing Your Skills Answers

6. OBSERVE: Answers may vary. (Possible answer: 101°C)
7. OBSERVE: Answers may vary. (Possible answer: 102°C)
8. OBSERVE: Answers may vary. (Possible answer: 104°C)
9. ANALYZE: Increasing the amount of solute in a solution increases the boiling point of the solution.

• TEACHING RESOURCES •

💿 **Teacher's Resources CD-ROM**
Lesson Review: Chapter 5, p. 11
Graph Paper: Visuals, p. 4
Designing an Experiment Rubric: Teaching Tools, p. 7
Designing an Experiment: Study Tools, p. 14

📼 **Laboratory Video**
Segment 6: Observing Boiling Point Elevation

Laboratory Manual
Lab. Skills Worksheet 5: Graphing, pp. 15–18

1 Introduce

✎ **STUDY HINT** Before beginning this lesson, have students explain Figure 5-21 in their own words.

Linking Prior Knowledge Have students review how to distinguish between physical and chemical changes.

2 Teach

Demonstration Ask students how they think a solute and solvent can be separated. Allow students to suggest possible methods. List their responses on the board. Then, put 10 mL of a copper sulfate solution in an evaporating dish. Heat the solution until the water boils away. Exhibit the residue of copper sulfate crystals. Point out that a solid solute can be recovered from a liquid solution by boiling or evaporating the solvent. **learning styles: visual, auditory**

Discussion Explain to students the Key Terms *evaporation*, *condensation*, and *distillation*. Evaporation is the change of a liquid to a gas at the surface of the liquid. This change occurs because the molecules at the surface of the liquid absorb enough energy from the environment to escape out of the liquid. Condensation is the opposite of evaporation. It occurs when a gas is cooled which causes it to change to a liquid. Distillation is a process that uses both evaporation and condensation to separate a solute and a solvent from a solution. **learning style: auditory**

Reinforcement Show students a distillation apparatus and, if possible, demonstrate distillation. (You can also use a photograph of a distillation apparatus.) Point out the tube-within-a-tube structure of the condenser. Explain that water in the outside tube cools the gases passing through the inside tube, thus causing the gases to condense. **learning styles: visual, auditory**

Answers to questions

▶ **INFER:** Let the water evaporate from the solution.

▶ **DEFINE:** change of a gas to a liquid

▶ **IDENTIFY:** evaporation and condensation

5-8 How can solutions be separated?

Objective
Describe two methods for separating the solute from the solvent in a solution.

Key Terms
evaporation (ee-vap-uh-RAY-shuhn): change from a liquid to a gas at the surface of the liquid

condensation (kahn-duhn-SAY-shuhn): change from a gas to a liquid

distillation (dihs-tuh-LAY-shuhn): process of evaporating a liquid and then condensing the gas back into a liquid

Evaporation A solute can be separated from a solution by evaporation. **Evaporation** is the change of a liquid to a gas at the surface of the liquid. The molecules at the surface of the liquid gain enough energy to break free of the liquid and move into the air as a gas.

You can separate copper sulfate crystals from a solution of copper sulfate and water. Place the solution in a shallow dish and let it stand. After a few days, all the water will have evaporated. Crystals of copper sulfate remain in the bottom of the dish.

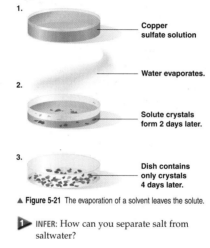

1.

Copper sulfate solution

Water evaporates.

2.

Solute crystals form 2 days later.

3.

Dish contains only crystals 4 days later.

▲ **Figure 5-21** The evaporation of a solvent leaves the solute.

▶ **INFER:** How can you separate salt from saltwater?

118

Condensation Have you ever come out of a hot shower to find drops of water on your bathroom mirror? The drops of water are the result of condensation. **Condensation** is the change of a gas to a liquid. Some of the shower water evaporates to form water vapor, an invisible gas. When the water vapor strikes the mirror, it is cooled. This causes the water vapor to change back to liquid water.

▶ **DEFINE:** What is condensation?

Distillation A liquid solution can be separated into its separate parts by the process of distillation. In the process of **distillation**, a liquid is heated until it evaporates. The gas is then cooled until it condenses back into a liquid.

When a solution is distilled, both the solvent and the solute can be recovered. The solution to be separated is heated. The solvent evaporates and forms a gas. The gas moves through a tube called a condenser. The condenser cools the gas, which changes back to a liquid. The liquid drips into a container. The solute remains in the original container. Both the solute and the solvent are recovered.

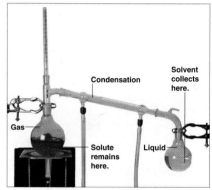

Condensation

Solvent collects here.

Gas

Solute remains here.

Liquid

▲ **Figure 5-22** Separation of a solution by distillation

▶ **IDENTIFY:** What two processes are involved in distillation?

Teaching Options

◇ INTEGRATING EARTH SCIENCE

Identifying a Salt Source The Great Salt Lake in Utah is the largest lake in the United States other than the Great Lakes. Its average area is about 4,400 square kilometers (1,700 square miles). Although freshwater streams feed into the lake, it is extremely salty because it has no outlet. Its minerals remain in the lake as the water evaporates. The size and salt concentration of the lake vary according to weather conditions. During wet periods, the lake becomes larger as it swells with water, and its salt concentration decreases. The lake shrinks during dry weather as its water evaporates, and the salt concentration increases. During dry conditions when the lake is smallest, its salt concentration can be twice as high as it is during wet periods. Because the lake is so salty, bathers can float easily in its waters. Millions of kilograms of salt are taken from the lake each year for human use.

Divide students into pairs. Have one of the partners research and report on the method used to obtain salt from the Great Salt Lake. Have the other partner research and report on the uses for the salt. **learning style: linguistic**

☑ CHECKING CONCEPTS

1. Evaporation changes a liquid to a _____.
2. Condensation changes a gas to a _____.
3. A solution can be separated into its solute and solvent by _____.
4. As a liquid is heated, the molecules at the liquid's _____ evaporate first.
5. A solvent can be evaporated from a solution to recover the _____.
6. Evaporation takes place at the _____ of a liquid.
7. During distillation, cooling the evaporated solute causes _____ to occur.

💡 THINKING CRITICALLY

8. **INFER:** What causes steam to escape from the spout of a teakettle?
9. **HYPOTHESIZE:** Why do droplets of water form on the underside of the lid of a pot of boiling water?

BUILDING SCIENCE SKILLS

Researching Distillation can be used to purify water. Chemists and pharmacists use distilled water to make solutions. Distilled water is also used in car batteries. Use library references to find out how distilled water is prepared. Why is it sometimes important to use distilled water instead of ordinary tap water? Write a brief report of your findings.

Science and Technology

FRACTIONAL DISTILLATION OF PETROLEUM

Petroleum is a mixture of different substances. Gasoline, kerosene, and heating oil are just some of the products obtained from petroleum. Petroleum is separated by the process of fractional distillation. In this process, petroleum is heated in a fractionating (FRAK-shuhn-ayt-ing) tower. The different substances in petroleum have different boiling points. Each substance, or fraction, changes to a vapor at a different temperature. The process of fractional distillation depends on each substance's boiling point.

As the temperature in the fractionating tower increases, each substance changes to a vapor. The vapors pass through pipes where they cool and condense. Then, they collect separately. The substances with the highest boiling points cool and condense and drain from the lower part of the tower. These substances include asphalt and lubricating oil. Substances that boil at a lower temperature rise higher in the tower before they cool and condense. Fuel oil and kerosene drain off in the middle of the tower. Gasoline, with the lowest boiling point, rises to the top of the tower and drains off. Once the petroleum is separated into liquid fractions, each liquid drains into its storage tank.

Thinking Critically Why do the substances with lower boiling points drain from the top of the tower, whereas those with higher boiling points drain from the bottom?

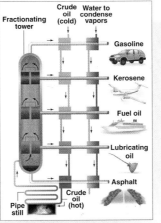

▲ **Figure 5-23** Fractional distillation

COOPERATIVE LEARNING

Presenting the Evidence Have a volunteer explain evaporation and condensation to the class. Have a second volunteer describe how evaporation and condensation occur in the process of distillation. **learning styles: linguistic, auditory**

• TEACHING RESOURCES •

Teacher's Resources CD-ROM
Lesson Review: Chapter 5, p. 12

MORE ON THE WEB

Diagramming Distillation Have students visit www.conceptsandchallenges.com to draw a model of a distiller and to show how it works. Students' diagrams should include a description of the distillation process.

---

3 Assess

☑ CHECKING CONCEPT ANSWERS

1. gas
2. liquid
3. distillation
4. surface
5. solute
6. surface
7. condensation

💡 THINKING CRITICALLY ANSWERS

8. **INFER:** evaporation
9. **HYPOTHESIZE:** The coolness of the lid causes the water vapor to change back to a liquid.

4 Close

BUILDING SCIENCE SKILLS

Researching Students' reports should describe how distilled water is prepared. Their reports should also indicate that it is sometimes important to use distilled water instead of ordinary tap water because tap water may contain minerals.

Science and Technology

FRACTIONAL DISTILLATION OF PETROLEUM

Interdisciplinary Connection In a sense, petroleum is stored sunlight. Solar energy was absorbed by organisms in the oceans between about 300 and 400 million years ago. The organisms used the Sun's energy to make organic compounds. When they died, the organisms settled on the ocean floor and were covered by layers of sediments. After millions of years, under great heat and pressure, the sediments became rock and their organic compounds were converted into petroleum.

Discussion Ask: *Why do you think petroleum is called a fossil fuel?* (Petroleum was produced from organisms that lived millions of years ago.) **learning style: auditory**

Thinking Critically Answer
The substances cool as they rise in the tower. Therefore, the substances with the highest boiling points will condense and drain from the bottom of the tower. The substances with the lowest boiling points will condense and drain from the top of the tower.

Lab Activity

(pp. 120–121)

1 Prepare the Lab

Making Supersaturated Solutions

SET-UP TIME: 🕐 **LAB TIME:** 🕐

BACKGROUND: To make a supersaturated solution, one must know the solubility of the solute, which relates to the amount of solute that can dissolve at a given temperature.

PURPOSE: Students will roughly determine the solubility of table salt, Epsom salt, and sugar. Also, students will make supersaturated solutions.

SCIENCE SKILLS: Students will **observe** and **collect data** on the experiment and **communicate** their findings in written form. They will use this experiment to **infer** how much solute is needed at a given temperature and to **model** a supersaturated solution.

2 Guide the Lab

PROCEDURE: Divide the class into groups of two or three students. Discuss the procedures. Emphasize to students to make rounded teaspoons for the solids. Also, in Step 5, tell students to remove the beaker from the hot plate with beaker tongs before adding more solid. Discuss data collection and reporting. Provide students with a copy of the Lab Activity Report found on the Teacher's Resources CD-ROM for students to record their observations and conclusions.

TROUBLESHOOTING: Often, if a saturated solution is allowed to cool undisturbed, the solute will not fall out of solution as the temperature drops. This creates a supersaturated solution. A supersaturated solution will not occur if any crystals of the solute settle out of the solution because the undissolved crystals act as "seeds" in forming crystals. Also, any disturbance to the solution can start crystal formation.

To produce a supersaturated solution, students will have to pour off some of the solution into another container, being careful not to get any undissolved crystals in the poured-off solution. If students are successful at creating a supersaturated solution, they will observe a dramatic change if they drop a crystal of the solute

---

BACKGROUND

The solubility of a solute is the amount of solute that will dissolve in a given amount of a certain solvent. This will produce a saturated solution. Increasing the temperature usually increases the solubility of a solute. To make a supersaturated solution, heat the solution, add more solute to it, and then cool it.

PURPOSE

In this activity, you will observe the solubility of different substances in solutions. Also, you will observe the relationship between solutes, solvents, and heat.

Materials
Safety goggles, lab apron, oven mitt, heat source, marking pen, 3 250-mL beakers, 100-mL graduated cylinder, glass stirrers, 3 plastic teaspoons, water, sugar, Epsom salt, table salt

▲ **STEP 2** Label each beaker.

PROCEDURE 🔒 👓 ♨ ✖

1. Copy the chart in Figure 5-24. Put on safety goggles and a lab apron.

2. Label each beaker with the following: table salt, Epsom salt, and sugar.

3. Add 100 mL of water to each beaker.

Observing the Effects of Heat on a Solute and a Solvent			
Beaker	Solute	Number of Teaspoons to Make Saturated Solution	Number of Teaspoons After Heating
1	Table salt		
2	Epsom salt		
3	Sugar		

▲ **Figure 5-24** Copy this chart and use it to record your observations.

120

Teaching Options

❗ FAST FACTS   More on Solubility

The solubility of most solids in water increases as the temperature increases. In some cases, the increase is small. For example, 36 g of table salt dissolves in 100 g of water at 25°C (77°F), while 40 g dissolves at 100°C (212°F). For other solids, the effect is much greater. At 25°C, 39 g of potassium nitrate, KNO_3, dissolves in 100 g of water, while at 100°C, the solubility increases to 246 g per 100 g of water. In a few cases, the solubility of a solid decreases as the temperature increases—an example is cerous sulfate, $Ce_2(SO_4)_3$. If a saturated solution of cerous sulfate at 50°C (122°F) is cooled to room temperature, it becomes unsaturated because the solution contains less solute than it can hold at room temperature.

ESL/ELL STRATEGY

Noting the Icons Students should pay close attention to the icons at the beginning of the Procedure. The icons indicate the precautions that should be taken during the lab.

▲ STEP 4 Make saturated solutions of each substance.

▲ STEP 5 Place the beaker on the heat source and stir the contents.

4. Make saturated solutions of each substance. For each solution, add a teaspoonful of table salt, Epsom salt, or sugar to the corresponding beaker. Stir for one minute. Continue adding the solute and stirring until some does not dissolve. Record how many teaspoonfuls you add to make each saturated solution.

5. Place the beaker that contains table salt on a heat source. Stir the mixture with a glass stirrer as it is heating. As soon as the solid particles dissolve, add another teaspoon of table salt and stir. Add more table salt until some table salt is left behind. Record the number of teaspoons you add.
⚠ CAUTION: Be extremely careful when handling anything on a hot plate.

6. Allow the solution to cool. As it cools, record your observations.

7. Repeat Step 4 with the beakers that contain the Epsom salt and the sugar. Record your observations.

CONCLUSIONS

1. OBSERVE: Describe the appearance of the solutions at room temperature.

2. OBSERVE: Describe what happened to the solutions upon heating.

3. INFER: Which part of the activity represents a supersaturated solution? How do you know?

4. ANALYZE: How is the knowledge of solubility useful for people who make drink mixes or instant soups?

Tips for Using Technology

Databases Have students use database software to record their observations on the effects of heat on a solute and a solvent. Databases allow students to enter and edit information, store and organize a lot of information easily, and search for specific information. Databases also allow students to arrange information by putting it in a specific order. Students can use database software to share their data with the class. Have students use the Database Planner on the Teacher's Resources CD-ROM to plan their databases.

• TEACHING RESOURCES •

Teacher's Resources CD-ROM
Lab Activity Report: Study Tools, pp. 16–17

Laboratory Activity Rubric: Teaching Tools, p. 8

Database Planner: Study Tools, p. 22

Laboratory Manual
Lab. Skills Worksheet 1: Using a Graduated Cylinder, pp. 5–8

into the supersaturated solution. Many crystals will suddenly form in the solution. The exception is sodium chloride, where few crystals, if any, will form.

If students are not able to produce supersaturated solutions, crystals will form in the Epsom salt and sugar solutions as these solutions cool.

SAFETY TIP: Caution students about using hot plates, hot glass, and hot solutions. Also, remind students to be careful when mixing hot solutions.

EXPECTED OUTCOME: Answers may vary, depending on the starting temperature and the temperature to which the solutions are heated. Students will find that table salt is the least soluble of the three solids.

3 Conclude the Lab

1. **OBSERVE:** Answers will depend on students' results. Students should describe their solutions as being clear.
2. **OBSERVE:** The extra solute began to dissolve upon heating.
3. **INFER:** when the salt solution was allowed to cool; because it held more solute than it normally could at a given temperature
4. **ANALYZE:** By knowing the solubility of different substances, you will not have extra mix on the bottom of the container. For example, the instructions on a drink mix or instant soup mix will list a specific amount of water to make the perfect drink or to make soup correctly.

Use the Laboratory Activity Rubric on the Teacher's Resources CD-ROM to assess students' lab activities. Fill in the rubric with the additional information below. For this activity, students should have:

• performed the activity according to the procedure and filled in the chart with data collected during the activity.

• correctly answered the questions in complete sentences.

4 Extend the Lab

Have students repeat the procedure for making a supersaturated sugar solution, using a thermometer to record the temperature at which the solution boils and to record the temperature of the solution periodically as it cools. Thermometers need to be attached to a clamp and then suspended in the solutions. Make sure that the thermometers do not touch the walls or bottoms of the beakers.

1 Introduce

✏️ **STUDY HINT** Have students write the lesson title and objective in their notebooks. As students read the lesson, tell them to write the sentence or sentences that provide the information that meets the objective.

Linking Prior Knowledge Before beginning this lesson, have students review what a crystal is (Lesson 4-5).

2 Teach

Demonstration Show students several three-dimensional models of crystals. Point out that crystals have an orderly arrangement of atoms. Show students samples of rocks that contain crystals. Inform them that many types of rocks contain crystals.
learning styles: visual, auditory

Discussion Bring in pictures of synthetic crystals that are used to develop new technologies. Such pictures might be found in science or technology magazines. Point out that these crystals can be grown in the appropriate size and shape to suit a specific purpose. **learning styles: visual, auditory**

Answers to questions

1 INFER: The particles that make up a salt crystal are arranged in a pattern that gives salt crystals their cube shape.

2 DEFINE: Adding a seed crystal causes the excess solute to come out of solution.

3 LIST: Possible answers: development of new technology, cutting and drilling through materials, and making medical instruments

Reinforcement Have students examine salt crystals with a powerful magnifying lens or microscope and sketch the shape of salt crystals in their notebooks. (Salt crystals are cubic.)
learning styles: visual, tactile

5-9 How are crystals formed?

Objective
Explain how crystals are formed from solutions.

Crystal Chemistry The particles that make up a crystal are arranged in a pattern. This pattern gives the crystal a definite shape. All crystals of the same substance have the same shape. Figure 5-25 shows how crystals of copper sulfate can "grow" from a saturated solution of this compound. As the saturated solution sits, water will evaporate. Copper sulfate crystals will appear in the bottom of the solution. These crystals will increase in size as more and more water evaporates.

◀ **Figure 5-25** Over time, water evaporates from the copper sulfate solution, leaving crystals of copper sulfate.

1 INFER: Why are all salt crystals shaped like a cube?

Seeding Another way to grow crystals is to use a supersaturated solution. Figure 5-29 shows how to grow crystals from a supersaturated solution of sodium acetate. After a saturated solution is prepared at a high temperature, let it cool to room temperature. Then add a small sodium acetate crystal to the solution. This sodium acetate "seed" causes the excess crystals of sodium acetate to come out of solution and settle quickly to the bottom of the container.

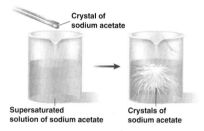

Crystal of sodium acetate

Supersaturated solution of sodium acetate

Crystals of sodium acetate

▲ **Figure 5-26** Growing sodium acetate crystals

2 DEFINE: How does a supersaturated solution allow you to grow crystals?

Synthetic Crystals Natural crystals may contain flaws or impurities, but synthetic, or human-made, crystals can be made flawless. They can be made to grow in a particular shape or size to suit specific needs. Synthetic crystals are crucial to the development of new technology.

Optical crystals made of sodium chloride, potassium chloride, and many other crystalline compounds can be used in the development of laser and fiber-optic communication. Silicon chips are very thin slices of artificially grown silicon crystals. They are used in many electronic devices, such as the circuit boards of computers, to hold information and control mechanical functions. "Smart cards" are credit or debit cards that have a microprocessor built into the silicon chip on the card. These cards may be used in the future to store and update personal bank or credit account information.

Teaching Options

RETEACH

Observing Crystal Formation
Make a saturated copper sulfate solution. Pour about 2 mL of the solution into a clear dish. Place the dish on an overhead projector. Focus the image that is produced. Have students observe the image as crystals form.
learning style: visual

EXTENDING THE LESSON

Existing in Two Crystalline Forms
Tell students that in some cases, a single element or compound can exist in more than one crystalline form. For example, the element carbon can exist as diamond or as graphite, which is part of the lead in a pencil. Ask students how the properties of these two forms of carbon are different.
(diamond: very hard and clear; graphite: soft and black)
learning styles: auditory, logical/mathematical

Synthetic gems such as diamonds are used in industry primarily because of their strength and durability. Saws set with diamonds and diamond-tipped drill bits are used to cut and drill through glass, ceramics, and rocks. Because they do not corrode, diamonds are also used in medical instruments like diamond-bladed scalpels for eye surgery. Other types of gems can also be made with synthetic crystals.

▲ Figure 5-27
A synthetic gem

▸ LIST: What are some uses of synthetic crystals?

✓ CHECKING CONCEPTS

1. When water is evaporated from a copper sulfate solution, copper sulfate _____ remain.

2. All crystals of the same substance have the same _____.

3. A supersaturated solution contains more _____ than it would normally hold at a given temperature.

4. Crystals form when extra _____ is added to a supersaturated solution.

💡 THINKING CRITICALLY

5. PREDICT: What will happen when sugar is added to a supersaturated solution of sugar and water?

BUILDING SCIENCE SKILLS

Organizing Information When you organize information, you put the information in some kind of order. Draw a chart showing the six basic crystal shapes. Use library references to identify a substance whose crystals have each type of shape.

⚛ Hands-On Activity

MAKING ROCK CANDY

You will need a sugar crystal, sugar-water solution prepared ahead of time, pencil, thread, large drinking glass, and paper towels.

1. From the container your teacher will supply, select a large sugar crystal. Remove it with tongs and dry it with a paper towel.

2. Pour some of the sugar-water solution from the container into a glass. Be careful not to pour any other crystals into the glass.

3. Tie one end of the thread to a pencil and the other end of the thread gently around the sugar crystal.

4. Balance the pencil over the opening of the glass so that the crystal is suspended in the solution. Do not let the crystal touch the bottom of the glass.

5. Let the glass sit undisturbed for several days to a week. Observe what grew on the string.

Practicing Your Skills

6. OBSERVE: What formed on the string after several days?

7. HYPOTHESIZE: What caused the result you observed?

▲ STEP 5 Observe the thread after a few days.

MORE ON THE WEB

The Synthetic Diamond Have students read about the struggle to be the first to create a synthetic diamond by visiting www.conceptsandchallenges.com. Then, have students create a timeline that details the individuals and scientific developments that led to the creation of the first synthetic diamond.

• TEACHING RESOURCES •

💿 **Teacher's Resources CD-ROM**
Lesson Review: Chapter 5, p. 13
Crystal Shapes: Visuals, p. 7

ONGOING ASSESSMENT

Describing How Crystals Are Formed Have students describe the three ways that crystals are formed. (allowing a saturated solution to evaporate, seeding a supersaturated solution, making a synthetic crystal)

---

3 Assess

✓ CHECKING CONCEPTS ANSWERS

1. crystals
2. shape
3. solute
4. solute

💡 THINKING CRITICALLY ANSWER

5. PREDICT: Sugar crystals will form.

4 Close

BUILDING SCIENCE SKILLS ANSWERS

Organizing Information The six basic crystal shapes are cubic (or isometric), hexagonal/trigonal, monoclinic, tetragonal, triclinic, and orthorhombic.
learning style: visual

Hands-On Activity

MAKING ROCK CANDY

TIME: 15–30 minutes; 1 week for observation

PURPOSE: observing, analyzing

ADVANCED PREPARATION: You will need to make the sugar-water solution at least 1 week in advance. To make the sugar-water solution, you will need 200 mL of water, 485 g of sugar, a hot plate, and a 1,000-L beaker or sauce pan. Pour the water into the 1,000-L beaker or sauce pan. Add the sugar. Heat the solution to boiling. Make sure that all the sugar dissolves. Next, cover the solution and let it stand undisturbed for 1 week. After 1 week, the solution will form large crystals that students can use in the Hands-On Activity.

ALTERNATIVE MATERIALS: Salt or Epsom salt can be used to replace sugar.

COOPERATIVE LEARNING: Have students work in pairs.

Practicing Your Skills Answers

6. OBSERVE: Crystals formed on the string.

7. HYPOTHESIZE: As the solvent evaporated, the dissolved sugar crystallized on the string and the crystal.

The Big Idea

(pp. 124–125)

1 Introduce

Objective Students will learn that crystals exist in a variety of forms and in many different places. Students will write a story about a crystal in their Science Logs.

Linking Prior Knowledge Ask students to recall two ways to grow crystals. (evaporating the solvent from a solution and using a supersaturated solution) Also, have students recall some examples of synthetic crystals.

2 Teach

Discussion After students read the article, encourage them to use reference materials to find additional examples of crystals, as well as the places where these crystals form. **learning styles: visual, linguistic**

Use the information in the article, in the captions, and in Fast Facts to help guide students in choosing a topic for their Science Logs.

THE BIG IDEA ONLINE

How are crystals formed on Earth? Have students research their Science Log Writing Activity at www.conceptsandchallenges.com. You can have students organize their log by completing the Big Idea activity online. Students may post their work in the Online Classroom Database for others to read.

Reinforcement Students can also use the Big Idea Planner or Big Idea Science Log Entry found on the Teacher's Resources CD-ROM.

◆ *Integrating Earth Science*

THE Big IDEA

How are crystals formed on Earth?

Gases and liquids are disordered. The molecules in a liquid or a gas bounce off each other and flow. Think about some perfume evaporating from a liquid into a gas. The perfume vapor spreads out. Your nose can easily prove that molecules of perfume in a gas state have flowed all around the room.

Solids, however, do not flow. If you put a solid into an empty jar, it just sits at the bottom of the jar. It does not spread out or flow. The solid stays together because its molecules are often ordered in regular geometric patterns called crystals.

How do crystals form? When a substance cools from liquid to solid, its flowing molecules slow down. The molecules begin to line up, forming rows and layers. They pack together tightly to form a crystal.

Crystals can be found in many places. You can find crystals in a kitchen in the form of sugar and salt. Rock candy is a giant sugar crystal. Diamonds are very hard crystals of carbon. In the heart of a battery-powered watch is a quartz crystal, which vibrates when electricity flows through it. Crystals can form in volcanoes, teakettles, caves, and candy shops. Crystals form anywhere molecules line up in geometric rows and layers.

Look at the photos that appear on these two pages. Then, follow the directions in the Science Log to find out more about "the big idea." ✦

124

The Caverns of Sonora
These crystalline structures form in caves over thousands of years. They are deposits of minerals called calcite and aragonite, which come from water dripping into the cave. This close-up shows calcite crystals.

Volcanic eruption of Kilauea, Hawaii
Geodes are hollow rocks lined with crystals. Some geodes can form as a result of certain lava flows.

Teaching Options

! FAST FACTS *Crystal Formation*

Several factors influence the growth of crystals. The size of crystals depends on the rate at which the liquid forming them cools. If the liquid cools slowly, large crystals may develop. If it cools quickly, many smaller crystals tend to form. When cooling takes place very rapidly, crystals may not form at all. Instead, the solid is smooth and shiny like glass.

Each substance has its own characteristic crystalline shape. For example, sodium chloride crystals are cubic. The planes that make up their outer surfaces, called faces, always meet at 90° angles. Crystals will be well-shaped if the crystal grows freely and undisturbed. If the crystal grows in a restricted space, it will take the shape of the area. A perfect crystal is rare, but regardless of the crystal's shape, the angles of its faces will remain the same.

ESL/ELL STRATEGY

Working With Peers Working with students who are proficient in English can help English-language learners to communicate. Pair an English-language learner with an English-proficient student. Have both students explain to each other the article and the captions in their own words.

Science Log

Some crystals are as ordinary as table salt; others are as rare as priceless gems. Find out more about crystals. Then, in your science log, write an extraordinary story about a crystal. Start your search at www.conceptsandchallenges.com.

Kitchen Crystals
Sometime crystals form in teakettles. Minerals dissolved in water crystallize when the water boils and evaporates. This close-up shows these crystals.

Tufa Towers at Mono Lake, CA
The formations you see here are made as saltwater evaporates, leaving the salty towers. This close-up shows salt crystals.

CHAPTER 5: Solutions **125**

3 Assess

Use the Writing Activity Rubric on the Teacher's Resources CD-ROM to assess students' Science Logs. Fill in the rubric with the additional information below. For this assignment, students should have:

- written an extraordinary story about a crystal, using some of the information about crystal formation provided in the Big Idea.

- used correct punctuation, capitalization, and grammar, and complete sentences.

4 Close

Crystal Poster Have pairs of students create a poster that relates information about one type of crystal that they learned about while studying the Big Idea. The posters should include the name of the crystal and information about its chemical composition, as well as how and where the crystal forms. Have students present their completed posters to the class.
learning styles: tactile, linguistic

Tips for Using Technology

Word Processing Software
Have students use word processing software to write a story about an extraordinary crystal. A simple word processing program allows them to do basic tasks such as entering and editing text. A more complex word processing program allows students to make tables, draw pictures, do math, and make graphs. Students can print out their word processing document to share with the class. Remind students to use proper margins and spacing for a neat paper.

• TEACHING RESOURCES •

Teacher's Resources CD-ROM
Big Idea: Chapter 5, p. 14
Big Idea Planner: Study Tools, pp. 11–12
Big Idea Science Log Entry: Study Tools, p. 13
Writing Activity Rubric: Teaching Tools, p. 9

Challenges (pp. 126-128)

Chapter Summary

Review Before students begin the Challenges, review the summary with them. If time permits, divide students into groups of three. Have each group of students describe the summary points from one of the lessons in their own words.
learning styles: linguistic, auditory

STUDY HINT Have students work in pairs to review the Key Terms. Students can alternate, with one student reading a definition of a Key Term and the other student identifying the Key Term.
learning styles: linguistic, auditory

Key Term Challenges

MATCHING

1. freezing point (5-6)
2. supersaturated solution (5-5)
3. condensation (5-8)
4. boiling point (5-7)
5. freezing point depression (5-6)
6. unsaturated solution (5-5)

FILL IN

7. saturated solution (5-5)
8. concentrated solution (5-5)
9. evaporation (5-8)
10. solute (5-2)
11. dissolves (5-4)
12. freezing point (5-6)

Chapter Summary

Lesson 5-1
- When a substance dissolves, it goes into **solution**, a mixture in which one substance is evenly mixed with another substance.

Lesson 5-2
- The substance that dissolves in a solution is called the **solute**. The **solvent** is the substance in which a solute dissolves.
- A substance that dissolves in another substance is **soluble** in that substance.

Lesson 5-3
- A molecule is polar if one end has a positive charge and the other end has a negative charge.
- Water is called the universal solvent because it can dissolve many different substances.

Lesson 5-4
- Stirring, crushing, or heating a solvent increases the rate at which a solute dissolves.

Lesson 5-5
- An **unsaturated solution** contains less solute than it can hold at a given temperature.
- A **saturated solution** contains all the solute it can hold at a given temperature.

Lesson 5-6
- Lowering the **freezing point** of a liquid solvent by adding solute is called **freezing point depression**.

Lesson 5-7
- The temperature at which a liquid changes to a gas is called its **boiling point**. Raising the boiling point of a liquid solvent by adding solute is called **boiling point elevation**.

Lesson 5-8
- **Evaporation** is the process by which a liquid changes to a gas at the surface of the liquid.
- **Condensation** is the process by which a gas changes to a liquid.

Lesson 5-9
- Crystals form when extra solute is added to a supersaturated solution.

126

Key Term Challenges

boiling point (p. 116)
boiling point elevation (p. 116)
concentrated solution (p. 112)
condensation (p. 118)
dilute solution (p. 112)
dissolve (p.104)
distillation (p. 118)
evaporation (p. 118)
freezing point (p. 114)
freezing point depression (p. 114)
insoluble (p. 106)
polar molecule (p. 108)
saturated solution (p. 112)
solubility (p. 106)
soluble (p. 106)
solute (p. 106)
solution (p. 104)
solvent (p. 106)
supersaturated solution (p. 112)
unsaturated solution (p. 112)

MATCHING Write the Key Term from above that best matches each description.

1. temperature at which a liquid changes to a solid
2. solution containing more solute than it can normally hold at a given temperature
3. change of a gas to a liquid
4. temperature at which a liquid changes to a gas
5. lowering the freezing point of a liquid solvent by adding solute
6. solution containing less solute than it can hold at a given temperature

FILL IN Write the Key Term from above that best completes each statement.

7. Extra solute sitting at the bottom of a solution indicates the solution is a _____.
8. Increasing the amount of solute in a solution can make a _____.
9. In distillation of a liquid, _____ occurs first and then condensation.
10. For a solution to form, a _____ must dissolve in a solvent.
11. Powdered sugar _____ faster than a sugar cube.
12. The _____ of pure water is 0°C.

Teaching Options

PREPARING STUDENTS FOR STANDARDIZED TESTS

Reading Strategy: Tell students to look for key words, such as *increase*, *decrease*, *raise*, and *lower*, to help them choose the best answer to each question.

Writing Strategy: Tell students to list the key points that they want to make before beginning to write to ensure that they do not omit any important information.

Interpreting Visuals: Remind students that when they are studying a graph, they should carefully read the title of the graph and the labels along each axis to fully understand the information that the graph provides.

ESL/ELL STRATEGY

Restating Processes English-language learners will benefit from restating processes in their own words. Have pairs of students work together to explain evaporation and condensation.

Content Challenges TEST PREP

MULTIPLE CHOICE **Write the letter of the term or phrase that best completes each statement.**

1. Extra solute sitting at the bottom of a solution indicates the solution is _____.
   a. dilute
   b. unsaturated
   c. saturated
   d. supersaturated

2. As the amount of solute in a solution increases, the _____ of the solution also increases.
   a. boiling point
   b. temperature
   c. freezing point
   d. solubility

3. In distillation, a liquid _____ and then condenses.
   a. sublimes
   b. freezes
   c. boils
   d. evaporates

4. For a solution to form, a _____ must dissolve in a solvent.
   a. chemical
   b. solute
   c. soda
   d. salt

5. Crystals of the same substance have the same _____.
   a. shape
   b. size
   c. faces
   d. irregularities

6. Powdered sugar dissolves _____ a sugar cube.
   a. more slowly than
   b. at the same rate as
   c. faster than
   d. the same way as

7. The _____ of pure water is 0°C.
   a. boiling point
   b. freezing point
   c. room temperature
   d. solubility

8. Adding antifreeze to a car's cooling system raises the _____ of the water it contains.
   a. amount
   b. freezing point
   c. concentration
   d. boiling point

9. Placing rock salt on an icy sidewalk lowers the _____ of melted ice.
   a. evaporation
   b. freezing point
   c. boiling point
   d. condensation

10. A _____ solution contains more solute than it can normally hold at a given temperature.
    a. dilute
    b. supersaturated
    c. unsaturated
    d. saturated

TRUE/FALSE **Write *true* if the statement is true. If the statement is false, change the underlined term to make the statement true.**

11. Stirring a solution <u>speeds up</u> the rate at which a solute dissolves.

12. The freezing point of salt water is <u>higher</u> than that of pure water.

13. Crystals form when extra solute is added to <u>an unsaturated</u> solution.

14. The ends of a water molecule are <u>electrically charged</u>.

15. As the amount of solute in a solution increases, the boiling point of the solution <u>decreases</u>.

CHAPTER 5: Solutions **127**

Content Challenges

MULTIPLE CHOICE

1. c (5-5)
2. a (5-7)
3. d (5-8)
4. b (5-2)
5. a (5-9)
6. c (5-4)
7. b (5-6)
8. d (5-7)
9. b (5-6)
10. b (5-5)

TRUE/FALSE

11. true (5-4)
12. false; lower (5-6)
13. false; a supersaturated (5-9)
14. true (5-3)
15. false; increases (5-7)

ALTERNATIVE ASSESSMENT

Comparing Students may write a Science Log entry that compares the freezing points and boiling points of the following: (1) pure water, (2) a dilute solution of sugar in water, and (3) a concentrated solution of sugar in water. Students may also describe ways in which the boiling points of all three substances can be increased and ways in which their freezing points can be lowered.

PORTFOLIO ASSESSMENT

Making Student Portfolios
Students can demonstrate their comprehension of the concepts in this chapter by making a portfolio. Encourage students to select their own work for inclusion in their portfolios. The Concept Map, the Big Idea Planner, and the Weekly Journal are some of the reproducibles on the Teacher's Resources CD-ROM that they can include in their portfolios. You can use the Portfolio Assessment Rubric also found on the Teacher's Resources CD-ROM to assess students' portfolios.

Concept Challenges

WRITTEN RESPONSE

1. **ANALYZE:** Water changes from one form to another when it evaporates, but the amount of water does not change. (5-8)
2. **COMPARE:** An increased amount of solute raises the boiling point and lowers the freezing point of a solution. (5-6, 5-7)
3. **INFER:** Substances have specific, known crystal shapes. (5-9)
4. **HYPOTHESIZE:** Evaporation increases the concentration of salt. (5-8)
5. **EXPLAIN:** The carbon dioxide gas comes out of solution into the air. (5-1)

INTERPRETING A GRAPH

6. about 110 g (5-5)
7. about 90°C (5-5)
8. about 180 g (5-5)
9. about 65 g (5-5)
10. The higher the temperature of the solvent, the more solute it can dissolve. (5-4)

Chapter Project Wrap-Up

SOLUTIONS GUESSING GAME

Students can play a guessing game to find out each other's solutions. Games can be played with the entire class, or students can be divided into small groups. You can use the Individual Activity Rubric found on the Teacher's Resources CD-ROM to assess students' projects. Fill in the rubric with the additional information below. For this project, students should have:

- thought of ten solutions.
- created five clues for each solution, including a clue that named the solute and the solvent.

Concept Challenges TEST PREP

WRITTEN RESPONSE Complete the exercises and answer each of the following questions in complete sentences.

1. **ANALYZE:** The law of conservation of matter states that matter cannot be created or destroyed but only changed from one form to another. How does the evaporation of water support this law?
2. **COMPARE:** Compare the effect of an increased amount of solute on both the boiling point and the freezing point of a solution.
3. **INFER:** How could information about crystal shape be used to identify an unknown substance?
4. **HYPOTHESIZE:** What effect does evaporation have on Earth's oceans?
5. **EXPLAIN:** Club soda contains carbon dioxide gas dissolved in liquid water. Explain why a bottle of club soda goes "flat" when it is left open at room temperature.

INTERPRETING A GRAPH Use Figure 5-28 to answer the following questions. Round off your numbers.

6. About how many grams of sodium nitrate can be dissolved in 100 g of water at a temperature of 50°C?
7. At what temperature will 100 g of water dissolve 160 g of sodium nitrate?
8. About how much sodium nitrate can be dissolved in 100 g of water at a temperature equal to the boiling point of pure water?
9. About how much sodium nitrate can be dissolved in 100 g of water at a temperature equal to the freezing point of pure water?
10. What is the relationship between the temperature of a solvent and the amount of solute it can dissolve?

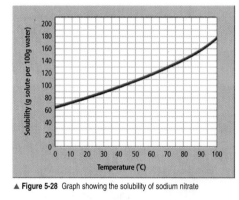

▲ **Figure 5-28** Graph showing the solubility of sodium nitrate

---

Teaching Options

• TEACHING RESOURCES •

Teacher's Resources CD-ROM

Key Term Review: Chapter 5, p. 15

Chapter 5 Test: pp. 16–18

Big Idea Planner: Study Tools, pp. 11–12

Weekly Journal: Study Tools, p. 19

Portfolio Assessment Rubric: Teaching Tools, p. 10

Individual Activity Rubric: Teaching Tools, p. 5

Chapter Self-Check: Teaching Tools, p. 11

PLANNING GUIDE

◆ **TEACHING THE CHAPTER** This chapter should take approximately 5–8 days to complete instruction and assessment.

	Skills and Features	Projects and Activities	Achieve Science Literacy	Meet Individual Needs
Chapter 6 Opener p. T129	RESEARCH	• Chapter Project		
Lesson 6-1 **What is a suspension?** pp. T130–T131 Standard: B1a	DEFINE, ANALYZE, CLASSIFY • Building Science Skills • Hands-On Activity	• Cooperative Learning • More on the Web • Lab Challenge	• Study Hint • Reading Strategy • Ongoing Assessment	• Reteach ○ CD-ROM Writing Activity Outline ▭ Laboratory Video
Lesson 6-2 **How can a suspension be separated?** pp. T132–T133 Standard: B1a	PREDICT, IDENTIFY, MODEL • Investigate • Building Science Skills • Integrating Earth Science	• More on the Web • Integrating Life Science	• Study Hint • Ongoing Assessment	• ESL/ELL Strategy
Lesson 6-3 **What is an emulsion?** pp. T134–T135	IDENTIFY, HYPOTHESIZE, CONTRAST • Web Infosearch • Hands-On Activity	• Cooperative Learning	• Study Hint • Ongoing Assessment	○ CD-ROM Fishbone Map
Lesson 6-4 **What is a colloid?** pp. T136–T137 Standard: B3c	DEFINE, EXPLAIN, COMPARE • Web Infosearch • Science and Technology	• Extending the Lesson • Lab Challenge	• Study Hint • Ongoing Assessment	• ESL/ELL Strategy ○ CD-ROM Enrichment Activity Venn Diagram
Big Idea **What suspensions, emulsions, or colloids do you eat?** pp. T138–T139	RESEARCH, COMMUNICATE, ANALYZE • Science Log: Writing Activity	• Big Idea Online • Integrating Life Science • Close Activity	• Tips for Using Technology	• ESL/ELL Strategy ○ CD-ROM Big Idea Planner

Planning Guide continues on next page.

Standards: For details on the correlation to National Science Standards see pages *xx–xxi*.

	Skills and Features	Projects and Activities	Achieve Science Literacy	Meet Individual Needs
Lesson 6-5 **What are air and water pollution?** pp. T140–T141	DEFINE, LIST, IDENTIFY • Health and Safety Tip • Hands-On Activity	• Cooperative Learning • Extending the Lesson • More on the Web	• Study Hint • Ongoing Assessment	 CD-ROM Enrichment Activity Cause-and-Effect Diagram
Lab Activity **Testing for the Tyndall Effect—Solution or Nonsolution?** pp. T142–T143 Standard: B3c	OBSERVE, MODEL, ANALYZE • Set-Up Time: 5 min • Lab Time: 20 min	• Extend the Lab Activity • Lab Skills Worksheets	• Tips for Using Technology	• ESL/ELL Strategy CD-ROM Lab Activity Report Spreadsheet
Chapter 6 Challenges pp. T144–T146	• Chapter Summary • Key Term Challenges • Content Challenges • Concept Challenges	• Chapter Project Wrap-Up • Unit Challenge Online	• Study Hint • Preparing Students for Standardized Tests	• ESL/ELL Strategy CD-ROM Chapter Self-Check Cause-and-Effect Diagram

Teacher Notes

_____

_____

_____

_____

_____

_____

_____

_____

_____

_____

_____

_____

Chapter 6 Suspensions

▲ Figure 6-1 A decorative, stained-glass window

Stained glass is used to decorate because light shines through, making colors look as if they are glowing. It is used in windows, lamp shades, and sculptures.

Clear glass is an unusual solution in which particles of sand and other substances are evenly mixed. Stained glass is different. It is actually a mixture in which color particles are suspended within the clear glass. The color particles are actually minerals. Cobalt makes blues. Copper makes greens and reds.

▶ What is the difference between the particles in two different colors?

Contents

UNIT 2: Types of Matter   **129**

Teaching Options

ASSESSMENT PLANNER

For assessment in the Student Edition, see the following pages:

Content Assessment
Checking Concepts: pp. 131, 133, 135, 137, 141
Thinking Critically: pp. 131, 133, 135, 137, 141
Chapter Challenges: pp. 144–146

Alternative Assessment
Building Skills: pp. 131, 133
Web InfoSearch: pp. 135, 137
Science Log: p. 139

Performance-Based Assessment
Hands-On Activity: pp. 131, 135, 141
Lab Activity: pp. 142–143

• TEACHING RESOURCES •

Teacher's Resources CD-ROM
Lesson Review: Chapter 6, pp. 2, 3, 4, 5, 8
Enrichment: Chapter 6, pp. 6, 9
Key Term Review: Chapter 6, p. 10
Chapter 6 Test: pp. 11–13
Laboratory Manual: pp. 5–8, 13–14, 41–44

Laboratory Video
Segment 7: Determining the Difference Between a Solution and a Suspension

---

Chapter 6
Suspensions

Chapter Overview

In this chapter, students will describe the characteristics of a suspension. They will describe some ways of separating a suspension and describe and give examples of an emulsion and a colloid. Finally, they will draw upon their knowledge of suspensions to describe causes of air pollution and water pollution.

About Figure 6-1 About 1,000 years ago, stained glass began to be used in the windows of buildings, such as castles and places of worship. The images created by using stained glass, such as the tree and the mountains in Figure 6-1, often told a story.

Some of the finer details of an image created by using stained glass may contain paint, but most of the colors are produced by the permanent suspension of particles instead of pigment from paint. For this reason, the brilliance of these glowing colors will not fade.

Answer The particles in different colors contain different minerals.

Linking Prior Knowledge

For this chapter, students should recall:
- the four states of matter (Lesson 1-3).
- how mixtures are separated (Lesson 4-3).
- the characteristics of mixtures (Lesson 4-4).
- the parts of a solution (Lesson 5-2).

Chapter Project

WATER FILTRATION POSTERS

MATERIALS: posterboard, marking pens
After students read the chapter, discuss how water from wells, lakes, rivers, or reservoirs is an example of a suspension because of the sediment that is contained in the water. Have students research how water treatment plants filter out these sediments. Have them create a poster that shows each step in the process. Allow students to present their posters to the class. **learning styles: visual, tactile**

1 Introduce

✏️ **STUDY HINT** Before beginning this lesson, have students copy the title of each section in outline format in their notebooks. As students read each section, they should write notes that support or explain each of the titles. Students can use the Writing Activity Outline found on the Teacher's Resources CD-ROM.

Linking Prior Knowledge Invite a volunteer to read the lesson title aloud. Ask students to recall what a solution is (Lesson 5-2). After reading the Key Term, ask students to predict how a suspension is similar to a solution (Lesson 5-2).

2 Teach

Demonstration Add some soil to a jar of water. Tighten the lid and shake the jar to make a suspension. Ask students to describe the mixture. (It will be cloudy.) Then, allow the mixture to stand for a while and have students observe what happens. Students will observe that the soil particles settle to the bottom. Ask students why they think the soil particles settled to the bottom. (Particles of soil are denser than water.) **learning styles: visual, auditory**

Discussion Have a volunteer read the definition of *suspension* aloud. Ask: *What are some properties of a suspension?* Guide students to recognize that a suspension is a type of mixture made of two or more substances that keep their chemical properties. A suspension lacks a definite chemical composition and can be separated by physical means.
learning styles: auditory, linguistic

Answers to questions

▶1 **DEFINE:** a mixture of two or more materials that separate on standing

▶2 **COMPARE:** Particles in a suspension are much larger than those in a solution.

▶3 **OBSERVE:** Both are mixtures.

▶4 **LIST:** Accept any two of the following: salad dressing, dust or smoke in the air, smog, fog, and clouds.

6-1 What is a suspension?

Objective
Describe the characteristics of a suspension.

Key Term
suspension (suh-SPEHN-shuhn): mixture of two materials or more that separate on standing

Suspensions If you add some soil to a jar of water, the water will become cloudy. If you let the mixture stand, you will notice that the soil particles settle to the bottom of the jar. A mixture of soil and water is an example of a suspension. A **suspension** is a mixture of two or more materials that separate on standing. An important thing to remember about suspensions is that most types of suspensions are temporary. The materials in an ordinary suspension may appear to be well mixed at first, but in time they will separate.

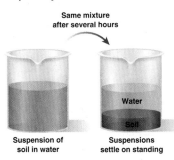

Same mixture after several hours

Suspension of soil in water

Suspensions settle on standing

Water

Soil

▲ **Figure 6-2** Soil and water make a temporary suspension.

In many cases the particles of a suspension will separate into layers. Think about a suspension of soil and water. If you were to examine this mixture after it has separated, you would notice that the soil has formed definite layers. Soil is made up of particles of different sizes and weights. As the particles settle, they form layers, with the heaviest particles on the bottom and the lightest particles on top.

▶1 **DEFINE:** What is a suspension?

130

Particles in Suspensions The particles in a solution are much too small to be seen, even with the aid of a microscope. That is because the particles in a solution are mixed at the smallest level possible—as atoms or molecules. However, the particles in a suspension are much larger. You can see the particles in some suspensions without a microscope. In other suspensions, the particles are visible with a microscope.

▶2 **COMPARE:** How does the size of the particles in a suspension compare with the size of the particles in a solution?

Properties of Suspensions An important property of suspensions is that the particles of a suspension scatter light. You can observe this property by darkening a room and shining a flashlight through a mixture of soil and water. The beam of light will be visible as it passes through the cloudy water. One way that you can tell the difference between a solution and a suspension is that the particles of a solution do not scatter light. Figure 6-3 compares some properties of solutions and suspensions.

PROPERTIES OF SOLUTIONS AND SUSPENSIONS	
Solution	**Suspension**
Mixture	Mixture
Clear	Cloudy
Particles evenly mixed	Particles settle on standing
Particles too small to be seen	Particles can be seen

▲ **Figure 6-3** Compare the properties of solutions and suspensions.

▶3 **OBSERVE:** What property do suspensions and solutions have in common?

Examples of Suspensions A familiar example of a suspension is an oil and vinegar salad dressing. If you shake a bottle of salad dressing, the contents mix together. Once you put the bottle down, however, the ingredients separate. That is why the labels on bottles of salad dressing often state "Shake well before using."

Teaching Options

COOPERATIVE LEARNING

Listing Suspensions Have students work in small groups to make lists of suspensions. Allow them to use the Internet and other resources. Students can find pictures or make their own drawings to illustrate each example. As a class, students can combine their lists to see how many suspensions they have listed. **learning styles: interpersonal, logical/mathematical**

RETEACH

Classifying a Mixture Pour a mixture of milk and water into a clear glass container. Darken the classroom and shine a flashlight on the container. Have students explain why this mixture is classified as a suspension. (The light is scattered as it passes through the liquid.) **learning styles: visual, auditory**

Not all suspensions involve liquids. A common suspension of a solid in a gas is dust or smoke particles suspended in the air. Smog, a suspension of smoke and fog in air, is a common pollutant. Clouds, another suspension, are made up of tiny particles of water or ice suspended in air.

▲ **Figure 6-4** A dust storm is a suspension of a solid in a gas.

 **LIST:** What are two common examples of suspensions?

✓ CHECKING CONCEPTS

1. If a suspension is allowed to stand, the substances will _____.
2. The appearance of a _____ is cloudy.
3. The _____ in a suspension are larger than atoms or molecules.
4. An example of a suspension of a solid in a gas is _____ suspended in air.
5. Solutions and suspensions are similar in that both are _____.

💡 THINKING CRITICALLY

6. CONTRAST: How are the particles in a suspension different from those in a solution?
7. CLASSIFY: Look at Figure 6-3. Are the properties listed physical or chemical properties?

BUILDING SCIENCE SKILLS

Analyzing Prepare mixtures of each of the following in water: salt, sand, pepper, and sugar. Stir each mixture and use what you have learned to decide whether each mixture is a solution or a suspension. Record all your observations and tell how you reached your conclusions.

Hands-On Activity

MAKING A SUSPENSION

You will need safety goggles, water, vegetable oil, starch, a spoon, and two small jars with lids.

1. Put on the goggles. Half-fill each jar with water.
2. To one jar, add two spoonfuls of starch.
3. Add vegetable oil to the other jar until it is about two-thirds full.
4. Put the lids tightly on both jars.
5. Shake each jar for about 30 seconds.
6. Allow the jars to remain still for five minutes.

Practicing Your Skills

7. EXPLAIN: Why did you shake the jars?
8. OBSERVE: What happened when you allowed the jars to sit?
9. ANALYZE: Are both of the mixtures you made suspensions? How do you know?

▲ **STEP 5** Shake each jar.

ONGOING ASSESSMENT

Making a Venn Diagram Have students make a Venn diagram to show how solutions and suspensions are alike and how they are different. Students can use the Venn Diagram found on the Teacher's Resources CD-ROM.

• TEACHING RESOURCES •

Teacher's Resources CD-ROM
Lesson Review: Chapter 6, p. 2
Writing Activity Outline: Study Tools, pp. 20–21

Laboratory Manual
Lab. Challenge: How do solutions, suspensions, and colloids compare? pp. 41–44

Laboratory Video
Segment 7: Determining the Difference Between a Solution and a Suspension

---

📖 **READING STRATEGY** Remind students that comparing means telling how two things are alike, and contrasting means telling how they are different. Encourage students to compare and contrast solutions and suspensions. **learning style: linguistic**

3 Assess

✓ CHECKING CONCEPTS ANSWERS

1. separate
2. suspension
3. particles
4. dust or smoke particles
5. mixtures

💡 THINKING CRITICALLY ANSWERS

6. CONTRAST: Possible answer: Particles are visible in a suspension but are too small to be seen in a solution.
7. CLASSIFY: physical properties

4 Close

BUILDING SCIENCE SKILLS ANSWERS

Analyzing Students should observe that only the sand-water mixture and the pepper-water mixture separate on standing. Therefore, they should classify these two mixtures as suspensions and the other two mixtures as solutions.

Hands-On Activity

MAKING A SUSPENSION

TIME: 15–20 minutes

PURPOSE: observing

SAFETY TIP: Caution students not to drink the liquids.

COOPERATIVE LEARNING: Have pairs of students share their responses with each other.

Practicing Your Skills Answers

7. EXPLAIN: to mix the ingredients
8. OBSERVE: The mixtures separated. In one jar, the vegetable oil settled on top of the water. In the other jar, the starch settled to the bottom.
9. ANALYZE: yes, because they separated on standing

1 Introduce

🔍 INVESTIGATE

TIME: 5-10 minutes

PURPOSE: Students will observe two methods of separating a suspension.

MATERIALS: 3 clear plastic glasses, teaspoon, sand, clay, pebbles, paper towel, rubber band, pail, water

PROCEDURE: Have students work in pairs. Explain that after Step 4, students should observe the contents of the undisturbed glass.

THINK ABOUT IT: Filtration was faster and better. It is a more thorough means of separating the substances.

✏️ **STUDY HINT** Before beginning this lesson, have students study Figures 6-5 and 6-6. Have them compare the two methods of separating suspensions.

Linking Prior Knowledge Ask students to recall how mixtures are separated (Lesson 4-3).

2 Teach

Demonstration Show students the undisturbed glass from the Investigate activity. Ask them to identify the order in which the sand, clay, and pebbles settled. (pebbles, sand, clay) Guide students to recognize that the size of particles determines the rate at which the particles settle. **learning styles: visual, auditory**

Discussion Ask students to describe what happens when a liquid falls on a waterproof item. (The liquid beads up and does not pass through.) Explain that such items are nonporous, or lack openings through which liquids can move. Inform students that filtering a suspension is based on a similar principle. Materials whose particles are bigger than the pores in a filter will not pass through.
learning style: auditory

Answers to questions

 EXLPAIN: ~~Clay~~ Sand; Its particles are larger.

PREDICT: They are trapped by the filter and do not pass through it.

6-2 How can a suspension be separated?

INVESTIGATE

Separating a Suspension
HANDS-ON ACTIVITY

1. Half-fill two clear plastic glasses with water. Add a teaspoon each of sand, clay, and pebbles to each glass and stir.
2. Allow one glass to stand undisturbed.
3. Place a piece of paper towel over a third plastic glass and hold it in place with a rubber band. Allow the paper towel to sag into the glass slightly.
4. Stir the mixture in the second glass and carefully pour the suspension through the paper towel into the third glass.

THINK ABOUT IT: Which method of separating the suspension was faster? Which separated better? Explain.

STEP 2

Objective

Describe some ways to separate a suspension.

Key Terms

filtration: separation of particles in a suspension by passing the suspension through filter paper or some other porous material

coagulation (koh-ag-yoo-LAY-shuhn)**:** use of chemicals to make the particles in a suspension clump together

Settling Particles in a suspension settle on standing. Large particles settle out quickly. Smaller particles take a longer time to settle. You can see how this works in Figure 6-5.

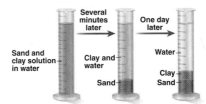

▲ **Figure 6-5** Suspensions separate on standing.

EXPLAIN: When sand and clay are mixed with water, which settles faster? Explain.

132

Filtration **Filtration** is the removal of particles in a suspension by passing the suspension through a filter. Filters can be made of paper, charcoal, or other materials. Filters are porous. They have tiny openings, or pores, through which some materials can pass and some cannot. Materials that cannot pass through the filter have particles that are larger than the pores in the filter.

Particles collect in filter held by the funnel.

Suspension

Liquid passes through filter.

▲ **Figure 6-6** Suspensions can be separated by filtration.

PREDICT: What happens to particles in a suspension that are larger than the pores in a filter?

Coagulation Another way to separate a suspension is to add chemicals that make the particles of the suspension stick together. The particles form clumps that are larger and heavier

---

Teaching Options

◇ INTEGRATING LIFE SCIENCE

Keeping the Body Healthy
Filtration occurs in different parts of the human body. The nasal passages are lined with hairs that filter dust and other suspended particles in air and prevent them from entering the body. Have students use different resources to find other filters in the human body. (The kidneys contain structures called nephrons that filter wastes from the blood. The lymphatic system filters disease-causing microorganisms from the fluids that surround body cells.)
learning styles: auditory, linguistic

ESL/ELL STRATEGY

Pour, Poor, and Pore Homophones, or words that have the same sound but different meanings, may be confusing for students acquiring language proficiency. Write the homophones *pour, poor,* and *pore* on the board. Then, discuss the meaning of each word, inviting volunteers to use each in a sentence.

than the original particles. As a result, the particles settle out more quickly. This process is called **coagulation.** Alum is a common coagulant. Coagulation takes place when you cut your finger. Chemicals in your blood cause the blood to coagulate and form a clot.

▶ **DEFINE:** What is coagulation?

Spinning A fourth way to separate a suspension is to spin a mixture at high speeds. The device used to spin a mixture is called a centrifuge (SEN-truh-fyooj). As the suspension is spun around, the particles in the suspension are pulled to the bottom of the container. Use of a centrifuge greatly increases the rate at which a suspension separates. The solid materials in blood cells are separated from the liquid materials, the plasma, by centrifugation.

▶ **IDENTIFY:** What is a centrifuge?

✔ CHECKING CONCEPTS

1. What happens when a suspension is left to stand overnight?
2. What is filtration?

3. What is coagulation?
4. How is a centrifuge used to separate the particles in a suspension?

💡 THINKING CRITICALLY

5. **ANALYZE:** Which method of separating a suspension is described? **a.** A solution of ammonium hydroxide and alum is added to a clay-and-water suspension. **b.** A suspension is passed through a piece of linen cloth.

BUILDING SCIENCE SKILLS

Modeling Make a model to show how coagulation works. Half-fill two test tubes with water. Add a small amount of clay to each. To one of the test tubes, add several drops of alum solution. Then, add several drops of ammonium hydroxide to the same test tube. Observe both test tubes for several minutes. In the test tube that you added the alum solution and the ammonium hydroxide, you should see a jellylike material form. This causes the clay particles to clump together. In which test tube do the clay particles settle faster? Why?

◈ Integrating Earth Science

TOPICS: sediments, rivers, erosion

THE MISSISSIPPI DELTA

As a river flows, it carries particles of clay, sand, and gravel. These particles are called sediments. The sediments are suspended in the water.

A river picks up sediments as it floods and erodes its banks. A fast-moving river carries the most sediments. As the banks of a river widen, the river slows down. When the river slows down, sediments settle out of the suspension and are deposited. Rocks and pebbles are deposited first because they are the heaviest and largest particles. Sand has the next largest particles. Silt and clay, having the smallest particles, are deposited last.

The widest part of a river is usually its mouth, where it empties into a larger body of water. The Mississippi River's mouth is located at the Gulf of Mexico. Here, the Mississippi moves so slowly that sediments from the river are deposited. Gradually, the sediments form new land called a delta. The land of the Mississippi delta is good for farming because new topsoil is always being deposited.

Thinking Critically Why do you think materials are deposited in the order given above?

▲ **Figure 6-7** Aerial view of Mississippi delta

▶ **DEFINE:** a process in which chemicals are used to make the particles in a suspension clump together

▶ **IDENTIFY:** a device used to separate a suspension by spinning it at high speeds

3 Assess

✔ CHECKING CONCEPTS ANSWERS

1. The particles settle out of the suspension.
2. the separation of particles in a suspension by passing the suspension through a filter
3. a process in which chemicals are used to make the particles in a suspension clump together
4. It spins the suspension at high speeds, causing the particles in the suspension to be pulled toward the bottom of the container.

💡 THINKING CRITICALLY ANSWERS

5. **ANALYZE: a.** coagulation **b.** filtration

4 Close

BUILDING SCIENCE SKILLS ANSWER

Modeling The clay particles in the test tube to which alum solution and ammonium hydroxide were added settle faster because the particles that clump together are larger than separate particles.

◈ Integrating Earth Science

TOPICS: sediments, rivers, erosion

THE MISSISSIPPI DELTA

Real-Life Connection The people of ancient cultures recognized that lands bordering Earth's rivers were suitable for farming. People living along the Nile River in northern Africa used the fertile soil in this region to raise crops as early as 5000 B.C.

Discussion Display a map of the United States in the classroom and have students identify the mouth of the Mississippi River. Ask students to name all the states that touch the river.

Thinking Critically Answer
The materials are deposited according to particle size.

MORE ON THE WEB

Writing About Anticoagulants Have students learn more about anticoagulants by visiting www.conceptsandchallenges.com. Then, have students write a short report about anticoagulants and how they are administered to patients.

• TEACHING RESOURCES •

🔘 **Teacher's Resources CD-ROM**
Lesson Review: Chapter 6, p. 3

ONGOING ASSESSMENT

Separating a Suspension Ask students to name and describe four ways to separate a suspension. (settling, filtration, coagulation, spinning)

1 Introduce

✎ **STUDY HINT** Before beginning this lesson, have students create word webs in their notebooks. The topic should be emulsions. As students read the lesson, they can add arms to their webs on which they record Key Terms with their definitions and other details about emulsions. Students can also use the Fishbone Map found on the Teacher's Resources CD-ROM.

Linking Prior Knowledge Ask students to define *matter*. Then, have them identify the four states of matter (Lesson 1-3). Explain that this lesson focuses on a type of suspension in which both parts are in the liquid state.

2 Teach

Demonstration Mix some cooking oil with water and then shake the mixture. Allow the mixture to stand and ask students what occurs. (The oil and water separate.) Point out that a mixture of oil and water is an emulsion. Define an emulsion as a suspension of two liquids. Ask students if they can think of other emulsions. (oil and vinegar salad dressing, medicines, gravy, soup). **learning styles: visual, auditory**

Discussion After reading about permanent emulsions, ask students why dairy manufacturers homogenize milk. (If milk is not homogenized, the milk and cream will separate into layers.) Explain to students that some cream is removed from fresh milk and used to create products such as half-and-half and whipping cream. **learning style: auditory**

Answers to questions

▶ **PREDICT:** It will separate on standing.

▶ **CONTRAST:** A temporary emulsion will separate. A permanent emulsion will not separate because its particles are small enough to stay in suspension.

▶ **IDENTIFY:** a substance that keeps an emulsion from separating

6-3 What is an emulsion?

Objective
Describe and give examples of an emulsion.

Key Terms
emulsion (ee-MUL-shuhn): suspension of two liquids

homogenization (huh-mahj-uh-nih-ZAY-shuhn): formation of a permanent emulsion

Emulsions When a liquid is suspended in another liquid, the result is an **emulsion.** Milk, paint, and many medicines are examples of emulsions.

You can make an emulsion by mixing some cooking oil with water, and then shaking the mixture. This emulsion will not stay mixed for long. If you let the mixture stand, the oil and water will soon separate. An emulsion that does not stay mixed is called a temporary emulsion.

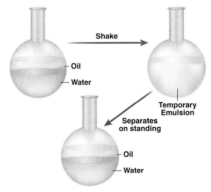

▲ **Figure 6-8** A temporary emulsion separates on standing.

▶ **PREDICT:** What will happen to a temporary emulsion?

Permanent Emulsions Many types of commercial products that are emulsions do not separate on standing. These emulsions are called permanent emulsions. The particles in a permanent

134

emulsion are much smaller than the particles in a temporary emulsion. The particles in a permanent emulsion are small enough to stay in suspension.

A familiar example of a permanent emulsion is homogenized milk. **Homogenization** is the formation of a permanent emulsion. Fresh milk is a temporary emulsion that quickly separates into milk and cream. Fresh milk is homogenized in a machine that breaks down the cream into very small particles. The small particles of cream remain permanently suspended in the milk.

▲ **Figure 6-9** The fresh milk coming from these cows is a temporary emulsion.

▶ **CONTRAST:** What is the difference between a temporary emulsion and a permanent emulsion?

Emulsifying Agents Many detergents or other cleaning products contain substances called emulsifying agents. An emulsifying agent keeps an emulsion from separating. The soap in cleaning products is an emulsifying agent. Soap breaks apart grease or dirt into smaller particles. These particles are small enough to form a permanent emulsion with water. The dirt or grease is washed away in the water.

Teaching Options

❗ FAST FACTS *Milk Processing*

Before raw milk is homogenized, it is pasteurized. During this process, the raw milk is heated to 63°C (145°F) for 30 minutes and then cooled quickly. This rapid heating and cooling process destroys any disease-causing bacteria present in the liquid. The cooled milk is then sent to a homogenizer, where it is pumped through tiny openings under great pressure. This action breaks down fat globules in the milk into tiny particles that are permanently suspended in the liquid. Vitamin D is then added to the homogenized milk to promote normal bone formation.

Other emulsifying agents include gelatin and egg yolk. These substances are often used in food to keep ingredients from separating.

▶ IDENTIFY: What is an emulsifying agent?

✓ CHECKING CONCEPTS

1. An emulsion is a suspension of a _____ in a liquid.
2. Oil and water separate on standing because they form a _____ emulsion.
3. The particles in a _____ emulsion are small enough to stay in suspension.
4. Soap is an example of an _____ agent.
5. Milk and cream form a permanent emulsion through the process of _____.

💡 THINKING CRITICALLY

6. HYPOTHESIZE: Bile is produced by the liver. It emulsifies the fats that a person eats. Why is this process important to the digestive process?

7. INFER: When you buy a can of paint, you usually have to stir the paint before you can use it. Why do you think it is necessary to stir the paint?

Web InfoSearch

Homogenization Fresh milk right from a cow is a temporary emulsion. It separates on standing into cream and milk. Before it is sold in stores, the milk is homogenized, making it a permanent emulsion.

SEARCH: Use the Internet to find out how milk is homogenized. Create a poster to illustrate the steps. Start your search www.conceptsandchallenges.com. Some key search words are **milk** and **homogenize**.

⚛ Hands-On Activity

MAKING AN EMULSION

You will need safety goggles, vinegar, vegetable oil, an egg, a bowl, a measuring cup, and an eggbeater.

1. Separate the yolk from the white of the egg. Put the yolk in the bowl.
2. Beat the egg yolk until it looks foamy.
3. Add 1/4 cup of vinegar to the egg yolk. Beat the mixture of vinegar and egg yolk.
4. Add 1/8 cup of oil to the mixture one tablespoon at a time. Beat the mixture thoroughly each time you add a tablespoon of oil.

Practicing Your Skills

5. OBSERVE: When did the mixture begin to thicken?
6. PREDICT: If the mixture is allowed to stand, will it separate?
7. ANALYZE: What is the emulsifying agent in the mixture?
8. PREDICT: What would happen if you did not add the egg yolk to the mixture?

▲ STEP 2 Beat the egg yolk.

---

3 Assess

✓ CHECKING CONCEPTS ANSWERS

1. liquid
2. temporary
3. permanent
4. emulsifying
5. homogenization

💡 THINKING CRITICALLY ANSWERS

6. HYPOTHESIZE: By breaking fats into smaller droplets, bile makes it easier for digestive enzymes to act on the fats.
7. INFER: Paint is an emulsion. The liquids that make up the paint have settled into layers.

4 Close

Web InfoSearch

Homogenization Have students use the Internet to find out how milk is homogenized. Have students create a poster to illustrate the steps. Some key search words are **milk** and **homogenize**. Have students begin their investigation by visiting www.conceptsandchallenges.com.

Hands-On Activity

MAKING AN EMULSION

TIME: 15–30 minutes

PURPOSE: observing, predicting

SAFETY TIP: Make sure students wear safety goggles and aprons. Caution students not to drink the liquid.

COOPERATIVE LEARNING: Have students work in pairs.

Practicing Your Skills Answers

5. OBSERVE: when oil was added
6. PREDICT: no
7. ANALYZE: egg yolk
8. PREDICT: The oil and vinegar would separate.

Discussion Inform students that they have made mayonnaise, which is an emulsion of oil and vinegar. The emulsifying agent is egg yolk.

COOPERATIVE LEARNING

Identifying an Emulsifying Agent
Have students work in pairs to find packaged food items that contain the emulsifying agent gelatin. Have students create a list of the foods that they found.
learning styles: visual, interpersonal

ONGOING ASSESSMENT

Contrasting Milk Ask students to explain why milk fresh from a cow is different from store-bought milk. (Milk from a store is homogenized.)

• TEACHING RESOURCES •

💿 **Teacher's Resources CD-ROM**
Lesson Review: Chapter 6, p. 4
Fishbone Map: Study Tools, p. 5

1 Introduce

📝 **STUDY HINT** Before beginning this lesson, have students study Figure 6-11. Have students compare the effect on light passing through both containers.

Linking Prior Knowledge Ask students to name the four phases of matter (Lesson 1-3). List the phases on the board. (solid, liquid, gas, and plasma)

2 Teach

Demonstration Pour some milk into a glass. Add water to dilute the milk. Then, shine a bright beam of light from a flashlight or slide projector through the glass of milk. Students will observe that the beam of light passes through the mixture of milk and water. Point out that the beam is visible because light is reflected by the particles in milk. Have students explain how the demonstration models what occurs when light from a car's headlights passes through fog. **learning styles: visual, auditory**

Discussion Define a colloid as a suspension in which the particles are permanently suspended. Ask students: *How do the particles in a colloid stay suspended?* (Small particles constantly bump into molecules of the surrounding material.) **learning styles: auditory, linguistic**

Answers to questions

1️⃣ DEFINE: a suspension in which the particles are permanently suspended

2️⃣ EXPLAIN: The particles are small enough to pass through the pores in a filter.

3️⃣ EXPLAIN: As light passes through the colloid, it strikes moving particles and is scattered.

Reinforcement Have students look at the images in Figure 6-10. Ask them to name the colloid that is also an emulsion. (homogenized milk) **learning styles: visual, auditory**

6-4 What is a colloid?

Objective
Describe and give examples of a colloid.

Key Term
colloid (KAHL-oid): suspension in which the particles are permanently suspended

Colloids What do whipped cream, fog, mayonnaise, and smoke have in common? All of these substances are colloids. A **colloid** is a suspension in which the particles are permanently suspended. Colloids can be mixtures of different phases of matter. Figure 6-10 shows some common types of colloids and examples of each type.

1️⃣ DEFINE: What is a colloid?

Colloid Particle Size The particles in a colloid are not as small as the particles in a solution. However, they are much smaller than the particles in an ordinary suspension. They cannot be seen with an ordinary microscope. Because the particles are so small, a colloid cannot be separated by normal means of filtration. A colloid such as homogenized milk passes right through filter paper. The particles in milk are smaller than the pores in the filter.

2️⃣ EXPLAIN: Why can a colloid not be separated by filtration?

Movement of Colloid Particles Have you ever traveled in a car on a foggy night? If so, you probably know that the car's headlight beams do not penetrate very far into the fog. Fog is a colloid made up of tiny water droplets suspended in air. When light passes through fog, the light strikes these droplets and is scattered, or spreads out. This scattering of light by the particles of a colloid is known as the Tyndall effect.

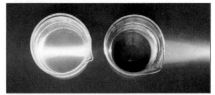

▲ **Figure 6-11** Light passes through a solution (right) but is scattered by a colloid (left).

Why do the particles of a colloid not settle out, much like the particles do in an ordinary suspension? After all, there is no emulsifying agent keeping them in suspension. The answer is that the very tiny particles of a colloid are constantly bumping into molecules of the surrounding material. For example, the water droplets in fog keep colliding with air molecules. These collisions keep the droplets from settling out of the colloid.

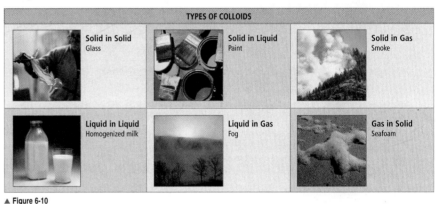

TYPES OF COLLOIDS

Solid in Solid	Solid in Liquid	Solid in Gas
Glass	Paint	Smoke
Liquid in Liquid	Liquid in Gas	Gas in Solid
Homogenized milk	Fog	Seafoam

▲ Figure 6-10

Teaching Options

ONGOING ASSESSMENT

Comparing Suspensions Have pairs of students make a Venn diagram that compares emulsions and colloids. Students can use the Venn Diagram found on the Teacher's Resources CD-ROM. **learning styles: visual, linguistic**

EXTENDING THE LESSON

Explaining a Rainbow Ask students to research what causes a rainbow to form. Have them use their findings to explain how a rainbow is related to the scattering of light by particles of a colloid. Students should organize their findings in a brief paragraph. **learning styles: visual, linguistic**

Instead, the droplets move rapidly through the air with a zigzag motion. When light passes through a colloid, it strikes the moving particles and is scattered, or spreads out. The cloudy appearance of a colloid is caused by the scattering of light.

▶ **EXPLAIN:** Why does a colloid appear cloudy?

✓ CHECKING CONCEPTS

1. How do the particles in a colloid compare in size with those in a solution?
2. Are colloids permanent or temporary suspensions?
3. What happens if a colloid is passed through a filter?
4. What happens to light that passes through a colloid?
5. Give an example of a colloid consisting of a solid in a liquid.

💡 THINKING CRITICALLY

6. **INFER:** Why can the beam of a flashlight be seen as it passes through a bowl of gelatin?

7. **COMPARE:** In what ways are colloids like solutions? In what ways are they different?
8. **EXPLAIN:** How is paint made that it can be classified as a colloid?

Web InfoSearch

Brownian Motion If you look at a colloid through a very powerful microscope, you will see that the particles of a colloid are in continuous random motion. This motion is called Brownian motion. Brownian motion is named for the biologist Robert Brown. Brown first noticed this motion while observing the motion of particles in a suspension of pollen grains in water.

SEARCH: Use the Internet to find out more about Brownian motion and the scientist who first noticed it. Write a short report. Start your search at www.conceptsandchallenges.com. Some key search words are **Robert Brown, biologist,** and **Brownian motion.**

Science and Technology
USE OF COLLOIDS TO PURIFY WATER

Do you know where your household water comes from? In many cases, the water you use in your home comes from wells or reservoirs some distance from your house. Before this water reaches your house, it goes to a treatment plant. At the treatment plant, the water passes through several stages before it is clean enough for people to use.

Water from wells or reservoirs is passed through screens, which remove debris. Then, the water is sent to tanks or ponds where suspended materials are allowed to settle. Even after settling has taken place, some fine particles still remain suspended. At one time, these fine particles were allowed to remain in the water. Today, colloids are used to trap and remove these undesirable materials from our drinking water. Next, the water is filtered through sand or charcoal. Then it is pumped to sprinklers that spray the water into the air. This aerated water is then treated with chemicals to purify it before it is sent to our homes.

Thinking Critically Which stage in water treatment removes the largest particles?

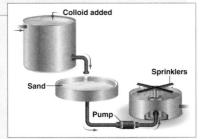
▲ Figure 6-12 Colloids are used to help purify water.

---

3 Assess

💡 CHECKING CONCEPTS ANSWERS

1. The particles in a colloid are not as small as the particles in a solution.
2. permanent suspensions
3. Its particles pass through the pores of the filter.
4. It strikes moving particles and is scattered.
5. paint

💡 THINKING CRITICALLY ANSWERS

6. **INFER:** Gelatin is a colloid. The particles in colloids scatter light.
7. **COMPARE:** In colloids and solutions, substances are mixed. The particles in a colloid are not as small as the particles in a solution.
8. **EXPLAIN:** a solid in a liquid

4 Close

Web InfoSearch

Brownian Motion Have students research Robert Brown and his observations of moving particles by visiting www.conceptsand challenges.com. Some key search words are **Robert Brown** and **Brownian Motion.**

Science and Technology
USE OF COLLOIDS TO PURIFY WATER

Real-Life Connection Some water contains dissolved minerals such as calcium and magnesium. Water that contains a large amount of dissolved minerals is called hard water. The term stems from the fact that it is often hard to get soap to form lather in this water. Water with few or no minerals is called soft water.

Discussion Explain that drinking water is often drawn from springs, wells, or reservoirs. Ask students to describe each of these sources of water. (A spring is a natural flow of groundwater that reaches Earth's surface. A well is a hole dug below the water table that fills with water. A reservoir is a lake made by people to store water.) Have students talk with family members to determine the source of their household water.

Thinking Critically Answer
the first stage, in which the water is passed through screens

---

ESL/ELL STRATEGY

Defining Homogeneous Have students look up the definition of the term *homogeneous* in a dictionary. Tell students to write in their own words how the meaning of *homogeneous* refers to homogenized milk.

• TEACHING RESOURCES •

Teacher's Resources CD-ROM
Lesson Review: Chapter 6, p. 5
Enrichment: Chapter 6, p. 6
Venn Diagram: Study Tools, p. 10

Laboratory Manual
Lab. Challenge: How do solutions, suspensions, and colloids compare? pp. 41–44

The Big Idea

(pp. 138–139)

1 Introduce

Objective Students will identify the properties of solutions, suspensions, colloids, and emulsions. Students will apply knowledge of these mixtures to foods they eat.

Linking Prior Knowledge Ask students to recall the properties of a suspension (Lesson 6-1). Have them remember the ways that emulsions and colloids are alike and different (Lessons 6-3 and 6-4).

2 Teach

Discussion Ask students to name their favorite foods. Record responses on the board. Invite volunteers to circle the entries that are suspensions.

Use the information in the article and in the captions to help guide students in choosing a topic for their Science Logs.

THE BIG IDEA ONLINE

What suspensions, emulsions, or colloids do you eat? Have students research their Science Log Writing Activity at www.conceptsandchallenges.com. You can have students organize their logs by completing the Big Idea activity online. Students may post their work in the Online Classroom Database for others to read.

Reinforcement Students can also use the Big Idea Planner or Big Idea Science Log Entry found on the Teacher's Resources CD-ROM.

◆ *Integrating Health*

THE Big IDEA

What suspensions, emulsions, or colloids do you eat?

You have learned that a solution is a mixture in which substances are evenly mixed. The dissolved particles in a solution are about the size of molecules. If a solution of salt water sits for 100 years without evaporating, the salt stays dissolved. Not all mixtures are solutions. A suspension is a cloudy mixture of different substances.

The Food Guide Pyramid is a guide to good nutrition. It reflects the findings of research on nutrition. The right amount of foods from each group is recommended for a balanced, healthy diet on a daily basis. Many of the foods we eat are suspensions, emulsion, or colloids. They are from different parts of the Food Guide Pyramid.

Salad dressing and split pea soup are suspensions. In a suspension, the particles in the mixture are big enough to be separated by gravity or by filtering. An emulsion is a special kind of suspension made from two liquids that are permanently mixed. Ever had an emulsion for breakfast? Milk is a delicious and nutritious emulsion. Eggs are the emulsifiers in some products, such as mayonnaise.

Permanent suspensions are called colloids. In a colloid, the particles are so tiny that they stay mixed. Flavored gelatin and whipped cream are tasty colloids.

Look at the illustrations, photographs, and text that appear on these two pages. Then, follow the directions in the Science Log to learn more about "the big idea." ✦

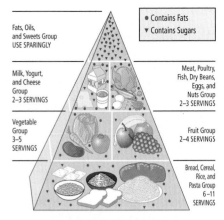

▲ **Figure 6-13** The Food Guide Pyramid shows what you should eat every day for a healthy diet.

- Contains Fats
- ▼ Contains Sugars

Fats, Oils, and Sweets Group USE SPARINGLY

Milk, Yogurt, and Cheese Group 2–3 SERVINGS

Meat, Poultry, Fish, Dry Beans, Eggs, and Nuts Group 2–3 SERVINGS

Vegetable Group 3–5 SERVINGS

Fruit Group 2–4 SERVINGS

Bread, Cereal, Rice, and Pasta Group 6–11 SERVINGS

Temporary Suspension
A soup, such as this one, is a mixture of many ingredients. A serving of soup contains several food groups, such as vegetables, proteins, and grains.

138

Teaching Options

◆ INTEGRATING LIFE SCIENCE

Balancing Your Meals The body gets the nutrients it needs to work properly from different kinds of foods. Diets that contain the right amount of nutrients are called balanced diets. The U.S. Department of Agriculture developed the Food Guide Pyramid to help people plan a balanced diet. The Food Guide Pyramid shows the types of foods that should be eaten daily. It also gives the recommended number of servings from each food group. Many food packages are labeled with the Food Guide Pyramid. Have students obtain a copy of the pyramid from an empty package. Then, have small groups of students use the pyramid to plan a balanced breakfast, lunch, and dinner.
learning styles: visual, interpersonal

ESL/ELL STRATEGY

Working in Pairs Pair English-language learners with English-proficient students to create the menu for the Close activity. English-language learners may be able to contribute examples of foods from their own cultures that are solutions or suspensions.

Emulsion

The egg yolks in mayonnaise keep the molecules of oil mixed with molecules of water. The egg yolks in mayonnaise function as emulsifiers. Because of its fat content, you should not eat too much mayonnaise.

Emulsion

Milk, fresh from a cow, separates into cream and milk. Milk that you buy in a store does not separate because it has been homogenized. The cream and the milk are permanently mixed. This emulsion is an important part of a healthy diet. 3–4 servings a day are recommended.

Colloid

Whipped cream is a colloid made by mixing gas into liquid cream. Cream is part of the milk and dairy group. Because it is high in fat, cream should be eaten sparingly. If you eat a small amount of it with a cup of strawberries, you have a healthy colloid-topped snack.

Temporary Suspension

A salad dressing with vinegar and oil is a suspension that will separate quickly. The harder it is shaken, the smaller the particles become, and the longer it remains mixed. A small amount of this suspension on a salad is part of a healthy diet.

WRITING ACTIVITY

Science Log

Many foods are suspensions. Pick a suspension that you enjoy eating and research how to make it. Describe other foods that you like to eat with the suspension. Here are some examples of foods that are suspensions: split pea soup, tomato sauce, applesauce, salad dressing, mayonnaise, whipped cream, butter, and jelly. Start your search at www.conceptsandchallenges.com.

CHAPTER 6: Suspensions **139**

3 Assess

Use the Writing Activity Rubric on the Teacher's Resources CD-ROM to assess students' Science Logs. Fill in the rubric with the additional information below. For this assignment, students should have:

- identified a favorite food that is a suspension.
- communicated, in paragraph form, accurate information about how the food is prepared or eaten.

4 Close

Creating a Menu Have small groups of students work together to create a menu in which every food choice is either a solution or suspension. You may choose to start the activity by having group members identify the suspension they wrote about in their Science Logs. Have each group present its completed menu to the class.

Tips for Using Technology

Word Processing Software

Have students use word processing software to record their descriptions of food suspensions. A simple word processing program allows them to do basic tasks such as entering and editing text. A more complex word processing program allows students to make tables, draw pictures, do math, and make graphs. Tell students to use the spell check feature before printing out their word processing documents to share with the class.

• TEACHING RESOURCES •

Teacher's Resources CD-ROM

Big Idea: Chapter 6, p. 7

Big Idea Planner: Study Tools, pp. 11–12

Big Idea Science Log Entry: Study Tools, p. 13

Writing Activity Rubric: Teaching Tools, p. 9

1 Introduce

STUDY HINT Before beginning this lesson, have students study Figure 6-14. Have them create a two-column chart. In one column, they should list the causes of air pollution, and in the other column, they should list the causes of water pollution.

Linking Prior Knowledge Ask students to describe experiences when they entered a room that was filled with cigarette smoke. Guide students to understand that the smoky air is a colloid that could harm a person's respiratory system.

2 Teach

Demonstration Wipe the outside of a window with a damp cloth. Have students observe the cloth with a hand lens. Explain that the particles that were picked up by the cloth came from the air. Have students consider whether the soiled cloth is evidence of air pollution. (It depends on the type of particles on the cloth.)
learning styles: visual, auditory

Discussion Write the term *pollution* on the board. Invite volunteers to identify words that come to mind when they hear this term. Ask students if pollution harms nonliving things. **learning styles: auditory, visual**

Answers to questions

1 DEFINE: substances that are harmful to the environment

2 LIST: Possible answers: exhaust from motor vehicles, waste products from factories, and the burning of fossil fuels

3 IDENTIFY: water that is safe to drink

4 INFER: Fewer cars would mean less car exhaust released into the air.

Reinforcement Ask a volunteer to explain the relationship between conserving fossil fuels and reducing air pollution. Point out that every time a person shuts off an unnecessary light, the person is conserving the fuels used to produce electricity. Reducing the amount of fuel that is burned reduces the amount of pollutants released into the air. **learning style: auditory**

6-5 What are air and water pollution?

Objective
Describe some causes of air and water pollution.

Key Terms
pollution (puh-LOO-shuhn): release of harmful substances into the environment

potable (POHT-uh-buhl) **water:** water that is safe to drink

Pollution What would happen if you did not have clean air to breathe or clean water to drink? One thing that would happen is that your health would be harmed. Every day our air and water resources are being threatened by pollution. **Pollution** is the adding of harmful substances, called pollutants, to the environment. Pollutants may be solids, liquids, or gases.

1 ▶ DEFINE: What are pollutants?

Causes of Pollution Most pollution is caused by human activities. Exhaust from cars, trucks, and buses is a major source of air pollution. Waste products from factories pollute air, land, and water. Burning fossil fuels releases harmful gases into the atmosphere.

2 ▶ LIST: What are three sources of pollution?

Safe Water There are many sources of water pollution. Agricultural use of pesticides and fertilizers is one major source. Another is the release of sewage and chemical wastes into rivers and lakes by cities and towns, factories, and even by individuals. Nuclear power plants release very hot water into nearby sources of water. This heats a river or stream to higher than normal temperatures. These pollutants harm fish and other organisms that live in the water. They also make the water unsafe to drink.

Water that is safe to drink is called **potable water.** Water can be made potable when it is passed through a series of steps in a process called purification (pyoor-uh-fih-KAY-shuhn). One of the steps is to add chemicals, such as chlorine, to kill germs. Other steps include settling, coagulation, and filtration. These steps remove solid particles that are suspended in water.

3 ▶ IDENTIFY: What is potable water?

Reducing Air Pollution Air pollution can be harmful to people in many ways. Gases and solid particles in the air can cause irritation of the eyes, nose, and throat. They can cause breathing problems and respiratory illness.

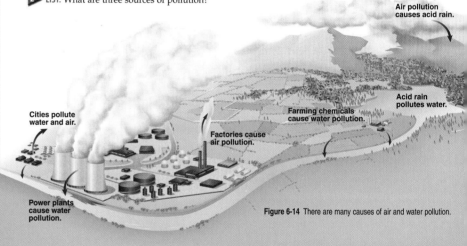

Figure 6-14 There are many causes of air and water pollution.

Labels on figure:
Air pollution causes acid rain.
Acid rain pollutes water.
Farming chemicals cause water pollution.
Factories cause air pollution.
Cities pollute water and air.
Power plants cause water pollution.

Teaching Options

COOPERATIVE LEARNING

Reading About It Ask students to find newspaper and magazine articles related to air and water pollution. Have small groups of students read and discuss the articles. Groups should summarize the articles and, if possible, develop a plan of action that might help solve the problem. Allow groups to present their summaries and plans to the class.
learning styles: visual, interpersonal

EXTENDING THE LESSON

Determining Air Quality Ask students to obtain the daily air-quality index readings from a local newspaper for a week. Have them display their findings in a chart. **learning styles: visual, tactile**

ONGOING ASSESSMENT

Making Cause-and-Effect Diagrams Have students make cause-and-effect diagrams for water pollution and air pollution. Students can use the Cause-and-Effect Diagram found on the Teacher's Resources CD-ROM.

▲ Figure 6-15 Air pollution over Montreal, Canada

Everyone can help to reduce air pollution. You can ride a bike or walk short distances instead of using a car or a bus. You might join a car pool with friends to help reduce the number of cars on the road. By lowering the temperature in your home, your family can use less heating oil. Find out what else you can do to help reduce air pollution.

4 ► INFER: How would fewer cars on the road help to reduce air pollution?

Hands-On Activity

OBSERVING POLLUTANTS IN AIR

You will need glass slides, petroleum jelly, and a hand lens.

1. Coat one side of several glass slides with a thin layer of petroleum jelly.
2. Choose several indoor and outdoor spots for testing the air quality.
3. At each spot, place a slide with the coated side up.
4. Record the location and the time when you placed each slide. Leave the slides overnight.
5. Collect the slides the next day. Record the time of collection.
6. Using the hand lens, examine each slide. Record your observations.

▲ STEP 6 Examine each slide with a hand lens.

Practicing Your Skills

7. OBSERVE: What kinds of particles did you see on the slides?
8. OBSERVE: Which slide had the most particles?
9. OBSERVE: Which slide had the fewest particles?
10. HYPOTHESIZE: How can you explain your results?

☑ CHECKING CONCEPTS

1. Substances that are harmful to the environment are _____.
2. Using less fuel to heat your home helps to reduce _____ pollution.
3. Water that is safe to drink is called _____.
4. Chemical wastes and sewage are major causes of _____ pollution.

💡 THINKING CRITICALLY

5. HYPOTHESIZE: Often trees that are planted along city streets do not grow well. What is a possible reason for this?

HEALTH AND SAFETY TIP

Never drink the water in a stream or brook. It may be polluted with chemicals or bacteria. Use library references to find out how you can purify water to make it safe for you to drink.

MORE ON THE WEB

Driving a "Green Vehicle"
Have students learn about cars that are better for the environment than other vehicles on the market. Then, have students create a poster that advertises the advantages of owning and driving an environmentally friendly car. Have students visit www.conceptsandchallenges.com for more details.

• TEACHING RESOURCES •

◎ **Teacher's Resources CD-ROM**
Lesson Review: Chapter 6, p. 8
Enrichment: Chapter 6, p. 9
Cause-and-Effect Diagram: Study Tools, p. 3

---

3 Assess

☑ CHECKING CONCEPTS ANSWERS

1. pollutants
2. air
3. potable water
4. water

💡 THINKING CRITICALLY ANSWER

5. HYPOTHESIZE: Possible answer: They are harmed by exhaust from motor vehicles.

HEALTH AND SAFETY TIP

Students' research should provide information on how to purify water, such as boiling for 5–10 minutes; adding 8 drops of chlorine bleach per gallon of water and allowing the water to stand for 30 minutes; adding 20 drops per gallon of a 2% tincture of iodine; or using water purification tablets, which can be purchased at drugstores or sporting goods stores.
learning style: visual

4 Close

Hands-On Activity

OBSERVING POLLUTANTS IN AIR

TIME: 10–15 minutes

PURPOSE: observing, hypothesizing

SAFETY TIP: Be sure that students wash their hands after handling the soiled slides.

COOPERATIVE LEARNING: Have students observe one another's slides.

Practice Your Skills Answers

7. OBSERVE: Possible answers: particles of dust, pollen, soot, and dead insects
8. OBSERVE: Answers will vary based on location.
9. OBSERVE: Answers will vary based on location.
10. HYPOTHESIZE: The pollutants came from the air and landed on the slides. The pollutants became trapped in the sticky petroleum jelly.

Lab Activity

(pp. 142–143)

1 Prepare the Lab

Testing for the Tyndall Effect—
Solution or Nonsolution?

SET-UP TIME: 🕐 **LAB TIME:** 🕐

BACKGROUND: The Tyndall effect is one way to show students that mixtures that are not solutions have particles large enough to scatter light.

PURPOSE: Students will make various liquid mixtures and observe which mixtures are solutions and which are not, using a Tyndall-effect tester that they will make.

ALTERNATIVE MATERIALS: Small plastic cups can be used in place of jars or beakers. If you do not have running water in your classroom, bring water in plastic milk bottles. If time is an issue, penlights can be used as solution testers instead of making solution testers in Step 4.

SCIENCE SKILLS: Students will **observe** and **collect data** on the experiment and **communicate** their findings in writing. They will use this experiment to **model** the Tyndall effect and to **infer** which mixtures are solutions and which are not solutions based on observations.

ADVANCE PLANNING: Gather materials you will need for the lab. Have an empty bucket on hand for collecting all the liquid mixtures after the experiment.

2 Guide the Lab

PROCEDURE: Divide the class into groups of two or three students. Discuss the procedures. Tell students to shake or stir mixtures before testing with the flashlight. Discuss data collection and reporting. Have students make their data charts before starting the experiment. Provide students with a copy of the Lab Activity Report found on the Teacher's Resources CD-ROM to record their observations and conclusions.

TROUBLESHOOTING: Be sure that the flashlights have new batteries and that the water is at room temperature. Use clear glass or clear plastic jars.

LAB ACTIVITY
Testing for the Tyndall Effect—Solution or Nonsolution?

Materials List

Goggles, apron,
6 jars with lids,
flashlight, funnel
rubbing alcohol,
black construction paper,
sharpened pencil,
powdered juice mix,
sugar, sand, whole milk,
vegetable oil, water,
10 mL and 100 mL
graduated cylinders,
teaspoon, eyedropper

BACKGROUND

Some mixtures that may appear to look like a solution may not be one after all. Some of these "nonsolutions" may be suspensions or colloids. If a path of light can be seen easily through a mixture, then the mixture is not a solution. This happens because the particles are large enough to scatter or reflect the light. This light scattering is called the Tyndall effect.

PURPOSE

In this activity, you will make various mixtures and observe the difference between solutions and non-solutions using the Tyndall effect.

PROCEDURE 🖐️ 🔒

1. Copy the chart in Figure 6-16. Put on safety goggles and a lab apron.

2. Label the jars A through F for the following mixtures to be tested:

   A. 1 teaspoon of powdered juice mix to 100 mL of water

   B. 10 mL of rubbing alcohol to 100 mL of water

   C. 5 drops of whole milk to 100 mL of water

   D. 1 teaspoon of sugar to 100 mL of water

   E. 10 mL of vegetable oil to 100 mL of water

   F. 1 teaspoon of sand to 100 mL of water

3. Shake each jar and observe the mixtures. Predict which mixtures will be solutions or nonsolutions.

▲ **STEP 2** Add mixtures to the jars labeled A–F.

▲ **STEP 3** Shake the jars with the mixtures.

142

Teaching Options

4. Make a solution tester. First cut out a small circle from a piece of black construction paper. The circle should just cover the lens of the flashlight. Use a sharpened pencil to punch a small hole in the center of the circle. Then, tape the paper circle over the flashlight lens.

5. In a darkened area of the room, press the solution tester very close to the jar holding mixture A. Record what you see. If you can see the path of light through the mixture, it is not a true solution.

6. Repeat Step 5 for mixtures B–F. Record your results.

▲ **STEP 5** Shine the solution tester into the jar.

Testing for the Tyndall Effect—Solution or Nonsolution?			
Beaker	Mixture	Observations Upon Mixing	Observations When Testing With Solution Tester
A	Powdered juice mix and water		
B	Rubbing alcohol and water		
C	Whole milk and water		
D	Sugar and water		
E	Vegetable oil and water		
F	Sand and water		

▲ **Figure 6-16** Copy this chart and use it to record your observations.

CONCLUSIONS

1. **OBSERVE:** Describe what you observed with each mixture.

2. **MODEL:** Which mixtures represented solutions? How do you know?

3. **MODEL:** Which mixtures represented nonsolutions?

4. **INFER:** Explain how the nonsolutions show the Tyndall effect.

5. **ANALYZE:** How might you be able to determine if the nonsolutions are suspensions or colloids?

Tips for Using Technology

Spreadsheets Have students use spreadsheet software to record the results of their experiments. Spreadsheets are tables that display data such as numbers, text, dates, or a combination of all three. Students can use spreadsheet software to present their data to the class. Tell students to carefully record their data. Have students use the Spreadsheet on the Teacher's Resources CD-ROM to plan their spreadsheets.

• TEACHING RESOURCES •

Teacher's Resources CD-ROM
Lab Activity Report: Study Tools, pp. 16–17

Laboratory Activity Rubric: Teaching Tools, p. 8

Spreadsheet: Study Tools, p. 23

Laboratory Manual
Lab. Skills Worksheet 1: Using a Graduated Cylinder, pp. 5–8

Lab. Skills Worksheet 4: Organizing and Analyzing Data, pp. 13–14

SAFETY TIP: Caution students not to look directly into the light source or shine it into anyone's eyes.

EXPECTED OUTCOME: The juice, rubbing alcohol, and sugar mixtures are solutions. The milk, oil, and sand mixtures are not solutions.

LAB HINT: Remind students to consider all variables when analyzing the results of the experiment.

3 Conclude the Lab

1. **OBSERVE:** The juice, rubbing alcohol, and sugar mixtures did not scatter light. The milk, oil, and sand mixtures did scatter light.

2. **MODEL:** Juice, rubbing alcohol, and sugar; They did not scatter light.

3. **MODEL:** milk, oil, and sand

4. **INFER:** The nonsolutions did not allow light to pass straight through. The light was scattered.

5. **ANALYZE:** Observe the nonsolutions after they have been standing for a long time. If they are colloids, the particles will still be suspended.

Use the Laboratory Activity Rubric on the Teacher's Resources CD-ROM to assess students' lab activities. Fill in the rubric with the additional information below. For this activity, students should have:

• performed the activity according to the procedure and filled in the chart with data collected during the activity.

• correctly answered the questions in complete sentences.

4 Extend the Lab

Mention to students that the Tyndall effect has a role in other areas of science. For example, the Tyndall effect can be used to measure the turbidity of rivers. Have students work in small groups to research other applications of the Tyndall effect.

Challenges (pp. 144–146)

Chapter Summary

Review Before students begin the Challenges, review the summary with them. Ask students to write one of the summary points in their own words.

🖊 **STUDY HINT** Have students use their summary points to create a question and answer. They can write the question on one side of an index card and the answer on the back. Then, have pairs of students quiz each other, using their cards.

Key Term Challenges

MATCHING

1. potable water (6-5)
2. coagulation (6-2)
3. homogenization (6-3)
4. colloid (6-4)
5. pollution (6-5)
6. emulsion (6-3)

FILL IN

7. suspension (6-1)
8. filtration (6-2)
9. emulsion (6-3)
10. coagulation (6-2)

Chapter Summary

Lesson 6-1
- A **suspension** is a mixture of two or more substances that settle out over time.
- The particles in a suspension are larger than the particles in a solution.
- The particles in a suspension scatter light.
- Some familiar examples of suspensions include salad dressing and dust in the air.

Lesson 6-2
- The particles in a suspension settle out.
- **Filtration** is a method of separating a suspension by passing it through a filter.
- **Coagulation** is a process in which chemicals are used to make the particles in a suspension clump together.
- A centrifuge is a device that separates a suspension by spinning it at high speeds.

Lesson 6-3
- An **emulsion** is a suspension of two liquids.
- Temporary emulsions separate on standing, whereas permanent emulsions do not.
- **Homogenization** is the formation of a permanent emulsion.
- Emulsifying agents are substances that prevent an emulsion from separating.

Lesson 6-4
- A **colloid** is a suspension in which the particles are permanently suspended.
- The particles of a colloid are larger than the particles of a solution but smaller than those of an ordinary suspension.
- The particles of a colloid are kept in suspension because they are always colliding with the molecules around them.

Lesson 6-5
- **Pollution** is the release of harmful substances into the environment.
- Most pollution is caused by human activities.
- Air pollution is harmful to people.
- Everyone can help to reduce air pollution.
- **Potable water** is safe to drink.

144

Key Term Challenges

coagulation (p. 132)
colloid (p. 136)
emulsion (p. 134)
filtration (p. 132)
homogenization (p. 134)
pollution (p. 140)
potable water (p. 140)
suspension (p. 130)

MATCHING Write the Key Term from above that best matches each description.

1. water that is safe to drink
2. making the particles in a suspension clump together
3. formation of a permanent emulsion
4. suspension in which particles are permanently suspended
5. release of harmful substances into the environment
6. suspension of two liquids

FILL IN Write the Key Term from above that best completes each statement.

7. A _____ is a cloudy mixture of two or more substances that settles on standing.
8. Passing a suspension through paper or other substances is called _____.
9. A suspension of two liquids is called an _____.
10. Particles in a suspension are clumped together by the process of _____.

Teaching Options

PREPARING STUDENTS FOR STANDARDIZED TESTS

Reading Strategy: Tell students that another way to be sure that they understand a passage is to restate it in their own words. First, they should read the passage. Then, they should identify keywords and the main idea. Finally, they should restate the entire passage in their own words.

Writing Strategy: Students can check that answers are in complete sentences by identifying the subject and predicate in each sentence.

Interpreting Visuals: Remind students that a diagram that shows a process, such as purifying water, is easy to understand if they focus on how each step in the process fits in the whole picture.

ESL/ELL STRATEGY

Peer Tutoring Peer-tutored hands-on activities help English-language learners in two ways. Working with peers encourages students to communicate, while hands-on activities help make scientific concepts easier to understand without the barriers of difficult scientific language.

Content Challenges TEST PREP

MULTIPLE CHOICE **Write the letter of the term or phrase that best completes each statement.**

1. If a suspension of clay, sand, and gravel is allowed to stand, the particles that settle out first would be
   a. clay.
   b. sand.
   c. gravel.
   d. water.

2. Colloids cannot be separated by filtration because colloid particles are
   a. round.
   b. too large.
   c. too small.
   d. clumped together.

3. A process that speeds up the separation of a suspension is
   a. homogenization.
   b. pollution.
   c. emulsification.
   d. coagulation.

4. An example of an emulsifying agent is
   a. milk.
   b. egg yolk.
   c. fog.
   d. oil and water.

5. A device that separates a suspension by spinning is called a
   a. centrifuge.
   b. homogenizer.
   c. filter.
   d. coagulator.

6. Both colloids and suspensions
   a. have large particles.
   b. are clear.
   c. scatter light.
   d. settle on standing.

7. The particles in a colloid are
   a. smaller than in a solution.
   b. smaller than in a suspension.
   c. smaller than molecules.
   d. larger than in a suspension.

8. An emulsifying agent makes an emulsion that is
   a. temporary.
   b. liquid.
   c. permanent.
   d. soapy.

9. All of the following are colloids except
   a. fog.
   b. salad dressing.
   c. smoke.
   d. whipped cream.

10. Settling, coagulation, and filtration are examples of
    a. suspensions.
    b. emulsifying agents.
    c. homogenization.
    d. separation methods.

TRUE/FALSE **Write *true* if the statement is true. If the statement is false, change the underlined term to make the statement true.**

11. Light is scattered by particles in a <u>suspension</u>.

12. Unhomogenized milk is a <u>temporary</u> suspension.

13. When a suspension is left standing, the <u>larger</u> particles are the last to settle.

14. Solutions, colloids, and suspensions are all <u>mixtures</u>.

15. An emulsion is a suspension of two <u>gases</u>.

Content Challenges

MULTIPLE CHOICE

1. c (6-2)
2. c (6-4)
3. d (6-2)
4. b (6-3)
5. a (6-2)
6. c (6-4)
7. b (6-4)
8. c (6-3)
9. b (6-4)
10. d (6-2)

TRUE/FALSE

11. true (6-1)
12. true (6-3)
13. false; smaller (6-2)
14. true (6-1, 6-4)
15. false; liquids (6-3)

ALTERNATIVE ASSESSMENT

Relating Information Students may create a three-column chart in their Science Logs comparing the properties of suspensions, emulsions, and colloids. Students may also define each type of mixture and give examples.

PORTFOLIO ASSESSMENT

Making Student Portfolios Portfolio Assessment is designed to evaluate a student's performance over an extended period of time. Encourage students to select their own work for inclusion in their portfolios. The Cause-and-Effect Diagram and the Big Idea Science Log Entry are some of the reproducibles on the Teacher's Resources CD-ROM that they can include in their portfolios. You can use the Portfolio Assessment Rubric also found on the Teacher's Resources CD-ROM to assess students' portfolios.

Concept Challenges

WRITTEN RESPONSE

1. **EXPLAIN:** An emulsifying agent keeps the particles in an emulsion from separating by breaking the particles into smaller pieces. (6-3)
2. **CONTRAST:** The particles in a colloid are permanently suspended. (6-4)
3. **EXPLAIN:** Particles in a colloid are kept in suspension because they are constantly bumping into the molecules around them. (6-4)
4. **EXPLAIN:** Wait for the mixture to settle. If it does, it is a noncolloidal suspension. If it does not, then test to see if it scatters light. If it does, it is a colloid. If it does not scatter light, it is a solution. (6-1, 6-2, 6-4)

INTERPRETING A VISUAL (6-5)

5. cities, power plants, and factories
6. cities, power plants, farming, and acid rain
7. gases: exhausts from cities, power plants, and factories; liquids and solids: waste products from cities, power plants, farming, and factories
8. by reducing consumption
9. probably not, because the lake has been polluted
10. Pollutants produced in another area, such as the one shown in Figure 6-17, may have entered the water that supplies the rural area. For example, the rural area may draw water from the same lake or from a river that drains the lake.

Chapter Project Wrap-Up

WATER FILTRATION POSTERS

Allow students to present their posters to the class and to explain how water treatment plants filter water. You can use the Individual Activity Rubric on the Teacher's Resources CD-ROM to assess students' projects. Fill in the rubric with the additional information below. For this project, students should have:

- carefully researched how a water treatment plant works.
- made a neat, clear, and accurate presentation of how water is filtered in a water treatment plant.

Concept Challenges TEST PREP

WRITTEN RESPONSE Complete the exercises and answer each of the following questions in complete sentences.

1. **EXPLAIN:** How does an emulsifying agent work?
2. **CONTRAST:** In what ways do colloids differ from ordinary suspensions?
3. **EXPLAIN:** How does the constant motion of colloid particles affect the properties of a colloid?
4. **EXPLAIN:** How could you test a mixture to find out if it is a solution, a suspension, or a colloid?

INTERPRETING A VISUAL Use Figure 6-17 to answer the following questions.

5. What sources of air pollution are shown in the picture?
6. What sources of water pollution are shown?
7. Which pollutants are gases? Which are liquids? Which are solids?
8. How could each source of air pollution be reduced?
9. Would you expect to find healthy fish and plants in the lake? Why or why not?
10. A rural area 20 km from the area shown in this picture has no factories or other industry. However, the town's water supply is polluted with chemical wastes. How might this be explained?

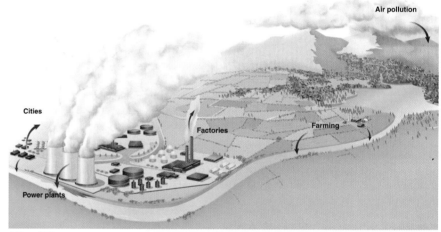

▲ Figure 6-17

Teaching Options

UNIT CHALLENGE ONLINE

Salty Seawater Instruct students to visit www.concepts andchallenges.com. Have them complete the online activity for Unit 2. Students will investigate the salinity of seawater, and collect and analyze data. Have students post their results on the Online Classroom Database.

• *TEACHING RESOURCES* •

Teacher's Resources CD-ROM

Key Term Review: Chapter 6, p. 10

Chapter 6 Test: pp. 11–13

Cause-and-Effect Diagram: Study Tools, p. 3

Big Idea Science Log Entry: Study Tools, p. 13

Portfolio Assessment Rubric: Teaching Tools, p. 10

Individual Activity Rubric: Teaching Tools, p. 5

Chapter Self-Check: Teaching Tools, p. 11

T146 UNIT 2: Types of Matter

PLANNING GUIDE

◆ **TEACHING THE CHAPTER** This chapter should take approximately 6–9 days to complete instruction and assessment.

	Skills and Features	Projects and Activities	Achieve Science Literacy	Meet Individual Needs
Chapter 7 Opener p. T147	EXPLAIN	• Chapter Project		
Lesson 7-1 **What is a chemical formula?** pp. T148–T149 Standards: B1b, B1c	DESCRIBE, IDENTIFY, STATE • Building Science Skills • Real-Life Science	• Cooperative Learning • More on the Web	• Study Hint • Writing Hint • Ongoing Assessment	• ESL/ELL Strategy ◎ CD-ROM Enrichment Activity
Lesson 7-2 **What is an oxidation number?** pp. T150–T151 Standards: B1b, B1c	IDENTIFY, INFER, STATE • Investigate • Interpreting Visuals	• Cooperative Learning • Extending the Lesson • More on the Web • Lab Challenge	• Study Hint • Reading Strategy	• Reteach ◎ CD-ROM Fishbone Map Energy Levels
Lesson 7-3 **How are chemical compounds named?** pp. T152–T153 Standards: B1b, B1c	PREDICT, INFER, IDENTIFY • Investigate • Web InfoSearch • People in Science • Cooperative Learning • Lab Skills Worksheet		• Study Hint • Ongoing Assessment	• ESL/ELL Strategy
Lesson 7-4 **What is a polyatomic ion?** pp. T154–T155 Standards: B1b, B1c	IDENTIFY, ANALYZE, CLASSIFY • Building Language Arts Skills • Science and Technology • Integrating Life Science • Extending the Lesson	• More on the Web	• Study Hint • Ongoing Assessment	◎ CD-ROM Enrichment Activity
Lab Activity **Constructing Chemical Formulas** pp. T156–T157 Standards: B1b, B1c	MODEL, CALCULATE • Set-Up Time: 5 min • Lab Time: 30 min	• Lab Skills Worksheet • Extend the Lab Activity	• Tips for Using Technology	• ESL/ELL Strategy • Reteach ◎ CD-ROM Lab Activity Report Thumbnail Sketch
Lesson 7-5 **What is a diatomic molecule?** pp. T158–T159 Standards: B1b, B1c	DEFINE, INFER, ANALYZE • Integrating Environmental Science	• Extending the Lesson • More on the Web	• Study Hint • Ongoing Assessment	• ESL/ELL Strategy ◎ CD-ROM Concept Map

Planning Guide continues on next page.

Standards: For details on the correlation to National Science Standards see pages *xx–xxi*.

	Skills and Features	Projects and Activities	Achieve Science Literacy	Meet Individual Needs
Lesson 7-6 **What is formula mass?** pp. T160–T161 Standards: B1b, B1c	INFER, CALCULATE, ANALYZE • Building Math Skills • Hands-On Activity	• More on the Web	• Study Hint	• Reteach  CD-ROM Flowchart
Big Idea **How is a chemical formula written?** pp. T162–T163 Standards: B1b, B1c	RESEARCH, COMMUNICATE, ANALYZE • Science Log: Writing Activity	• Big Idea Online • Close Activity	• Tips for Using Technology	CD-ROM Big Idea Planner
Chapter 7 Challenges pp. T164–T166 Standards: B1b, B1c	• Chapter Summary • Key Term Challenges • Content Challenges • Concept Challenges	• Chapter Project Wrap-Up	• Study Hint • Preparing Students for Standardized Tests	• ESL/ELL Strategy CD-ROM Chapter Self-Check Flowchart Concept Map

Teacher Notes

_____

_____

_____

_____

_____

_____

_____

_____

_____

_____

_____

_____

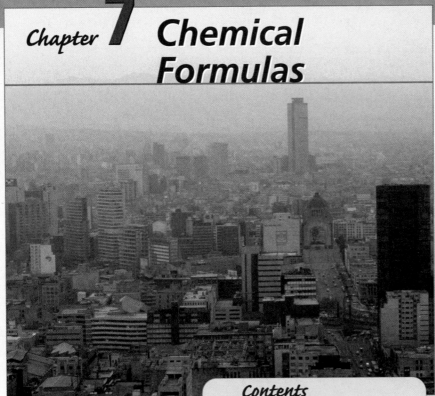

Chapter 7 Chemical Formulas

▲ **Figure 7-1** Smog forms over a city.

Oxygen is an important part of the air we breathe. Each molecule of this substance is made up of two oxygen atoms. Smog contains a different form of oxygen, called ozone. A molecule of ozone is made up of three oxygen atoms. Ozone can make breathing very difficult. As you can see in Figure 7-1, the ozone in smog is very different from the oxygen in clean air. Yet, the two gases are made up of the same element.

►How do the properties of oxygen found in clean air compare with those found in ozone?

Contents

UNIT 3: The Behavior of Matter **147**

Teaching Options

ASSESSMENT PLANNER

For assessment in the Student Edition, see the following pages:

Content Assessment
Checking Concepts: pp. 149, 151, 153, 155, 159, 161
Thinking Critically: pp. 149, 151, 153, 155, 159, 161
Interpreting Visuals: p. 151
Chapter Challenges: pp. 164–166

Alternative Assessment
Building Skills: pp. 149, 155, 161
Web InfoSearch: p. 153
Science Log: p. 163

Performance-Based Assessment
Hands-On Activity: p. 161
Lab Activity: pp. 156–157

• TEACHING RESOURCES •

Teacher's Resources CD-ROM
Lesson Review: Ch. 7, pp. 2, 4, 5, 6, 8, 9

Enrichment: Ch. 7, pp. 3, 7

Key Term Review: Ch. 7, p. 11

Chapter 7 Test: pp. 12–14

Laboratory Manual: pp. 13–14, 45–48

Chapter 7
Chemical Formulas

Chapter Overview

In this chapter, students will learn how chemical formulas are written, describe how to use oxidation numbers to write the chemical formula of a compound and explain how chemical compounds are named. They will also recognize the chemical formula for a polyatomic ion and apply the steps needed to calculate formula mass.

About Figure 7-1 Ozone formed near Earth's surface is a health hazard. It may cause serious damage to crops in addition to making it difficult for some people to breathe. However, ozone higher in the atmosphere absorbs much of the ultraviolet radiation that would harm life on Earth if it reached the surface. This ozone layer has been damaged by chlorine-containing chemicals called chlorofluorocarbons.

Answer Oxygen found in clean air is essential to most life on Earth. Ozone causes breathing difficulties.

Linking Prior Knowledge

For this chapter, students should recall:
- how to find the atomic mass and mass number of an atom (Lesson 3-5).
- the periodic table (Lesson 3-7).
- what a molecule is (Lesson 4-2).

Chapter Project

CHEMICAL FORMULA DISPLAY

MATERIALS: posterboard, stencils, markers, scissors, magazines

Students will create a posterboard that shows how a chemical formula is written. Have students carefully study the Big Idea on pages 162 and 163. Divide students into small groups. Each group should create a display similar to the Big Idea. Each group will choose three or four chemical formulas from the chapter. They will show how the chemical formulas are written according to the four steps in the Big Idea. They can also include on their posterboards pictures of the compounds that the chemical formulas represent. **learning styles: tactile, visual**

1 Introduce

✏️ **STUDY HINT** Have students study Figure 7-2. Have them compare the chemical name of each compound to the elements that make up each compound.

Linking Prior Knowledge Ask students to recall the definition of a compound (Lesson 4-2). Remind them that a compound has properties different from those of the elements that formed it.

2 Teach

Discussion To introduce the lesson, write the symbols for several elements on the board, such as oxygen (O), hydrogen (H), sodium (Na), and chlorine (Cl). Ask students to identify the symbols. Then, ask why we use symbols to represent elements. (They are abbreviations for the names of elements.) Point out that, just as chemical symbols are shorthand for the names of elements, chemical formulas are shorthand for the names of compounds. Refer students to the column labeled *chemical name* in Figure 7-2. Read aloud a few of the chemical names and have students tell you what the chemical formula is for each compound. **learning styles: auditory, visual**

Reinforcement Give students practice in identifying the elements in chemical formulas. Write the chemical formulas of a variety of compounds on the board. Ask students what elements make up each compound and how many atoms of each element would be found in one unit of the compound. **learning styles: auditory, visual**

Answers to questions

▸ STATE: Fe

▸ DESCRIBE: a way of writing the name of a compound using chemical symbols

▸ INFER: 22

▸ STATE: $AlCl_3$

7-1 What is a chemical formula?

Objective
Write chemical formulas.

Key Terms
chemical formula: way of writing the name of a compound using chemical symbols

subscript: number written to the lower right of a chemical symbol in a chemical formula

Chemical Symbols Chemical symbols are used to represent elements. Each element has its own symbol. Symbols for all the known elements are made up of one or two letters. For example, C is the chemical symbol for carbon. Fe is the symbol for iron. Permanent names for some synthetic elements, elements made in a laboratory, have not yet been agreed on. For these elements, temporary names and three-letter symbols have been assigned. For example, Uun is the temporary symbol for ununnilium.

▸ **STATE:** What is the chemical symbol for iron?

Chemical Formulas Compounds are made up of two or more elements that are chemically combined. Scientists use a chemical formula to show the elements that make up a compound. A **chemical formula** is a way of writing the name of a compound using chemical symbols. The compound water contains the elements hydrogen and oxygen. Each molecule of water contains two atoms of hydrogen and one atom of oxygen.

The chemical symbol for hydrogen is H. The chemical symbol for oxygen is O. The chemical formula for water is H_2O. The chemical formula includes the symbols for each element in the compound. Figure 7-2 shows the chemical formulas of some common compounds.

▸ **DESCRIBE:** What is a chemical formula?

Subscripts Chemical formulas also indicate how many atoms of each element are in a molecule or an ion of a compound. The number of atoms of each element is indicated by a subscript. A **subscript** is a number written to the lower right of a chemical symbol. The 2 in the chemical formula H_2O is a subscript. It indicates that there are two atoms of hydrogen in a molecule of water. There is one atom of oxygen in a molecule of water, however, there is no subscript written after the O in H_2O. This is because the number 1 is never written in a chemical formula. When there is no subscript after a symbol in a formula, you know that there is only one atom of that element.

▸ **INFER:** How many atoms of hydrogen are in a molecule of table sugar with the chemical formula $C_{12}H_{22}O_{11}$?

Writing Chemical Formulas In some compounds, a metal is chemically combined with a nonmetal. For example, sodium chloride is made up of the metal sodium and the nonmetal chlorine. In a chemical formula, the symbol for the metallic element is always written first. The chemical formula for the compound sodium chloride is

CHEMICAL FORMULAS OF SOME COMMON COMPOUNDS

Common name	Chemical name	Chemical formula	Elements
Table salt	Sodium chloride	NaCl	Sodium, chlorine
Stomach acid	Hydrochloric acid	HCl	Hydrogen, chlorine
Lye	Sodium hydroxide	NaOH	Sodium, oxygen, hydrogen
Ammonia	Ammonia	NH_3	Nitrogen, hydrogen
Laughing gas	Nitrous oxide	N_2O	Nitrogen, oxygen
Vinegar	Acetic acid	CH_3COOH	Hydrogen, carbon, oxygen

▲ Figure 7-2

148

Teaching Options

COOPERATIVE LEARNING

Playing a Game Make up sets of cards so that small groups of students have two sets each: one set of chemical formulas, such as those found in Figure 7-2, and one set of names of elements, such as sodium, chlorine, and oxygen. Students should use the cards to play a matching game. For each of the chemical formulas, students should match the appropriate element cards. Circulate around the room as students play to be sure that they correctly associate the names of elements with the symbols in compounds. **learning styles: interpersonal, tactile**

ONGOING ASSESSMENT

Examining Chemical Formulas Write the names and chemical formulas of several compounds on the board. For each compound, ask students: *What are the elements that make up this compound? How many atoms of each element are there in one molecule? How can you tell? Which of the elements in the compound is metallic? How do you know?* **learning styles: auditory, visual**

NaCl. Figure 7-3 shows some compounds and the metals and nonmetals that make them up.

SOME COMPOUNDS MADE OF METALS AND NONMETALS

Compound	Chemical formula	Metallic element	Nonmetallic element
Sodium chloride	NaCl	Na (Sodium)	Cl (Chlorine)
Aluminum chloride	$AlCl_3$	Al (Aluminum)	Cl (Chlorine)
Silver sulfide	Ag_2S	Ag (Silver)	S (Sulfur)

▲ Figure 7-3

4 STATE: What is the chemical formula for aluminum chloride?

☑ **CHECKING CONCEPTS**

1. The chemical symbol for hydrogen is _____.

2. The chemical formula for acetic acid is _____.

---

3. The nonmetal in sodium chloride is _____.

4. In a chemical formula, the symbol for a _____ element is always written first.

💡 **THINKING CRITICALLY**

5. CONTRAST: The chemical formula for water is H_2O. The chemical formula for hydrogen peroxide is H_2O_2. How does a molecule of water differ from a molecule of hydrogen peroxide?

BUILDING SCIENCE SKILLS

Identifying Elements List the names of the elements that make up each of the following compounds.

a. carbon dioxide (CO_2)

b. ammonia (NH_3)

c. calcite ($CaCO_3$)

⚛ *Real-Life Science*

PLASTICS

Plastics are long-chain polymer molecules made up of carbon, hydrogen, nitrogen, chlorine, and sulfur. Plastics can be molded, stretched, bent, and drawn into fibers. It all begins by heating hydrocarbons (compounds containing hydrogen and carbon). This process leads to a series of small molecules called monomers. One type of monomer is vinyl chloride. Its chemical formula is C_2H_3Cl. Monomers can be recombined into different long-chain polymers. These polymers make up plastics that have a variety of properties and characteristics.

▲ Figure 7-4 Products made of plastics

Today's world is filled with plastics. From medicine bottles, food containers, computer parts, and toys to carpet and clothing fibers, plastics are used every day. Scientists have discovered many specialized plastics and are looking to develop new polymer chains that can be used to make other useful products. The many different ways in which plastics can be used make them very important compounds.

Thinking Critically Why do you think plastics can be considered one of the most important inventions?

✏ **WRITING HINT** Tell students that when they write a chemical formula, they should make sure that the second letter of a chemical symbol is lowercase.

3 Assess

☑ **CHECKING CONCEPTS ANSWERS**

1. H
2. CH_3COOH
3. chlorine
4. metallic

💡 **THINKING CRITICALLY ANSWER**

5. CONTRAST: A molecule of water contains only one atom of oxygen. A molecule of hydrogen peroxide contains two atoms of oxygen.

4 Close

BUILDING SCIENCE SKILLS

Identifying Elements a. carbon, oxygen b. nitrogen, hydrogen c. calcium, carbon, oxygen

Real-Life Science

PLASTICS

Real-Life Connection Share with students that polyvinyl chloride (PVC) is noted for its chemical resistance, long-term stability, and waterproofness. These qualities make it an excellent material for use in pipes, siding, windows, medical blood bags, medical tubing, and bottles.

Discussion Ask students: *Why are plastics better material to use for medical tubing than metal?* Explain that plastics are used in medicine because they do not react with chemicals in the body, as most metals do. Point out that plastics are used to join broken bones, make contact lenses, and replace body parts, such as heart valves, joints, and limbs.
learning style: auditory

Thinking Critically Answer
Plastics have a wide range of properties, which can be suited to a variety of uses.

MORE ON THE WEB

Reviewing Chemical Symbols
Have students visit
www.conceptsandchallenges.com
to learn and review the names of the elements and their chemical symbols.

• TEACHING RESOURCES •

◎ Teacher's Resources CD-ROM
Lesson Review: Chapter 7, p. 2
Enrichment: Chapter 7, p. 3

ESL/ELL STRATEGY

Defining the Prefix sub- Tell students that the prefix *sub-* can mean "under, below, or beneath." Ask students to define *subscript.*

7-2 (pp. 150–151)

1 Introduce

🔍 INVESTIGATE

TIME: 10–15 minutes

PURPOSE: Students will model the valence electrons in various atoms.

MATERIALS: Valence Electrons charts found on the Teacher's Resources CD-ROM, counters (bingo chips or disks that are 1–2 cm in diameter), element cards (Make cards for elements with atomic numbers 1–20.)

PROCEDURE: Have students work independently. Give each student a different element card. Be sure to emphasize the use of the Valence Electrons chart (Figure 7-5).

THINK ABOUT IT: electrons
learning styles: visual, tactile

✏️ **STUDY HINT** Before beginning this section, have students read the Key Terms and their definitions aloud. Then, have students study Figures 7-6 and 7-7 and apply the Key Terms to the figures.
learning styles: visual, auditory

Linking Prior Knowledge Have students recall how electrons are arranged in an atom. (in energy levels around the nucleus; Lesson 3-6) Students should recall that atoms gain or lose electrons, becoming more stable (Lessons 4-6 and 4-7).

2 Teach

Discussion Draw Figure 7-6 on the board to show the valence electrons in sodium and chlorine. Remind students that atoms tend to complete their outermost energy levels by gaining, losing, or sharing electrons. Point out that chlorine and sodium complete their outermost energy levels by transferring an electron from one atom to the other. Refer students to the diagrams on the board and ask them to identify which atom loses an electron and which atom gains an electron.
learning styles: visual, auditory

Demonstration Draw a number line that includes positive and negative numbers on the board. Remind students that a compound has no charge, so the total number of positive charges must equal the

---

7-2 What is an oxidation number?

🔍 INVESTIGATE

Modeling Valence Electrons
HANDS-ON ACTIVITY

1. Obtain a Valence Electrons Chart (Figure 7-5), counters, and an element card from your teacher. Look up the atomic number of the element on the periodic table. The atomic number is the number of counters that you will place on the chart.

2. Place the counters on top of the small circles in the order in which the circles are numbered. Observe how many counters there are in the last energy level you filled.

THINK ABOUT IT: The chart represents how electrons are arranged around the nucleus of an atom. What do you think the counters represent?

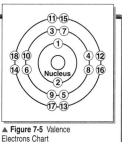

▲ **Figure 7-5** Valence Electrons Chart

Objective
Describe how to use oxidation numbers to write the chemical formula of a compound.

Key Terms
valence electron: electron in the outermost energy level of an atom

oxidation number: number of electrons an atom gains, loses, or shares when it forms a chemical bond

Valence Electrons You have learned that electrons move around the nucleus of an atom in energy levels. The lowest or first energy level of an atom can hold up to two electrons. For energy levels beyond the first level, eight is a very important number. Whenever the outermost energy level of an atom contains eight electrons, the atom is very stable, or complete. Atoms tend to gain, lose, or share electrons by bonding with other atoms in order to reach this stable arrangement. The electrons in an atom's outermost energy level are called **valence electrons**.

▶ **IDENTIFY:** How many electrons are in the outermost energy level of a stable atom?

Oxidation Number An **oxidation number** shows how many electrons an atom gains, loses, or shares when it forms a chemical bond. In general, atoms of nonmetals tend to gain electrons, and atoms of metals tend to lose electrons. For example, a chlorine

atom has seven valence electrons. To complete its outermost energy level, the atom must gain one electron from another atom. An atom that gains electrons has a negative oxidation number. When it gains an electron, it gains a negatively charged particle. Thus, the chlorine atom becomes an ion with a negative charge. Therefore, the oxidation number of chlorine is 1–.

An atom that loses electrons has a positive oxidation number. The outermost energy level of a sodium atom contains one electron. If the sodium atom loses its one valence electron, then the next lower energy level becomes its outermost energy level. This level has eight electrons, so it is complete. When a sodium atom loses its one valence electron, it becomes an ion with a positive charge. Therefore, the oxidation number of sodium is 1+.

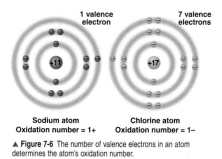

1 valence electron   **7 valence electrons**

Sodium atom
Oxidation number = 1+

Chlorine atom
Oxidation number = 1–

▲ **Figure 7-6** The number of valence electrons in an atom determines the atom's oxidation number.

▶ **INFER:** If an atom loses an electron, what kind of oxidation number will it have?

Teaching Options

EXTENDING THE LESSON

Looking Closer at the Periodic Table Have students use the periodic table on pages 66 and 67 to make models for the following elements in Group 1: hydrogen, lithium, sodium, and potassium. Ask students if they notice a pattern in the atoms of these elements. They should realize that all of the atoms of these elements have the same number of valence electrons. Inform students that all of the elements in a group have the same number of valence electrons but different numbers of energy levels.
learning styles: visual, tactile

RETEACH

Using the Periodic Table Show students a periodic table that includes oxidation numbers. Write the names and oxidation numbers of different elements on the board. Have volunteers come up to the board and write whether each element gains or loses electrons when it bonds with other atoms.
learning style: visual

Determining the Signs of Oxidation Numbers

In general, the location of an element on the periodic table can tell you whether its oxidation number will be positive or negative. Look back at the periodic table on pages 66 and 67. The elements to the left of the dark zigzag line, with the exception of hydrogen, are metals. Metals tend to lose electrons during a chemical reaction. Therefore, metals have positive oxidation numbers.

Elements to the right of the dark zigzag line on the periodic table are nonmetals. Nonmetals tend to gain electrons. So, nonmetals usually have negative oxidation numbers. Knowing the signs of the oxidation number of elements can help you to write the chemical formulas for different compounds.

▶ **INFER:** What kind of oxidation numbers do nonmetals usually have?

Writing Chemical Formulas The oxidation number of an element tells you if it tends to lose (+) or gain (−) electrons when forming a chemical bond. When writing a chemical formula, remember that the oxidation numbers of the elements in a compound must add up to zero. For example, sodium chloride is a compound made up of sodium and chlorine. The oxidation number of sodium is 1+. The oxidation number of chlorine is 1−. The oxidation numbers of the elements add up to zero:

$$(1+) + (1-) = 0$$

In the compound sodium chloride, one atom of sodium forms an ionic bond with one atom of chlorine. The chemical formula for sodium chloride is NaCl.

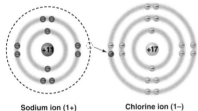

Sodium ion (1+)   Chlorine ion (1−)

▲ **Figure 7-7** An ionic bond forms between an atom of sodium and an atom of chlorine.

▶ **STATE:** What is the sum of the oxidation numbers of the elements in a compound?

✓ CHECKING CONCEPTS

1. What is the number of electrons that an atom gains, loses, or shares when it forms a chemical bond called?
2. What determines how many electrons an atom will gain, lose, or share when it forms a chemical bond?
3. Is the oxidation number of an atom that gains electrons positive or negative?
4. How many valence electrons does an atom of chlorine have?
5. In general, does a metal tend to gain electrons or lose electrons?
6. What kind of elements are to the right of the dark zigzag line on the periodic table?

💡 THINKING CRITICALLY

7. EXPLAIN: What is true about the oxidation numbers of the elements in a chemical formula?
8. ANALYZE: What is the oxidation number of aluminum in AlCl₃? What is the oxidation number of chlorine? Explain how you arrived at your answers.
9. PREDICT: The oxidation number of magnesium is 2+ and of sulfur is 2−. What is the formula for magnesium sulfide?
10. CALCULATE: The chemical formula for calcium oxide is CaO. If the oxidation number for calcium is 2+, what is the oxidation number for oxygen?

INTERPRETING VISUALS

Explain how the electron dot diagram shows how an atom of sodium and an atom of chlorine combine to make sodium chloride.

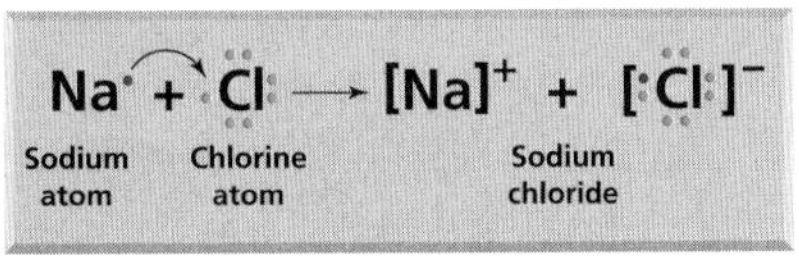

$$Na \cdot + \overset{\cdots}{\underset{\cdots}{Cl}} \cdot \longrightarrow [Na]^+ + [\overset{\cdots}{\underset{\cdots}{Cl}}]^-$$

Sodium   Chlorine   Sodium
atom   atom   chloride

▲ **Figure 7-8** An electron dot diagram for the formation of sodium chloride

---

total number of negative charges. Show them how to use the number line to determine the formulas of the compounds formed from various combinations of positive and negative ions. For example, the formula for a compound formed from Fe^{2+} and Br^- is $FeBr_2$ because two bromide ions have a charge equal but opposite to that of one iron ion. Possible ions to use: Fe^{2+}, Al^{3+}, Na^+, Mg^{2+}, Ca^{2+}, K^+, Cl^-, S^{2-}, N^{3-}, and I^-.
learning styles: logical/mathematical, visual

Answers to questions

▶ IDENTIFY: two if the atom is hydrogen or helium; eight for other atoms

▶ INFER: positive

▶ INFER: negative

▶ STATE: zero

📖 **READING STRATEGY** Have students fill out a graphic organizer, such as the Fishbone Map found on the Teacher's Resources CD-ROM. The main idea should be *oxidation number*. The supporting details should include information from each subhead. **learning style: linguistic**

3 *Assess*

✓ CHECKING CONCEPTS ANSWERS

1. oxidation number
2. the number of valence electrons
3. negative
4. seven
5. lose
6. nonmetals

💡 THINKING CRITICALLY ANSWERS

7. EXPLAIN: They add up to zero.
8. ANALYZE: 3+; 1−; There are three atoms of Cl for every atom of Al. The oxidation numbers must add up to zero.
9. PREDICT: MgS
10. CALCULATE: 2−

INTERPRETING VISUALS ANSWER

To acquire a stable electron configuration, sodium gives up its valence electron to chlorine, which fills its outermost energy level. Because both atoms become electrically charged, they form ions of the compound sodium chloride.

COOPERATIVE LEARNING

Making Models Have pairs of students make models of two atoms, one with an oxidation number of 1+ and one with an oxidation number of 1−. Using their models, students can show how the atoms become stable. Students can also use the Valence Electrons chart found on the Teacher's Resources CD-ROM.
learning styles: visual, tactile

• TEACHING RESOURCES •

💿 **Teacher's Resources CD-ROM**
Lesson Review: Chapter 7, p. 4
Valence Electrons Chart: Visuals, p. 8
Fishbone Map: Study Tools, p. 5
Laboratory Manual
Lab. Challenge: What factors can cause iron to undergo a chemical change? pp. 45–48

AlCl₃
(3+) + (−1·3)
3+ + −3
0

1 Introduce

INVESTIGATE

TIME: 10–15 minutes

PURPOSE: Students will identify the elements in compounds that have negative oxidation numbers and those that have positive oxidation numbers and conclude which is written first when writing the name of a compound.

MATERIALS: notebook paper, pencil

PROCEDURE: Students can work independently. They can also use the periodic table on pages 66 and 67 to identify the elements. Students should recall that metals have positive oxidation numbers and nonmetals usually have negative oxidation numbers. If students have difficulty identifying the second element in each compound, have them examine the words and determine how their endings were changed. *Chloride*, for example, looks like *chlorine*. *Oxide* indicates that the compound contains oxygen.

THINK ABOUT IT: The metallic element has a positive oxidation number; The metallic element comes first in the name of the compound.
learning styles: visual, linguistic

STUDY HINT Have students write the lesson title and objective in their notebooks. As they read this lesson, they should write the information that meets the objective.

2 Teach

Discussion Inform students that binary compounds contain two elements. Write the names of a variety of binary compounds, such as sodium chloride, aluminum oxide, and calcium bromide, on the board. Ask students to name the two elements that make up each compound and to tell which element of each compound has a positive oxidation number based on its position in the compound's name.
learning styles: visual, auditory

Reinforcement Write *copper (I) oxide* and *copper (II) oxide* on the board, and be sure that students understand that these are two different compounds. Emphasize the importance of including the Roman numeral in the name of the compound. Remind students that the Roman numeral indicates oxidation number, not the number of atoms present. **learning styles: auditory, visual**

7-3 How are chemical compounds named?

INVESTIGATE
Identifying Elements in Compounds
HANDS-ON ACTIVITY

1. Copy the chart onto a sheet of notebook paper.
2. Look at the list of compounds. Each compound is made up of only two elements.
3. Fill in the chart.

THINK ABOUT IT: In each compound, which element has a positive oxidation number? When writing the name of a compound with only two elements, which one do you write first?

IDENTIFYING ELEMENTS IN COMPOUNDS		
Compound	Element with positive oxidation number	Element with negative oxidation number
Sodium chloride		
Iron oxide		
Copper oxide		

▲ **Figure 7-9**

Objective
Explain how chemical compounds are named.

Key Term
binary (BY-nuhr-ee) **compound:** compound containing two elements

Binary Compounds Two different elements that are chemically combined form a **binary compound**. The name of a binary compound tells which two elements are found in the compound. Sodium chloride is an example of a binary compound. It is formed from the elements sodium and chlorine. The name of the element with a positive oxidation number is written first. Sodium has a positive oxidation number, 1+. If the second element only has one oxidation number, the name of that element is changed to end in -*ide* and is written last. For example, chlorine is changed to chloride when naming sodium chloride.

1 **PREDICT:** What elements would you expect to find in the compound hydrogen chloride?

Different Oxidation Numbers Many elements have more than one oxidation number. For example, the oxidation number of iron can be either 2+ or 3+. Scientists indicate different oxidation numbers of an element by including a Roman numeral in parentheses after the name of the

element. Iron (II) shows that an atom of iron has an oxidation number of 2+. Iron (III) shows that an atom of iron has an oxidation number of 3+.

Iron and chlorine can combine to form the compound $FeCl_2$. Iron and chlorine can also combine to form the compound $FeCl_3$. $FeCl_2$ and $FeCl_3$ are two different compounds with different properties. These compounds are identified as iron (II) chloride and iron (III) chloride. In both cases, chlorine has an oxidation number of 1−.

▲ **Figure 7-10** Iron and chlorine can combine to form iron (II) chloride (left) and iron (III) chloride (right).

2 **INFER:** What is the oxidation number of an atom of gold (III)?

Other Elements Most elements that have more than one oxidation number are usually metals. For example, tin can have an oxidation number of 4+ or 2+. Copper can have an oxidation number of 2+ or 1+. The Roman numeral in the name of a compound shows the oxidation

Teaching Options

COOPERATIVE LEARNING

Playing a Memory Game Make a set of cards for each of several small groups of students. Half of the cards should show the symbols for ions of metals that have more than one oxidation number. (Refer to Figure 7-11 for examples.) The other half of the cards should show the name of each of the ions. For example, one card would have Fe^{3+} written on it, while another would have *iron (III)*. Have students shuffle the cards and place them facedown in rows. Each row should have no more than four or five cards. Then, students can use the cards to play a memory game. Players take turns turning over two cards at a time. To make a match, students need to turn over the two cards that have the symbol for the ion and its name. **learning styles: visual, tactile**

number of the element in the compound. Figure 7-11 lists some metals that have more than one oxidation number.

OXIDATION NUMBERS OF SOME METALS

Metal	Higher oxidation number	Lower oxidation number
Iron	3+, iron (III)	2+, iron (II)
Mercury	2+, mercury (II)	1+, mercury (I)
Copper	2+, copper (II)	1+, copper (I)
Tin	4+, tin (IV)	2+, tin (II)
Nickel	3+, nickel (III)	2+, nickel (II)
Gold	3+, gold (III)	1+, gold (I)

▲ Figure 7-11

3 IDENTIFY: What is the oxidation number of copper in the compound copper (II) chloride?

✓ CHECKING CONCEPTS

1. The oxidation number of iron (III) is _____.

2. Iron (II) chloride and iron (III) chloride are different _____.

3. In the compound hydrogen chloride (HCl), _____ has a positive oxidation number.

4. Because the compound water contains the elements hydrogen and oxygen, it is a _____ compound.

5. The name mercury (II) bromide indicates that the oxidation number of _____ is 2+.

💡 THINKING CRITICALLY

6. INFER: The chemical formula for oxygen gas is O_2. Is this a binary compound?

Web InfoSearch

Prefixes In naming compounds made up of two nonmetals, prefixes are used. For example, the compound carbon monoxide contains one atom of oxygen. The prefix *mono-* means "one."

SEARCH: Use the Internet to find other compounds whose names start with prefixes. List the elements and the number of each kind of atom that make up each compound. Start your search at www.conceptsandchallenges.com. Some key search words are **compound**, **chemical formula**, and **prefixes**.

⚛ People in Science

NIELS BOHR (1885–1962)

In order to write chemical formulas, the atomic structure of an atom has to be known. Much of our present knowledge of atomic structure is based on the work of the Danish physicist Niels Bohr.

Niels Bohr proposed that the electrons in an atom travel in fixed energy levels around the nucleus, like planets orbiting the Sun. He also continued to explain that atoms could absorb an amount, or quantum, of energy that allows the electrons to jump to higher energy levels. When the atoms lose the energy, the electrons fall back to their original energy levels. When this happens, the atoms release the same quantum of energy that they absorbed. The released energy is often in the form of light. This work earned Bohr the Nobel Prize in 1922. Niels Bohr's work with electrons also led to the understanding of valence electrons.

▲ **Figure 7-12** Niels Bohr studied the structure of atoms.

Thinking Critically How does the work of Niels Bohr relate to writing chemical formulas?

Answers to questions

1 PREDICT: hydrogen and chlorine

2 INFER: 3+

3 IDENTIFY: 2+

3 Assess

✓ CHECKING CONCEPTS ANSWERS

1. 3+
2. compounds
3. hydrogen
4. binary
5. mercury

💡 THINKING CRITICALLY ANSWER

6. INFER: No; An O_2 molecule contains two atoms but only one element. A binary compound contains two different elements.

4 Close

Web InfoSearch

Prefixes Have students visit www.conceptsandchallenges.com to find compounds whose names include prefixes. Students should list the elements and the number of each kind of atom that make up each compound.

People in Science

NIELS BOHR (1885–1962)

Discussion Share with students that Bohr's work led to the idea that electrons exist in energy levels. Have students look back at page 56 to review Bohr's atomic model. The number of electrons in the outermost energy level determines the chemical properties of an atom. Bohr eventually came to the United States and helped develop the first atomic bomb. He also worked on developing peaceful uses for atomic energy. In 1997, the element with atomic number 107 was named bohrium (Bh) in honor of Niels Bohr and his contributions to science.

Thinking Critically Answer
Knowing how many valence electrons are in an atom is essential to predicting oxidation numbers. Oxidation numbers are needed to write chemical formulas.

ONGOING ASSESSMENT

Naming Compounds Write the formulas $FeCl_2$ and $FeCl_3$ on the board. Ask students to name the compounds and explain the differences between the two.

ESL/ELL STRATEGY

Defining the Prefix bi- To help students remember that a binary compound is made up of only two elements, point out that the prefix *bi-* means "two," as in bicycle or bicentennial.

• TEACHING RESOURCES •

💿 **Teacher's Resources CD-ROM**
Lesson Review: Chapter 7, p. 5
Laboratory Manual
Lab. Skills Worksheet 4: Organizing and Analyzing Data, pp. 13–14

1 Introduce

✏️ **STUDY HINT** Write the title of each section on the board. Have students copy these titles in their notebooks in outline format. As students read each section, they should write the information that supports or explains each section title. Students can also use the Writing Activity Outline found on the Teacher's Resources CD-ROM.

Linking Prior Knowledge Ask students to recall what an ion is. (an atom with an electrical charge; Lesson 4-5)

2 Teach

Discussion Refer students to Figure 7-13. Ask them to look at the nitrate ion and to point out the part of the diagram that represents nitrogen and the parts that represent oxygen. Follow the same process for the sulfate ion and the hydroxide ion. Then, remind students that the electrical charge that is shown in the upper right-hand corner is the charge for the entire ion, not for the last element in the ion's formula. **learning styles: visual, auditory**

Answers to questions

▶ **DEFINE:** a group of atoms that acts as a single-charged atom when combining with other atoms

▶ **IDENTIFY:** OH^-

▶ **ANALYZE:** $1+$

▶ **IDENTIFY:** 3

Reinforcement Be sure that students understand that when polyatomic ions take part in a chemical reaction, these groups of atoms behave as if they were a single unit. Tell students to treat polyatomic ions as a single ion when writing chemical formulas. Point out the parentheses in $Ba(OH)_2$. Show students that the parentheses indicate more than one unit of a polyatomic ion made of oxygen and hydrogen. Ask them to determine the oxidation number of Ba, given that the charge of the hydroxide ion is $1-$. (The oxidation number of Ba is $2+$.) **learning styles: auditory, visual**

7-4 What is a polyatomic ion?

Objective
Identify the chemical formula for polyatomic ions.

Key Term
polyatomic (pahl-ee-uh-TAHM-ihk) **ion:** group of atoms that acts as a charged atom, or ion, when combining with other atoms

Polyatomic Ions Sometimes a group of atoms stays together when chemically combining with other atoms. The atoms in this group are bound very tightly to each other. Thus, the group acts as a single atom with an electrical charge. A group of atoms that acts as a single charged atom, or ion, when combining with other atoms is called a **polyatomic ion.** The prefix *poly-* means "more than one." The group of atoms is called an ion because it has an overall electrical charge. The atoms in a polyatomic ion are held together by covalent bonds. Figure 7-13 shows some polyatomic ions. Notice how the electrical charge for each atom is written to the upper right of the chemical formula and the molecular model.

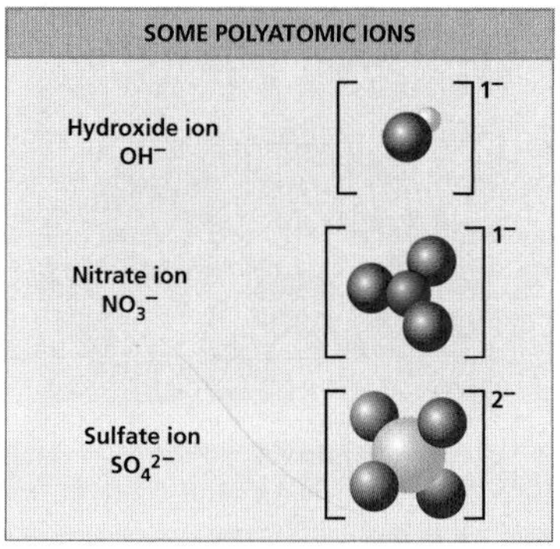

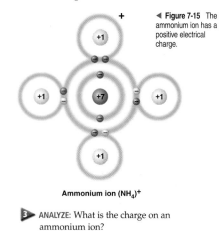

SOME POLYATOMIC IONS

Hydroxide ion OH^- 1^-

Nitrate ion NO_3^- 1^-

Sulfate ion SO_4^{2-} 2^-

▲ **Figure 7-13** The chemical formulas and molecular models of some polyatomic ions.

▶ **DEFINE:** What is a polyatomic ion?

154

Hydroxide Ions An example of a polyatomic ion is the hydroxide ion. The hydroxide ion is made up of one oxygen atom and one hydrogen atom. The oxygen atom and the hydrogen atom are joined together by a covalent bond. The hydroxide ion has a negative electrical charge. The chemical formula for the hydroxide ion is OH^-.

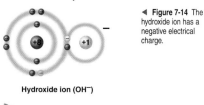

◀ **Figure 7-14** The hydroxide ion has a negative electrical charge.

Hydroxide ion (OH^-)

▶ **IDENTIFY:** What is the formula for the hydroxide ion?

Ammonium Ions The ammonium ion is made up of one nitrogen atom, three hydrogen atoms, and one hydrogen ion. The chemical formula for the ammonium ion is NH_4^+. The ammonium ion is a common polyatomic ion with a positive electrical charge.

◀ **Figure 7-15** The ammonium ion has a positive electrical charge.

Ammonium ion (NH_4)$^+$

▶ **ANALYZE:** What is the charge on an ammonium ion?

Teaching Options

◆ **INTEGRATING LIFE SCIENCE**

Nitrates and Nitrites in Food
Nitrates and nitrites are often used in the food industry. These substances are added to fresh meat to prevent the growth of harmful organisms and to give meat a particular flavor and color. Encourage students to use reference materials to find out why the addition of nitrates and nitrites might not be safe for people who eat those foods. Students may want to bring in food labels from packages of ham, bacon, hot dogs, and bologna and look for nitrates and nitrites in the lists of ingredients.

EXTENDING THE LESSON

Making Models Guide students as they use Figure 7-13 to make models of polyatomic ions. They might use gumdrops and toothpicks to construct the ions. Students can work in small groups to make their models. They can display the models on a desktop or table. Students from another group can label the models with the chemical formulas for the ions. If students are unable to label the ions, encourage them to determine how to make the ions easy to identify. Caution students not to eat anything in a laboratory setting.
learning styles: visual, tactile

Writing Chemical Formulas To write the formula for a polyatomic ion, you follow the same rules for writing other chemical formulas. However, if there is more than one polyatomic ion in a compound, you would write the chemical formula for the polyatomic ion in parentheses. The number of polyatomic ions would be written as a subscript after the parentheses. For example, in $Ba(OH)_2$, two hydroxide ions chemically combine with a barium atom to form barium hydroxide.

▶ IDENTIFY: How many hydroxide ions are there in $Al(OH)_3$?

CHECKING CONCEPTS

1. A polyatomic ion contains _____ one atom.
2. The polyatomic ion made up of an oxygen and hydrogen atom is the _____ ion.
3. The hydroxide ion has a _____ electrical charge.
4. The nitrate ion contains one nitrogen atom and _____ oxygen atoms.

THINKING CRITICALLY

5. CLASSIFY: Look at the following chemical compounds. Which ones contain hydroxide ions? Which do not? Explain your answers.
   a. Limewater, $Ca(OH)_2$
   b. Milk of magnesia, $Mg(OH)_2$
   c. Table salt, NaCl
   d. Water, H_2O
   e. Lye, NaOH
6. INFER: When atoms of different elements combine to form polyatomic ions, what holds these atoms together?
7. INFER: How many sulfate ions are there in a molecule of potassium sulfate, K_2SO_4?

BUILDING LANGUAGE ARTS SKILLS

Building Vocabulary The prefix *poly-* means "more than one." Use a dictionary to find the definitions of the words *polygon*, *polymer*, and *polysyllabic*. Write the definitions on a sheet of paper.

Science and Technology
NITRATES IN FERTILIZERS

The nitrate polyatomic ion plays a major role in fertilizers and plant life. It is made up of one nitrogen atom and three oxygen atoms. Plants need nitrogen to make proteins. Plants can obtain the needed nitrogen from the nitrates that are naturally found in soil and in both organic and commercial fertilizers. Nitrogen fertilizers include ammonium nitrate, NH_4NO_3, and calcium nitrate, $Ca(NO_3)_2$. The presence of nitrates in soil can improve plant growth.

▲ **Figure 7-16** Spreading nitrogen-rich fertilizer

People have used fertilizers for thousands of years. Before their benefits were known scientifically, people observed that animal droppings, ashes, and certain minerals helped plants thrive. All of these substances contain nitrates. Today, farmers spend thousands of dollars on commercial fertilizers each year. Farmers add a certain amount of fertilizers to soil to ensure that plants will have the nitrogen needed to grow healthy and plentiful.

Thinking Critically Why does adding fertilizers to soil help plants grow?

---

3 *Assess*

✓ CHECKING CONCEPTS ANSWERS

1. more than
2. hydroxide
3. negative
4. three

THINKING CRITICALLY ANSWERS

5. CLASSIFY: **a**, **b**, **e**; They all contain OH in their chemical formulas.
6. INFER: covalent bonds
7. INFER: one

4 *Close*

BUILDING LANGUAGE ARTS SKILLS ANSWERS

Building Vocabulary polygon—a closed plane figure with three or more straight sides; polymer—a chemical compound made up of many small, repeating units; polysyllabic—having more than three syllables **learning style: linguistic**

Science and Technology
NITRATES IN FERTILIZERS

Discussion Natural soil usually has all the nutrients that are required for plants to grow. If the same parcel of land is used to grow crops year after year, however, the land may become depleted of nutrients. Farmers use fertilizers to add those essential nutrients back to the soil. Nitrogen, phosphorus, and potassium are the nutrients most commonly found in fertilizers. Nitrogen can be found in natural fertilizers, such as manure and bones. Some legume crops, such as soybeans or peanuts, can be rotated with other crops. Bacteria in the roots of legumes change atmospheric nitrogen into a form that plants can use. When the fields are plowed under, nitrogen from the plants is added back to the soil.

Thinking Critically Answer
Possible answer: Fertilizers add nutrients to soil.

MORE ON THE WEB

More on Polyatomic Ions Have students learn how polyatomic ions are named by visiting www.conceptsandchallenges.com. Have students take an online quiz for review.

• TEACHING RESOURCES •

◉ **Teacher's Resources CD-ROM**
Lesson Review: Chapter 7, p. 6
Enrichment: Chapter 7, p. 7
Writing Activity Outline: Study Tools, pp. 20–21

ONGOING ASSESSMENT

Explaining Polyatomic Ions Ask students: *Why do the atoms in a polyatomic ion stay together and act as a single atom?* (They are bound very tightly to one another.)

Lab Activity

(pp. 156–157)

1 Prepare the Lab

Constructing Chemical Formulas

SET-UP TIME: ⏱ **LAB TIME:** 🕘

BACKGROUND: Individual atoms have one or more oxidation numbers that indicate how many electrons an atom will lose, gain, or share to become stable. Because a polyatomic ion contains more than one element, each of which has its own oxidation number, *oxidation number* is not a term that applies to a polyatomic ion as a whole. The term *charge* is used to show the total of the oxidation numbers of the elements in the ion. For example, in PO_4^{3-}, the P has an oxidation number of $5+$ and each O has an oxidation number of $2-$. The charge on the ion is $3-$, which is the sum of $(5+) + 4(2-)$.

PURPOSE: Students will use "building blocks" to model examples of chemical formulas for several compounds.

ALTERNATIVE MATERIALS: Students can make building blocks out of self-stick notes.

SCIENCE SKILLS: Students will **model** how to balance oxidation numbers and charges to form stable compounds. They will **calculate** oxidation numbers to make sure that they add up to zero. They will use correct chemical notation, including symbols and subscripts, as they write the formulas of compounds that they form.

ADVANCE PLANNING: Be sure that the graph paper you provide has a metric grid.

2 Guide the Lab

PROCEDURE: Have pairs of students cut 60 squares. Remind them that the numbers in parentheses show how many of each atom they need to make. Be sure that students understand that the charges on the polyatomic ions apply to the whole group of atoms. The charge for CO_3^{2-}, for example, applies to the entire group of atoms, not only to the oxygen atoms. Remind students that elements or ions with positive oxidation numbers or charges are always listed first in a chemical formula. Provide students with a copy of the Lab Activity Report found on the Teacher's Resources CD-ROM to record their observations and conclusions.

LAB ACTIVITY
Constructing Chemical Formulas

Materials
Graph paper
Ruler
Marker
Construction paper
Scissors
Glue or tape

▲ **STEP 1** Make 3 cm × 3 cm boxes.

▲ **STEP 3** Prepare a list of chemical formulas.

BACKGROUND

In order to write the chemical formula of a compound, you must know the oxidation numbers of the elements or the charges of the polyatomic ions of that particular compound. The oxidation numbers of the elements or the charges of the polyatomic ions in a compound must add up to zero.

PURPOSE

In this activity, you will model various examples of elements and polyatomic ions with their oxidation numbers and charges. Also, you will construct various chemical formulas of common substances.

PROCEDURE

1. On graph paper, make about 60 3 cm × 3 cm boxes.

2. In each box, write the following chemical symbols and chemical formulas with their oxidation numbers. The number in the parentheses to the left of the chemical symbol tells you how many of each element or polyatomic ion you should make.

(8) H^{1+}	(6) Cl^{1-}
(4) Na^{1+}	(6) OH^{1-}
(4) Ca^{2+}	(4) O^{2-}
(4) Mg^{2+}	(4) S^{2-}
(4) Al^{3+}	(4) SO_4^{2-}
(4) CO_3^{2-}	

▲ **Figure 7-17** Chemical symbols with the oxidation numbers for certain elements and with the charges for certain polyatomic ions.

156

Teaching Options

RETEACH

Creating a Chart Students may benefit from working together on creating a simple chart to show that elements combine to create compounds. Make a grid on the board with six rows and five columns. Label the rows with the following ions: H^+, NH_4^+, Au^{3+}, K^+, Fe^{2+}, and Al^{3+}. Label the columns with the following ions: Cl^-, Br^-, N^{3-}, CO_3^{2-}, and S^{2-}. Have students fill in the chart to show the compound formed by each pair. Have them check to be sure that the oxidation numbers and charges add up to zero and that the formulas show the smallest ratio possible. For example, Fe^{2+} and CO_3^{2-} form $FeCO_3$, not $Fe_2(CO_3)_2$. Remind students that parentheses must be used around more than one unit of a polyatomic ion in a compound.
learning styles: interpersonal, logical/mathematical

ESL/ELL STRATEGY

Pairing Students English-language learners may have difficulty following the procedure. Pair an English-language learner with an English-proficient student during this lab. The English-proficient student can help the English-language learner in carrying out the procedure, as well as help in interpreting the results.

3. Cut out all of your boxes. On a sheet of construction paper, label the top *Constructing Chemical Formulas*. Using your boxes, construct the chemical formulas listed in Figure 7-18 on construction paper.

4. Glue or tape your chemical formulas onto the paper. Label each chemical formula.

5. With the leftover boxes, try to construct other possible chemical formulas. (REMEMBER: oxidation numbers must equal zero.) Glue or tape them to your construction paper.

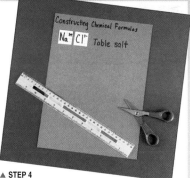
▲ STEP 4
Label each chemical formula.

Some Chemical Formulas			
table salt	NaCl	sulfuric acid	H_2SO_4
water	H_2O	"rotten egg" smell	H_2S
lye	NaOH	lime water	$Ca(OH)_2$
marble chips	$CaCO_3$	bauxite	Al_2O_3
Epsom salt	$MgSO_4$	milk of magnesia	$Mg(OH)_2$

▲ Figure 7-18

CONCLUSIONS

1. CALCULATE: What do you notice about the sum of the oxidation numbers and charges of all the chemical formulas that you have constructed?

2. MODEL: Use an example from the list to explain how the boxes help in writing a chemical formula.

3. CALCULATE: List the chemical formulas that you constructed on your own. Do the oxidation numbers and charges of all the elements in each formula add up to zero?

Tips for Using Technology

Presenting Chemical Formulas
Have students use presentation software to show their chemical formulas. Presentation software allows them to use a computer to put text and art together into a slide show. They can use a scanner to incorporate their own art into their slide show. Students can then print their slide show and use it as a handout for others to follow during their presentation. Have students use the Thumbnail Sketch on the Teacher's Resources CD-ROM to plan their presentations.

• TEACHING RESOURCES •

Teacher's Resources CD-ROM
Lab Activity Report: Study Tools, pp. 16–17
Laboratory Activity Rubric: Teaching Tools, p. 8
Thumbnail Sketch: Study Tools, p. 24

Laboratory Manual
Lab. Skills Worksheet 4: Organizing and Analyzing Data, pp. 13–14

EXPECTED OUTCOME: Students should create other possible chemical formulas, such as Na_2O, Na_2S, Na_2SO_4, CaO, $MgCO_3$, and H_2CO_3. Some of the compounds they create may not actually exist, but the oxidation numbers and charges should add up to zero.

3 Conclude the Lab

1. **CALCULATE:** The sum of the oxidation numbers and charges is always zero.
2. **MODEL:** Possible answer: For the compound H_2O, oxygen has an oxidation number of 2−. To have a neutral compound, the other part of the compound needs to have a total oxidation number of 2+. Hydrogen has an oxidation number of 1+, so two hydrogen atoms are needed.
3. **CALCULATE:** Answers will vary. Expect students to prove that the oxidation numbers and charges add up to zero.

Use the Laboratory Activity Rubric on the Teacher's Resources CD-ROM to assess students' lab activities. Fill in the rubric with the additional information below. For this activity, students should have:

• performed the activity according to the procedure and filled in the chart with data collected during the activity.

• correctly answered the questions in complete sentences.

4 Extend the Lab

Transition elements, which are those in Groups 3–12 on the periodic table, usually have multiple oxidation numbers. Refer students to Figure 7-11 on page 153 for examples of elements that have more than one oxidation number. Have students write formulas of compounds formed from ions of the same element but with different oxidation numbers. For example, iron has oxidation numbers of 2+ and 3+. Iron forms FeO and Fe_2O_3 with oxygen, which has an oxidation number of 2−.

1 Introduce

✎ **STUDY HINT** Before beginning this lesson, have students begin a word web in their notebooks. They should write the term *diatomic molecule* and circle it. Then, they should draw arms leading from the circle on which they can record information about diatomic molecules, such as the definition and examples. Students can also use the Concept Map on the Teacher's Resources CD-ROM.

Linking Prior Knowledge Ask students to recall the definition of a molecule (Lesson 4-2). You might also review the definition of a covalent bond and discuss the differences between covalent and ionic bonds (Lessons 4-5 and 4-6).

2 Teach

Discussion Explain that not all diatomic molecules are made up of two atoms of the same element. For example, carbon monoxide (CO) is a gas made up of diatomic molecules of carbon and oxygen. Nitrous oxide (NO), laughing gas, is another gas that is made up of diatomic molecules of nitrogen and oxygen.
learning style: auditory

Demonstration On the board, draw electron dot diagrams for two chlorine atoms. Each diagram should show the symbol for chlorine (Cl) surrounded by seven valence electrons, written as three pairs of electrons and one unpaired electron. Show students how, if the atoms share the two unpaired electrons, each atom will have eight valence electrons, which is a stable electron configuration.
learning style: visual

Reinforcement Make sure students understand that molecular models and electron dot diagrams only show the valence electrons around atoms. For example, oxygen has an atomic number of eight but only six electrons are drawn in a molecular model and in an electron dot diagram. The two electrons that are unaccounted for are found in the first energy level and so, are not valence electrons.

7-5 What is a diatomic molecule?

Objective
Identify a diatomic molecule.

Key Term
diatomic molecule: molecule made up of only two atoms

Hydrogen Molecules An atom of hydrogen has one electron in its first energy level. A hydrogen atom needs another electron in order to complete this energy level. It can receive that extra electron from another hydrogen atom. By sharing two electrons, the two hydrogen atoms complete their first energy levels. The two hydrogen atoms combine to form a hydrogen molecule, H_2. Hydrogen gas is always made up of pairs of hydrogen atoms.

▶ 1 **INFER:** How many electrons does an atom of hydrogen need to complete its energy level?

Diatomic Molecules The molecule formed by the covalent bonding between two hydrogen atoms is called a diatomic molecule. A **diatomic molecule** is made up of only two atoms. Most elements that are gases form diatomic molecules. For example, carbon monoxide (CO) is a diatomic molecule. Atoms in a diatomic molecule are usually held together by a covalent bond.

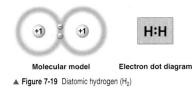

▲ **Figure 7-19** Diatomic hydrogen (H_2)

▶ 2 **DEFINE:** What is a diatomic molecule?

Oxygen Molecules Oxygen is another element that can form a diatomic molecule. Oxygen gas (O_2) in the air is formed when two oxygen atoms share two pairs of electrons. However, oxygen can also form molecules made up of three oxygen atoms. This substance is called ozone (O_3). Ozone is a triatomic molecule. A layer of ozone is found

158

in Earth's atmosphere from about 10 km to about 45 km above Earth's surface.

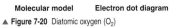
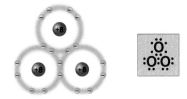

Molecular model **Electron dot diagram**
▲ **Figure 7-20** Diatomic oxygen (O_2)

Molecular model **Electron dot diagram**
▲ **Figure 7-21** Triatomic oxygen (O_3), also called ozone

▶ 3 **CONTRAST:** How do oxygen gas and ozone differ?

Other Diatomic Molecules Other elements can be found as diatomic molecules, too. For example, an atom of chlorine has seven valence electrons. It can complete its outermost energy level by forming a covalent bond with another chlorine atom. By sharing a pair of electrons, both chlorine atoms can complete their outermost energy levels. Figure 7-22 lists other elements that can form diatomic molecules.

SOME DIATOMIC MOLECULES		
Molecule	**Chemical formula**	**Physical state**
Iodine	I_2	Solid
Nitrogen	N_2	Gas
Chlorine	Cl_2	Gas
Fluorine	F_2	Gas
Bromine	Br_2	Liquid

▲ **Figure 7-22**

▶ 4 **LIST:** Name some elements that form diatomic molecules.

Teaching Options

EXTENDING THE LESSON

Building Vocabulary Based on the definition of *diatomic molecule*, have students guess what the prefix *di-* means. (two) Have students use a dictionary to verify their answers. Then, have them find the definitions of the following words: *diagonal*, *dicotyledon*, *dibromide*, and *dichloride*. (*diagonal:* extending between the corners of any two nonadjacent angles; *dicotyledon:* flowering plant with two seed cotyledons; *dibromide:* containing two bromine atoms; *dichloride:* containing two chlorine atoms)
learning style: linguistic

ONGOING ASSESSMENT

Identifying True/False Statements Give students simple statements and ask them to tell whether the statements are true or false. Have students change false statements to make them true. Examples: Diatomic molecules are usually liquids at room temperature. (false; Diatomic molecules are usually gases at room temperature.) Atoms in a diatomic molecule are usually held together by a covalent bond. (true)

1. A hydrogen atom needs _____ electrons to complete its first energy level.
2. A molecule that contains only two atoms is called a _____ molecule.
3. Most elements that are _____ form diatomic molecules.
4. A molecule of _____ contains three atoms of oxygen.
5. The atoms in a diatomic molecule are held together by a _____ bond.
6. Diatomic molecules of _____ can form a liquid.

7. CLASSIFY: Which of the following molecules are diatomic molecules?
    a. Br_2
    b. CO_2
    c. H_2O
    d. Cl_2
8. APPLY: The elements fluorine (F), chlorine (Cl), bromine (Br), iodine (I), and astatine (At) are called halogens. As gases, the halogens exist as diatomic molecules. Write the formula for one molecule of each of these elements.
9. ANALYZE: In a diatomic molecule of hydrogen, how many valence electrons does each atom of hydrogen have?

Integrating Environmental Science

TOPIC: the atmosphere

DESTRUCTION OF THE OZONE LAYER

Ozone is a triatomic molecule. It forms in the atmosphere when ultraviolet rays from the Sun strike oxygen molecules in the air. A layer of ozone in the atmosphere absorbs most of the Sun's harmful ultraviolet radiation.

Certain chemicals called chlorofluorocarbons, or CFCs, destroy ozone molecules. CFCs are compounds that contain carbon, fluorine, and chlorine. In many countries, CFCs were used in spray cans, air conditioners, refrigerators, and aircraft engines. However, it has been found that when CFCs are released into the atmosphere, they break down ozone molecules. As a result of the use of CFCs, the ozone layer has thinned. The thinning of the ozone layer is especially noticeable in the section over Antarctica.

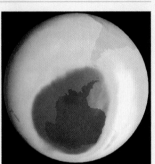

▲ **Figure 7-23** The dark blue ring in the photograph shows the size of the hole in the ozone layer above Antarctica.

In 1987, the United States government and other industrialized nations agreed to reduce the use of CFCs. Then, after further destruction of the ozone layer, another agreement was signed by most industrialized nations to stop using CFCs by 2000. However, some countries still use CFCs. Because CFC molecules can last a long time, they can still be found in the atmosphere.

Thinking Critically Why have some countries banned the use of CFCs?

Answers to questions

▶1 **INFER:** one

▶2 **DEFINE:** a molecule made up of only two atoms

▶3 **CONTRAST:** Possible answer: Oxygen gas contains two atoms of oxygen. Ozone contains three atoms of oxygen.

▶4 **LIST:** iodine, nitrogen, chlorine, fluorine, bromine, oxygen, and hydrogen

3 Assess

✓ **CHECKING CONCEPTS ANSWERS**

1. one
2. diatomic
3. gases
4. ozone
5. covalent
6. bromine

💡 **THINKING CRITICALLY ANSWERS**

7. CLASSIFY: **a** and **d**
8. APPLY: F_2, Cl_2, Br_2, I_2, At_2
9. ANALYZE: two

4 Close

Integrating Environmental Science

TOPIC: the atmosphere

DESTRUCTION OF THE OZONE LAYER

Discussion Ask how the ozone layer helps people. (The ozone layer absorbs most of the Sun's harmful ultraviolet radiation, protecting people from skin cancer and eye damage.) Inform students that the hole in the ozone layer that scientists often refer to is not a true hole. It is an area where the ozone layer has thinned to a great degree. Ask: *What elements make up CFCs?* (carbon, fluorine, and chlorine) Ask students whether the banning of CFCs has solved the problem of the destruction of the ozone layer. Students should realize that the hole in the ozone layer cannot be easily repaired. CFC molecules last a long time, so they will not be eliminated immediately, even if all nations ban their use. **learning style: auditory**

Thinking Critically Answer
CFCs break down ozone and thin the ozone layer, causing people to have more direct exposure to harmful

---

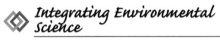

MORE ON THE WEB

More on Diatomic Molecules
Have students use the Internet to review diatomic molecules. Then, have students take an online quiz for review at www.conceptsandchallenges.com.

• **TEACHING RESOURCES** •

⊙ **Teacher's Resources CD-ROM**
Lesson Review: Chapter 7, p. 8
Concept Map: Study Tools, p. 4

ESL/ELL STRATEGY

Reinforcing Diatomic Molecules
Have English-language learners draw molecular models and electron dot diagrams to show that diatomic molecules are always made up of two atoms.

7-6 *(pp. 160–161)*

1 Introduce

STUDY HINT Before beginning this lesson, have students draw a flowchart showing the steps in finding formula mass. Students can also use the Flowchart on the Teacher's Resources CD-ROM. As they read the lesson, students can refer to the chart to find the formula mass of different compounds.

Linking Prior Knowledge Ask students to recall the definition of a molecule. (smallest part of a substance that has all the properties of the substance; Lesson 4-2) Students should also explain what atomic mass is. (total mass of protons and neutrons in an atom; Lesson 3-5)

2 Teach

Discussion Review the concept of mass number with students. Have them recall that the mass number of an atom is equal to the total number of protons and neutrons in its nucleus. Describe the formula mass of a molecule. From this description, develop the idea that the mass of one molecule is equivalent to the total mass of the atoms that make up the molecule. Have students study Figure 7-24. Inform them that the mass of a molecule of water is too small to be measured on any scale. However, if the mass of a water molecule could be measured, it would equal the formula mass of the molecule. **learning style: auditory**

Demonstration Use plastic-foam balls to represent the atoms of a molecule of ethyl chloride. On each ball, write the symbol of the element and its atomic mass. Join the balls together with toothpicks to make the molecule. Use the model to help calculate the formula mass of ethyl chloride. Students can use plastic-foam balls to make additional models and can then calculate the formula mass of each molecule or ionic compound. **learning styles: visual, tactile**

Answers to questions

1 DEFINE: the sum of the mass numbers of all the atoms in a molecule or ions in an ionic compound

2 INFER: 1

3 CALCULATE: 18

T160   UNIT 3: The Behavior of Matter

7-6   What is formula mass?

Objective
Explain how to find formula mass.

Key Term
formula mass: sum of the mass numbers of all the atoms in a molecule or ions in an ionic compound

Formula Mass A molecule contains atoms chemically joined together. Each atom in a molecule has its own mass number. Remember that the mass number of an atom is the number of protons and neutrons in the nucleus. It is equal to the atomic mass rounded to the nearest whole number. The sum of the mass numbers of all the atoms in a molecule is called the **formula mass** of the molecule. Formula mass is also the sum of the mass numbers of all the ions in an ionic compound.

▲ **Figure 7-24** If you could put a molecule of water on a scale, you would find its formula mass.

1 DEFINE: What is formula mass?

Finding Formula Mass Neon is an element that can exist as a molecule with only one atom. Therefore, a molecule of neon contains one atom of neon. The mass number of neon is 20. Because there is only one atom in a molecule of neon, the formula mass of neon is also 20. However, most molecules and ionic compounds contain more than one atom. To find the formula mass of molecules or ions in ionic compounds that contain more than one atom, use the following steps.

160

Step 1 Write the chemical formula of the compound.

Step 2 Use the periodic table on pages 66 and 67 to find the atomic mass of each element in the compound. Round the atomic mass to find the mass number.

Step 3 Multiply the mass number of each element by its subscript. If there is no subscript, multiply the mass number by 1.

Step 4 Add the total masses of all the atoms in the compound. The total is the formula mass of the compound.

2 INFER: If there is no subscript for an element, what do you multiply the mass number by?

Formula Mass of Ethyl Chloride You can find the formula mass of the compound ethyl chloride by following the steps listed above.

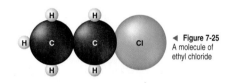

◄ **Figure 7-25**
A molecule of ethyl chloride

- Write the chemical formula for ethyl chloride. The formula for ethyl chloride is C_2H_5Cl.

- Find the mass number of each element in the compound. The mass number of C = 12, H = 1, and Cl = 35. Then, multiply the mass number of each element by its subscript: $12 \times 2 = 24$; $1 \times 5 = 5$; $35 \times 1 = 35$.

- Add the total masses of all the elements in the compound: $24 + 5 + 35 = 64$. The formula mass of ethyl chloride is 64.

3 CALCULATE: If the mass number of hydrogen is 1 and the mass number of oxygen is 16, what is the formula mass of water (H_2O)?

Teaching Options

! FAST FACTS   *Calculating in Chemistry*

- The atomic mass of a substance is expressed in atomic mass units (amu). An atomic mass unit is equal to approximately 1.66×10^{-24} g.

- The study of chemistry that deals with calculations based on chemical reactions is called stoichiometry (stoi-kee-AHM-uh-tree).

- Formula mass is sometimes called molecular mass. Molecular mass is the sum of the mass numbers of all the atoms in a molecule. For molecular substances, it is correct to use either term. However, for ionic compounds, substances that are made up of ions, the only correct term to use is *formula mass*.

✓ CHECKING CONCEPTS

1. Each type of atom in a molecule has its own __________.
2. The mass number of an atom is the number of protons and __________ in the nucleus.
3. The mass number of an atom of neon is the same as the __________ of a molecule of neon.
4. The first step in finding the formula mass of a molecule is to write the __________ of the compound.
5. The formula mass is the sum of the __________ of all the atoms in a molecule or ionic compound.
6. When finding formula mass, multiply the mass number of each element by its __________.
7. The final step in finding the formula mass of a molecule is to __________ the total masses of all the atoms in the molecule.

THINKING CRITICALLY

8. INFER: The mass number of a certain element is the same as the formula mass of the element. What does this tell you about a molecule of that element?
9. HYPOTHESIZE: Could the formula mass of an element ever be less than the mass number of the element?
10. CALCULATE: What is the formula mass of a molecule of sugar, $C_{12}H_{22}O_{11}$?
11. ANALYZE: Could the formula mass of a compound ever contain a decimal point?

BUILDING MATH SKILLS

Predicting Formula Mass The chemical formula of the compound carbon monoxide is CO. The chemical formula of the compound carbon dioxide is CO_2. Predict how the formula mass of both molecules differ. Check the accuracy of your prediction by calculating the formula mass of each molecule.

Hands-On Activity

HOW TO FIND FORMULA MASS

You will need a pencil and a sheet of paper.

1. Review the steps to follow when calculating formula mass.
2. Copy the table in Figure 7-26 onto a sheet of paper. Use the periodic table on pages 66 and 67 to fill in the table.

Practicing Your Skills

3. CALCULATE: What is the atomic mass of sodium? What is its mass number?
4. EXPLAIN: What is the difference between the atomic mass and the mass number of an element? Which is used to calculate formula mass?

CALCULATING FORMULA MASS

Compound	Elements	Mass number	Sub-script	Mass of each element	Formula mass
NO_2 Nitrogen dioxide	Nitrogen	14	1	14	46
	Oxygen	16	2	32	
H_2O_2 Hydrogen peroxide					
$CaCO_3$ Calcium carbonate					
Na_3PO_4 Sodium phosphate					

▲ Figure 7-26

3 *Assess*

✓ CHECKING CONCEPTS ANSWERS

1. mass number
2. neutrons
3. formula mass
4. chemical formula
5. mass numbers
6. subscript
7. add

THINKING CRITICALLY ANSWERS

8. INFER: Possible answer: A molecule of the element has no subscript.
9. HYPOTHESIZE: no, because mass numbers are added to calculate formula mass
10. CALCULATE: 342
11. ANALYZE: no (The atomic mass is rounded to the nearest one.)

4 *Close*

BUILDING MATH SKILLS ANSWER

Predicting Formula Mass CO_2 will have a greater formula mass than CO. The formula mass of CO is 28, and the formula mass of CO_2 is 44.

Hands-On Activity

HOW TO FIND FORMULA MASS

TIME: 10–15 minutes

PURPOSE: calculating, explaining

Practicing Your Skills Answers

3. CALCULATE: 22.990; 23
4. EXPLAIN: Atomic mass is the average mass of all the atoms in a sample of an element. Mass number is the number of protons and neutrons in the nucleus. Mass numbers are used to calculate formula mass.

CALCULATING FORMULA MASS

Compound	Elements	Mass number	Sub-script	Mass of each element	Formula mass
H_2O_2 Hydrogen peroxide	Hydrogen	1	2	2	34
	Oxygen	16	2	32	
$CaCO_3$ Calcium carbonate	Calcium	40	1	40	100
	Carbon	12	1	12	
	Oxygen	16	3	48	
Na_3PO_4 Sodium phosphate	Sodium	23	3	69	164
	Phosphorus	31	1	31	
	Oxygen	16	4	64	

MORE ON THE WEB

Finding Formula Mass Have students visit www.conceptsandchallenges.com to practice the calculation of formula masses.

RETEACH

Finding Formula Mass If students are having a hard time following the steps in finding formula mass, you can have them draw a model of the molecule. In each atom, they can write the chemical symbol for the element and the mass number. Instead of following the steps, they can just add the mass numbers of all the atoms.

• *TEACHING RESOURCES* •

Teacher's Resources CD-ROM

Lesson Review: Chapter 7, p. 9

Flowchart: Study Tools, p. 6

The Big Idea

(pp. 162–163)

1 Introduce

Objective Students will review the steps for using oxidation numbers to write chemical formulas. They will write chemical formulas using elements from Group 2 and Group 16 of the periodic table.

Linking Prior Knowledge Ask students to recall what they learned about oxidation numbers. Students should recall that the oxidation numbers and charges in a chemical compound must add up to zero. You might also focus students' attention on the lab activity, reminding them of the steps they took to create chemical formulas.

2 Teach

Discussion After students read the article and the steps, encourage them to look at the periodic table on pages 66 and 67 to make connections on how to write a chemical formula. Then, guide them in writing a sample chemical formula using an element from Group 2 and an element from Group 16. **learning styles: visual, logical/mathematical**

Use the information in the article and the steps in the captions to help guide students in writing chemical formulas in their Science Logs.

THE BIG IDEA ONLINE

How is a chemical formula written? Have students research their Science Log Writing Activity at www.conceptsandchallenges.com. You can have students organize their log by completing the Big Idea activity online. Students may post their work in the Online Classroom Database for others to read.

Reinforcement Students can also use the Big Idea Planner or Big Idea Science Log Entry found on the Teacher's Resources CD-ROM.

◆ *Integrating Mathematics*

THE Big IDEA

How is a chemical formula written?

The formation of a chemical bond involves the transfer or sharing of valence electrons between atoms. An oxidation number tells how many electrons an atom can give, receive, or share when forming chemical bonds.

Water is a compound made up of hydrogen and oxygen. Hydrogen has an oxidation number of 1^+ because it tends to give up its one electron when forming chemical bonds. Oxygen has six valence electrons. It needs two electrons to complete its outermost energy level, so its oxidation number is 2^-.

The oxidation numbers of all the atoms in one molecule of water must add up to zero. So, for every oxygen atom (oxidation number 2^-), there must be two hydrogen atoms ($1^+ + 1^+ = 2^+$).

Water (H_2O)
Three fourths of Earth is covered by water. Hydrogen and oxygen combine to form the compound water.

STEP 1 Write the chemical formula.
H_2O

STEP 2 Write each atom and its oxidation number as an equation that equals zero.
$H^{1+} + H^{1+} + O^{2-} = 0$

STEP 3 Write the oxidation numbers of each atom as an equation that equals zero.
$1 + 1 + (-2) = 0$

STEP 4 Make sure that the left side of the equation adds up to zero.
$2 + (-2) = 0$

Iron (III) Oxide (Fe_2O_3)
Tapes in audio cassettes are often coated with iron oxide. Iron combines with oxygen forming ferric oxide, also called iron (III) oxide or rust.

STEP 1 Write the chemical formula.
Fe_2O_3

STEP 2 Write each atom and its oxidation number as an equation that equals zero.
$Fe^{3+} + Fe^{3+} + O^{2-} + O^{2-} + O^{2-} = 0$

STEP 3 Write the oxidation numbers of each atom as an equation that equals zero.
$3 + 3 + (-2) + (-2) + (-2) = 0$

STEP 4 Make sure that the left side of the equation adds up to zero.
$6 + (-6) = 0$

162

Teaching Options

! FAST FACTS *The Big Idea Compounds*

Water Ancient philosophers thought that water was a basic element. This idea about water did not change until the end of the eighteenth century. At that time, a British chemist made water by igniting a mixture of hydrogen and air. Two years later, a French chemist proved that water was a compound made of hydrogen and oxygen rather than an element.

Iron(III) Oxide This compound (Fe_2O_3) is found in the mineral hematite, which is an important ore of iron. Hematite is also used in making abrasives and pigments.

Magnesium Nitride Because magnesium is a metal that burns easily, it is used in flash powder, incendiary bombs, and signal flares. When magnesium burns in air, the main product formed is magnesium oxide. Although oxygen is much more reactive than nitrogen, some nitrogen from the air reacts with magnesium, and magnesium nitride also forms.

Sulfur Dioxide Sulfur dioxide is a colorless, poisonous gas with an odor like that of rotten eggs. This gas forms when sulfur is burned in air. It is released in the air by the burning of fossil fuels, such as gas, petroleum, and coal. This gas is a major source of air pollution and is one cause of acid rain.

The formula for one molecule of water is H_2O. The element that gives electrons, hydrogen, is written first in the chemical formula. The subscript "2" written to the right of the hydrogen symbol indicates that there are two atoms of hydrogen in a molecule of water. If there is no number after a chemical symbol in a formula, it means that there is only one atom of that element. Because there is no number written to the right of the oxygen symbol, that means that there is only one atom of oxygen in a molecule of water.

Study the steps on writing chemical formulas in the examples below. Then, follow the directions in the Science Log to learn more about "the big idea."✦

WRITING ACTIVITY

Science Log

Look at the periodic table on pages 66 and 67. Group 2 elements have oxidation numbers of 2+. Group 16 elements have oxidation numbers of 2−. In your science log, write chemical formulas using an element from each group. Search the Internet to see if any of your chemical formulas are used to make products. Start your search at www.conceptsandchallenges.com.

Magnesium Nitride (Mg_3N_2)
Early photographers used magnesium flash powder to take pictures in low light before flashbulbs were invented. When magnesium and nitrogen combine, the compound magnesium nitride is formed.

STEP 1 Write the chemical formula.

Mg_3N_2

STEP 2 Write each atom and its oxidation number as an equation that equals zero.

$Mg^{2+} + Mg^{2+} + Mg^{2+} + N^{3-} + N^{3-} = 0$

STEP 3 Write the oxidation numbers of each atom as an equation that equals zero.

$2 + 2 + 2 + (-3) + (-3) = 0$

STEP 4 Make sure that the left side of the equation adds up to zero.

$6 + (-6) = 0$

Sulfur Dioxide (SO_2)
Sulfur dioxide is produced when coal containing sulfur is burned, such as in these coal-burning stacks. Sulfur burns in air forming sulfur dioxide.

STEP 1 Write the chemical formula.

SO_2

STEP 2 Write each atom and its oxidation number as an equation that equals zero.

$S^{4+} + O^{2-} + O^{2-} = 0$

STEP 3 Write the oxidation numbers of each atom as an equation that equals zero.

$4 + (-2) + (-2) = 0$

STEP 4 Make sure that the left side of the equation adds up to zero.

$4 + (-4) = 0$

3 Assess

Use the Writing Activity Rubric on the Teacher's Resources CD-ROM to assess students' Science Logs. Fill in the rubric with the additional information below. For this assignment, students should have:

- created chemical formulas using elements from Group 2 and Group 16, and balanced their chemical formulas so that the oxidation numbers add up to zero.
- indicated which of the formulas represent actual compounds that are used or manufactured.

4 Close

Chemical Formula Display Have students work on their chapter projects. Make sure that students' posterboards clearly show the steps in writing a chemical formula.

Tips for Using Technology

Searching the Internet Remind students that one important tool for finding information on the Internet is a search engine. A search engine allows the user to type in a keyword or phrase. The engine then searches thousands of sites on the Internet for those that contain the keyword or phrase. After a few seconds, the search engine returns many addresses for links related to the topic.

• TEACHING RESOURCES •

Teacher's Resources CD-ROM

Big Idea: Chapter 7, p. 10

Big Idea Planner: Study Tools, pp. 11–12

Big Idea Science Log Entry: Study Tools, p. 13

Writing Activity Rubric: Teaching Tools, p. 9

Challenges (pp. 164–166)

Chapter Summary

Review Before students begin the Challenges, review the summary with them. If time permits, give each pair of students one summary point to describe in their own words.

STUDY HINT Have students use the material on these pages to review the Key Terms. Have one student define a Key Term to another student who sketches or writes an example of the term.

Key Term Challenges

MATCHING

1. subscript (7-1)
2. valence electron (7-2)
3. binary compound (7-3)
4. diatomic molecule (7-5)
5. formula mass (7-6)
6. chemical formula (7-1)
7. polyatomic ion (7-4)
8. oxidation number (7-2)

FILL IN

9. subscript (7-1)
10. diatomic molecule (7-5)
11. valence electrons (7-2)
12. binary compound (7-3)
13. formula mass (7-6)
14. polyatomic ion (7-4)

Chapter Summary

Lesson 7-1
- Every element has its own chemical symbol.
- A **chemical formula** identifies the elements in a compound.
- The symbol for a metallic element is always written first in a chemical formula.

Lesson 7-2
- **Valence electrons** are the number of electrons in an atom's outermost energy level.
- Atoms that lose electrons have positive **oxidation numbers**.
- Atoms that gain electrons have negative oxidation numbers.

Lesson 7-3
- A **binary compound** contains atoms of two elements.
- An element can have more than one oxidation number.

Lesson 7-4
- A group of atoms that acts as a charged atom, or ion, when combining with other atoms is called a **polyatomic ion**.
- The atoms in a polyatomic ion are held together by covalent bonds.

Lesson 7-5
- A **diatomic molecule** contains only two atoms.
- Atoms in a diatomic molecule are usually held together by a covalent bond.

Lesson 7-6
- Each atom in a molecule or ion of an ionic compound has its own mass number.
- The sum of the mass numbers of all the atoms in a molecule or ion of an ionic compound is equal to the **formula mass** of the molecule.

Key Term Challenges

binary compound (p. 152)
chemical formula (p. 148)
diatomic molecule (p. 158)
formula mass (p. 160)
oxidation number (p. 150)
polyatomic ion (p. 154)
subscript (p. 148)
valence electron (p. 150)

MATCHING Write the Key Term from above that best matches each description.

1. number written to the lower right of a chemical symbol
2. electron in an atom's outermost energy level
3. compound containing two elements
4. molecule made up of only two atoms
5. sum of the mass numbers of all the atoms in a molecule
6. chemical symbols that identify the elements that make up a compound
7. group of atoms that acts as a charged atom, or ion, when combining with other atoms
8. 1− for an atom of chlorine

FILL IN Write the Key Term from above that best completes each statement.

9. The "2" in the formula H_2O is a _____.
10. A molecule of hydrogen gas is an example of a _____.
11. Chlorine has seven _____ in its outermost energy level.
12. Sodium chloride is an example of a _____.
13. The _____ of ethyl chloride is 64.
14. The ammonium ion is an example of a _____.

Teaching Options

PREPARING STUDENTS FOR STANDARDIZED TESTS

Reading Strategy: Tell students that, when taking multiple-choice tests, they should first eliminate items that they are certain are wrong. This strategy will help them narrow their choices.

Writing Strategy: Tell students to proofread their writing for mistakes in spelling, grammar, and organization. Remind them to use words that clearly signal steps in a process, such as *first*, *last*, *next*, and *finally*.

Interpreting Visuals: Remind students to look at graphic organizers for titles, captions, and other information that will help them interpret what is shown in the graphic organizer.

ESL/ELL STRATEGY

Definitions To help students learn new vocabulary words, have them write each unfamiliar term, such as *polyatomic ion*, on one side of an index card. Then, pair English-proficient students with English-language learners to write the definition for the unfamiliar term on the other side of the index card to use as flash cards to study for tests.

Content Challenges TEST PREP

MULTIPLE CHOICE Write the letter of the term or phrase that best completes each statement.

1. Scientists represent elements by using
   a. atomic numbers.
   b. subscripts.
   c. chemical symbols.
   d. words.

2. The compound NaOH contains the elements
   a. sodium and hydrogen.
   b. sodium and oxygen.
   c. oxygen and hydrogen.
   d. sodium, oxygen, and hydrogen.

3. The formula mass of neon is equal to its
   a. mass number.
   b. atomic number.
   c. atomic mass.
   d. oxidation number.

4. The oxidation numbers of the elements in a compound must add up to
   a. 8.
   b. 0.
   c. 1.
   d. 7.

5. The oxidation number of iron in iron (II) chloride is
   a. 2+.
   b. 2–.
   c. 3+.
   d. 0.

6. An example of a binary compound is
   a. NaOH.
   b. O_2.
   c. NaCl.
   d. Na.

7. A polyatomic ion always has
   a. no electrical charge.
   b. a positive charge.
   c. a negative charge.
   d. an electrical charge.

8. A common polyatomic ion with a positive charge is the
   a. nitrate ion.
   b. ammonium ion.
   c. sulfate ion.
   d. phosphate ion.

9. Of the following molecules, the one that is <u>not</u> a diatomic molecule is
   a. ozone.
   b. oxygen.
   c. hydrogen.
   d. iodine.

10. Diatomic molecules of nitrogen and oxygen are
    a. solids.
    b. liquids.
    c. gases.
    d. crystals.

TRUE/FALSE Write *true* if the statement is true. If the statement is false, change the underlined term to make the statement true.

11. A binary compound contains atoms of <u>two</u> elements.

12. The mass number of an atom is equal to the <u>atomic mass</u> rounded to the nearest whole number.

13. Chemical symbols are made up of one or two <u>numbers</u>.

14. The chemical formula of a compound tells you what <u>valences</u> the compound contains.

Content Challenges

MULTIPLE CHOICE

1. c (7-1)
2. d (7-1)
3. a (7-6)
4. b (7-2)
5. a (7-3)
6. c (7-3)
7. d (7-4)
8. b (7-4)
9. a (7-5)
10. c (7-5)

TRUE/FALSE

11. true (7-3)
12. true (7-6)
13. false; letters (7-1)
14. false; elements (7-1)

ALTERNATIVE ASSESSMENT

Relating Information Students may write a science log entry explaining how to write a chemical formula using the oxidation numbers for each of the elements in a compound. They could also compare and contrast polyatomic ions with diatomic molecules and write examples of each.

PORTFOLIO ASSESSMENT

Making Student Portfolios Students can demonstrate their comprehension of the concepts in this chapter by making a portfolio. Encourage students to select their own work for inclusion in their portfolios. The Flowchart, the Concept Map, and the Big Idea Science Log Entry are some of the reproducibles on the Teacher's Resources CD-ROM that they can include in their portfolios. You can use the Portfolio Assessment Rubric also found on the Teacher's Resources CD-ROM to assess students' portfolios.

Concept Challenges

WRITTEN RESPONSE

1. **HYPOTHESIZE:** Possible answer: The symbols and formulas are universal and can be understood by all scientists. (7-1)
2. **CALCULATE: a.** 40 **b.** 36 **c.** 143 **d.** 102 **e.** 84 (7-6)
3. **EXPLAIN:** The number of valence electrons an atom has determines its oxidation number. (7-2)
4. **HYPOTHESIZE:** Carbon is equally likely to gain or lose its four electrons. (7-2)

INTERPRETING A TABLE (7-1)

5. metallic: Na, Al, Ag; nonmetallic: Cl, S
6. metallic
7. 3+
8. Ag_2S; $AlCl_3$

Chapter Project Wrap-Up

CHEMICAL FORMULA DISPLAY

Allow each group to present its posterboard to the class. A designated speaker for each group can describe how the chemical formulas for the compounds that the group chose are written. You can use the Group Activity Rubric found on the Teacher's Resources CD-ROM to assess students' projects. Fill in the rubric with the additional information below. For this project, groups should have:

- shown the way to write the chemical formulas for three or four compounds in a format similar to that of the Big Idea.

- a logical, neat overall presentation.

Concept Challenges TEST PREP

WRITTEN RESPONSE Complete the exercises and answer each of the following questions in complete sentences.

1. **HYPOTHESIZE:** Why do you think chemical symbols and chemical formulas are an important part of communication among scientists?
2. **CALCULATE:** Find the formula mass for each of the following compounds.
   a. NaOH **b.** HCl **c.** AgCl **d.** Al_2O_3 **e.** $NaHCO_3$
3. **EXPLAIN:** What is the relationship between an atom's oxidation number and the number of valence electrons the atom has?
4. **HYPOTHESIZE:** Why do you think carbon can have an oxidation number of 4+ or 4–? (Hint: Carbon has four valence electrons.)

INTERPRETING A TABLE Use Figure 7-27 to answer each of the following questions.

5. What are the metallic elements listed in this table? What are the nonmetallic elements?
6. What kind of element is written first in the chemical formulas of the compounds?
7. What is the oxidation number of aluminum in aluminum chloride?
8. Which compound is made up of three atoms? Four atoms?

SOME COMPOUNDS MADE OF METALS AND NONMETALS			
Compound	Chemical formula	Metallic element	Nonmetallic element
Sodium chloride	NaCl	Na (Sodium)	Cl (Chlorine)
Aluminum chloride	$AlCl_3$	Al (Aluminum)	Cl (Chlorine)
Silver sulfide	Ag_2S	Ag (Silver)	S (Sulfur)

▲ Figure 7-27

Teaching Options

• TEACHING RESOURCES •

Teacher's Resources CD-ROM

Key Term Review: Chapter 7, p. 11

Chapter 7 Test: pp. 12–14

Flowchart: Study Tools, p. 6

Concept Map: Study Tools, p. 4

Big Idea Science Log Entry: Study Tools, p. 13

Portfolio Assessment Rubric: Teaching Tools, p. 10

Group Activity Rubric: Teaching Tools, p. 6

Chapter Self-Check: Teaching Tools, p. 11

PLANNING GUIDE

◆ **TEACHING THE CHAPTER** This chapter should take approximately 7–10 days to complete instruction and assessment.

	Skills and Features	Projects and Activities	Achieve Science Literacy	Meet Individual Needs
Chapter 8 Opener p. T167	DEMONSTRATE	• Chapter Project		
Lesson 8-1 What is a chemical reaction? pp. T168–T169 Standard: B1b	DESCRIBE, DEFINE, EXPLAIN • Building Math Skills • Hands-On Activity	• More on the Web • Lab Challenge	• Study Hint • Reading Strategy	• ESL/ELL Strategy • Reteach CD-ROM Enrichment Activity Concept Map Laboratory Video
Lab Activity Changing the Speed of a Chemical Reaction pp. T170–T171 Standards: B1b, B1c	OBSERVE, HYPOTHESIZE, ANALYZE • Set-Up Time: 15 min • Lab Time: 30 min	• Integrating the Sciences • Lab Skills Worksheet • Extend the Lab Activity	• Tips for Using Technology	CD-ROM Lab Activity Report Spreadsheet
Lesson 8-2 What is a chemical equation? pp. T172–T173 Standard: B1b	STATE, EXPLAIN, CALCULATE • Investigate • Building Science Skills	• Cooperative Learning • More on the Web	• Study Hint	• ESL/ELL Strategy • Reteach CD-ROM Enrichment Activity Flowchart
Lesson 8-3 What are oxidation and reduction? pp. T174–T175	CONTRAST, ANALYZE, DEFINE • Web InfoSearch • Science and Technology	• Extending the Lesson	• Study Hint • Reading Strategy • Ongoing Assessment	
Lesson 8-4 What is a synthesis reaction? pp. T176–T177 Standards: B1b, B1c	IDENTIFY, DEFINE, INFER • Real-Life Science • Interpreting Visuals	• Extending the Lesson • More on the Web • Cooperative Learning	• Study Hint • Ongoing Assessment	CD-ROM Writing Activity Outline
Lesson 8-5 What is a decomposition reaction? pp. T178–T179 Standard: B1b	INFER, ANALYZE, DEFINE • Designing an Experiment • Science and Technology	• More on the Web	• Study Hint • Ongoing Assessment	• Reteach CD-ROM Concept Map Designing an Experiment

Planning Guide continues on next page.

Standards: For details on the correlation to National Science Standards see pages *xx–xxi*.

	Skills and Features	Projects and Activities	Achieve Science Literacy	Meet Individual Needs
Lesson 8-6 **What is a single-replacement reaction?** pp. T180–T181 Standards: B1b, B1c	DEFINE, INFER, ANALYZE • Health and Safety Tip • Hands-On Activity	• Cooperative Learning • More on the Web • Lab Skills Worksheets	• Study Hint • Writing Hint	• Reteach CD-ROM Enrichment Activity
Lesson 8-7 **What is a double-replacement reaction?** pp. T182–T183 Standards: B1b, B1c	DEFINE, DESCRIBE, ANALYZE • Integrating Life Science	• Cooperative Learning • Extending the Lesson • More on the Web	• Study Hint	CD-ROM Enrichment Activity Laboratory Video
Big Idea **What are deep-sea vents?** pp. T184–T185 Standards: B1b, B1c	RESEARCH, COMMUNICATE, ANALYZE • Science Log: Writing Activity	• Big Idea Online • Close Activity	• Tips for Using Technology	CD-ROM Big Idea Planner
Chapter 8 Challenges pp. T186–T188	• Chapter Summary • Key Term Challenges • Content Challenges • Concept Challenges	• Chapter Project Wrap-Up	• Study Hint • Preparing Students for Standardized Tests	• ESL/ELL Strategy CD-ROM Chapter Self-Check Concept Map Flowchart

Teacher Notes

_____

_____

_____

_____

_____

_____

_____

_____

_____

_____

Chapter 8 Chemical Reactions

▲ Figure 8-1 Fireworks over the Statue of Liberty at night

The sky lights up in brilliant colors over the Statue of Liberty. Not only is this a celebration, it is an example of how chemical reactions can produce new substances. The colors produced by the burning of fireworks are evidence that new substances are forming. The color of the Statue of Liberty in daylight also indicates that a chemical reaction has taken place. The statue used to look like a shiny new penny. Now, after many years of exposure to gases in air and water, it has become a bluish green.

▶ What do the fireworks and the Statue of Liberty have in common?

Contents

Teaching Options

ASSESSMENT PLANNER

For assessment in the Student Edition, see the following pages:

Content Assessment
Checking Concepts: pp. 169, 173, 175, 177, 179, 181, 183
Thinking Critically: pp. 169, 173, 175, 177, 179, 181, 183
Interpreting Visuals: p. 177
Chapter Challenges: pp. 186–188

Alternative Assessment
Building Skills: pp. 169, 173
Web InfoSearch: p. 175
Science Log: p. 185

Performance-Based Assessment
Hands-On Activity: pp. 169, 181
Designing an Experiment: p. 179
Lab Activity: pp. 170–171

• TEACHING RESOURCES •

💿 **Teacher's Resources CD-ROM**
Lesson Review: Ch. 8, pp. 2, 4, 6, 7, 8, 9, 11
Enrichment: Ch. 8, pp. 3, 5, 10, 12
Key Term Review: Ch. 8, p. 14
Chapter 8 Test: pp. 15–17
Laboratory Manual: pp. 5–10, 13–14, 49–52

📼 **Laboratory Videos**
Segments 4, 8, 9

Chapter 8
Chemical Reactions

Chapter Overview

In this chapter, students will describe what happens in chemical reactions. They will write and balance chemical equations. Students will then compare and contrast oxidation and reduction reactions. Finally, they will classify chemical reactions.

About Figure 8-1 Fireworks are used for both entertaining and for signaling. Most fireworks are made by putting a mixture of chemicals in a paper case. The exact ingredients depend on what color is to be produced and how quickly the reaction is to occur. When the fireworks are lit, oxygen combines with the chemicals, and heat and light are produced by the reaction that occurs.

Answer They both show evidence of chemical reactions taking place.

Linking Prior Knowledge

For this chapter, students should recall:
- chemical changes (Lesson 1-5).
- the gain and loss of electrons (Lesson 4-5).
- how to write a chemical formula (Lesson 7-1).

Chapter Project

CHEMICAL REACTIONS DEMONSTRATION

MATERIALS: Materials will vary.

Have pairs of students choose an everyday chemical reaction, such as burning, rusting, cooking, electrochemical reactions in batteries, or the discoloring of an apple. Approve each reaction to ensure that it is a chemical reaction and that students can demonstrate it safely. At the end of the chapter, have students demonstrate and discuss their chosen reaction. Discussion could include whether the reaction is oxidation-reduction or not, the signs of chemical reaction that occur during the reaction, the type of reaction it is, and general reactants and products.
learning styles: tactile, visual

1 Introduce

📓 **STUDY HINT** Have students create word webs in their notebooks, centering on the phrase *chemical reaction*. As students read, they can add arms to their webs on which they record Key Terms with their definitions and other details about chemical reactions.

Linking Prior Knowledge Pose a scenario for students: An adult in your family placed twigs in a fireplace and lit them with a match. Ask: *What happened to the twigs?* (The twigs caught fire and burned into ashes.) Point out that the burning of the twigs is a chemical change (Lesson 1-5).

2 Teach

Discussion Help students understand the differences between a physical change and a chemical change. Light a match, and then tear up a piece of paper. Ask students to identify the physical change (tearing up the piece of paper) and the chemical change (burning of the match). Ask students which type of change results in a new substance. (the chemical change) Define a chemical reaction as a process by which new substances are formed.
learning styles: auditory, visual

📖 **READING STRATEGY** Tell students that text features can help them better understand what they are reading. Point out the subheads and let students know that subheads can provide a preview of the section content and help them formulate questions they want to answer as they read. The boldface words signify new vocabulary terms. Students can look for context clues surrounding the boldface words to understand the words' meanings.

Answers to questions

▶ **DESCRIBE:** New substances with new physical and chemical properties are formed.

▶ **DEFINE:** a substance that is changed in a chemical reaction

---

8-1 What is a chemical reaction?

Objective
Describe what happens in a chemical reaction.

Key Terms
chemical reaction: process in which new substances with new chemical and physical properties are formed
reactant: substance that is changed in a chemical reaction
product: substance that is formed in a chemical reaction
law of conservation of matter: law that states that matter cannot be created or destroyed by a chemical change

Chemical Reactions New substances are formed as a result of a chemical change. During a chemical change, chemical bonds are formed or broken. The process by which a chemical change takes place is called a chemical reaction. In a **chemical reaction,** new substances with new chemical and physical properties are formed.

Chemical reactions are taking place around you all the time. If you have noticed rust that has formed on an iron fence, then you have seen the results of a chemical reaction. The iron in the fence has combined with the oxygen in air to form a new substance—rust. Figure 8-2 lists some signs that a chemical reaction has taken place.

SOME SIGNS OF A CHEMICAL REACTION	
Evidence	**Example**
Production of a gas	Carbon dioxide is produced when a log burns.
A change in color	When iron combines with oxygen, it changes to a reddish color.
A change in energy	When fuel burns, a large amount of energy is released.

▲ Figure 8-2

▶ **DESCRIBE:** What always happens in a chemical reaction?

168

Reactants and Products In any chemical reaction, certain substances are present at the start of the reaction and different substances are present at the end of the reaction. A substance that is present at the start of a chemical reaction is called a reactant. A **reactant** is a substance that is changed in a chemical reaction. A substance that is present at the end of a chemical reaction is called a product. A **product** is a substance that is formed as a result of a chemical reaction.

▶ **DEFINE:** What is a reactant?

Conservation of Matter When a log burns, a chemical reaction takes place. The wood burns away and ashes are left. What has happened? Has matter really disappeared? Can matter be lost during a chemical reaction? The answer is no. In addition to ashes, water vapor and carbon dioxide are also produced when a log burns. If you could add the masses of each of these products, you would find that their total mass equals the mass of the original log. This example illustrates an important scientific law called the **law of conservation of matter.** This law states that matter cannot be created or destroyed by a chemical change. In a chemical reaction, the amount of matter present in the products must always equal the amount of matter present in the reactants.

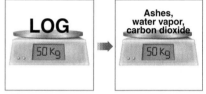

▲ Figure 8-3 In a chemical reaction, the amount of mass never changes.

▶ **STATE:** What is the law of conservation of matter?

Teaching Options

RETEACH

Describing Chemical Reactions
Name various processes, some of which are chemical reactions. Ask students to give a thumbs up when you name a chemical reaction. Call on volunteers to explain their responses. Chemical reactions to name may include rusting, the burning of gasoline in a car engine, baking bread batter in an oven, and digestion. Nonreactions may include painting a wall, an earthquake, mixing raisins and nuts to make trail mix, and blowing up a balloon. **learning style: auditory**

ESL/ELL STRATEGY

Illustrating Conservation of Mass
To help English-language learners understand the concept presented in Figure 8-3, have them draw a before and after illustration of a log burning and the ashes and smoke left after the log has completely burned. Have students write a brief caption for their illustrations.

Changing the Speed of a Chemical Reaction

Some chemical reactions occur very fast and some chemical reactions occur very slowly. A dynamite explosion takes place very quickly. The formation of rust takes place more slowly. By changing certain factors, the speed of some chemical reactions can also be changed.

To speed up a chemical reaction, the particles of the reactants need to come together more often. Increasing the temperature, increasing the surface area of the reactants, and adding certain kinds of catalysts (KAT-uh-lihsts) are ways to speed up some reactions. A catalyst is a chemical that changes the rate of a reaction without itself being changed.

To slow down chemical reactions, the particles of the reactants need to be brought together less often. Lowering the temperature, decreasing the surface area, and adding catalysts that slow down a reaction are some ways to decrease the speed of some chemical reactions.

4 ▶ DEFINE: What is a catalyst?

Hands-On Activity

OBSERVING A CHEMICAL REACTION

You will need safety goggles, an apron, plastic gloves, a balloon, a funnel, water, paper towels, a narrow-necked bottle, vinegar, baking soda, and a teaspoon.

1. Put on an apron, safety goggles, and plastic gloves. Stretch out the balloon by inflating and deflating it a few times.
2. Insert the narrow end of a funnel into the opening of the deflated balloon. Pour two teaspoonfuls of baking soda into the funnel so that the baking soda settles to the bottom of the balloon. Remove the funnel from the balloon.
3. Rinse the funnel with water and dry it with a paper towel. Insert the narrow end into the narrow-necked bottle. Pour six spoonfuls of vinegar into the funnel.
4. Carefully stretch the opening of the balloon over the neck of the bottle, making sure that the baking soda does not fall out of the balloon.
5. Lift the balloon so that the baking soda falls into the bottle. Observe what happens as the baking soda combines with the vinegar.

▲ **STEP 4** Stretch the balloon over the neck of the bottle.

Practicing Your Skills

6. **DESCRIBE:** What signs are there that a chemical change has taken place?
7. **HYPOTHESIZE:** What happened inside of the bottle?

CHAPTER 8: Chemical Reactions **169**

---

3 ▶ STATE: Matter cannot be created or destroyed by a chemical change.

4 ▶ DEFINE: a chemical that changes the rate of a reaction without itself being changed

3 Assess

✓ CHECKING CONCEPTS ANSWERS

1. reactant
2. destroyed
3. chemical reaction
4. increase

💡 THINKING CRITICALLY ANSWER

5. **EXPLAIN:** Rust has different chemical and physical properties than iron.

4 Close

BUILDING MATH SKILLS ANSWER

Calculating Matter is conserved, so the mass of the product is 48 kg + 6 kg, or 54 kg.

Hands-On Activity

OBSERVING A CHEMICAL REACTION

TIME: 10–15 minutes

PURPOSE: observing, describing, hypothesizing

SAFETY TIP: Caution students to be sure that the balloons are firmly on the bottles before combining the baking soda and vinegar. Be sure that they wear safety goggles the entire time the reaction is taking place.

COOPERATIVE LEARNING: Place students in small groups. Be sure that different students prepare the balloon, prepare the bottle, and assemble the balloon and bottle.

ADVANCE PLANNING: Demonstrate each of the steps for students so that they understand how to put the balloon on the bottle without letting baking soda drop out of the balloon.

Practicing Your Skills Answers

6. **DESCRIBE:** A gas is released, as seen when the balloon expands. The mixture fizzes with bubbles on the surface.
7. **HYPOTHESIZE:** As the chemicals in the mixture reacted, they formed a gas that made the balloon expand.

• TEACHING RESOURCES •

◉ **Teacher's Resources CD-ROM**
Lesson Review: Chapter 8, p. 2
Enrichment: Chapter 8, p. 3
Concept Map: Study Tools, p. 4
Laboratory Manual
Lab. Challenge: What is the law of conservation of matter? pp. 49–52

📼 **Laboratory Video**
Segment 8: Observing a Chemical Reaction

Lab Activity

(pp. 170–171)

1 Prepare the Lab

Changing the Speed of a Chemical Reaction

SET-UP TIME: ⏱ **LAB TIME:** ⏱

BACKGROUND: The speed of a reaction depends on how many reactant particles come in contact with each other over a period of time. A large surface area increases the number of particles available for direct contact. Higher temperatures increase the speed of the particles, increasing the number of collisions. Both factors can cause a chemical reaction to proceed more quickly.

PURPOSE: Students will observe the effects of surface area and temperature on the chemical reaction between an effervescent antacid tablet and water.

SCIENCE SKILLS: Students will **observe** and **collect data** on this experiment and **communicate** their findings in written from. They will use this experiment to **analyze** and **infer** the effects of surface area and temperature on the speed of a reaction.

ADVANCE PLANNING: Gather materials you will need for the lab. If you do not have running water in your classroom, bring hot water (not boiling) in a thermos bottle and cold water in plastic milk bottles. Have an empty bucket on hand for collecting antacid-water mixtures after the experiment.

2 Guide the Lab

PROCEDURE: Divide students into groups of two or three. Discuss the procedure. Emphasize to students that they should stop the timing when the bubbling or foaming stops. Discuss collection and reporting of data. Have students make their data charts before starting the experiment. Provide students with a copy of the Lab Activity Report found on the Teacher's Resources CD-ROM to record their observations and conclusions.

TROUBLESHOOTING: Be sure that there is at least a 20°C (68°F) difference between the hot water and the room-temperature water, and between the room-temperature water and the cold water.

LAB ACTIVITY
Changing the Speed of a Chemical Reaction

BACKGROUND

All chemical reactions are affected by the physical conditions and the environment in which they occur. For example, a campfire is easier to start with small twigs and branches rather than with a large log. Also, food lasts longer in warm weather if it is stored in an ice-cold cooler. Surface area, in the case of the wood for the fire, and temperature, in the case of the food, play a role in the speed of a chemical reaction.

PURPOSE

In this activity, you will be comparing the speed of chemical reactions by changing the surface area and the temperature of the reactants.

PROCEDURE

1. Copy the chart shown in Figure 8-4.

2. Put on safety goggles and an apron.

3. With a marking pen, label two plastic foam cups *Ice,* two plastic foam cups *Room,* and two plastic foam cups *Hot.*

4. Put on plastic gloves. Place one antacid tablet into each of the three small plastic bags. Carefully break each tablet into three or four pieces.

5. Measure the temperature of the ice water. Record the temperature on your chart.

Materials
Safety goggles,
Apron, plastic gloves,
6 plastic foam cups,
6 antacid tablets,
Room-temperature
water, ice water,
Hot water, thermometer,
Stopwatch,
3 small plastic bags,
Marking pen

▲ **STEP 3** Label the plastic foam cups.

▲ **STEP 4** Carefully break each antacid tablet.

170

Teaching Options

◈ INTEGRATING THE SCIENCES

Catalysts are also factors that can increase the rate of chemical reactions.

Biology Enzymes are catalysts that regulate the speed of many chemical reactions in organisms. In animals, certain enzymes help to convert food into substances required for tissue-building and cellular replacement. The energy released in other chemical reactions is used to make the heart beat, the lungs expand and contract, and the limbs move.

Technology Platinum can act as a catalyst in the reaction of carbon monoxide (CO) with oxygen (O_2) to form carbon dioxide (CO_2). This reaction is promoted in catalytic converters to eliminate carbon monoxide from exhaust gases. The catalytic converter provides a platinum surface on which the reaction can take place. The platinum surface attracts O_2 molecules and weakens the bond between the two oxygen atoms, allowing carbon monoxide to break the bond more easily and react with the oxygen to produce carbon dioxide.

6. Half-fill both cups labeled *Ice* with the ice water. At the same time, drop one whole antacid tablet into one of the cups and in the other cup, empty one of the plastic bags containing broken pieces of an antacid tablet. Record the time it takes for each tablet to completely dissolve.

7. Repeat Steps 5 and 6 using hot water and room-temperature water.
   ⚠ CAUTION: Hot water can burn. Allow your teacher to pour the water into your cup.

▲ STEP 6 Drop a whole antacid tablet into one cup and pieces of a broken antacid tablet into the other cup.

Changing the Speed of a Chemical Reaction

	Temperature	Time of Reaction with Whole Tablet	Time of Reaction with Tablet Pieces
Cups marked Ice			
Cups marked Hot			
Cups marked Room			

▲ **Figure 8-4** Copy this chart onto a sheet of paper. Enter your observations from your experiment.

CONCLUSIONS

1. **OBSERVE:** In which cup did the chemical reaction take place the fastest? In which cup did the chemical reaction take place the slowest?

2. **HYPOTHESIZE:** What does the effect of surface area have on the speed of a chemical reaction? What does the effect of temperature have on the speed of a chemical reaction? Explain your hypothesis using the results of your experiment.

3. **ANALYZE:** Which do you think will mix in a cup of hot tea faster, a lump of sugar or a teaspoon of sugar?

Tips for Using Technology

Spreadsheets Have students use spreadsheet software to record the results of their experiments. Spreadsheets are tables that display data such as numbers, text, dates, or a combination of all three. Students can make their data look special by using spreadsheets, doing math to analyze numerical data, and making graphs and charts to present data in a colorful way. Students can use spreadsheet software to present their data to the class. Have students use the Spreadsheet on the Teacher's Resources CD-ROM to plan their spreadsheets.

• TEACHING RESOURCES •

🔘 **Teacher's Resources CD-ROM**
Lab Activity Report: Study Tools, pp. 16–17

Laboratory Activity Rubric: Teaching Tools, p. 8

Spreadsheet: Study Tools, p. 23

Laboratory Manual
Lab. Skills Worksheet 4: Organizing and Analyzing Data, pp. 13–14

SAFETY TIP: Caution students on handling the hot water. Students should wear lab aprons to protect themselves from spills. Caution students against eating or drinking anything in a laboratory setting.

EXPECTED OUTCOME: The reaction with the broken tablet and hot water should be fastest. The reaction with the whole tablet and cold water should be slowest.

3 Conclude the Lab

1. **OBSERVE:** The fastest reaction occurred in the cup with the broken tablet in hot water. The slowest reaction occurred in the cup with the whole tablet in cold water.

2. **HYPOTHESIZE:** A large surface area increases the speed of a chemical reaction. A higher temperature increases the speed of a chemical reaction. The broken tablet in hot water produced the fastest reaction. Breaking the tablet increased its surface area.

3. **ANALYZE:** a teaspoon of sugar

Use the Laboratory Activity Rubric on the Teacher's Resources CD-ROM to assess students' lab activities. Fill in the rubric with the additional information below. For this activity, students should have:

- performed the activity according to the procedure and filled in the chart with data collected during the activity.

- correctly answered the questions in complete sentences.

4 Extend the Lab

Have students provide everyday examples in which increased surface area or increased temperature increases the rate of a reaction. Examples include using granulated or powdered materials for cooking and increasing the temperature of a stove burner or oven to increase the rate of cooking. Have students provide other examples in which decreased surface area or decreased temperature decreases the rate of a reaction. An example of decreasing surface area is painting an iron railing to decrease the surface exposed to oxygen in the air. Keeping batteries and film in a refrigerator makes them last longer because the chemical reactions that change them are slowed down.

1 Introduce

INVESTIGATE

TIME: 10–15 minutes

PURPOSE: Students will make models that illustrate the law of conservation of mass.

MATERIALS: connecting cubes (or other materials that will connect to make models of molecules, such as toothpicks, sugar cubes, and gumdrops), paper, pencil

PROCEDURE: Have students work in pairs. Remind them that they should use all of the materials they were given to build their models. Compare the building materials in the models to atoms in molecules.

THINK ABOUT IT: The models have the same number of atoms. The models show that the atoms can be rearranged, but mass is conserved because all of the pieces are still there.
learning styles: visual, tactile

🖊 **STUDY HINT** As students read the steps for balancing a chemical equation, have them draw a flowchart or write a numbered list to record those steps. Students can use the Flowchart found on the Teacher's Resources CD-ROM to guide them as they balance chemical equations.

Linking Prior Knowledge Ask students to recall what subscripts in chemical formulas mean (Lesson 7-1). Write a few chemical formulas on the board and prompt students to read them.

2 Teach

Discussion On the board, write in words the chemical reaction for photosynthesis: six molecules of carbon dioxide and six molecules of water yields one molecule of sugar and six molecules of oxygen. Then, write the chemical equation for photosynthesis below its word description:

$$6CO_2 + 6H_2O \rightarrow C_6H_{12}O_6 + 6O_2$$

Discuss the use of chemical equations. Elicit from students that a chemical equation is easier to interpret than the longer statement. Tell students that chemical equations contain universal symbols that all chemists can understand. **learning styles: visual, auditory**

8-2 What is a chemical equation?

INVESTIGATE

Modeling Conservation of Mass
HANDS-ON ACTIVITY

1. Obtain connecting cubes from your teacher. Connect the cubes to form models of two "molecules." Make a drawing of your models on a sheet of paper.
2. Take apart your models and create two new ones. Next to your first drawing, make a drawing of the new models.

THINK ABOUT IT: Look at your drawings. What do you notice is similar about all of your models? How do your models show the law of conservation of mass?

STEP 1

Objectives
Explain how a chemical equation describes a chemical reaction. Write balanced chemical equations.

Key Terms
chemical equation: statement in which chemical formulas are used to describe a chemical reaction
coefficient (koh-uh-FIHSH-uhnt): number that shows how many molecules of a substance are involved in a chemical reaction

Chemical Equations Scientists use a special "language" to describe chemical reactions. They use chemical equations. A **chemical equation** is a statement in which chemical symbols and chemical formulas are used to describe a chemical reaction. It tells you what substances are the reactants and what substances are the products in a chemical reaction.

▶ **DEFINE:** What is a chemical equation?

Writing Chemical Equations To write a chemical equation, first write the correct symbols or formulas for the reactants and the products. The chemical formulas for the reactants are always written on the left side of a chemical equation followed by an arrow. The arrow indicates what substances are formed. It is like an equal sign and is read as "yields." The chemical formulas for the

172

products are written to the right of the arrow. When there are two or more reactants or two or more products, a plus sign (+) is placed between the chemical formulas of the different substances.

The following chemical equation shows the reaction between two reactants that produce one product.

$$\underset{\text{reactant}}{2Na} + \underset{\text{reactant}}{Cl_2} \rightarrow \underset{\text{product}}{2NaCl}$$

Read the equation as the reaction of "sodium and chlorine yields sodium chloride."

The production of water and oxygen from hydrogen peroxide (H_2O_2) is an example of a reaction in which one reactant yields two products.

$$\underset{\text{reactant}}{2H_2O_2} \rightarrow \underset{\text{product}}{2H_2O} + \underset{\text{product}}{O_2}$$

The formation of tarnish (Ag_2S) on silver is an example of a chemical reaction in which three reactants yield two products.

$$4Ag + 2H_2S + O_2 \rightarrow 2Ag_2S + 2H_2O$$

▶ **EXPLAIN:** In a chemical equation, where are the chemical formulas for the products written?

Teaching Options

RETEACH

Balancing Equations Write the following equation on the board, which represents the production of water and oxygen from hydrogen peroxide: $2H_2O_2 \rightarrow 2H_2O + O_2$. Cut circles from paper to represent the atoms. Show that on the left side of the equation there are four hydrogen atoms and four oxygen atoms. On the right side, there are also four of each atom. Allow students to manipulate atoms in other chemical equations, such as the formation of tarnish on silver (Ag_2S) and the formation of salt ($NaCl_2$), to reinforce the concept.
learning styles: visual, tactile

COOPERATIVE LEARNING

Balancing Equations Write a variety of simple unbalanced equations on separate index cards. Place all the index cards in a bag. Then, have small groups of students choose a card and work together to balance the equation on that card. Groups should explain the process they used to balance the equations.
learning styles: visual, interpersonal

Balanced Chemical Equations A chemical equation shows the atoms and molecules that are involved in a chemical reaction. Recall that matter cannot be created or destroyed during a chemical reaction. So, in a chemical equation the total number of atoms of each element must be the same on both sides of the equation. When the number of atoms of each element is the same on both sides of the equation, the equation is said to be balanced.

To balance a chemical equation, you place numbers called coefficients in front of chemical formulas. A **coefficient** is a number that shows how many molecules or atoms of a substance are involved in a chemical reaction. Look at the reaction between sodium (Na) and chlorine (Cl_2). If the equation were written with just the formulas for the reactants and the products, it would read as follows:

$$Na + Cl_2 \longrightarrow NaCl$$

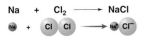

There are two chlorine atoms on the left side of the equation and only one chlorine atom on the right side. Write a 2 before the product:

$$Na + Cl_2 \longrightarrow 2NaCl$$

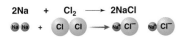

Now the chlorine atoms are balanced, but the sodium atoms are not. Write another 2 on the left side of the equation before the Na:

$$2Na + Cl_2 \longrightarrow 2NaCl$$

Now the equation is balanced.

3 DEFINE: What is a coefficient?

---

1. A chemical equation describes a _____.
2. The arrow in a chemical equation means _____.
3. A plus sign (+) in a chemical equation means _____.
4. The reactants in a chemical equation are written on the _____ side of the equation.
5. A balanced chemical equation must show the same number of _____ of each element on both sides of the equation.
6. The reaction of hydrogen peroxide is an example of a reaction in which one reactant yields _____.
7. A _____ shows how many molecules or atoms of a substance are involved in a chemical reaction.

THINKING CRITICALLY

8. ANALYZE: Count the atoms. Which of the following equations are balanced?
   a. $H_2O_2 \rightarrow H_2O + O_2$
   b. $CO + O_2 \rightarrow CO_2$
   c. $Si + O_2 \rightarrow SiO_2$
   d. $2KClO_3 \rightarrow 2KCl + 3O_2$
   e. $N_2 + H_2 \rightarrow NH_3$
9. CALCULATE: Write balanced equations for the unbalanced equations in exercise 8.
10. INFER: When there is no number in front of a chemical formula in a chemical equation, what number is understood?
11. EXPLAIN: How do you read the following equation?
    $$Fe + 2S \rightarrow FeS_2$$

BUILDING SCIENCE SKILLS

Stating the Problem The following equations are not balanced correctly. What errors were made?
   a. $Cl_2 + NaBr \rightarrow Br_2 + NaCl$
      $2Cl + 2NaBr \rightarrow 2Br + 2NaCl$
   b. $Mg + O_2 \rightarrow MgO$
      $Mg + O \rightarrow MgO$
   c. $Na + O_2 \rightarrow Na_2O$
      $2Na + 2O_2 \rightarrow 2Na_2O$

Answers to questions

1 DEFINE: a statement in which chemical formulas are used to describe a chemical reaction

2 EXPLAIN: to the right of the arrow

3 DEFINE: a number that shows how many molecules or atoms of a substance are involved in a chemical reaction

Reinforcement To help students understand chemical equations, you may wish to compare chemical equations with addition problems. Relate the reactants to the addends, the arrow to the equal sign, and the products to the sum. If students have difficulty balancing chemical equations, demonstrate how to randomly use different coefficients until the equations are balanced. Use unbalanced equations such as the following to reinforce the concept:

Not balanced: $C + Br_2 \rightarrow CBr_4$
balanced: $C + 2Br_2 \rightarrow CBr_4$

3 Assess

✔ CHECKING CONCEPTS ANSWERS

1. chemical reaction
2. yields
3. and
4. left
5. atoms
6. two products
7. coefficient

THINKING CRITICALLY ANSWERS

8. ANALYZE: c
9. CALCULATE: $2H_2O_2 \rightarrow 2H_2O + O_2$;
   $2CO + O_2 \rightarrow 2CO_2$;
   $2KClO_3 \rightarrow 2KCl + 3O_2$;
   $N_2 + 3H_2 \rightarrow 2NH_3$
10. INFER: one
11. EXPLAIN: Possible answer: One iron atom and two sulfur atoms yield one molecule of iron sulfide.

4 Close

BUILDING SCIENCE SKILLS ANSWERS

Stating the Problem
   a. The subscripts of Cl and Br were changed into coefficients.
   b. The subscript was removed from O_2.
   c. The subscripts were ignored in balancing the equation.

MORE ON THE WEB

Making Balancing a Sna
Have students use the Int
to learn how to balance
chemical equations. Then
students take an online q
review. Have them visit
www.conceptsandchallen
for more details.

ESL/ELL STRATEGY

Reading Chemical Equat
an English-language lea
an English-proficient student to
practice reading the equations in
this lesson.

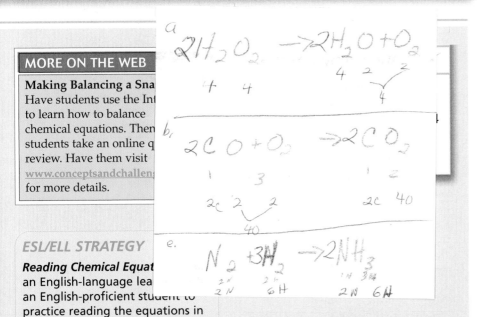

1 Introduce

✏ **STUDY HINT** Read the Key Terms aloud and have students repeat them. Then, ask students to list the two terms as column heads in their notebooks. As they read, they can take notes about each process.

Linking Prior Knowledge Ask students to explain how electrons are lost and gained in some chemical reactions (Lesson 4-5).

2 Teach

Discussion Students may be confused by the definition of the term *reduction* because the terms *reduce* and *gain* are usually thought of as opposites. Associate the term *reduction* with the negative charge of an electron to help students better understand its scientific meaning. Using a number line to add a negative number will help students see the effect.
learning styles: visual, logical/mathematical

Demonstration Demonstrate the oxidation of iron. Use a pair of tongs to hold a piece of steel wool over a flame. Have students observe the new substance, iron(III) oxide, formed by this chemical reaction. Then, describe redox reactions, using the formation of iron oxide as an example. Tell students that iron is oxidized by losing electrons, and oxygen is reduced by gaining electrons. **learning styles: visual, auditory**

Answers to questions

▶ **CONTRAST:** In oxidation, electrons are lost. In reduction, electrons are gained.

▶ **ANALYZE:** redox reactions

▶ **DEFINE:** a chemical change in which electrons are lost, or a chemical reaction in which a substance combines chemically with oxygen

📖 **READING STRATEGY** Remind students that comparing means telling how two things are alike, and contrasting means telling how they are different. Encourage students to compare and contrast oxidation and reduction as they read.

8-3 What are oxidation and reduction?

Objective
Compare oxidation and reduction reactions.

Key Terms
oxidation (ahk-sih-DAY-shuhn): chemical change in which electrons are lost

reduction (rih-DUK-shuhn): chemical change in which electrons are gained

Oxidation and Reduction When different substances (elements and compounds) react chemically, electrons are transferred or shared among the atoms that make up those substances. Some atoms gain electrons in the reaction. Other atoms lose electrons. When the atoms of an element lose electrons, the reaction is called oxidation. **Oxidation** is any chemical change in which electrons are lost. When the atoms of an element gain electrons, the reaction is called reduction. **Reduction** is any chemical change in which electrons are gained.

▶ **CONTRAST:** What is the difference between oxidation and reduction?

Redox Reactions Oxidation and reduction always take place together. The electrons lost by one element are gained by another element. Reactions involving oxidation and reduction are often referred to as "redox" reactions. In redox reactions, some elements are oxidized (lose electrons), and other elements are reduced (gain electrons).

The chemical reaction between sodium and chlorine is an example of an oxidation and reduction reaction. The chemical equation for this reaction is as follows:

$$2Na + Cl_2 \rightarrow 2NaCl$$

Each sodium atom loses an electron and is oxidized. Each chlorine atom gains an electron and is reduced.

174

The combination of hydrogen and chlorine forms a strong substance called hydrochloric acid. This is another example of a reaction involving oxidation and reduction. Each hydrogen atom loses an electron and is oxidized. Each chlorine atom gains an electron and is reduced.

$$H_2 + Cl_2 \rightarrow 2HCl$$

▶ **ANALYZE:** What are reactions that involve oxidation and reduction often called?

Combining with Oxygen The most familiar kind of oxidation and reduction reactions involve oxygen. The formation of rust is an example of a reaction in which an element combines with oxygen. The chemical equation for the production of iron oxide (rust) is as follows:

$$4Fe + 3O_2 \rightarrow 2Fe_2O_3$$

Each iron atom loses three electrons and is oxidized. Each oxygen atom gains two electrons and is reduced. When a substance combines chemically with oxygen, the chemical reaction is also called oxidation. Other examples of this type of oxidation reaction include the burning of a match and the burning of fireworks.

▲ **Figure 8-5** The burning of fireworks is an example of oxidation.

▶ **DEFINE:** What is oxidation?

Teaching Options

❗ **FAST FACTS** *The Statue of Liberty*

The Statue of Liberty's formal name is "Liberty Enlightening the World." The statue, which is 46 m (about 152 ft) high, depicts a woman escaping the chains of tyranny, which lie at her feet. The burning torch in her right hand symbolizes liberty, while her left hand holds a tablet with the date "July 4, 1776," the date that the United States declared its independence from Great Britain. The seven rays on the statue's crown stand for the seven seas and continents. The surface of the statue is made of hammered copper sheets. These sheets are 2.4 mm (0.09 in.) thick and are riveted to a framework made of iron. A French engineer, Gustave Alexandre Eiffel, designed the iron framework. (He also designed the Eiffel Tower in Paris.) The rehabilitation of the statue was done in preparation for the centennial of the statue in 1986. A French-American team repaired the statue, cleaned the surface, and replaced the glass and metal torch with a torch covered in gold leaf.

✓ CHECKING CONCEPTS

1. When rust forms, iron chemically combines with _____.
2. In an oxidation reaction, electrons are _____.
3. In a reduction reaction, electrons are _____.
4. Oxidation and _____ reactions always occur together.
5. When a substance combines chemically with oxygen, the chemical reaction is also called _____.
6. The burning of a match and the burning of fireworks are examples of _____.

💡 THINKING CRITICALLY

7. ANALYZE: Why must oxidation and reduction always happen together in a chemical reaction?
8. HYPOTHESIZE: Is oxygen always needed in order for an oxidation reaction to occur? Explain your answer.

Web InfoSearch

Reactions and Energy Some chemical reactions give off energy. This energy may be in the form of heat, light, or mechanical energy. Reactions that give off energy are called exothermic (ehk-soh-THUR-mihk) reactions. Other chemical reactions absorb energy. They need a steady supply of energy in order to take place. Reactions that absorb energy are called endothermic (ehn-doh-THUR-mihk) reactions.

SEARCH: What kinds of chemical reactions are endothermic or exothermic? Use the Internet to find out. Start your search at www.conceptsandchallenges.com. Some key search words are **chemical reaction, exothermic,** and **endothermic.**

⚛ Science and Technology

COPPER OXIDATION

Copper is used for pipes, electrical wires, and other building materials. You may have seen buildings with copper roofs. When they are first built, these roofs look like shiny new pennies. As the roofs are exposed to gases in air and water, an oxidation reaction takes place that changes the color of the copper. First, the copper changes from pink to brown, then to black. Finally, the copper is coated with a blue-green material called a patina (puh-TEE-nuh). The patina is made of copper sulfate, a compound of copper and sulfur. Once copper has a patina, air cannot touch the surface and corrosion stops. The copper may last for hundreds of years.

Because it resists corrosion, copper was used as the covering, or skin, on the Statue of Liberty. The Statue of Liberty has been exposed to air, water, and other forms of weathering for more than one hundred years. In 1986, the Statue of Liberty was restored. Because of its patina, very little of the statue's skin needed to be replaced. This copper skin will continue to protect the Statue of Liberty for another hundred years.

Thinking Critically Why do you think copper is a good material to use to make pipes?

▲ **Figure 8-6** Statue of Liberty

---

3 Assess

✓ CHECKING CONCEPTS ANSWERS

1. oxygen
2. lost
3. gained
4. reduction
5. oxidation
6. oxidation

💡 THINKING CRITICALLY ANSWERS

7. ANALYZE: Electrons must have a source, and there must be some place for them to go. Electrons lost by one reactant must be gained by another.
8. HYPOTHESIZE: No; Oxidation occurs whenever reactants lose electrons.

4 Close

Web InfoSearch

Reactions and Energy Have students find out what kinds of chemical reactions are endothermic reactions and what kinds are exothermic reactions. Students should begin their search at www.conceptsandchallenges.com.

Science and Technology

COPPER OXIDATION

Real-Life Connection Copper's resistance to corrosion makes copper a good material for many common products. A primary use of copper is as electrical wire in homes, businesses, automobiles, electrical equipment, and electric motors. Another important use is for pipes for indoor plumbing and natural gas lines. Pianos rely on copper to provide their musical tones. Brass musical instruments contain about 70–75 percent copper.

Thinking Critically Answer
It resists corrosion.

EXTENDING THE LESSON

Drawing Electron Dot Models Have students draw electron dot models showing the redox reactions between sodium and chlorine, hydrogen and chlorine, and iron and oxygen. Tell students to label the reactants and products in each of their models. Have them explain their models to the rest of the class.
learning style: visual

• TEACHING RESOURCES •

Teacher's Resources CD-ROM
Lesson Review: Chapter 8, p. 6

ONGOING ASSESSMENT

Losing and Gaining Electrons Tell students that, in the formation of table salt, sodium atoms lose electrons to chlorine atoms. Ask: *Which element is oxidized?* (sodium) *Which element is reduced?* (chlorine)

1 Introduce

STUDY HINT Write the title of each section on the board. Have students copy these titles in their notebooks to use as main topics in outlines. As students read each section, they should write notes that support or explain each of the main topics. Encourage them to include definitions and diagrams. Students can use the Writing Activity Outline reproducible found on the Teacher's Resources CD-ROM.

Linking Prior Knowledge Ask students to recall what happens in a chemical change (Lesson 1-5). To represent a chemical change, write a simple chemical equation on the board. Ask students to identify the reactants and the products.

2 Teach

Discussion Introduce the lesson by reviewing the reaction between iron and oxygen. Point out that during the reaction, two elements combine to produce a new substance, the compound iron (III) oxide. Tell students that many reactions involving the oxidation of metals are synthesis reactions. Develop the understanding that in a synthesis reaction, two or more simple substances combine, to form, or synthesize, a more complex substance.
learning style: auditory

Demonstration Using building blocks, gumdrops, and toothpicks, or some other simple materials, make models to demonstrate a synthesis reaction such as one of the reactions shown in Figure 8-7. Students will notice that the number of atoms in the reactants and products is the same, and that a product is formed with properties different from those of the reactants. Allow students to use the models to represent the remaining reactions in Figure 8-7. **learning styles: visual, tactile**

Answers to questions

1▶ DEFINE: a reaction in which two or more substances combine to form a more complex substance

2▶ INFER: iron and sulfur

8-4 What is a synthesis reaction?

Objective
Describe what happens in a synthesis reaction.

Key Term
synthesis (SIHN-thuh-sihs) **reaction:** reaction in which substances combine to form a more complex substance

Synthesis Reactions There are many types of chemical reactions. One type of chemical reaction is called a **synthesis reaction.** To *synthesize* means "to put together." In a synthesis reaction, two or more substances combine to form a more complex substance. The reactants in a synthesis reaction can be elements, compounds, or both. The product of a synthesis reaction is always a compound.

1▶ DEFINE: What is a synthesis reaction?

Examples of Synthesis Reactions The formation of iron sulfide (FeS_2), also known as pyrite or fool's gold, is an example of a synthesis reaction. The formation of table salt (NaCl) is also a synthesis reaction.

$$Fe + S_2 \rightarrow FeS_2$$
$$2Na + Cl_2 \rightarrow 2NaCl$$

2▶ INFER: What elements form iron sulfide?

Oxidation Reactions Many oxidation reactions are synthesis reactions. The burning of carbon to form carbon dioxide (CO_2) and the oxidation of magnesium to form magnesium oxide (MgO) are also synthesis reactions.

$$C + O_2 \rightarrow CO_2$$
$$2Mg + O_2 \rightarrow 2MgO$$

3▶ EXPLAIN: How are the formation of carbon dioxide and magnesium oxide examples of synthesis reactions?

Synthesis Reactions Involving Compounds Some synthesis reactions involve the combination of a compound and an element. When the compound carbon monoxide (CO) burns, it combines with an element, oxygen, to produce a more complex compound, carbon dioxide.

$$2CO + O_2 \rightarrow 2CO_2$$

Two compounds react when calcium oxide (CaO) combines with water to produce calcium hydroxide.

$$CaO + H_2O \rightarrow Ca(OH)_2$$

4▶ IDENTIFY: Give an example of a compound that combines with an element to form a more complex compound.

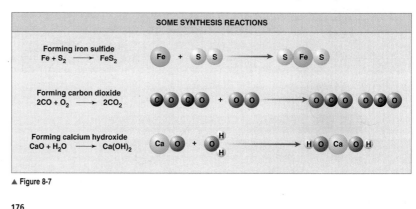

SOME SYNTHESIS REACTIONS

Forming iron sulfide
$Fe + S_2 \longrightarrow FeS_2$

Forming carbon dioxide
$2CO + O_2 \longrightarrow 2CO_2$

Forming calcium hydroxide
$CaO + H_2O \longrightarrow Ca(OH)_2$

▲ Figure 8-7

176

Teaching Options

EXTENDING THE LESSON

Investigating the Synthesis Reactions That Make Acid Rain Challenge students to find out what substances combine with water in synthesis reactions to form acid rain. (sulfur oxides, SO_2 and SO_3, and the nitrogen oxide NO_2) Students can use the text or reference materials to help them write equations to show how these acids are formed.
($SO_2 + H_2O \rightarrow H_2SO_3$,
$SO_3 + H_2O \rightarrow H_2SO_4$,
$2NO_2 + H_2O \rightarrow HNO_2 + HNO_3$)

ONGOING ASSESSMENT

Determining a Balanced Synthesis Equation Write the following chemical equation on the board: $3Ti + 2N_2 \rightarrow Ti_3N_4$. Ask students if the equation is balanced. (yes) Then, ask if it is a synthesis reaction. (yes) Ask students how they can tell. (The reactants and products have the same number of atoms of the elements, and two elements form a more complex substance.)

Synthesis Reactions With More Than Two Reactants Some synthesis reactions can involve the combination of more than two reactants. Sulfuric acid (H_2SO_4), a substance found in acid rain, is formed when sulfur dioxide gas (SO_2) and oxygen in the air combine with water.

$$2SO_2 + O_2 + 2H_2O \rightarrow 2H_2SO_4$$

▶ **IDENTIFY:** What three reactants combine to form sulfuric acid?

✓ CHECKING CONCEPTS

1. To synthesize means "_____."
2. In a synthesis reaction, the product formed is always a _____.
3. In a synthesis reaction, two or more substances produce a _____ substance.
4. When carbon monoxide combines with oxygen, _____ is produced.
5. Three _____ combine in a synthesis reaction to form sulfuric acid.

Real-Life Science

DEVELOPMENT OF SYNTHETIC FABRICS

Do you own a rayon blouse or a polyester shirt? Can some of your clothes be washed and then worn with little or no ironing? Are your bathing suits or exercise clothes made of a special material that stretches for a good fit? If you answered yes to any of these questions, then you are familiar with synthetic (sihn-THEHT-ihk) fabrics.

Synthetic fabrics are materials that were invented by chemists to take the place of natural fibers such as silk, cotton, and wool. Synthetic fabrics are made from very large molecules called polymers. Polymers are made up of many smaller molecules joined together in long chains.

▲ **Figure 8-9** Making synthetic fabric

The first synthetic fiber to be developed was rayon. Rayon was invented at the end of the nineteenth century. Rayon is manufactured from cellulose. Cellulose comes from wood pulp. This synthetic fiber can be treated to resemble wool, cotton, linen, or silk. Nylon was introduced in 1938 as a substitute for silk. It soon replaced silk in the manufacture of stockings.

Thinking Critically Why do you think people would buy materials made from synthetic fabrics?

THINKING CRITICALLY

6. **ANALYZE:** Which of the following reactions are synthesis reactions?

   a. $2H_2O \rightarrow 2H_2 + O_2$
   b. $N_2 + 2O_2 \rightarrow 2NO_2$
   c. $4Al + 3O_2 \rightarrow 2Al_2O_3$
   d. $Zn + 2HCl \rightarrow ZnCl_2 + H_2$
   e. $CaO + H_2O \rightarrow Ca(OH)_2$

7. **APPLY:** Explain why the following general equation describes a synthesis reaction.

   $$A + B \rightarrow C$$

INTERPRETING VISUALS

Look at the diagram of a synthesis reaction in Figure 8-8. Write the balanced equation for the synthesis reaction.

▲ **Figure 8-8** The formation of water

▶ **EXPLAIN:** In both reactions, substances combine to form a more complex substance.

▶ **IDENTIFY:** Possible answer: carbon monoxide, which combines with oxygen to form carbon dioxide

▶ **IDENTIFY:** sulfur dioxide, oxygen, and water

Reinforcement Be sure that students understand that a synthesis reaction involves two or more reactants. Review the various synthesis reactions shown in the lesson to reinforce this idea.
learning styles: auditory, visual

3 Assess

✓ CHECKING CONCEPTS ANSWERS

1. to put together
2. compound
3. more complex
4. carbon dioxide
5. reactants or substances

THINKING CRITICALLY ANSWERS

6. **ANALYZE:** b, c, and e
7. **APPLY:** Two reactants combine to form a new and different product.

INTERPRETING VISUALS ANSWER

$$2H_2 + O_2 \rightarrow 2H_2O$$

4 Close

Real-Life Science

DEVELOPMENT OF SYNTHETIC FABRICS

Real-Life Connection Illustrate the wide use of synthetic fabrics by asking students how many of them are wearing clothing made of nylon, polyester, rayon, or some other synthetic fabric. Most students probably will be wearing some type of synthetic fabric.

Discussion Ask students to identify the first synthetic fiber to be developed. (rayon) Have students name some natural fibers and their sources. (silk from silkworms, cotton from plants, wool from sheep)

Thinking Critically Answer
Possible answer: The materials may stretch to fit well, and can be washed and then worn with little or no ironing.

MORE ON THE WEB

Reviewing Synthesis Reactions
Have students use the Internet to review synthesis reactions. Then, have students answer the questions that follow this activity at www.conceptsand challenges.com.

• TEACHING RESOURCES •

Teacher's Resources CD-ROM
Lesson Review: Chapter 8, p. 7
Writing Activity Outline: Study Tools, pp. 20–21

COOPERATIVE LEARNING

Writing a Synthesis Equation
Have pairs of students write the balanced equation for the synthesis reaction that forms water (H_2O). ($2H_2 + O_2 \rightarrow 2H_2O$)

1 Introduce

✎ **STUDY HINT** Before beginning this lesson, have students create a word web in their notebooks. They should write the term *decomposition reaction* and circle it. Then, they should draw arms leading from the circle on which they can record information about these types of reactions. They can include a definition as well as specific examples of decomposition reactions and what conditions are necessary for such reactions to occur.

Linking Prior Knowledge Ask students to recall what happens in a synthesis reaction. Ask what they think may be the opposite of a synthesis reaction (Lesson 8-4).

2 Teach

Discussion Compare decomposition reactions with synthesis reactions. Point out that the two types of reactions are opposite. In synthesis reactions, simple substances combine to produce more complex substances. In decomposition reactions, complex substances break down to produce simpler substances. **learning style: auditory**

Discussion Inform students that during electrolysis of water, the volume of hydrogen produced is always twice the volume of oxygen produced. Ask students why they think the volume ratio is always two hydrogen to one oxygen. (Water contains two atoms of hydrogen for every atom of oxygen.) **learning styles: auditory, logical/mathematical**

Answers to questions

▶1 **DEFINE:** a reaction in which a complex substance is broken down into two or more simpler substances

▶2 **EXPLAIN:** Heat needs to be added.

▶3 **DESCRIBE:** An electric current is passed through water, and the water decomposes into hydrogen and oxygen.

▶4 **STATE:** Hydrogen peroxide will decompose into water and oxygen without energy being added.

8-5 What is a decomposition reaction?

Objective
Describe what happens in a decomposition reaction.

Key Terms
decomposition (dee-kahm-puh-ZISH-uhn) **reaction:** reaction in which a complex substance is broken down into two or more simpler substances

electrolysis (ee-lehk-TRAHL-ih-sihs): process by which a substance is decomposed using an electric current

Decomposition Reactions When a substance breaks down into simpler substances, the reaction is called a **decomposition reaction.** Decomposition reactions are the opposite of synthesis reactions. In a decomposition reaction, a single complex substance is broken down into two or more simpler substances. The products of a decomposition reaction can be elements, compounds, or both.

▶ **DEFINE:** What is a decomposition reaction?

The Need for Energy Most decomposition reactions need energy from an outside source in order to take place. The energy is usually in the form of heat or electricity. Chemists often show the type of energy that is needed for a decomposition reaction by writing a symbol above the arrow in the chemical equation. A triangle drawn above the arrow means that heat needs to be added. You can see how this symbol is used in the following equation. This equation shows the decomposition of mercuric oxide.

$$2HgO \xrightarrow{\triangle} 2Hg + O_2$$

▶ **EXPLAIN:** What does a triangle drawn above an arrow in a chemical equation mean?

Electrolysis of Water An example of a decomposition reaction is the electrolysis of water. In **electrolysis,** a substance is decomposed using an electric current. The energy from the electric current causes a chemical reaction to take place.

178

When an electric current is passed through water, the water breaks down, or decomposes, into oxygen and hydrogen.

$$2H_2O \rightarrow 2H_2 + O_2$$

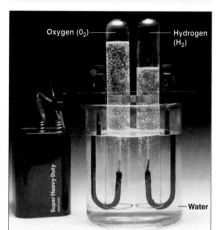
Oxygen (O_2) — Hydrogen (H_2) — Water

▲ **Figure 8-10** Electrolysis of water

Electrolysis can be used to break down other substances as well. Although difficult to do, sodium chloride can be melted. Once melted, it can be decomposed by an electric current.

$$2NaCl \rightarrow 2Na + Cl_2$$

▶ **DESCRIBE:** What happens during the electrolysis of water?

Decomposition Reactions Without Added Energy Some decomposition reactions do not require added energy. Hydrogen peroxide (H_2O_2) is a substance used to clean skin wounds. Over time, hydrogen peroxide will decompose into water and oxygen.

$$2H_2O_2 \rightarrow 2H_2O + O_2$$

▶ **STATE:** Give an example of a decomposition reaction that does not require added energy.

Teaching Options

RETEACH

Classifying Reactions Write equations for several simple chemical reactions—some synthesis and some decomposition—on the board or on an overhead transparency. Ask students to work in pairs to classify the reactions and record them in a two-column chart with the headings *Synthesis* and *Decomposition*. **learning styles: visual, interpersonal**

ONGOING ASSESSMENT

Identifying True/False Statements Give students simple statements and ask them to decide whether the statements are true or false. Have students change false statements to make them true. Examples: Most decomposition reactions do not require added energy to take place. (False; Most decomposition reactions require added energy.) Water is synthesized during electrolysis. (False; Water is decomposed during electrolysis.) The production of a decomposition reaction may be elements or compounds. (true)

CHECKING CONCEPTS

1. What are the kinds of products formed in decomposition reactions?
2. What is the opposite of a decomposition reaction called?
3. How many reactants are there in a decomposition reaction?
4. What are the products when water decomposes?
5. What forms of energy are usually needed in decomposition reactions?
6. What is used to decompose water in an electrolysis reaction?
7. What are the products in a decomposition reaction of table salt?
8. What kind of symbol is used to show that heat is needed in a decomposition reaction?

THINKING CRITICALLY

9. ANALYZE: If substance AB is broken down into simpler substances in a decomposition reaction, how would you represent the products?
10. INFER: Why can the reactant in a decomposition reaction never be an element?
11. INFER: Over time, what does hydrogen peroxide decompose into?

DESIGNING AN EXPERIMENT

Design an experiment to solve the following problem. Include a hypothesis, variables, a procedure, and a type of data to study.

PROBLEM: The sugar glucose ($C_6H_{12}O_6$) can be broken down into simpler substances. What products are formed when glucose is decomposed by heating?

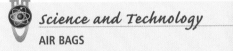
Science and Technology

AIR BAGS

Chemistry provides a way of inflating a pillow to help cushion passengers during an automobile crash. The pillow is called an air bag.

Air bags are made of nylon. They can be located inside steering wheels, dashboards, and door mounts. A chemical decomposition reaction puts the air in air bags. If a crash occurs, a sensor device installed in the car activates the inflation system. Decomposition reactions take place and produce nitrogen gas, N_2. The nitrogen gas comes from the decomposition of sodium azide, NaN_3. Air bags can inflate at rates close to 200 miles per hour.

Studies show that air bags can reduce the risk of fatal injuries by more than 30% during frontal automobile crashes. Most new vehicles are built with air bags in the steering wheel and in the dashboard in front of the passenger seat. Future vehicles may contain as many as eight air bags for overall protection.

Thinking Critically What do you think will be the effect of increasing the number of air bags in automobiles?

▲ **Figure 8-11** Air bags can protect passengers during an auto crash.

---

3 Assess

CHECKING CONCEPTS ANSWERS

1. elements, compounds, or both
2. synthesis reaction
3. one
4. hydrogen and oxygen
5. electricity or heat
6. electric current
7. sodium and chlorine
8. a triangle positioned over the arrow

THINKING CRITICALLY ANSWERS

9. ANALYZE: A + B
10. INFER: An element cannot be broken down into simpler substances.
11. INFER: water and oxygen

4 Close

DESIGNING AN EXPERIMENT

Use the Designing an Experiment Rubric on the Teacher's Resources CD-ROM to assess students' experiments. Fill in the rubric with the additional information below. For this assignment, students should have:

- hypothesized that carbon, hydrogen, and oxygen are the decomposition products.
- developed a logical procedure that involves heating.

Science and Technology

AIRBAGS

Real-Life Connection The science of airbags is based on momentum. A moving car consists of the car itself, the people inside the car, and loose objects inside. The people and objects inside the car have momentum, so if the car crashes, they will continue to move. In a head-on collision, for example, a passenger may crash into the dashboard. The person's forward motion is instantly stopped, and serious injury can result.

Discussion Discuss why on some cars drivers can disable the airbag on the passenger side. (The airbag inflates with such force that children can be injured or killed by the airbag itself. For safety, children should ride in the back seat. If there is no back seat, disabling the passenger-side airbag may be the next-safest option.)

Thinking Critically Answer
Fatal injuries from crashes will most likely occur less frequently.

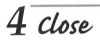

1 Introduce

✎ **STUDY HINT** Before beginning this lesson, have students write the objective in their notebooks. As students read the lesson, they should write information that supports the objective.

Linking Prior Knowledge Relate the formation of ionic bonds to redox reactions (Lesson 4-5). Explain that when free elements are oxidized, they form positive ions, and when they are reduced, they become negative ions.

2 Teach

Demonstration Have students act out the examples of single-replacement reactions described on pages 180 and 181. Have students use string to represent chemical bonds. Explain that students connected by a string represent a compound involved in a reaction. The other students represent free elements. Give each student a sheet of white paper labeled with the symbol of the element the student represents. For example, give two students sheets labeled *H*. Each of these students should be connected by a string to one other student labeled *Cl*. A fifth student, labeled *Zn*, should replace both of the *H* students, who then become connected to each other by another string.
learning styles: visual, kinesthetic

Reinforcement If students need help remembering what happens in a single-replacement reaction, you might demonstrate with objects such as connecting cubes or building blocks. Make an element and a compound, using the cubes or the blocks. Take them apart and put them back together to represent a replacement reaction. Students may want to use the cubes or the blocks to make models of their own to better understand the concept. **learning styles: visual, tactile**

Answers to questions

▶1 **DEFINE:** a reaction in which one element replaces another element in a compound

▶2 **INFER:** hydrogen and a salt

8-6 What is a single-replacement reaction?

Objective
Describe what happens in a single-replacement reaction.

Key Term
single-replacement reaction: reaction in which one element replaces another element in a compound

Single-Replacement Reactions In certain types of chemical reactions, one element replaces another element in a compound. This type of chemical reaction is called a **single-replacement reaction.** All single-replacement reactions begin with a compound and a free element. When the element and the compound react, the free element replaces one of the elements in the compound. The element that is replaced then becomes a free element. The reactants in a single-replacement reaction are always a compound and a free element. The products are always a new compound and a new free element. This general equation will help you to remember what happens in a single-replacement reaction.

$$A + BC \rightarrow AC + B$$

▶1 **DEFINE:** What is a single-replacement reaction?

Single-Replacement Reactions with Metals Three common groups of substances are acids, bases, and salts. A salt is an ionic compound made up of a positive metallic ion and a negative nonmetallic ion, such as sodium chloride. Many metals react with acids to produce hydrogen gas and a salt. In this type of reaction, the metal is the free element and the acid is the compound. When the metal and the acid react, the metal replaces hydrogen in the acid. When the reaction is over, hydrogen is the free element, which escapes as a gas. A salt is the new compound.

You can see how this works by looking at the equation below for the reaction between zinc and hydrochloric acid (HCl).

Zn	+	$2HCl$	$\rightarrow$	$ZnCl_2$	+	H_2
metal		acid		salt		hydrogen

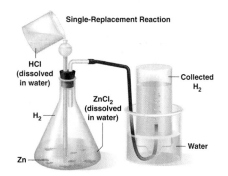

▲ **Figure 8-12** The reaction between zinc and hydrochloric acid is a single-replacement reaction.

▶2 **INFER:** What is produced when a metal reacts with an acid?

Other Examples Some other types of single-replacement reactions include the reaction between sodium and water, and the reaction between chlorine and sodium bromide (NaBr).

$2Na$	+	$2H_2O$	$\rightarrow$	$2NaOH$	+	H_2
Cl_2	+	$2NaBr$	$\rightarrow$	$2NaCl$	+	Br_2

One way in which the element copper (Cu) can be obtained from a rock containing copper oxide (CuO) is in a single-replacement reaction. If carbon can be made to react with copper oxide, carbon dioxide will form and copper will become the free element.

$2CuO$	+	C	$\rightarrow$	CO_2	+	$2Cu$
copper oxide		carbon		carbon dioxide		copper

Teaching Options

RETEACH

Reinforcing Understanding of Single-Replacement Reactions
Write the three equations at the bottom of page 180 on the board. Lead students as they determine which element is being replaced in each reaction. Write an incomplete sentence on the board: _____ replaces _____ in the compound _____ to form _____ and _____. Students can work with you to fill in the blanks for each of the reactions. **learning styles: visual, logical/mathematical**

COOPERATIVE LEARNING

Making Up a Quiz Students can work in small groups to construct a quiz made up of true/false and multiple-choice questions. Provide an example or two to spark their thinking. Be sure that they create answer keys. Once you have checked the quizzes for accuracy, have groups trade their quizzes and then complete them. **learning styles: visual, interpersonal**

◀ **Figure 8-13** The element copper can be obtained in a single-replacement reaction.

▶ INFER: What is the compound produced in the reaction between chlorine and sodium bromide?

✓ CHECKING CONCEPTS

1. A single-replacement reaction always takes place between an element and a _____.
2. In a single-replacement reaction, one element _____ another element.

3. The products of a single-replacement reaction are always a compound and an _____.
4. When zinc reacts with hydrochloric acid, hydrogen is replaced by _____.
5. When the reaction between zinc and hydrochloric acid is complete, _____ is the free element.

💡 THINKING CRITICALLY

6. ANALYZE: Tell what is happening in the following reaction.

$$Cu + AgNO_3 \rightarrow CuNO_3 + Ag$$

HEALTH AND SAFETY TIP

The element sodium is dangerous to handle. Sodium reacts explosively with water. As a result, sodium must be stored in oil. What safety precautions do you think scientists must use when handling sodium?

⚛ Hands-On Activity

REPLACING METALS

You will need safety goggles, copper sulfate, silver nitrate, water, two ungalvanized nails, two copper strips, two 100-mL beakers, four test tubes, a graduated cylinder, a clock or timer, and a balance.

1. Prepare a copper sulfate solution in a 100-mL beaker by adding 2 g of copper sulfate to 100 mL of water.
2. Half-fill two test tubes with the solution.
3. Place a nail in one test tube and a copper strip in the other. Wait 5 minutes.
4. Pour the copper sulfate solution out of both test tubes. Remove the nail and the copper strip. Observe any changes.
5. Repeat steps 1 to 3 substituting silver nitrate for the copper sulfate.

Practicing Your Skills
6. OBSERVE: What happened to the iron nail?
7. OBSERVE: What happened to the copper strip?
8. ANALYZE: Which element is replaced?

▲ **Figure 8-14** A nail in copper sulfate (left) and a strip of copper in copper sulfate (right)

MORE ON THE WEB

Single-Replacement Reactions
Have students use the Internet to learn more about single-replacement reactions. Have students complete the practice problems at www.conceptsand challenges.com.

• TEACHING RESOURCES •

💿 **Teacher's Resources CD-ROM**
Lesson Review: Chapter 8, p. 9
Enrichment: Chapter 8, p. 10
Laboratory Manual
Lab. Skills Worksheet 1: Using a Graduated Cylinder, pp. 5–8
Lab. Skills Worksheet 2: Using a Triple-Beam Balance, pp. 9–10

▶ INFER: sodium chloride, NaCl

✏ **WRITING HINT** Remind students that they need to provide labels when they draw visuals, such as the diagram in Figure 8–12. You might have them create a visual for one of the steps in the Hands-On Activity. **learning style: visual**

3 Assess

✓ CHECKING CONCEPTS ANSWERS

1. compound
2. replaces
3. element
4. zinc
5. hydrogen

💡 THINKING CRITICALLY ANSWER

6. ANALYZE: Copper replaces silver in silver nitrate to form copper nitrate and silver.

4 Close

HEALTH AND SAFETY TIP ANSWER

Scientists must be sure that the sodium does not come in contact with any water, even water in the air.

Hands-On Activity

REPLACING METALS

TIME: 30 minutes

PURPOSE: observing, analyzing

SAFETY TIP: All chemicals should be used carefully. Silver nitrate will stain skin and clothing. Be sure that students wear lab aprons, safety goggles, and plastic gloves during the experiment.

DISCUSSION: Have students discuss which of the metals used is more reactive and will better replace other elements in compounds. (Iron is more reactive because it replaced copper and silver in both compounds.)

Practicing Your Skills Answers

6. OBSERVE: Copper and silver formed on it.
7. OBSERVE: Silver formed on it.
8. ANALYZE: Silver and copper are replaced.

1 Introduce

✏️ **STUDY HINT** Before beginning this lesson, have students study Figure 8-15. Ask them to describe what is happening in the photographs.

Linking Prior Knowledge Have students recall what they learned about single-replacement reactions (Lesson 8-6). Ask them to predict what double-replacement reactions are, based on what they know about single-replacement reactions.

2 Teach

Discussion Write chemical equations on the board that show a single-replacement reaction and a double-replacement reaction. Lead students to compare and contrast single-replacement reactions and double-replacement reactions. Write the general equations for each reaction to help students make their comparisons.
learning styles: visual, auditory

Discussion A solution of $AgNO_3$ can be mixed with NaCl, NaBr, or NaI to show various double-replacement reactions. In each reaction, one of the salts formed will precipitate out of solution. Each of the precipitates is also light-sensitive and will darken when exposed to light. You may wish to tell students that such light-sensitive compounds are used extensively in photographic emulsions.
learning style: visual

Answers to questions

▶ **DEFINE:** a reaction in which elements from two different compounds replace each other, forming two new compounds

▶ **DEFINE:** a solid that settles to the bottom of a mixture

▶ **DESCRIBE:** An acid and a base react to form water and a salt.

Reinforcement Clarify that a redox reaction is any reaction that involves the gain and loss of electrons. However, not every reaction is a redox reaction. If an element changes oxidation number during

---

8-7 What is a double-replacement reaction?

Objective
Describe what happens in a double-replacement reaction.

Key Terms
double-replacement reaction: reaction in which elements from two different compounds replace each other, forming two new compounds
precipitate (pree-SIHP-uh-tayt)**:** solid that settles to the bottom of a mixture

Double-Replacement Reactions In certain types of chemical reactions, the elements from two different compounds replace each other, forming two new compounds. This type of reaction is called a **double-replacement reaction.** A double-replacement reaction can be shown by the following general equation.

$$AB + CD \rightarrow AD + CB$$

Have you ever taken medicine to relieve an upset stomach? If you have, the medicine may have contained magnesium carbonate ($MgCO_3$). This substance can cause a double-replacement reaction to take place. Magnesium carbonate can help break down the substance hydrochloric acid (HCl), which is produced in your stomach. In this reaction, the magnesium and the hydrogen replace each other. Magnesium chloride ($MgCl_2$) and carbonic acid (H_2CO_3) are produced.

$$MgCO_3 + 2HCl \rightarrow MgCl_2 + H_2CO_3$$

The carbonic acid produced in the double-replacement reaction then goes through a decomposition reaction that produces water and carbon dioxide. Your upset stomach is relieved.

▶ **DEFINE:** What is a double-replacement reaction?

Formation of a Precipitate Double-replacement reactions take place in solutions. Although water does not take part in these reactions, it does help to

182

speed them up. In many double-replacement reactions, a substance called a precipitate is formed. A **precipitate** is a solid that settles to the bottom of a mixture. For example, in the double-replacement reaction between lead nitrate and potassium iodide, lead iodide is one of the products. As it forms, this compound settles out as a yellow precipitate.

$$\underset{\text{lead nitrate}}{Pb(NO_3)_2} + \underset{\text{potassium iodide}}{2KI} \rightarrow \underset{\text{potassium nitrate}}{2KNO_3} + \underset{\text{lead iodide}}{PbI_2}$$

▲ **Figure 8-15** When potassium iodide is poured into lead nitrate, lead iodide is the precipitate that forms.

In the double-replacement reaction between silver nitrate and sodium chloride, silver chloride is the precipitate.

$$\underset{\text{silver nitrate}}{AgNO_3} + \underset{\text{sodium chloride}}{NaCl} \rightarrow \underset{\text{sodium, nitrate}}{NaNO_3} + \underset{\text{silver chloride}}{AgCl}$$

In the double-replacement reaction between aluminum sulfate and barium chloride, aluminum chloride is the precipitate.

$$\underset{\text{aluminum sulfate}}{Al_2(SO_4)_3} + \underset{\text{barium chloride}}{3BaCl_2} \rightarrow \underset{\text{barium sulfate}}{3BaSO_4} + \underset{\text{aluminum chloride}}{2AlCl_3}$$

▶ **DEFINE:** What is a precipitate?

Teaching Options

EXTENDING THE LESSON

Forming a Precipitate Conduct a scientific experiment to form a precipitate in a double-replacement reaction. Materials needed are potassium carbonate, calcium chloride, two 100-mL beakers, a graduated cylinder, a balance, and a stirring rod. Measure 2 g of potassium carbonate and 2 g of calcium chloride and place each compound into a separate beaker. Using the graduated cylinder, add 50 mL of distilled water to each beaker, and stir each solution with a clean stirring rod. Mix both solutions together and stir. Ask students to observe what the solutions looked like before they were mixed together and what happens as the solutions are mixed. (Both solutions are clear before mixing. The resulting liquid is cloudy.) Ask students what precipitate forms. (calcium carbonate) Tell students that they can check a table of solubilities to help them determine which product precipitates. **learning style: visual**

Acid-Base Reactions Another common type of double-replacement reaction is the reaction that takes place between an acid and a base. This type of reaction produces a salt and water. It is called a neutralization (noo-truh-lih-ZAY-shuhn) reaction. In a neutralization reaction, an acid and a base combine to form a salt and water. The following equation describes the reaction between the base sodium hydroxide (NaOH) and hydrochloric acid (HCl).

$$NaOH + HCl \rightarrow NaCl + H_2O$$

▶ DESCRIBE: What happens in a neutralization reaction?

✓ CHECKING CONCEPTS

1. In a double-replacement reaction, two new _____ are formed.
2. A precipitate is a _____ that settles to the bottom of a mixture.

3. When lead nitrate and potassium iodide react, the precipitate formed is _____.
4. Double-replacement reactions take place in _____.
5. When a _____ and an acid react, water and a salt are formed.

💡 THINKING CRITICALLY

6. PREDICT: What products are formed in the following reaction?

   KOH + HCl → ? + ?

7. ANALYZE: Which of the following reactions are double-replacement reactions?

   a. $2Al_2O_3 \rightarrow 4Al + 3O_2$
   b. $Ca + 2H_2O \rightarrow Ca(OH)_2 + H_2$
   c. $AgNO_3 + NaBr \rightarrow AgBr + NaNO_3$
   d. $2Na + Br_2 \rightarrow 2NaBr$
   e. $2NaOH + H_2SO_4 \rightarrow Na_2SO_4 + 2H_2O$

◆ Integrating Life Science

TOPIC: digestive system

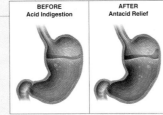

▲ Figure 8-16 In the stomach, antacids can relieve indigestion (left) by breaking down hydrochloric acid (right).

RELIEVING INDIGESTION

Your stomach produces a strong substance called gastric juice. Gastric juice contains hydrochloric acid (HCl) and other molecules that help you to digest food. Special cells found inside the lining of your stomach produce hydrochloric acid by taking H⁺ ions and Cl⁻ ions from substances in your blood.

Sometimes your stomach produces too much hydrochloric acid. This can cause a condition called acid indigestion to occur. Antacids are medicines that can relieve the pain of acid indigestion by breaking down hydrochloric acid. Calcium carbonate, sodium bicarbonate, and magnesium hydroxide are common ingredients in antacids. All of these compounds can react with H⁺ ions to break down the acid in a double-replacement reaction.

For example:

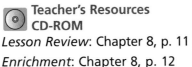

$NaHCO_3$	+	HCl	→	$NaCl$	+	H_2O	+	CO_2
sodium bicarbonate		hydrochloric acid		salt		water		carbon dioxide

The salt and water produced pass through your digestive system. Carbon dioxide may be released as a burp.

Thinking Critically Why are these medicines called antacids?

---

the reaction, it is a redox reaction. Have students examine equations for the four basic types of reactions. Have them determine which of these types are redox reactions and which are not. (Synthesis, decomposition, and single-replacement reactions are redox reactions; double-replacement reactions are not.)
learning style: logical/mathematical

3 Assess

✓ CHECKING CONCEPTS ANSWERS

1. compounds
2. solid
3. lead iodide
4. solutions
5. base

💡 THINKING CRITICALLY ANSWERS

6. PREDICT: KCl and H_2O
7. ANALYZE: c and e

4 Close

◆ Integrating Life Science

TOPIC: digestive system

RELIEVING INDIGESTION

Real-Life Connection In many cases, indigestion is caused by poor eating habits, such as eating too much, eating too quickly, swallowing air while eating, or not chewing food properly. Excessive amounts of fatty foods, foods that are not properly cooked, and certain vegetables may also cause indigestion.

Discussion Explain why the reaction of sodium bicarbonate and stomach acid is a double-replacement reaction. (Sodium chloride and carbonic acid form in this double-replacement reaction.) Ask: *What happens to the products of the double-replacement reaction?* (Much of the salt and water is absorbed into the blood. Carbonic acid decomposes into water and carbon dioxide. Carbon dioxide may be exhaled.)

Thinking Critically Answer
The prefix *ant-* (or *anti-*) means "against." Antacids can be thought of as being "against acids."

COOPERATIVE LEARNING

Classifying Reactions Write chemical reactions on index cards, one equation per card. Have students work in small groups to balance the chemical equations and then classify them.
learning styles: interpersonal, visual

• TEACHING RESOURCES •

💿 **Teacher's Resources CD-ROM**
Lesson Review: Chapter 8, p. 11
Enrichment: Chapter 8, p. 12

📼 **Laboratory Video**
Segment 9: Forming a Precipitate

The Big idea

(pp. 184–185)

1 Introduce

Objective Students will find out about chemical reactions that take place at vents on the deep ocean floor. They will research what the conditions are like around these vents and what life-forms can be found there.

Linking Prior Knowledge Ask students what happens during a chemical reaction. (New substances with new chemical properties are formed; Lesson 8-1.)

2 Teach

Discussion After students read the article and the captions, encourage them to use reference materials to find out more about the deep ocean floor and how the density of life decreases as ocean depth increases. This will help them understand how unusual the concentration of organisms is around ocean vents.

Use the information in the article, the captions, and Fast Facts to help you guide students in choosing a topic for their Science Logs.

Reinforcement Students can also use the Big Idea Planner or Big Idea Science Log Entry found on the Teacher's Resources CD-ROM.

◆ *Integrating Earth Science*

THE Big IDEA

What are deep-sea vents?

Chemical reactions occur deep on the ocean floor. One particular set of chemical reactions affects the shape of the ocean floor. Another set of chemical reactions helps a community of bacteria live there.

Deep in the Atlantic and Pacific Oceans, researchers have found formations called black smokers. These tall structures are made up of certain minerals. These minerals are the result of chemical reactions that take place when hot fluids come in contact with the cold ocean floor.

In Earth's crust, these chemical reaction causes the formation of sulfur compounds. The black color of these compounds gives black smokers their name.

Black smokers look like tall chimneys with black smoke blowing out of them into the water. These structures can be as tall as a fifteen-story building.

These underwater formations are actually vents or cracks in the ocean floor. Hot water pours out of them. The water is heated by magma, which is hot, melted rock found deep in the ocean's crust. The heat of the water in the vents causes the minerals in the crust to become dissolved in the water. As the water rises out through the vents, it is cooled by the surrounding ocean water. The sulfur compounds precipitate out of the rising water and add to the tops of the chimneys.

Certain types of bacteria can live off the sulfur compounds. These bacteria go through chemical reactions in a process called chemosynthesis. During this process, bacteria use the sulfur in a similar way to which plants use the Sun for photosynthesis. The energy released by the chemical reaction is used by the bacteria to make food. Larger organisms then eat the bacteria and a food chain is established. This deep-sea vent community is home to giant clams, tube worms, and other creatures found nowhere else on Earth.

Study the black smoker on these two pages. Then follow the directions in the Science Log to learn more about "the big idea." ✦

184

Bacteria Certain bacteria live in deep-sea vents. These bacteria form the basis of food chains.

2°C

Crust

400°C

1200°C

▲ **Figure 8-17** A deep-sea vent

Teaching Options

❗ FAST FACTS *Exploring a Black Smoker*

Since the first deep ocean vent was discovered in 1977, scientists have identified more than 300 species of vent organisms. As new vents are discovered, the list of species grows.

Bacteria are the key organisms at the base of the food chain at the vent. These bacteria synthesize organic matter from inorganic matter present in the waters around the vents. Vestimentiferan tube worms are among the most abundant of the organisms that live in the vent communities. Tube worms rely on bacteria living in them to provide their nutrition. Vescomyid clams and bathymodiolid mussels are similar to the clams and mussels we eat, but, like tube worms, they rely mostly on bacteria that live in their gills for most of their nutrition.

Scientists are interested in the vents for several reasons. Large amounts of heat and matter are carried from deep within Earth to Earth's surface at these sites. This in turn affects the chemical content of ocean water. Also, these ecosystems are the only known communities on Earth where sunlight is not the immediate source of energy. Some scientists think that life on Earth may have first evolved in environments similar to that around the vents. Studying the vents may give scientists new insights into how life formed millions of years ago.

Black Smoker
Black "smoke" erupts from a chimney on the ocean floor. This "smoke" is filled with minerals.

Cloud of minerals

Deep-Sea Vent Community
Deep-sea vents are home to many creatures, such as giant tube worms and crabs.

Chimney

Vent

Hot sea water

Magma

WRITING ACTIVITY

Science Log

Black smokers are found in very deep water. Light from the Sun does not reach such far depths. Research what the conditions are like around a black smoker. In your science log, describe the kinds of life-forms that can be found around them. Start your search at www.conceptsandchallenges.com.

CHAPTER 8: Chemical Reactions **185**

3 Assess

Use the Writing Activity Rubric on the Teacher's Resources CD-ROM to assess students' Science Logs. Fill in the rubric with the additional information below. For this assignment, students should have:

- described conditions around a black smoker, such as water temperature, mineral content of the water, and appearance of the chimneys.
- described organisms found around black smokers, including bacteria, tube worms, clams, mussels, and shrimp.

4 Close

Writing a Travel Diary Have students write a travel diary entry about a research trip to a black smoker. They should include how they arrived at the black smoker, what they observed, and what was the most exciting aspect of the trip. Students can post their diary entries on a Web page for other students to read.

Tips for Using Technology

Searching the Internet Remind students that one important tool for finding information on the Internet is a search engine. A search engine allows the user to type in a keyword or phrase. The engine then searches thousands of sites on the Internet for those that contain the keyword or phrase. After a few seconds, the search engine lists many sites related to the topic.

• TEACHING RESOURCES •

Teacher's Resources CD-ROM

Big Idea: Chapter 8, p. 13

Big Idea Planner: Study Tools, pp. 11–12

Big Idea Science Log Entry: Study Tools, p. 13

Writing Activity Rubric: Teaching Tools, p. 9

Challenges (pp. 186–188)

Chapter Summary

Review Before students begin the Challenges, review the summary with them. Consider reading the statements aloud, turning the boldface words into blanks. Students can fill in the blanks with the correct answers.

STUDY HINT Have students use the information in the Chapter Summary to create a glossary of terms for Chapter 8. Be sure that they define the terms in their own words.

Key Terms Challenges

MATCHING

1. product (8-1)
2. reduction (8-3)
3. electrolysis (8-5)
4. oxidation (8-3)
5. reactant (8-1)
6. single-replacement reaction (8-6)
7. precipitate (8-7)

FILL IN

8. double-replacement reaction (8-7)
9. chemical equation (8-2)
10. law of conservation of matter (8-1)
11. decomposition reaction (8-5)
12. synthesis reaction (8-4)
13. electrolysis (8-5)
14. coefficient (8-2)

Chapter Summary

Lesson 8-1
- A **chemical reaction** is a process in which new substances with new physical and chemical properties are formed.
- The **law of conservation of matter** states that matter cannot be created or destroyed by a chemical change.

Lesson 8-2
- A **chemical equation** is a statement in which chemical formulas are used to describe a chemical reaction.
- To balance chemical equations, numbers called **coefficients** are placed in front of chemical formulas.

Lesson 8-3
- **Reduction** is any chemical change in which electrons are gained.
- **Oxidation** is any chemical change in which electrons are lost.
- When a substance chemically combines with oxygen, the reaction is called **oxidation.**

Lesson 8-4
- In a **synthesis reaction,** two or more substances chemically combine to form a more complex substance.

Lesson 8-5
- In a **decomposition reaction,** a complex substance is broken down into two or more simpler substances.

Lesson 8-6
- In a **single-replacement reaction,** one element replaces another element in a compound.

Lesson 8-7
- In a **double-replacement reaction,** elements from two different compounds replace each other, forming two new compounds.

Key Term Challenges

chemical equation (p. 172)	oxidation (p. 174)
chemical reaction (p. 168)	precipitate (p. 182)
coefficient (p. 172)	product (p. 168)
decomposition reaction (p. 178)	reactant (p. 168)
	reduction (p. 174)
double-replacement reaction (p. 182)	single-replacement reaction (p. 180)
electrolysis (p. 178)	synthesis reaction (p. 176)
law of conservation of matter (p. 168)	

MATCHING Write the Key Term from above that best matches each description.

1. substance formed in a chemical reaction
2. chemical reaction in which electrons are gained
3. decomposition using an electric current
4. chemical reaction in which electrons are lost
5. substance changed in a chemical reaction
6. chemical reaction in which one element replaces another element in a compound
7. solid that settles out of a mixture

FILL IN Write the Key Term from above that best completes each statement.

8. In a _____, two new compounds are formed.
9. A _____ describes a chemical reaction.
10. The _____ states that matter cannot be created or destroyed by a chemical change.
11. The opposite of a synthesis reaction is a _____.
12. A more complex substance is formed from two simpler substances in a _____.
13. During _____, water is broken down into hydrogen and oxygen.
14. To balance a chemical equation, you would use a _____.

186

Teaching Options

PREPARING STUDENTS FOR STANDARDIZED TESTS

Reading Strategy: Tell students that when taking multiple-choice tests, they should look for words such as *always* and *never*. These words often signal incorrect answers.

Writing Strategy: Tell students to proofread their writing for mistakes in spelling, grammar, and organization. Remind them to use precise words.

Interpreting Visuals: Remind students to look at the title of a graphic to get an overall idea of what the graphic shows. Encourage them to look for labels and other explanatory material. They should consider the purposes of various types of graphics. For example, ask them what kind of information would be provided in a map, a diagram, or a flowchart.

ESL/ELL STRATEGY

Restating Terms English-language learners will benefit from restating terms in their own words. Have pairs of students work together to explain terms such as *chemical reaction, synthesis reaction,* and *decomposition reaction.*

Content Challenges TEST PREP

MULTIPLE CHOICE **Write the letter of the term or phrase that best completes each statement.**

1. The substance produced when iron is oxidized is
   a. water.
   b. oxygen.
   c. iron precipitate.
   d. rust.

2. The reactants in the equation $2H_2 + O_2 \rightarrow 2H_2O$ are
   a. hydrogen and energy.
   b. hydrogen and oxygen.
   c. water and energy.
   d. oxygen and water.

3. In a chemical reaction, matter cannot be
   a. created or destroyed.
   b. conserved.
   c. seen.
   d. measured.

4. The arrow in a chemical equation means
   a. "yields."
   b. "and."
   c. "balances."
   d. "changes."

5. The number of atoms of each element on both sides of a chemical equation must always be
   a. greater than one.
   b. less than two.
   c. different.
   d. equal.

6. The chemical formula $3H_2O$ means
   a. Three atoms of hydrogen and three atoms of oxygen.
   b. Six atoms of hydrogen and three atoms of oxygen.
   c. Three atoms of water.
   d. Three atoms of hydrogen and two atoms of oxygen.

7. The burning of a match is an example of
   a. rusting.
   b. oxidation.
   c. synthesis.
   d. respiration.

8. In a chemical reaction, atoms gain and lose
   a. oxygen.
   b. protons.
   c. electrons.
   d. matter.

9. The product of a synthesis reaction is always
   a. an element.
   b. a solid.
   c. a precipitate.
   d. a compound.

10. In electrolysis, an electric current produces a chemical reaction by providing
    a. reactants.
    b. energy.
    c. oxygen.
    d. water.

TRUE/FALSE **Write *true* if the statement is true. If the statement is false, change the underlined term to make the statement true.**

11. In a synthesis reaction, the product is always an <u>element</u>.

12. The electrolysis of water is a <u>single-replacement</u> reaction.

13. Many metals replace hydrogen when they react with <u>acids</u>.

14. A double-replacement reaction involves the reaction of <u>two elements</u>.

15. A <u>neutralization</u> reaction involves an acid and a base.

16. You can recognize a precipitate because it settles at the <u>surface</u> of a mixture.

Content Challenges

MULTIPLE CHOICE

1. d (8-3)
2. b (8-2)
3. a (8-1)
4. a (8-2)
5. d (8-2)
6. b (8-2)
7. b (8-3)
8. c (8-3)
9. d (8-4)
10. b (8-5)

TRUE/FALSE

11. false; compound (8-4)
12. false; decomposition (8-5)
13. true (8-6)
14. false; two compounds (8-7)
15. true (8-7)
16. false; bottom (8-7)

ALTERNATIVE ASSESSMENT

Recording Information Students may write a science log entry explaining each of the different types of chemical reactions. They can list each type of reaction, explain what happens in each type, and provide a chemical equation and a drawing of a model to illustrate each one.

PORTFOLIO ASSESSMENT

Making Student Portfolios Portfolio Assessment provides an opportunity for students who are generally not good test-takers to demonstrate their learning in another way. Students can demonstrate their comprehension of the concepts in this chapter by making a portfolio. The Lab Activity Report and the Concept Map are some of the reproducibles on the Teacher's Resources CD-ROM that they can include in their portfolios. You can use the Portfolio Assessment Rubric also found on the Teacher's Resources CD-ROM to assess students' portfolios.

Concept Challenges

WRITTEN RESPONSES

1. **EXPLAIN:** The same number and type of atoms are found on both sides of a balanced equation. (8-2)

2. **ANALYZE:** New substances are formed by a rearrangement of the atoms in the reactants. (8-2)

3. **COMPARE:** Electrons are lost, or oxygen is involved in a chemical reaction. (8-3)

4. **CONTRAST:** In a single-replacement reaction, a free element takes the place of an element in a compound. In a double-replacement reaction, elements from two different compounds replace each other. (8-6, 8-7)

5. **APPLY:** Solid silver chloride precipitates and sodium nitrate remains in solution as the result of a double-replacement reaction. (8-7)

6. **CLASSIFY: a.** synthesis **b.** double-replacement **c.** synthesis **d.** single-replacement **e.** decomposition **f.** double-replacement **g.** synthesis **h.** single-replacement **i.** decomposition **j.** double-replacement (8-4, 8-5, 8-6, 8-7)

INTERPRETING A DIAGRAM (8-5)

7. decomposition
8. electrolysis of water
9. water
10. hydrogen and oxygen

Chapter Project Wrap-Up

CHEMICAL REACTIONS DEMONSTRATION

Students' projects can be explained orally, or students can present a written report or other presentation. You can use the Group Activity Rubric found on the Teacher's Resources CD-ROM to assess students' projects. Fill in the rubric with the additional information below. For this project, students should have:

- identified a common chemical reaction.
- provided as much information as possible about the reaction.

Concept Challenges TEST PREP

WRITTEN RESPONSES Complete the exercises and answer each of the following questions in complete sentences.

1. **EXPLAIN:** How do balanced chemical equations illustrate the law of conservation of matter?

2. **ANALYZE:** How can you tell from a chemical equation that a chemical change is taking place?

3. **COMPARE:** Discuss the two different meanings of the term *oxidation*.

4. **CONTRAST:** Explain the difference between a single-replacement reaction and a double-replacement reaction.

5. **APPLY:** Describe the physical and chemical changes that take place when silver nitrate reacts with sodium chloride.

6. **CLASSIFY:** Identify each of the following reactions as synthesis, decomposition, single-replacement, or double-replacement.

   a. $2Mg + O_2 \rightarrow 2MgO$
   b. $BaCl_2 + H_2SO_4 \rightarrow BaSO_4 + 2HCl$
   c. $Si + O_2 \rightarrow SiO_2$
   d. $Zn + 2HCl \rightarrow ZnCl_2 + H_2$
   e. $H_2CO_3 \rightarrow CO_2 + H_2O$
   f. $NaOH + HBr \rightarrow NaBr + H_2O$
   g. $2CO + O_2 \rightarrow 2CO_2$
   h. $Ca + 2H_2O \rightarrow Ca(OH)_2 + H_2$
   i. $2H_2O_2 \rightarrow 2H_2O + O_2$
   j. $BaCl_2 + Na_2SO_4 \rightarrow BaSO_4 + 2NaCl$

INTERPRETING A DIAGRAM Use Figure 8-18 to answer the following questions.

7. What kind of a reaction is shown?
8. What is this reaction called?
9. What are the reactants in this reaction?
10. What are the products?

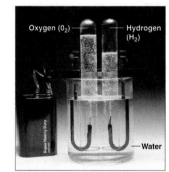

◀ **Figure 8-18** Use this photo to answer questions 7 through 10.

Teaching Options

• TEACHING RESOURCES •

Teacher's Resources CD-ROM

Key Term Review: Chapter 8, p. 14

Chapter 8 Test: pp. 15–17

Lab Activity Report: Study Tools, pp. 16–17

Concept Map: Study Tools, p. 4

Portfolio Assessment Rubric: Teaching Tools, p. 10

Group Activity Rubric: Teaching Tools, p. 6

Chapter Self-Check: Teaching Tools, p. 11

PLANNING GUIDE

◆ **TEACHING THE CHAPTER** This chapter should take approximately 6–9 days to complete instruction and assessment.

	Skills and Features	Projects and Activities	Achieve Science Literacy	Meet Individual Needs
Chapter 9 Opener p. T189	CONTRAST	• Chapter Project		
Lesson 9-1 What is an acid? pp. T190–T191 Standards: B1a, B1b, B1c	IDENTIFY, NAME, CLASSIFY • Health and Safety Tip • Science and Technology	• Extending the Lesson • More on the Web	• Study Hint • Ongoing Assessment	• Reteach CD-ROM Fishbone map
Lesson 9-2 What is a base? pp. T192–T193 Standards: B1a, B1b, B1c	IDENTIFY, EXPLAIN, DESCRIBE • Investigate • Health and Safety Tip • Real-Life Science	• More on the Web	• Study Hint • Ongoing Assessment	• Reteach CD-ROM Venn Diagram
Lesson 9-3 What are indicators? pp. T194–T195 Standard: B1b	DESCRIBE, ANALYZE, CLASSIFY • Designing an Experiment • Hands-On Activity	• Cooperative Learning • More on the Web • Lab Skills Worksheet	• Study Hint • Writing Hint	• Reteach CD-ROM Designing an Experiment Laboratory Video
Lesson 9-4 What is the pH scale? pp. T196–T197 Standard: B1a	IDENTIFY, EXPLAIN, DEFINE • Building Mathematics Skills	• Extending the Lesson • More on the Web	• Study Hint • Reading Strategy • Writing Hint • Ongoing Assessment	CD-ROM Enrichment Activity Writing Activity Outline Graph Paper Laboratory Video
Lab Activity Classifying Household Materials as Acids or Bases pp. T198–T199 Standard: B1c	OBSERVE, ANALYZE, HYPOTHESIZE • Set-Up Time: 10 min • Lab Time: 30 min	• Integrating Earth Science • Extend the Lab Activity • Lab Skills Worksheet	• Tips for Using Technology	CD-ROM Lab Activity Report Database Planner
Big Idea How does pH affect the blood? pp. T200–T201 Standard: B1c	RESEARCH, COMMUNICATE, ANALYZE • Science Log: Writing Activity	• Big Idea Online • Extending the Lesson • Close Activity	• Tips for Using Technology	CD-ROM Big Idea Planner

Planning Guide continues on next page.

	Skills and Features	Projects and Activities	Achieve Science Literacy	Meet Individual Needs
Lesson 9-5 **What is neutralization?** pp. T202–T203 Standards: B1b, B1c	DESCRIBE, DEFINE, EXPERIMENT • Building Science Skills • Real-Life Science	• More on the Web • Integrating Life Science • Lab Skills Worksheet	• Study Hint • Writing Hint • Ongoing Assessment	 CD-ROM Enrichment Activity
Lesson 9-6 **What is an electrolyte?** pp. T204–T205 Standards: B1a, B1b, B1c	INFER, DEFINE, CLASSIFY • Designing an Experiment • Hands-On Activity	• Extending the Lesson • More on the Web • Lab Challenge	• Study Hint • Ongoing Assessment	• ESL/ELL Strategy CD-ROM Designing an Experiment
Chapter 9 Challenges pp. T206–T208	• Chapter Summary • Key Term Challenges • Content Challenges • Concept Challenges	• Unit Challenge Online • Chapter Project Wrap-Up	• Study Hint • Preparing Students for Standardized Tests	• ESL/ELL Strategy CD-ROM Chapter Self-Check Cause-and-Effect Diagram Spider Map

Teacher Notes

Chapter 9 Acids and Bases

▲ Figure 9-1 This pattern is etched on glass.

Patterns can be produced on glass by etching it with hydrofluoric acid. Hydrofluoric acid is a very strong acid that can cause severe burns if not used correctly. The first step in glass etching is the preparation of the glass. The surface to be etched is covered with a protective layer called a resist. This layer is usually made of vinyl. The desired pattern is then cut from the resist. Next, the glass is placed in an acid bath, and the exposed parts of the glass are eaten away, or etched. After removing the glass from the bath, the artist grinds the etched portions to give them an opaque finish.

▶ Why is it important to be careful when using acids?

Contents

UNIT 3: The Behavior of Matter   **189**

Teaching Options

ASSESSMENT PLANNER

For assessment in the Student Edition, see the following pages:

Content Assessment
Checking Concepts: pp. 191, 193, 195, 197, 203, 205
Thinking Critically: pp. 191, 193, 195, 197, 203, 205
Chapter Challenges: pp. 206–208

Alternative Assessment
Building Skills: pp. 197, 203
Science Log: p. 201

Performance-Based Assessment
Hands-On Activity: pp. 195, 205
Designing an Experiment: pp. 195, 205
Lab Activity: pp. 198–199

• TEACHING RESOURCES •

Teacher's Resources CD-ROM
Lesson Review: Ch. 9, pp. 2, 3, 4, 5, 8, 10
Enrichment: Ch. 9, pp. 6, 9
Key Term Review: Ch. 9, p. 11
Chapter 9 Test: pp. 12–13
Laboratory Manual: pp. 5–8, 13–14, 53–56

Laboratory Videos
Segment 10, Segment 11

Chapter Overview

In this chapter, students will learn about acids and bases. Students will describe how indicators are used to identify acids and bases and how the pH scale is used to measure the strength of acids and bases. They will describe what happens when an acid reacts with a base and explain how ions in solution conduct electricity.

About Figure 9-1 Hydrofluoric acid (HF) is a dangerous acid found in some cleaning agents that remove difficult stains, such as rust and tar. Hydrofluoric acid can easily penetrate skin, causing severe burns. Once in the body, it can produce seizures, destroy bone, and cause death. When using a cleaning product, check the label to see if it contains hydrofluoric acid or ammonium bifluoride, which is converted to hydrofluoric acid. Take precautions when using these products. Wear protective clothing over all bare skin, safety glasses, and heavy-duty gloves. Use the product only in a well-ventilated area.

Answer because acids can cause severe burns

Linking Prior Knowledge

For this chapter, students should recall:
- ionic bonds (Lesson 4-5).
- solutions (Lesson 5-10).
- single-replacement reactions (Lesson 8-6).

Chapter Project

CONTRASTING ACIDS AND BASES

MATERIALS: posterboard, magazines, scissors, colored markers, glue

After reading this chapter, have students work in small groups to create posters that show the contrasting properties of acids and bases. Students' posters should include the properties of acids and bases, how these substances react in water, and examples and pictures of both types of substances. Students should also use indicators and the pH scale to show the differences between acids and bases. **learning styles: visual, tactile**

1 Introduce

✎ **STUDY HINT** Before beginning this lesson, have students make a two-column chart in their notebooks. *Properties of Acids* can be one of the column heads, and *Examples of Acids* can be the other column head. As students read the lesson, they can fill in the two columns.

Linking Prior Knowledge Ask students: *What are some acids that you are familiar with?* List the acids they name on the board. Ask: *What properties do these acids have in common?* (Possible answers may include several physical or chemical properties that students know.)

2 Teach

Discussion Display several substances that contain acids, such as vinegar, lemons, and sour cream. Do not allow students to taste the substances, but ask students to describe what taste the substances have in common. Point out that each substance tastes sour because it contains an acid and water. When an acid dissolves in water, it releases hydrogen ions. Hydrogen ions give foods a sour taste. **learning styles: visual, auditory**

Demonstration If possible, combine some hydrochloric acid and zinc. Have students note the bubbles that form during the reaction. Point out that the bubbles indicate that hydrogen gas is being released. The hydrochloric acid reacts with the metal zinc to release hydrogen. **learning styles: visual, auditory**

Answers to questions

▶1 IDENTIFY: acid or hydrogen ions

▶2 NAME: proton donor

Reinforcement Have students review the acids listed in Figure 9-3. Ask students to identify the elements that make up each acid and the number of atoms of each element that combine to form one molecule of the acid. Emphasize that acids can be recognized by the fact that the symbol for hydrogen appears first in the chemical formula. **learning styles: visual, logical/mathematical**

9-1 What is an acid?

Objective
Define and give some examples of acids.

Key Term
acid: substance that releases hydrogen ions (H^+) when dissolved in water

Acids What do vinegar, lemons, and sour milk have in common? They all taste sour. This is true because they all contain acids. An **acid** is a substance that releases hydrogen ions (H^+) when dissolved in water. It is the presence of these H^+ ions that give an acid its sour taste.

▲ **Figure 9-2** Citrus fruits have a sour taste.

Acids are found in many common materials. Figure 9-3 lists the names and chemical formulas of some common acids and where they can be found.

COMMON ACIDS		
Acid	**Chemical Formula**	**Found In**
Acetic acid	$HC_2H_3O_2$	Vinegar
Boric acid	H_3BO_3	Antiseptic
Carbonic acid	H_2CO_3	Club soda
Citric acid	$H_3C_6H_5O_7$	Citrus fruit flavors
Hydrochloric acid	HCl	Digestive juices
Nitric acid	HNO_3	Fertilizers
Sulfuric acid	H_2SO_4	Fertilizers, batteries

▲ **Figure 9-3**

Notice that the symbol for hydrogen appears first in the chemical formula for an acid. All acids contain hydrogen.

▶1 IDENTIFY: What is it that gives lemons their sour taste?

Properties of Acids All acid solutions have the following properties in common.

- Acids taste sour. Remember that you should never taste or touch a substance to find out what it is.
- Acids conduct electricity.
- Acids are corrosive. Some acids can cause painful burns to the skin.
- Acids react with certain chemicals to produce predictable color changes.

Some acids react with some metals to release hydrogen gas. Figure 9-4 shows what happens when hydrochloric acid is added to zinc metal.

$$2HCl + Zn \rightarrow ZnCl_2 + H_2$$

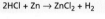
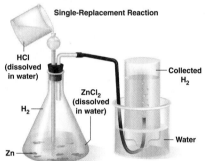
▲ **Figure 9-4** Hydrogen is released when an acid reacts with some metals.

When an acid is dissolved in water, the acid forms positive ions (H^+) and negative ions. For example, hydrochloric acid (HCl) forms positive hydrogen ions and negative chloride ions. The chemical equation for this reaction is shown here.

$$HCl \rightarrow H^+ + Cl^-$$
hydrochloric acid → hydrogen ions + chloride ions

Teaching Options

EXTENDING THE LESSON

Describing Hydronium Ions Explain to students that hydrogen ions (H^+) are attracted to water molecules (H_2O) and readily combine with them to form hydronium ions (H_3O^+). Draw a hydrogen ion, a water molecule, and a hydronium ion on the board. Ask a volunteer to explain why a hydronium ion has a positive charge. (A hydrogen ion is a proton and has a positive charge, which it adds to the neutral water molecule.) **learning styles: visual, auditory**

RETEACH

Naming Properties of Acids Have students make graphic organizers to show the properties of acids. Students can use the Fishbone Map found on the Teacher's Resources CD-ROM.

ONGOING ASSESSMENT

Listing Acids Ask students to name some products found in their homes that contain acids. **learning style: auditory**

A hydrogen atom is made up of one proton and one electron. A hydrogen ion is simply a hydrogen atom that has lost its single electron. In other words, a hydrogen ion is the same as a proton. For this reason, acids are sometimes called proton donors. A strong acid is one that has a strong tendency to release its hydrogen ion.

NAME: What is another name for an acid?

✓ CHECKING CONCEPTS

1. Club soda contains _____ acid.
2. The stomach produces _____ acid to aid in digestion.
3. Acids release _____ ions when placed in water.
4. Acids are _____ donors
5. Vinegar contains _____ acid.
6. Some acids react with some _____ to release hydrogen gas.

THINKING CRITICALLY

7. **INFER:** Why are acids called proton donors?
8. **CLASSIFY:** Which of the following chemical formulas are not acids? How do you know?

   a. HCl   e. $HC_2H_3O_2$
   b. NaCl   f. KBr
   c. H_3PO_4 g. CO_2
   d. $CaSO_4$ h. H_2CO_3

HEALTH AND SAFETY TIP

Strong acids, such as sulfuric acid, can be very dangerous if they come in contact with your skin. They also are poisonous. Use library references to find out how to handle acids safely in a science laboratory. Draw a poster to show what you learned about laboratory safety.

Science and Technology

SULFURIC ACID

One of the most important chemical compounds in the world is sulfuric acid (H_2SO_4). Each year, the United States uses more than 80 billion pounds of it, more than 325 pounds per person. Most of the sulfur mined around the world is used to make sulfuric acid.

Sulfuric acid has many uses. Much of it goes into the production of fertilizer. Batteries, paints, dyes, and paper all contain some sulfuric acid. Petroleum refining and metal processing also make use of sulfuric acid. It is also the raw material used to make other chemicals.

You can tell how well our country's economy is doing by looking at the production of sulfuric acid. During periods of economic growth, industries are busy and they need a lot of sulfuric acid. During difficult times, its production is very low.

Thinking Critically Why is sulfuric acid so important?

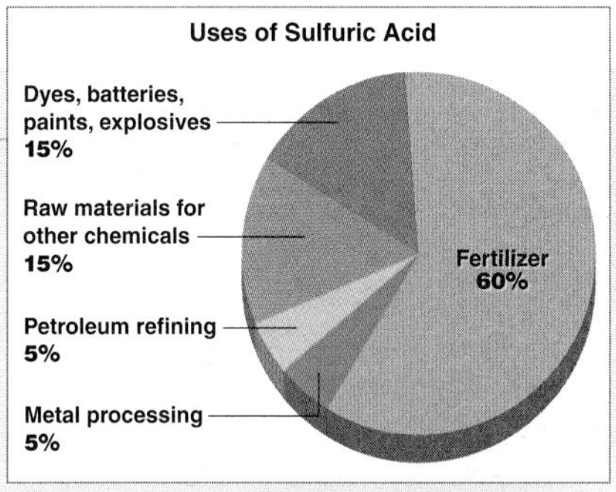

Uses of Sulfuric Acid

Dyes, batteries, paints, explosives **15%**
Raw materials for other chemicals **15%**
Petroleum refining **5%**
Metal processing **5%**
Fertilizer **60%**

▲ **Figure 9-5** This circle graph shows the breakdown of the major uses of sulfuric acid.

---

3 Assess

✓ CHECKING CONCEPTS ANSWERS

1. carbonic
2. hydrochloric
3. hydrogen
4. proton
5. acetic
6. metals

THINKING CRITICALLY ANSWERS

7. **INFER:** They release hydrogen ions, which are protons.
8. **CLASSIFY:** b. NaCl, d. $CaSO_4$, f. KBr, g. CO_2; Their formulas do not begin with the letter *H*.

4 Close

HEALTH AND SAFETY TIP

Students' posters should illustrate how to handle acids safely. Posters may include these tips: use extreme care when working with acids, never pour water into an acid, always pour acid into water, and wear safety goggles and lab aprons. You may wish to display the posters in the classroom.
learning styles: visual, tactile

Science and Technology

SULFURIC ACID

Background Although sulfuric acid is very useful, it can be harmful if it is in the atmosphere. One way it can get into the atmosphere is when coal with a high sulfur content is burned for energy. Sulfur dioxide released as a waste product reacts with water in the air, ultimately forming sulfuric acid. This acid can fall to the ground as precipitation known as acid rain, causing erosion of buildings and monuments and injuring crops and forests.

Discussion Tell students that acids in the atmosphere move from where they originated to other areas with winds and the movement of air masses. Ask students what effects this might have.
learning styles: auditory, linguistic

Thinking Critically Answer
Possible answer: It has many uses.

MORE ON THE WEB

Acid Cola Have students learn more about the acids found in soft drinks by visiting www.conceptsandchallenges.com. Then, have students write a short explanation of why these drinks are relatively safe to drink.

• TEACHING RESOURCES •

Teacher's Resources CD-ROM
Lesson Review: Chapter 9, p. 2
Fishbone Map: Study Tools, p. 5

QUICK CONVERSIONS

	Metric/SI	English
Yearly U.S. sulfuric acid use	36 billion kg	80 billion lb
Yearly sulfuric acid use per person	147 kg	325 lb

1 Introduce

INVESTIGATE

TIME: 10–15 minutes

PURPOSE: Students will determine which cleaning agent is best for cleaning butter or margarine.

MATERIALS: paper towels, butter or margarine, 3 plates, 3 sponges, water, ammonia water, liquid soap

PROCEDURE: Have students work in groups of four to complete this activity. One student can rub the butter or margarine on the plates. Each of the other three students can use a different liquid to try to clean the plates. **learning styles: visual, tactile**

SAFETY TIP: Caution students to be careful when using the ammonia water and to wipe up spills of any liquids immediately.

THINK ABOUT IT: liquid soap and water; Possible answer: Soap is made to remove oil.

STUDY HINT Before beginning this lesson, have students write the lesson title and the head of each section using an outline format in their notebooks. As students read the lesson, tell them to write the main idea of each section.

Linking Prior Knowledge Have students review what they learned about the parts of an atom (Lesson 3-3).

2 Teach

Demonstration Wet a bar of soap and ask students to feel it. Ask students to describe the feel of the soap. Explain that the soap contains a base, which causes the slippery feel. **learning styles: tactile, auditory**

Discussion Display some substances containing bases in front of the classroom, such as a bar of soap, milk of magnesia, ammonia solution, and limewater. Tell students that each substance contains a base. Define a base as a substance that releases hydroxyl ions when dissolved in water. **learning styles: visual, auditory**

Answers to questions

> **DESCRIBE:** by chemically combining fats or oils with a base

---

9-2 What is a base?

INVESTIGATE

Comparing Cleaning Agents
HANDS-ON ACTIVITY

1. Rub some butter or margarine on three plates.
2. Try to clean the first plate with a sponge soaked in plain water.
3. Use a sponge soaked in ammonia water on the second plate, and a sponge soaked in water and liquid soap on the third plate.

THINK ABOUT IT: Which cleaning agent removed the grease most easily? Why?

STEP 2

Objective

Define and give some examples of a base.

Key Terms

base: substance that releases hydroxyl ions (OH⁻) when dissolved in water

hydroxyl (hy-DRAHKS-ihl) **ion:** negative ion made up of one atom of hydrogen and one atom of oxygen

Bases Early settlers in the United States made their own soap from animal fat and ashes. Today, soaps are made by chemically combining fats or oils with a type of chemical compound called a base. A **base** is a substance that releases hydroxyl ions (OH⁻) when dissolved in water. Ashes contain the bases sodium hydroxide (NaOH) and potash (KOH).

▲ **Figure 9-6** Early settlers made their own soap.

Like acids, bases are found in many common materials. Figure 9-7 lists the names and chemical formulas of some common bases and where they can be found.

> **DESCRIBE:** How are soaps made?

192

Properties of Bases All base solutions have the following properties in common. You will find that some of these properties are very similar to the properties of acids.

- Bases taste bitter and feel slippery. Never taste or touch a substance to find out what it is.
- Bases conduct electricity.
- Bases can be corrosive and may cause painful burns to the skin.
- Bases react with certain chemicals to produce predictable color changes.

> **IDENTIFY:** What are two properties of bases?

Composition of Bases When some active metals are placed in water, a chemical reaction takes place. The reaction produces a base plus hydrogen gas. For example, sodium, a very active metal, reacts with water to produce sodium hydroxide, a strong base, and hydrogen gas.

$$Na + H_2O \rightarrow NaOH + H$$
sodium + water → sodium hydroxide + hydrogen

COMMON BASES		
Base	Chemical Formula	Found In
Calcium hydroxide	Ca(OH)₂	Plaster, cement, mortar
Magnesium hydroxide	Mg(OH)₂	Laxatives, antacids
Potassium hydroxide	KOH	Soap, bleach, drain cleaners
Sodium hydroxide	NaOH	Soap, paper, textiles, some drain cleaners

▲ **Figure 9-7**

Teaching Options

! FAST FACTS *Defining Acids and Bases*

Acids and bases were defined in 1884 by a Swedish chemist, Svante Arrhenius. He defined an acid as a substance that releases hydrogen ions in water and a base as a substance that forms hydroxide ions in water. In 1923, Danish chemist Johannes Brønsted and British chemist Thomas Lowry independently proposed that an acid is a proton donor and a base is a proton acceptor. Later, the idea was added that an acid is a substance that accepts an electron pair and a base is a substance that donates an electron pair.

ONGOING ASSESSMENT

Identifying the Composition of a Base Have students study the chemical formulas of the bases listed in Figure 9-7. Ask students what all these bases have in common. Make sure that students understand that these four bases contain the hydroxyl (OH) group and that all bases cause the formation of hydroxyl ions when dissolved in water. **learning styles: visual, auditory**

Look at the chemical formulas of the bases listed in Figure 9-7. They all contain a group called a **hydroxyl ion.** The hydroxyl ion, OH^-, is a negative ion made up of one atom of hydrogen and one atom of oxygen. All bases release hydroxyl ions when dissolved in water.

$$NaOH \rightarrow Na^+ + OH^-$$

Hydroxyl ions can combine with hydrogen ions to form water. A hydrogen ion is a proton. Therefore, bases are also known as proton acceptors. The more hydroxyl ions a base releases in water, the stronger the base.

▶ **EXPLAIN:** Why are bases often called proton acceptors?

✔ CHECKING CONCEPTS

1. Soaps are made by chemically combining _____ with fats or oils.
2. Strong bases are dangerous to handle because they can _____.
3. Bases form when some active _____ react with water.

Real-Life Science

SOAP

Soaps are made up of large molecules whose ends have different properties. One end of a soap molecule is soluble in water. This end has a negative charge, so it is attracted to the positive ends of water molecules. The other end has no charge, so it is soluble in oil. This is why soap can remove grease and oil from clothes or from your skin.

What happens when you wash dirty clothes in soapy water? Soap molecules gather around a grease spot with their oil-soluble ends pointing in. The water-soluble ends of the molecules point out into the water. The grease then forms little drops covered by soap. These drops can then easily mix with the water and be washed away.

Soap is made by boiling fats with lye. Lye contains either sodium hydroxide or potassium hydroxide. Soaps can be made with either one.

| fat | + | lye | → | soap | + | glycerin |

Sometimes the glycerin is left in the soap. Glycerin can also be used to make cellophane, printer's ink, cosmetics, and medicines.

Thinking Critically Explain how soap can remove grease and oil from your skin.

4. The negative ion found in all bases is called the _____ ion.
5. Bases are proton _____.

💡 THINKING CRITICALLY

6. **HYPOTHESIZE:** How does the concentration of hydroxyl ions affect the strength of a base?
7. **APPLY:** Write the chemical formula for each base.

   a. calcium hydroxide
   b. potassium hydroxide
   c. sodium hydroxide
   d. ammonium hydroxide

   1. NaOH
   2. Ca(OH)$_2$
   3. NH$_4$OH
   4. KOH

HEALTH AND SAFETY TIP

Strong bases, such as sodium hydroxide, can be dangerous if they come in contact with your skin. They also are poisonous. Use library references to find out how to handle bases safely in a science laboratory.

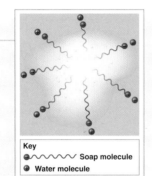

Key
● ∿∿∿ Soap molecule
● Water molecule

▲ **Figure 9-8** Soap molecules surround an oil drop in water.

▶ **IDENTIFY:** Accept any two of the following: taste bitter, feel slippery, conduct electricity, can be corrosive, may cause burns to skin, and react with certain chemicals to produce predictable color changes.

▶ **EXPLAIN:** The hydroxyl ions released by bases can combine with hydrogen ions (protons) to form water.

3 Assess

✔ CHECKING CONCEPTS ANSWERS

1. a base
2. cause burns to the skin
3. metals
4. hydroxyl
5. acceptors

💡 THINKING CRITICALLY ANSWERS

6. **HYPOTHESIZE:** The greater the concentration of hydroxyl ions, the stronger is the base.
7. **APPLY: a.** 2 **b.** 4 **c.** 1 **d.** 3

4 Close

HEALTH AND SAFETY TIP

Students' research findings may include: never pour water into a base, always pour a base into water, and wear safety goggles and a lab apron.

Real-Life Science

SOAP

Background The end of a soap molecule that is soluble in water is hydrophilic. The end of a soap molecule that is soluble in oil is hydrophobic. Have students look up the definitions of the terms *hydrophilic* and *hydrophobic* in a dictionary. Tell students to write in their own words how the meanings of these two terms relate to the action of a soap molecule. learning styles: auditory, linguistic

Thinking Critically Answer
The oil-soluble ends of soap molecules are attracted to the grease and oil on your skin. The other ends of the molecules are attracted to water. When the soap molecules are rinsed off with water, the grease and oil that are attracted to the oil-soluble ends are also washed away.

RETEACH

Comparing Acids and Bases Have students make Venn diagrams that compare the properties of acids and bases. Ask volunteers to explain their diagrams to the class. Students can use the Venn diagram found on the Teacher's Resources CD-ROM.
learning style: visual

• TEACHING RESOURCES •

◉ **Teacher's Resources CD-ROM**
Lesson Review: Chapter 9, p. 3
Venn Diagram: Study Tools, p. 10

MORE ON THE WEB

Acids, Bases, and Salts Have students answer the quiz questions on acids and bases at www.conceptsandchallenges.com.

1 Introduce

✏️ **STUDY HINT** Before beginning this lesson, have students read the captions and art labels. This will allow them to preview what is to come as well as to focus on the most important ideas in the lesson.

Linking Prior Knowledge Ask students to recall what a solution is. (a mixture in which one substance is evenly distributed in another substance; Lesson 5-1)

2 Teach

Demonstration Divide the class into small groups. Distribute various indicators, such as litmus paper and bromthymol blue. Then, give each group different samples of weak acids and bases. Have students test each sample to determine if it is an acid or a base. Tell students to use Figure 9-11 as a guide. After all groups have completed their tests, have a student from each group write the group's findings on the board. Review the findings of all groups as a class.
learning styles: visual, tactile

Discussion Ask students what the purpose of an indicator is. (to identify a substance as an acid or a base) Discuss why using an indicator is better than using other properties of acids and bases. (Some properties are similar. It would be dangerous to test some properties by tasting or touching.)
learning styles: auditory, linguistic

Answers to questions

▶ **1 DESCRIBE:** to determine whether a substance is an acid or a base

▶ **2 NAME:** Accept any three of the following: litmus, phenolphthalein, methyl red, congo red, or bromthymol blue.

▶ **3 EXPLAIN:** They have pink flowers in basic soil and blue flowers in acidic soil.

✏️ **WRITING HINT** Tell students that tables and charts, such as Figure 9-11, help organize information visually and make ideas easier to understand.

9-3 What are indicators?

Objective
Describe how indicators are used to identify acids and bases.

Key Term
indicator: (IHN-dih-kayt-uhr): substance that changes color in an acid or a base

Color Change Suppose you have an unknown solution and you want to know if it is an acid or a base. How might you find out? Remember—you should never taste or touch anything to find out what it is. So, how can you identify your unknown solution? You can test it with an indicator. An **indicator** is a chemical that changes color in an acid or a base.

▶ **DESCRIBE:** What are indicators used for?

Indicators Litmus is an indicator that turns red in acids and blue in bases. Paper treated with litmus can be used to test acids and bases. For example, vinegar is acidic and soap is basic. If you dip one end of a strip of blue litmus paper into vinegar, the blue litmus turns red. If you dip one end of a strip of red litmus paper into soapy water, the red litmus turns blue.

Vinegar   **Soapy water**

▲ **Figure 9-9** Litmus paper is an indicator.

194

Phenolphthalein (fee-nohl-THAL-een) is another indicator. Phenolphthalein is colorless in acids and ranges from pink to red in bases.

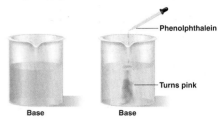

— Phenolphthalein

— Turns pink

Base   **Base**

▲ **Figure 9-10** Phenolphthalein changes color in bases.

The indicator methyl red is red in acids and yellow in bases. The indicator bromthymol blue will turn blue in a base. Figure 9-11 shows some common indicators and the colors they turn in acids and bases.

INDICATORS		
Indicator	**Color in Acids**	**Color in Bases**
Litmus	Red or pink	Blue
Phenolphthalein	Colorless	Pink or red
Methyl red	Red	Yellow
Congo red	Blue	Red
Bromthymol blue	Yellow	Blue

▲ **Figure 9-11**

▶ **2 NAME:** What are three common indicators?

Everyday Indicators Many common, everyday substances are indicators. Grape juice is a good indicator. It will change color depending on how much acid or how much base is present. Red cabbage, beets, rhubarb, cherries, blueberries, and blackberries all can be used as indicators.

Hydrangeas (hy-DRAYN-juhz) are a special kind of flower that act as indicators. They have pink flowers in basic soil and blue flowers in acidic soil.

Teaching Options

RETEACH

Comparing Ions Write *Water + Acid* on the board. From this head, draw an arrow to the head *Hydrogen Ions.* Write *Water + Base* on the board. From this head, draw an arrow to the head *Hydroxyl Ions.* Ask students what the chemical symbols for these ions are. (H^+ and OH^-) Write these symbols on the board. Have students copy this graphic organizer in their notebooks.
learning styles: visual, auditory

COOPERATIVE LEARNING

Comparing Indicators Have students work in pairs to make posters that compare the colors that different indicators turn in acids and bases. Have volunteers explain their posters to the class. Display posters in the classroom.
learning styles: visual, auditory

▲ **Figure 9-12** These hydrangeas are growing in soil that is acidic in some places and basic in others.

 EXPLAIN: How do hydrangeas act as acid-base indicators?

✓ CHECKING CONCEPTS

1. Blue litmus paper turns red in _____.
2. Phenolphthalein turns _____ in bases.
3. Methyl red turns yellow in _____.
4. Congo red turns _____ in acids.
5. Hydrangeas have _____ flowers in basic soil.

💡 THINKING CRITICALLY

6. **ANALYZE:** An unknown solution turns bromthymol blue from yellow to blue. Is the solution an acid or a base? How do you know?
7. **CLASSIFY:** Identify each of the following properties as belonging to an acid or a base.
   a. tastes bitter
   b. reacts with metals to produce hydrogen
   c. turns methyl red from red to yellow
   d. feels slippery
   e. tastes sour
   f. turns phenolphthalein from colorless to pink

DESIGNING AN EXPERIMENT

Design an experiment to solve the following problem. Include a hypothesis, variables, a procedure, and a type of data to study.

PROBLEM: If you plant hydrangeas in your garden, will the flowers be pink or blue?

Hands-On Activity

MAKING AN INDICATOR

You will need red cabbage leaves, a heat source, water, a beaker, a strainer, samples to be tested, and a graduated cylinder.

1. Boil several red cabbage leaves in water until the mixture turns dark red. ⚠CAUTION: Be careful when boiling liquids.
2. Let the mixture cool. Pour the liquid through a strainer into a beaker. This is the indicator.
3. Choose several samples to be tested, for example, milk, fruit juice, shampoo, household cleaner, soda, liquid soap. Pour a small amount of each sample into a separate container.
4. Add 2 mL of red cabbage indicator to each of your samples. Observe what happens.

▲ **STEP 4** Add 2 mL of the indicator to each sample.

Practicing Your Skills

5. **OBSERVE:** What color did the indicator turn in each sample?
6. **OBSERVE:** What is the color of the indicator in acids?
7. **OBSERVE:** What is the color of the indicator in bases?

CHAPTER 9: Acids and Bases **195**

MORE ON THE WEB

Natural Indicators Have students visit www.concepts andchallenges.com to learn how red cabbage can be used as an indicator. Then, have students write an explanation of why red cabbage is a natural indicator.

• TEACHING RESOURCES •

Teacher's Resources CD-ROM
Lesson Review: Chapter 9, p. 4
Designing an Experiment: Study Tools, p. 14
Designing an Experiment Rubric: Teaching Tools, p. 7

Laboratory Manual
Lab. Skills Worksheet 1: Using a Graduated Cylinder, pp. 5–8

Laboratory Video
Segment 10: Making an Indicator

---

3 Assess

✓ CHECKING CONCEPTS ANSWERS

1. acids
2. pink or red
3. bases
4. blue
5. pink

💡 THINKING CRITICALLY ANSWERS

6. **ANALYZE:** A base; Bromthymol blue is an indicator that turns blue in bases.
7. **CLASSIFY:** **a.** base **b.** acid **c.** base **d.** base **e.** acid **f.** base

4 Close

DESIGNING AN EXPERIMENT

Use the Designing an Experiment Rubric on the Teacher's Resources CD-ROM to assess students' experiments. Fill in the rubric with the additional information below. For this assignment, students should have:

- written a hypotheses, included variables and a procedure, and recorded data.
- included, in the procedure, a method for testing the soil in the garden.

Hands-On Activity

MAKING AN INDICATOR

TIME: 20–30 minutes

PURPOSE: observing, comparing

SAFETY TIP: Caution students to be careful when handling hot solutions. Also, caution them not to get the indicator on their skin or clothing.

COOPERATIVE LEARNING: Have students work in groups. Have a volunteer from each group share the group's results with the class.

Practicing Your Skills Answers

5. **OBSERVE:** Answers will vary according to the samples used. Milk, fruit juice, and soda will turn red. Shampoo, household cleaner, and liquid soap will turn green.
6. **OBSERVE:** red
7. **OBSERVE:** green

1 Introduce

✎ **STUDY HINT** Before beginning this lesson, have students copy the title of each section in outline format in their notebooks. As students read this lesson, they should write the main idea of each section. Students can also use the Writing Activity Outline reproducible found on the Teacher's Resources CD-ROM.

Linking Prior Knowledge Ask students to rank the weather today on a scale of 1 to 10 with 10 being the perfect day. Tell students that scales have many uses. For example, doctors try to evaluate their patients by asking them to rank their pain on a scale of 1 to 10. Point out that these scales are based on opinion or subjective information. Other scales, such as the pH scale, are based on measurable data. **learning styles: auditory, logical/mathematical**

2 Teach

Discussion Explain that the pH scale is used to determine how acidic or basic a solution is. Ask students what a pH number below 7 describes. (an acidic solution) Ask what a pH number above 7 describes. (a basic solution) Make sure that students understand that the higher the number, the more basic the substance is. The lower the number, the more acidic the substance is. A pH of 7 indicates a neutral solution. **learning styles: auditory, logical/mathematical**

Demonstration Have students use pH paper to test the pH of various acids and bases. Ask students to rank the acids and bases from lowest pH to highest pH. **learning styles: tactile, logical/mathematical**

📖 **READING STRATEGY** Inform students that the pH scale looks like a number line, but it is not a number line. As you read a number line, the values go higher as you move farther toward the right. However, on a pH scale, the numbers do not necessarily indicate a value. They indicate the relative strength of acids and bases.

9-4 What is the pH scale?

Objective
Describe how the pH scale is used to measure the strength of acids and bases.

Key Terms
pH scale: measure of the concentration of hydrogen ions in a solution
neutral: neither acidic nor basic

Strength of Acids and Bases Acids and bases can be strong or weak. Sulfuric acid and nitric acid are strong acids that can burn the skin. Carbonic acid and boric acid are weak acids. Boric acid is even used as an antiseptic to kill germs. Sodium hydroxide and potassium hydroxide are strong bases. Ammonium hydroxide is a weak base that is used as a household cleaner. Aluminum hydroxide is a weak base that is used as an antacid.

The strength of acids or bases depends on their tendency to release ions when dissolved in water. A strong acid, such as hydrochloric acid (HCl) releases many hydrogen ions when dissolved in water. A weak acid, such as carbonic acid (H_2CO_3) releases only a few hydrogen ions in solution. Strong bases, such as sodium hydroxide (NaOH) release many hydroxyl ions, whereas weak bases, such as ammonium hydroxide (NH_3OH) release few hydroxyl ions.

▶ **IDENTIFY:** What determines the strength of an acid or a base?

Concentration of Acids and Bases The terms *concentrated* and *dilute* are often used to describe acids and bases. A concentrated solution contains a large amount of acid or base compared with the amount of water in which it is dissolved. A dilute solution contains a small amount of acid or base compared with the amount of water present.

The amount of water present in a solution does not change the strength of an acid or a base. Hydrochloric acid is a strong acid, regardless of whether it is in a concentrated solution or a dilute solution. However, adding water to an acidic or a basic solution makes the solution safer to use. The addition of water tends to spread out the ions that make the acid or base so reactive.

▶ **EXPLAIN:** How is it possible for a strong acid to be dilute?

The pH Scale Scientists have developed a scale to measure how acidic or basic a solution is. This scale is called the pH scale. The **pH scale** indicates the concentration of hydrogen ions in a solution.

The pH scale is a series of numbers from 0 to 14. A neutral solution has a pH of 7. A **neutral** solution is neither acidic nor basic. Acids have a pH below 7. Strong acidic solutions have a low pH. Bases have a pH that ranges from 7 to 14. Strong basic solutions have a high pH.

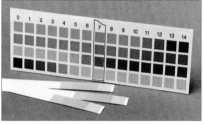

▲ **Figure 9-13** The pH of items can be tested using pH paper. The pH paper uses a range of colors to help make the test more accurate.

▶ **DEFINE:** What is a neutral solution?

Indicators and pH Indicators can be used to help find the pH of an acid or a base. pH paper is an indicator that changes color depending on the pH of the solution. In strong acids, pH paper is red. It is yellow in weak acids and green in weak bases. In strong bases, pH paper is blue.

▶ **PREDICT:** What color will concentrated sulfuric acid turn pH paper?

196

Teaching Options

EXTENDING THE LESSON

Testing Rain The normal pH of rainwater is 5.5, but acids in the atmosphere can lower the pH considerably. When fossil fuels burn, they release gases into the atmosphere. Some of these gases combine with water vapor to form sulfuric acid and other acids, which fall as acid rain.

Have students collect samples of rainwater on the next rainy day and bring them to class. Have students test the samples with pH paper to determine the pH of the rainwater.
learning styles: tactile, auditory

ONGOING ASSESSMENT

Identifying Acids and Bases by pH Write the numbers *0* to *14* on separate index cards. Place all the cards in a bag and mix them up. Have students take turns choosing a card. Ask students to state whether the number on the card they pick indicates an acid, a base, or a neutral solution. You may also wish to vary this activity by having students pick two cards and state which number indicates the stronger acid or base.
learning styles: visual, auditory

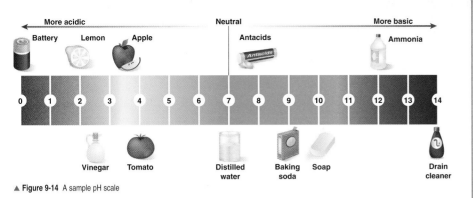

More acidic — Neutral — More basic

Battery Lemon Apple Antacids Ammonia

0 1 2 3 4 5 6 7 8 9 10 11 12 13 14

Vinegar Tomato Distilled water Baking soda Soap Drain cleaner

▲ **Figure 9-14** A sample pH scale

✓ CHECKING CONCEPTS

1. Sulfuric acid is a _____ acid.
2. Nitric acid is a _____ acid.
3. Ammonium hydroxide is a _____ base.
4. Sodium hydroxide is a _____ base.
5. The strength of a base depends on the number of _____ ions in a solution.
6. Acids have a pH _____ 7.
7. A solution with a pH of 12 is _____.

💡 THINKING CRITICALLY

Use the pH scale in Figure 9-14 to answer the following questions.

8. **ANALYZE:** What is the pH of the following substances?
   a. baking soda
   b. distilled water
   c. soap
   d. drain cleaner
   e. lemon
   f. antacids
   g. apple

9. **INTERPRET:** Which of the substances shown on the pH scale are acids?

10. **INTERPRET:** Which of the substances shown on the pH scale are bases?

11. **INTERPRET:** Which of the substances shown on the pH scale are neutral?

BUILDING MATHEMATICS SKILLS

Graphing Many common household products are acids or bases. Make a list of products around your house that are acids and a list of those that are bases. Use library references to identify the acid or base present in each product. Then, find out the pH.

Create a bar graph such as the one in Figure 9-15. Compare the different pH levels. Label the y axis from 0 to 14. Label the x axis with each product you found.

▲ **Figure 9-15** Make a bar graph like this one.

Answers to questions

1️⃣ **IDENTIFY:** the number of hydrogen or hydroxyl ions released in water

2️⃣ **EXPLAIN:** A strong acid is dilute if a solution contains a small amount of the acid compared to the amount of water present.

3️⃣ **DEFINE:** Possible answer: a solution that is neither acidic nor basic

4️⃣ **PREDICT:** red

3 *Assess*

✓ CHECKING CONCEPTS ANSWERS

1. strong
2. strong
3. weak
4. strong
5. hydroxyl
6. below
7. a base or basic

💡 THINKING CRITICALLY ANSWERS

8. **ANALYZE: a.** 9 **b.** 7 **c.** 10 **d.** 14 **e.** 2 **f.** 8 **g.** between 3 and 4
9. **INTERPRET:** battery acid, vinegar, lemon juice, apple juice, and tomato juice
10. **INTERPRET:** antacids, baking soda, soap, ammonia, and drain cleaner
11. **INTERPRET:** distilled water

4 *Close*

BUILDING MATH SKILLS

Graphing Have students share their graphs with the class and tell about the products they listed as acids and bases. Check graphs for an x-axis that is labeled with products and a y-axis that is labeled from 0 to 14.

✏️ **WRITING HINT** Remind students that they need to label the x-axis and y-axis when they draw graphs. They should also include a title for their graphs.

MORE ON THE WEB

Learning the pH Scale Have students use the Internet to learn the pH of many common materials. Then, have students take an online quiz. Students will be asked to rank several materials in order of decreasing acidity. Have students visit www.conceptsandchallenges.com for more details.

• TEACHING RESOURCES •

💿 **Teacher's Resources CD-ROM**
Lesson Review: Chapter 9, p. 5
Enrichment: Chapter 9, p. 6
Writing Activity Outline: Study Tools, pp. 20–21
Graph Paper: Visuals, p. 4

📼 **Laboratory Video**
Segment 11: Using Indicators to Show Whether a Solution Is Acidic or Basic

Lab Activity

(pp. 198–199)

1 Prepare the Lab

Classifying Household Materials as Acids or Bases

SET-UP TIME: ⏱   **LAB TIME:** 🕐

BACKGROUND: The household materials in this activity are useful acids and bases. Some materials found in homes are strong acids and bases that are useful, but they can be dangerous when not used properly. Caution needs to be taken around all acids and bases. Labels should be checked for warnings, and directions should always be followed.

PURPOSE: Students will predict and classify various household materials as acids or bases and then use pH paper to find the pH of each material.

ALTERNATIVE MATERIALS: Other household materials can be used. However, avoid using any strong acids or bases.

SCIENCE SKILLS: Students will **predict** which materials are acids and which are bases. Then, students will **observe** and **collect data** as they use pH paper to **test** each material. They will **analyze** their data to check their predictions and determine which materials are the strongest acid and the strongest base. Students will also **form a hypothesis** about the pH of spoiled milk.

ADVANCE PLANNING: Gather the materials you will need for the lab.

2 Guide the Lab

PROCEDURE: Divide students into groups of two to four. Discuss the procedure. Emphasize the importance of using a clean stirring rod for each material to avoid contamination. Tell students to leave space between the labels on their paper towels. Discuss data collection and have students copy the data chart before beginning the activity. Provide students with a copy of the Lab Activity Report found on the Teacher's Resources CD-ROM for students to record their observations and conclusions.

LAB ACTIVITY
Classifying Household Materials as Acids or Bases

Materials
Safety goggles,
Lab apron, gloves,
12 stirring rods,
12 small test tubes and test tube rack,
Eyedroppers,
pH paper and pH chart,
Various household liquids:
Wax pencil and markers,
Paper towels

▲ **STEP 4** Clearly label the paper towels.

▲ **STEP 6** Test each liquid with pH paper.

BACKGROUND

Many times, we think of acids and bases as dangerous substances. However, your home is filled with many useful acids and bases. Many of these materials are part of your everyday life.

PURPOSE

In this activity, you will predict and classify various household materials as acids or bases. Then, you will determine the pH level of each item.

PROCEDURE 🛡 🥽 ✂ 🗑

1. Copy the chart in Figure 9-16 onto a sheet of paper. Make your predictions as to which materials will be acids and which will be bases.

2. Put on your safety goggles, lab apron, and plastic gloves. Place a few sheets of paper towel on your area.

3. Obtain 12 small test tubes and a test-tube rack. Using a wax pencil, label the test tubes with the corresponding numbers from the chart.

4. Label areas on the paper towels with the same numbers. You will leave the pH paper to dry on the paper towels.

5. Add ten drops of each household liquid into its corresponding numbered test tube.

6. Dip a clean stirring rod into the test tube. Place a drop of the material onto the pH paper. Place the pH paper on the paper towel under the correct number.

7. Allow the pH paper to dry for 1 to 2 minutes. Compare the color change to the pH chart. Record your results.

198

Teaching Options

◈ INTEGRATING EARTH SCIENCE

Testing Drinking Water The pH level of drinking water is important to know. For example, if drinking water is very acidic, the high level of acid could be an indication that lead, copper, or other metals may be leaking into the water supply. If drinking water is highly basic, it can also be an indication of contamination by substances that make the water unsafe to drink. Drinking water, as well as pool water and water from wells, lakes, and reservoirs, can be tested by using water-testing kits. These kits are available at many home centers and scientific supply houses.

Testing Soil Some soils are acidic, and some are basic. Certain types of plants grow best within a certain pH range. Demonstrate how soils are tested. Soil-testing kits can be obtained from scientific supply houses or local nurseries. Have students collect samples of soil from different areas. If possible, use some soil found under evergreens and some from open grassy fields. Indicators such as litmus paper or pH paper also can be used to test soils.
learning styles: visual, tactile

8. Repeat Steps 6 and 7 for each material. Use a new stirring rod for each material tested. Otherwise, thoroughly clean the one you have after each test.

9. Dispose of the household materials properly. Wash your hands thoroughly after all work is finished.

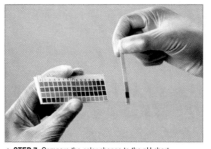

▲ **STEP 7** Compare the color change to the pH chart.

Classifying Household Materials as Acids or Bases

Material	Prediction	Observation of pH Paper	pH According to Chart
1. Ammonia			
2. Apple cider			
3. Distilled water			
4. Ginger ale			
5. Liquid soap			
6. Milk			
7. Milk of magnesia			
8. Mineral water			
9. Orange juice			
10. Salt water			
11. Tap water			
12. Tomato juice			

▲ **Figure 9-16** Copy this chart and use it to record your observations.

CONCLUSIONS

1. OBSERVE: Which household materials were acids? Which were bases? Which were neutral?

2. ANALYZE: Which household materials did not match your prediction? Explain the reason behind your prediction.

3. ANALYZE: Which household item was the strongest acid? Strongest base?

4. HYPOTHESIZE: The pH of cow's milk is about 6.5. When milk spoils, we say that it has gone sour because of the lemonlike taste. What has happened to the milk's pH?

Tips for Using Technology

Databases Have students use database software to record their observations and classifications of household materials. Databases allow students to enter and edit information, store and organize a lot of information easily, and search for specific information. Databases also allow students to arrange information by putting it in a specific order and to present information by using special layouts. Students can use database software to share their data with the class. Have students use the Database Planner on the Teacher's Resources CD-ROM to plan their databases.

• TEACHING RESOURCES •

Teacher's Resources CD-ROM
Lab Activity Report: Study Tools, pp. 16–17

Laboratory Activity Rubric: Teaching Tools, p. 8

Database Planner: Study Tools, p. 22

Laboratory Manual
Lab. Skills Worksheet 4: Organizing and Analyzing Data, pp. 13–14

TROUBLESHOOTING: Observe students and make sure that they are not contaminating the materials. Make sure that students have written numbers on their paper towels and are placing the pH papers under the correct numbers.

SAFETY TIP: Caution students not to allow any of the materials to contact their skin and eyes, and remind them to wipe up spills immediately.

EXPECTED OUTCOME: Outcomes may vary slightly. The pH of each material is approximate. (ammonia 12, apple cider 3, distilled water 7, ginger ale 3, liquid soap 10, milk 6.5, milk of magnesia 10, mineral water 7, orange juice 3, salt water 8.5, tap water 7, tomato juice 4)

LAB HINT: To increase the accuracy of the data collected, have students compare their results to the results of other groups.

3 Conclude the Lab

1. OBSERVE: Possible answer: acids: apple cider, ginger ale, orange juice, milk, and tomato juice; bases: ammonia, liquid soap, and milk of magnesia; neutral: salt water, distilled water, mineral water, and tap water
2. ANALYZE: Answers will vary but should include logical reasons behind students' original predictions.
3. ANALYZE: The strongest acid was likely to be orange juice, apple cider, or ginger ale. The strongest base was likely to be ammonia.
4. HYPOTHESIZE: It has decreased.

Use the Laboratory Activity Rubric on the Teacher's Resources CD-ROM to assess students' lab activities. Fill in the rubric with the additional information below. For this activity, students should have:

- performed the activity according to the procedure and filled in the chart with data collected during the activity.
- correctly answered the questions in complete sentences.

4 Extend the Lab

Tell students that skin has a pH of between 4 and 7. Ask them to predict the pH of various skin products and shampoos. Interested students can collect samples of various products to test their pH. Have these students make posters showing their results and present the posters to the class.

The Big Idea

(pp. 200–201)

1 Introduce

Objective Students will tell a chemical story about a hemoglobin molecule as it moves through the human body. Students will describe how hemoglobin picks up oxygen in the lungs and carbon dioxide from cells. Students will also tell how hemoglobin reacts to the changes in pH in different parts of the body.

Linking Prior Knowledge Have students review what they learned about acids and pH (Lessons 9-1 and 9-4). Ask students what they already know about hemoglobin. (It contains iron and carries oxygen.) Tell students that the pH of the blood affects how well hemoglobin carries oxygen.

2 Teach

Discussion After students have read the article, ask them what happens to their breathing when they are exercising. (It becomes faster and deeper.) Ask why this is necessary. (Muscles need more oxygen and produce more carbon dioxide as a waste product.) Tell students that when muscle cells release carbon dioxide into the blood, the carbon dioxide combines with water in the blood and forms carbonic acid. Ask what happens when carbonic acid dissolves in water. (Hydrogen ions are released, and blood becomes more acidic.) Make sure that students understand that blood that contains the most hydrogen ions is acidic and is found near the muscles. Blood that contains the least amount of hydrogen ions is least acidic and is found in the lungs because carbon dioxide is exhaled. Hemoglobin tends to pick up and hold oxygen best in the lower acidity in the lungs and release it in the higher acidity near muscle cells.
learning styles: auditory, linguistic

◆ *Integrating Life Science*

THE Big IDEA

How does pH affect the blood?

Our bodies need a balance of acid and base. Some body systems need to be acidic, like the stomach. On the other hand, blood fluid, called plasma, needs to be slightly basic. A drastic change in the pH of blood plasma can be deadly. Blood pH affects many chemical reactions in the human body, including the way oxygen gets from our lungs to our cells.

Getting oxygen to all the body cells is the job of hemoglobin, a protein in red blood cells that contains iron. Hemoglobin changes its chemical characteristics depending on pH.

When muscle cells turn sugar into energy for movement, they take up oxygen and release carbon dioxide. When you exercise, you use more energy and need more oxygen. You breathe faster and more deeply. Oxygen carried by hemoglobin flows through the bloodstream to your muscle cells. Carbon dioxide is carried back to the lungs. The more oxygen you need in your cells, the better hemoglobin gets at doing its job.

Here is how it works: In the lungs, carbon dioxide is released. This causes the pH of the blood to increase, becoming more basic. This makes hemoglobin better at grabbing oxygen molecules. In the tiny blood vessels that supply the muscles, the pH is lower. This makes the hemoglobin molecule lose its chemical grip on the oxygen that it is carrying. Hemoglobin unloads oxygen right where the muscle cells need it.

Look at the illustrations and text boxes that appear on these two pages. Then, follow the directions in the Science Log to find out more about "the big idea."◆

200

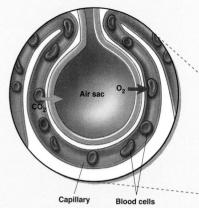

pH is Higher in Lungs
In the lungs, the pH of the blood is higher. This increases the attraction of oxygen to hemoglobin. Oxygen in the air sacs moves across the capillary membranes. The red blood cells easily pick up the needed oxygen.

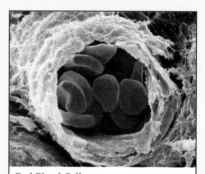

Red Blood Cells
Red blood cells travel through blood vessels. Oxygen is carried throughout the body by hemoglobin in the red blood cells.

Teaching Options

! FAST FACTS

The Human Body and pH

The pH of different fluids in the human body varies. However, each fluid has a pH range that is normal for that fluid. For example, blood has a pH that ranges from about 7.3 to 7.5, the pH of gastric juice in the stomach ranges from about 1.0 to 3.0, the pH of saliva ranges from about 6.5 to 7.5, and the pH of urine ranges from about 4.6 to 8.0.

EXTENDING THE LESSON

Taking Oxygen's Place Carbon monoxide is a poisonous gas that is released when materials, such as natural gas in furnaces, are burned. Carbon monoxide has a much stronger attraction to the hemoglobin in blood than oxygen does. When hemoglobin carries carbon monoxide, it can carry less oxygen. Carbon monoxide poisoning can result. Have interested students find out more about carbon monoxide poisoning including its symptoms.
learning styles: auditory, linguistic

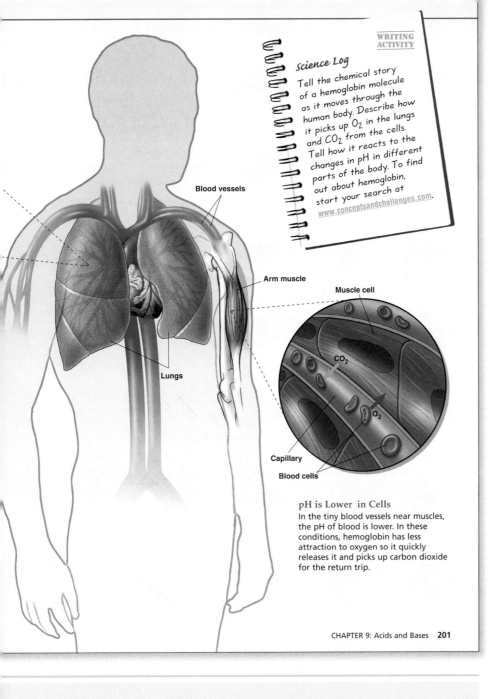

Science Log

Tell the chemical story of a hemoglobin molecule as it moves through the human body. Describe how it picks up O_2 in the lungs and CO_2 from the cells. Tell how it reacts to the changes in pH in different parts of the body. To find out about hemoglobin, start your search at www.conceptsandchallenges.com

Blood vessels

Arm muscle

Muscle cell

CO_2

O_2

Capillary

Blood cells

Lungs

pH is Lower in Cells
In the tiny blood vessels near muscles, the pH of blood is lower. In these conditions, hemoglobin has less attraction to oxygen so it quickly releases it and picks up carbon dioxide for the return trip.

CHAPTER 9: Acids and Bases **201**

Use the information in the article and in the captions to help guide students in choosing a topic for their Science Logs.

THE BIG IDEA ONLINE

How does pH affect the blood?
Have students research their Science Log Writing Activity at www.conceptsandchallenges.com. You can have students organize their log by completing the Big Idea activity online. Students may post their work in the Online Classroom Database for others to read.

Reinforcement Students can also use the Big Idea Planner or Big Idea Science Log Entry found on the Teacher's Resources CD-ROM.

3 Assess

Use the Writing Activity Rubric on the Teacher's Resources CD-ROM to assess students' Science Logs. Fill in the rubric with the additional information below. For this assignment, students should have:

- described how hemoglobin picks up oxygen in the lungs and carbon dioxide from cells.

- told how hemoglobin reacts to the changes in pH in different parts of the body.

4 Close

Making a Diagram Have students work in pairs to make a diagram of the chemical processes that occur in their stories. Students' diagrams should show what is happening to hemoglobin, oxygen, carbon dioxide, and pH in the lungs and in the muscles. Have volunteers present their diagrams to the class.
learning styles: visual, auditory

Tips for Using Technology

Word Processing Software Have students use word processing software to record their stories of a hemoglobin molecule as it moves through the human body. A simple word processing program allows them to do basic tasks such as entering and editing text. A more complex word processing program allows students to make tables, draw pictures, do math, and make graphs. Remind students to use the spell check before printing their word processing documents to share with the class.

• TEACHING RESOURCES •

Teacher's Resources CD-ROM
Big Idea: Chapter 9, p. 7
Big Idea Planner: Study Tools, pp. 11–12
Big Idea Science Log Entry: Study Tools, p. 13
Writing Activity Rubric: Teaching Tools, p. 9

1 Introduce

✎ **STUDY HINT** Before beginning this lesson, read the lesson objective with students. Then, have students review the Key Terms and their definitions.

Linking Prior Knowledge Before beginning this lesson, have students review double-replacement reactions (Lesson 8-7).

2 Teach

Discussion Display a bottle of table salt. Point out that table salt is one of many different kinds of salts. Explain that a salt is produced when an acid reacts with a base. Write the double-replacement neutralization reaction that takes place between hydrochloric acid and sodium hydroxide on the board. Ask volunteers to explain the equation to the class. **learning styles: visual, auditory**

Demonstration To demonstrate that a neutralization reaction results in a neutral substance, test a solution of table salt and water with red litmus paper and blue litmus paper. Students will observe that the indicators do not change color. **learning style: visual**

Answers to questions

▸ **DESCRIBE:** Sodium chloride and water are formed.

▸ **DEFINE:** a reaction between an acid and a base

▸ **IDENTIFY:** when an acid reacts with a base

Reinforcement Write the chemical equation $HCl + NaOH \rightarrow NaCl + H_2O$ on the board. Ask students to describe how the chemical reaction is a double-replacement reaction. (Sodium and hydrogen replace each other, forming two new compounds.)

✎ **WRITING HINT** Suggest that students use complete sentences to write a conclusion for experiments they perform. This improves the quality of their thinking as well as their writing.

9-5 What is neutralization?

Objective

Describe what happens when an acid reacts with a base.

Key Terms

neutralization (noo-truh-lih-ZAY-shuhn): reaction between an acid and a base to produce a salt and water

salt: substance formed from the negative ion of an acid and the positive ion of a base

Mixing Acids and Bases Some acids and bases are dangerous, corrosive compounds. However, different compounds are formed when acids and bases are mixed together. Hydrochloric acid and sodium hydroxide can cause burns if they are spilled on the skin. When they are mixed together, they form sodium chloride and water. Sodium chloride is a common substance known as table salt. The chemical reaction between hydrochloric acid and sodium hydroxide produces two new compounds with different properties.

▸ **DESCRIBE:** What happens when hydrochloric acid is mixed with sodium hydroxide?

Neutralization The reaction between an acid and a base forms a neutral substance. When red litmus paper is placed in a solution of table salt and water, the paper does not change color. When blue litmus paper is placed in a solution of table salt and water, the paper does not change color. Salt water is neither acidic nor basic. It is a neutral substance.

When acids and bases are mixed, a **neutralization** reaction takes place. Neutralization reactions are double-replacement reactions. Water and a salt are always formed in a neutralization reaction.

▸ **DEFINE:** What is a neutralization reaction?

Salts Sodium chloride is common table salt. It is just one of many different salts. A salt is a substance produced when an acid reacts with a base. A salt is made up of the negative ion from the acid and the positive ion from the base. Mixing sulfuric acid with sodium hydroxide produces the salt sodium sulfate and water.

▸ **IDENTIFY:** When is a salt produced?

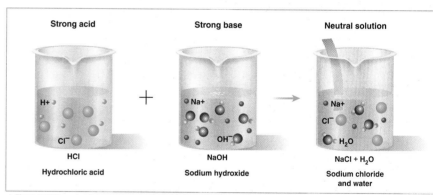

▲ **Figure 9-17** These two dangerous compounds react to form safe salt water. If the water evaporates, crystals of sodium chloride will be left.

Teaching Options

◈ INTEGRATING LIFE SCIENCE

Protecting the Stomach The lining of the human stomach contains millions of microscopic glands. Some of these glands release pepsin, an enzyme that helps in the digestion of protein. Pepsin only works in a very acidic environment, so the stomach also produces hydrochloric acid, which reduces the pH of the stomach contents to between 1 and 3. Hydrochloric acid kills many pathogens, such as bacteria, in the food.

Other glands in the stomach lining produce mucus, which lubricates the food and protects the stomach lining from the hydrochloric acid. The mucus forms a protective layer over the stomach lining, preventing the hydrochloric acid from damaging it. Have interested students research other uses of hydrochloric acid. Students can share the results of their research with the class. **learning style: auditory**

✓ CHECKING CONCEPTS

1. What is a neutral substance?
2. Why is sodium hydroxide dangerous?
3. What happens when hydrochloric acid and sodium hydroxide are mixed together?
4. What is sodium chloride?
5. What is a neutralization reaction?
6. What is a salt?
7. What happens when red litmus paper and blue litmus paper are placed in a solution of salt and water?

💡 THINKING CRITICALLY

8. Match the salts in the second column with the acids and bases in the first column from which they were formed.

Acid + Base → Salt

a. HCl + NaOH	**1.** $CaSO_4$
b. H_2SO_4 + $Ca(OH)_2$	**2.** NaCl
c. HNO_3 + HN_4OH	**3.** K_3PO_4
d. H_3PO_4 + KOH	**4.** NH_4NO_3

BUILDING SCIENCE SKILLS

Experimenting You can compare the strengths of acids by neutralizing them with a base. Try this experiment. Place 10 mL of an acid into a beaker. Add a few drops of phenolphthalein. Add a base one drop at a time to the acid and indicator. Stop when the phenolphthalein turns light pink. How many drops of base did you add? Repeat this experiment with a different acid. The stronger the acid, the more base you will have to add to neutralize it. Make a table like the one in Figure 9-18. List each acid you are testing. Record the number of drops of base needed for each.

Acid	Name and Number of Drops of Base

▲ **Figure 9-18** Copy this table. Use it to record your observations.

⚛ *Real-Life Science*

HISTORY OF SALT

The saying that people are "worth their salt" comes from a time when salt had great value. Being described as the salt of the earth was a great compliment. In many places, spilling salt was considered bad luck because it was too valuable to be wasted. Salt was so valuable in ancient Rome that soldiers were paid so they could buy it. This part of their wages was called their salary.

When table salt (NaCl) is added to water, a substance called brine is produced. Brine is used to pickle and preserve many different types of foods. Before canning and refrigeration were available, pickling was used to keep meat and vegetables from spoiling.

Today, salt is used to make ice cream, dyes, rubber, soap, leather, and many other items. Salt can be readily obtained by the evaporation of seawater, but it is usually mined like other minerals. Deposits of salt are found where prehistoric inland seas have dried up.

Thinking Critically Why do we find salt where dried-up seas used to be?

▲ **Figure 9-19** Lake Grassmere Salt Works

✓ CHECKING CONCEPTS ANSWERS

1. a substance that is neither acidic nor basic
2. It can cause burns if spilled on the skin.
3. They form sodium chloride and water.
4. table salt
5. a reaction between an acid and a base to produce a salt and water
6. a substance formed from the negative ion of an acid and the positive ion of a base
7. They do not change color.

💡 THINKING CRITICALLY ANSWERS

8. **a.** 2 **b.** 1 **c.** 4 **d.** 3

4 *Close*

BUILDING SCIENCE SKILLS

Experimenting Caution students to use safety procedures while working with acids and bases. Check for accurate data collection and recording. Have students share their results with the class.

Real-Life Science

HISTORY OF SALT

Real-Life Connection Some areas do not have enough fresh water for drinking, washing, or irrigating crops. These areas may have access to large amounts of ocean water, but drinking ocean water makes people sick and using ocean water for irrigation kills crops. The desalting, or desalinization, of ocean water results in fresh water. Some desalinization plants use a heat source to evaporate the water from ocean water. The evaporated water then condenses and is collected. This distilled water is fresh water.

Discussion Ask students: *What is left behind as a waste product after desalinization of ocean water?* (salt) Discuss what effects dumping the wastes back into the ocean might have. (It might make the ocean water too salty, which could be bad for organisms living in the area.) Ask: *What else might be done with the wastes?* (Use the salt.) learning styles: auditory, linguistic

Thinking Critically Answer
The salt was left behind when the water evaporated from the salt water in the seas.

MORE ON THE WEB

Interactive Learning Have students use the Internet to watch an interactive movie about the pH scale and neutralization. Students can also submit questions about acids and bases, view a timeline about the history of the pH scale, and do an online activity at www.conceptsand challenges.com.

ONGOING ASSESSMENT

Explaining Neutralization Ask volunteers to explain Figure 9-17 to other students.
learning styles: visual, auditory

• *TEACHING RESOURCES* •

◎ **Teacher's Resources CD-ROM**
Lesson Review: Chapter 9, p. 8
Enrichment: Chapter 9, p. 9
Laboratory Manual
Lab. Skills Worksheet 4:
Organizing and Analyzing Data, pp. 13–14

9-6 (pp. 204–205)

1 Introduce

STUDY HINT Before beginning this lesson, have students make a two-column chart. The head for the first column should be *Electrolytes*, and the head for the second column should be *Nonelectrolytes*. As students read the lesson, they should fill in both columns.

Linking Prior Knowledge Have students review ionic bonds (Lesson 4-5).

2 Teach

Demonstration Refer back to page T69 to set up a conductivity tester. Ask students if the bulb will light if you add distilled water to the tester. Place distilled water in the tester and have students observe that the bulb does not light. Ask students if the bulb will light if you add some acetic acid to the water. Add some acetic acid and have students observe that the bulb lights. Point out that acetic acid is an electrolyte because it conducts electricity when it is dissolved in water. **learning styles: visual, auditory**

Discussion Write *Distilled water, Sugar dissolved in water, Acid dissolved in water, Base dissolved in water,* and *Salt dissolved in water* on the board. Ask students which of these solutions contains an electrolyte. Circle the electrolytes. (acid, base, and salt) Explain that these substances are electrolytes because they form ions when they are dissolved in water. Distilled water contains no ions, and sugar does not form ions when it is dissolved in water. **learning styles: visual, auditory**

Answers to questions

▶ **INFER:** yes; because it conducts electricity

▶ **DEFINE:** the formation of ions

▶ **CLASSIFY:** nonelectrolyte

9-6 What is an electrolyte?

Objective

Explain how ions in a solution conduct electricity.

Key Terms

electrolyte (ee-LEHK-troh-lyt): substance that conducts an electric current when it is dissolved in water

ionization (eye-uh-nih-ZAY-shuhn): formation of ions

nonelectrolyte: substance that will not conduct an electric current when it is dissolved in water

Electrolytes A substance that conducts an electric current when it is dissolved in water is called an **electrolyte.** Pure distilled water is not a good conductor of electricity. Figure 9-20 shows what happens when electrodes connected to a battery are placed in pure water. The bulb does not light. This indicates that electricity does not flow through the circuit.

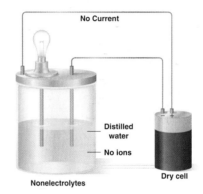

▲ **Figure 9-20** Distilled water is not a good conductor.

204

Figure 9-21 shows what happens when a small amount of hydrochloric acid is added to the water. The bulb lights. A slightly acidic solution of water is a good conductor of electricity.

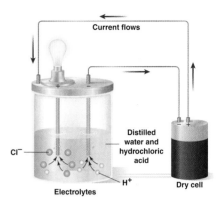

▲ **Figure 9-21** A slightly acidic solution is a good conductor.

▶ **INFER:** Is hydrochloric acid an electrolyte? Why or why not?

Ionization Electrolytes can conduct electricity because they form ions when they dissolve in water. A solution that contains ions can conduct an electric current. The ions move and carry the current through the solution.

The formation of ions is called **ionization.** When sodium chloride dissolves in water, it forms sodium (Na^+) ions and chloride (Cl^-) ions. When hydrochloric acid is added to water, it separates into hydrogent (H^+) ions and chloride (Cl^-) ions. The base potassium hydroxide forms potassium (K^+) ions and hydroxide (OH^-) ions in solution.

▶ **DEFINE:** What is ionization?

Teaching Options

EXTENDING THE LESSON

Distinguishing Between Strong and Weak Electrolytes Different compounds form ions at different rates. Strong electrolytes have higher rates of ionization than weak electrolytes. When strong electrolytes dissolve, there are more ions in solution. Such a solution is a better conductor of electricity than a solution containing a weak electrolyte. Ask students if acetic acid or hydrochloric acid is a stronger electrolyte. (hydrochloric acid) Ask a volunteer to explain why. (It forms more ions.) **learning style: auditory**

ESL/ELL STRATEGY

The Prefix **non-** The prefix *non-* means "not" and usually makes the root word mean the opposite. Ask students to add *non-* to some of the words in the lesson, such as *conductor* and *electrolyte.*

ONGOING ASSESSMENT

Identifying Electrolytes Name some electrolytes and nonelectrolytes. Have students indicate which ones are electrolytes by giving a thumbs-up sign.

Nonelectrolytes A substance that does not conduct an electric current when it is dissolved in water is called a **nonelectrolyte**. A sugar solution does not conduct electricity. Sugar is a nonelectrolyte. Nonelectrolytes do not conduct an electric current because they do not form ions in a solution.

▶ CLASSIFY: Is sugar an example of an electrolyte or a nonelectrolyte?

☑ CHECKING CONCEPTS

1. Pure water _____ conduct electricity.
2. A solution of hydrochloric acid and water is an example of an _____.
3. Acids, bases, and salts are all good _____.
4. A substance that forms _____ in a solution is a good electrolyte.
5. Sugar is an example of a _____.
6. The separation of a salt into ions is called _____.

💡 THINKING CRITICALLY

7. What ions will be formed in solutions of the following acids, bases, and salts?
   a. KCl
   b. NH$_4$OH
   c. CaCl$_2$
   d. HI
   e. Ca(OH)$_2$
   f. HNO$_3$
   g. NaBr
   h. MgSO$_4$

DESIGNING AN EXPERIMENT

Design an experiment to solve the following problem. Include a hypothesis, variables, a procedure, and a type of data to study.

PROBLEM: How can you identify a substance as an electrolyte or a nonelectrolyte?

⚛ Hands-On Activity

TESTING HOUSEHOLD MATERIALS FOR ELECTRICAL CONDUCTIVITY

You will need distilled water, several plastic cups, a conductivity tester provided by your teacher, wet paper towels, and several different samples to be tested.

1. Choose several samples to be tested, such as table salt, sugar, vinegar, ammonia, lemon juice, and baking soda.
2. Pour about 50 mL of distilled water in a clean plastic cup. Add a small amount of the sample to be tested and stir.
3. Test the sample with your conductivity tester.
4. Record your observations. Clean the electrodes (wires) one at a time with a wet paper towel.
5. Repeat Steps 2, 3, and 4 for each material to be tested.

Practicing Your Skills

6. ANALYZE: Which of your samples are electrolytes? How do you know?
7. ANALYZE: Which of your samples are nonelectrolytes? How do you know?

▲ STEP 3 Place the electrodes into the sample to test it.

MORE ON THE WEB

Learning About Fuel Cells
Have students use the Internet to learn more about fuel cells and how they are more environmentally friendly than other methods of generating electricity. Have students visit www.conceptsandchallenges.com for more details.

• TEACHING RESOURCES •

◎ **Teacher's Resources CD-ROM**
Lesson Review: Chapter 9, p. 10
Designing an Experiment: Study Tools, p. 14
Designing an Experiment Rubric: Teaching Tools, p. 7
Laboratory Manual
Lab. Challenge: Do all solutions conduct electricity? pp. 53–56

---

3 Assess

☑ CHECKING CONCEPTS ANSWERS

1. does not
2. electrolyte
3. electrolytes or conductors of electricity
4. ions
5. nonelectrolyte
6. ionization

💡 THINKING CRITICALLY ANSWERS

7. **a.** K$^+$, Cl$^-$ **b.** NH$_4$$^+$, OH$^-$ **c.** Ca^{2+}, Cl$^-$
   d. H$^+$, I$^-$ **e.** Ca^{2+}, OH$^-$ **f.** H$^+$, NO$_3$$^-$
   g. Na$^+$, Br$^-$, **h.** Mg^{2+}, SO$_4$$^{2-}$

4 Close

DESIGNING AN EXPERIMENT

Use the Designing an Experiment Rubric on the Teacher's Resources CD-ROM to assess students' experiments. Fill in the rubric with the additional information below. For this assignment, students should have:

- formed a hypothesis that states what makes a substance an electrolyte.
- designed a procedure in which a substance is dissolved in water and the solution is then tested for electrical conductivity.

Hands-On Activity

TESTING HOUSEHOLD MATERIALS FOR ELECTRICAL CONDUCTIVITY

TIME: 15–30 minutes

PURPOSE: analyzing, interpreting

SAFETY TIP: Caution students to be careful when using conductivity testers and household materials. Be sure that students wipe the electrodes with a clean, wet paper towel after each test.

ADVANCED PREPARATION: Refer to page T69 to make a conductivity tester.

TROUBLESHOOTING: If samples are not conducting electricity, use a battery that has more voltage or increase the concentration of the electrolytes by adding more of each sample to the distilled water.

Practicing Your Skills Answers

6. ANALYZE: Salt, vinegar, ammonia, lemon juice, and baking soda; they all conducted electricity when dissolved in water.

7. ANALYZE: Sugar; It did not conduct electricity when dissolved in water.

Challenges (pp. 206–208)

Chapter Summary

Review Before students begin the Challenges, review the summary with them. If time permits, have students work in pairs. Give students one summary point to describe in their own words.

STUDY HINT Have students use index cards to create flash cards for each Key Term. Have students write the Key Term on one side of the index card and the definition on the other side. Then, have students work in pairs to review the Key Terms, using their flash cards.

Key Term Challenges

MATCHING

1. base (9-2)
2. neutral (9-4)
3. indicator (9-3)
4. neutralization (9-5)
5. ionization (9-6)
6. electrolyte (9-6)
7. hydroxyl ion (9-2)

FILL IN

8. salt (9-5)
9. nonelectrolyte (9-6)
10. indicator (9-4)
11. acid (9-1)
12. pH scale (9-4)

Chapter Summary

Lesson 9-1
- **Acids** are chemical compounds that produce hydrogen ions (H⁺) when dissolved in water. They are called proton donors.

Lesson 9-2
- **Bases** are chemical compounds that produce **hydroxyl ions** (OH⁻) when dissolved in water. They are called proton acceptors.

Lesson 9-3
- Litmus paper can be used to identify both acids and bases.
- **Indicators** are chemical substances that change color in acids and bases.

Lesson 9-4
- The strength of an acid or a base depends on the number of hydrogen or hydroxyl ions in the solution.
- The **pH scale** is a measure of the concentration of H⁺ ions in a solution.

Lesson 9-5
- When acids and bases are mixed, new compounds with different properties are formed.
- The reaction between an acid and a base forms a neutral substance.
- Water and a salt are always formed in a **neutralization** reaction.
- A **salt** is made up of the negative ion from an acid and the positive ion from a base.

Lesson 9-6
- An **electrolyte** is a substance that conducts electricity when it is dissolved in water.
- Electrolytes conduct electricity because they form ions when they dissolve in water.
- The formation of ions is called **ionization**.
- **Nonelectrolytes** do not conduct electricity because they do not form ions when they dissolve in water.

Key Term Challenges

acid (p. 190)
base (p. 192)
electrolyte (p. 204)
hydroxyl ion (p. 192)
indicator (p. 194)
ionization (p. 204)
neutral (p. 196)
neutralization (p. 202)
nonelectrolyte (p. 204)
pH scale (p. 196)
salt (p. 202)

MATCHING Write the Key Term from above that best matches each description.

1. formed when metals react with water
2. neither acidic nor basic
3. changes color in acids and bases
4. reaction between an acid and a base
5. formation of ions
6. conducts an electric current in water
7. negative ion made up of a hydrogen atom and an oxygen atom

FILL IN Write the Key Term from above that best completes each statement.

8. A _____ is always formed in a neutralization reaction.
9. Sugar is a _____ because it does not conduct an electric current when it is dissolved in water.
10. Scientists use the _____ to measure the strengths of acids and bases.
11. Vinegar is an example of an _____.
12. On a _____, a neutral solution has a pH of 7.

Teaching Options

PREPARING STUDENTS FOR STANDARDIZED TESTS

Reading Strategy: Suggest to students that as they read a question on a test, they anticipate the correct answer and look for keywords in the answer choices.

Writing Strategy: Tell students that they can circle important words in a question or write keywords in the margin to make it easier to go back and check answers.

Interpreting Visuals: Remind students that when referring to the pH scale, acids are on the left side of the scale (below 7) and bases are on the right side of the scale (above 7).

ESL/ELL STRATEGY

Fill-In Questions Have English-language learners turn the fill-in sentences into questions. This may help them come up with the missing words.

Content Challenges TEST PREP

MULTIPLE CHOICE Write the letter of the term or phrase that best completes each statement.

1. Acids are sometimes called
   a. proton donors.
   b. proton acceptors.
   c. electron donors.
   d. electron acceptors.

2. When they are placed in water, all bases release
   a. chloride ions.
   b. ammonium ions.
   c. hydrogen ions.
   d. hydroxyl ions.

3. Phenolphthalein and bromthymol blue are
   a. acids.
   b. bases.
   c. electrolytes.
   d. indicators.

4. If you put a strip of blue litmus paper into a cup of vinegar, the litmus paper will turn
   a. red.
   b. yellow.
   c. green.
   d. colorless.

5. The pH of a neutral solution is
   a. 0.
   b. 7.
   c. 10.
   d. 14.

6. A solution with a pH of 2 is
   a. strongly basic.
   b. weakly basic.
   c. strongly acidic.
   d. weakly acidic.

7. A neutralization reaction is a reaction between
   a. an acid and a base.
   b. a salt and water.
   c. an acid and water.
   d. a base and water.

8. A reaction between hydrochloric acid and sodium hydroxide produces water and
   a. sodium chloride.
   b. sulfur hydroxide.
   c. hydrochloric acid.
   d. sodium sulfate.

9. Electrolytes can conduct electricity when they are dissolved in water because they form
   a. molecules.
   b. compounds.
   c. ions.
   d. salts.

10. Of the following substances, the one that is a nonelectrolyte is
    a. sodium chloride.
    b. acetic acid.
    c. potassium hydroxide.
    d. sugar.

TRUE/FALSE Write *true* if the statement is true. If the statement is false, change the underlined term to make the statement true.

11. Acids react with metals to release <u>oxygen</u> gas.

12. All bases release <u>hydrogen</u> ions in water.

13. Chemicals, such as phenolphthalein, that change color in acids and bases are called <u>indicators</u>.

14. A neutral solution has a pH of <u>4</u>.

15. A salt contains <u>positive</u> ions from an acid.

16. A neutralization reaction is a <u>double-</u>replacement reaction.

CHAPTER 9: Acids and Bases **207**

Content Challenges

MULTIPLE CHOICE

1. a (9-1)
2. d (9-2)
3. d (9-3)
4. a (9-3)
5. b (9-4)
6. c (9-4)
7. a (9-5)
8. a (9-5)
9. c (9-6)
10. d (9-6)

TRUE/FALSE

11. false; hydrogen (9-1)
12. false; hydroxyl (9-2)
13. true (9-3)
14. false; 7 (9-4)
15. false; negative (9-5)
16. true (9-5)

ALTERNATIVE ASSESSMENT

Defining Key Terms Students may define the Key Terms for this chapter in their science logs. They can also write a sentence using each Key Term. You can use the Writing Activity Rubric on the Teacher's Resources CD-ROM to evaluate students' entries.

PORTFOLIO ASSESSMENT

Making Student Portfolios Portfolio Assessment is designed to evaluate a student's performance over an extended period of time. The Chapter Self-Check and the Cause-and-Effect Diagram are some of the reproducibles on the Teacher's Resources CD-ROM that they can include in their portfolios. You can use the Portfolio Assessment Rubric also found on the Teacher's Resources CD-ROM to assess students' portfolios.

Concept Challenges

WRITTEN RESPONSE

1. **ANALYZE:** Acids and bases are corrosive and can cause burns. (9-1, 9-2)
2. **CLASSIFY:** The unknown solution is an acid. (9-3, 9-4)
3. **PREDICT:** Yes; Possible answers: It is an acid, and acids release ions when they are dissolved in water. Ions in water conduct electricity. Acids are electrolytes. Acids conduct electricity. (9-6)
4. **EXPLAIN:** Possible answer: An acid, such as acetic acid or hydrochloric acid, releases hydrogen ions when dissolved in water. A base, such as sodium hydroxide or potassium hydroxide, releases hydroxyl ions when dissolved in water. (9-1, 9-2)

INTERPRETING A TABLE (9-1)

5. hydrogen
6. $HC_2H_3O_2$
7. nitric acid and sulfuric acid
8. $H_3C_6H_5O_7$; citric acid

Chapter Project Wrap-Up

CONTRASTING ACIDS AND BASES

Students' projects can be exhibited around the classroom. Students can present their posters to the class. You can use the Group Activity Rubric found on the Teacher's Resources CD-ROM to assess students' projects. Fill in the rubric with the additional information below. For this project, students should have:

- created posters that show the contrasting properties of acids and bases, including the properties of both types of substances, how these substances react in water, and pictures and examples of acids and bases.

- used indicators and the pH scale to show the differences between acids and bases.

Concept Challenges TEST PREP

WRITTEN RESPONSE Answer each of the following questions in complete sentences.

1. **ANALYZE:** Why should you never taste an unknown substance to identify it as an acid or a base?
2. **CLASSIFY:** An unknown solution is found to have a pH of 3. Congo red turns blue in this solution, and bromthymol blue turns yellow. Is the unknown solution an acid or a base?
3. **PREDICT:** Will the unknown solution in exercise 2 conduct an electric current? How do you know?
4. **EXPLAIN:** What is the difference between an acid and a base? Use specific examples to explain.

INTERPRETING A TABLE Use Figure 9-22 to answer each of the following questions.

5. What element do all of the acids listed have in common?
6. What is the chemical formula for acetic acid?
7. Which acids are used to make fertilizers?
8. What is the chemical formula of the acid found in citrus fruits? What is the name of this acid?

COMMON ACIDS		
Acid	Chemical Formula	Found In
Acetic acid	$HC_2H_3O_2$	Vinegar
Boric acid	H_3BO_3	Antiseptic
Carbonic acid	H_2CO_3	Club soda
Citric acid	$H_3C_6H_5O_7$	Citrus fruit flavors
Hydrochloric acid	HCl	Digestive juices
Nitric acid	HNO_3	Fertilizers
Sulfuric acid	H_2SO_4	Fertilizers, batteries

▲ Figure 9-22

Teaching Options

UNIT CHALLENGE ONLINE

Acids and Bases Send students to www.conceptsand challenges.com. Have them complete the online activity for Unit 3. Students will research the use of health and industrial acids and bases, and investigate the pH of various substances. Have students post their results on the Online Classroom Database.

• TEACHING RESOURCES •

Teacher's Resources CD-ROM

Key Term Review: Chapter 9, p. 11

Chapter 9 Test: pp. 12–13

Writing Activity Rubric: Teaching Tools, p. 9

Chapter Self-Check: Teaching Tools, p.11

Cause-and-Effect Diagram: Study Tools, p. 3

Portfolio Assessment Rubric: Teaching Tools, p. 10

Group Activity Rubric: Teaching Tools, p. 6

PLANNING GUIDE

◆ **TEACHING THE CHAPTER** This chapter should take approximately 6–9 days to complete instruction and assessment.

	Skills and Features	Projects and Activities	Achieve Science Literacy	Meet Individual Needs
Chapter 10 Opener p. T209	OBSERVE	• Chapter Project		
Lesson 10-1 What is an ore? pp. T210–T211 Standards: B1b, B1c	OBSERVE, DEFINE, IDENTIFY • Building Science Skills • Real-Life Science	• More on the Web • Integrating Earth Science	• Study Hint • Ongoing Assessment	CD-ROM Flowchart Writing Activity Outline
Lesson 10-2 How are metals removed from their ores? pp. T212–T213 Standard: B1b	ANALYZE, SEQUENCE, DESCRIBE • Building Science Skills • Integrating Environmental Science	• Cooperative Learning • More on the Web	• Study Hint • Reading Strategy • Writing Hint	• Reteach
Lesson 10–3 What are alloys? pp. T214–T215 Standards: B1b, B1c	DEFINE, IDENTIFY, INFER • Investigate • Web InfoSearch	• Cooperative Learning • Lab Skills Worksheet	• Study Hint	• ESL/ELL Strategy CD-ROM Enrichment Activity
Big Idea What is the importance of alloys in bike design? pp. T216–T217 Standards: B1b, B1c	RESEARCH, COMMUNICATE, ANALYZE • Science Log: Writing Activity	• Big Idea Online • Close Activity	• Tips for Using Technology	CD-ROM Big Idea Planner
Lesson 10-4 Why are some metals more active than others? pp. T218–T219 Standard: B1b	EXPLAIN, IDENTIFY, INFER • Designing an Experiment • People in Science	• Cooperative Learning • More on the Web	• Study Hint • Reading Strategy	CD-ROM Designing an Experiment
Lesson 10-5 What is corrosion? pp. T220–T221 Standard: B1b	DESCRIBE, IDENTIFY, PREDICT • Health and Safety Tip • Hands-On Activity	• Extending the Lesson • More on the Web • Lab Challenge	• Study Hint • Ongoing Assessment	CD-ROM Concept Map Laboratory Video

Planning Guide continues on next page.

Standards: For details on the correlation to National Science Standards see pages *xx–xxi*.

	Skills and Features	Projects and Activities	Achieve Science Literacy	Meet Individual Needs
Lab Activity **Testing Activity and Corrosion of Metals** pp. T222–T223 Standard: B1b	OBSERVE, INFER, ANALYZE • Set-Up Time: 15 min • Lab Time: 30–40 min and 15–20 min needed 4 or 5 days later	• Lab Skills Worksheets • Extend the Lab Activity	• Tips for Using Technology	CD-ROM Lab Activity Report Database Planner
Lesson 10-6 **How are metals plated?** pp. T224–T225	ANALYZE, HYPOTHESIZE, DEFINE • Designing an Experiment • Hands-On Activity	• More on the Web	• Study Hint • Ongoing Assessment	• ESL/ELL Strategy CD-ROM Concept Map Designing an Experiment
Chapter 10 Challenges pp. T226–T228	• Chapter Summary • Key Term Challenges • Content Challenges • Concept Challenges	• Chapter Project Wrap-Up	• Study Hint • Preparing Students for Standardized Tests	• ESL/ELL Strategy CD-ROM Chapter Self-Check Weekly Journal

Teacher Notes

_____

_____

_____

_____

_____

_____

_____

_____

_____

_____

_____

_____

_____

Chapter 10 Metals

▲ Figure 10-1 Copper mine at Bingham Canyon, Utah

All minerals are elements or compounds with definite chemical compositions. Minerals form by natural processes. To get minerals from Earth, they must be mined. Raw mineral ores are usually part of the rocks mined. Once mined, ores must undergo a process to separate the pure metals from the rest of the ore. Metals have properties that make them very useful. Most metals are strong and conduct heat and electricity. Metals can also be mixed with other metals to form alloys such as brass, bronze, and sterling silver.

▶Why do you think raw ores must be processed?

Contents

Teaching Options

ASSESSMENT PLANNER

For assessment in the Student Edition, see the following pages:

Content Assessment
Checking Concepts: pp. 211, 213, 215, 219, 221, 225
Thinking Critically: pp. 211, 213, 215, 219, 221, 225
Chapter Challenges: pp. 226–228

Alternative Assessment
Building Skills: pp. 211, 213
Web InfoSearch: p. 215
Science Log: p. 217

Performance-Based Assessment
Designing an Experiment: pp. 219, 225
Hands-On Activity: pp. 221, 225
Lab Activity: pp. 222–223

• TEACHING RESOURCES •

Teacher's Resources CD-ROM
Lesson Review: Ch. 10, pp. 2, 3, 4, 8, 9, 10
Enrichment: Ch. 10, pp. 5, 6
Key Term Review: Ch. 10, p. 11
Chapter 10 Test: pp. 12–13
Laboratory Manual: pp. 5–10, 13–14, 57–60

Laboratory Video
Segment 12: Determining the Relative Activity of Different Metals

---

Chapter 10
Metals

Chapter Overview

In this chapter, students will learn about common ores, the metals they contain, and how metals are removed from ores. Students will identify alloys, list the most active metals from the periodic table, explain what causes metals to corrode, and describe how metals are plated.

About Figure 10-1 The Bingham Canyon open-pit copper mine has yielded more than 11 billion kg (12 million tons) of copper since its opening in 1906. It is about 4.0 km (2.5 mi) wide and has a depth of about 0.8 km (0.5 mi).

Answer Pure metals must be separated from the other materials with which they are mixed.

Linking Prior Knowledge

For this chapter, students should recall:

• the properties of metals (Lesson 3-8).

• writing and balancing chemical equations and identifying oxidation and reduction (Lessons 8-2 and 8-3).

Chapter Project

CORROSION PREVENTION DISPLAY

MATERIALS: iron strips or nails, paint or oil, magnesium ribbon

The most common type of corrosion is rust, the product of a chemical reaction between oxygen from air and iron. Before students read the chapter, have them protect iron strips or nails with paint or oil to prevent contact with the air. Then, have them fasten a piece of magnesium ribbon to a nail. (Magnesium reacts more readily than iron does, and it will corrode first, protecting the iron.) Have students place unprotected and protected nails in a warm, moist environment that would promote rusting. At the end of the chapter, students can display the results of their experiment. They can also write a report on the procedures and resulting conclusions. Students can use the Lab Activity Report found on the Teacher's Resources CD-ROM. **learning styles: visual, tactile**

10-1 (pp. 210–211)

1 Introduce

STUDY HINT Have students copy the title of each section in outline format in their notebooks. As students read this lesson, they should write the main idea of each section.

Linking Prior Knowledge Ask students to recall the definition of a compound (Lesson 4-1). Write the chemical formula for the compound iron disulfide (FeS_2) on the board, and have students identify the two elements that make up the compound. (iron and sulfur)

2 Teach

Discussion Discuss with students that even though a rock or mineral contains a metal, it is not necessarily an ore. Sometimes the metal makes up only a small percentage of the material in the rock or mineral. Sometimes the process to remove the metal is so involved that it costs more to recover the metal than the metal is worth. Any time it is not economical to recover a metal from a mineral or rock, the mineral or rock is not considered to be an ore.
learning style: auditory

Demonstration Display several ores and the metals derived from each. Have students note the color and luster of each ore. Define an ore as a rock or mineral from which a useful metal or other element can be removed economically. Ask students to name some useful metals.
learning styles: visual, auditory

Reinforcement For each ore in Figure 10-2, ask students to identify the elements in the compound and how many atoms of each element are represented in the chemical formula. **learning styles: visual, logical/mathematical**

Answers to questions

▶1 DEFINE: a rock or mineral from which a useful metal or other element can be removed economically

▶2 ANALYZE: iron

▶3 IDENTIFY: magnesite

10-1 What is an ore?

Objective
Name some common ores and the metals that are obtained from them.

Key Term
ore: rock or mineral from which a useful metal or element can be removed economically

Ores Metals are found in nature, usually in Earth's crust. They are often combined with other elements. The metals have to be removed from their compounds before they can be used. An **ore** is a rock or mineral from which an element, often a metal, can be removed. Many types of ores are found in nature.

Metals are a useful part of your life. Some of the most common metals are iron, copper, aluminum, and lead. These metals are used to make cars, appliances, electrical wires, jewelry, and many other objects. Metals are shiny and are usually good conductors of both heat and electricity. Other useful properties of most metals are their abilities to be stretched into thin wires and pounded into thin sheets.

▶1 DEFINE: What is an ore?

Common Ores All rock contains minerals. Rock often contains small quantities of a metal or valuable mineral. However, if the metal or mineral is not present in great enough amounts, the rock is not an ore. It is not mined. Pyrite is a good example of such a rock.

Pyrite, also called fool's gold, is yellow and has a shiny surface. Its chemical name is iron sulfide. As its name implies, pyrite contains iron. However, it does not contain enough iron to make it worthwhile to mine.

Hematite is an ore that is mined because iron is present in greater quantities. Pure iron can be removed from hematite by heating it. Figure 10-2 shows some other common ores and the metals that can be removed from them.

▶2 ANALYZE: What metal is obtained from the ore hematite?

Types of Ores The metals in an ore are usually combined with oxygen, sulfur, or carbon. A metal combined with oxygen is called an oxide. A metal combined with sulfur is called a sulfide. A metal combined with carbon and oxygen is called a carbonate.

▶3 IDENTIFY: Which of the ores in Figure 10-2 is a carbonate?

METALLIC ORES

| Hematite Iron Fe_2O_3 | Bauxite Aluminum Al_2O_3 | Galena Lead PbS |
| Cuprite Copper Cu_2O | Sphalerite Zinc ZnS | Magnesite Magnesium $MgCO_3$ |

▲ **Figure 10-2** This chart shows some ores, their formulas, and the metal obtained from that ore.

210

Teaching Options

◆ INTEGRATING EARTH SCIENCE

Concentrating Copper Ores Copper ore often contains less than 10 percent copper, usually in the form of chalcopyrite ($CuFeS_2$). Copper ore also contains large amounts of iron sulfide and other material. Transporting and processing the ore in this stage would be too costly. To reduce the cost, the copper is concentrated by a method called flotation. The first step in this method is to pulverize the ore. The ore is then mixed with oil and water in a large tank. The oil adheres to the iron sulfide and copper sulfide, while the water wets the other materials. Compressed air is pumped onto the mix, causing it to froth. The buoyancy of the froth lifts the sulfides to the top of the tank as the other materials fall. The froth is skimmed off and then dried, yielding an ore with increased concentrations of copper and iron sulfide for further processing. Have students create flowcharts that show this process. Students can use the Flowchart found on the Teacher's Resources CD-ROM.

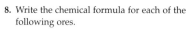

☑ CHECKING CONCEPTS

1. An ore is made of a _____ and other elements.

2. Three types of ores are sulfides, oxides, and _____.

3. Pyrite is a combination of sulfur and _____.

4. Useful _____ can be removed from rocks and minerals.

💡 THINKING CRITICALLY

5. INFER: What element must be removed from an oxide ore in order to obtain the useful metal?

6. INFER: What element must be removed from sphalerite in order to obtain zinc?

7. ANALYZE: Gold and silver are not found combined with other elements. Are gold and silver examples of oxides, sulfides, or carbonates? How do you know?

8. Write the chemical formula for each of the following ores.

   a. sphalerite
   b. magnesite
   c. hematite
   d. bauxite
   e. cuprite
   f. galena

BUILDING SCIENCE SKILLS

Observing Metals are a useful part of your life. Look at the objects you use around the house. Make a list of all the objects that are made of metal. How many objects have metal parts? Do most of the objects have some parts that are metal? What kinds of metals are used?

Real-Life Science

DESIGNING AND MAKING JEWELRY

Even before Columbus arrived in the Americas, the Incas of South America crafted jewelry of gold and silver. There is evidence in both South America and Central America that jewelry making was widespread. Metal articles that have been discovered are the forerunners of southwestern-style jewelry.

During the mid 1800s, Mexican silversmiths introduced the art of designing silver jewelry to the Navajo. Because silver was in short supply, early Navajo silversmiths used Mexican and U.S. coins as their source of this metal. Sometimes they melted down silver candlesticks and teapots. By the 1920s, silver could be purchased in the form of sheet metal and wire.

The Navajo incorporated local minerals, such as turquoise, in their jewelry designs. Turquoise, a blue compound, contains copper and aluminum phosphate. Deposits of iron in the mineral cause it to have a greener color. Most of the turquoise used by the Navajo and other Native Americans comes from Mexico, Arizona, New Mexico, Nevada, and Colorado.

Thinking Critically Why do you think the Navajo used coins and other objects for their supply of silver?

▲ **Figure 10-3** This person is making turquoise and silver jewelry.

CHAPTER 10: Metals **211**

---

3 Assess

☑ CHECKING CONCEPTS ANSWERS

1. metal
2. carbonates
3. iron
4. metals

💡 THINKING CRITICALLY ANSWERS

5. INFER: oxygen
6. INFER: sulfur
7. ANALYZE: Gold and silver are not oxides, sulfides, or carbonates because they are found as pure elements instead of in compounds.
8. a. ZnS
   b. $MgCO_3$
   c. Fe_2O_3
   d. Al_2O_3
   e. Cu_2O
   f. PbS

4 Close

BUILDING SCIENCE SKILLS

Observing Answers will vary. Students will probably notice that metallic items differ according to use. Items that require strength, such as structural metals, use materials such as steel that contain strong metals. Metals such as aluminum or magnesium are used in objects such as baseball bats, lawn chairs, and umbrellas, which require a metal with relatively little weight.

Real-Life Science

DESIGNING AND MAKING JEWELRY

Real-Life Connection Many craft and hobby shops offer courses in jewelry making. Tell students who would like to learn more about designing and making jewelry to contact a local craft store.

Discussion Ask students who may have jewelry made of metals, beads, or gemstones to identify the materials and, if possible, show them to the rest of the class. Ask students to identify some properties of metals and gemstones that make them useful in jewelry making.

Thinking Critically Answer
The Navajo used Mexican and U.S. silver coins and objects because pure silver was in short supply.

MORE ON THE WEB

Fool's Gold Pyrite, or fool's gold, is a popular ore for collectors and hobbyists. Have students visit www.concepts andchallenges.com to learn more about pyrite. Then, have students answer the questions that follow this activity.

● TEACHING RESOURCES ●

Teacher's Resources CD-ROM
Lesson Review: Chapter 10, p. 2

Writing Activity Outline: Study Tools, pp. 21–22

Flowchart: Study Tools, p. 6

ONGOING ASSESSMENT

Determining Ores Ask students: *When would a rock not be considered an ore?* (when it does not contain a metal that would yield a certain value)

10-2 (pp. 212–213)

1 Introduce

STUDY HINT Before beginning this lesson, have students make a three-column chart with the titles of each section in the columns. As students read the lesson, they should fill in the steps for removing metals from each type of ore.

Linking Prior Knowledge Have students review chemical reactions (Lesson 8-1), chemical equations (Lesson 8-2), and oxidation and reduction (Lesson 8-3).

2 Teach

Discussion Discuss the two steps needed to remove a metal from a sulfide or carbonate ore. Be sure that students understand that two steps are necessary to remove a metal from a sulfide or carbonate ore, whereas only one step is needed to remove a metal from an oxide ore.
learning style: auditory

READING STRATEGY Remind students that when they read chemical equations, the arrow that points to the right is read as "yields."

Answers to questions

1 DESCRIBE: by reduction, in which oxygen is removed from an ore

2 IDENTIFY: by roasting, which removes sulfur from the ore, forming an oxide, and then by reduction, which removes oxygen

3 EXPLAIN: to drive off carbon dioxide gas

WRITING HINT Tell students that when they write a chemical formula, they should make sure that they balance the equation. The number of atoms of each element on either side of the arrow must be the same.

10-2 How are metals removed from their ores?

Objective
Describe how some metals are removed from their ores.

Key Terms
reduction: process of removing oxygen from an ore

roasting: process in which an ore is heated in air to produce an oxide

Removing Metals from Oxide Ores Metals are removed from their ores through chemical processes. The three common types of ores are oxides, sulfides, and carbonates. The different types of ores require different processes to remove the metals they contain. Metals are usually removed from oxides.

Suppose you want to separate copper from cuprite (Cu_2O). You could combine two parts of cuprite to one part of carbon and heat the mixture. This process is shown in the following chemical equation.

$$2Cu_2O + C \rightarrow 4Cu + CO_2\uparrow$$
cuprite   carbon   copper   carbon dioxide

One atom of carbon and two atoms of oxygen combined to form one molecule of carbon dioxide. The CO_2 escaped as a gas, as shown by the arrow pointing upward. The oxygen was separated from the copper. When the carbon dioxide was formed, four atoms of copper were left over.

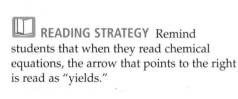
▼ **Figure 10-4** When ore is processed, the resulting metals are in liquid form until they cool.

For any oxide ore, the metal is obtained by removing the oxygen. The process of removing oxygen from an ore is called **reduction**.

1 DESCRIBE: How is a metal removed from an oxide?

Metals from Sulfide Ores Two steps are needed to remove the metal from a sulfide ore. The first step is called roasting. In **roasting**, an ore is heated in air to produce an oxide. For example, suppose galena (PbS) is roasted. Galena is a sulfide. After roasting, it forms an oxide called litharge. This process is shown in the following chemical equation.

$$2PbS + 3O_2 \rightarrow 2PbO + 2SO_2$$
galena   oxygen   litharge   sulfur dioxide

Once the ore has been changed into an oxide, the oxygen can be removed by reduction.

$$2PbO + C \rightarrow 2Pb + CO_2\uparrow$$
litharge   carbon   lead   carbon dioxide

2 IDENTIFY: How is a metal removed from a sulfide?

Metals from Carbonate Ores A two-step process is also used to separate metals from carbonate ores. For example, the first step in removing calcium from limestone, $CaCO_3$, is to heat the limestone in the absence of air. This process drives off carbon dioxide gas as shown in the following equation.

$$CaCO_3 + heat \rightarrow CaO + CO_2\uparrow$$
calcium   calcium   carbon dioxide
carbonate   oxide

The second step in the process is to pass an electric current through melted calcium oxide. The passage of the electric current causes the compound to decompose, or break down, into its elements, calcium and oxygen.

$$2CaO + electricity \rightarrow 2Ca + O_2\uparrow$$

3 EXPLAIN: What is the purpose of heating a carbonate ore?

Teaching Options

COOPERATIVE LEARNING

Reducing and Roasting Ores
Have students work in pairs. Have one partner write a description of removing metals from oxide ores, while the other partner writes a balanced equation illustrating the method. Have students reverse roles to describe the removal of metals from carbonate and sulfide ores.
learning styles: interpersonal, logical/mathematical

RETEACH

Reduction and Roasting Use different-colored gumdrops or clay spheres (representing ions and atoms) and toothpicks (representing chemical bonds) to model cuprite (Cu_2O) and carbon (C). Then, show how chemical bonds are broken and re-formed when cuprite and carbon react, forming copper and carbon dioxide according to the chemical equation $2Cu_2O + C \rightarrow 4Cu + CO_2$. Ask students to model the two steps involved in obtaining lead from galena.
learning styles: visual, tactile

METALLURGY

✓ CHECKING CONCEPTS

1. Obtaining metals from _____ ores is usually a two-step process.

2. Metals are usually removed from _____ ores.

3. In the process of _____, a sulfide or carbonate is made into an oxide.

4. Both roasting and reduction require energy in the form of _____.

5. In the process of _____, oxygen is removed from the ore.

💡 THINKING CRITICALLY

6. **ANALYZE:** Look at the chemical equations for removing magnesium from magnesite ($MgCO_3$). What is missing from each equation?

   $MgCO_3 + heat \rightarrow$ _____ $+ CO_2$

   2 _____ $+ electricity \rightarrow 2Mg + O_2$

---

7. **SEQUENCE:** The following two equations show the two steps involved in removing zinc from the ore sphalerite. Which equation shows Step 1? Which equation shows Step 2?

   $$2ZnO + C \rightarrow 2Zn + CO_2$$

   $$2ZnS + 3O_2 \rightarrow 2ZnO + 2SO_2$$

8. **ANALYZE:** In exercise 7, how many molecules of sphalerite were used in Step 1? How many molecules of zinc were produced in Step 2?

BUILDING SCIENCE SKILLS

Balancing Equations Write balanced equations for the following reduction reactions.

$$C + CuO \rightarrow Cu + CO_2$$

$$C + PbO \rightarrow Pb + CO_2$$

$$C + ZnO \rightarrow Zn + CO_2$$

▲ **Figure 10-5** Open-pit iron mines near Lake Superior

◈ Integrating Environmental Science

TOPICS: mining, the environment

METALLURGY

Metallurgy (MEHT-uh-luhr-jee) is the science and art of separating metals from their ores. Metallurgy began in about 4000 B.C. in the Middle East. Copper was the first metal to be used. The remains of copper mines have been found throughout parts of the Middle East. Over the centuries, ores containing tin, iron, silver, and gold were successfully mined and the metals separated from their ores.

Ores must be removed from Earth by mining before the metals can be obtained. For example, at one time an important source of the iron ore called hematite was in Minnesota. This mine was near Lake Superior. Open-pit mining was the process used. It has damaged the environment.

A two step process is used to separate a metal from its ore. First, the ore is broken up and crushed. The smaller particles are then separated either by hand or by using machines. Next, the metal is removed from the remaining bits of ore. This process can involve roasting and reduction, or simply heating the ore in a furnace. The metal that results from the second step is almost, but not quite, pure. Further refining of the metal is necessary to obtain a completely pure metal. Once the needed purity is reached, the metal can be worked. This means the metal can be used for the purpose intended.

Thinking Critically How might mining damage the environment?

MORE ON THE WEB

Describing Types of Ores
Have students visit
www.conceptsandchallenges.com
to learn about the types of ores found in the three most common groups: sulfides, carbonates, and oxides. Then, have students write a short report describing the types of ores found in each of the three groups.

• TEACHING RESOURCES •

◎ **Teacher's Resources CD-ROM**
Lesson Review: Chapter 10, p. 3

---

3 Assess

✓ CHECKING CONCEPTS ANSWERS

1. sulfide and carbonate
2. oxide
3. roasting
4. heat
5. reduction

💡 THINKING CRITICALLY ANSWERS

6. **ANALYZE:** MgO, MgO
7. **SEQUENCE:**

   Step 1: $2ZnS + 3O_2 \overset{\Delta}{\rightarrow} 2ZnO + 2SO_2$

   Step 2: $2ZnO + C \overset{\Delta}{\rightarrow} 2Zn + CO_2$

8. **ANALYZE:** 2; 2

4 Close

BUILDING SCIENCE SKILLS ANSWERS

Balancing Equations

$C + 2CuO \rightarrow 2Cu + CO_2$
$C + 2PbO \rightarrow 2Pb + CO_2$
$C + 2ZnO \rightarrow 2Zn + CO_2$

◈ Integrating Environmental Science

TOPICS: mining, the environment

METALLURGY

Environmental-Science Connection The work of medieval alchemists contributed to the science of metallurgy. Alchemists were people who tried to turn less costly metals into gold or silver. Although they were not successful, the work of alchemists was important because they discovered and compiled a great deal of information about metals and their uses.

Discussion Ask students: *What is metallurgy?* (the science and art of separating metals from their ores) *Why is it considered both a science and an art?* (Possible answer: A scientific method is followed, and the result can be a pleasing arrangement or use of the metal.)

Thinking Critically Answer
Possible answers: Habitats are destroyed; mining wastes pollute the land; and open mining areas are unsightly. Be sure to inform students that in most areas, open-pit mines must be reclaimed when they are no longer used. The land must be leveled, replanted, and otherwise restored.

10-3 (pp. 214–215)

1 Introduce

🔍 INVESTIGATE

TIME: 15 minutes

PURPOSE: Students will compare the properties of two types of alloys.

MATERIALS: safety goggles, empty soda can and empty vegetable can, balance, magnet, towel, hammer

SAFETY TIP: Be sure that the cans do not have any sharp edges. If there are sharp edges, have students use tongs to handle the cans. Be sure that students wear safety goggles while anyone in the class is trying to crush the cans.

PROCEDURE: Thoroughly wash each can and let it air-dry. Have students preview the activity and construct a data table for their observations. Even though students may not be able to lift a can with the magnet, have students note if they detect any type of magnetic attraction. To safely test the crushability of the cans, have students place the cans on their sides, place a towel over the cans, and then use a hammer to try to crush them.

THINK ABOUT IT: Possible answers: The vegetable can has a greater mass than the soda can. The vegetable can is slightly attracted to the magnet, whereas the soda can is not. The soda can is easier to crush than the vegetable can. Each can is made up of different types of metals.

🖊️ **STUDY HINT** Have students write the lesson title and objective in their notebooks. As students read the lesson, tell them to write the information that meets the objective.

Linking Prior Knowledge Have students recall the characteristics of a mixture (a material made up of two or more substances that can be separated by a physical change; Lesson 4-2)

2 Teach

Discussion Point out that alloys are mixtures of metals that are produced to take advantage of the properties of each of the metals they contain. For example, airplanes use alloys that include magnesium, titanium, and aluminum, which are strong and lightweight.
learning style: auditory

10-3 What are alloys?

🔍 INVESTIGATE

Comparing Alloys
HANDS-ON ACTIVITY

1. Take an empty soda can and an empty vegetable can.
2. Find the mass of each can.
3. With a magnet, try to pick up each type of can.
4. Placing the cans on the floor, attempt to crush each one.
5. Record your results.

THINK ABOUT IT: What differences did you notice between the two cans? Explain why these differences occur.

STEP 2

Objective
Identify some alloys and their uses.

Key Term
alloy: material made of a mixture of two or more metals

Pure Metals Through roasting and reduction, a metal can be separated from its ore. Pure metals have certain properties.

- They are solids at room temperature (21°C). The only exception is mercury, which is a liquid.
- They are malleable. They can be hammered into different shapes.
- They are ductile. They can be made into wires.
- Most are good conductors of both heat and electricity.

1️⃣ **LIST:** What are the properties of pure metals?

Alloys Two pure metals or more can be mixed to form a material called an **alloy**. The properties of an alloy differ from the properties of the original metals. They may form a solid solution or they may just be a mixture of the metals. For example, brass is an alloy of copper and zinc. Brass is harder than either copper or zinc. Brass is used in water pipes because it lasts longer than either copper or zinc. Many things you use are made of an alloy instead of pure metal. This is because most alloys are

214

stronger than pure metals. Figure 10-6 shows some alloys, the metals that make them up, and some uses for the different alloys.

ALLOYS		
Alloy	**Elements**	**Uses**
Steel	Iron, chromium, nickel, carbon	Bridges, buildings, tools
Brass	Copper, zinc	Plumbing
Bronze	Copper, tin	Machine parts
Pewter	Tin, copper, antimony	Dishes, cups
Sterling silver	Silver, copper	Jewelry
Alnico	Iron, aluminum, nickel, cobalt	Magnets
Nichrome	Nickel, iron, chromium, manganese	Electrical wires

▲ Figure 10-6

2️⃣ **DEFINE:** What is an alloy?

Alloys of Steel Steel is one of the most useful alloys ever developed. Iron is the main element used to make steel. By combining iron with different amounts of chromium, nickel, and carbon, different alloys of steel can be made. One alloy of steel used today is called low-alloy steel. Low-alloy steel contains small amounts of nickel, chromium, molybdenum, tungsten, titanium, niobium, and vanadium. Low-alloy steel is very strong and sturdy. It is used to make machine parts and the metal supports on bridges and buildings. Stainless steel is a type of low-alloy steel.

Teaching Options

❗ FAST FACTS Types of Alloys

Most alloys are solid solutions, homogenous mixtures containing a metal. Alloys are produced by mixing melted metal with one or more other elements and allowing the mixture to cool and solidify into metallic crystals.

Substitutional Alloys Substitutional alloys are alloys in which the atoms of the mixed metals are about the same size. Because of the atoms' similar sizes, an atom of one metal can replace, or substitute, for an atom of another metal in the metal crystal. Brass (an alloy of zinc and copper) is an example of a substitutional alloy.

Interstitial Alloys Alloys in which the atoms of one metal are much smaller than the other are called interstitial alloys. Because of the difference in size, the smaller atoms can easily fit into the interstices, the spaces between the larger atoms in the metallic crystal. Examples include the many alloys of steel in which carbon atoms fill the spaces between the much larger iron atoms in the metallic crystal, making it stronger.

▲ **Figure 10-7** A turbofan engine on a KC-135 Strato tanker

Another alloy of steel is called high-alloy steel. High-alloy steel contains larger amounts of nickel, chromium, and the other metals found in low-alloy steel. High-alloy steel is very shiny. It is used to make cooking utensils, cutting tools, and jet-engine parts.

▶ **IDENTIFY:** What is the main element in any steel alloy?

Ancient to Modern Uses of Bronze The Bronze Age was a period in history that existed for nearly 2,000 years. Over 4,000 years ago, people discovered that combining copper with tin produced a very strong alloy called bronze. Pots, bowls, weapons, and other utensils were made from bronze. With the discovery of iron, the Bronze Age ended.

▲ **Figure 10-8** Bronze can be easily cast into many useful objects, including sculptures.

Today, bronze is still used, although it is more expensive than brass. It can often be found in plumbing fixtures. Bronze is also used when there will be exposure to salt water because it does not react with the minerals in salt water.

▶ **EXPLAIN:** What makes bronze such a useful alloy?

✓ CHECKING CONCEPTS

1. _____ is an alloy of iron, carbon, and other elements such as nickel or chromium.

2. Most metals are _____ at room temperature.

3. Pewter is a combination of tin, _____, and antimony.

4. _____ is harder than the metals that are used to make it.

5. All _____ are malleable.

6. _____ is the only metal that is liquid at room temperature (21°C).

7. Pure metals _____ good conductors of heat and electricity.

8. Because metals are _____, they can be made into wires.

9. _____ is made of silver and copper.

💡 THINKING CRITICALLY

10. **INFER:** Electrical wires are usually made of copper. Why is a pure metal better than an alloy for electrical wires?

11. **ANALYZE:** Why do you think there are different types of alloys of steel?

Web InfoSearch

Amalgam An alloy of mercury is called an amalgam (uh-MAL-guhm). One of the most used amalgams is made up of mercury, silver, tin, copper, and zinc. This amalgam is sometimes used by dentists for filling teeth. The advantage of this alloy is that it will fill a cavity completely. It becomes rigid and can withstand the temperature changes in the mouth from hot and cold foods.

SEARCH: Use the Internet to find out more about amalgam. Start your search at www.conceptsandchallenges.com. Some key search words are **amalgam, amalgam mercury,** and **amalgam harmful.**

Answers to questions

▶ **LIST:** They are solids at room temperature (except for mercury), malleable, ductile, and good conductors of heat and electricity.

▶ **DEFINE:** a material made of a mixture of two or more metals

▶ **IDENTIFY:** iron

▶ **EXPLAIN:** It is strong and does not react with the minerals in salt water.

3 Assess

✓ CHECKING CONCEPTS ANSWERS

1. Steel
2. solids
3. copper
4. An alloy (such as brass or steel)
5. metals
6. Mercury
7. are
8. ductile
9. Sterling silver

💡 THINKING CRITICALLY ANSWERS

10. **INFER:** A pure metal is a better conductor of electricity.

11. **ANALYZE:** Different types of alloys of steel have different properties for different uses.

4 Close

Web InfoSearch

Amalgam Have students use the Internet to find out more about the controversy surrounding amalgams. Then, have students write a short report explaining both sides of the issue. Students should conclude their reports with their views on the subject. Some key search words are **amalgam, amalgam harmful,** and **amalgam mercury.** Students should begin their search at www.conceptsandchallenges.com.

COOPERATIVE LEARNING

Using Alloys Have one student randomly read aloud the name of an alloy in Figure 10-6. Have another student name the metals that make up the alloy and a third student name some of the alloy's uses. **learning style: auditory**

ESL/ELL STRATEGY

Naming Alloys English-language learners may know the names of some alloys in their native languages. Ask students to share these names with the class.

• TEACHING RESOURCES •

💿 **Teacher's Resources CD-ROM**
Lesson Review: Chapter 10, p. 4

Enrichment: Chapter 10, pp. 5, 6

Laboratory Manual
Lab. Skills Worksheet 2: Using a Triple-Beam Balance, pp. 9–10

The Big Idea

(pp. 216–217)

1 Introduce

Objective Students will design a bike for a specific function. They will identify its function and the design features that help it function. They will describe the types, compositions, and properties of alloys used to construct the frame and other components of the bike.

Linking Prior Knowledge Have students recall the properties of metals and alloys (Lessons 3-8 and 10-3).

2 Teach

Discussion Have students share information on the different types of bikes they know about such as trail, touring, hybrid, dirt, and stunt. Help students identify the characteristics of each type. Have students explain how each characteristic makes the bike suitable for its purpose.

Use the information in the articles and captions to help guide students in choosing a topic for their Science Logs.

THE BIG IDEA ONLINE

What is the importance of alloys in bike design? Have students research their Science Log Writing Activity at www.conceptsandchallenges.com. You can have students organize their log by completing the Big Idea activity online. Students may post their work in the Online Classroom Database for others to read.

Reinforcement Students can also use the Big Idea Planner or Big Idea Science Log Entry found on the Teacher's Resources CD-ROM.

THE Big IDEA

What is the importance of alloys in bike design?

Bikes are great machines. They are fun, durable, and pollution-free. They are better at turning energy from our muscles into motion than any other machine. The first step in building a great bicycle is determining its purpose. Bikes for different purposes are designed differently and built with different alloys.

The main part of a bike is the frame. It should be strong, lightweight, and a bit flexible. The metal frame comes from ores that have been mined, refined, and formed into tubes. Frame tubes are formed by rolling narrow sheets of metal into tubes and then joining the seam, or by drilling out a solid rod to form a seamless hollow tube.

The rest of the bike is made of components such as a seat, pedals, wheels, brakes, a drive train, and shocks. The components are what make the bike go. They are attached to the frame.

Steel, an alloy of iron and carbon, is strong, durable, and easy to weld. Steel alloys can be made containing chromium, vanadium, molybdenum, manganese, nickel, and titanium. Adding chromium, for example, helps steel resist corrosion. Chromium molybdenum steel (called chro-moly) is popular for bikes. It is twice as strong as carbon steel.

Aluminum comes from bauxite ore. It is strong and light, and much stiffer than steel. To improve its performance, aluminum is alloyed with copper, silicon, zinc, and sometimes scandium.

Some people consider titanium excellent for building bikes. It is used for racing bikes, where every ounce counts. The latest in bike design, though, is an alloy made with zirconium. Bikes made with this are 15% stronger than steel and 15% lighter than titanium.

Look at the photo and text that appear on these two pages. Then, follow the directions in the Science Log to find out more about "the big idea." ✦

216

Wheels
In bike racing, any rotating mass ne to save weight. Weight is focused ir the hub, so the wheel rims are mad from aluminum. This makes them lightweight and stiff. The spokes contain combinations of aluminum, steel, or even titanium to keep then stiff and lightweight.

▲ **Figure 10-9** Professional racing mountain bikes like this one need to be strong, stiff, and light. The combination of components and frame is important in making the entire racing bike.

Teaching Options

! FAST FACTS *A Specialized Alloy*

Just as bikes are made of alloys that are strong and lightweight, certain other new alloys have found widespread use based on their properties. One of the most interesting of these alloys is called nitinol, which is an alloy of nickel and titanium.

Properties and Uses of Nitinol Nitinol is lightweight and does not easily corrode. However, many metals and their alloys have these properties. The property of nitinol that makes it so unusual is that it returns to its previous shape when it is heated or the stress that causes its shape to change is removed. If frames for eyeglasses that are made from nitinol are bent, they return to their original shape. Dental braces retain their shape and require fewer adjustments.

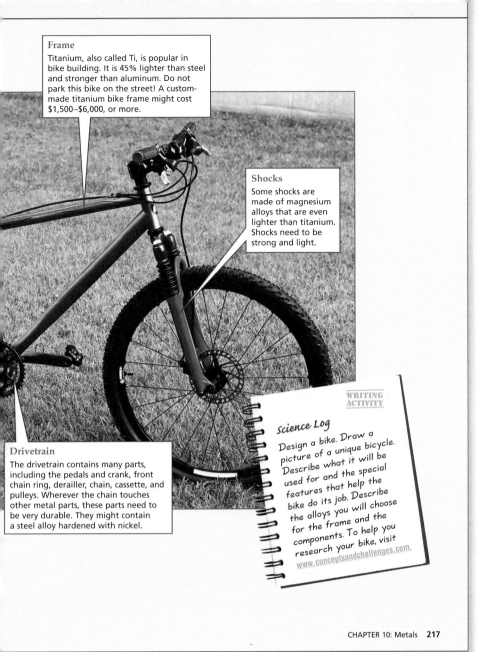

Frame
Titanium, also called Ti, is popular in bike building. It is 45% lighter than steel and stronger than aluminum. Do not park this bike on the street! A custom-made titanium bike frame might cost $1,500–$6,000, or more.

Shocks
Some shocks are made of magnesium alloys that are even lighter than titanium. Shocks need to be strong and light.

Drivetrain
The drivetrain contains many parts, including the pedals and crank, front chain ring, derailler, chain, cassette, and pulleys. Wherever the chain touches other metal parts, these parts need to be very durable. They might contain a steel alloy hardened with nickel.

WRITING ACTIVITY

Science Log
Design a bike. Draw a picture of a unique bicycle. Describe what it will be used for and the special features that help the bike do its job. Describe the alloys you will choose for the frame and the components. To help you research your bike, visit www.conceptsandchallenges.com.

3 Assess

Use the Individual Activity Rubric on the Teacher's Resources CD-ROM to assess students' Science Logs. Fill in the rubric with the additional information below. For this assignment, students should have:

- designed a bike for a specific function, describing its features and how alloys used in its frame and other components help it function.
- communicated, in drawing a design of the bike and in paragraph form, accurate descriptions of the bike's function and construction.

4 Close

Preparing a Sales Brochure Have groups of students compare their designs and come up with one plan for a group design. Have students prepare a sales brochure for the group design, emphasizing its features and how the bike's design allows it to meet its function.

Tips for Using Technology

Working With Photographs
If you or your students have a photograph file that you wish to make changes to, you can use photo-editing software to do so. Most photo-editing software allows the user to crop and resize a photograph. To do this, tell students to select the portion of the photograph that they wish to crop by clicking and dragging the mouse pointer in a diagonal direction. This should create a rectangle in the photograph. Then, they can choose Crop.

• TEACHING RESOURCES •

Teacher's Resources CD-ROM
Big Idea: Chapter 10, p. 7
Big Idea Planner: Study Tools, pp. 11–12
Big Idea Science Log Entry: Study Tools, p. 13
Individual Activity Rubric: Teaching Tools, p. 5

10-4 (pp. 218–219)

1 Introduce

✎ **STUDY HINT** Before beginning this lesson, read the list of Key Terms aloud so that students can hear their pronunciations. Then, have students make a two-column chart. Have students list the properties of alkali metals and examples in one column, and the properties of alkaline metals and examples in the other column.

Linking Prior Knowledge Have students review the terms *family* (vertical column), *group* (vertical column), and *period* (horizontal row) of the periodic table (Lesson 3-7).

2 Teach

Discussion Have students refer back to the periodic table on pages 66 and 67. Have them identify the alkali metals and the alkaline earth metals. Ask: *How is the atomic structure of alkali metals different from the atomic structure of alkaline earth metals?* (The alkali metals have one electron in their outermost energy levels. The alkaline earth metals have two electrons in their outermost energy levels.)

Discussion Ask students to use Figure 10-11 to predict what would happen if a copper wire was placed in an iron sulfate solution. (There would be no reaction because copper is less active than iron.)
learning styles: auditory, logical/mathematical

Answers to questions

▶ **IDENTIFY:** lithium, sodium, potassium, rubidium, cesium, and francium

▶ **IDENTIFY:** beryllium, magnesium, calcium, strontium, barium, and radium

▶ **ANALYZE:** lithium, potassium, barium, calcium, and sodium

📖 **READING STRATEGY** Inform students that when they read Figure 10-11, the electromotive series of metals, they should realize that the metals at the top are the most active so they replace metals below them in the table.

10-4 Why are some metals more active than others?

Objective
List the most active metals in the periodic table.

Key Terms
alkali metals: metals in Group 1 of the periodic table
alkaline earth metals: metals in Group 2 of the periodic table

Group 1 Metals Some metals are chemically active. These metals readily combine with certain nonmetals. One group of very active metals is called the **alkali metals**. The alkali metals include lithium, sodium, potassium, rubidium, cesium, and francium. The most common alkali metals are lithium, sodium, and potassium.

Found in Group 1 of the periodic table, atoms of these metals have one electron in their outermost energy level. Each alkali metal has one valence electron. Figure 10-10 shows the Group 1 metals as they appear in the periodic table. The alkali metals are so chemically active that they are always found combined with other elements. These metals are not found as pure metals in nature. The structure of each Group 1 metal is similar to the others.

▶ **IDENTIFY:** What are the six Group 1 metals?

Group 2 Metals The metals next to the alkali metals in the periodic table are the **alkaline earth metals.** These metals include beryllium, magnesium, calcium, strontium, barium, and radium. Found in Group 2 of the periodic table, atoms of these metals have two electrons in their outer shell. Figure 10-10 shows the Group 2 metals as they appear in the periodic table. These metals are also chemically active. They readily combine with other elements. Although less active than the Group 1 metals, the extra valence electron makes the Group 2 metals harder and stronger than the Group 1 metals. The most active Group 2 metals are beryllium, magnesium, and barium.

▶ **IDENTIFY:** What are the six Group 2 metals?

218

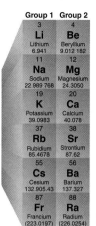

Group 1	Group 2
3 **Li** Lithium 6.941	4 **Be** Beryllium 9.012 182
11 **Na** Sodium 22.989 768	12 **Mg** Magnesium 24.3050
19 **K** Potassium 39.0983	20 **Ca** Calcium 40.078
37 **Rb** Rubidium 85.4678	38 **Sr** Strontium 87.62
55 **Cs** Cesium 132.905.43	56 **Ba** Barium 137.327
87 **Fr** Francium (223.0197)	88 **Ra** Radium (226.0254)

◀ **Figure 10-10**
Group 1 and 2 metals

Electromotive Series
Some metals are more active than others. In a chemical reaction, some metals will replace other metals in a compound. For example, when iron is placed in a copper sulfate solution, the iron will replace the copper to form iron sulfate.

Figure 10-11 shows the electromotive series of metals. The most active metals are at the top of the table. The least active metals are at the bottom of the table. A metal will replace those metals below it on the list. For example, lithium will replace sodium, but sodium will not replace calcium.

▶ **ANALYZE:** Which metals will replace magnesium in a chemical reaction?

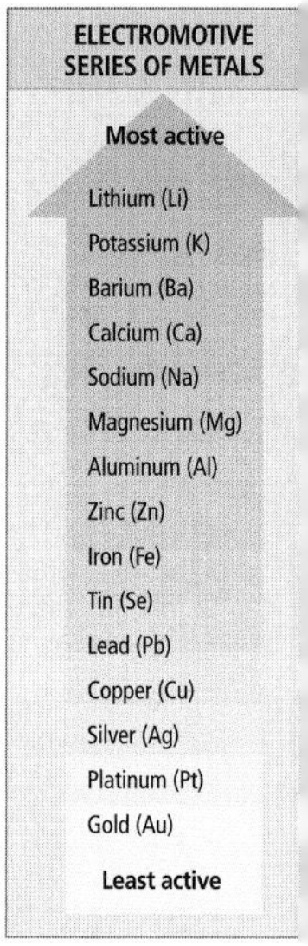

ELECTROMOTIVE SERIES OF METALS

Most active

Lithium (Li)
Potassium (K)
Barium (Ba)
Calcium (Ca)
Sodium (Na)
Magnesium (Mg)
Aluminum (Al)
Zinc (Zn)
Iron (Fe)
Tin (Se)
Lead (Pb)
Copper (Cu)
Silver (Ag)
Platinum (Pt)
Gold (Au)

Least active

▲ **Figure 10-11**

Teaching Options

❗ **FAST FACTS** *Metals Reacting With Nonmetals*

The electromotive series compares the activity of one metal replacing another metal in a chemical reaction. But metals can react with nonmetals also. When combining with nonmetals, the overall chemical activity of an alkali metal or an alkaline earth metal increases with atomic number. In a chemical reaction, an alkali metal will form an ion by losing its single valence electron. The alkali metal that has the strongest attraction for its single valence electron will be the least active.

Lithium is the smallest Group 1 atom, so its valence electron is closest to the nucleus. This closeness means that lithium's valence electron is the most tightly held of the Group 1 elements. Therefore, a lithium atom is least likely to lose its valence electron. As a result, lithium is the least active of the alkali metals when combining with nonmetals. As one moves down the group, the size of an atom of an alkali metal increases. As a result, the activity of the alkali metal increases as one moves down the group. A similar trend occurs in the alkaline earth metals, with beryllium being the least active alkaline earth metal and radium the most active.

✓ CHECKING CONCEPTS

1. Another name for the Group 1 metals is the _____ metals.

2. Another name for the Group 2 metals is the _____ metals.

3. In the electromotive series, a metal can be replaced by a metal _____ it on the list.

4. The alkali metals are found in _____ of the periodic table.

5. The alkaline earth metals are found in _____ of the periodic table.

6. The most active metal in the electromotive series is _____.

7. The least active metal in the electromotive series is _____.

THINKING CRITICALLY

8. EXPLAIN: Look at the following chemical equation.

$$Fe + CuSO_4 \rightarrow Cu + FeSO_4$$

Why was iron able to replace copper in copper sulfate? Is the copper oxidized or reduced?

9. INFER: Why is gold usually found as a pure metal in nature, unlike most of the other metals?

DESIGNING AN EXPERIMENT

Design an experiment to solve the following problem. Include a hypothesis, variables, a procedure, and a type of data to study.

PROBLEM: How can you compare the chemical activity of two metals or more?

People in Science

WELDER

Welding is a process used to join two pieces of metal. The process usually involves heating a metal and hammering it into shape. Several layers of metals can be heated and hammered together. This process is known as forge welding. A forge is a furnace in which the metal is heated for welding.

Today, most welders use a technique known as arc welding. In arc welding, heat from an electric current is used to weld together two pieces of metal. Another type of welding uses lasers. The intense light from a laser heats and melts the metals, welding them together. High-frequency, or ultrasonic, sounds can also be used in welding. The vibrations from the sound waves are transferred to the metals where they are changed to heat energy. The heat is used to weld the metals.

Welders need to take many safety precautions. The woman in Figure 10-12 is looking through a special mask to protect her eyes from the bright light. Special equipment is also needed to protect the welders from the intense heat produced. Welders may work for automobile manufacturers, for construction companies, or in other industries.

Thinking Critically What are four different types of welding? How do they differ from one another?

▲ **Figure 10-12** Welders use a heat source to join two metals together.

---

3 Assess

✓ CHECKING CONCEPTS ANSWERS

1. alkali
2. alkaline earth
3. above
4. Group 1
5. Group 2
6. lithium
7. gold

THINKING CRITICALLY ANSWERS

8. EXPLAIN: Iron is more active than copper. The copper is reduced.
9. INFER: because gold is the least active metal

4 Close

DESIGNING AN EXPERIMENT

Use the Designing an Experiment Rubric on the Teacher's Resources CD-ROM to assess students' experiments. Fill in the rubric with the additional information below. For this assignment, students should have:

- used the electromotive series of metals in developing their hypotheses.
- developed a data table to use in recording data.

People in Science

WELDER

Real-Life Connection Ultrasonic welding is used to weld materials that have low melting points such as plastics, or to fuse metals to plastics. The temperatures produced by ultrasonic welding are usually not much higher than the melting points of the materials. On the other hand, laser-welding techniques can produce temperatures well above the boiling points of metals. One technique uses a laser beam that can produce temperatures as high as 25,000°C (45,000°F).

Thinking Critically Answer
In forge welding, several pieces of metal are heated and joined by hammering them together. In arc welding, heat from an electric current is used to join the metals. In laser welding, intense heat from laser light melts the metals and joins them. In ultrasonic welding, vibrations of sound waves absorbed by the metals are converted to heat energy, which melts and joins the metals.

• TEACHING RESOURCES •

Teacher's Resources CD-ROM
Lesson Review: Chapter 10, p. 8

Designing an Experiment Rubric: Teaching Tools, p. 7

Designing an Experiment: Study Tools, p. 14

COOPERATIVE LEARNING

Comparing Metals Have one student randomly read aloud the names of any two elements listed in Figure 10-11. Have another student state which metal would replace the other in a chemical reaction. **learning styles: interpersonal, auditory**

1 Introduce

✎ **STUDY HINT** Have students make a concept map. The main topic should be *Corrosion*. The titles of each section should be the extensions, and students should write the supporting information in each extension. Students can use the Concept Map found on the Teacher's Resources CD-ROM.

Linking Prior Knowledge Have students recall that oxidation is a loss of electrons (Lesson 8-3).

2 Teach

Discussion Ask students to share personal experiences that deal with corrosion. Experiences might include rust on a car or bike, pennies turning dark or green, and silverware tarnishing. Ask students what their family might have done to minimize this corrosion. Most suggestions will probably involve protecting the metal from the source of the corrosion.
learning style: auditory

Demonstration Demonstrate iron rusting. Moisten a piece of plain steel wool with acetic acid (vinegar) and stuff it into the bottom of a test tube. (The acetic acid speeds up the reaction.) Insert a 15-cm piece of glass tubing halfway through a one-hole stopper. Stopper the test tube and invert it into a beaker of water so that the glass tube is submerged by about 5 cm. Use a stand and clamp to hold the inverted test tube. Have students check the apparatus periodically for several days for evidence of rusting and for water rising in the tube. The rise of water in the tube indicates that oxidation is taking place. Oxygen in the air inside the tube is combining with iron in the steel wool. **learning style: visual**

Answers to questions

▶ **DESCRIBE:** It changes color and loses its shine.

▶ **IDENTIFY:** rust and tarnish

▶ **DESCRIBE:** It loses one or more electrons.

▶ **LIST:** painting metals, covering them with oil, and using an alloy

---

10-5 What is corrosion?

Objective
Explain what causes corrosion.

Key Term
corrosion: chemical change in a metal

Corrosion Metals are chemically active. One result of this chemical activity is **corrosion**. Corrosion is a chemical change on the surface of metals. It results from the reaction of metals with chemicals in the environment. When a metal becomes corroded, its properties change. The metal changes color and loses its shine.

▶ **DESCRIBE:** What happens when a metal becomes corroded?

Types of Corrosion The most common example of corrosion is rust. Iron that is exposed to air and moisture will become rusted. The rusted iron has a reddish brown color and no shine. Rust, or iron oxide, is much weaker than iron. Tarnish is another example of corrosion. A tarnished metal loses its shine and has a dull color. For example, tarnished silver looks dark and dull because of a coating of silver sulfide.

▲ Figure 10-13 Iron rusts when exposed to air and moisture.

220

Corrosion forms layers on the surface of a metal. When you polish silver, you remove the layers of tarnish. Once the corrosion is removed, the surface of the metal is exposed again with its usual color and shine.

▶ **IDENTIFY:** Name two types of corrosion.

Cause of Corrosion Corrosion is often caused by oxidation. Remember that oxidation is a loss of electrons. Rust forms when iron combines with oxygen in the air to form iron oxide. The chemical equation for this is as follows.

$$4Fe + 3O_2 \rightarrow 2Fe_2O_3$$

An atom of iron has three valence electrons to "give away." An oxygen atom needs to gain two electrons. In this reaction, the four atoms of iron will lose 12 electrons. The six atoms of oxygen will gain the 12 electrons. Water also helps facilitate this process.

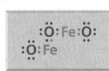

◀ **Figure 10-14** This is an electron dot diagram of one molecule of iron oxide.

▶ **DESCRIBE:** What happens to a metal during oxidation?

Preventing Corrosion Corrosion may wear away and weaken metals. Therefore, it is important to prevent metals from corroding. There are several ways to prevent corrosion.

▲ **Figure 10-15** Coating metals with paint helps prevent corrosion.

Teaching Options

EXTENDING THE LESSON

Cleaning Tarnished Silver Chemically Tell students that a chemical change can clean tarnished silver. Lay some crumpled aluminum foil in the bottom of a stainless steel pan and place a tarnished spoon on top of it. Cover with water. Stir in some baking soda and heat the water for few minutes. Have students observe the spoon. Have students use Figure 10-11 to explain why the silver tarnish disappears. (Al is more active than Ag, and it will replace silver in silver sulfide. Silver atoms and aluminum sulfide form.)
learning styles: visual, auditory

Painting is an effective way to prevent rust. A layer of paint over a piece of iron will keep air and moisture away from the surface of the metal. Coating the surface of a metal with oil also protects the metal from corrosion.

Using alloys is a way of avoiding rust. For example, stainless steel is an alloy of iron. Unlike iron, stainless steel will not rust. Even though an alloy is usually more expensive than the pure metal, it is often less expensive in the long run to use the alloy.

▲ LIST: What are three ways to prevent corrosion in metals?

✓ CHECKING CONCEPTS

1. What is corrosion?
2. What is the chemical formula for rust?
3. What causes corrosion?
4. Why is it important to prevent metals from corroding?
5. How does painting a metal prevent corrosion?
6. What happens when iron combines with oxygen in the air?

💡 THINKING CRITICALLY

7. PREDICT: Can corrosion take place if a metal is kept in a vacuum? Why or why not?
8. INFER: Why do ships always have more rust along their bottom than on any other part of the ship?

HEALTH AND SAFETY TIP

Corrosion wears away metal, and it can also be harmful to people. Rust tends to chip and peel, and can leave sharp, jagged edges that can harbor germs and that cause serious injury. If you accidentally cut yourself with a rusted object, you should see a doctor right away. Use first aid books or other reference materials to find out why cuts from rusty objects are dangerous. Find out what treatment you must receive to prevent further problems. Show what you learned on a poster.

⚛ Hands-On Activity

OBSERVING THE TARNISHING OF SILVER

You will need a silver spoon and a hard-boiled egg.
1. Peel the hard-boiled egg and remove the yolk.
2. Place the silver spoon into the egg yolk. Leave it in the yolk for 10 to 20 minutes.
3. Remove the spoon from the yolk. Observe the appearance of the spoon.

Practicing Your Skills
4. OBSERVE: What did the spoon look like when you removed it from the egg yolk?
5. INFER: Egg yolk contains sulfur. What do you think happened when you placed the silver spoon into the egg yolk?
6. PREDICT: How could you remove tarnish from the silver spoon?

▲ STEP 2 Place the spoon in the yolk for 10 to 20 minutes.

3 Assess

✓ CHECKING CONCEPTS ANSWERS

1. a chemical change in a metal
2. Fe_2O_3
3. most often oxidation
4. Corrosion may wear away and weaken metals.
5. The paint keeps air (oxygen) and moisture away from the surface of the metal.
6. Rust forms.

💡 THINKING CRITICALLY ANSWERS

7. PREDICT: No; The metal is not exposed to oxygen or other elements.
8. INFER: The bottom is in water, which promotes corrosion.

4 Close

HEALTH AND SAFETY TIP ANSWERS

Rusty objects may have harmful bacteria growing on them. One type of bacterium may cause the potentially fatal disease tetanus. A person who gets cut with a rusted metal object should see a doctor immediately to get a tetanus shot if the person's tetanus vaccination is not current.

Hands-On Activity

OBSERVING THE TARNISHING OF SILVER

TIME: 40 minutes

PURPOSE: observing, inferring, predicting

SAFETY TIP: Be sure that students are aware that they should not eat or drink anything in the laboratory. Tell students to discard the shell, white, and yolk of the egg in the trash and wash their hands thoroughly after handling any part of the egg.

PROCEDURE: Be sure that the metal object is silver and not stainless steel, which will not react with sulfur.

Practicing Your Skills Answers

4. OBSERVE: dull, tarnished
5. INFER: Silver and sulfur combined.
6. PREDICT: Rub away the layer of tarnish by polishing the spoon, or expose the tarnished silver to a more active metal, such as aluminum.

MORE ON THE WEB

Careers in Corrosion Have students search the Internet for careers related to corrosion. Then, have students write a help-wanted advertisement. Visit www.conceptsand challenges.com for more details.

ONGOING ASSESSMENT

Classifying Corrosion Ask students: *Is corrosion a physical or chemical change? How do you know?* (chemical; because a new substance with new properties is produced)

• TEACHING RESOURCES •

Teacher's Resources CD-ROM
Lesson Review: Chapter 10, p. 9
Concept Map: Study Tools, p. 4

Laboratory Manual
Lab. Challenge: How can tarnish be removed from silver? pp. 57–60

Laboratory Video
Segment 12: Determining the Relative Activity of Different Metals

Lab Activity

(pp. 222–223)

1 Prepare the Lab

Testing Activity and Corrosion of Metals

SET-UP TIME: 🕐 **LAB TIME:** 🕐

(30–40 minutes for the initial lab session followed 4–5 days later by a second lab session of 15–20 minutes for observations)

BACKGROUND: Corrosion is a chemical change in which a metal changes color and loses its shine when exposed to various substances.

PURPOSE: Students will compare the corrosion that occurs when different metals are placed in water, salt solution, and distilled white vinegar.

ALTERNATIVE MATERIALS: You may want to try drywall screws, masonry nails, or small reinforcement bars for concrete instead of iron nails.

SCIENCE SKILLS: Students will **observe** physical properties of metal objects before and after subjecting them to corrosive liquids and then **organize data** and **communicate** results. They will use this experiment to **compare** properties and **infer** ways by which the corrosion of metals may be reduced.

ADVANCE PLANNING: Gather the materials that you will need for the lab. Prepare the salt water by dissolving 50 g of table salt in 1 L of water. Set aside a shelf or drawer for students to store the solution cups. Have an empty bucket on hand for collecting liquids after the experiment.

2 Guide the Lab

PROCEDURE: Divide the class into small groups. Discuss the procedure. Discuss data collection and reporting. Have students copy the observation chart from Figure 10-16 before starting the experiment. Point out the location where students will store their cups for further observation. Provide students with a copy of the Lab Activity Report found on the Teacher's Resources CD-ROM to record their observations and conclusions.

LAB ACTIVITY
Testing Activity and Corrosion of Metals

Materials
Safety goggles,
Lab apron, gloves,
3 plastic cups,
100-mL graduated cylinder,
Forceps,
Plastic wrap,
Paper towels,
Wax pencil,
Water, salt,
White vinegar,
3 ungalvanized nails,
3 galvanized nails,
3 metal paper clips,
3 plastic-coated paper clips,
3 pennies,
3 quarters

▲ **STEP 4** Organize the metals to be tested.

▲ **STEP 6** Carefully place the samples in each cup.

BACKGROUND

There are many types of metals that we use in our daily lives. Metals are used in things such as cars, bicycles, cans for food, and coins. Since metals are reactive, one problem is corrosion. People need to understand how to prevent metals from becoming corroded.

PURPOSE

In this activity, you will observe and compare the rates of corrosion of various samples of metals in different liquids.

PROCEDURE 🛡️🧤

1. Copy the chart in Figure 10-16.

2. Put on your safety goggles, lab apron, and gloves. Using a wax pencil or labeling marker, label three plastic cups *Water*, *Salt*, and *Vinegar*. Also, write your initials on each cup.

3. Using a graduated cylinder, pour 100 mL of water into the cup labeled *Water*. Measure 100 mL of vinegar into the next cup. Measure 100 mL of salt water into the last cup.

4. Place these items on a paper towel: three ungalvanized nails, three galvanized nails, three metal paper clips, three plastic-coated paper clips, three pennies, and three quarters.

5. Use a paper towel to wipe off the nails, paper clips, and coins. Record the appearance—shine and color—of the samples in the section of the chart area labeled *Before*.

6. Using forceps, place one of each item into the liquids in the plastic cups. Cover each cup with a piece of plastic wrap. Place the cups in a separate area of the classroom. Let them stand undisturbed for 4 to 5 days.

222

Teaching Options

❗ FAST FACTS *How Iron Rusts*

Iron will not rust in dry air. The rusting process requires water containing dissolved oxygen. Iron atoms oxidize (lose electrons) and form iron ions when exposed to water in the following way:

$$2Fe \rightarrow 2Fe^{2+} + 4e^-$$

Oxygen molecules in the water are reduced (gain electrons) and form hydroxide ions.

$$O_2 + 2H_2O + 4e^- \rightarrow 4OH^-$$

The overall reaction is given by:

$$2Fe + O_2 + 2H_2O \rightarrow 2Fe(OH)_2$$

$Fe(OH)_2$ is iron(II) hydroxide, an insoluble compound. It is further oxidized to iron(III) hydroxide, which is also insoluble.

$$4Fe(OH)_2 + O_2 + 2H_2O \rightarrow 4Fe(OH)_3$$

When dried, the iron(III) hydroxide forms Fe_2O_3, rust.

7. After 4 to 5 days, bring the cups back to your work area. Lay down a few paper towels and label them *Water*, *Salt Water*, and *Vinegar*. Use the forceps to carefully remove the samples from the cups. Place the samples on the corresponding labeled sheets of paper towel.

8. Observe the items carefully for any signs of metal corrosion. This can include loss of shine, change in color, and rusting. Record your observations in the section of the chart labeled *After*.

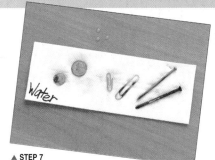
▲ STEP 7
Look for signs of corrosion.

Testing Activity and Corrosion of Metals

Samples	Before	After Water	After Salt Water	After Vinegar
Ungalvanized nail				
Galvanized nail				
Metal paper clip				
Plastic-coated paper clip				
Penny				
Quarter				

▲ **Figure 10-16** Copy this chart and use it to record your observations.

CONCLUSIONS

1. OBSERVE: According to your observation, which objects changed most? Which objects changed least?

2. OBSERVE: Which solution caused the most corrosion?

3. INFER: Why did the galvanized nail and plastic-coated paper clip not change much?

4. INFER: According to your observations, which metallic sample is the most active and why?

5. ANALYZE: A builder uses galvanized nails to build a wooden deck. With what you know about the activity and corrosion of metals, explain why galvanized nails are a better choice than ungalvanized nails.

Tips for Using Technology

Databases Have students use database software to record their observations of metal corrosion. Databases allow students to enter and edit information, store and organize a lot of information easily, and search for specific information. Databases also allow students to arrange information by putting it in a specific order and to present information by using special layouts. Students can use database software to share their data with the class. Have students use the Database Planner on the Teacher's Resources CD-ROM to plan their databases.

• TEACHING RESOURCES •

Teacher's Resources CD-ROM
Lab Activity Report: Study Tools, pp. 16–17
Laboratory Activity Rubric: Teaching Tools, p. 8
Database Planner: Study Tools, p. 22
Laboratory Manual
Lab. Skills Worksheet 1: Using a Graduated Cylinder, pp. 5–8
Lab. Skills Worksheet 4: Organizing and Analyzing Data, pp. 13–14

TROUBLESHOOTING: You may wish to have some of the original nails and coins available during the second lab session so that students can compare them to nails and coins from their cups in case they have overlooked some initial observations. Try to use pennies minted before 1982.

EXPECTED OUTCOME: Observations may vary. Ungalvanized nails and metal paper clips will show changes in all three solutions. Pennies may show changes in salt solution and vinegar. The galvanized nail, plastic-coated paper clip, and quarter may not show any change.

LAB HINT: Lead students to realize that the "Before" observations represent the controls in this experiment.

Use the Laboratory Activity Rubric on the Teacher's Resources CD-ROM to assess students' lab activities. Fill in the rubric with the additional information below. For this activity, students should have:

- performed the activity according to the procedure and filled in the chart with data collected during the activity.
- correctly answered the questions in complete sentences.

3 Conclude the Lab

1. OBSERVE: Possible answer: The ungalvanized nail and paper clip changed most. The galvanized nail and plastic-coated paper clip changed least.
2. OBSERVE: vinegar
3. INFER: The coatings did not react and prevented the underlying metal from reacting with water, vinegar, or salt water.
4. INFER: Possible answer: The ungalvanized nails are most reactive because the iron in them reacted in all three liquids.
5. ANALYZE: Since galvanized nails are less likely to corrode than ungalvanized nails, galvanized nails will last longer in a wooden deck.

4 Extend the Lab

Have students look for evidence of corrosion inside and outside the school and their homes. Ask students to consider conditions in which they would expect to find corrosion. (moist conditions) Discuss corrosion prevention.

1 Introduce

✎ **STUDY HINT** Have students create word webs in their notebooks. The topic should be *Protecting Metals*. As students read this lesson, they can add arms to their webs on which they record the Key Terms with their definitions and other details about protecting metals.

Linking Prior Knowledge Have students recall how electrons are lost and gained in oxidation-reduction reactions (Lesson 8-3).

2 Teach

Discussion Show samples of plated metals to the class. Describe coating with a corrosive-resistant metal as a method of protecting another metal from corrosion. Point out that the shiny chrome bumpers of vintage cars are made of steel plated with corrosion-resistant chromium. Explain further that some metals are coated with more expensive metals, such as copper, to enhance their appearance. For example, pennies minted in 1982 or later are mostly zinc electroplated with copper. Ask students which metal is more expensive. (copper) **learning styles: visual, auditory**

Answers to questions

▶1 **DEFINE:** coating one metal with another metal

▶2 **ANALYZE:** copper ion

▶3 **HYPOTHESIZE:** because they are positive ions

Reinforcement Refer to Figure 10-18. Be sure that students understand that the plated copper atoms come from the copper ions present in the solution of copper sulfate. Ask students what ions are present in the copper sulfate solution. (Cu^{2+}, SO_4^{2-}) Represent the ions as Cu^{2+} and SO_4^{2-}. Emphasize that in chemical reactions, only electrons are transferred. Show that Cu^{2+} gains two electrons at the negative electrode, becoming metallic copper, and that SO_4^{2-} transfers two electrons to the positive electrode. Ask students at what electrode the reduction of copper takes place. (negative electrode) **learning styles: auditory, visual**

10-6 How are metals plated?

Objective
Explain how metals are plated.

Key Terms
plating: coating one metal with another metal
electroplating (ee-LEHK-troh-playt-ing)**:** use of an electric current to plate one metal with another metal

Protecting Metals
One way to protect metals from corrosion is through the process of **plating**. In this process, a metal is coated with another metal. For example, a plating of zinc on the surface of iron will prevent the iron from rusting. Iron coated with zinc is called galvanized

▲ Figure 10-17
Galvanized screws

(GAL-vuh-nyzed) iron. When the zinc corrodes, it forms zinc oxide. The layer of zinc oxide prevents any further corrosion. Garbage cans, nails, and snow shovels often are made of galvanized iron.

Aluminum is "self-plating." When aluminum is exposed to air, a thin coating of aluminum oxide forms on the surface of the metal. This compound forms a protective coating for the aluminum beneath and keeps it from corroding further. The aluminum oxide gives the metal a dull appearance.

▶1 **DEFINE:** What is the process of plating?

Electrolysis Electrolysis is a process used to separate a compound into the elements it contains. It requires a chemical change in which atoms of an element are separated from other atoms in the compound. The process is used to remove pure metals from its ore or to plate a surface with a metal.

Figure 10-18 shows a setup for electrolysis. Two carbon rods are placed into a solution of copper sulfate. The copper sulfate is the electrolyte. The carbon rods are attached to the terminals of a

224

battery. The carbon rod attached to the positive terminal becomes the positive electrode. The rod attached to the negative terminal becomes the negative electrode.

Positively charged copper ions move to the negative electrode. At the negative electrode, each ion gains two electrons and becomes a copper atom.

$$Cu^{2+} + 2 \text{ electrons} \rightarrow Cu$$

The pure copper is seen plated onto the carbon rod.

▶2 **ANALYZE:** What ion moves to the negative electrode in the electrolysis of copper nitrate?

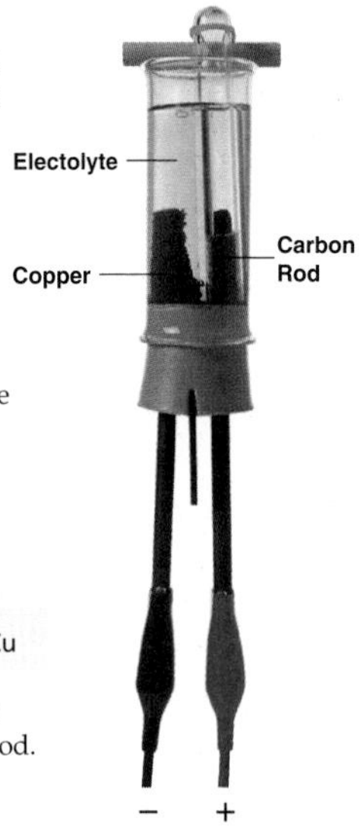

▲ Figure 10-18 In this setup, electrolysis is used to plate copper onto the negative carbon electrode.

Electroplating Electricity is often used to plate metals onto other surfaces. This process is called **electroplating**. Nickel, silver, copper, and zinc can be used in electroplating. Brass is an alloy of copper and zinc. Copper and zinc can be used to electroplate a metal surface with brass.

▼ Figure 10-19 Electroplating with brass

Teaching Options

❗FAST FACTS *Commercial Electroplating*

In the commercial process of copper electroplating, a piece of pure copper is used as the positive electrode rather than the carbon rod as shown in Figure 10-18. In this process, the loss and gain of electrons can be described as follows:

Metallic copper (Cu^0) is oxidized (loses electrons) at the positive electrode.

$$Cu^0 \rightarrow Cu^{2+} + 2e^-$$

Copper ions are reduced (gain electrons) at the negative electrode.

$$Cu^{2+} + 2e^- \rightarrow Cu^0$$

ESL/ELL STRATEGY

***Learning About* Electro** As students read the lesson, have them copy in their notebooks words that contain the word part *electro*. (electroplating, electroplated, electrolyte, electrode, electrons, electrolysis) Have students discuss what they think *electro* means. ("involving electricity")

To plate an object with brass, the object is placed in a solution of copper and zinc, as shown in Figure 10-19. The copper and zinc in this solution are positively charged. When the current flows, these positive ions are attracted to the negative electrode, or the object to be plated.

▶ **HYPOTHESIZE:** Why are ions of metals attracted to negative electrodes?

✓ CHECKING CONCEPTS

1. Iron that has a coating of zinc is called _____ iron.

2. A layer of zinc will prevent iron from _____.

3. When a protective layer of zinc corrodes, it forms _____.

4. Plating a metal by using an electric current is _____.

5. When electroplating with copper, the copper ions will be attracted to the _____ electrode.

💡 THINKING CRITICALLY

6. **PREDICT:** A solution of zinc sulfate ($ZnSO_4$) is used as an electrolyte for electroplating. Which electrode will the zinc ions, Zn^{2+}, be attracted to?

7. **HYPOTHESIZE:** Galvanized iron is used to make garbage cans and snow shovels. What is the advantage of using galvanized iron for these objects?

8. **ANALYZE:** Suppose you want to electroplate an object with silver. To which electrode would you attach the object? Explain. Is the silver being oxidized or reduced?

DESIGNING AN EXPERIMENT

Design an experiment to solve the following problem. Include a hypothesis, variables, a procedure, and type of data to collect and study.

PROBLEM: How can you determine if an object is silver-plated or is made of pure silver?

🔬 Hands-On Activity

PROTECTING METALS FROM CORROSION

You will need three ungalvanized nails, three beakers of water, vinegar, clear nail polish, and oil or petroleum jelly.

1. Cover one ungalvanized nail with clear nail polish. Let the nail polish dry completely.

2. Coat a second nail with oil or petroleum jelly.

3. Do not put anything on the third nail.

4. Label each beaker. Put each nail into a beaker of water. Add a little vinegar to the water to speed up the rusting process.

5. Remove the nails from the water and vinegar after several days. Record your observations.

Practicing Your Skills

6. **OBSERVE:** Which nail shows signs of rust?

7. **ANALYZE:** How do the nail polish and oil or petroleum jelly affect the corrosion of the ungalvanized nails?

8. **INFER:** Can you think of other substances that would keep the nails from rusting? What are they?

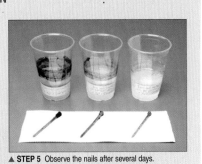

▲ **STEP 5** Observe the nails after several days.

---

3 Assess

✓ CHECKING CONCEPTS ANSWERS

1. galvanized
2. rusting or corroding
3. zinc oxide
4. electroplating
5. negative

💡 THINKING CRITICALLY ANSWERS

6. **PREDICT:** the negative electrode

7. **HYPOTHESIZE:** They will not rust when exposed to air and moisture.

8. **ANALYZE:** The negative electrode; The positive silver ions will be attracted to the negative electrode. The silver is being reduced.

4 Close

DESIGNING AN EXPERIMENT

Use the Designing an Experiment Rubric on the Teacher's Resources CD-ROM to assess students' experiments. Fill in the rubric with the additional information below. For this assignment, students should have:

- developed a procedure that is clear and concise.

- stated a hypothesis that might involve either determining density or scratching the object.

Hands-On Activity

PROTECTING METALS FROM CORROSION

TIME: 30 minutes

PURPOSE: observing, analyzing, inferring

SAFETY TIP: Have students apply the nail polish in a well-ventilated area.

ALTERNATIVE MATERIALS: Galvanized nails may be substituted to eliminate the need to coat iron nails with clear polish, oil, or petroleum jelly.

Practicing Your Skills Answers

6. **OBSERVE:** the nail without any coating

7. **ANALYZE:** They prevent the corrosion of the ungalvanized nail.

8. **INFER:** Possible answers: paint or another type of metal, such as zinc

---

MORE ON THE WEB

Gold Plating Have students visit www.conceptsand challenges.com to learn what some companies can plate with gold. Then, have students make a list of things that they own that they might want to have gold-plated.

ONGOING ASSESSMENT

Explaining Figure 10-18 Have students explain how copper is plated on the negative electrode in Figure 10-18.

• TEACHING RESOURCES •

🖲 **Teacher's Resources CD-ROM**

Lesson Review: Chapter 10, p. 10

Concept Map: Study Tools, p. 4

Designing an Experiment Rubric: Teaching Tools, p. 7

Designing an Experiment: Study Tools, p. 14

Challenges (pp. 226–228)

Chapter Summary

Review Before students begin the Challenges, review the summary with them. Tell pairs of students to make flash cards by writing a true/false, completion, or multiple-choice question for each summary point on the front of an index card and its answer on the back.

STUDY HINT Have pairs of students exchange the flash cards and quiz each other.

Key Term Challenges

MATCHING

1. ore (10-1)
2. plating (10-6)
3. roasting (10-2)
4. alkali metals (10-4)
5. alkaline earth metals (10-4)
6. alloy (10-3)
7. corrosion (10-5) or plating (10-6)
8. electroplating (10-6)
9. reduction (10-2)

FILL IN

10. alloy (10-3)
11. electroplating (10-6)
12. alkali metal (10-4)
13. alkaline earth metals (10-4)
14. roasting (10-2)
15. corrosion (10-5)
16. plating (10-6)
17. ore (10-1)
18. reduction (10-2)

Chapter Summary

Lesson 10-1
- Metals are usually found combined with other elements.
- An **ore** is a rock or mineral from which a useful metal can be removed.
- Three types of ores are oxides, sulfides, and carbonates.

Lesson 10-2
- Metals are removed from their ores through chemical processes.
- For oxides, the metal is removed through the process of **reduction**.
- For sulfides and carbonates, the metal is removed by first **roasting** and then reducing the ore.

Lesson 10-3
- The metals removed from ores are pure metals.
- An **alloy** is a mixture of two pure metals or more.
- Alloys have different properties from the metals that make them up.

Lesson 10-4
- The Group 1 metals, or **alkali metals**, are chemically active. They include lithium, sodium, potassium, rubidium, cesium, and francium. The alkali metals have one valence electron.
- The Group 2 metals, or **alkaline earth metals**, are also chemically active. They include beryllium, magnesium, calcium, strontium, barium, and radium. The alkaline earth metals have two valence electrons.
- Some metals can replace others in a chemical reaction.

Lesson 10-5
- **Corrosion** is a chemical change on the surface of metals.
- Two examples of corrosion are rust and tarnish.
- Corrosion is usually caused by oxidation.
- Two ways to prevent corrosion are sealing a surface with paint or oil and by using alloys.

Lesson 10-6
- In **plating**, a protective layer of one metal is placed over another metal.
- A type of plating called **electroplating** uses an electric current.

226

Key Term Challenges

alkali metals (p. 218)	ore (p. 210)
alkaline earth metals (p. 218)	plating (p. 224)
alloy (p. 214)	reduction (p. 212)
corrosion (p. 220)	roasting (p. 212)
electroplating (p. 224)	

MATCHING Write the Key Term from above that best matches each description.

1. rock or mineral from which a useful metal can be removed
2. coating of one metal on another metal
3. heating an ore in air
4. group 1 metals
5. group 2 metals
6. substance made up of two metals or more
7. process that changes the surface of metals
8. electrically coating one metal with another metal
9. removing oxygen from an ore

FILL IN Write the Key Term from above that best completes each statement.

10. Steel is an _____ of iron, carbon, and other elements, such as chromium or nickel.
11. In _____, a copper rod is sometimes used as an electrode.
12. Sodium is an _____.
13. Another name for the Group 2 metals is _____.
14. Sulfides and carbonates are converted to oxides by the process of _____.
15. One of the best examples of _____ is rust.
16. A layer of zinc placed over iron is an example of _____.
17. Litharge is an _____ of lead.
18. The process of _____ is used to separate a metal from an oxide ore.

Teaching Options

PREPARING STUDENTS FOR STANDARDIZED TESTS

Reading Strategy: Remind students that comparing means telling how two things are alike, and contrasting means telling how they are different.

Writing Strategy: In a one-paragraph response, tell students first to write the response in outline form. Then, they can write the topic sentence for the paragraph from the outline. They should support the topic sentence with additional sentences offering details and further information.

Interpreting Visuals: Remind students to read diagram labels carefully to understand more fully what they are seeing.

ESL/ELL STRATEGY

Restating English-language learners will benefit from restating processes in their own words. Have pairs of students work together to summarize the processes presented in the chapter.

Content Challenges TEST PREP

MULTIPLE CHOICE Write the letter of the term or phrase that best completes each statement.

1. Corroded metals are
   a. smooth and shiny.
   b. dull and discolored.
   c. silvery.
   d. reddish brown.

2. Most metals are not found in their pure form in nature because they are
   a. chemically active.
   b. rusted.
   c. tarnished.
   d. corroded.

3. The ores from which we usually remove metals are
   a. sulfides.
   b. carbonates.
   c. oxides.
   d. alloys.

4. Brass is an alloy of
   a. copper and tin.
   b. iron and gold.
   c. copper and zinc.
   d. copper and chromium.

5. Corrosion should be prevented because corrosion
   a. causes surfaces to react.
   b. discolors metal.
   c. makes the metal shiny.
   d. plates metal.

6. All of the following are ways to reduce corrosion except
   a. painting.
   b. electroplating.
   c. exposing to air.
   d. using alloys.

7. Silver is more active than
   a. lithium.
   b. copper.
   c. calcium.
   d. gold.

8. The ore from which aluminum is removed is
   a. cuprite.
   b. bauxite.
   c. galena.
   d. hematite.

9. Each of the following is a property of pure metals except being
   a. ductile.
   b. malleable.
   c. solid.
   d. a poor conductor of heat.

10. The two steps in removing a metal from a sulfide ore are
    a. roasting followed by reduction.
    b. reduction followed by roasting.
    c. reduction followed by oxidation.
    d. oxidation followed by roasting.

TRUE/FALSE Write *true* if the statement is true. If the statement is false, change the underlined term to make the statement true.

11. An ore is a combination of a <u>metal</u> and another element.

12. <u>Lead</u> can be removed from bauxite.

13. When iron rusts, it forms <u>iron oxide</u>.

14. Electroplating is one way to prevent <u>corrosion</u>.

15. When a metal is oxidized, it <u>gains</u> electrons.

16. Two examples of corrosion are rust and <u>tarnish</u>.

17. Bronze is a combination of copper and <u>iron</u>.

18. To remove a metal from a <u>sulfide</u> ore, the ore is roasted.

CHAPTER 10: Metals **227**

Content Challenges

MULTIPLE CHOICE

1. b (10-5)
2. a (10-4)
3. c (10-2)
4. c (10-3)
5. b (10-5)
6. c (10-5)
7. d (10-4)
8. b (10-1)
9. d (10-3)
10. a (10-2)

TRUE/FALSE

11. true (10-1)
12. false; Aluminum (10-1)
13. true (10-5)
14. true (10-6)
15. false; loses (10-5)
16. true (10-5)
17. false; tin (10-3)
18. false; oxide (10-2)

ALTERNATIVE ASSESSMENT

Summarizing Information Have students choose a metallic element in the text and write a science log entry summarizing information about the metal, such as the ore from which it is extracted, the method used to remove the metal from the ore, alloys it forms, what causes it to corrode, and methods to prevent its corrosion. You can use the Writing Activity Rubric found on the Teacher's Resources CD-ROM to assess students' work.

PORTFOLIO ASSESSMENT

Making Student Portfolios Portfolio Assessment can provide an opportunity for students who are generally not good test-takers to demonstrate their learning in another way. Students can demonstrate their comprehension of the concepts in this chapter by making a portfolio. The Lab Activity Report and the Weekly Journal are some of the reproducibles on the Teacher's Resources CD-ROM that they can include in their portfolios. You can use the Portfolio Assessment Rubric also found on the Teacher's Resources CD-ROM to assess students' portfolios.

Concept Challenges

WRITTEN RESPONSE

1. **EXPLAIN:** A metal's valence electrons make it a good conductor of electricity, which is the flow of electrons. (10-3)
2. **HYPOTHESIZE:** The technology needed to produce bronze was developed before the technology needed to produce iron. (10-3)
3. **INFER:** The copper is being oxidized. (10-5)
4. **EXPLAIN:** Lithium has only one valence electron. (10-4)

INTERPRETING A DIAGRAM (10-6)

5. electrolysis or electroplating
6. carbon
7. copper sulfate solution
8. Copper has been plated on the electrode.

Chapter Project Wrap-Up

CORROSION PREVENTION DISPLAY

Have students show the results of their projects and explain how each method prevents corrosion. You can use the Individual Activity Rubric found on the Teacher's Resources CD-ROM to assess students' projects. Fill in the rubric with the additional information below. For this project, students should have:

- organized a display of the effects of corrosion protection on iron.
- included a clear, well-written report of the procedures and conclusions.

Concept Challenges TEST PREP

WRITTEN RESPONSE Answer each of the following questions in complete sentences.

1. **EXPLAIN:** What part of a metal's atomic structure makes it a good conductor of electricity?
2. **HYPOTHESIZE:** Some periods of human history are known by the metals that were used during that time. The Bronze Age was about 6,000 years ago. The Iron Age was about 3,000 years ago. What does this tell you about the technology needed to produce bronze and iron?
3. **INFER:** The Statue of Liberty in New York Harbor is made of copper. Why do you think the statue has a green color? (Hint: You may have seen a similar green coating on old copper pennies.)
4. **EXPLAIN:** Lithium is the most active metal in the electromotive series of metals. It is an alkali metal. Why is lithium so active?

INTERPRETING A DIAGRAM Use Figure 10-20 to answer each of the following questions.

5. What process does the figure show?
6. What is the positive electrode made of?
7. What is the electrolyte?
8. What has happened at the negative electrode?

Copper sulfate solution

◀ Figure 10-20

−   +

228

Teaching Options

• TEACHING RESOURCES •

Teacher's Resources CD-ROM

Key Term Review: Chapter 10, p. 11

Chapter 10 Test: pp. 12–13

Chapter Self-Check: Teaching Tools, p. 11

Lab Activity Report: Study Tools, pp. 16–17

Writing Activity Rubric: Teaching Tools, p. 9

Weekly Journal: Study Tools, p. 19

Portfolio Assessment Rubric: Teaching Tools, p. 10

PLANNING GUIDE

◆ **TEACHING THE CHAPTER** This chapter should take approximately 4–7 days to complete instruction and assessment.

	Skills and Features	Projects and Activities	Achieve Science Literacy	Meet Individual Needs
Chapter 11 Opener p. T229	COMMUNICATE	• Chapter Project		
Lesson 11-1 **What elements are not metals?** pp. T230–T231 Standard: B1b	OBSERVE, NAME, LIST • Investigate • Interpreting Visuals	• More on the Web • Lab Skills Worksheet	• Study Hint • Reading Strategy • Ongoing Assessment	• Reteach
Lesson 11-2 **What are metalloids?** pp. T232–T233 Standard: B1b	DESCRIBE, CONTRAST, EXPLAIN • Designing an Experiment • Science and Technology	• More on the Web	• Study Hint • Reading Strategy	• ESL/ELL Strategy ◎ CD-ROM Enrichment Activity Designing an Experiment
Lesson 11-3 **What are radioactive elements?** pp. T234–T235 Standards: B1b, B3a	EXPLAIN, DEFINE, INFER • Health and Safety Tip • People in Science	• Extending the Lesson • More on the Web	• Study Hint • Ongoing Assessment	• Reteach ◎ CD-ROM Enrichment Activity Concept Map
Big Idea **How is half-life used to date fossils and rocks?** pp. T236–T237	RESEARCH, COMMUNICATE, ANALYZE • Science Log: Writing Activity	• Big Idea Online • Integrating Life Science • Close Activity	• Tips for Using Technology	◎ CD-ROM Big Idea Planner

Planning Guide continues on next page.

Standards: For details on the correlation to National Science Standards see pages *xx–xxi*.

	Skills and Features	Projects and Activities	Achieve Science Literacy	Meet Individual Needs
Lesson 11-4 **What are nuclear reactions?** pp. T238–T239 Standards: B2a, B3a, B3e, B3f	ANALYZE, INFER, LIST • Web InfoSearch • Hands-On Activity	• Lab Challenge	• Study Hint • Reading Strategy • Ongoing Assessment	• Reteach CD-ROM Nuclear Fission and Nuclear Fusion
Lab Activity **Modeling Half-Life** pp. T240–T241	OBSERVE, ANALYZE, COMPARE • Set-Up Time: 1 hr • Lab Time: 45 min	• Lab Skills Worksheets • Extend the Lab Activity	• Tips for Using Technology	CD-ROM Lab Activity Report Graph Paper Spreadsheet
Chapter 11 Challenges pp. T242–T244	• Chapter Summary • Key Term Challenges • Content Challenges • Concept Challenges	• Chapter Project Wrap-Up • Unit Challenge Online	• Study Hint • Preparing Students for Standardized Tests	• ESL/ELL Strategy CD-ROM Chapter Self-Check Concept Map

Teacher Notes

_____

_____

_____

_____

_____

_____

_____

_____

_____

_____

_____

_____

_____

_____

_____

Chapter 11 Nonmetals, Metalloids, and Radioactive Elements

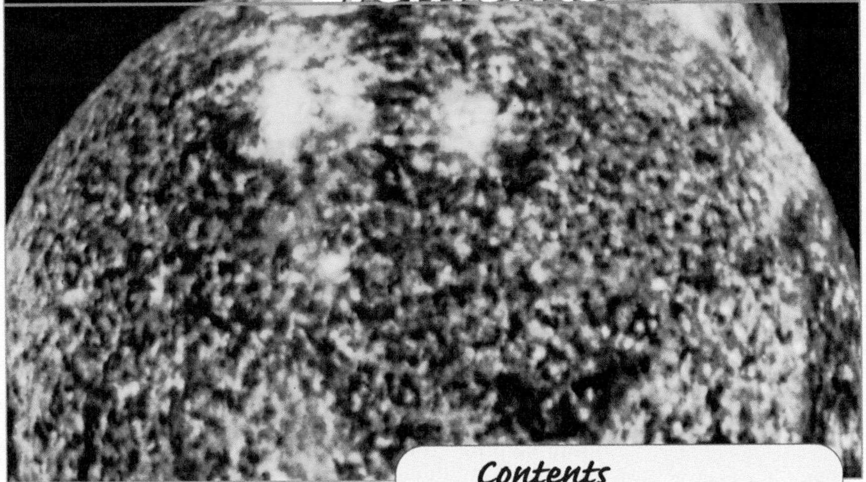

▲ **Figure 11-1** Scientists hope to someday reproduce the nuclear reactions of the Sun.

The Sun's energy is produced by nuclear fusion reactions that take place deep inside the Sun. A fusion reaction occurs when nuclei of lighter elements combine to form nuclei of heavier elements. Such reactions release great amounts of energy. Scientists are trying to produce fusion reactions that they can control. Hopefully, controlled fusion reactions will someday be used to meet many of our energy needs.

▶Why is it important for scientists to find new sources of energy?

Contents

Teaching Options

ASSESSMENT PLANNER

For assessment in the Student Edition, see the following pages:

Content Assessment
Checking Concepts: pp. 231, 233, 235, 239
Thinking Critically: pp. 231, 233, 235, 239
Interpreting Visuals: p. 231
Chapter Challenges: pp. 242–244

Alternative Assessment
Web InfoSearch: p. 239
Science Log: p. 237

Performance-Based Assessment
Hands-On Activity: p. 239
Designing an Experiment: p. 233
Lab Activity: pp. 240–241

• TEACHING RESOURCES •

Teacher's Resources CD-ROM
Lesson Review: Ch. 11, pp. 2, 3, 5, 8
Enrichment: Ch. 11, pp. 4, 6
Key Term Review: Ch. 11, p. 9
Chapter 11 Test: pp. 10–11
Laboratory Manual: pp. 13–18, 61–64

Chapter 11 Nonmetals, Metalloids, and Radioactive Elements

Chapter Overview

In this chapter, students will learn about nonmetals, metalloids, and radioactive elements. Students will describe properties of nonmetals and metalloids. Students will locate radioactive elements on the periodic table and explain the processes of nuclear fission and nuclear fusion.

About Figure 11-1 The temperature at the core of the Sun is nearly 16,000,000°C (approximately 29,000,000°F). This extreme heat, along with intense pressure, makes nuclear fusion possible. A small amount of the energy produced by fusion travels to Earth as radiant energy. It takes just over 8 minutes for this radiant energy to travel from the Sun to Earth.

Answer Possible answers: Most of the energy that people use comes from a limited supply of resources that are nonrenewable and cause pollution.

Linking Prior Knowledge

For this chapter, students should recall:

- the Periodic Table of Elements (Lesson 3-7).
- the definition of an isotope (Lesson 3-10).

Chapter Project

FAMILY OF ELEMENTS SONG OR POEM

MATERIALS: periodic table, research materials

Divide students into five groups. Assign each group one of the families on the periodic table. Each group will write either a song or a poem about the assigned family, including information about the characteristics of the family and the properties of the elements in the family. Students may include information about the history of the elements, what the elements are used for, and where they can be found.
learning styles: linguistic, auditory

1 Introduce

○ INVESTIGATE

TIME: 10–15 minutes

PURPOSE: Students will identify and list objects in their classroom as metals or not metals.

MATERIALS: notebook, pen or pencil, objects in classroom

PROCEDURE: Emphasize that some objects may have parts that are metallic and parts that are not, and that students can consider each part of an object. Point out that there are many more metallic elements than nonmetallic elements. However, because so many organic (carbon-based) compounds exist, students might see more nonmetallic materials than metallic ones. **learning style: visual**

THINK ABOUT IT: The column that has more items listed will depend on the number of metal and nonmetal objects in the classroom and which objects students chose to list. Conclusions and explanations should be consistent with students' lists.

✏ **STUDY HINT** Have students write the lesson title and objectives in their notebooks. As students read this lesson, they should write the information that meets the objectives.

Linking Prior Knowledge Have students review the periodic table (Lesson 3-7) and the properties of metals and nonmetals (Lesson 3-8). Ask students how they can tell the difference between metals and nonmetals in the periodic table. (by the element's position to the left or right of the dark, zigzag line and by the color of the element's square) **learning styles: auditory, visual**

2 Teach

Discussion Have students look at Figure 11-2. Ask students where nonmetallic elements are located in the periodic table. (to the right of the zigzag line and at the top of Group 1) Then, ask what elements are neither metals nor nonmetals. (metalloids) Point out the properties of nonmetals. (dull luster, brittle, poor conductors of heat and electricity) Make sure that students understand that metalloids have properties of both metals and nonmetals.

11-1 What elements are not metals?

INVESTIGATE

○ *Identifying Metals and Nonmetals*
HANDS-ON ACTIVITY

STEP 1

1. Look carefully at some of the different objects in your classroom.
2. Make a two-column chart in your notebook. Label one column "Metal" and the other column "Not a Metal."
3. Walk around the room and list as many objects as you can under the appropriate heading on your chart.
4. Read over your list. Compare the number of items you listed in each column.

THINK ABOUT IT: Which column has more items listed? Do you think there will always be more of one type of material than the other? Explain.

Objectives
Describe some of the properties of nonmetals. List the families of nonmetals and describe their features.

Key Terms
luster: the way a material reflects light
nonmetals: elements that have different properties from metals

Metals, Nonmetals, and Metalloids Look at the periodic table in Figure 11-2. Notice that there are three main classes of elements: metals, nonmetals, and metalloids. The heavy zigzag line separates elements that are metals from those that are not metals. Elements that are metals make up the largest class by far. Nonmetals are located at the right side of the table. In between the metals and the nonmetals is a small class of elements known as metalloids. These elements have some properties of metals and some properties of nonmetals.

▷ **OBSERVE:** How many groups of the periodic table have one or more elements that are nonmetals?

Properties of Nonmetals **Nonmetals** are elements that have different properties from metals. The way a material reflects light is called **luster.** Solid nonmetals have a dull luster and tend to be brittle, or easily broken. These properties are different from the properties of metals. Most metals are good conductors of heat and electricity. Nonmetals are generally poor conductors of heat and electricity.

Nonmetals exist in all three states of matter: solid, liquid, and gas. Only one nonmetal, bromine, is found in nature as a liquid. The rest are either solids or gases. Carbon, sulfur, and iodine are examples of solid nonmetals. Helium, oxygen, and radon are gaseous nonmetals.

▷ **NAME:** What are three properties of nonmetals?

Families of Nonmetals Look at the simplified Periodic Table of Elements in Figure 11-2. Notice that most nonmetals are found in Groups 14, 15, 16, 17, and 18. Although most of the nonmetals are contained in these five groups, each group is unique.

The nonmetals in a group have some properties similar to the other nonmetals in that group. The first three groups, or families, are named by the element in the top row of the group.

- **The Carbon Family** Group 14 is called the carbon family. In fact, carbon is the only nonmetal in the group. Carbon is a very important element found in all living things and in many nonliving things.
- **The Nitrogen Family** Group 15 is called the nitrogen family. Nitrogen and phosphorus are

---

Teaching Options

RETEACH

Grouping Nonmetals in Families
Write *The Carbon Family, The Nitrogen Family, The Oxygen Family, The Halogen Family,* and *The Noble Gases* in a row across the top of the board. Then, write *Nonmetals* under each family and ask students to name the nonmetals that are in each family. List each nonmetal under the appropriate family name. Make sure that students understand that some of the families also contain metalloids and metals.

ONGOING ASSESSMENT

Explaining the Families of Nonmetals
Ask volunteers to explain how the first three families of nonmetals are named. (by the element in the top row of the group) Then, ask what the other two families are named. (the halogen family and the noble gases) **learning styles: auditory, linguistic**

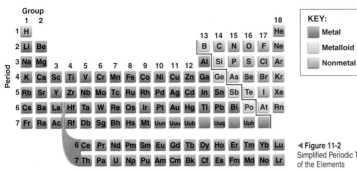

◀ Figure 11-2
Simplified Periodic Table
of the Elements

KEY:
- Metal
- Metalloid
- Nonmetal

the two nonmetals in this family. Nitrogen gas makes up most of Earth's atmosphere and is an important nutrient in soil. Phosphorus is used to make fertilizers, pesticides, matches, and fireworks.

- **The Oxygen Family** Group 16 is called the oxygen family. Oxygen, sulfur, and selenium are the three nonmetals in this family. Oxygen is an important part of our atmosphere. We must breathe in oxygen to survive. Oxygen also makes up ozone, a protective layer of gas in the upper atmosphere. Sulfur is used to make batteries, fertilizers, tires, and some medicines. Selenium is used in photographic equipment and photocopy machines.

- **The Halogen Family** Group 17 is called the halogens. The halogens are chemically very active. They combine with other elements to make very useful compounds. There are four nonmetals in this family: fluorine, chlorine, bromine, and iodine. Fluorine occurs in many minerals and is added to toothpaste. It is also found in most of the coolants used in air conditioners and refrigerators. Chlorine is found in many salts, including table salt. It is also used to purify drinking water. Bromine is used in dyes. Iodine is found in products used to prevent infections.

- **The Noble Gases** Group 18 is called the noble gases. Unlike the elements of the halogen family, the noble gases are chemically inactive. They do not easily take part in chemical reactions. All six elements in this family are nonmetals. These elements are helium, neon,

argon, krypton, xenon, and radon. Helium is used to inflate balloons. Neon, argon, krypton, and xenon are all used for lighting. Radon is not known to have a useful purpose.

▶ LIST: Name the five families of nonmetals.

✓ CHECKING CONCEPTS

1. There are fewer _____ than metals in the periodic table.
2. Nonmetals exist in all three states of _____ .
3. Nonmetals have few of the properties of _____ .
4. Elements in Group 17 are called _____ .
5. Group 18 is called the _____ .

💡 THINKING CRITICALLY

6. CONTRAST: How do nonmetals differ from metals?
7. INFER: How might the properties of neon compare with those of argon? Explain.

INTERPRETING VISUALS

Use Figure 11-2 to answer the following questions.

8. OBSERVE: Which group includes two nonmetals, two metalloids, and one metal?
9. OBSERVE: Which group contains no metals or metalloids?
10. INFER: Which nonmetal probably has properties similar to the properties of nitrogen?

• TEACHING RESOURCES •

Teacher's Resources CD-ROM
Lesson Review: Chapter 11, p. 2

Laboratory Manual
Lab. Skills Worksheet 4: Organizing and Analyzing Data, pp. 13–14

Reinforcement Have students refer to Figure 11-2. Give students the names and symbols of nonmetallic elements in random order and ask students to name each element's family.
learning styles: auditory, visual

Answers to questions

1. OBSERVE: 5
2. NAME: Possible answers: dull luster, brittle or easily broken, and poor conductors of heat and electricity
3. LIST: the carbon family, the nitrogen family, the oxygen family, the halogen family, and the noble gases

📖 READING STRATEGY Have students identify the prefix and suffix used in the terms *nonmetal* and *metalloid* that change the meaning of *metal*. Then, ask students what they think the prefix *non-* and the suffix *-oid* mean. Have students use a dictionary to check their meanings and then list other words that have the same prefix or suffix.
learning styles: auditory, linguistic

3 Assess

✓ CHECKING CONCEPTS ANSWERS

1. nonmetals or metalloids
2. matter
3. metals
4. halogens
5. noble gases

💡 THINKING CRITICALLY ANSWERS

6. CONTRAST: Possible answers: Nonmetals have dull luster; tend to be brittle, or easily broken; can be solid, liquid, or gas at room temperature; and are generally poor conductors of heat and electricity. Metals have shiny luster, are malleable and ductile, are usually solid at room temperature, and are good conductors of heat and electricity.
7. INFER: Their properties would be similar because they are both in the noble gas family.

4 Close

INTERPRETING VISUALS ANSWERS

8. OBSERVE: Group 15
9. OBSERVE: Group 18
10. INFER: phosphorus

1 Introduce

STUDY HINT Before beginning this lesson, have students study Figures 11-3 and 11-4. Have them find the elements in Figure 11-3 on the table in Figure 11-4.

Linking Prior Knowledge Ask students if they or someone in their family has used a silicone spray, which contains the metalloid silicon. If so, ask them to tell how it was used. Students may have experiences with silicone spray for lubricating bicycle parts, skateboard wheels, or exercise equipment. Explain that silicone spray is used to lubricate parts on machines to reduce friction and to allow the parts to move more easily. **learning styles: auditory, linguistic**

2 Teach

Demonstration Display sand, a piece of glass, a cleaning product that contains borax and boric acid (eyedrops). Tell students that these products contain metalloids. Sand is a natural source of silicon, and most glass is made from sand. The cleaning product and the boric acid contain boron.
learning styles: visual, auditory

Answers to questions

1 CONTRAST: They are separated by a zigzag line. Metals are to the left of the line, and nonmetals are to the right of the line.

2 DESCRIBE: Metalloids have properties of both metals and nonmetals, such as conducting heat and electricity better than nonmetals but not as well as metals.

3 OBSERVE: aluminum

4 DESCRIBE: Possible answer: It is the most common element in Earth's crust.

READING STRATEGY A good strategy to use with struggling readers is making connections. Ask students if they have ever read a mystery book, seen a movie, or watched a television program in which arsenic was used. Ask volunteers what they learned about arsenic from the book, movie, or program. **learning styles: auditory, linguistic**

11-2 What are metalloids?

Objective
Describe the properties of metalloids.

Key Term
metalloid: element that has properties of both metals and nonmetals

Locating the Metalloids on the Periodic Table A zigzag line separates the metals from the nonmetals on the periodic table. The elements along this line are called metalloids. The section of the periodic table containing the metalloids is shown in Figure 11-3.

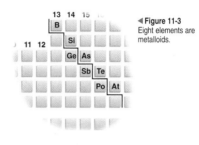

◀ **Figure 11-3**
Eight elements are metalloids.

1 CONTRAST: How do metals and nonmetals differ in their location on the periodic table?

Properties of Metalloids Metalloids are elements that have properties of both metals and nonmetals. You have learned that metals are usually hard, shiny, and good conductors of heat and electricity. Nonmetals are usually softer than metals, dull, and poor conductors of heat and electricity.

Because a metalloid may have properties of both metals and nonmetals, it may conduct heat and electricity better than a nonmetal but not as well as a metal. All metalloids on the periodic table are solids.

2 DESCRIBE: How would you describe the properties of metalloids?

Examples of Metalloids The eight metalloids are arranged along the zigzag line of the periodic table. Except for aluminum, each element that touches the zigzag line is a metalloid. Figure 11-4 lists the names and symbols of the eight metalloids.

METALLOIDS		
Element Name	Symbol	Atomic Number
Boron	B	5
Silicon	Si	14
Germanium	Ge	32
Arsenic	As	33
Antimony	Sb	51
Tellurium	Te	52
Polonium	Po	84
Astatine	At	85

▲ **Figure 11-4**

3 OBSERVE: What element located next to the zigzag line of the periodic table is not a metalloid?

Uses for Some Metalloids

- **Boron (B)** Boron is used to make insect poisons and to provide the bright green color in fireworks. Boron is also used in the production of boric acid. Many cleaning products contain compounds of boron.

- **Silicon (Si)** Silicon is the most common element in Earth's crust. It combines with oxygen to produce silicon dioxide, the main mineral in sand. Silicon has many uses. Perhaps its most familiar uses are in the production of glass and computer chips.

- **Germanium (Ge)** Germanium is very important in the production of transistors. It is also used in some alloys, in fluorescent lights, and in lenses and other optical equipment.

- **Arsenic (As)** Arsenic and its compounds are poisonous. The compounds are used in farming to fight insects. An arsenic compound is also used in lasers to convert electricity directly to light.

232

Teaching Options

! FAST FACTS *Mendeleev Predicts Germanium*

When Mendeleev developed the first table of elements organized by properties in 1869, he left spaces between elements so that the elements known at that time would belong to groups with similar properties. He predicted that the spaces would be filled by elements that had not been discovered yet. In 1871, he predicted that one of the spaces would be filled by an unknown element that had properties similar to those of silicon. He referred to the element as *ekasilicon*. In 1886, a German scientist, Clemens Winkler, discovered an unknown element that had the properties attributed to ekasilicon. He named the element germanium. Tell students that *eka-* means "standing or assumed to stand next in order beyond (a specified element) in the same family in the periodic table." Ask students why they think Mendeleev suggested the name ekasilicon for the unknown element. (He predicted it would have properties similar to silicon.) Have students located Si and Ge in Figure 11-3. Point out that germanium is located just below silicon in the same family. Then, ask students why they think Winkler named the element germanium. (to honor his country) **learning styles: auditory, linguistic**

- **Antimony (Sb)** Oxides of antimony are used in the production of paints, glass, and pottery.

4 **DESCRIBE:** What makes silicon unusual among the metalloids?

✓ CHECKING CONCEPTS

1. The elements along the zigzag line on the periodic table are called _____.
2. There are _____ elements that are metalloids.
3. All metalloids are found in the _____ state of matter.
4. The only element along the zigzag line that is not a metalloid is _____.
5. The metalloid _____ is used in the production of glass and computer chips.

💡 THINKING CRITICALLY

6. **INFER:** Which is a better conductor of electricity, germanium or copper? Explain.
7. **EXPLAIN:** Why is it possible for the metalloid silicon to conduct heat better than the nonmetal oxygen?
8. **ANALYZE:** What property of arsenic and arsenic compounds make these substances both useful and dangerous?

DESIGNING AN EXPERIMENT

Design an experiment to solve the problem below. Include a hypothesis, variables, a procedure, and a type of data to study.

PROBLEM: Which metalloid is the best conductor of electricity?

Science and Technology

COMPUTER CHIPS

The metalloid silicon is an important part of today's fastest computers. Silicon makes up the computer's microprocessor, also called a computer chip. The invention of the silicon chip helped to make computers much faster, more powerful, and much more compact.

Silicon is a perfect choice for making computer chips because it is a semiconductor. A semiconductor is a material that conducts electricity only under certain conditions. Electronic devices such as computers need the flow of electricity to be controlled by semiconductors like silicon.

How are silicon chips made? Silicon comes from one of the most common substances on Earth—sand. Silicon compounds are mined and shipped to companies that specialize in converting the compounds into purified silicon. Eventually, the silicon is made into very thin pieces to be used for computer chips. Then, thousands of electrical devices are built onto the silicon chip.

Scientists keep trying to improve the silicon chip by putting even more electrical devices on the chip. By improving the chip, they hope to make computers even faster and more powerful. What will future computers be like? Although we will have to wait and see, we expect that silicon will continue to play a major part in chip production.

Thinking Critically How have faster computer chips changed the way we use computers?

▲ **Figure 11-5** This silicon chip, which is smaller than your fingernail, can hold millions of circuits.

---

3 Assess

✓ CHECKING CONCEPTS ANSWERS

1. metalloids
2. eight
3. solid
4. aluminum
5. silicon

💡 THINKING CRITICALLY ANSWERS

6. **INFER:** Copper is a better conductor of electricity because it is a metal. Germanium is a metalloid, which does not conduct electricity as well as a metal.
7. **EXPLAIN:** A metalloid conducts heat better than a nonmetal because a metalloid has some properties of metals.
8. **ANALYZE:** They are poisonous, so they can be used to kill insects but are dangerous to humans.

4 Close

DESIGNING AN EXPERIMENT

Use the Designing an Experiment Rubric on the Teacher's Resources CD-ROM to assess students' experiments. Fill in the rubric with the additional information below. For this assignment, students should have:

- mentioned one of the eight metalloids as the best conductor of electricity in the hypothesis.
- included a conductivity tester and a sample of each of the eight metalloids in the procedure.

Science and Technology

COMPUTER CHIPS

Real-Life Connection Microprocessors have changed the convenience of using appliances. For example, computer chips in coffeepots allow people to program the coffeepot to automatically turn on and off at certain times. Computer chips are also used in such products as cars, traffic lights, cell phones, vending machines, interactive toys, and electronic guitars and synthesizers.

Thinking Critically Answer
Possible answer: Faster chips make it easier to use computers to play games, communicate on the Internet, and listen to music.

MORE ON THE WEB

Researching Solar Cells Have students use the Internet to learn how silicon-based solar cells work. Then, have students answer the questions that follow this activity at www.concepts andchallenges.com.

ESL/ELL STRATEGY

Researching Latin Origins Inform students that the names of many elements have Latin origins. For example, *boron* comes from *boracium*, and *silicon* comes from *silicium*. Have students find the Latin origins of other elements' names.

• TEACHING RESOURCES •

💿 **Teacher's Resources CD-ROM**
Lesson Review: Chapter 11, p. 3
Enrichment: Chapter 11, p. 4
Designing an Experiment: Study Tools, p. 14
Designing an Experiment Rubric: Teaching Tools, p. 7

11-3 *(pp. 234–235)*

1 Introduce

STUDY HINT Have students use the Key Terms and their definitions to make a concept map that shows how the terms relate to one another. Students can also use the Concept Map found on the Teacher's Resources CD-ROM.

Linking Prior Knowledge Have students review the parts of an atom (Lesson 3-3) and isotopes (Lesson 3-10). Ask students: *What makes up the nucleus of an atom?* (protons and neutrons) *What part of an atom determines what element the atom is?* (the number of protons) *What are isotopes?* (atoms of an element with different numbers of neutrons)

2 Teach

Demonstration Join two small, round, different-colored pieces of clay together to model the nucleus of an atom. Each piece of clay represents either the numbers of protons or the neutrons. Inform students that since there is a balance between the protons and neutrons in this nucleus, the atom is stable. Make another model with one of the pieces of clay noticeably larger than the other. Tell students that because the nucleus does not have a balance between the numbers of protons and the neutrons, the atom is likely to be unstable. The nucleus will break down, or decay. **learning style: visual**

Answers to questions

1 EXPLAIN: an element that has a nucleus that breaks down, or decays

2 CLASSIFY: the energy or particles released when the nuclei of radioactive elements break down

3 ANALYZE: Possible answer: Their nuclei do not hold together as well as smaller nuclei, and they tend to break down, making these elements radioactive.

4 DEFINE: isotopes that release radiation

T234 UNIT 4: Exploring the Periodic Table

11-3 What are radioactive elements?

Objectives
Locate radioactive elements on the periodic table and describe their properties.

Key Terms
radioactive element: unstable element whose nucleus breaks down
radiation: energy and particles released from the nucleus of a radioactive element
radioisotope: isotope that releases radiation

Radioactive Elements Some elements are unstable. These elements are unstable because the nuclei of their atoms break down, or decay. When the nuclei of these atoms break down, energy and particles are released. Elements with unstable nuclei are called **radioactive elements.**

1 EXPLAIN: What makes an element unstable?

Radiation When the nuclei of radioactive elements break down, the energy released is called **radiation.** The release of radiation is called radioactivity. There are small amounts of radiation all around you. You cannot see, smell, taste, touch, or hear radioactivity. There is even some radioactivity inside your body.

2 CLASSIFY: What is radiation?

Large Nuclei Look at the location of the radioactive elements in the periodic table in Figure 11-6. All of the radioactive elements have atomic numbers equal to or greater than 83. This means that these elements have large nuclei, with at least 83 protons and at least that many neutrons. It has been found that large atomic nuclei do not hold together as well as smaller nuclei. So, the large nuclei tend to break down, making these elements radioactive.

3 ANALYZE: What is true of elements that have large nuclei?

Radioactive Isotopes Some atoms of elements with smaller nuclei may also be radioactive. Every element has isotopes. Isotopes are atoms of an element with the same number of protons but a different number of neutrons. Hydrogen is an example of an element with three isotopes. All three isotopes have a single proton but different numbers of neutrons. The three isotopes of hydrogen are hydrogen-1, hydrogen-2, and hydrogen-3. The numbers 1, 2, and 3 represent the mass numbers of the isotopes.

A number of elements have some isotopes that are stable and others that are unstable. The unstable isotopes release radiation. Such isotopes are called radioactive isotopes, or **radioisotopes.**

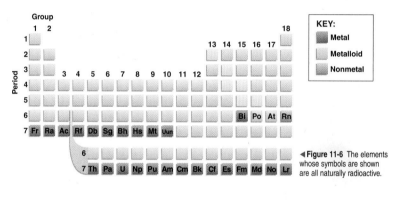

◄ **Figure 11-6** The elements whose symbols are shown are all naturally radioactive.

234

Teaching Options

RETEACH

Locating Radioactive Elements
Ask students how they could locate radioactive elements on a periodic table if the table did not have a key that identified them. (All elements with an atomic number of 83 or more are radioactive.) Give students practice finding radioactive elements on the periodic table by giving them the names of elements and asking if these elements are radioactive. Be sure to include some elements from atomic numbers 58–71. These elements are located near radioactive elements but are not radioactive.
learning styles: visual, auditory

EXTENDING THE LESSON

Using Radiation on Foods
Another use of radiation is the irradiation of foods to make them safer and last longer. The radiation kills insects, bacteria, pathogens, and microorganisms that make the foods spoil. Although irradiating foods does not cause the foods to become radioactive, some people object to eating foods that have been irradiated. Encourage volunteers to find out more about the concerns some people have about eating irradiated foods. Encourage other volunteers to find out what foods have the Food and Drug Administration's approval for irradiation. **learning style: auditory**

Consider the element carbon, for example. The nuclei of most carbon atoms contain six protons and six neutrons. This isotope, called carbon-12 (C-12), is stable. C-13 is also a stable isotope of carbon. However, some carbon isotopes contain six protons and eight neutrons. This isotope, called carbon-14, is unstable. It is radioactive. Carbon-14 isotopes are used to determine the age of certain rocks and fossils.

Many radioactive isotopes are important in our lives. Americium-241, an isotope of americium (Am), is used in smoke detectors and to measure lead amounts in paint. Californium-252 (Cf-252) is used by airlines in the detectors that check luggage for hidden explosives. Cesium-137 (Cs-137) is used to treat cancer cells. Cobalt-60 (Co-60) is used to sterilize medical equipment used in surgery.

▲ **DEFINE:** What are radioisotopes?

✓ **CHECKING CONCEPTS**

1. What happens when the nuclei of radioactive elements break down, or decay?

2. What is a radioactive element?

3. Name four elements on the periodic table that are naturally radioactive.

4. How are radioisotopes different from stable isotopes?

💡 **THINKING CRITICALLY**

5. **CONCLUDE:** What is released from a nucleus that breaks down?

6. **INFER:** What can you infer about the element radon, which has an atomic number of 86? Explain.

HEALTH AND SAFETY TIP

Exposure to radiation can be dangerous to living things. Find out what kind of protective clothing scientists, doctors, and other workers wear when dealing with radioactive elements. Find out what to do if you are exposed to some radioactive source.

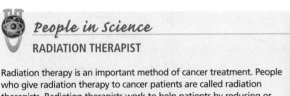

People in Science

RADIATION THERAPIST

Radiation therapy is an important method of cancer treatment. People who give radiation therapy to cancer patients are called radiation therapists. Radiation therapists work to help patients by reducing or eliminating cancer cells in their bodies. In some treatments, drugs containing radioactive elements are given to patients to destroy cancer cells. Another method of treatment is to radiate cancerous tumors. Radiation can often destroy the cancer cells.

A radiation therapist has many different tasks. Radiation therapists work closely with oncologists, doctors who specialize in cancer treatment. Radiation therapists use computers to help them do their job. Computers help therapists find the best way to give the radiation treatment, to know how much radiation to give, and to decide how long the treatment will take.

Most radiation therapists work in hospitals. Others work in doctors' offices, clinics, and laboratories. To become a radiation therapist, a person must graduate from high school and complete a training program in radiation therapy. Most training programs last two years. Many hospitals, vocational or technical schools, and colleges and universities offer training programs.

Thinking Critically Why is a radiation therapist's job challenging?

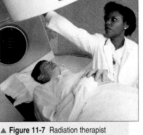

▲ **Figure 11-7** Radiation therapist at work

MORE ON THE WEB

Radioisotopes in Medicine
Have students use the Internet to learn about the uses of radioisotopes in medicine. Then, have students write a short report about their findings. Have students visit www.conceptsandchallenges.com for more details.

• TEACHING RESOURCES •

🔘 **Teacher's Resources CD-ROM**
Lesson Review: Chapter 11, p. 5
Enrichment: Chapter 11, p. 6
Concept Map: Study Tools, p. 4

---

3 Assess

✓ **CHECKING CONCEPTS ANSWERS**

1. They release energy and particles, or radiation.
2. an unstable element whose nucleus breaks down
3. Accept any four of the elements listed in Figure 11-6.
4. Radioisotopes are unstable and release radiation.

💡 **THINKING CRITICALLY ANSWERS**

5. **CONCLUDE:** Accept any of the following: radiation, energy, or energy and particles.
6. **INFER:** Radon is a radioactive element because it has an atomic number greater than 83.

4 Close

HEALTH AND SAFETY TIP ANSWERS

Students should find that protective clothing worn by workers who deal with radioactive elements often contains lead, which will help shield the worker by absorbing radiation. Workers also often wear some type of badge that detects radiation exposure. Exposure to a radioactive source requires treatment by a health care professional and depends on the length and type of exposure.
learning style: linguistic

People in Science

RADIATION THERAPIST

Technology Connection Radiation therapists use a wide variety of technology in their work. They must be able to accurately and safely operate this technology to determine the exact dosage of radiation, protect the areas of patients' bodies that do not need treatment, and administer the radiation. Some of the equipment they use includes computers, X-ray machines, CT scanners, and linear accelerators. The radioactive elements and radiation that therapists use to kill cancer cells can damage normal cells if not used correctly.

Thinking Critically Answer
Possible answers: The job involves working with people who have serious illnesses and with complicated equipment that must be operated safely and efficiently.

The Big Idea

(pp. 236–237)

1 Introduce

Objective Students will find examples of artifacts that were dated using carbon-14. Students will draw and describe the artifacts and explain why it is important to know the age of artifacts.

Linking Prior Knowledge Ask students whether they have been to a museum that had fossils of dinosaurs. Ask volunteers to tell about the dinosaurs and what they remember about how old the dinosaur fossils are.

2 Teach

Discussion Ask students to name a radioactive isotope that is used to find the age of fossils. (carbon-14) Have students review the captions and labels. Ask volunteers to describe the different fossils that scientists have learned about by measuring the amount of carbon-14 in the fossils.

Be sure that students understand that carbon-14 cannot be used to date all materials. If the material is not organic (does not contain carbon), it will not contain carbon-14. Radioactive isotopes such as uranium-238 are used to date inorganic materials, such as rocks. Moreover, if an organic artifact is more than about 50,000 years old, the amount of carbon-14 contained in it is so small that its measurement might not be accurate. **learning styles: visual, auditory**

Use the information in the article and the captions to help guide students in choosing a topic for their Science Logs.

THE BIG IDEA ONLINE

How is half-life used to date fossils and rocks? Have students research their Science Log Writing Activity at www.conceptsandchallenges.com. You can have students organize their log by completing the Big Idea activity online. Students may post their work in the Online Classroom Database for others to read.

◆ *Integrating Earth Science*

THE Big IDEA

How is half-life used to date fossils and rocks?

Scientists who specialize in the study of Earth's history often rely on radioactive isotopes to help them find out how old something is.

Radioactive isotopes do not stay radioactive forever. Over time, the nuclei of a radioactive element decay. When this happens, energy is released and a different element is formed. For example, when an atom of uranium-238 decays, it eventually forms an atom of lead-206, which is not radioactive.

Different radioactive elements decay at different rates. The half-life of an element is the time it takes for half the atoms in a sample of the element to decay. Scientists can use the half-life of certain radioactive isotopes to determine the ages of rocks, fossils, and other materials. This process is called radiometric dating.

Uranium-238 has a half-life of 4.5 billion years. That is the estimated age of Earth. Figure 11-8 below shows a simplified example of how the age of a very old rock containing uranium-238 can be found.

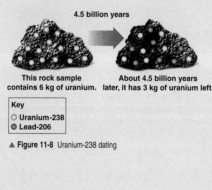

4.5 billion years

This rock sample contains 6 kg of uranium. About 4.5 billion years later, it has 3 kg of uranium left.

Key
○ Uranium-238
◉ Lead-206

▲ **Figure 11-8** Uranium-238 dating

A different radioactive isotope, carbon-14, is used to calculate the age of things that were once living. All living things contain carbon-12, which is not radioactive. They also contain much smaller amounts of carbon-14, which is formed in the atmosphere. Carbon-14 has a half-life of 5,730 years. As soon as something dies, the carbon-14 atoms decay and are not replaced. These atoms change to atoms of nitrogen-14, which are released into the environment. Scientists can date fossils and artifacts by comparing the amount of carbon-14 to the total amount of carbon in them.

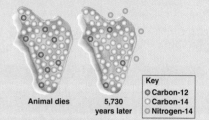

Animal dies | **5,730 years later**

Key
◉ Carbon-12
○ Carbon-14
○ Nitrogen-14

▲ **Figure 11-9** Carbon-14 dating

Look at the photos and illustrations on these two pages. Then, follow the directions in the Science Log to find out more about "the big idea."◆

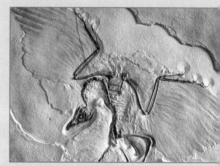

Archaeopteryx Fossil
Radioactive isotopes that have very long half-lives, such as U-238, can only be used to date very old rocks and fossils. The rock containing this fossil of the first known bird, called the archaeopteryx, is more than 100 million years old.

236

Teaching Options

◆ INTEGRATING LIFE SCIENCE

Finding Carbon-14 in Living Things Carbon-12 and carbon-14 are both found in carbon dioxide molecules in the air, but how do they get from the environment into living things? Plants acquire carbon when they take in carbon dioxide from the air. During the chemical reaction of photosynthesis, plants use energy from sunlight to change carbon dioxide and water into simple sugars and oxygen. Simple sugars contain carbon from the carbon dioxide. Most of this carbon is carbon-12, and a much smaller amount is carbon-14. When animals eat plants, they are eating molecules containing carbon. Animals use these carbon-containing molecules for energy and to make molecules that become part of the animals' bodies. The molecules, such as proteins, carbohydrates, and lipids, that make up living things contain carbon-12 and carbon-14. Have students draw diagrams that show the path of carbon from carbon dioxide in the air to the foods that they eat. **learning styles: auditory, visual**

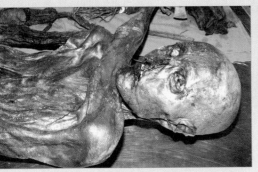

The Iceman
In 1991, the body of a man was found frozen in ice high in the Alps. He was nicknamed the Iceman. Scientists found the Iceman's age by measuring tiny amounts of carbon-14 in his remains and in tools found with him. The Iceman was found to be 5,300 years old!

Living Fossils
Bristlecone pine trees can live for more than 4,000 years. Scientists count the tree rings of dead bristlecone pines. Then, they measure their carbon-14 content. In this way, researchers have been able to make carbon-14 dating more accurate.

> **WRITING ACTIVITY**
>
> *Science Log*
> Find examples of fossils and artifacts that were dated using radioisotopes of uranium-238 or carbon-14. Draw sketches of the fossils and artifacts, and write descriptions of them. Why is it important to know the age of fossils and ancient artifacts? Start your search at www.conceptsandchallenges.com.

CHAPTER 11: Nonmetals, Metalloids, and Radioactive Elements **237**

Reinforcement Students can also use the Big Idea Planner or Big Idea Science Log Entry found on the Teacher's Resources CD-ROM.

3 *Assess*

Use the Writing Activity Rubric on the Teacher's Resources CD-ROM to assess students' Science Logs. Fill in the rubric with the additional information below. For this assignment, students should have:

- drawn and described fossils and artifacts that were dated using uranium-238 or carbon-14.
- explained why it is important to know the age of fossils and artifacts.

4 *Close*

Making a Timeline of Artifacts Have students work in small groups to make a timeline that puts their artifacts in order from the oldest to the youngest. Students' timelines should include the artifacts and their ages. Have volunteers present their timelines to the class.
learning styles: visual, logical/mathematical

Tips for Using Technology

Searching the Internet Remind students that one important tool for finding information on the Internet is a search engine. A search engine allows the user to type in a keyword or phrase. The engine then searches thousands of sites on the Internet for those that contain the keyword or phrase. After a few seconds, the search engine returns many addresses of sites related to the topic.

• *TEACHING RESOURCES* •

Teacher's Resources CD-ROM
Big Idea: Chapter 11, p. 7
Big Idea Planner: Study Tools, pp. 11–12
Big Idea Science Log Entry: Study Tools, p. 13
Writing Activity Rubric: Teaching Tools, p. 9

1 Introduce

✏️ **STUDY HINT** Have students write the lesson title and the title of each section in their notebooks. As students read this lesson, they should write the main idea of each section.

Linking Prior Knowledge Ask students to name the three isotopes of hydrogen. (protium, deuterium, and tritium; Lesson 3-10) Ask students how these isotopes differ from one another. (Protium has no neutron, deuterium has one neutron, and tritium has two neutrons.)
learning styles: linguistic, auditory

2 Teach

Discussion Ask students to explain what happens to nuclei in nuclear fission and what is released. (A large nucleus splits into smaller nuclei. Energy and neutrons are released.) Ask students to explain what happens to nuclei in nuclear fusion and what is released. (Two smaller nuclei are joined together to form a larger nucleus. Energy is released. Students may also say that a neutron is released.) Point out that both reactions release energy.
learning style: auditory

Answers to questions

1️⃣ **LIST:** nuclear fission and nuclear fusion

2️⃣ **ANALYZE:** A chain reaction is started when the neutrons released by a fission reaction crash into other nuclei, causing them to split.

3️⃣ **INFER:** to control the chain reaction of nuclear fission by absorbing neutrons

4️⃣ **CONTRAST:** Possible answer: Nuclear fission is the splitting of nuclei, and nuclear fusion is the joining of nuclei.

📖 **READING STRATEGY** A good strategy to use with struggling readers is making connections. Ask students what they know about the controversy surrounding the use of nuclear power to produce electrical energy. Ask them to explain why some people are so opposed to it.
learning style: linguistic

11-4 What are nuclear reactions?

Objective
Explain the processes of nuclear fission and nuclear fusion.

Key Terms:
nuclear energy: energy stored in the nucleus of the atom and released during a nuclear reaction
nuclear fission: reaction in which a large nucleus is split into smaller nuclei and energy is released
chain reaction: uncontrolled series of fission reactions
nuclear fusion: reaction in which two smaller nuclei are joined to form a larger nucleus

Nuclear Reactions There is tremendous energy stored in the nucleus of an atom. This energy, called **nuclear energy**, is released during a nuclear reaction. The breakdown of nuclei of radioactive elements is a natural process. For example, suppose you had a sample of pure uranium-238, a naturally radioactive element. It would take over 4 billion years for all of the nuclei to decay and form more stable nuclei of other elements.

If something happens to cause the nuclei of all of the atoms of a radioactive element to change suddenly, the energy stored in the nuclei may be released all at once. Nuclear energy can be released in two types of nuclear reactions. These reactions are called nuclear fission and nuclear fusion.

1️⃣ **LIST:** Name the two types of nuclear reactions.

Nuclear Fission Nuclear energy has been an important energy source for over a half century. The type of reaction that produces this energy is nuclear fission. **Nuclear fission** is a reaction in which a large nucleus is split into two smaller nuclei. Figure 11-10 shows what happens when the nucleus of an atom of uranium-235 (U-235) is split. Radiation and neutrons are released.

A fission reaction does not have to stop there, however. If the neutrons released are free to crash into other nuclei, those nuclei can also split. This will release more energy and more neutrons. The

238

fission process can go on and on, producing a chain reaction. A **chain reaction** is a continuing, uncontrolled series of fission reactions.

▲ Figure 11-10 Nuclear fission

2️⃣ **ANALYZE:** How is a chain reaction started?

Nuclear Reactors A nuclear reactor is a device used to control fission reactions and to make use of the energy they release. Control rods absorb neutrons to keep the chain reaction under control. A nuclear reactor is located in a nuclear power plant. The fuel used in most nuclear reactors is uranium. Carefully controlled uranium fission reactions are used to release large amounts of heat energy. This heat energy is then used to boil water and make steam. The steam leaves the reactor and is used to turn turbines and generate electricity. Figure 11-11 shows how fission reactions can be used to produce steam.

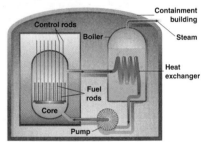

▲ Figure 11-11 In a nuclear reactor, fission reactions are used to generate steam.

3️⃣ **INFER:** What is the purpose of the control rods in a nuclear reactor?

Teaching Options

❗ **FAST FACTS** *Is It Smoke or Steam?*

The large towers of a nuclear power plant can be seen from many miles away. They are not smokestacks with smoke pouring out of them. They are cooling towers with condensed water vapor rising from them. Excess heat from the reactors heats water that is pumped from an outside source, thus cooling the reactor itself. This hot water is then piped to these towers to cool. Because it is hot when it reaches the cooling tower, the water quickly evaporates and rises from the towers. As the rising water vapor cools, it condenses into steam. Sometimes a reactor is shut down for repairs. Ask students how people who live in the area can tell the reactor is shut down. (There is no cloud or steam above the cooling tower). **learning style: auditory**

Nuclear Fusion Another type of nuclear reaction is called nuclear fusion. **Nuclear fusion** is a reaction in which two smaller nuclei are joined together, or fused, to form a larger, more stable nucleus. A great amount of energy is released from a fusion reaction. Fusion reactions produce the energy released by our Sun and other stars.

▲ **Figure 11-12** In a nuclear fusion reaction, nuclei of two different hydrogen isotopes can be joined to form a helium nucleus.

At present, scientists are trying to develop a method of starting and controlling fusion reactions. If a practical fusion reactor can be made, fusion will be the major energy source of the future. The problem is that fusion reactions take place only at very high temperatures and pressures. Such conditions exist in stars, but are difficult to control here on Earth.

4 CONTRAST: How does nuclear fusion differ from nuclear fission?

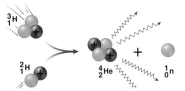

Hands-On Activity
MODELING NUCLEAR FUSION IN THE SUN

You will need two colors of modeling clay.

1. Using modeling clay, make several small spheres of equal size. Make two spheres one color. These will represent protons. Then, make three spheres of a second color to represent neutrons.

2. Combine one proton and one neutron to make a nucleus of hydrogen-2 (H-2). Combine one proton and two neutrons to make a nucleus of hydrogen-3 (H-3).

3. On a flat surface, move the two nuclei toward each other until they collide and stick together. Then, remove one neutron and set it to one side. You have just completed the type of fusion reaction that takes place in the Sun.

PRACTICING YOUR SKILLS

4. ANALYZE: What is the atomic number of the element formed when two nuclei collide in Step 3?

5. IDENTIFY: Use the Periodic Table to identify this element.

▲ **Step 1** Make several small spheres of equal size.

✓ CHECKING CONCEPTS

1. The two types of nuclear reactions are _____ and fusion.

2. Fusion reactions take place in the _____.

3. In nuclear _____, a large nucleus is split into smaller, more stable nuclei.

4. An uncontrolled series of fission reactions is called a _____.

💡 THINKING CRITICALLY

5. PREDICT: Will there be more hydrogen atoms or helium atoms in our Sun in 4 billion years?

Web InfoSearch

Nuclear Waste Waste from nuclear fission reactors remains radioactive for tens of thousands of years. It must be carefully stored to protect the environment.
SEARCH: Use the Internet to find out how the government is dealing with this problem. Go to www.conceptsandchallenges.com. Some key search words are **nuclear waste disposal** and **nuclear reactor management.**

---

3 Assess

✓ CHECKING CONCEPTS ANSWERS

1. fission
2. Sun or stars
3. fission
4. chain reaction

💡 THINKING CRITICALLY ANSWER

5. PREDICT: helium atoms

4 Close

Web InfoSearch

Nuclear Waste Have students visit www.conceptsandchallenges.com to find out how the government is dealing with nuclear waste. Some key search words are **nuclear waste disposal** and **nuclear reactor management.**

Hands-On Activity
MODELING NUCLEAR FUSION IN THE SUN

TIME: 10–15 minutes

PURPOSE: modeling, analyzing, identifying

DISCUSSION: Tell students that fusion reactions are impractical at this time on Earth. No known material can withstand the temperature and pressure required to contain such a reaction. Currently, the cost of producing energy by fusion is much greater than the value of the energy produced.

COOPERATIVE LEARNING: Have students work in groups of four. Have one student make the proton models, another student make the neutron models, a third student assemble the atoms, and the last student model the fusion reaction.
learning styles: tactile, interpersonal

Practicing Your Skills Answers

4. ANALYZE: 2
5. IDENTIFY: helium

RETEACH

Modeling a Chain Reaction Line up dominoes so that if you push the first domino, it starts a chain reaction and all the dominoes fall over. Ask a student to push the first domino. Point out that the energy of the student's push caused a chain reaction. Ask students if a chain reaction occurs in nuclear fission or nuclear fusion. (nuclear fission)

ONGOING ASSESSMENT

Explaining Figure 11-11 Ask volunteers to explain the function of each of the parts of the nuclear reactor in Figure 11-11.

• TEACHING RESOURCES •

💿 **Teacher's Resources CD-ROM**
Lesson Review: Chapter 11, p. 8
Nuclear Fission and Nuclear Fusion: Visuals, p. 9
Laboratory Manual
Lab. Challenge: What happens in a nuclear chain reaction such as fission? pp. 61–64

Lab Activity
(pp. 240–241)

1 Prepare the Lab

Modeling Half-Life

SET-UP TIME: LAB TIME:

BACKGROUND: In a given amount of a radioactive element, the number of nuclei that will decay in a certain length of time can be predicted. A radioactive element's half-life is the time it takes for half the nuclei in a given sample to decay. The half-life of a specific element is constant, but the half-life of different elements varies greatly from millionths of a second to billions of years.

PURPOSE: Students will use marked cardboard squares to represent radioactive nuclei of an element and model the half-life of the element.

ALTERNATIVE MATERIALS: Any objects that are two-sided and have one side that is different or can be marked, such as playing cards, can be used in place of the small cardboard squares.

SCIENCE SKILLS: Students will **collect and record data** about the number of cardboard nuclei that have decayed. Then, they will use a formula to **calculate** the percentage of nuclei that decayed. Students will **analyze** what fraction of the nuclei they would expect to decay in each trial and **compare** this fraction with their results. Students will also **infer** what they would expect if they did a fifth trial. Then, they will **observe** the shape of their line graph and **analyze** the graph to determine what the half-life of the substance is.

ADVANCE PLANNING: Ask volunteers to bring shoeboxes with removable lids to class ahead of time. For each group, make 200 cardboard squares with an *X* marked on one side of each square. Make sure that students have graph paper available.

2 Guide the Lab

PROCEDURE: Have students copy the data chart before beginning the activity. Provide students with a copy of the Lab Activity Report found on the Teacher's Resources CD-ROM for students to record their observations and conclusions.

LAB ACTIVITY
Modeling Half-Life

Materials
200 small cardboard squares with an X marked on one side, Shoebox with lid, Pencil and paper, Graph paper

▲ **STEP 2** Place all of the cardboard squares in the box with the *X*s facing up.

▲ **STEP 3** Shake the box to mix the squares.

BACKGROUND
When the nuclei of a radioactive element decay, energy is released and nuclei of a different element are produced. The nuclei of a radioactive element decay at a constant rate. The rate of decay is based on the element's half-life. The half-life of an element is the length of time it takes for one-half of its nuclei to decay.

PURPOSE
In this activity, you will model the half-life of an element by causing "nuclei" to decay.

PROCEDURE

1. Copy the data table shown in Figure 11-13.

2. The cardboard squares represent atomic nuclei. A square with the *X* facing up represents a nucleus that is radioactive. A square with the *X* facing down represents a nucleus that has decayed and is no longer radioactive. Place each of the 200 squares in the lid of a shoebox. Arrange the squares so that all of the *X*s are facing up. All of these "nuclei" are radioactive.

3. Place the bottom of the box over the lid. Hold the box securely, and shake it to mix the squares thoroughly. Then, set the box, lid down, on your work surface and open it. Take out all of the squares that do not have the *X* facing up. These nuclei have decayed.

4. Count the number of nuclei that decayed and the number that did not decay. Record this data in your table.

5. Repeat Steps 3 and 4 three more times, each time leaving the undecayed nuclei in the box lid.

240

Teaching Options

! FAST FACTS *Amazing Carbon*

Several isotopes of carbon occur naturally on Earth. Over 98 percent of this carbon is carbon-12. About 1 percent is carbon-13. Because carbon-12 and carbon-13 are stable, neither of them has a half-life. Their amounts on Earth remain the same. Other isotopes of carbon are radioisotopes. Carbon-14 is the most common of carbon's radioisotopes. Carbon-14 is constantly being made when radiation hits nitrogen-14 high in the atmosphere. This carbon-14 drifts toward the surface of Earth and becomes a part of living organisms when plants take in carbon dioxide. After 5,730 years, half of the carbon-14 decays and becomes nitrogen-14. Scientists can measure the amount of radiation given off per minute per gram by a fossil to determine its age. Carbon-14 that was formed in the present releases 15 radiation units per minute per gram. Ask students how old a fossil would be if it releases 7.5 radiation units per minute per gram. (5,730 years) **learning styles: auditory, logical/mathematical**

6. For each trial, calculate the percentage that decayed using this formula:

% decayed = number removed ÷ number before shaking × 100

7. On a sheet of graph paper, copy the axes shown in Figure 11-14. Then, prepare a graph of your results.

▲ STEP 4 Count and record the data.

Trial Number	Number of Objects Before Shaking	Number of Objects "Decayed"	% of Decaying
1			
2			
3			
4			

▲ Figure 11-13 Copy this chart and use it to record your observations.

CONCLUSIONS

1. ANALYZE: What fraction of the nuclei in the box would you expect to decay each time you shake the box?

2. COMPARE: How did your results compare to the prediction above?

3. INFER: If you were to shake the box for a fifth trial, about how many nuclei would you expect to decay? Explain.

4. OBSERVE: What is the shape of the line on your graph?

5. ANALYZE: If each trial represents 1,000 years, what is the half-life of substance X in years?

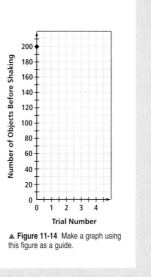
▲ Figure 11-14 Make a graph using this figure as a guide.

TROUBLESHOOTING: Make sure that students remove the squares without X sides facing up for each trial and set them aside after counting them. Trial 2 is conducted with only the squares with X sides still showing from trial 1. If the experimental results are considerably different from those expected, students might not be shaking the squares enough between trials.

EXPECTED OUTCOME: Approximately 50 percent of the squares will decay with each trial.

LAB HINT: To increase the validity of the data collected, have students make a classroom data table that lists the data for all the groups. Explain to students that a large sample increases the validity of the data.

3 Conclude the Lab

1. **ANALYZE:** One-half of the nuclei would be expected to decay each time.
2. **COMPARE:** Answers will depend on students' results, but students will probably find that their results were close to the prediction in question 1.
3. **INFER:** Most students will probably say that approximately six or seven nuclei would decay in a fifth trial because half the sample remaining from trial 4 will decay.
4. **OBSERVE:** a steep, downward curve
5. **ANALYZE:** 1,000 years

Use the Laboratory Activity Rubric on the Teacher's Resources CD-ROM to assess students' lab activities. Fill in the rubric with the additional information below. For this activity, students should have:

• performed the activity according to the procedure and filled in the chart with data collected during the activity.

• correctly answered the questions in complete sentences.

4 Extend the Lab

Ask students the following question for an element with a half-life of 500 years: *If 400 squares represent the amount of the element in an animal when it died, how old is the animal's fossil if it currently contains 25 squares?* (2,000 years old) Have students perform an experiment, collect data, and record the data in a table and in a graph to prove their answer. Have students present their data and conclusions to the class. **learning styles: auditory, logical/mathematical**

Tips for Using Technology

Spreadsheets Have students use spreadsheet software to make a graph of the percentage of X sides that decayed. Spreadsheets are tables that display data such as numbers, text, dates, or a combination of all three. Students can use spreadsheet software to present their data to the class. Tell students to create graphs that are easy to read. Have students use the Spreadsheet on the Teacher's Resources CD-ROM to plan their spreadsheets.

• TEACHING RESOURCES •

Teacher's Resources CD-ROM
Lab Activity Report: Study Tools, pp. 16–17

Laboratory Activity Rubric: Teaching Tools, p. 8

Graph Paper: Visuals, p. 4

Spreadsheet: Study Tools, p. 23

Laboratory Manual
Lab. Skills Worksheet 5: Graphing, pp. 15–18

Challenges (pp. 242–244)

Chapter Summary

Review Before students begin the Challenges, review the summary with them. If time permits, have students work in pairs. Give students one summary point to describe in their own words.

STUDY HINT Have students make a graphic organizer to determine relationships among several Key Terms or concepts in the chapter. For example, students might make a concept map to explain nuclear reactions. Students can use the Concept Map found on the Teacher's Resources CD-ROM. **learning style: visual**

Key Term Challenges

MATCHING

1. metalloid (11-2)
2. nuclear fission (11-4)
3. radioactive element (11-3)
4. radioisotope (11-3)
5. nuclear energy (11-4)

FILL IN

6. radiation (11-3)
7. nonmetals (11-1)
8. chain reaction (11-4)
9. nuclear fusion (11-4)
10. luster (11-1)

Chapter Summary

Lesson 11-1
- **Nonmetals** are elements that lack most of the properties of metals.
- Solid nonmetals have a dull **luster** and are brittle. Most nonmetals do not conduct heat and electricity well.
- The families of nonmetals are the carbon family, the oxygen family, the nitrogen family, the halogens, and the noble gases.

Lesson 11-2
- **Metalloids** are elements that have properties of both metals and nonmetals.
- Metalloids are located along the zigzag line of the periodic table.

Lesson 11-3
- **Radioactive elements** are unstable elements whose nuclei decay. When this happens, **radiation** is released.
- Elements with an atomic number higher than 83 are radioactive.
- Elements of any size may have a radioactive isotope, which is called a **radioisotope.**

Lesson 11-4
- **Nuclear fission** is a reaction in which a large nucleus is split into smaller nuclei.
- An uncontrolled series of fission reactions produce a **chain reaction.**
- **Nuclear fusion** is a reaction in which two smaller nuclei are joined to form a larger nucleus.

Key Term Challenges

chain reaction (p. 238)
luster (p. 230)
nonmetals (p. 230)
metalloid (p. 232)
nuclear energy (p. 238)
nuclear fission (p. 238)
nuclear fusion (p. 238)
radiation (p. 234)
radioactive element (p. 234)
radioisotope (p. 234)

MATCHING Write the Key Term from above that best matches each description.

1. element that has properties of both metals and nonmetals
2. reaction in which a large nucleus is split into smaller nuclei
3. unstable element whose nucleus breaks down
4. isotopes that release radiation
5. energy stored in the nucleus of the atom that can be released during a nuclear reaction

FILL IN Write the Key Term from above that best completes each statement.

6. Energy released from a radioactive element is called _____.
7. Elements that have a dull luster and are brittle are _____.
8. An uncontrolled fission reaction that goes on and on is a _____.
9. The type of reaction that takes place in the Sun is called _____.
10. The way the surface of a material reflects light is called _____.

Teaching Options

PREPARING STUDENTS FOR STANDARDIZED TESTS

Reading Strategy: Tell students that carefully reading and thinking about each answer choice will help them avoid making mistakes. Tell them to eliminate answers that are obviously wrong.

Writing Strategy: Tell students to first write a quick outline when answering essay or other questions that require several sentences to answer. The outline will provide structure and a logical flow of thought.

Interpreting Visuals Strategy: Remind students to pay attention to labels and legends, which help explain a diagram or an illustration.

ESL/ELL STRATEGY

Improving Communications Skills Working with peers encourages English-language learners to communicate. Have students work in pairs. One student should make up three questions about the chapter and read them aloud to the other student. The partner should answer the questions. Then, partners should reverse roles. Partners should check each other's replies to make sure that the correct answers were given.

Content Challenges   TEST PREP

MULTIPLE CHOICE **Write the letter of the term or phrase that best completes each statement.**

1. Radiation is the energy released from a
   a. metallic element.
   b. radioactive element.
   c. nonmetallic element.
   d. metalloid.

2. On the periodic table, the number of groups that contain nonmetals is
   a. two.
   b. three.
   c. four.
   d. five.

3. A group that is not one of the families of nonmetals is
   a. the halogens.
   b. the noble gases.
   c. the boron family.
   d. the oxygen family.

4. Metalloids are located
   a. in Group 7.
   b. in Group 10.
   c. to the left of the zigzag line.
   d. along the zigzag line.

5. One element that is a metalloid is
   a. boron.
   b. neon.
   c. oxygen.
   d. aluminum.

6. Isotopes are elements with
   a. the same number of neutrons but a different number of protons.
   b. the same number of protons but a different number of neutrons.
   c. the same number of protons but a different number of electrons.
   d. the same number of electrons but a different number of protons.

7. Radioactive elements have atomic numbers greater than
   a. 13.
   b. 43.
   c. 73.
   d. 83.

8. Fusion reactions are difficult to control because they
   a. use highly radioactive materials.
   b. take place so slowly.
   c. take place at very high temperatures.
   d. involve helium.

9. Fusion reactions in the Sun change
   a. helium to hydrogen.
   b. helium to oxygen.
   c. hydrogen to helium.
   d. oxygen to helium.

10. To determine if radiation is around you, you can
    a. see it.
    b. smell it.
    c. feel it.
    d. none of the above

TRUE/FALSE **Write** *true* **if the statement is true. If the statement is false, change the underlined term to make the statement true.**

11. Elements with the properties of both metals and nonmetals are <u>gases</u>.

12. <u>Radioactive</u> elements are elements whose nuclei break down.

13. A reaction in which a large nucleus is split into smaller nuclei is called <u>fission</u>.

14. Group 15 is called the <u>carbon</u> family.

15. Isotopes that release radiation are called <u>radioisotopes</u>.

Content Challenges

MULTIPLE CHOICE

1. b (11-3)
2. d (11-1)
3. c (11-1)
4. d (11-2)
5. a (11-2)
6. b (11-3)
7. d (11-3)
8. c (11-4)
9. c (11-4)
10. d (11-3)

TRUE/FALSE

11. false; metalloids (11-2)
12. true (11-3)
13. true (11-4)
14. false; nitrogen (11-1)
15. true (11-3)

CUMULATIVE ASSESSMENT

Assessing Students' Progress You may wish to administer the midterm examination found on the Teacher's Resources CD-ROM at this point. Distribute copies of the Scantron Sheet, also found on the Teacher's Resources CD-ROM, for students to record their answers.

PORTFOLIO ASSESSMENT

Making Student Portfolios Students can demonstrate their comprehension of the concepts in this chapter by making a portfolio. It is important that students include work that they are proud of or that they have put great effort into completing. The Concept Map and the Chapter Self-Check are some of the reproducibles on the Teacher's Resources CD-ROM that they can include in their portfolios. You can use the Portfolio Assessment Rubric also found on the Teacher's Resources CD-ROM to assess students' portfolios.

Concept Challenges

WRITTEN RESPONSE

1. **CONTRAST:** During fusion, two smaller nuclei join to form a larger nucleus. During fission, a large nucleus splits into smaller nuclei. Fusion needs the very high temperatures and pressures found in stars, while fission can take place on Earth. (11-4)
2. **EXPLAIN:** Metals are located on the left side of the zigzag line on the periodic table. Nonmetals are located on the right side of the zigzag line. Metalloids are located along the zigzag line. (11-1 and 11-2)
3. **EXPLAIN:** The temperature and pressure in Earth's interior are not high enough. (11-4)
4. **ANALYZE:** Bromine is a liquid at room temperature. Also, elements used to make pots and pans need to conduct heat well, and bromine is a nonmetal, which is a poor conductor of heat. (11-1)
5. **EXPLAIN:** An isotope of an element is radioactive when it is an unstable isotope. (11-3)

INTERPRETING VISUALS (11-1)

6. left side
7. Left side; Metals are good conductors of heat and electricity.
8. 1; Group 18, the noble gases
9. 3; Sn, Pb, and Uuq
10. Rn; It has the largest atomic number of the noble gases.

Chapter Project Wrap-Up

FAMILY OF ELEMENTS SONG OR POEM

Allow each group to present its poem or song to the class. The songs and poems can also be written on paper and framed so that they can be displayed in the classroom. You can use the Group Activity Rubric found on the Teacher's Resources CD-ROM to assess students' projects. Fill in the rubric with the additional information below. For this project, students should have:

- written a song or poem about the family of elements assigned to them.
- included information about the characteristics of the family and information about the elements in the family.

Concept Challenges TEST PREP

WRITTEN RESPONSE Answer each of the following questions in complete sentences.

1. **CONTRAST:** What are two ways that fusion is different from fission?
2. **EXPLAIN:** Where are metals, nonmetals, and metalloids located on the periodic table?
3. **EXPLAIN:** Why do fusion reactions take place in stars but not in Earth's interior?
4. **ANALYZE:** Why would the element bromine not be used to make pots and pans?
5. **EXPLAIN:** When is an isotope of an element radioactive?

INTERPRETING VISUALS Use the simplified periodic table in Figure 11-15 to complete the following questions.

6. On which side of the zigzag line are more elements?
7. On which side of the periodic table do you find the elements that are good conductors of heat and electricity? Explain.
8. How many groups contain only nonmetals? ~~Name them.~~
9. How many elements in the carbon family are metals? ~~Name them.~~
10. Which noble gas is most likely to be more radioactive? Explain.

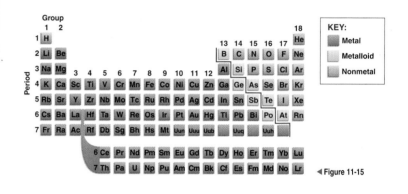

◄ Figure 11-15

244

Teaching Options

• TEACHING RESOURCES •

Teacher's Resources CD-ROM

Key Term Review: Chapter 11, p. 9

Chapter 11 Test: pp. 10–11

Concept Map: Study Tools, p. 4

Chapter Self-Check: Teaching Tools, p. 11

Portfolio Assessment Rubric: Teaching Tools, p. 10

Group Activity Rubric: Teaching Tools, p. 6

Scantron Sheet: Teaching Tools, p. 12

PLANNING GUIDE

◆ **TEACHING THE CHAPTER** This chapter should take approximately 9–12 days to complete instruction and assessment.

	Skills and Features	Projects and Activities	Achieve Science Literacy	Meet Individual Needs
Chapter 12 Opener p. T245	EXPERIMENT	• Chapter Project		
Lesson 12-1 **What is a force?** pp. T246–T247 Standards: B2a, B2b, B2c	INFER, DEFINE, IDENTIFY • Hands-On Activity	• More on the Web	• Study Hint • Reading Strategy	• Reteach ◎ CD-ROM Enrichment Activity Writing Activity Outline
Lesson 12-2 **What is gravity?** pp. T248–T249 Standard: B2a	NAME, CALCULATE, DESCRIBE • Science and Technology • Interpreting Visuals	• More on the Web	• Study Hint	• ESL/ELL Strategy ◎ CD-ROM Enrichment Activity
Big Idea **What keeps planets and satellites in their orbits?** pp. T250–T251 Standards: B2a, B2c	RESEARCH, COMMUNICATE, ANALYZE • Science Log: Writing Activity	• Big Idea Online • Integrating Earth Science • Lab Skills Worksheet • Close Activity	• Tips for Using Technology	• ESL/ELL Strategy ◎ CD-ROM Big Idea Planner
Lesson 12-3 **How does a spring scale work?** pp. T252–T253	IDENTIFY, INFER, CALCULATE • Web InfoSearch • Hands-On Activity	• Extending the Lesson	• Study Hint • Writing Hint • Ongoing Assessment	
Lesson 12-4 **What is friction?** pp. T254–T255 Standards: B2b, B2c	EXPLAIN, CLASSIFY, LIST • Hands-On Activity	• Cooperative Learning • More on the Web	• Study Hint • Reading Strategy	◎ CD-ROM Spider Map
Lesson 12-5 **How can friction be changed?** pp. T256–T257 Standard: B2c	HYPOTHESIZE, CALCULATE, EXPLAIN • Designing an Experiment • Real-Life Science	• More on the Web • Integrating Life Science	• Study Hint • Reading Strategy • Ongoing Assessment	◎ CD-ROM Designing an Experiment Writing Activity Outline

Planning Guide continues on next page.

Standards: For details on the correlation to National Science Standards see pages *xx–xxi*.

	Skills and Features	Projects and Activities	Achieve Science Literacy	Meet Individual Needs
Lesson 12-6 What is air resistance? pp. T258–T259 Standards: B2a, B2b, B2c	PREDICT, DESCRIBE, HYPOTHESIZE • Investigate • Web InfoSearch • How Do They Know That?	• Extending the Lesson • Cooperative Learning	• Study Hint • Ongoing Assessment	CD-ROM Enrichment Activity
Lesson 12-7 What is pressure? pp. T260–T261	ANALYZE, LIST, CALCULATE • Building Math Skills • Hands-On Activity	• Extending the Lesson • More on the Web	• Study Hint • Ongoing Assessment	• Reteach CD-ROM Writing Activity Outline
Lesson 12-8 What is air pressure? pp. T262–T263	IDENTIFY, HYPOTHESIZE, DEFINE • Web InfoSearch	• Cooperative Learning	• Study Hint • Writing Hint • Ongoing Assessment	• ESL/ELL Strategy
Lesson 12-9 What is water pressure? pp. T264–T265	HYPOTHESIZE, DESCRIBE, EXPLAIN • Health and Safety Tip • Hands-On Activity	• Cooperative Learning • More on the Web • Lab Challenge	• Study Hint • Reading Strategy	• Reteach CD-ROM Enrichment Activity Laboratory Video
Lab Activity Making a Cartesian Diver pp. T266–T267	HYPOTHESIZE, INFER, OBSERVE • Set-Up Time: 15 min • Lab Time: 45 min	• Extend the Lab Activity	• Tips for Using Technology	CD-ROM Lab Activity Report Database Planner
Chapter 12 Challenges pp. T268–T270	• Chapter Summary • Key Term Challenges • Content Challenges • Concept Challenges	• Chapter Project Wrap-Up	• Study Hint • Preparing Students for Standardized Tests	• ESL/ELL Strategy CD-ROM Chapter Self-Check Weekly Journal

Teacher Notes

Chapter 12 Force

▲ Figure 12-1 An electromagnet at work

The machine shown in Figure 12-1 uses magnetic force to lift and move car bodies and other large metal objects. If you have ever had to push a car, you know how much force is needed to move the car. Now think about the amount of force the machine can exert. The best part is that, unlike a permanent magnet, the magnetic force applied by the machine is supplied by electricity and can be turned on and off.

►Can you name other machines that use force to move things?

Contents

Teaching Options

ASSESSMENT PLANNER

For assessment in the Student Edition, see the following pages:

Content Assessment
Checking Concepts: pp. 247, 249, 253, 255, 257, 259, 261, 263, 265
Thinking Critically: pp. 247, 249, 253, 255, 257, 259, 261, 263, 265
Interpreting Visuals: p. 249
Chapter Challenges: pp. 268–270

Alternative Assessment
Building Skills: p. 261
Science Log: p. 251
Web InfoSearch: pp. 253, 259, 263

Performance-Based Assessment
Designing an Experiment: p. 257
Hands-On Activity: pp. 247, 253, 255, 261, 265
Lab Activity: pp. 266–267

• TEACHING RESOURCES •

Teacher's Resources CD-ROM
Lesson Review: Ch. 12, pp. 2, 4, 7, 8, 9, 10, 12, 13, 14
Enrichment: Ch. 12, pp. 3, 5, 11, 15
Key Term Review: Ch. 12, p. 16
Chapter 12 Test: pp. 17–19
Laboratory Manual: pp. 15–18, 65–68

Laboratory Video
Segment 13: Relating Depth and Water Pressure

Chapter 12
Force

Chapter Overview

In this chapter, students will define *force*, describe forces such as gravity and friction, and identify balanced and unbalanced forces. They will also define *pressure*, describe how a spring scale is used to measure weight, and relate air resistance and Bernoulli's principle to flight.

About Figure 12-1 The size of the force involved in pushing a car is different from the size of the force involved in lifting a car. Pushing a stationary car to get it moving requires a force exerted in the direction that the car is to move and is equal in size to the force of static friction between the tires and the road. Keeping the car in motion requires a force equal in size to the force of sliding friction between the tires and the road. Both of these forces are smaller than the weight of the car. Lifting a car requires an upward force equal in size to the weight of the car.

Answer Possible answers: a hydraulic lift, a forklift, or a crane

---

Linking Prior Knowledge

For this chapter, students should recall:
- that mass is the amount of matter in an object (Lesson 1-2).
- that the newton (N) is the SI unit of force (Lesson 2-5).

Chapter Project

AIR LIFT

MATERIALS: construction paper

After students have read Lesson 12-8 on Bernoulli's principle, have pairs of students design and build a paper airplane that will remain aloft for at least 4 seconds. Requirements are that students launch the plane by hand and that they may not touch the plane once it is airborne. Students will then draw a force diagram illustrating the forces acting on the plane while it is in flight. Allow students time to design, build, and test their planes.
learning styles: visual, tactile

1 Introduce

✏️ **STUDY HINT** Before beginning this lesson, have students copy the titles of each section in their notebooks, using an outline format. As students read each section, they should write the main idea of the section in their notebooks. Students can use the Writing Activity Outline found on the Teacher's Resources CD-ROM.

Linking Prior Knowledge Have students recall that a floating object has two equal forces acting on it (Lesson 2-5). Have students identify the forces and their directions. (weight, downward; buoyant force, upward)

2 Teach

Demonstration Using a double-pan balance, place two weights of equal mass on each pan. Have students observe that equal forces are keeping the pan balanced. Remove one weight. Have students observe that unbalanced forces made the pan holding the remaining weight drop. **learning style: visual**

Discussion Explain to students that a force has a size and a direction. Have students look at Figure 12-2. Ask students: *What is used to represent a force?* (an arrow) Point out that the length or thickness of the arrow usually represents the size of the force, and the direction that the arrow points represents the force's direction. Ask students: *What do the two arrows tell you about the two forces?* (The forces are equal and opposite.) *What do the two arrows in Figure 12-3 tell you about those two forces?* (They are not equal in size and are opposite in direction.)

Answers to questions

1. **DEFINE:** a push or a pull
2. **PREDICT:** There will be no effect.
3. **IDENTIFY:** unbalanced forces
4. **PREDICT:** Accept any of the following: It may speed up, slow down, stop moving, or change direction.
5. **IDENTIFY:** gravity

12-1 What is a force?

Objectives
Define force and give some examples of forces in nature. Identify balanced and unbalanced forces and describe their effects.

Key Terms
force: a push or a pull
balanced forces: forces that are equal in size but opposite in direction
unbalanced forces: forces that cause a change in the motion of an object

Force A **force** is a push or a pull. To open a door, you have to push or pull the door. In other words, you have to exert a force on the door. A force always acts in some direction. When you push on a door, the force is in the direction of the push. When you pull on a doorknob, the force is in the direction of the pull. If the force is strong enough, the door will move in the direction of the force.

▶ **DEFINE:** What is force?

Balanced Forces To describe a force, you must know two things—the size of the force and the direction of the force. For example, think about two teams in a tug of war. Each team pulls with equal force in opposite directions, as shown in Figure 12-2. Neither team can make the other move.

▲ **Figure 12-2** Balanced forces

246

Forces that are equal in size and opposite in direction are called **balanced forces.** As the name suggests, balanced forces acting on an object do not cause a change in the motion of the object.

▶ **PREDICT:** What effect will balanced forces have on a book?

Unbalanced Forces Look at Figure 12-3. A member of one team has fallen and let go of the rope. One team now pulls harder than the other, and the rope moves. The forces acting on the rope are no longer balanced. **Unbalanced forces** cause a change in the motion of an object.

▲ **Figure 12-3** Unbalanced forces

▶ **IDENTIFY:** What kinds of forces cause an object to move?

Forces and Motion Unbalanced forces can change the motion of an object in two ways.

- When unbalanced forces act on an object at rest, the object will move.
- When unbalanced forces act on a moving object, the motion of the object will change. The object may speed up, slow down, stop moving, or change direction.

▶ **PREDICT:** What might happen when unbalanced forces act on a moving car?

Teaching Options

RETEACH

Balancing More Than Two Forces On the board, draw two arrows of equal length that originate at the same spot. One arrow should point to the left, and the other arrow should point to the right. Explain that the arrows represent the balanced forces exerted by two equally strong teams in a tug-of-war. Then, draw a third arrow of the same length, pointing straight down from the spot. Ask: *Are all three forces balanced?* (no) *In which direction will the spot move?* (straight down) *How do you know?* (because it is the only unbalanced force acting on the spot) *What force would balance the other three?* (a force represented by an arrow of the same length as the others but pointing straight up) **learning style: visual**

Forces in Nature You experience many different kinds of forces every day. A few examples of these forces are described here.

- How much do you weigh? The weight of an object is a measure of the force of gravity acting between Earth and the object.
- The attraction of a magnet for a paper clip is an example of a magnetic force.
- A kite flies in the air as a result of wind pushing against it. The force of the wind results from the moving air pushing against the kite.
- The force of falling water in a waterfall is caused by Earth's gravity acting on the water.

5 IDENTIFY: What force causes a rock to roll down the side of a mountain?

CHECKING CONCEPTS

1. A __________ is a push or a pull.
2. To describe a force, you must know the size and __________ of the force.
3. Balanced forces are equal in size and __________ in direction.
4. Unbalanced forces cause a change in the __________ of an object.
5. The weight of an object is a measure of the force of __________ acting on it.
6. The force of the __________ is produced by moving air.

THINKING CRITICALLY

7. INFER: Describe the two forces that act on a flying kite.

Hands-On Activity

INTERPRETING FORCE DIAGRAMS

You will need a metric ruler.

1. Look at Figure 12-4. The arrow represents the force used to push a desk across the floor. Use a metric ruler to measure the length of the arrow.
2. Look at Figure 12-5. It shows a second force helping to push the desk. Measure the total length of the two arrows.
3. Look at Figure 12-6. It shows a force pushing in the opposite direction. Measure the length of the arrow pointing in the opposite direction.

Practicing Your Skills

4. CALCULATE: Force is measured in newtons (N). If 1 cm = 1 N, what force was used to push the desk in Figure 12-4?
5. CALCULATE: What was the total force used to push the desk in Figure 12-5?
6. CALCULATE: Look at Figure 12-6. **a.** What force was used to push the desk in the opposite direction? **b.** Subtract that force from the result in question 5 to find the total force acting on the desk.

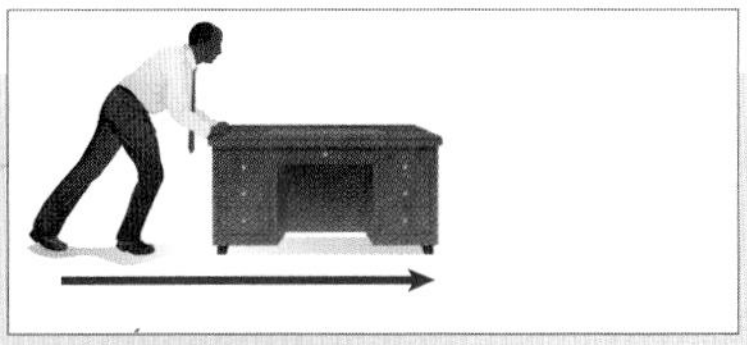

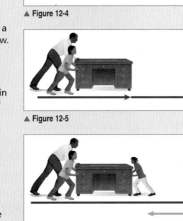

▲ Figure 12-4

▲ Figure 12-5

▲ Figure 12-6

MORE ON THE WEB

Writing About Avalanches Have students visit www.conceptsandchallenges.com to learn how avalanches occur. Students can also view some photographs of avalanches in action. Have students write a short report identifying the forces involved in the formation of an avalanche.

• *TEACHING RESOURCES* •

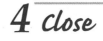

Teacher's Resources CD-ROM

Lesson Review: Chapter 12, p. 2

Enrichment: Chapter 12, p. 3

Writing Activity Outline: Study Tools, pp. 20–21

Reinforcement Make sure that students understand that unbalanced forces can cause a stationary object to move and can cause moving objects to speed up, slow down, stop moving, or change direction.

READING STRATEGY Explain to students that *un-* is a prefix that means "not." When added to an adjective, it reverses the meaning of the adjective. Tell students that there are other prefixes with the same meaning (*in-*, *il-*, *im-*, *ir-*, and *non-*) and that *un-* can be added to verbs to mean "do the opposite of," such as *uncover* and *unfasten*. Have students compare and contrast the terms *balanced forces* and *unbalanced forces*.

3 *Assess*

CHECKING CONCEPTS ANSWERS

1. force
2. direction
3. opposite
4. motion
5. gravity
6. wind

THINKING CRITICALLY ANSWER

7. INFER: gravity and the force of the wind

4 *Close*

Hands-On Activity

INTERPRETING FORCE DIAGRAMS

TIME: 15 minutes

PURPOSE: measuring, calculating

DISCUSSION: A force diagram represents forces, using arrows drawn to scale. The resultant force can be determined.

ALTERNATIVE MATERIALS: Students can carefully trace the arrows onto 1-cm scale graph paper and then use the paper to measure the lengths of the arrows and determine the forces.

Practicing Your Skills Answers

4. CALCULATE: 4 N to the right
5. CALCULATE: 7 N to the right
6. CALCULATE: **a.** 2 N to the left **b.** 5 N to the right

12-2 (pp. 248–249)

1 Introduce

✏️ **STUDY HINT** Have students study Figure 12-8. Ask them why they think the top arrows are different in size from the bottom arrows. (The sizes of the forces are different.)

Linking Prior Knowledge Ask students to recall the definition of *mass* (Lesson 1-2). Inform students that the force of gravity is affected by mass.

2 Teach

Discussion Inform students that gravity is a force of attraction between all objects. However, the mass of the objects as well as the distance between the objects affect the amount of gravitational pull between them. Earth has a large gravitational pull on objects located at its surface because Earth has a large mass. Two objects lying next to each other, such as two spoons, also have a gravitational pull between them. However, the masses of the spoons are so small that the gravitational pull between them is hard to see.

Demonstration Have students observe as you drop an apple from one hand to the other. Point out that when the apple is released, Earth's force of gravity changes the motion of the apple because the force is unbalanced. On the board, sketch the apple and a downward arrow representing Earth's force of gravity on the apple. Explain that as the apple falls, it exerts an unbalanced force on Earth. Sketch an upward arrow much smaller in size than the first and have students identify it as representing the apple's force of gravity on Earth. Ask students why Earth does not move upward toward the apple. Explain that the effect of a force in changing the motion of an object decreases as the mass of the objects increases. Because Earth's mass is very large, the change in its motion is so small that it is unobservable.
learning styles: visual, auditory

Answers to questions

▶ **NAME:** Newton's law of gravity or universal gravitation

▶ **DESCRIBE:** toward Earth's center

12-2 What is gravity?

Objective
Explain Newton's law of gravity.

Key Term
gravity: force of attraction between all objects in the universe

Sir Isaac Newton Isaac Newton was a famous scientist. He was born in England over 350 years ago. Newton wondered why all objects fall to the ground. He hypothesized that there is a force that makes all objects move toward each other. This force is gravity. All objects in the universe are attracted to one another because of the force of gravity between them. This idea is now known as Newton's law of gravity, or universal gravitation.

▲ **Figure 12-7** A falling apple provided Newton's "inspiration."

▶ **NAME:** What scientific law explains why objects fall?

Gravity Gravity is a force of attraction between all objects in the universe. On Earth, all objects fall toward the center of Earth's mass. An apple falls to the ground because it is pulled by Earth's gravity. In fact, every object near Earth's surface is pulled toward Earth's center.

▶ **DESCRIBE:** In which direction does an object fall on Earth?

248

Gravity and Mass The amount of gravitational force between two objects depends on the mass of each object. Earth's mass appears to be concentrated in Earth's center. When an apple falls from a tree, the gravitational force between Earth and the apple tends to pull them toward each other. However, because Earth has much more mass than the apple, Earth does not seem to move at all.

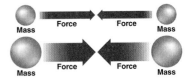
▲ **Figure 12-8** Larger masses exert greater gravitational force.

▶ **EXPLAIN:** Why is the force of Earth's gravity so strong?

Gravity and Distance The force of gravity between two objects decreases as the distance between them increases. When you stand on Earth at sea level, the amount of gravitational force you feel is your weight. If you were far away from Earth, the gravitational force between you and Earth would be less. The force of gravity decreases by an amount equal to one divided by the distance (d) squared, or $1/d^2$. For example, if the moon were twice as far from Earth, the force of gravity between Earth and the Moon would be $1/2^2$ or $1/4$ of its present value.

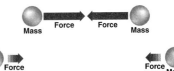
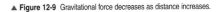
▲ **Figure 12-9** Gravitational force decreases as distance increases.

▶ **CALCULATE:** If you were twice as far from Earth's center as you are now, how much would you weigh?

Teaching Options

❗ FAST FACTS *An Insider's Weight*

As an object moves away from Earth's surface, the force of gravity on the object decreases with the square of the distance from Earth's center. In other words, the farther an object is from Earth's surface, the less it weighs. Inside Earth, it is a different story. If Earth were a sphere with a uniform density, the force of gravity would be zero at its center, so at the center an object would be weightless. (All the material around the object would be pulling on it equally in all directions. The effect of all these balanced forces would be the same as not having any force on the object.) At a distance of 3,200 km (2,000 mi) from Earth's center, about half the distance to Earth's surface, the object would weigh 50 percent of its surface weight. At 4,800 km (3,000 mi) from Earth's center, about three-quarters of the distance to Earth's surface, an object would weigh 75 percent of its surface weight, and so on. However, Earth is neither perfectly spherical nor of uniform density. Therefore, the force of gravity inside Earth actually varies in a more complex way.

☑ CHECKING CONCEPTS

1. The idea of universal gravitation was suggested by _____.
2. All objects in the universe are attracted to each other because of the force of _____.
3. Near Earth's surface, all objects fall in the direction of Earth's _____.
4. The farther away you are from Earth, the _____ you weigh.
5. Gravity between two objects decreases as the distance between the objects _____.

💡 THINKING CRITICALLY

6. ANALYZE: Why does an apple fall toward Earth, instead of Earth moving toward the apple?
7. INFER: The Moon travels in an orbit around Earth. What force keeps the Moon from flying off into space?

INTERPRETING VISUALS

Look at the three pairs of masses labeled a, b, and c shown in Figure 12-10.

8. Compare the forces of gravity acting between each pair of spheres and tell how you reached your conclusion.

a.

b.

c.

▲ **Figure 12-10** Compare mass, distance, and gravitational force.

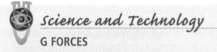

Science and Technology
G FORCES

Gravity pulls your body toward Earth's center. You feel that pull as your weight. Pilots and astronauts refer to this force as 1 G. Sometimes you may have the sensation of having more or less than 1 G of force on your body. For example, as you plunge down the first hill of a roller coaster, your body lifts up off the seat. This action is caused by the fact that the seat is moving down away from you. When you reach the bottom and start up the next hill, your seat pushes up against you. This action makes it feel as if you are being pushed down into your seat. These sensations aredue to changing forces on your body.

▲ **Figure 12-11** As this pilot turns, he feels increased G forces.

During flight, test pilots experience much greater changes in forces. The human body cannot withstand more than 9 Gs of force. As forces increase, blood is forced from the brain and the heart cannot pump it back quickly enough. After a short time, a person loses consciousness.

To deal with increased forces, pilots wear special suits. Tubes along the sides of these suits inflate, preventing the blood from rushing from the brain.

Thinking Critically What might happen to a pilot that experienced more than 9 Gs of force during a flight maneuver?

CHAPTER 12: Force **249**

3️⃣ EXPLAIN: because Earth's mass is large

4️⃣ CALCULATE: 1/4 of your surface weight

3 Assess

☑ CHECKING CONCEPTS ANSWERS

1. Isaac Newton
2. gravity
3. center
4. less
5. increases

💡 THINKING CRITICALLY ANSWERS

6. ANALYZE: because Earth has much more mass than the apple
7. INFER: Earth's gravitational pull

INTERPRETING VISUALS ANSWERS

8. Figure *b* shows the greatest force of gravity because the objects are large and close together. Figure *a* shows less gravity than Figure *b* because one object is small, but it shows more gravity than Figure *c* because one object is larger and they are closer together. In Figure *c*, the objects are smaller and far apart, showing the least gravity.

4 Close

Science and Technology
G FORCES

Real-Life Connection Riding an elevator is similar to riding a roller coaster but much less dramatic. For example, when you initially start descending in an elevator, the elevator changes its downward speed more rapidly than you do. During that time, you feel that you are being lifted from the floor. In reality, the floor is falling faster than you are. As you come to a stop, the elevator must support your weight as well as slow you down. Therefore, it exerts an upward force on you that is slightly larger than your weight. Because you are in contact with the floor, you sense this stopping force in your feet as an increase in weight, as if you are being pushed downward. The push on you is actually upward.

Discussion Ask students what term they would use to describe a feeling of 0 G. (weightless)

Thinking Critically Answer
The pilot might lose consciousness.

MORE ON THE WEB

Weighing Yourself Have students visit www.concepts andchallenges.com to view a short movie on gravity and to use a gravity simulator to calculate their weight on Mars.

ESL/ELL STRATEGY

Relating Gravity to Its Origin
To help students understand the word *gravity*, tell them that it comes from a Latin word meaning "heavy." Ask students how the definition of *gravity* is related to its Latin origin.

• TEACHING RESOURCES •

💿 **Teacher's Resources CD-ROM**
Lesson Review: Chapter 12, p. 4
Enrichment: Chapter 12, p. 5

The Big Idea

(pp. 250–251)

1 Introduce

Objective Students will form and test hypotheses concerning how balanced or unbalanced forces affect the motion of an object.

Linking Prior Knowledge Have students recall the possible effects that unbalanced forces have on a moving object. (Unbalanced forces may speed up, slow down, stop, or change the direction of a moving object.)

2 Teach

Discussion Ask students what force exists between the Sun and a planet. (gravity) Point out that the Sun's gravity on a planet is the only force that causes the planet to orbit the Sun. Explain that this force is an unbalanced force. For planets traveling in nearly circular orbits (Earth, Venus, and Neptune), the force changes the direction of the planet's motion but not its speed so that the planet constantly falls toward the Sun. This falling motion causes the planet to follow a circular path. The Sun's gravity causes the speed and direction of motion of the other planets in the solar system to change so that the planets travel in elliptical orbits.

Use the information in the article and captions to help guide students in choosing a topic for their Science Logs.

THE BIG IDEA ONLINE

What keeps planets and satellites in their orbits? Have students research their Science Log Writing Activity at www.conceptsand challenges.com. You can have students organize their log by completing the Big Idea activity online. Students may post their work in the Online Classroom Database for others to read.

Integrating Earth Science

THE Big IDEA

What keeps planets and satellites in their orbits?

The great physicist Albert Einstein liked to do something he called thinking physics. He performed thought experiments to try out new ideas in his imagination. Sometimes he did this before doing mathematical proofs or calculations. Let's try a thought experiment to visualize the forces keeping planets and satellites in orbit.

Imagine that Earth has no atmosphere, so there will be no air resistance to slow the ball down in this experiment. You are standing on top of a very tall mountain as shown in the figure on the right. You throw a ball straight out, parallel to the ground. The harder you throw the ball, the farther the ball travels before hitting the ground. The falling ball traces a curved path as it is pulled by Earth's gravity. The more force you use to throw the ball, the longer the curve.

Because there is no air resistance, if the ball is thrown hard enough, its curved falling-path matches the curve of Earth's surface. So the ball will fall continuously without hitting Earth. It will be in orbit. It is falling without reaching the ground.

Orbit happens when the velocity of an object is such that the forward motion of the object keeps the object from falling directly toward a surface. The object travels in a circular or elliptical path. When a planet orbits the Sun, it is pulled toward the Sun's surface by the powerful force of gravity between the planet and the Sun. However, the forward motion of the planet is great enough to keep the planet from falling straight to the Sun's surface. Instead, the planet goes around the Sun.

Look at the illustrations that appear on these two pages. Then, follow the directions in the Science Log to find out more about "the big idea." ✦

250

Earth "Falling" Around The Sun
The Sun's gravitational force pulls Earth toward the center of the Sun. However, the forward motion of Earth is equal to its motion toward the Sun, and Earth remains in an orbital path around the Sun.

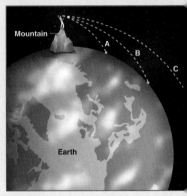

Mountain

Earth

Throwing a Ball into Orbit
A ball thrown straight out from a very high mountain peak would follow a curved path (A and B) as it fell to Earth's surface. If it were thrown hard enough, its forward motion will be equal to its downward motion. This ball (C) would go into orbit around Earth.

Teaching Options

◆ INTEGRATING EARTH SCIENCE

Escaping Gravity The minimum speed at which an object will escape the force of gravity is called escape velocity. If an object on Earth is given a speed of 11.2 km/s, it will neither fall back to Earth nor go into orbit around Earth. It will venture into space. An object can attain this speed if it is equipped with large rocket boosters. The escape velocity of a celestial body depends only on the mass and radius of the body. The table gives the escape velocities of Earth, Mercury, Mars, and Venus. Have students prepare a bar graph that illustrates the information in the table.

QUICK CONVERSIONS

Body	Escape Velocity	
	Metric/SI	**English**
Earth	11.2 km/s	25,100 mi/h
Mercury	3.8 km/s	8,500 mi/h
Mars	5.0 km/s	11,000 mi/h
Venus	10.3 km/s	23,000 mi/h

ESL/ELL STRATEGY

Defining Words To help students define unfamiliar words, have them write each word on one side of an index card. On the other side of the card, have students define the word.

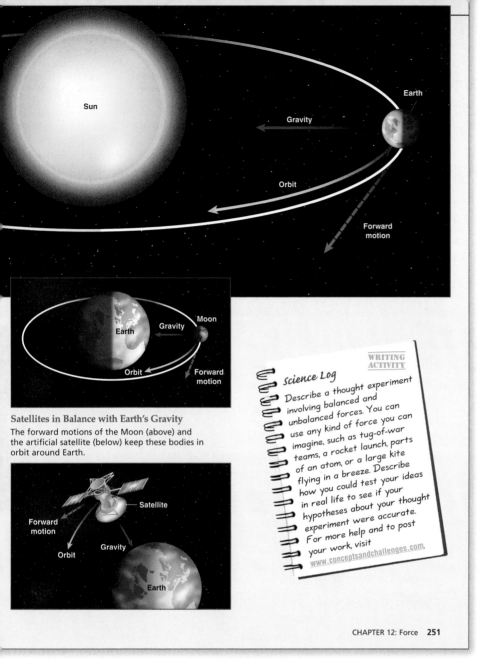

Sun

Earth

Gravity

Orbit

Forward motion

Moon

Earth

Gravity

Orbit

Forward motion

Satellites in Balance with Earth's Gravity
The forward motions of the Moon (above) and the artificial satellite (below) keep these bodies in orbit around Earth.

Satellite

Forward motion

Gravity

Orbit

Earth

WRITING ACTIVITY

Science Log

Describe a thought experiment involving balanced and unbalanced forces. You can use any kind of force you can imagine, such as tug-of-war teams, a rocket launch, parts of an atom, or a large kite flying in a breeze. Describe how you could test your ideas in real life to see if your hypotheses about your thought experiment were accurate. For more help and to post your work, visit www.conceptsandchallenges.com.

3 Assess

Use the Writing Activity Rubric on the Teacher's Resources CD-ROM to assess students' Science Logs. Fill in the rubric with the additional information below. For this assignment, students should have:

- mentioned, in the hypothesis, that balanced forces do not change the motion of an object or, conversely, that unbalanced forces cause an object at rest to start moving or a moving object to speed up, slow down, stop, or change direction.

- measured, in the procedure, speed, or direction, or both.

4 Close

Drawing and Interpreting Force Diagrams
Have students work in pairs. Have one student draw a force diagram of one situation. The diagram should show balanced or unbalanced forces acting on an object. Have the other student interpret the diagram.
learning styles: visual, interpersonal

Tips for Using Technology

Word Processing Software
Have students use word processing software to write about their thought experiments. A simple word processing program allows students to do basic tasks such as entering and editing text. A more complex word processing program allows students to make tables, draw pictures, do math, and make graphs. Students can print their word processing documents to share with the class.

• TEACHING RESOURCES •

Teacher's Resources CD-ROM
Big Idea: Chapter 12, p. 6
Big Idea Planner: Study Tools, pp. 11–12
Big Idea Science Log Entry: Study Tools, p.13
Writing Activity Rubric: Teaching Tools, p.9
Laboratory Manual
Lab. Skills Worksheet 5: Graphing, pp. 15–18

1 Introduce

STUDY HINT Have students study Figure 12-12. Ask them to hypothesize how a spring scale works.

Linking Prior Knowledge Have students look back at Figure 2-19 on page 44. Ask students to name the instrument supporting the rock. (spring scale) Ask them what it is measuring. (weights of the rock in air and water)

2 Teach

Demonstration Demonstrate the effects of force on springlike materials. Loop three identical, heavy rubber bands over a pencil and then suspend the pencil horizontally between two upright books. Hang a paper clip bent into a hook from each rubber band. Pass around a small object (such as a 100-g mass) so that students can feel its weight. Hang the object from one of the hooks. Pass around two more objects identical to the first. Then, hang both of them from one of the hooks. Allow students to observe the change in length (elongation) of the rubber bands that support those two hooks. Ask students to predict the change in length of the third rubber band if all three objects were hung from it. Allow students to test their prediction. **learning styles: tactile, logical/mathematical**

Answers to questions

1 **IDENTIFY:** the force of gravity on the object

2 **IDENTIFY:** weight (force)

3 **LIST:** laboratory spring scales, some bathroom scales, some grocers' scales

WRITING HINT Tell students that when referring to a unit of measurement in a sentence, the unit term is written in full. For example, the unit of force is the newton. When a unit is given as part of a measurement, the abbreviation of the unit is used. For example, a book might weigh 12 N.

12-3 How does a spring scale work?

Objective
Describe how a spring scale is used to measure weight.

Key Term
newton: SI unit of force

The SI Unit of Force There are different SI units for different types of measurements. For example, the basic unit of distance is the meter (m). The basic unit of mass is the kilogram (kg). The **newton** (N) is the basic SI unit of force. The unit is named in honor of Sir Isaac Newton. On Earth, it takes a force equal to 9.8 N to lift a 1-kg mass.

Weight is a familiar example of force. An object's weight is a measure of the force of gravity acting on the object. When you weigh an object, you measure the pull of gravity on the object. Because weight is a force, an object's weight is measured in newtons. For example, an object that weighs 15 N is heavier than an object that weighs 10 N when weighed at the same location.

1 **IDENTIFY:** What are you measuring when you weigh an object?

Using a Spring Scale A spring scale is used to measure weight. A spring scale measures the force of gravity on an object. Figure 12-12 shows the main parts of a spring scale.

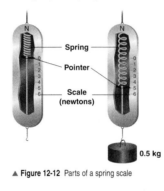

Spring
Pointer
Scale (newtons)
0.5 kg

▲ **Figure 12-12** Parts of a spring scale

252

To use the scale, attach a mass to the hook. The weight of the mass stretches the spring. The pointer moves down along the scale. The number at which the pointer stops is the object's weight. For example, suppose one mass moves the pointer to 5, and another mass moves the pointer to 1. The first mass weighs five times as much as the other mass.

2 **IDENTIFY:** What does a spring scale measure?

Types of Spring Scales There are many types of spring scales. The scale shown in Figure 12-12 is similar to the type of spring scale used in a science lab. Many bathroom scales are also spring scales. When you stand on the scale, your weight pushes on a spring. The spring causes a circular scale to turn until the number on the scale lines up with the pointer. This number shows your weight.

Another type of spring scale is the one you see in the fruit and vegetable section of a market. If you place some grapes or apples on the scale, the weight of the fruit pulls a spring. The spring turns the pointer to show the weight of the fruit.

▲ **Figure 12-13** A grocer's scale can weigh fruits and vegetables.

3 **LIST:** What are three types of spring scales?

Teaching Options

! FAST FACTS *Defining Weight With a Spring Scale*

One definition of the weight of an object is "the reading of a spring scale from which the object is suspended." This definition is valid anywhere—on Earth's surface, on the Moon, or in outer space. The reading for each location reflects the weight of the object determined by the force of gravity that exists at that location.

Finding weight by using a spring scale has other applications. The difference in the readings of the spring scale when an object is suspended in a vacuum and when it is submerged in a gas or in a liquid is used to determine the buoyant force exerted on the object by the gas or the liquid.

✓ CHECKING CONCEPTS

1. The SI unit of force is the _____.
2. Weight is a _____ measured in newtons.
3. The greater the mass of an object the _____ its weight will be.
4. A spring scale is used to measure _____.
5. A bathroom scale is a kind of _____.

💡 THINKING CRITICALLY

6. **INFER:** It takes 10 N to lift an object. What is the object's weight? How do you know?
7. **IDENTIFY:** What force is being measured when you use a spring scale to measure weight?
8. **CALCULATE:** One object causes the spring of a scale to stretch four times farther than a second object. If the second object weighs 3 N, what is the weight of the first object?

Web InfoSearch

Bathroom Scale Have you ever wondered how your bathroom scale is able to measure over 200 pounds while being so thin and small? Most bathroom scales use spring scales like those found in supermarkets. However, bathroom scales use ratios to allow smaller, less powerful springs to accurately measure heavier weights.

SEARCH: Use the Internet to find out how a bathroom scale works. What is a ratio? How is a bathroom scale able to use a small spring to measure heavy weights? Start your search at www.conceptsandchallenges.com. Some key search words are **how bathroom scale works, inside bathroom scale,** and **bathroom spring scale.**

⚛ Hands-On Activity

USING A SPRING SCALE

You will need a spring scale, a small mass, and several small objects.

1. Be sure that the pointer of the spring scale is at zero when nothing is hanging from it.
2. Carefully place a mass on the hook of the spring scale. Do not let the mass drop. This might damage the spring scale.
3. Observe where the pointer stops on the scale. If the pointer stops between two numbers, round the number to the nearest half. Record your measurement.
4. Use the spring scale to weigh several small objects. Record and compare your measurements.

▲ **STEP 2** Place a mass on the hook.

Practicing Your Skills

5. **ANALYZE:** What force are you measuring when you weigh an object?
6. **COMPARE:** How much does a 1-kg mass weigh in newtons?
7. **OBSERVE:** In newtons, what are the weights of the masses measured in the activity?

---

3 Assess

✓ CHECKING CONCEPTS ANSWERS

1. newton
2. force
3. greater
4. force or weight
5. spring scale

💡 THINKING CRITICALLY ANSWERS

6. **INFER:** 10 N; Lifting it overcomes the force of gravity acting on it, which is its weight.
7. **IDENTIFY:** Earth's force of gravity
8. **CALCULATE:** 12 N

4 Close

Web InfoSearch

Bathroom Scale Have students use the Internet to find out how a bathroom scale works. Some key search words are **how bathroom scale works, inside bathroom scale,** and **bathroom spring scale.** Students should begin their search at www.conceptsandchallenges.com.

Hands-On Activity

USING A SPRING SCALE

TIME: 15 minutes

PURPOSE: measuring, analyzing, comparing, observing

SAFETY TIP: Have students hold the spring scale in one hand and attach the objects with the other hand. They should then slowly lower each object so that it does not abruptly stretch the spring in the scale.

DISCUSSION: Have students explain why it is important not to damage the spring in the scale. (If the spring is permanently stretched, the readings will not be accurate.)

Practicing Your Skills Answers

5. **ANALYZE:** Earth's force of gravity on the object
6. **COMPARE:** 9.8 N
7. **OBSERVE:** Answers will depend on the mass of the objects that were used.

EXTENDING THE LESSON

Balancing Forces Show and identify the pair of balanced forces acting in Figure 12-12. Sketch the figure on the board. Draw equal and opposite vertical arrows on the mass. Label the down arrow *weight (force of gravity on 0.5-kg mass), 5 N, down.* Label the up arrow *pull of spring on 0.5-kg mass, 5 N, up.* Draw identical arrows on the spring. Have students identify each arrow, for example, *pull of 0.5-kg mass on spring, 5 N, down* and *pull of scale on spring, 5 N, up.* **learning styles: visual, logical/mathematical**

• *TEACHING RESOURCES* •

 Teacher's Resources CD-ROM
Lesson Review: Chapter 12, p. 7

ONGOING ASSESSMENT

Stating Basic SI Units Ask students: *What is the basic SI unit of distance?* (the meter) *What is the basic SI unit of mass?* (the kilogram) *What is the basic SI unit of force?* (the newton) *How much force would it take to lift a 1-kg mass?* (9.8 N)

1 Introduce

✎ **STUDY HINT** Have students sketch a graphic organizer that relates information about friction. Have them write *friction* in a circle in the center of the page. As they read the lesson, have them record information about friction on arms that extend from the circle. Students can also use the Spider Map found on the Teacher's Resources CD-ROM.

Linking Prior Knowledge Ask students what they wear on their feet during snowy weather. Lead them to understand that the treads on snow boots are designed to prevent the wearer from slipping in the snow.

2 Teach

Discussion Inform students that snow can be slippery. Therefore, to walk through snow, a person needs a force that opposes the motion of sliding on the snow. This force is called friction. Friction is the force that causes a toy car to stop rolling across the floor. It is also the force that skiers and roller skaters use to come to a stop.
learning style: auditory

Demonstration Place a large baking sheet on a desk or table. Set a ceramic coffee mug (or other flat-bottomed item of similar weight) on the sheet near one edge of the sheet. Lift that edge until the mug begins to slide. Explain that there are two opposing forces acting on the mug as it slides: gravity and friction. Next, coat the baking sheet with a lubricant, such as vegetable oil. Repeat the demonstration, lifting the edge of the sheet to the same height as before. The mug should now slide faster than before. Ask: *Why did adding oil make the mug slide faster?* (It reduced friction.)
learning style: visual

📖 **READING STRATEGY** Have students note that the term *friction* starts with *fr*. Explain that the sound of the two letters together is an example of a consonant blend. Blends most often are found at the beginning of a word. Have students look in the lesson for other words that include consonant blends. (*slides, slows,* and *stops*)

12-4 What is friction?

Objective
Identify examples of friction.

Key Term
friction: force that opposes the motion of an object

Forces and Motion To stop a moving object, a force must act in the direction opposite to the direction of motion. If you give your book a push across your desk, the book will move. The force of the push moves the book. As the book slides across the desk, it slows down and stops moving.

▷ **OBSERVE:** Give your textbook a slight push across your desk. What must you do to keep the book moving?

Friction A force that opposes the motion of an object is called **friction.** Look at Figure 12-14. At first, the book is at rest. A push (F) causes the book to start sliding across the desk. As the book slides across the desk, a force of friction (f) acts in the opposite direction. The friction slows the motion of the book. Finally, the book is once again at rest.

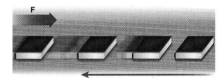

▲ **Figure 12-14** What force slows the moving book?

▷ **DEFINE:** What is friction?

Types of Friction There are different types of friction. A book sitting on a desk has static friction. This is the force that must be overcome to start the book moving. A book moving across the desk is an example of sliding friction. As the book slides across the desk, the bottom of the book is touching the desk. The source of the friction is the contact between the surface of the book and the desk. Air

254

resistance is a type of friction. As an object falls, air resistance pushes up on the object. When you ride a bicycle, the contact between the tires and the road is an example of rolling friction.

▷ **STATE:** When does friction occur?

Useful Friction On Earth, friction makes motion possible. When you ride a bicycle, the friction between the road and the bicycle wheels is necessary to keep the bicycle in motion. Without friction, you would not be able to stop the bicycle. You would not be able to climb a rope, throw a ball, or even walk down the street. Pencils would not work, and kites, birds, and airplanes would not be able to fly. As you can see, life without friction would be very different and very difficult.

▲ **Figure 12-15** Drag racers depend on friction between their tires and the track.

▷ **LIST:** Name several activities that would not be possible without friction.

Harmful Friction Sometimes friction is not helpful. For example, think about trying to ski down a hill covered with grass instead of snow. You might be able to do it, but friction between the grass and the skis would make it a slow, bumpy ride.

Unwanted friction can also be found in machines and engines. Many machines have moving metal parts that touch. The rubbing together of these parts produces heat and can cause parts to wear out.

▷ **EXPLAIN:** Why is it sometimes useful to reduce friction?

Teaching Options

❗ FAST FACTS *Friction and Athletics*

Obtaining peak athletic performance often requires minimizing friction. In sports where speed is most important, athletes generally try to reduce friction caused by air or water resistance. Sprinters, cyclists, snow skiers, and luge racers wear body-hugging suits that offer less resistance than loose-fitting garments. The head is covered as well, either by part of the suit or by a sleek helmet. Helmets for cyclists may extend far behind the head to further reduce friction. Many swimmers also compete in bodysuits and, like cyclists, shave the hair on any part of their body that is not covered by the suit.

Maintaining the correct body position is another way to reduce friction in sports. Cyclists and skiers assume a crouched position when racing, luge racers lie flat, and ski jumpers extend their bodies over their skis while in the air.

In sports where objects are thrown through the air, the objects encounter less air resistance if they have the proper orientation in flight. A football thrown in a tight spiral travels farther than one that tumbles end over end. Similarly, a javelin or discus travels farther if it travels through the air without wobbling.

✓ CHECKING CONCEPTS

1. A book sliding across a desk will come to a stop because of the force of _____.

2. A book sliding across a desk is an example of _____ friction.

3. The type of friction that acts on an object falling through the atmosphere is called _____.

4. Friction makes _____ possible.

💡 THINKING CRITICALLY

5. INFER: When a car's tires are stuck in snow or mud, is it better to have more or less friction? Why?

6. HYPOTHESIZE: Sand is often placed on top of ice on roads and highways. Why do you think the sand is used?

7. CLASSIFY: Decide which of the following is an example of sliding friction, rolling friction, or air resistance. **a.** an airplane descending **b.** a person roller-skating **c.** a person ice skating **d.** a falling leaf

8. CALCULATE: Copy the diagram in Figure 12-16 onto a sheet of paper. A force of 10 N is causing the object to slide across a tabletop from left to right. There is a 3-N force of friction opposing that motion. Complete the diagram, using arrows to show all the forces acting on the object.

▲ **Figure 12-16** Complete the diagram.

⚛ *Hands-On Activity*

MEASURING FRICTION

You will need a spring scale, a small object, a long sheet of sandpaper, and tape.

1. Place the small object on a tabletop. Attach the spring scale to the object. Pull the object across the table at a constant speed. Record the amount of force shown on the spring scale.

2. The force measured in Step 1 is the force of friction on the object from the tabletop.

3. Repeat Steps 1 to 3. This time use the sheet of sandpaper. Tape the sandpaper to the tabletop. Use the spring scale to pull the object across the sandpaper at the same speed as before.

Practicing Your Skills

4. OBSERVE: What was the force of friction on the object from the tabletop?

5. OBSERVE: What was the force of friction on the object from the sandpaper?

6. INFER: Does a smooth surface offer less friction or more friction than a rough surface?

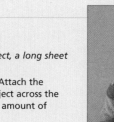

▲ **STEP 3** Pull the object across the sandpaper with the spring scale.

Answers to questions

1️⃣ OBSERVE: keep pushing it

2️⃣ DEFINE: a force that opposes the motion of an object

3️⃣ STATE: when two surfaces are in contact

4️⃣ LIST: Possible answers: bicycling, climbing a rope, walking, throwing a ball

5️⃣ EXPLAIN: Friction can produce heat and wear away surfaces.

3 Assess

✓ CHECKING CONCEPTS ANSWERS

1. friction
2. sliding
3. air resistance
4. motion

💡 THINKING CRITICALLY ANSWERS

5. INFER: More friction; The tires would be able to grip the surface and stop spinning.

6. HYPOTHESIZE: Sand increases friction between tires and the road surface.

7. CLASSIFY: **a.** air resistance **b.** rolling friction **c.** sliding friction **d.** air resistance

8. CALCULATE: Students should add a 3-N arrow pointing to the left. Its length should be 30% that of the 10-N arrow.

4 Close

Hands-On Activity

MEASURING FRICTION

TIME: 15 minutes

PURPOSE: measuring, observing, inferring

ALTERNATIVE MATERIALS: Books or blocks of wood work well.

DISCUSSION: Have different pairs of students use different grades of sandpaper. Before performing the activity, ask students to predict how the grade of sandpaper will affect their results. Be sure that students justify their predictions.

Practicing Your Skills Answers

4. OBSERVE: Answers will vary.

5. OBSERVE: Answers will vary.

6. INFER: less friction

MORE ON THE WEB

The History of Matches Have students use the Internet to learn about the invention and perfection of friction matches. Then, have students answer the questions that follow this activity at www.conceptsand challenges.com.

• *TEACHING RESOURCES* •

◎ Teacher's Resources CD-ROM
Lesson Review: Chapter 12, p. 8
Spider Map: Study Tools, p. 9

COOPERATIVE LEARNING

Listing Examples of Friction Have small groups of students create a three-column chart to list more examples of sliding friction, air resistance, and rolling friction.

1 Introduce

STUDY HINT Have students read the Real-Life Science feature before beginning this lesson. Discuss the concepts presented in the feature. Ask students how they think this information relates to topics they have already studied or to the lesson they are about to study.

Linking Prior Knowledge Ask students why oil is used in a car and what happens to a car if it runs out of oil. (Oil reduces friction between moving parts of the engine. If a car runs out of oil, the parts rub against each other and can become damaged.)

2 Teach

Demonstration Draw a large object on the board. Under it, draw an arrow that points right, label it *10 N*, and inform students that it represents the force of friction on the object. Next, draw an identical arrow that points to the left inside the object. Label it *10 N* and inform students that it represents the pushing force. Ask students: *How will the object move?* (It will not move because the forces are balanced.) Have a volunteer draw an arrow that represents a pushing force that would move the object. (a bigger arrow to the left)

READING STRATEGY Encourage students to think about situations relevant to what they are reading. For example, in a situation where they had to push something heavy, did they ask someone to help them push the object or did they use a lubricant to make it easier to move the object?

Answers to questions

1 CALCULATE: a force greater than 16 N

2 EXPLAIN: You would not be able to exert a force large enough to overcome friction and, therefore, you would not be able to move the object.

3 IDENTIFY: when you need to reduce friction between moving parts

4 HYPOTHESIZE: to increase the friction between shoe soles and the surface of the steps

---

12-5 How can friction be changed?

▲ **Figure 12-18** Using rolling friction

Objective
Describe some ways to change friction.

Key Term
lubricants (LOO-brih-kuhnts): materials that reduce friction

Moving Against Friction Friction makes it hard to move objects. Force is needed to overcome the force of friction. Suppose you wanted to push a heavy wooden box across the floor. As you push against the box, sliding friction equal to a force of 5 N pushes in the opposite direction. This means that it will take a total force greater than 5 N to push the box.

▲ **Figure 12-17** Overcoming sliding friction

1 CALCULATE: If the force of friction is 16 N, how much force is needed to move the object?

Using Rolling Friction Reducing friction makes it easier to move an object. One way to reduce friction is to change sliding friction to rolling friction. When you try to push a wooden box across a floor, you have to overcome sliding friction. The size of this frictional force depends on the types of surfaces in contact with each other. In this case, the bottom of the box is in contact with the floor. If you put the box on a wheeled cart, there will be much less friction. Rolling friction is always less than sliding friction. With the box on wheels, you use less force to push the box.

2 EXPLAIN: Why must you reduce friction in order to move certain objects?

Using Lubricants You can also reduce friction by using lubricants. **Lubricants** are materials that reduce friction. For example, in a car's engine, metal parts called pistons are in contact with other metal parts. When two pieces of metal touch, there is a lot of friction. Oil is used to reduce the friction between the metal parts. Oil is a lubricant. It separates the metal parts from one another. Without the oil, the metal parts would scrape against one another. This would make the engine overheat and wear out more quickly.

3 IDENTIFY: When would it be helpful to use a lubricant?

Not Enough Friction Have you ever slipped on an icy sidewalk or seen a car skid out of control? These things happen when there is not enough friction between surfaces such as your feet and the ice or the tires and the road. In such cases, it is necessary to increase friction. This can be done by spreading sand on an icy surface or using tires with a deeper tread.

Athletes often wear special footwear to increase friction between their feet and the surfaces over which they move. Basketball players wear shoes with soles designed not to slip on a hardwood floor. In several sports, players wear shoes with spiked soles to give their feet a better grip on the ground.

Teaching Options

◈ INTEGRATING LIFE SCIENCE

Explaining Friction Between Bones Inform students that a joint is the area where two bones meet. Explain how joints affect movement between bones. A joint is surrounded by a sac that produces a lubricant called synovial fluid. The fluid is absorbed by cartilage, spongy material at the end of bones. When the bones are moving, synovial fluid is pressed out of the cartilage and lubricates the bones. The lubricant reduces friction and makes movement between bones easier. When bones are held rigid, the cartilage absorbs the fluid, causing friction between bones to increase. The increased friction can cause pain when the bones start to move. Have interested students research and report on how diseases such as arthritis affect the movement of joints. Students can also use the Writing Activity Outline found on the Teacher's Resources CD-ROM to organize the information that they gather.
learning styles: visual, auditory

▲ **Figure 12-19** Sometimes it helps to increase friction.

4 HYPOTHESIZE: Why do staircases often have rubber mats on the steps?

✓ CHECKING CONCEPTS

1. Because of friction, it takes _____ force to move an object.
2. When friction is _____ , it is easier to move an object.
3. Waxing a floor makes the floor slippery because wax is a _____ .
4. If you wear roller skates instead of shoes, you _____ the friction between your feet and the floor.

💡 THINKING CRITICALLY

5. ANALYZE: Is it easier to push a heavy object across a carpeted floor or across a polished wooden floor? Why?
6. CALCULATE: Find the amount of force in each example. **a.** If it takes 20 N to slide a wooden crate across the floor, what is the force of friction? **b.** By putting wheels on the crate, the force of friction is reduced to 2 N. How much force is now needed to push the crate?
7. HYPOTHESIZE: On rainy days, the amount of friction between the road and the wheels of a car can sometimes be reduced by half. Why would reducing friction not be helpful in this case?

DESIGNING AN EXPERIMENT

Design an experiment to solve the following problem. Include a hypothesis, variables, a procedure, and a data table to be completed.

PROBLEM: Which is more effective in reducing friction between a block of steel and a smooth, flat surface, rollers or a lubricant?

⚛ *Real-Life Science*

FRICTION AND SKIING

Friction is one of the major forces that affects the movement of skis across a snow-covered surface. Friction can slow the speed of a downhill racer. That same friction makes it possible for another skier to make sharp turns while maneuvering through a slalom course.

A good ski run can be affected by the type of snow on the course. In some cases, the snow might be icy or crusty. At other times, it may be soft and sticky. Skiers often apply wax to the bottom of their skis in order to adapt to the snow conditions, especially when the snow is soft or wet.

The type of equipment a skier uses is also important. The skis used for cross-country skiing are longer and narrower than those used for downhill skiing.

Thinking Critically What things can a skier do to adapt to varying snow conditions?

▲ **Figure 12-20** Waxing skis reduces friction and helps to increase speed.

3 Assess

✓ CHECKING CONCEPTS ANSWERS

1. more
2. reduced
3. lubricant
4. decrease

💡 THINKING CRITICALLY ANSWERS

5. ANALYZE: A polished wooden floor; There is less friction on a polished wooden floor.
6. CALCULATE: **a.** less than 20 N **b.** more than 2 N
7. HYPOTHESIZE: The car would not be able to stop in the same distance as it would when traveling at the same speed on a dry road.

4 Close

DESIGNING AN EXPERIMENT

Use the Designing an Experiment Rubric on the Teacher's Resources CD-ROM to assess students' experiments. Fill in the rubric with the additional information below. For this assignment, students should have:

- described, in the hypothesis, friction as a force that opposes the motion of an object.
- mentioned, in the procedure, a method of measuring the force necessary to (a) slide the object on rollers and (b) slide the same object across a lubricated surface.

Real-Life Science

FRICTION AND SKIING

Background In downhill skiing, the weight of the skier tends to pull the skier down the hill. If the force of friction, directed uphill, acting on the skier balances the downhill force on the skier, the skier will move down the hill at constant speed. If the force of friction is less than the downhill force, the skier will move down the hill faster and faster. If the force of friction is greater than the downhill force, the moving skier will slow to a stop.

Discussion Ask students how reducing friction affects a skier's speed. (Reducing friction increases a skier's speed.)

Thinking Critically Answer
Possible answers: Apply wax to the bottom of skis or change the type of skis.

ONGOING ASSESSMENT

Identifying a Force Slide a book across a tabletop. Ask students to identify the force that opposes the motion of the book and the direction of that force. (friction, opposite the motion of the book)

• TEACHING RESOURCES •

💿 **Teacher's Resources CD-ROM**
Lesson Review: Chapter 12, p. 9
Designing an Experiment Rubric: Teaching Tools, p. 7
Designing an Experiment: Study Tools, p.14
Writing Activity Outline: Study Tools, pp. 20–21

1 Introduce

🔍 INVESTIGATE

TIME: 10 minutes

PURPOSE: Students will observe that the shape of an object affects how it falls.

MATERIALS: two identical sheets of paper, chair

PROCEDURE: Be sure that students hold the uncrumpled sheet of paper parallel to the floor and that they simultaneously release both sheets of paper.

THINK ABOUT IT: The air pushed up on the uncrumpled sheet of paper more than it did on the crumpled sheet of paper as both fell.

✏️ **STUDY HINT** Before beginning this lesson, have students recall what they learned about friction and gravity. Ask them to predict which would land first if dropped from the same height—a penny or a basketball.

Linking Prior Knowledge Have students recall that the term *speed* relates to the question *How quickly am I moving?* Have them recall that the term *acceleration* relates to the question *How quickly is my speed changing?*

2 Teach

Discussion Discuss with students the meaning of the word *terminal*. Point out that this and related terms, such as *terminate*, all refer to something being final or at the end.

Demonstration Review the Investigate activity with students. Have them compare a crumpled sheet of paper to an uncrumpled sheet of paper. Ask them to describe the differences between both sheets. (The uncrumpled sheet has more surface area.) Explain to students that because the uncrumpled sheet has more surface area, more air can push against it. The greater air resistance slows the uncrumpled sheet down. However, if both objects were dropped in a vacuum, they would land at the same time. Ask students why this is so. (Because there is no air in a vacuum, there is no air resistance.)

learning styles: visual, auditory

12-6 What is air resistance?

🔍 INVESTIGATE

Observing Air Resistance
HANDS-ON ACTIVITY

1. Obtain two identical sheets of paper. Crumple one sheet into a ball.
2. Hold the crumpled sheet of paper in one hand and the uncrumpled sheet in the other hand. Extend your arms straight out in front of you at shoulder height.
3. Release both sheets of paper at the same time and observe them fall.

THINK ABOUT IT: Both sheets of paper are identical, yet one fell faster than the other. Why do you think this happened?

STEP 2

Objective
Explain how air resistance affects moving objects.

Key Terms
air resistance: force that opposes the movement of an object in air

terminal velocity: speed at which air resistance and gravity acting on a falling object are equal

vacuum: empty space

Falling Objects The force that opposes the downward motion of objects falling through Earth's atmosphere is called **air resistance.** Air resistance is not the same for all objects. The greater the surface area of an object, the greater the air resistance. Suppose, for example, an oak leaf and an acorn fall from a tree. The leaf flutters slowly to the ground, whereas the acorn drops straight down. As each object falls, air pushes up against the surfaces of the objects. The leaf has a greater surface area than the acorn. As a result, air pushes with more force against the leaf than it does against the acorn. The leaf is slowed more than the acorn, so the acorn hits the ground first.

▶ **PREDICT:** Which falling object will hit the ground first, a marble or a feather?

Terminal Velocity When an object is dropped from a high place, gravity pulls the object toward Earth. As it falls, gravity causes the object to accelerate. Its velocity and air resistance increase at steady rates. At some point, the upward force of air resistance becomes equal to the downward pull of gravity. At this point, the object reaches its **terminal velocity.** It stops accelerating and its velocity remains the same for the rest of its downward trip.

▶ **DESCRIBE:** What happens to an object's velocity as it falls?

Free Fall A **vacuum** is empty space. If a bowling ball and a sheet of paper were dropped from the same height in a vacuum, they would hit the ground at the same time. Because there is no air in a vacuum, there is no air resistance to slow the objects as they fall.

▲ **Figure 12-21** When on the Moon's surface, an astronaut dropped a hammer and a feather to test the idea of free fall.

Teaching Options

⚠️ FAST FACTS

Galileo's Hypothesis

Galileo was able to support his hypothesis that all objects fall with the same acceleration by investigating the motion of balls rolling down inclines. Galileo deduced that a ball rolling down an incline has a constant acceleration because its speed increases by equal amounts during equal time periods. Therefore, he argued that the observation of two objects of different weights, each dropped from the same height, reach the ground in the same amount of time. This implies that both objects have the same acceleration.

EXTENDING THE LESSON

Dropping Objects on the Surface of the Moon In 1971, when astronaut David Randolph Scott dropped a hammer and a feather at the same time while standing on the surface of the Moon, millions of viewers on Earth saw that both objects landed at the same time. Viewers became witnesses to the fact that since there is no air on the Moon, there was no air resistance to slow down either object.

All objects fall at the same speed in a vacuum. When the Apollo astronauts landed on the moon, they tested this idea. There is no air on the moon. One of the astronauts dropped a feather and a hammer at the same time and from the same height. Look at Figure 12-21. What do you think happened? The hammer and the feather hit the ground at the same time!

▶ **DEFINE:** What is a vacuum?

✓ CHECKING CONCEPTS

1. When an object is first dropped, its speed _____.

2. As an object falls, it will reach _____ because of air resistance.

3. When you drop an object, _____ slows it down.

4. There is no _____ in a vacuum.

5. All objects accelerate at the same rate in a _____.

6. HYPOTHESIZE: Certain birds spread their wings before they land. Why do they do this? Explain.

Web InfoSearch

Effects of Streamlining A large truck and a sports car traveling at the same speed both have to overcome air resistance. Because of its size and shape, the truck has more air resistance acting on it than does the sports car. The sports car has less surface area. Also, the sports car is streamlined. Its shape has been designed to help reduce air resistance.

SEARCH: Cars, airplanes, and other vehicles all have to overcome air resistance as they move. Use the Internet to find out how engineers design shapes to reduce air resistance. Start your search at www.conceptsandchallenges.com. Some key search words are **streamlining air resistance, wind tunnel streamlining,** and **streamlining airplanes.**

🔬 *How Do They Know That?*

WEIGHT DOESN'T MATTER

All falling objects speed up as they fall. Until Galileo, everyone believed that if two objects of different weight were dropped from some height at the same time, the heavier object would reach the ground first. During a storm, Galileo watched hailstones of different size and weight fall. Based on what he saw, Galileo hypothesized that weight had little or no effect on the change in speed of a falling object.

Legend has it that, to test his idea, Galileo climbed to the top of the Leaning Tower of Pisa. He dropped two rocks of different weight from the tower at the same time. People at the base of the tower saw the two rocks hit the ground at the same time. It is not clear whether or not Galileo actually did this experiment. But he did test and prove his hypothesis.

Perhaps Galileo's most important contribution to science was his use of the scientific method. Galileo served as a model for all later scientists.

Thinking Critically If a 10-N stone and a 2-N stone are dropped from a tall building at the same time, which will hit the ground first? Explain.

▲ **Figure 12-22** Galileo may have tested his hypothesis at the leaning tower of Pisa.

CHAPTER 12: Force **259**

Answers to questions

1 **PREDICT:** a marble

2 **DESCRIBE:** It increases until it reaches terminal velocity and then remains the same.

3 **DEFINE:** empty space

3 Assess

✓ CHECKING CONCEPTS ANSWERS

1. increases
2. terminal velocity
3. air resistance
4. air or matter
5. vacuum

💡 THINKING CRITICALLY ANSWER

6. HYPOTHESIZE: It increases air resistance, helping the birds slow down as they land.

4 Close

Web InfoSearch

Effects of Streamlining Have students use the Internet to find out how engineers design shapes to reduce air resistance. Students should begin their search at www.conceptsandchallenges.com.

How Do They Know That?

WEIGHT DOESN'T MATTER

Background If a 20-cm diameter solid lead ball and a 20-cm solid plastic ball were both dropped from the top of the Leaning Tower of Pisa, each would strike the ground 3.4 s later traveling at a speed of 33 m/s (110 ft/s). During each second of fall, their speeds would increase by 9.8 m/s (32 ft/s).

Discussion Ask students what unbalanced force exerted on the balls causes each ball to fall with the same acceleration. (Earth's force of gravity)

Thinking Critically Answer They will hit the ground at the same time because weight does not affect the change in speed of a falling object.

ONGOING ASSESSMENT

Explaining Terminal Velocity Have students explain how gravity and air resistance are related to terminal velocity. Then, have them explain why a falling object never reaches terminal velocity in a vacuum.

• TEACHING RESOURCES •

Teacher's Resources CD-ROM
Lesson Review: Chapter 12, p. 10
Enrichment: Chapter 12, p. 11

COOPERATIVE LEARNING

Experimenting With Weight Have pairs of students design an experiment that uses a basketball and a beach ball to show that weight does not affect the speed of a falling object.

1 Introduce

✒️ **STUDY HINT** Before beginning this lesson, write the title of each section on the board. Have students copy these titles in their notebooks, using an outline format. As students read each section, they should write important concepts from the section in their notebooks.

Linking Prior Knowledge Have student recall that density of a material is mass per unit volume (Lesson 2-2). Ask students how to calculate density. (Divide mass by volume.) Ask students what the unit of density is for a solid or a liquid. (g/cm^3) Tell students that they will use division to calculate a new concept, called pressure, and its unit of measurement.

2 Teach

Discussion Discuss with students how pressing with the sharp edge of a knife increases the pressure produced by the knife. Even though the dull edge does not have a great deal more area than the sharp edge does, it has enough to decrease the pressure produced when you cut with it.

Demonstration Show how the same force can produce different pressures. Use a block of wood, nails, and a hammer. Wear safety goggles. Have students also wear safety goggles. Hold a nail with its point down on the wood and strike it with one blow of the hammer. Repeat with a nail pointed head down. Have students observe and feel the block of wood and nails. Have students compare the penetration of the nails. Help students conclude that the greater penetration occurred when the same force acted over a smaller area.
learning styles: tactile, visual

Answers to questions

▶ **CALCULATE:** $3 N/m^2$

▶ **LIST:** change force and change area

▶ **LIST:** Possible answers: air pressure and pressure of rocks against each other deep below Earth's surface

---

12-7 What is pressure?

Objective
Identify pressure as a force acting on a unit area.

Key Term
pressure: force per unit area

Force and Area The amount of force acting on a unit of area is called pressure. **Pressure** is equal to force divided by area. Suppose you hold a can as shown in Figure 12-23. If the can weighs 10 N, it presses down on your hand with a force of 10 N. Now suppose the bottom of the can has an area of 100 cm². The pressure caused by the weight of the can on your hand can be found by using the equation:

$$pressure = force \div area$$
$$pressure = 10\ N \div 100\ cm^2$$
$$pressure = 0.1\ N/cm^2$$

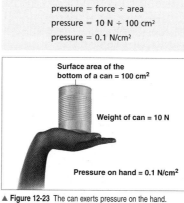

Surface area of the bottom of a can = 100 cm²

Weight of can = 10 N

Pressure on hand = 0.1 N/cm²

▲ **Figure 12-23** The can exerts pressure on the hand.

▶ **CALCULATE:** How much pressure is produced by a 30-N force acting on an area of 10 m²?

Changing Pressure Pressure can be changed by changing the force. When the area stays the same, increasing the amount of force increases the pressure. Think of a pencil point. Press the point gently against a piece of modeling clay. The point of the pencil will make a small dent in the clay. If you press a little harder, you increase the force and the pressure. The pencil point will sink deeper into the clay.

Pressure can also be changed by changing the area on which the force is pushing. If you apply the same amount of force to a larger area, the pressure is decreased. Think of the same pencil. Turn it around and gently press the eraser against the clay with the same force you used before. The pencil will barely make a mark on the clay. If you increase the force, the eraser will dent the clay but will not sink into the clay as far as the pencil point did. This shows that the pressure applied with the eraser is less than the pressure applied with the point of the pencil.

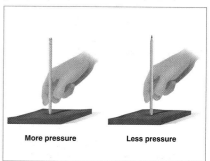

More pressure   Less pressure

▲ **Figure 12-24** The pencil point exerts more pressure than the eraser.

▶ **LIST:** What are two ways to change the amount of pressure being exerted?

Pressure in Nature Pressure can also be found and felt in nature. When pumped into a tire or a balloon, air exerts pressure to keep the item inflated. The air pressure in a tire can be great enough to support the weight of a truck. The pressure exerted by moving air, or wind, can turn the vanes of a windmill or keep a kite flying.

Deep below Earth's surface, pressure is very great. The weight of rocks and soil above can cause dramatic changes in rocks at great depths. Pressures build up to cause volcanoes to erupt and earthquakes to occur.

▶ **LIST:** Name some examples of pressure in nature.

Teaching Options

RETEACH

Demonstrating Pressure and Area
Prepare two packets by sandwiching a sheet of fresh carbon paper between two sheets of paper for each packet. Place a packet on the floor and have a student stand on it with one foot. Have the same student stand on the toes of one foot on the second packet. Open the packets and have students observe and compare the size and darkness of the impressions. Relate the darker impression to the increased pressure of the student's weight being exerted on a smaller area.
learning style: visual

EXTENDING THE LESSON

Falling Through Ice
Inform students that if a person falls through ice, a rescuer has to lie on his or her stomach and inch over to the person who has fallen through. The rescuer also has to pull the person out the same way. Ask students to explain why the rescuer has to lie down on the ice. (The rescuer needs to decrease the area on which his or her weight is exerted to avoid breaking the ice.)
learning style: auditory

✓ CHECKING CONCEPTS

1. Pressure is equal to force divided by _____.

2. Pressure can be measured in _____ /cm².

3. You can decrease pressure by _____ the amount of force on the same area.

4. If you increase the area on which a force acts, you will _____ the pressure.

THINKING CRITICALLY

5. CALCULATE: Find the amount of pressure for each of the following examples. **a.** How much pressure is applied when a 50-N force acts over an area of 10 m²? **b.** What will happen to the pressure if the force is increased to 60 N? **c.** How could you decrease the pressure from 6 N/m² to 3 N/m²?

6. ANALYZE: A rectangular building brick rests on a tabletop. How can you change the amount of pressure the brick exerts on the tabletop?

7. ANALYZE: You can get a stronger spray of water from a garden hose if you make the opening of the hose smaller. Explain why.

BUILDING MATH SKILLS

Calculating When you measure, you compare an unknown quantity with a known quantity. You can use the equation pressure = force ÷ area to find the force. To find force, rearrange the equation as follows:

$$\text{force} = \text{pressure} \times \text{area}$$

Use the equation above to find the force for each of the following examples:

8. A pressure of 12 N/m² is applied over an area of 10 m².

9. The contents of a spray can are at a pressure of 1,500 N/mm². The opening of the spray nozzle has an area of 0.2 mm².

10. A pressure of 250 N/cm² is applied to a nail. The point of the nail has an area of 0.25 cm².

⚛ Hands-On Activity

OBSERVING AIR PRESSURE

You will need a 2-L plastic bottle with cap, hot water, and cold water.

1. Half-fill a 2-L plastic bottle with hot tap water and screw the cap on tightly.

2. Swirl the hot water around in the bottle for a few seconds.

3. Remove the cap, pour the water out, and quickly replace the cap.

4. Hold the bottle under the cold-water tap for several seconds. Then stand the bottle on a flat surface and observe what happens.

Practicing Your Skills

5. DESCRIBE: What happened to the bottle? What caused this to happen?

6. INFER: What effect did filling the bottle with hot water have?

▲ **STEP 2** Swirl the water in the bottle.

MORE ON THE WEB

Understanding Air Pressure
Have students use the Internet to learn more about air pressure. Have students take the online quiz at www.conceptsand challenges.com.

ONGOING ASSESSMENT

Reviewing Pressure Ask students: *What is the formula for pressure?* (pressure = force/area) *What is the SI unit for force?* (newton) *What units can be used to measure force?* (N/cm²)

• TEACHING RESOURCES •

◎ **Teacher's Resources CD-ROM**
Lesson Review: Chapter 12, p. 12

Writing Activity Outline: Study Tools, pp. 20–21

---

3 Assess

✓ CHECKING CONCEPTS ANSWERS

1. area
2. N
3. decreasing
4. decrease

THINKING CRITICALLY ANSWERS

5. CALCULATE: **a.** 5 N/m² **b.** The pressure will increase to 6 N/m². **c.** Increase the area to 20 m² or reduce the force to 30 N.

6. ANALYZE: Lay it on another side.

7. ANALYZE: If the opening has less area, the pressure will be greater.

4 Close

BUILDING MATH SKILLS ANSWERS

Calculating
8. 120 N
9. 300 N
10. 63 N

Hands-On Activity

OBSERVING AIR PRESSURE

TIME: 15 minutes

PURPOSE: describing, inferring

BACKGROUND: Gas pressure and temperature are directly related. In a closed system, as temperature increases, pressure increases. As temperature decreases, so does pressure.

DISCUSSION: Explain that the bottle collapses because the outside air pressure is greater than the inside air pressure, resulting in an unbalanced force. The lower air pressure inside the bottle occurs because when the air is warmed by the hot water, some of the air leaves the bottle. When the bottle is sealed, the air inside cools and the air pressure decreases. As a result, the air pressure inside the bottle is less than the air pressure outside the bottle.

Practicing Your Skills Answers

5. DESCRIBE: The bottle collapsed slightly. The air pressure on the outside was greater than the air pressure inside the bottle. The greater pressure pushed the sides in.

6. INFER: The hot water warmed the bottle, which, in turn, warmed the air.

1 Introduce

✎ **STUDY HINT** Before beginning this lesson, reads the list of Key Terms aloud so that students can hear their pronunciations.

Linking Prior Knowledge Ask students if they have ever visited locations that were at very high elevations or very low elevations. For those who answered yes, ask them if they had any trouble breathing. Inform students that air pressure changes with elevation. Because of the difference in air pressure, students may have experienced headaches, dehydration, or difficulty in breathing.

2 Teach

Discussion Inform students that gravity pulls air molecules toward the center of Earth. These air molecules make up the atmosphere. They exert pressure on the surface of Earth. Air pressure is greatest near Earth's surface. As you move farther away from Earth's surface, air pressure decreases because there is less air. Ask students: *Where is air pressure greater, at the top of a mountain or in a valley?* (in a valley)

Demonstration Demonstrate Bernoulli's principle by using a funnel and a table tennis ball or a small, plastic-foam ball. Hold the funnel with its tapered end up and hold the ball inside the funnel. Blow hard over the tapered end and let go of the ball. The ball should stay inside the funnel because the air pressure above the funnel has decreased. The air pressure below the funnel is now greater and pushes the ball upward.

Answers to questions

▸ **INFER:** The air pressure is less at the top of the mountain.

▸ **IDENTIFY:** air pressure

▸ **DEFINE:** As the speed of a fluid increases, the pressure it exerts decreases.

▸ **IDENTIFY:** lift

▸ **IDENTIFY:** thrust

12-8 What is air pressure?

Objective
Explain what causes air pressure and how it is measured.

Key Terms
air pressure: pressure caused by the force exerted by Earth's atmosphere

barometer (buh-RAHM-uht-uhr): instrument used to measure air pressure

Bernoulli's principle: as the speed of a fluid increases, its pressure decreases

Air Pressure Earth's atmosphere is made up of a mixture of gases. This mixture is called air. Air molecules are in constant motion and are pulled toward Earth's center by gravity. The force of all these moving air molecules causes **air pressure.** Most of the air in Earth's atmosphere is concentrated near Earth's surface. So air pressure is greatest near Earth's surface and decreases as altitude increases.

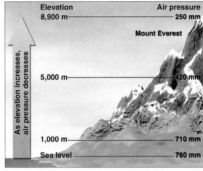

▲ **Figure 12-25** Air pressure decreases as altitude increases.

▸ **INFER:** How does air pressure at the top of a mountain compare with the air pressure at sea level?

Measuring Air Pressure Air pressure is measured with an instrument called a **barometer.** Figure 12-25 shows how a barometer works. The open container and the glass tube contain mercury, a very heavy liquid. The space above the mercury in the tube is a vacuum. As air presses down on the surface of the mercury in the container, the air pressure holds the column of mercury in the glass tube. The greater the air pressure, the higher the mercury will rise in the tube. Normal air pressure at sea level will support a column of mercury 760 mm high in the glass tube. Air pressure decreases with altitude. So, if you carried the barometer up a mountain, the level of the mercury in the tube would move down.

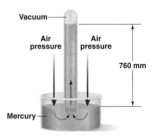

▲ **Figure 12-26** A mercury barometer

▸ **IDENTIFY:** What does a barometer measure?

Bernoulli's Principle Air that is still exerts pressure on Earth's surface. When moving, as in wind, that same air will exert less pressure on the surface. This change in pressure is explained by Bernoulli's principle. **Bernoulli's principle** states that as the speed of a fluid—any gas or liquid—increases, the pressure it exerts decreases. You can try a simple experiment to show this principle. Hold a sheet of paper in front of you. Blow over the top of the paper. The sheet of paper will rise. This shows that the air pressure above the paper has decreased. It is now less than the air pressure beneath the paper, which pushes the paper up.

▸ **DEFINE:** What is Bernoulli's principle?

Teaching Options

❗ FAST FACTS *The Wind Took My Breath*

On windy days, a person might say that the wind "takes my breath." This feeling is a result of the Bernoulli principle. On a windy day, the outside air is moving faster than the air inside the mouth and lungs. Therefore, the outside air pressure is less than the air pressure inside the mouth and lungs. Wind moves from an area of greater air pressure to an area of lower air pressure. As a result, the air inside the lungs and mouth is pushed out.

ESL/ELL STRATEGY

***Explaining the Origin of* Meter** Explain to students that *meter* comes from a Greek word meaning "measure." Ask students how the word *barometer* is related to its Greek origin. Then, have students look up the following words in a dictionary and relate them to their Greek origins: *thermometer, speedometer,* and *hydrometer.*

Air Pressure and Wing Shape Airplane wings are designed to make use of Bernoulli's principle. Look at the shape of the wing in Figure 12-27. Notice that the top of the wing is more curved than the bottom. As the airplane moves through the air, the shape of the wing causes air pressure on top of the wing to be reduced. So the pressure of the air pushing up on the wing is greater than the pressure of the air pushing down. This unbalanced force, called lift, helps to push the wing up.

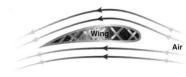

▲ **Figure 12-27** The shape of an airplane wing helps to create unbalanced forces on the wing.

4▶ IDENTIFY: What force pushes up on an airplane wing?

Flight Four forces act on an airplane in flight. Figure 12-28 shows a view of an airplane. The arrows show the directions of the four forces.

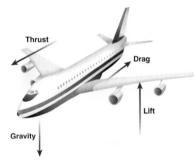

▲ **Figure 12-28** Four forces act on an airplane in flight.

- The weight of the airplane is due to gravity. This force pulls the plane toward the ground.
- The upward force on the bottom of the airplane's wings is called lift. This force pushes the wings up. In normal flight, the lift is equal to the weight of the airplane.

- The forward force on the plane is called thrust. The plane's engines provide the force, or thrust, needed to move the plane forward.
- The flow of air over the wings is a form of air resistance. This frictional force is called drag. Drag slows an airplane down. Too much drag causes the plane to use too much fuel. Engineers design planes that will reduce drag. The process of reducing drag is called streamlining.

5▶ IDENTIFY: What is the forward force a plane needs in order to fly?

☑ **CHECKING CONCEPTS**

1. Air pressure is caused by the force of moving _____.
2. A barometer measures _____.
3. Air pressure _____ as altitude increases.
4. As the speed of a fluid increases, the pressure it exerts _____.
5. The force that tends to slow a moving airplane is called _____.

💡 **THINKING CRITICALLY**

6. HYPOTHESIZE: A plane flying into a strong wind feels more drag than in calm air. Explain.
7. HYPOTHESIZE: When a plane is landing, the flaps under the wings are used to give the plane more drag. Why is this necessary?

Web InfoSearch

Aneroid Barometers Mercury barometers are not always practical to use because they take up so much space. Another type of barometer, called an aneroid barometer, is widely used for its convenience.

SEARCH: Use the Internet to find out how aneroid barometers work and how they can be used to measure altitude. What does *aneroid* mean? Start your search at www.conceptsandchallenges.com. Some key search words are **aneroid barometer, how aneroid barometer works,** and **how barometer works.**

Reinforcement Ask students to bring model airplanes to class. Using the models, describe the four forces that act on an airplane in flight. Ask students to identify balanced forces, including their directions, when the plane is flying (lift and gravity, up and down; thrust and drag, forward and backward) **learning styles: visual, auditory**

3 Assess

☑ **CHECKING CONCEPTS ANSWERS**

1. air molecules
2. air pressure
3. decreases
4. decreases
5. drag

💡 **THINKING CRITICALLY ANSWERS**

6. HYPOTHESIZE: There is more air resistance in a strong wind.
7. HYPOTHESIZE: to slow the plane

✏️ **WRITING HINT** Tell students that when they refer to the type of force caused by gravitational attraction acting on a body, they should use the term *force of gravity* or *gravity*. When referring to the value of the force of gravity acting on an object, they should use the term *weight*.

4 Close

Web InfoSearch

Aneroid Barometers Have students use the Internet to find out how aneroid barometers work and what *aneroid* means. Some key search words are **aneroid barometer, how aneroid barometer works,** and **how barometer works.** Students should begin their search at www.conceptsandchallenges.com.

COOPERATIVE LEARNING

Observing Bernoulli's Principle
Give pairs of students strips of notebook paper and have them perform the activity described in the section Bernoulli's Principle. As one student performs the activity, the other student can record the observations.
learning styles: tactile, interpersonal

• TEACHING RESOURCES •

💿 **Teacher's Resources CD-ROM**
Lesson Review: Chapter 12, p. 13

ONGOING ASSESSMENT

Explaining Figure 12-26 Ask students to explain Figure 12-26, the mercury barometer. Ask students: *What will happen as air presses down on the surface of the mercury?* (The mercury will rise higher in the tube.)

1 Introduce

✎ **STUDY HINT** Before beginning this lesson, have students study Figure 12-29. Ask them to hypothesize the answer to the question.

Linking Prior Knowledge Tell students that they are familiar with pressure changes in fluids. Have students feel their pulse by placing the fingertips of the second and third fingers of their right hand on the wrist of their left hand, just below the thumb. Explain that they are feeling changes in the pressure of the blood as it moves through an artery. Explain to students that their pulse can also be felt in the carotid artery in the side of their neck.

2 Teach

Discussion Inform students that water molecules have weight, so they exert pressure. In a body of water, water pressure increases with depth because the weight of the water molecules above presses down on the water molecules below. Increased pressure with increased depth is the reason a diver feels increased pressure, especially in the ears, as the diver goes deeper and deeper.

Answers to questions

▸ **DESCRIBE:** Water pressure increases with depth.

▸ **EXPLAIN:** Gravity provides water pressure.

▸ **DESCRIBE:** The pressure travels throughout the fluid.

📖 **READING STRATEGY** Before students read each section, have them read the question at the end of the section. As they read, they can focus on the part of the section that provides the answer to the question.

12-9 What is water pressure?

Objective
Identify water pressure as the pressure caused by the weight and movement of water molecules.

Water Pressure Like air, water is a fluid. However, water is a liquid. Water molecules are more tightly packed than the molecules that make up air. Water exerts pressure because of the weight and movement of the water molecules. If you place an object in a container of water, the water applies pressure to the object in all directions.

Water pressure changes with depth. There is more pressure on a submarine the deeper it goes underwater. Below certain depths, the pressure from the water is so great that it can crush an object. Submarines are built to withstand a great deal of force from water pressure.

When you dive to the bottom of a swimming pool, you can feel the water pressure, especially against your ears. The pressure of the water is greater than that of the air that normally presses against your body.

▲ Figure 12-29 How does water pressure at depth *y* compare with that at depth *x*?

▸ **DESCRIBE:** How does water pressure change with depth?

Water Pressure at Home What happens when you open a faucet at home? Hopefully, water comes flowing out in a steady stream. This shows that you have good water pressure in your home. Where does this pressure come from? Some force must be pushing the water out of the faucet.

264

If your family has its own well, you probably have a system for pumping water up from the well and through the water pipes of your house. The pump provides your water pressure. Chances are your water comes from some central source, such as a town or city water system. In such systems, water is obtained from wells, lakes, or rivers. After being cleaned and purified, the water is pumped into large tanks. The tanks may be on a hill or some location higher than that of the homes they will supply with water. Gravity supplies the force that provides water pressure in such systems.

▲ Figure 12-30 Gravity provides the force that creates pressure for the water coming from this water tank.

▸ **EXPLAIN:** Why are water tanks located in high places?

Hydraulics Fluids, especially liquids, can transfer pressure. This is the idea behind hydraulic (hy-DRAW-lihk) systems. Look at the hydraulic system shown in Figure 12-31.

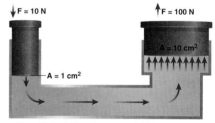

▲ Figure 12-31 Fluid transfers pressure in this hydraulic system.

Teaching Options

RETEACH

Water Pressure Varies With Depth in a Precise Way. Tell students that for each meter below the water's surface, the pressure increases by 9,800 N/m². At a depth of 10 m, the pressure would be 98,000 N/m², which is about the same as air pressure at sea level. At a depth of 20 m, the pressure would be twice what it was at a depth of 10 m. Ask students what the pressure would be at 20 m. (196,000 N/m²) Have students draw a diagram to illustrate their answers.
learning styles: auditory, visual

COOPERATIVE LEARNING

Researching Hydraulic Devices Have pairs of students choose a hydraulic device to research. They should draw a diagram of the device and describe how the device works in a brief paragraph. Some hydraulic devices that students can research are hydraulic brakes, barbers' chairs, automobile lifts, and rescue ladders. Allow volunteers to share their diagrams with the class.
learning styles: visual, linguistic

This system is filled with a liquid and has two movable pistons. The smaller piston has an area of 1 cm². If you push down on this piston with a force of 10 N, you will apply a pressure of 10 N/cm². This pressure will travel throughout the fluid. When it reaches the larger piston, this pressure will be applied over the entire area of that piston, which is 10 cm². So, a downward force of 10 N on the small piston will produce an upward force of 100 N on the large piston.

3 ▸ DESCRIBE: What happens when pressure is applied to an enclosed fluid?

✓ CHECKING CONCEPTS

1. Water pressure is caused by the weight and _____ of water molecules.

2. Water pressure is _____ than air pressure.

3. _____ provides the force for the water pressure in most homes and offices.

4. Water pressure at a depth of 1 m will be _____ than the pressure at a depth of 5 m.

5. _____ can transfer pressure.

💡 THINKING CRITICALLY

6. HYPOTHESIZE: Why does water pressure increase as you move deeper into the water?

HEALTH AND SAFETY TIP

Snorkeling and scuba diving can be educational and great fun. However, these activities can be dangerous. You should always swim and dive with a partner. Don't snorkel or dive in unfamiliar waters. Learn as much as you can about the area you plan to investigate. Be sure to follow all safety precautions. Before diving, take a course and get a dive license.

Hands-On Activity
RELATING PRESSURE AND DEPTH

You will need a milk carton or plastic soda bottle, pencil, paper, metric ruler, modeling clay, basin, apron and safety goggles.

1. Use a pencil to make a hole in a milk carton about 5 cm from the bottom. Plug the hole with modeling clay.

2. Repeat Step 1, making two more holes at distances of 10 cm and 15 cm from the bottom.

3. Put on safety goggles and fill the milk carton with water.

4. Place the carton in a basin or sink and remove the clay plug at the 15-cm hole. Measure and record how far the water squirts.

5. Replug the hole and refill the milk carton with water. Repeat Step 4 for the 10-cm hole and the 5-cm hole.

▲ STEP 2 Make small holes in the carton.

Practicing Your Skills

6. DESCRIBE: From which hole did water squirt the greatest distance? The least distance?

7. INFER: From your observations, how does pressure change with depth?

• TEACHING RESOURCES •

◉ **Teacher's Resources CD-ROM**
Lesson Review: Chapter 12, p. 14
Enrichment: Chapter 12, p. 15

Laboratory Manual
Lab. Challenge: How does depth affect water pressure? pp. 65–68

📼 **Laboratory Video**
Segment 13: Relating Depth and Water Pressure

3 Assess

✓ CHECKING CONCEPTS ANSWERS

1. movement
2. greater
3. Gravity
4. less
5. Fluids

💡 THINKING CRITICALLY ANSWER

6. HYPOTHESIZE: The weight of the water increases with depth.

4 Close

HEALTH AND SAFETY TIP

Ask students if they have ever gone scuba diving. Have any students who have been scuba diving describe their experiences to the class. Have them focus on the safety aspects of diving.

Hands-On Activity
RELATING PRESSURE AND DEPTH

TIME: 15 minutes

PURPOSE: describing, inferring

DISCUSSION: In most cases, students will observe that the water from the bottom hole projects farther than the water from the top hole. Students can infer that the speed of the water coming from the bottom hole is greater than the speed of the water coming from the top hole. Therefore, the water pressure is greater at the bottom hole than at the top hole. Students will see that water pressure increases with depth.

Practicing Your Skills Answers

6. DESCRIBE: bottom hole; top hole

7. INFER: Pressure increases with depth.

Lab Activity

(pp. 266–267)

1 Prepare the Lab

Making a Cartesian Diver

SET-UP TIME: 🕐 **LAB TIME:** 🕐

BACKGROUND: A Cartesian diver demonstrates how a submarine works.

PURPOSE: Students will construct a Cartesian diver and observe how pressure changes affect its tendency to float or sink in water.

ALTERNATIVE MATERIALS: Any kind of flexible wire can be wrapped around the pipette. Glass eyedroppers can be used instead of the plastic pipettes. Wire is not needed with glass eyedroppers.

SCIENCE SKILLS: Students will **observe** volume changes in the air within a Cartesian diver and changes in its motion. Students will also **infer** that pressure changes caused the density of the diver to change.

ADVANCE PLANNING: Obtain the materials needed before class. Have paper towels on hand in case of spills. You may wish to have a completed Cartesian diver made for demonstration purposes.

2 Guide the Lab

PROCEDURE: There are different kinds and sizes of plastic pipettes. It may be necessary to modify the construction procedures slightly to ensure maximum performance. Narrow-tube pipettes can be shortened by cutting off about one-third of the tube. The shortening will enable the divers to dive a greater distance before striking the bottom. Wide-tube pipettes are more difficult to keep the water inside when shortened. About 10–30 cm of wire may be needed to offset the buoyancy of the plastic pipette.

Divide students into groups of three. Have them make one Cartesian diver for their group to use. Demonstrate the construction process and how to fill the pipette with water to adjust its buoyancy.

Provide students with a copy of the Lab Activity Report found on the Teacher's Resources CD-ROM for students to record their observations and conclusions.

LAB ACTIVITY
Making a Cartesian Diver

Materials
Safety goggles
2-L plastic bottle with cap
Plastic pipette
Insulated bell wire
Water
Permanent marker
Metric ruler

▲ **STEP 2** Prepare the pipette for diving.

▲ **STEP 5** Remove some water from the pipette bulb.

BACKGROUND

Pressure affects water and air differently. A plastic bottle filled with air can easily be squeezed with your fingers so that it dents. The pressure applied to the outside of the bottle is transferred to the air inside, squeezing it into a smaller space. However, the same bottle filled with water cannot be squeezed so that it dents. The water inside is not as compressible as air.

What will happen if a bottle that has both air and water inside is squeezed? You can find out by constructing and testing a Cartesian (kahr-TEE-zhuhn) diver.

PURPOSE

In this activity, you will construct a Cartesian diver and experiment with the effects of changing water pressure.

PROCEDURE 🥽

1. Copy the chart in Figure 12-32 on a sheet of paper.

2. Use a ruler and marking pen to place marks 5 mm apart on the bulb of the pipette. Then, wrap 10 to 12 coils of insulated bell wire around the pipette. The pipette will be your model diver.

3. Put on safety goggles. Fill a 2-L plastic bottle almost to the top with water.

4. Squeeze the bulb of the pipette and insert the tip into the water. Relax the bulb to draw water into the pipette. Fill the pipette with water.

5. Squeeze the pipette bulb to empty out a small amount of water. Shake it gently to move the air bubble into the bulb.

6. Place the pipette into the bottle and cap it. In your chart, record the level of the water in the pipette.

266

Teaching Options

❗ FAST FACTS *Diving Science*

A Cartesian diver descends to the bottom of a closed bottle when pressure on the outside of the bottle is increased. As pressure is increased on the outside of the bottle, the increased pressure is transferred through the water. The increased pressure pushes water into the diver. The water that is pushed into the diver compresses the air trapped within it. The compressed air displaces less water than before. As a result, the buoyant force on the diver is reduced because, as Archimedes' principle states, the buoyant force acting on a submerged or partially submerged object is equal to the weight of the displaced fluid. Because the reduced buoyant force is less than the weight of the diver, the diver sinks. When the pressure on the compressed air in the diver decreases, the air expands, displaces more water, and as a result, increases the buoyant force acting on the diver so that it rises.

▲ STEP 7 Squeeze the bottle containing the diver.

▲ STEP 9 Try to control the depth of the diver.

7. Squeeze the bottle with your hands. If the pipette dives to the bottom, go to Step 8. If the pipette does not dive to the bottom, remove it and squeeze a bit more water out of it. Place it back in the bottle and see if it will dive.

8. Observe and record the water level inside the pipette. Squeeze the bottle to make the diver go to the bottom. Does the water level inside the diver change? If so, how much does it change? Record your observations in the table.

9. Try to make the diver stop halfway to the bottom. Observe and record the water level again.

Comparison of Cartesian Diver Depth with Air Chamber Volume		
Depth	Air Chamber Mark	Change (mm)
Surface		
Middle		
Bottom		

▲ Figure 12-32 Copy this chart and use it to record your observations.

CONCLUSIONS

1. OBSERVE: What happened to the Cartesian diver when you squeezed the bottle?

2. INFER: What happens to the pressure created by squeezing the bottle?

3. ANALYZE: What caused the diver to dive?

4. HYPOTHESIZE: Based on your observations, how does a submarine stay underwater?

5. HYPOTHESIZE: Why does a diver's ears hurt when he or she descends underwater?

Tips for Using Technology

Databases Have students use database software to record their comparisons of diver depth with air-chamber volume. Databases allow students to enter and edit information, store and organize a lot of information easily, and search for specific information. Databases also allow students to arrange information by putting it in a specific order and to present information by using special layouts. Students can use database software to share their data with the class. Have students use the Database Planner on the Teacher's Resources CD-ROM to plan their databases.

• *TEACHING RESOURCES* •

Teacher's Resources CD-ROM

Lab Activity Report: Study Tools, pp. 16–17

Laboratory Activity Rubric: Teaching Tools, p. 8

Database Planner: Study Tools, p. 22

TROUBLESHOOTING: Students may have trouble adjusting the buoyancy of their divers. Make sure that the diver just floats on the surface of the water before sealing it into the bottle. Have students fill their bottles and seal the diver inside at a sink before taking the bottle back to their workstations. Make sure that they return to the sink to open the bottles.

EXPECTED OUTCOMES: Students will observe that the size of the air pocket in the diver will decrease and the diver will descend as outside pressure is increased.

LAB HINT: To make adjusting the buoyancy of the divers easier, fill an aquarium with enough water to float the pipettes and permit students to adjust the buoyancy of the divers in the aquarium.

3 Conclude the Lab

1. **OBSERVE:** It descended.
2. **INFER:** The pressure increases.
3. **ANALYZE:** As the increased pressure was transferred through the water, water entered the diver and compressed the air trapped within the diver. The compressed air displaced less water. As a result, the density of the diver increased, causing the diver to sink.
4. **HYPOTHESIZE:** The air in its holding tanks is compressed or expanded to change the buoyant force on the submarine.
5. **HYPOTHESIZE:** The pressure on the outside of the eardrum is greater than the pressure on the inside of the eardrum.

Use the Laboratory Activity Rubric on the Teacher's Resources CD-ROM to assess students' lab activities. Fill in the rubric with the additional information below. For this activity, students should have:

- performed the activity according to the procedure and filled in the chart with data collected during the activity.

- correctly answered the questions in complete sentences.

4 Extend the Lab

Have students adjust the pressure so that the diver remains suspended. Have them discuss the relationship between the weight of the diver and the buoyant force on it. (They are equal but act in opposite directions.) Lead students to identify the two forces as balanced forces.

Challenges (pp. 268–270)

Chapter Summary

Review Before students begin the Challenges, review the summary with them. If time permits, have students work in pairs. Give each pair of students one summary point to describe in their own words.

STUDY HINT Assign each student a different figure in the chapter. Tell students to study the figure and its caption. Then, allow them time to explain each figure to the class.

Key Term Challenges

MATCHING

1. newton (12-3)
2. lubricants (12-5)
3. vacuum (12-6)
4. pressure (12-7)
5. barometer (12-8)
6. force (12-1)
7. Bernoulli's principle (12-8)
8. friction (12-4)
9. terminal velocity (12-6)
10. gravity (12-2)

FILL IN

11. friction (12-4)
12. Bernoulli's principle (12-8)
13. terminal velocity (12-6)
14. gravity (12-2)
15. gravity (12-2)
16. friction (12-5)

Chapter Summary

Lesson 12-1
- A **force** is a push or a pull.
- A force always acts in a certain direction.
- Weight is a force.

Lesson 12-2
- All objects are attracted to each other because of the force of **gravity** between them.
- The gravitational force between two objects depends on their masses and the distance between them.

Lesson 12-3
- The **newton** (N) is the metric unit of force.
- Weight is a force that is measured in newtons.

Lesson 12-4
- **Friction** is a force that opposes the motion of an object. There are different types of friction.

Lesson 12-5
- Friction can be reduced by changing sliding friction to rolling friction and by using a **lubricant.**

Lesson 12-6
- **Air resistance** is the force that opposes objects moving through air.

Lesson 12-7
- **Pressure** is the amount of force acting on a unit area of a surface.
- Pressure can be changed by changing the amount of force acting on an area or by changing the area on which a force acts.

Lesson 12-8
- **Air pressure** is caused by the weight and movement of air molecules.
- Air pressure is measured with a **barometer.**
- **Bernoulli's principle** says that as the speed of a fluid increases, its pressure decreases.

Lesson 12-9
- Water pressure is caused by the weight and movement of water molecules.
- Water pressure increases with depth.

268

Key Term Challenges

air pressure (p. 262)   gravity (p. 248)
air resistance (p. 258)   lubricants (p. 256)
balance forces (p. 246)   newton (p. 252)
barometer (p. 262)   pressure (p. 260)
Bernoulli's principle (p. 262) terminal velocity (p. 258)
force (p. 246)   unbalanced forces (p. 246)
friction (p. 254)   vacuum (p. 258)

MATCHING Write the Key Term from above that best matches each description.

1. metric unit of force
2. substances used to reduce friction
3. empty space
4. force divided by area
5. instrument for measuring air pressure
6. push or pull
7. deals with the pressure of moving fluids
8. force opposing motion
9. maximum velocity for a falling object
10. force of attraction between all objects

FILL IN Write the Key Term from above that best completes each statement.

11. When you walk across the floor, there is _____ between your shoes and the floor.
12. As water flows faster through pipes, the pressure on the pipes from the water is decreased. This is an example of _____.
13. When skydivers jump from an airplane, they will reach _____ before landing.
14. Objects fall to the ground because of the force of _____.
15. Earth's force of _____ pulls objects in the direction of Earth's center.
16. The wheels on a skateboard help to reduce _____.

Teaching Options

PREPARING STUDENTS FOR STANDARDIZED TESTS

Reading Strategy: Remind students to read the question and answer choices carefully to avoid giving a wrong answer to a question. Tell them to be sure that they understand what the question is asking. Have them look for keywords such as *all*, *not*, or *none*.

Writing Strategy: Tell students to always make sure that they answer both parts of a two-part question.

Interpreting Visuals: Explain to students that the first step in reading a diagram is to identify the subject or topic of the diagram. Often this information is presented in the title. Sometimes knowing the title is all students need to answer a question.

ESL/ELL STRATEGY

Restating in Your Own Words English-language learners will benefit from restating processes in their own words. Have pairs of students work together to summarize each process in the lesson.

Content Challenges <u>TEST PREP</u>

MULTIPLE CHOICE Write the letter of the term or phrase that best completes each statement.

1. As the wheels of a bicycle move over the surface of the road, they must overcome
   a. sliding friction.
   b. gravity.
   c. rolling friction.
   d. air resistance.

2. An apple falls to the ground because of
   a. a magnetic force.
   b. an electric force.
   c. a gravitational force.
   d. a force of friction.

3. If it takes 25 N to push a car at a constant speed, the friction between the road and the car's tires is
   a. 20 N.
   b. 25 N.
   c. 15 N.
   d. 5 N.

4. A hydraulic lift uses force from
   a. weight.
   b. fluid pressure.
   c. air pressure.
   d. friction.

5. A submarine rising to the surface of the water from deep in the ocean is going from
   a. low pressure to high pressure.
   b. high pressure to low pressure.
   c. zero pressure to high pressure.
   d. high pressure to zero pressure.

6. A ball rolls off a table and hits the floor. The force that caused the ball to hit the floor is
   a. gravity.
   b. friction.
   c. air pressure.
   d. a magnetic force.

7. As an airplane lands, it lowers the flaps under the wings in order to
   a. increase air resistance.
   b. decrease air resistance.
   c. increase the plane's weight.
   d. decrease the plane's weight.

8. A barometer is used to measure
   a. friction.
   b. air pressure.
   c. gravity.
   d. water pressure.

9. An airplane can fly because the pressure on the plane's wings is
   a. greater on the top of the wings.
   b. zero.
   c. greater on the bottom of the wings.
   d. equal on both sides of the wings.

TRUE/FALSE Write *true* if the statement is true. If the statement is false, change the underlined term to make the statement true.

10. Weight is a <u>force</u>.

11. Pressure is equal to force <u>times</u> area.

12. Near Earth's surface, all objects fall in the direction of Earth's <u>center</u>.

13. Air pressure <u>decreases</u> as altitude increases.

14. Moving a box across the floor is an example of <u>rolling</u> friction.

15. A spring scale measures <u>weight</u>.

16. Air resistance <u>slows</u> the speed of a falling object.

17. A lubricant reduces <u>pressure</u>.

18. <u>Friction</u> slows down the motion of objects.

19. The upward force acting on an airplane's wing is called <u>drag</u>.

20. At Earth's surface, a feather falls more slowly than a rock because of <u>air resistance</u>.

Content Challenges

MULTIPLE CHOICE
1. c (12-5)
2. c (12-2)
3. b (12-5)
4. b (12-9)
5. b (12-9)
6. a (12-2)
7. a (12-8)
8. b (12-8)
9. c (12-8)

TRUE/FALSE
10. true (12-2)
11. false; divided by (12-7)
12. true (12-2)
13. true (12-8)
14. false; sliding (12-4)
15. true (12-3)
16. true (12-6)
17. false; friction (12-5)
18. true (12-4)
19. false; lift (12-8)
20. true (12-6)

ALTERNATIVE ASSESSMENT

Discussing Forces Draw a line across the board. Ask students what force caused the chalk to mark the board. (friction) Ask on what object the force was acting. (the piece of chalk) Ask in what direction the force was acting. (opposite the motion of the chalk)

PORTFOLIO ASSESSMENT

Making Student Portfolios
Portfolio Assessment is designed to evaluate a student's performance over an extended period of time. Students can demonstrate their comprehension of the concepts in this chapter by making a portfolio. The Chapter Self-Check, the Big Idea Planner, and the Weekly Journal are some of the reproducibles on the Teacher's Resources CD-ROM that students can include in their portfolios. You can use the Portfolio Assessment Rubric also found on the Teacher's Resources CD-ROM to assess students' portfolios.

Concept Challenges

WRITTEN RESPONSE

1. **DESCRIBE:** Air pressure decreases with altitude. Because the force of moving air molecules causes air pressure, and most of the air in Earth's atmosphere is concentrated near Earth's surface, air pressure is greatest near Earth's surface and decreases with altitude. (12-8)
2. **HYPOTHESIZE:** Possible answer: Movement would be impossible. (12-4)
3. **PREDICT:** More pressure is exerted when you stand on your toes than when you stand flat-footed. Because pressure is force per unit area, your weight acting over the smaller area of your toes causes a greater pressure than your weight acting on the larger area of your feet. (12-7)
4. **EXPLAIN:** Astronauts experience apparent weightlessness when they are in orbit. (12-2)
5. **EXPLAIN:** A hydraulic system is filled with a liquid and has two movable pistons. When a force is exerted on the small piston, the pressure travels through the enclosed fluid in the system to the large piston. The pressure acting on the large piston causes a much larger upward force on the large piston than the original downward force on the small piston. (12-9)

INTERPRETING A DIAGRAM (12-8)

6. drag
7. lift
8. thrust
9. lift
10. drag and gravity

Chapter Project Wrap-Up

AIR LIFT

Students' projects can be exhibited around the classroom. Have students launch their planes simultaneously and observe the planes' motion. They can use watches with second hands to time the flights. You can use the Individual Activity Rubric found on the Teacher's Resources CD-ROM to assess students' projects. Fill in the rubric with the additional information below. For this project, students should have:

- designed and constructed a paper airplane that flies for at least 4 seconds.
- illustrated the three forces acting on the paper airplane in flight: lift, weight, and drag.

Content Challenges TEST PREP

WRITTEN RESPONSE Complete the exercises and answer each of the following questions in complete sentences.

1. **DESCRIBE:** What effect does altitude have on air pressure? Explain.
2. **HYPOTHESIZE:** How would the world be different if there were no friction?
3. **PREDICT:** Will you exert more pressure when you stand on your toes or when you stand flat-footed? Explain.
4. **EXPLAIN:** Why does an astronaut need to learn about apparent weightlessness?
5. **EXPLAIN:** Use the principle of hydraulics to explain how some car jacks work.

INTERPRETING A DIAGRAM Use Figure 12-33 to answer the following questions.

6. What force tends to slow the airplane's forward motion?
7. What force opposes the force of gravity?
8. What force is provided by the airplane's engines?
9. Bernoulli's principle helps to explain what force acting on the airplane?
10. What two forces tend to take over when the airplane prepares to land?

▲ **Figure 12-33** Forces acting on an airplane in flight

270

Teaching Options

• TEACHING RESOURCES •

Teacher's Resources CD-ROM

Key Term Review: Chapter 12, p. 16

Chapter 12 Test: pp. 17–19

Individual Activity Rubric: Teaching Tools, p. 5

Chapter Self-Check: Teaching Tools, p. 11

Big Idea Planner: Study Tools, pp. 11–12

Weekly Journal: Study Tools, p. 19

Portfolio Assessment Rubric: Teaching Tools, p. 10

Chapter 13 Motion

PLANNING GUIDE

◆ **TEACHING THE CHAPTER** This chapter should take approximately 6–9 days to complete instruction and assessment.

	Skills and Features	Projects and Activities	Achieve Science Literacy	Meet Individual Needs
Chapter 13 Opener p. T271	DEMONSTRATE	• Chapter Project		
Lesson 13-1 **What are motion and speed?** pp. T272–T273 Standard: B2a	EXPLAIN, COMPARE, CALCULATE • Building Math Skills • Hands-On Activity	• Extending the Lesson • More on the Web	• Study Hint • Reading Strategy • Ongoing Assessment	CD-ROM Venn Diagram
Lesson 13-2 **What are velocity and acceleration?** pp. T274–T275 Standards: B2a, B2c	INFER, COMPARE, ANALYZE • Building Math Skills • Hands-On Activity	• More on the Web • Lab Challenge	• Study Hint • Reading Strategy	• Reteach CD-ROM Enrichment Activity
Lesson 13-3 **What is momentum?** pp. T276–T277 Standards: B2a, B2c	DESCRIBE, CALCULATE, IDENTIFY • Designing an Experiment • Integrating Life Science	• More on the Web	• Study Hint • Writing Hint	• Reteach CD-ROM Designing an Experiment
Big Idea **How does safety technology change momentum?** pp. T278–T279 Standards: B2a, B2c	RESEARCH, COMMUNICATE, ANALYZE • Science Log: Writing Activity	• Big Idea Online • Close Activity	• Tips for Using Technology	• ESL/ELL Strategy CD-ROM Big Idea Planner
Lesson 13-4 **What is Newton's first law of motion?** pp. T280–T281 Standards: B2a, B2b, B2c	EXPLAIN, PREDICT, IDENTIFY • Investigate • Interpreting Visuals • Real-Life Science	• More on the Web • Integrating Earth Science • Cooperative Learning	• Study Hint • Ongoing Assessment	• ESL/ELL Strategy
Lesson 13-5 **What is Newton's second law of motion?** pp. T282–T283 Standards: B2a, B2c	CALCULATE, DESCRIBE, IDENTIFY • Interpreting Visuals • People in Science	• Cooperative Learning • More on the Web	• Study Hint • Ongoing Assessment	• Reteach CD-ROM Enrichment Activity

Planning Guide continues on next page.

	Skills and Features	Projects and Activities	Achieve Science Literacy	Meet Individual Needs
Lesson 13-6 **What is Newton's third law of motion?** pp. T284–T285 Standard: B2a	CONTRAST, CLASSIFY, STATE • Investigate • Web InfoSearch	• Cooperative Learning	• Study Hint • Reading Strategy • Ongoing Assessment	• Reteach CD-ROM Cause-and-Effect Diagram
Lab Activity **Investigating Newton's Second and Third Laws** pp. T286–T287 Standards: B2a, B2c	OBSERVE, ANALYZE • Set-Up Time: 15 min • Lab Time: 30 min	• Extend the Lab Activity	• Tips for Using Technology	• ESL/ELL Strategy CD-ROM Lab Activity Report Database Planner
Chapter 13 Challenges pp. T288–T290	• Chapter Summary • Key Term Challenges • Content Challenges • Concept Challenges	• Chapter Project Wrap-Up	• Study Hint • Preparing Students for Standardized Tests	• ESL/ELL Strategy CD-ROM Chapter Self-Check Weekly Journal

Teacher Notes

Chapter 13 Motion

▲ **Figure 13-1** It is the motion of a roller coaster that makes it fun.

A roller coaster can be a lesson in motion. Imagine that everywhere you look, things are moving. Standing on the ground, you see that the roller coaster is moving. If you were in one of the cars, you would feel the motion and see things move past at very fast speeds. Now, suppose you were sitting next to a friend. Throughout the ride, your friend stays beside you. Has your friend moved? Have you?

▶ How can you tell when you or something around you is moving?

Contents

UNIT 5: Force, Motion, And Energy **271**

Teaching Options

ASSESSMENT PLANNER

For assessment in the Student Edition, see the following pages:

Content Assessment
Checking Concepts: pp. 273, 275, 277, 281, 283, 285
Thinking Critically: pp. 273, 275, 277, 281, 283, 285
Interpreting Visuals: pp. 281, 283
Chapter Challenges: pp. 288–290

Alternative Assessment
Building Skills: pp. 273, 275
Web InfoSearch: p. 285
Science Log: p. 279

Performance-Based Assessment
Hands-On Activity: pp. 273, 275
Designing an Experiment: p. 277
Lab Activity: pp. 286–287

• TEACHING RESOURCES •

Teacher's Resources CD-ROM
Lesson Review: Ch. 13, pp. 2, 3, 5, 7, 8, 10
Enrichment: Ch. 13, pp. 4, 9
Key Term Review: Ch. 13, p. 11
Chapter 13 Test: pp. 12–13
Laboratory Manual: pp. 69–72

Chapter 13
Motion

Chapter Overview

In this chapter, students will learn about motion, explain what motion is, differentiate between instantaneous speed and average speed, and calculate average speed. They will differentiate between speed, velocity, and acceleration, calculate acceleration, and describe how to calculate momentum. They will also describe Newton's first law of motion, second law of motion, and third law of motion.

About Figure 13-1 As the roller coaster in the picture moves quickly around the curve, its passengers will experience momentum, inertia, and a change in velocity. Their bodies will try to keep going in a straight line, but safety devices in the roller coaster keep them inside the turning cars. The passengers will feel the pull of various forces, including the pull of gravity as they plunge over each hill.

Answer Possible answers: You see objects moving past you or objects change position relative to some fixed object or place.

Linking Prior Knowledge

For this chapter, students should recall:

- the definition of mass (Lesson 1-2).
- the difference between balanced and unbalanced forces (Lesson 12-1).
- that weight is a force measured in newtons (Lesson 12-3).

Chapter Project

NEWTON'S LAWS OF MOTION EXPERIMENT BOOKLET

MATERIALS: several marbles (at least two of equal size), ruler with a center groove, tape, paper, marking pens

As students read the chapter, they should consider how to demonstrate each law of motion, using the materials listed above. Have groups of students create an experiment booklet that describes and shows diagrams of at least three different experiments about motion. Invite students to demonstrate their experiments and to share their booklets with the class.
learning styles: visual, tactile

1 Introduce

STUDY HINT Before beginning this lesson, have students study Figure 13-2. Have them answer the question and explain their answers.

Linking Prior Knowledge Ask students how they know if an object has moved. Ask students how they know they are moving when they are passengers in a car. Point out that they only know because their position changes relative to some object that is not moving, such as a tree, a building, or the road.

2 Teach

Demonstration Have volunteers measure the length of the classroom in meters. Record the measurement on the board. Ask a volunteer to walk the length of the classroom. Using a stopwatch or clock with a second hand, measure how long it takes the student to walk the length of the classroom. On the board, calculate the student's average speed by dividing the distance by the time. Point out that in this example, the average speed is represented in meters per second.
learning styles: visual, auditory

Reinforcement Give students several practice problems for calculating average speed using meters and kilometers, and time in seconds, minutes, and hours. Make sure that students give the appropriate SI units with their answers, such as 35 km/h. Point out that a number, such as 20, tells nothing about speed without units.
learning styles: auditory, logical/mathematical

Answers to questions

1 EXPLAIN: Possible answers: Its position has changed relative to some fixed object or place.

2 CALCULATE: Neither, they are traveling at the same speed.

3 CALCULATE: 90 km/h

13-1 What are motion and speed?

Objective
Explain that an object is moving if it changes position relative to some object that is not moving.

Key Terms
motion: change in position relative to some fixed object or place

speed: distance traveled per unit of time

average speed: total distance traveled divided by the time it takes to travel that distance

Motion Has anything like this ever happened to you? You see a mail truck parked in front of your house. You run upstairs to get a letter you want to mail. When you come out, the truck is no longer in front of your house. It is now in front of the house next door.

▲ **Figure 13-2** (Top) The position of the mail truck is in front of the house. (Bottom) How do you know the truck has moved?

272

This example shows that you do not have to see something move to know that motion has taken place. **Motion** is a change in position relative to some fixed object or place. Because you know that your house did not move, the mail truck must have changed position relative to your house.

1 EXPLAIN: How do you tell something moved?

Motion and Speed When dealing with moving objects, you often want to know how fast something moves. In other words, you want to know how far something travels and how long it takes to make the trip. **Speed** is the distance traveled per unit of time. The SI unit for distance is the meter. Kilometer is often used to measure long distances. The equation for finding speed is shown below.

speed = distance ÷ time

2 CALCULATE: Which is moving faster, a car traveling 150 km in 3 hours or one traveling 100 km in 2 hours?

Average Speed When traveling in a car, you can tell how fast you are moving at any given instant by looking at the speedometer. This tells your *instantaneous speed*. You might travel at the same speed for some time. During this time, you would be traveling at a *constant speed*.

▲ **Figure 13-3**
An automobile speedometer

However, you seldom travel at the same speed for an entire trip. You probably speed up, slow down, and stop many times. When you finally get to your destination, you can find your average speed for the trip. **Average speed** is the total distance traveled divided by the time it takes to travel that distance.

average speed = total distance ÷ time

3 CALCULATE: If you traveled 360 km in 4 hours, what was your average speed?

Teaching Options

QUICK CONVERSIONS	
Distance	
Metric/SI	**English**
1 km	0.62 mi
50 km	31 mi
90 km	56 mi
100 km	62 mi
150 km	93 mi
200 km	124 mi
360 km	223 mi

✓ CHECKING CONCEPTS

1. A change in position relative to some fixed object or place is called _____.
2. The equation for calculating speed is _____ divided by time.
3. The speedometer of a car tells you your _____ speed.
4. Speed that does not change is called _____ speed.
5. The total distance traveled divided by the time it takes to travel that distance gives you the _____.

THINKING CRITICALLY

6. COMPARE: Explain the difference between instantaneous speed and average speed.
7. CALCULATE: If a car travels at an average speed of 90 km/h, how long will it take the car to travel 360 km?
8. INFER: A car makes a trip of 400 km in 4 hours. The return trip takes $3\frac{1}{2}$ hours. What can you infer about the average speed of the car on two trips?

BUILDING MATH SKILLS

Analyzing a Graph The distance an object travels in a certain amount of time can be shown on a graph. Figure 13-4 shows distance and time for a car trip. How far does the car travel in 5 hours? What was the average speed of the car during that time? What was the speed of the car between the second and third hours? What was the car's average speed during the first 2 hours? The last 2 hours?

▲ Figure 13-4

Hands-On Activity

MEASURING AVERAGE SPEED

You will need a book, a piece of cardboard, a metric ruler, a watch or clock with a second hand, and a marble.

1. You will need about 1.5 m of floor space. Fold the piece of cardboard lengthwise. Place one end of the cardboard on a book so that the end of the cardboard is raised 1.5 cm off the floor.
2. Hold the marble at the raised end of the cardboard. Release the marble and let it roll down the center of the cardboard and across the floor.
3. Measure the distance in centimeters the marble rolls from the end of the cardboard in 2 seconds. Record your measurement in a table.
4. Repeat Steps 2 and 3 three more times. Record your measurements.

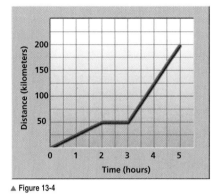

▲ STEP 2 Allow the marble to roll down the slope.

Practicing Your Skills

5. OBSERVE: What was the average distance the marble rolled in 2 seconds?
6. CALCULATE: What was the average speed of the marble?

CHAPTER 13: Motion **273**

• TEACHING RESOURCES •

Teacher's Resources CD-ROM
Lesson Review: Chapter 13, p. 2
Venn Diagram: Study Tools, p. 10

READING STRATEGY Comparing and contrasting information can help students understand and remember what they read. Students can use the Venn Diagram found on the Teacher's Resources CD-ROM to show the similarities and differences between instantaneous speed and average speed. learning styles: visual, auditory

3 Assess

✓ CHECKING CONCEPTS ANSWERS

1. motion
2. distance
3. instantaneous
4. constant
5. average speed

THINKING CRITICALLY ANSWERS

6. COMPARE: Instantaneous speed is the speed at any given instant, while average speed is an average of the different speeds traveled over a distance.
7. CALCULATE: 4 hours
8. INFER: The average speed during the return trip was greater.

4 Close

BUILDING MATH SKILLS ANSWERS

Analyzing a Graph 200 km; 40 km/h; 0 km/h; 25 km/h; 75 km/h. Make sure that students understand that between the second and third hours, the car did not cover any distance.
learning styles: visual, logical/mathematical

Hands-On Activity

MEASURING AVERAGE SPEED

TIME: 20–30 minutes
PURPOSE: observing, calculating

Practicing Your Skills Answers

5. OBSERVE: Average distances will vary. Each group can find their average distance by adding the distances from their four trials together and dividing by 4.
6. CALCULATE: Average speeds will vary. Each group can find their average speed by dividing total distance by 8 s.

1 Introduce

✎ **STUDY HINT** Before beginning this lesson, have students read the captions and the art labels that appear in the lesson. This will allow them to preview what is to come.

Linking Prior Knowledge Ask students for examples of acceleration. Make sure that students understand that when something is traveling at a constant speed and in the same direction, it is not accelerating.

2 Teach

Demonstration Have two volunteers come to the front of the room. Have the two students walk around the room in opposite directions. Tell the class to assume that both volunteers are walking at the same speed. Ask students what is different about their velocities. Make sure that students know that velocity is speed and direction. **learning styles: visual, kinesthetic**

Discussion Ask students what the difference between velocity and acceleration is. (Velocity is speed and direction, while acceleration is a change in velocity, or a change in speed or direction.) Then, describe how to measure acceleration by using the problem on pages 274 and 275 as an example. **learning styles: auditory, logical/mathematical**

Answers to questions

▶ INTERPRET: 90 km/h east; 90 km/h west

▶ INFER: Its direction is changing.

▶ INFER: 0 m/sec

📖 **READING STRATEGY** Students may be confused by the use of the term *acceleration*. In everyday language, people use *acceleration* to mean "speeding up" and *deceleration* to mean "slowing down." In science, *acceleration* refers to speeding up, slowing down, or changing direction. Have students look up *accelerate*, *acceleration*, and *decelerate* in a dictionary. Point out that one of the definitions of *acceleration* is "a change in velocity." Remind students that velocity includes both speed and direction.

13-2 What are velocity and acceleration?

Objective
Differentiate between speed, velocity, and acceleration.

Key Terms
velocity (vuh-LAHS-uh-tee): speed and direction
acceleration (ak-sehil-uh-RAY-shuhn): rate of change in velocity over time

Speed, Velocity, and Direction When you move from place to place, you travel at different speeds. However, to describe your motion, you need to know more than just your average speed. You must also know the direction in which you are moving. Speed and direction describe **velocity**. An example of velocity is 90 km/h west. Your speed is 90 km/h and your direction is west. Together, these two values describe your velocity.

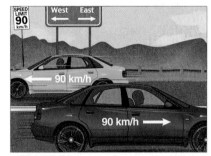

▲ **Figure 13-5** The cars are traveling at the same speed but their velocities are different.

▶ INTERPRET: In Figure 13-5, what is the velocity of the red car? The blue car?

Acceleration When a car changes speed or direction, it is accelerating. **Acceleration** is a change in velocity. When a car speeds up, its velocity is changing. The car is accelerating. When a car slows down, it is also changing velocity. It is

274

accelerating. When a car goes around a curve or turns a corner, it is changing direction. A change in direction is a change in velocity. The car is accelerating. The initial velocity of the runners in Figure 13-6 is 0. So, as soon as they move down the track, they are accelerating.

◀ **Figure 13-6** From the minute they leave the starting blocks, these runners are accelerating.

▶ INFER: Why is a car accelerating when it turns a corner?

Measuring Acceleration Acceleration describes how fast the velocity of a moving object is changing. To find average acceleration, you must know the change in velocity and the time it takes for the change to occur. The equation for finding acceleration in a straight line is shown here.

acceleration = change in velocity ÷ time, or
acceleration = (final velocity − initial velocity) ÷ time

Suppose a car is stopped at a red light. When the light turns green, the car accelerates to a speed of 150 m/sec. The car takes 10 seconds to reach this speed. What is its acceleration?

acceleration = (150 m/s − 0 m/s) ÷ 10 s
acceleration = 150 m/s ÷ 10 s
acceleration = 15 m/s/s

Teaching Options

❗ FAST FACTS
Negative Acceleration

An object's average acceleration will be a negative number if the object is slowing down. For example, a car is traveling at a speed of 100 m/s and slows to 20 m/s in 10 s. Its acceleration is 20 m/s − 100 m/s ÷ 10 s. The acceleration of the car is a deceleration of 8 meters per second per second.

RETEACH

Accelerating Quickly A car's ability to accelerate quickly is an important safety feature. In some circumstances, the quicker a car can accelerate, the less chance there is of an accident. Ask students: *What kind of circumstances would require the ability to accelerate quickly?* (when turning onto a highway, merging from an entrance ramp onto a road, or passing another vehicle) **learning styles: auditory, linguistic**

The acceleration is 15 meters per second per second, or 15 m/s². This means that the car's velocity increases 15 m/s every second.

 INFER: What is the initial velocity of the car?

✓ CHECKING CONCEPTS

1. What is velocity?
2. What does velocity tell you about a moving object?
3. What is a change in velocity called?
4. What is the formula for finding acceleration?
5. How do you find a change in velocity?

💡 THINKING CRITICALLY

6. COMPARE: A truck is traveling east on a highway at 80 km/h. What is its velocity?
7. ANALYZE: A highway speed limit is 90 km/h. Is this average speed or instantaneous speed? Explain.

BUILDING MATH SKILLS

Interpreting Tables When an object falls through the air, it accelerates as it falls. When it is released, its speed is zero. As it falls, its speed increases. Figure 13-7 shows how the speed of a falling object changes.

ACCELERATION OF A FALLING OBJECT

Time (seconds)	Velocity (m/sec downward)
0	0
1	9.8
2	19.6
3	29.4
4	39.2
5	0

▲ Figure 13-7

What is the object's acceleration from 0 to 1s? From 0 to 3s? From 2s to 4s? Based on your calculations, what can you say about the acceleration of a falling object?

⚛ Hands-On Activity

CHANGING ACCELERATION

You will need a large rubber band, a toy car, a metric ruler, a pencil, and paper.

1. Place the car on the floor. Hold one end of the rubber band on one side of the car while a partner holds the other end.
2. Pull the rubber band and the car a distance of 5 cm, as shown in the picture. Release the rubber band. Measure and record the distance the car travels.
3. Repeat Steps 1 and 2 two more times. The first time pull the rubber band and car back 10 cm. The second time pull them back 15 cm.

Practicing Your Skills

4. ANALYZE: What supplied the force to make the car accelerate?
5. OBSERVE: How did increasing the force affect the acceleration of the car?

▲ STEP 2 Making the car accelerate

MORE ON THE WEB

Fast Cars Have students visit www.conceptsandchallenges.com to read about some of the fastest accelerating vehicles ever made. Have students make a list of the five fastest-accelerating cars.

QUICK CONVERSIONS

Distance	
Metric/SI	English
9.8 m	10.72 yd
19.6 m	21.43 yd
29.4 m	32.15 yd
39.2 m	42.87 yd

• TEACHING RESOURCES •

💿 **Teacher's Resources CD-ROM**
Lesson Review: Chapter 13, p. 3
Enrichment: Chapter 13, p. 4
Laboratory Manual
Lab. Challenge: What happens when an object accelerates? pp. 69–72

Reinforcement Give students several practice problems for calculating acceleration. Include various final velocities, initial velocities, and times. You might choose numbers that are easy to divide. Remind students to give the appropriate SI units with their answers. learning styles: auditory, logical/mathematical

3 Assess

✓ CHECKING CONCEPTS ANSWERS

1. speed and direction
2. its speed and direction
3. acceleration
4. change in velocity/time or (final velocity − initial velocity)/time
5. Subtract the initial velocity from the final velocity.

💡 THINKING CRITICALLY ANSWERS

6. COMPARE: 80 km/h east
7. ANALYZE: Possible answers: instantaneous speed because if it was average speed, cars would be able to exceed the limit some of the time

4 Close

BUILDING MATH SKILLS ANSWERS

Interpreting Tables 9.8 m/s/s [change in velocity/time]; 9.8 m/s/s [(29.4 m/s)/3 s]; 9.8 m/s/s [(39.2 m/s − 19.6 m/s)/2 s]; It is constant or does not change until the object lands. learning styles: visual, logical/mathematical

Hands-On Activity

CHANGING ACCELERATION

TIME: 20–30 minutes

PURPOSE: analyzing, observing

SAFETY TIP: Caution students to be careful when using rubber bands. You might want students to wear safety goggles.

Practicing Your Skills Answers

4. ANALYZE: pulling and releasing the rubber band
5. OBSERVE: Increasing the force increased the acceleration.

1 Introduce

STUDY HINT Before beginning this lesson, have students study Figures 13-9 and 13-10. Ask students to explain what is happening in both figures.

Linking Prior Knowledge Have students review the definition of *mass* (Lesson 1-2).

2 Teach

Demonstration Use a marble and cardboard ramp like the one in the activity on page 273. With one end of the cardboard raised 1.5 cm off the floor, release the marble at the top of the cardboard. Have a volunteer mark where the marble stops with a piece of masking tape. Ask students to predict how far the marble will travel if the end of the cardboard is raised to 5 cm. Then, release the marble at 5 cm off the floor. Ask students what caused the marble to travel farther. Point out that the mass of the marble did not change, but because the marble had a higher velocity, it had more momentum. **learning styles: visual, logical/mathematical**

Discussion Ask students why football players, especially linemen, are usually big. (because they have to block the other team) Explain that linemen need a lot of momentum in order to stop the players on the other team. The greater their mass, the more momentum the football players have. **learning styles: visual, auditory**

Answers to questions

▶ **IDENTIFY:** mass and velocity

▶ **CALCULATE:** 200 kg-m/s

▶ **INFER:** Three spheres will fly out from the other end.

WRITING HINT When students design an experiment, encourage them to write in complete sentences. This helps improve the quality of their writing. It also helps others to be able to understand and conduct their experiment.

13-3 What is momentum?

Objective
Define and describe how to calculate momentum.

Key Terms
momentum: a property of all moving objects

law of conservation of momentum: total momentum of any isolated system always remains the same

Momentum Picture a bowling ball with a mass of 5 kg rolling toward the pins at the end of the alley. In the next alley, a ball with a mass of 8 kg is rolling toward the pins with the same velocity. Which ball do you think is likely to knock over more pins? If you answered the ball with the greater mass, you are correct. As long as the two bowling balls are moving with the same velocity, the ball with the greater mass will strike the pins with greater energy. The combined effect of the mass and velocity of an object is momentum. **Momentum** is a property of all moving objects.

▲ **Figure 13-8** Momentum is transferred from the ball to the pins.

▶ **IDENTIFY:** What two factors determine momentum?

Calculating Momentum The momentum of an object can be found by multiplying its mass by its velocity.

$$\text{momentum} = \text{mass} \times \text{velocity}$$

Let's look at the two bowling balls described earlier. Suppose the velocity of each ball is 20 m/s. Find the momentum of the 5-kg ball.

$$5 \text{ kg} \times 20 \text{ m/s} = 100 \text{ kg-m/s}$$

The 5-kg ball has a momentum of 100 kg-m/s. Now find the momentum of the 8-kg ball.

$$8 \text{ kg} \times 20 \text{ m/s} = 160 \text{ kg-m/s}$$

The 8-kg ball has a momentum of 160 kg-m/s. The ball with more momentum will knock over more pins.

▶ **CALCULATE:** Find the momentum of a 10-kg object moving at a velocity of 20 m/s.

Conservation of Momentum When one moving object collides with another object, the motion of both objects changes. For example, when a bowling ball strikes the pins, the bowling ball slows down. It loses momentum. The pins move. The pins gain momentum. The important thing to remember is that the total momentum of the ball and the pins remains the same. In any isolated system, momentum can be transferred but cannot be lost. This is the **law of conservation of momentum.**

Figure 13-9 demonstrates this idea. If a sphere on the left is swung and strikes the row of spheres, a sphere on the other end will move. The momentum of the first sphere is transferred through the row of spheres to the sphere at the other end. No momentum is lost.

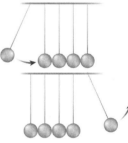

▲ **Figure 13-9** Momentum is conserved as it is transferred from sphere to sphere.

Teaching Options

RETEACH

Increasing Momentum If possible, take students to an area where it is safe to run. Use masking tape to mark a line on the floor in the middle of the room. This will be the finish line. Ask a volunteer to walk at a normal pace toward the line. Yell "stop" when the volunteer reaches the line. Have another student use masking tape to mark where the volunteer stopped. Then, have the same volunteer run toward the line. Make sure that the student does not slow down before you yell "stop." Have students observe the difference between the two places where the volunteer stopped. Point out that the volunteer's mass was the same in both trials, but the momentum was different because the velocity was different.
learning styles: visual, kinesthetic

Now suppose two spheres are allowed to strike the remaining row of spheres. Figure 13-10 shows what would happen.

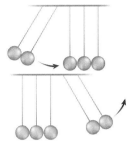

▲ Figure 13-10 Momentum is still conserved.

▶ INFER: What will happen if three spheres are allowed to strike the row of spheres?

✓ CHECKING CONCEPTS

1. The momentum of an object depends on its _____ and its velocity.

2. When a bowling ball strikes the pins, the ball _____ momentum.

3. If the velocity of a car traveling at 50 km/h changes to 30 km/h, the momentum of the car will _____.

4. If several objects are traveling at the same velocity, the object with the greatest mass will have the greatest _____.

💡 THINKING CRITICALLY

5. **DESCRIBE:** Describe the momentum changes that might occur when a large glass marble rolling across a smooth surface makes a direct hit on a smaller glass marble that is not moving.

6. **CALCULATE:** Find the momentum of a 25-kg mass moving with a velocity of 25 m/sec.

DESIGNING AN EXPERIMENT

Design an experiment to solve the following problem. Include a hypothesis, variables, a procedure, and a type of data to study.

PROBLEM: How can you show that the momentum of an object is related to its mass?

 **Integrating Life Science**

TOPICS: birds, bones

ANIMALS AND MOMENTUM

Most birds can fly. Their hollow bones make for a light body weight. The most difficult parts of a bird's flight are the takeoff and the landing. Both require a change in momentum.

▲ Figure 13-11 Flamingos during takeoff

In order to take off, birds have to build up enough speed so that the lift from their wings is greater than their body weight. Small birds can take off with a hop and a flap of their wings. Larger birds, like the flamingos in Figure 13-11, have more of a problem. Because they have more mass, they need more momentum to reach the speed needed to take off. They do this by running as fast as they can while they flap their wings.

For some birds, landing is even harder than taking off. Birds cannot just stop flapping their wings. They would drop like a stone. Instead, they twist and spread their wings so that they slow down gradually. In other words, they lose momentum slowly enough to allow them to make a safe landing.

Thinking Critically Why do large birds need more momentum than small birds do in order to take off?

• TEACHING RESOURCES •

💿 **Teacher's Resources CD-ROM**
Lesson Review: Chapter 13, p. 5
Designing an Experiment: Study Tools, p. 14
Designing an Experiment Rubric: Teaching Tools, p. 7

---

3 Assess

✓ CHECKING CONCEPTS ANSWERS

1. mass
2. loses
3. decrease
4. momentum

💡 THINKING CRITICALLY ANSWERS

5. **DESCRIBE:** Possible answers: Momentum is transferred from the large marble to the small marble, the large marble loses momentum or its momentum decreases, and the small marble gains momentum or its momentum increases.

6. **CALCULATE:** 625 kg-m/sec

4 Close

DESIGNING AN EXPERIMENT

Use the Designing an Experiment Rubric on the Teacher's Resources CD-ROM to assess students' experiments. Fill in the rubric with the additional information below. For this assignment, students should have:

- formed a hypothesis, named variables, designed a procedure, and collected and recorded data.
- included, in the procedure, a method to measure the momentum of objects of different mass.

◈ **Integrating Life Science**

TOPICS: birds, bones

ANIMALS AND MOMENTUM

Life-Science Connection Birds gain enough momentum to fly because of the physical features that they have. Wings, hollow bones, feathers, strong chest muscles, and streamlined bodies are some of the features that make flight possible. One or two of these features alone is not enough for a bird to fly. Some groups of birds, such as ostriches, have feathers and wings, but cannot fly. Ostriches hold their wings away from their bodies for balance, while their powerful leg muscles give them momentum for running on land.

Thinking Critically Answer
They need more momentum to overcome their greater body weight.

The Big Idea

(pp. 278–279)

1 Introduce

Objective Students will think of some safety devices that protect people in moving vehicles or in sports. Students will choose a piece of safety gear to draw and describe in their Science Logs.

Linking Prior Knowledge Have students review what they learned about transferring momentum.

Ask students what safety gear they have used or know about. (various helmets, kneepads, elbow pads, air bags) List the safety gear on the board. Ask volunteers to share experiences in which safety gear protected them. Point out that many safety devices help protect people by changing momentum.

2 Teach

Discussion After students have read the article, ask them how safety devices change a moving object's momentum. Have them review the captions. Then, ask volunteers to explain how momentum is slowed in each example.
learning styles: visual, auditory

Use the background information in Fast Facts to help guide students in choosing a piece of safety gear for their Science Logs.

THE BIG IDEA ONLINE

How does safety technology change momentum? Have students research their Science Log Writing Activity at www.conceptsandchallenges.com. You can have students organize their log by completing the Big Idea activity online. Students may post their work in the Online Classroom Database for others to read.

Reinforcement Students can also use the Big Idea Planner or Big Idea Science Log Entry found on the Teacher's Resources CD-ROM.

◆ *Integrating Technology*

THE Big IDEA

How does safety technology change momentum?

Momentum is a property of all moving objects. An object's momentum can be found by multiplying its mass by its velocity. Many safety devices, such as automobile airbags and protective helmets, are designed to decrease an object's momentum gradually. They do this by changing the velocity—and thus the momentum—of the moving object over as long a time as possible. This is what the mattress does. Physicists use the term *impulse* to describe change in momentum over a given period of time.

Think about how an automobile airbag works. When a person moving at a high speed hits an inflated airbag, the person's momentum is transferred to the particles of air in the bag. The particles speed up. The person loses velocity, and momentum, slowly and safely. If that person were to hit a hard object, such as the dashboard, that person's velocity and momentum would change all at once, perhaps resulting in serious injury.

Protective headgear, such as a bicycle helmet, has some sort of protective lining. When a hard object strikes the helmet, the lining absorbs much of the shock. The object loses momentum slowly, so the effect of its impact on your head is less severe.

Look at the photos and text that appear on these two pages. Then, follow the directions in the Science Log to find out more about "the big idea." ✦

Stuntperson's Fall Cushion
The trick to falling safely from a tall building is to land on something that moves with you when you hit it. The air-filled "pillow" at the base of the building acts like the airbag in a car. It allows the stuntperson to lose momentum slowly and safely.

278

Teaching Options

! FAST FACTS *Elasticity in Safety Gear*

Mountain Climbing Mountain climbers have many kinds of ropes to choose from. These ropes need to support their weight and also need to have some elasticity in them. An elastic rope is better than a rigid rope because an abrupt yank on a rigid rope could injure the climber.

Circus High-Wire Act At the circus, the net under the high wire is another example of safety gear. The elasticity in the net protects the performers from injury by gradually reducing their momentum.

ESL/ELL STRATEGY

Defining Words To help students define unfamiliar words, have them write each word on one side of an index card. On the other side of the card, have students define the word. English-proficient students can help English-language learners study the words and their definitions.

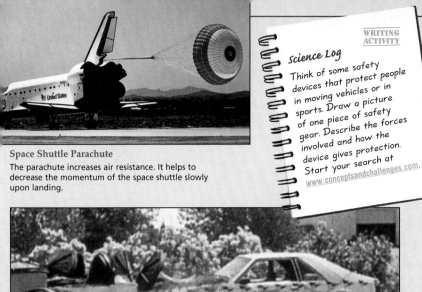

Space Shuttle Parachute
The parachute increases air resistance. It helps to decrease the momentum of the space shuttle slowly upon landing.

WRITING ACTIVITY

Science Log

Think of some safety devices that protect people in moving vehicles or in sports. Draw a picture of one piece of safety gear. Describe the forces involved and how the device gives protection. Start your search at www.conceptsandchallenges.com.

Highway Crash Barriers
These plastic containers are filled with sand. If a car hits such a container, much of the car's momentum is transferred to the sand. The car loses momentum much more slowly than it would if it ran directly into the concrete.

Car Airbags
Airbags give accident victims more time to slow down than they would have if they crashed into something hard such as a steering wheel.

CHAPTER 13: Motion **279**

3 Assess

Use the Writing Activity Rubric on the Teacher's Resources CD-ROM to assess students' Science Logs. Fill in the rubric with the additional information below. For this assignment, students should have:

- drawn a picture of one piece of safety gear.
- described the forces involved and how the device provides protection.

4 Close

Making a Poster Have groups of students make a poster that combines their individual drawings and descriptions. Encourage students to add pictures of safety gear from magazines to their posters. Students' posters should show safety gear, the forces involved, and how the gear provides protection. Have volunteers present their posters to the class.
learning styles: visual, linguistic

Tips for Using Technology

Creating Graphics and Illustrations Most graphics-creation software uses similar tools to create graphics and illustrations. Some of these tools include shape tools, text tools, and pencil tools. Shape tools allow students to create different types of shapes in their illustrations. The bucket tool allows students to fill a shape or an object that they have created with a color. The text tool allows students to enter text into their illustrations. The pencil, or drawing, tool allows students to draw in freehand in their illustrations.

• TEACHING RESOURCES •

Teacher's Resources CD-ROM
Big Idea: Chapter 13, p. 6
Big Idea Planner: Study Tools, pp. 11–12
Big Idea Science Log Entry: Study Tools, p. 13
Writing Activity Rubric: Teaching Tools, p. 9

1 Introduce

🔍 INVESTIGATE

TIME: 10–15 minutes

PURPOSE: Students will predict and then test how an increase in mass will affect the amount of force needed to move that mass.

MATERIALS: 2-m long board, toy car, meterstick, 2 pieces of modeling clay

PROCEDURE: Have students work in groups of three to complete this activity. One student can lift the board until the car starts to move and hold the board at that height. Another student can measure and record the height of the board. The third student can retrieve the car and add clay to it. Make sure that students hold the boards at the height at which the car just begins to move and do three trials: car only, car with one piece of clay, and car with two pieces of clay. **learning styles: visual, tactile**

THINK ABOUT IT: inertia; gravity

✏️ **STUDY HINT** Before beginning this lesson, read the lesson objective with students. Then, have them review the Key Term and its definition.

Linking Prior Knowledge Have students review what they learned about balanced and unbalanced forces (Lesson 12-1). Ask volunteers to describe these forces and their effects on objects.

2 Teach

Discussion Ask students: *What is the tendency of an object to stay at rest called?* (inertia) Point out that inertia also applies to moving objects. Ask students to describe what happens when they are in a moving vehicle that stops suddenly. Make sure that students understand that their bodies keep moving forward until an unbalanced force stops them. Seat belts and air bags are some forces that can stop them.
learning styles: auditory, linguistic

Answers to questions

1️⃣ IDENTIFY: inertia

2️⃣ PREDICT: It will remain at rest.

3️⃣ EXPLAIN: because your body has inertia

13-4 What is Newton's first law of motion?

🔍 INVESTIGATE

Observing Newton's First Law
HANDS-ON ACTIVITY

1. Lay a board about 2 m long on the floor. Place a toy car at one end of the board.
2. Slowly lift the end of the board with the toy car until the car starts to move. Hold the end of the board at that level. Have a partner measure the height to which the end of the board was raised. Record this measurement.
3. Press a piece of modeling clay on the top of the toy car to increase its mass. Repeat Steps 1 and 2.
4. Predict how adding a second piece of clay to the car will affect the height you will have to raise the board before the car moves. Record your prediction. Repeat Steps 1 and 2 to test your prediction.

THINK ABOUT IT: What keeps the car from moving along the board as it begins to rise? What outside force finally causes the car to move?

STEP 2

Objective

Describe Newton's first law of motion.

Key Term

inertia (ihn-UR-shuh): tendency of an object to stay at rest or in motion

Inertia Place a book on your desk. Does the book move? Unless you push the book, it will remain where you put it without moving. Imagine a spacecraft moving through space. When the engines are turned off, the spacecraft will coast through space at the same speed and in the same direction. The book and the spacecraft have **inertia**. Because of inertia, an object at rest tends to stay at rest. An object in motion tends to keep moving at a constant speed in a straight line.

1️⃣ IDENTIFY: What causes a book on a table to remain at rest?

Newton's First Law Newton's first law of motion explains how inertia affects moving and nonmoving objects. Newton's first law states that an object will remain at rest or move at a constant speed in a straight line unless it is acted on by an unbalanced force.

According to Newton's first law, an unbalanced force is needed to move the book on your desk. You could supply the force by pushing the book. An unbalanced force is needed to change the speed or direction of the spacecraft. This force could be supplied by the spacecraft's engines.

2️⃣ PREDICT: According to Newton's first law of motion, what will happen to an object at rest if no unbalanced force acts on it?

Effects of Inertia You can see the effects of inertia everywhere. In baseball, for example, to overcome inertia a base runner has to "round" the bases instead of making sharp turns.

◀ **Figure 13-12**
The base runner is fighting to overcome inertia as he rounds the bases.

280

Teaching Options

🔷 INTEGRATING EARTH SCIENCE

Exploring Space A spacecraft can be sent to explore distant planets because of inertia. Once the spacecraft is launched with enough force to overcome Earth's gravity, inertia keeps it going. Space has very few molecules to cause friction or air resistance. Because unbalanced forces have very little effect on the spacecraft's inertia, the spacecraft will continue to move in a straight line through space until it is affected by gravity or the force of a rocket engine. Have students research the forces involved in landing a spacecraft on the surface of another planet. Ask volunteers to share what they learned with the class. **learning styles: auditory, linguistic**

COOPERATIVE LEARNING

Explaining Crash-Test Dummies
Have pairs of students explain how crash-test dummies illustrate inertia. **learning styles: interpersonal, linguistic**

ONGOING ASSESSMENT

Wearing Seat Belts Ask volunteers to explain why seat belts could be called anti-inertia belts. (A seat belt fights the inertia of the passenger.) **learning styles: auditory, linguistic**

As a more familiar example of inertia, think about riding in a car. You and the car have inertia. If the car comes to a sudden stop, your body tends to keep moving forward. When the car starts moving again, your body tends to stay at rest. You move forward because the car seat exerts an unbalanced force on your body.

3 EXPLAIN: Why do you keep moving forward when the car in which you are riding stops?

✓ CHECKING CONCEPTS

1. In space, a spacecraft with its engines turned off will move with constant speed in the same _____.

2. A book will not move by itself because it has _____.

3. A book will remain at rest unless it is acted on by an _____ force.

4. When a car stops suddenly, your body tends to keep moving _____.

5. Newton's first law explains how inertia affects moving and _____ objects.

Real-Life Science
SPORTS AND INERTIA

Inertia plays an important role in most sports. Look at the soccer ball in Figure 13-14. It's just sitting there. Because of inertia, it will stay there until some force causes it to move. As you can see, that force is on the way! Think of the goalkeeper waiting for a ball to be sent speeding toward the goal. If his reflexes are quick enough, he will be able to change the speed or direction of any ball coming his way.

A downhill skier deals with inertia throughout her run. At the top of the mountain, she has to push off to overcome her own inertia. Once she gets moving, inertia will tend to keep her moving down the slope in a straight line. But the course has a lot of curves! So she has to use all of her skill to twist and turn down the course. At the end, she must overcome inertia to bring herself to a safe stop.

Try to think of a sport or game that does not require a person to deal with inertia. Even a checker will stay on a square until someone moves it to another square!

Thinking Critically Who would have to overcome more inertia to move the ball, a golfer or a soccer player?

▲ Figure 13-14 The inertia of the soccer ball is about to be changed by an unbalanced force.

💡 THINKING CRITICALLY

6. PREDICT: Push a roller skate across a smooth surface. Will the skate keep moving when you stop pushing? Explain.

INTERPRETING VISUALS

Look at Figure 13-13 to answer the following question.

7. In terms of inertia, explain what happens to the coin when the card is flicked away.

▲ Figure 13-13

---

3 Assess

✓ CHECKING CONCEPTS ANSWERS

1. direction
2. inertia
3. unbalanced
4. forward
5. nonmoving

💡 THINKING CRITICALLY ANSWER

6. PREDICT: Yes; An object in motion tends to keep moving.

INTERPRETING VISUALS ANSWER

7. The coin falls into the glass because the coin tends to stay at rest when the card is flicked away.

---

4 Close

Real-Life Science
SPORTS AND INERTIA

Real-Life Connection Unbalanced forces are needed to overcome inertia. In sports, the force comes from people's muscles. Ask students to think about riding a bicycle as you describe the forces involved. The force of muscles pushing down on the pedals or pushing off the ground overcomes the inertia of the bicycle and makes it move. Inertia will keep it moving even if pedaling stops. According to Newton's first law, the bicycle will continue moving unless it is acted on by an unbalanced force. The forces of friction and air resistance slow down the bicycle, and it will eventually stop unless pedaling continues. If the surface is not level, the rider will notice the force of gravity affecting the bicycle's inertia.

Discussion If a bicycle is going up or down an incline, gravity is an unbalanced force that affects its inertia. Ask students to describe how gravity affects the inertia of a bicycle going up a hill and down a hill. Then, ask them to name the forces that affect the inertia of objects in bicycling and other sports.
learning styles: auditory, linguistic

Thinking Critically Answer
The soccer player would have to overcome more inertia because a soccer ball has more mass than a golf ball.

MORE ON THE WEB

Viewing Inertia Have students view animations of real-life inertia and answer questions about inertia at www.conceptsandchallenges.com.

• TEACHING RESOURCES •

💿 **Teacher's Resources CD-ROM**
Lesson Review: Chapter 13, p. 7

ESL/ELL STRATEGY

Illustrating Inertia To better understand how inertia is related to motion, have students draw diagrams illustrating an object at rest and an object in motion. Then, have students explain their diagrams orally.

1 Introduce

✏️ **STUDY HINT** Have students write the formula for Newton's second law in their notebooks ($F = m \times a$). As students read the lesson, they should identify each variable in the equation and describe the relationship between the variables.

Linking Prior Knowledge Remind students that a force is a push or a pull (Lesson 12-1).

2 Teach

Demonstration Use two cardboard ramps like the one in the Hands-On Activity on page 273. Raise one end of both pieces of cardboard 1.5 cm off the floor. Fold two index cards in half and place one in front of each ramp with the fold up. Hold a marble at the top of one ramp and a table tennis ball at the top of the other ramp. Have students predict which card will be moved farther. Release the marble and ball. Ask students what caused the card that was hit by the marble to travel farther. Make sure that students understand that the marble has more mass than the table tennis ball and, therefore, has more momentum and exerts more force. **learning styles: visual, auditory**

Discussion Ask students to think of times that they have tried to push or pull a heavy object. Remind students that inertia kept the object in place until they could push or pull with enough force to create an unbalanced force. Ask what would happen if someone helped push or pull the object. Make sure that students understand that the other person provides added force.

Reinforcement Make sure that students understand that according to Newton's second law, an object will begin to move, speed up, slow down, change direction, or come to a stop only when a force acts on the object. **learning style: auditory**

13-5 What is Newton's second law of motion?

Objective
Describe Newton's second law of motion.

Key Term
newton: SI unit of force

Effects of Unbalanced Forces Unbalanced forces cause acceleration. When an unbalanced force acts on an object, the motion of the object is changed. If the object is at rest, the force makes it move. If the object is in motion, the force changes its velocity. Any change in velocity is an acceleration.

▶ 1 **DESCRIBE:** What effect does an unbalanced force have on a moving object?

Force, Mass, and Acceleration The amount by which an object accelerates depends on three things. They are the size of the force, the direction in which the force acts, and the mass of the object. Look at Figure 13-15. If two forces act on the same object, the greater force will produce more acceleration than the smaller force.

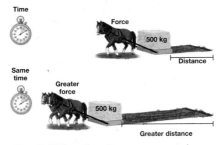

▲ **Figure 13-15** When acting on the same mass, a greater force moves the mass a greater distance over the same period of time.

Now look at Figure 13-16, which shows the same amount of force applied to two objects with different masses. The object with the smaller mass will be accelerated more than the object with the larger mass.

282

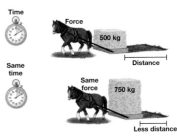

▲ **Figure 13-16** When acting on different masses, the same force will move the smaller mass a greater distance over the same period of time.

▶ 2 **IDENTIFY:** What three factors affect the acceleration of an object?

Newton's Second Law Newton's second law describes the relationship among force, mass, and acceleration. Newton's second law states that the unbalanced force acting on an object is equal to the mass of the object times its acceleration. Newton's second law can be described by this equation.

$$F = m \times a.$$

In this equation, F is the force, m is the mass, and a is the acceleration. When the mass is measured in kilograms and the acceleration is measured in meters per second per second, the force is measured in newtons (N). A newton is the SI unit of force. An unbalanced force of 1 N will accelerate a mass of 1 kg at 1 m/s^2. One newton of force is equal to one kilogram-meter per second per second (1 $kg\text{-}m/s^2$).

▶ 3 **DEFINE:** What is 1 N of force equal to?

Using Newton's Second Law If no friction is involved, how much force would you have to apply to 10-kg object to make it accelerate at a rate of 45 m/s^2? This may seem like a difficult problem at first. However, if you use the equation for Newton's second law, it becomes easy.

Teaching Options

RETEACH

Reviewing Units Write the terms *mass, acceleration,* and *force* on the board. Ask students to name the units for each of these terms. (mass: gram and kilogram; acceleration: meters or kilometers per second per second; force: newton) **learning styles: visual, logical/mathematical**

COOPERATIVE LEARNING

Describing Newton's Second Law Have students make up word problems based on Newton's second law. Have students switch problems with a partner and solve each other's problems. **learning styles: auditory, linguistic**

$$F = m \times a$$
$$F = 10 \text{ kg} \times 45 \text{ m/s}^2$$
$$F = 450 \text{ kg-m/s}^2$$

You would have to apply a force of 450 kg-m/s², or 450 N.

4 CALCULATE: How much force is needed to give a 5-kg mass an acceleration of 20 m/s²?

✓ CHECKING CONCEPTS

1. When it is acted on by an unbalanced force, an object will _____.
2. When an unbalanced force acts on an object at rest, the object will _____.
3. A change in velocity is called _____.
4. A large force will cause _____ acceleration than a small force.
5. Newton's second law of motion states that force is equal to _____ times acceleration.
6. The _____ is a unit of force equal to 1 kg-m/s².

People in Science

SIR ISAAC NEWTON (1642–1727)

Isaac Newton was born in England on December 25, 1642. He was a physicist, an astronomer, and a mathematician. At the age of 45, Newton published his theories of motion and gravity. Newton's great book is usually called the *Principia*. It is considered one of the most important works in the history of science.

In the *Principia*, Newton explained his three laws of motion and his theory of gravitation. Newton also invented a branch of mathematics called calculus to help predict motion using his three laws. Newton also made many important discoveries about light and color.

Newton was a professor of mathematics at Cambridge University and a member of the Royal Society. He was knighted by Queen Anne in 1705. Newton once said about himself, "If I have seen further than others, it is because I have stood on the shoulders of giants."

Thinking Critically What do you think Newton meant by his statement?

▲ Figure 13-18 Sir Isaac Newton

🔆 THINKING CRITICALLY

Use the equation F = m × a to answer the following questions. Show your calculations.

7. CALCULATE: What force is needed to accelerate a 2-kg mass at rest to a rate of 1 m/s²?
8. With what force would you have to push a 50-kg skater to increase the skater's speed by 2 m/s²?

INTERPRETING VISUALS

Look at Figure 13-17 to answer the question.

9. Will the acceleration of the piano be greater in A or in B? Use Newton's second law of motion to explain your answer.

▲ Figure 13-17

Answers to questions

1 DESCRIBE: The force changes its velocity.

2 IDENTIFY: size of the force, the direction in which the force acts, and the mass of the object

3 DEFINE: one kilogram-meter per second per second (1 kg-m/s²)

4 CALCULATE: 100 kg-m/s²

3 Assess

✓ CHECKING CONCEPTS ANSWERS

1. accelerate
2. move
3. acceleration
4. more
5. mass
6. newton

💡 THINKING CRITICALLY ANSWERS

7. CALCULATE: F = 2 kg × 1 m/s² = 2 kg-m/s² or 2 N
8. F = 50 kg × 2 m/s² = 100 kg-m/s² or 100 N

INTERPRETING VISUALS ANSWER

9. The acceleration will be greater in B because a larger force is applied.

4 Close

People in Science

SIR ISAAC NEWTON (1642–1727)

Real-Life Connection Newton made one of the first reflecting telescopes. It used a concave mirror to reflect light instead of convex lenses to refract light. The large telescopes of today are reflecting telescopes.

One of Newton's discoveries about light and color was that sunlight is made up of all colors. Students might be interested to know that although Newton did not publish his book until he was in his forties, he made most of his discoveries when he was in his twenties.

Thinking Critically Answer
Possible answer: He accomplished what he did because he built his work upon the work of other scientists.

MORE ON THE WEB

Calculating Have students visit www.conceptsandchallenges.com to perform an online experiment to calculate force.

ONGOING ASSESSMENT

Calculating Force Give students some practice problems to calculate force. Provide them with different masses and accelerations. Ask students: *What force would have to be applied to a mass of xx to make it accelerate at a rate of xx?* learning styles: auditory, logical/mathematical

• TEACHING RESOURCES •

⊙ **Teacher's Resources CD-ROM**
Lesson Review: Chapter 13, p. 8
Enrichment: Chapter 13, p. 9

13-6 (pp. 284–285)

1 Introduce

🔍 INVESTIGATE

TIME: 10–15 minutes

PURPOSE: Students will use a balloon to observe Newton's third law of motion.

MATERIAL: balloon

PROCEDURE: Encourage students to point the balloon away from other students as they hold the balloon at arm's length and release it. Students should carefully observe the direction the opening of the balloon faces before it is released and the direction it travels after it is released. Have students pick up their balloons. Students might want to repeat the activity. Make sure that students picked up their own balloons.

THINK ABOUT IT: The balloon flew or moved through the air. Possible answers: Air pushed out of the balloon and pushed the balloon forward. The balloon moved in the opposite direction than the neck of the balloon was facing.

✏️ **STUDY HINT** Before beginning this lesson, have students write the lesson objective in their notebooks. As students read the lesson, tell them to write the information that meets the objective.

Linking Prior Knowledge Give students the following scenario: A frog jumps off a lily pad. Ask: *What do you think happens to the lily pad as the frog moves forward?* (The lily pad moves backwards, away from its original position.)

2 Teach

Demonstration Hold a tennis ball at arm's length and drop it. Catch the ball as it bounces off the floor. Point out that the ball hitting the floor is the action force, and the floor pushing back is the reaction force. Holding the tennis ball at the same height, use a small amount of force to throw the ball straight to the floor. Catch the ball as it bounces back. Ask students what happened when the action force was increased. (The reaction force also increased.) Encourage volunteers to repeat this demonstration.
learning styles: visual, kinesthetic

13-6 What is Newton's third law of motion?

🔍 INVESTIGATE

Observing Newton's Third Law
HANDS-ON ACTIVITY

1. Blow up a balloon. Hold the neck of the balloon tightly to prevent air from escaping.
2. Hold the balloon at arm's length and observe which direction the neck of the balloon is facing.
3. Release the balloon and observe what happens.

THINK ABOUT IT: What happened when you released the balloon? What do you think caused this to happen? How was the behavior of the balloon related to the direction in which the neck of the balloon was facing?

STEP 2

Objective
Describe Newton's third law of motion.

Key Terms
action force: force acting in one direction
reaction force: force acting in the opposite direction

Action and Reaction Forces always act in pairs. The two forces act in opposite directions. When you push on an object, the object pushes back with an equal force. When the basketball player in Figure 13-19 shoots the ball, he pushes against it. This is the **action force.**

▲ **Figure 13-19** When the player exerts a force on the ball, the ball exerts an equal force on him.

284

The ball pushes back against the player with a force of the same size. This **reaction force** will cause the wheelchair to move backwards. Notice that the two forces act on different objects. The action force acts on the ball. The reaction force acts on the player.

▶ **1 CONTRAST:** How are action and reaction forces different?

Newton's Third Law Newton's third law of motion describes action and reaction forces. The law states that for every action force, there is an equal and opposite reaction force. Imagine hitting a tennis ball. The racket exerts a force on the ball. This is the action force. The ball exerts an equal and opposite force on the racket. This is the reaction force.

◀ **Figure 13-20** The tennis racket is about to exert an action force on the ball.

Teaching Options

❗ FAST FACTS

Rockets in Space

A rocket in space changes velocity because of action and reaction forces. The action force occurs when the engines burn fuel and produce gases. The engines push these gases out the back of the rocket. Pushing the gases is the action force. The gases pushing back is the reaction force that moves the rocket. The rocket does not need air molecules in space to push.

RETEACH

Relating Sports to Newton's Third Law Explain to students how Newton's third law can help athletes. If a basketball player is aware that increasing velocity during a jump can make her jump higher because of the increase in the reaction force, than she can train towards increasing the strength in her jumping ability.

Newton's third law explains how many sports injuries are caused. The more force you use to hit a tennis ball, the more reaction force your arm receives from the racket. Every time your feet hit the ground when you are running, the ground hits your feet with an equal and opposite force.

▶ **STATE:** What does Newton's third law of motion state?

Balloons and Rockets Newton's third law explains how balloons and rocket engines work. When the neck of an inflated balloon is released, the stretched rubber material pushes against the air in the balloon. The air rushes out of the neck of the balloon. The action of the air rushing from the balloon pushes against the balloon, moving it in the opposite direction.

When rocket fuel is burned, hot gases are produced. These gases expand rapidly and are forced out of the back of the rocket. This is the action force. The gases exert an equal and opposite force on the rocket itself. This is the reaction force. This force pushes the rocket upward.

▲ **Figure 13-21** Action and reaction forces during liftoff

▶ **INFER:** What effect would blowing more air into a balloon have on the motion of the balloon when released?

✔ CHECKING CONCEPTS

1. Forces always act in _____.
2. A table exerts an upward _____ on objects resting on the table.
3. For every action force, there is an equal and _____ reaction force.
4. In a rocket engine, the _____ force pushes the rocket upward.
5. Action forces and reaction forces always act on _____ objects.

💡 THINKING CRITICALLY

6. **INFER:** An object resting on a table weighs 100 N. With what force is the object pushing on the table? With what force is the table pushing on the object?
7. **CLASSIFY:** When you walk, your feet push against the ground. At the same time, the ground pushes against your feet. Which is the action force? Which is the reaction force?
8. **HYPOTHESIZE:** When you walk, you move forward. Does Earth move in the opposite direction? Explain your answer.

Web InfoSearch

VentureStar In 1996, NASA started plans to develop a replacement for the space shuttle. This replacement, called VentureStar, was to have many improvements over the present shuttle. At present, this project has been postponed. It may be revived in the future.

SEARCH: Use the Internet to find out what types of improvements NASA plans to incorporate in its next generation of space shuttles. What is the X-33? Why does NASA call the VentureStar a Reusable Launch Vehicle? Start your search at www.conceptsandchallenges.com. Some key search words are **X-33, Reusable Launch Vehicle, VentureStar,** and **Lockheed Martin VentureStar.**

Answers to questions

▶ **CONTRAST:** They act in opposite directions.

▶ **STATE:** For every action force, there is an equal and opposite reaction force.

▶ **INFER:** It would move faster and farther.

📖 **READING STRATEGY** Action and reaction forces have a cause-and-effect relationship. Tell students that a cause makes something happen and an effect is what results from the cause. An action force is a cause. A reaction force is the effect. Have students create a cause-and-effect diagram of the action and reaction forces mentioned on pages 284 and 285. Students can also use the Cause-and-Effect Diagram found on the Teacher's Resources CD-ROM.

3 Assess

✔ CHECKING CONCEPTS ANSWERS

1. pairs
2. force
3. opposite
4. reaction
5. different

💡 THINKING CRITICALLY ANSWERS

6. **INFER:** 100 N; 100 N
7. **CLASSIFY:** The action force is your feet pushing against the ground. The reaction force is the ground pushing against your feet.
8. **HYPOTHESIZE:** Possible answer: No; Earth has so much mass compared to a person that the force of a person's feet has very little effect on the movement of Earth.

4 Close

Web InfoSearch

VentureStar Have students use the Internet to find out what types of improvements NASA plans to incorporate in its next generation of space shuttles. Some key search words are **X-33 Reusable Launch Vehicle, VentureStar,** and **Lockheed Martin VentureStar.** Students should begin their search at www.conceptsandchallenges.com.

COOPERATIVE LEARNING

Explaining Sports Have different groups of students pick a sport or an activity and explain to the class how Newton's third law applies to it.

ONGOING ASSESSMENT

Reviewing Newton's Third Law of Motion Ask students: *When you bounce a basketball on the floor, what is the action force?* (the ball pushing against the floor) *What is the reaction force?* (the floor pushing against the ball)

• TEACHING RESOURCES •

💿 **Teacher's Resources CD-ROM**
Lesson Review: Chapter 13, p. 10
Cause-and-Effect Diagram: Study Tools, p. 3

Lab Activity

(pp. 286–287)

1 Prepare the Lab

**Investigating Newton's
Second and Third Laws**

SET-UP TIME: ⏱   **LAB TIME:** ◔

BACKGROUND: A Newton cart is a device that can be used to investigate Newton's second and third laws of motion. In this activity, when stretched rubber bands are released, they propel a film canister off the cart. The canister being pushed off the cart is the action force. A reaction force causes the Newton cart to move in the opposite direction. Because the canister has less mass than the cart, the canister will travel a longer distance than the cart does. The acceleration and therefore the action force of the canister can be increased by using more rubber bands. This will increase the reaction force of the cart, increasing the distance it travels.

PURPOSE: Students will vary the number of rubber bands used to propel a canister off a Newton cart to experiment with the relationship among mass, acceleration, and force.

ALTERNATIVE MATERIALS: When constructing the cart, large wood screws can be substituted for the nails. The canisters can be filled with metal washers or other masses.

SCIENCE SKILLS: Students will **observe** and **measure** the distances that the canister and the cart travel when they cut the string. Then, they will vary the number of rubber bands used to provide force. Students will **analyze** why the cart moved. Then, they will **analyze their data** to **explain** the relationship between the amount of force being applied to the canister and the number of rubber bands used.

ADVANCE PLANNING: Construct the Newton carts from pieces of 1 × 4-in. wood. Cut the wood to 8-in. lengths. (If you purchase wood from a lumberyard, ask to have the wood cut.) Pound nails in the wood as shown in the pictures. Obtain empty film canisters from a store that develops film. You may wish to fill the canisters ahead of time rather than having students fill them in Step 5. You might have students tape the lids to avoid spills.

LAB ACTIVITY
Investigating Newton's Second and Third Laws

Materials
Newton cart
Safety goggles
Plastic drinking straws
3 rubber bands
Film canister
Sand
Meter stick
String
Scissors

▲ **STEP 3** Use drinking straws to make a track.

▲ **STEP 4** Attach a string loop and rubber band to the Newton cart.

BACKGROUND

Newton's second law describes how force, mass, and acceleration are related. The ability of a rocket to take off from Earth's surface and climb into space depends on the generation of enough force. Newton's third law deals with the action-reaction forces at work when a rocket engine lifts the rocket and pushes it into space. Together, these two laws explain how a rocket is launched into space.

PURPOSE 🕹

In this activity, you will experiment with the relationship of mass, acceleration, and force.

PROCEDURE

1. On a separate sheet of paper, make a chart like the one shown in Figure 13-22.

2. Cut three 15-cm pieces of string. Tie the ends of each piece of string to form three loops. Make each loop the same size.

3. On a flat surface, make a track of 20 plastic drinking straws. Lay the straws parallel to each other 4 cm apart.

4. Slip a rubber band through one of the string loops. Slide the rubber band over the two end posts of a Newton cart. Stretch the rubber band until you can slide the string loop over the third post of the cart.

5. Fill a film canister with sand. Place the canister snugly inside the stretched rubber band on the cart.

6. Set the Newton cart on the straws near one end of the track. Point the end of the cart with the single post down the track.

286

Teaching Options

❗ FAST FACTS *Rocket Power*

As a rocket engine burns rocket propellants, pressure builds up inside the engine. The gases formed by the burning rush out of the rocket engine. This creates a force that is exerted on the rocket. The rocket, in turn, exerts an equal force on the gases. The gases have mass, and the speed at which they leave the engine is their acceleration. To generate enough force to reach space, a rocket engine has to eject a large mass of gas at a very high acceleration. The Space Shuttle generates over 30 million newtons of force to travel into space. As it climbs through the atmosphere, flames of hot gases 152-m long stream out of the engines.

ESL/ELL STRATEGY

Filling in Data Charts When filling in a data chart, it may be helpful for English-language learners to add illustrations as well as describe their observations.

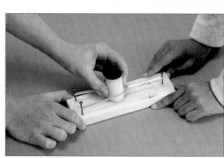
▲ STEP 5 Place the canister on the Newton cart.

▲ STEP 7 Launch the Newton cart down the track of straws.

7. Put on safety goggles. Then, carefully cut the string and quickly pull the scissors out of the way. Measure and record the distances that the cart travels.

8. Repeat the activity using two rubber bands and again using three rubber bands. Each additional rubber band increases the force.

Comparison of Acceleration and Distance for the Newton Cart		
Trial	Number of Rubber Bands	Distance Cart Traveled
1		
2		
3		

▲ Figure 13-22 Copy this chart and use it to record your observations.

CONCLUSIONS

1. OBSERVE: What happened to the cart when you cut the string? What happened to the canister?

2. ANALYZE: What supplies the action force in this activity?

3. ANALYZE: What is the relationship between the amount of force applied and the distance the cart moved?

Tips for Using Technology

Databases Databases allow students to enter and edit information, sort and organize a lot of information easily, and search for specific information. Databases also allow students to arrange information by putting it in a specific order and to present information by using special layouts. Have students use database software to record the distances that the canister and cart travel. Students can use database software to share their data with the class. They can also use the Database Planner found on the Teacher's Resources CD-ROM.

• TEACHING RESOURCES •

Teacher's Resources CD-ROM
Lab Activity Report: Study Tools, pp. 16–17

Laboratory Activity Rubric: Teaching Tools, p. 8

Database Planner: Study Tools, p. 22

2 *Guide the Lab*

PROCEDURE: Discuss the procedure. Demonstrate how to tie the string loops, attach the rubber band to the cart, place the canister on the cart, and cut the string. Discuss data collection, and have students copy the data chart before beginning the activity. Provide students with a copy of the Lab Activity Report found on the Teacher's Resources CD-ROM to record their observations and conclusions.

EXPECTED OUTCOME: The canister (action force) and the cart (reaction force) will move in opposite directions. The canister will travel farther than the cart because it has less mass. Each time the number of rubber bands is increased, the cart travels farther.

LAB HINT: Give students an extra piece of string and have them try the experiment one time for practice before conducting the actual experiment.

3 *Conclude the Lab*

1. **OBSERVE:** The cart rolled across the straws or traveled a distance. The canister traveled in the opposite direction.
2. **ANALYZE:** Possible answers: A force was exerted on the cart when the string was cut or a force was exerted on the canister, which caused a reaction force to move the cart.
3. **ANALYZE:** As more rubber bands were used, the force increased and the canister and the cart moved farther apart.

Use the Laboratory Activity Rubric on the Teacher's Resources CD-ROM to assess students' lab activities. Fill in the rubric with the additional information below. For this activity, students should have:

• performed the activity according to the procedure and filled in the chart with data collected during the activity.

• correctly answered the questions in complete sentences.

4 *Extend the Lab*

Have volunteers use the same laboratory setup to investigate the relationship of mass to force. Make sure that they set up the Newton cart with three rubber bands for each trial but vary the amount of mass inside the canister. Have students present their data and conclusions to the class.

Challenges (pp. 288–290)

Chapter Summary

Review Before students begin the Challenges, review the summary with them. If time permits, have students work in pairs. Give each pair of students one summary point to describe in their own words.

✏ **STUDY HINT** Have students use index cards to create flash cards for each Key Term. Have students write a Key Term on one side of the index card and the definition on the other side. Then, have students work in pairs to review the Key Terms.

Key Term Challenges

MATCHING

1. velocity (13-2)
2. acceleration (13-2)
3. momentum (13-3)
4. newton (13-5)
5. motion (13-1)
6. inertia (13-4)
7. speed (13-1)

FILL IN

8. speed (13-1)
9. momentum (13-3)
10. action (13-6)
11. inertia (13-4)
12. motion (13-1)

Chapter Summary

Lesson 13-1
- **Motion** is a change in position.
- **Average speed** is equal to the total distance traveled divided by the total time for the trip.

Lesson 13-2
- **Velocity** describes the speed and direction of a moving object.
- An object is accelerating when there is change in its velocity.
- To find **acceleration,** you must know the change in velocity and the time for the change to occur.

Lesson 13-3
- **Momentum** is a property of all moving objects.
- The momentum of an object is equal to its mass times its velocity.
- The **law of conservation of momentum** states that momentum may be transferred but cannot be lost.

Lesson 13-4
- **Inertia** is the tendency of an object to remain at rest or in motion.
- Newton's first law of motion states that an object will remain at rest or move at a constant speed in a straight line unless it is acted on by an unbalanced force.
- The effects of inertia can be felt every day.

Lesson 13-5
- Unbalanced forces cause objects to accelerate.
- The acceleration of an object depends on the mass of the object and the size and direction of the force acting on it.
- Newton's second law of motion describes the relationship among force, mass, and acceleration ($F = m \times a$).

Lesson 13-6
- Forces always act in pairs.
- Newton's third law of motion states that for every **action force,** there is an equal and opposite **reaction force.**
- Newton's third law explains how rocket engines work.

288

Key Term Challenges

acceleration (p. 274)
action force (p. 284)
average speed (p. 272)
inertia (p. 280)
law of conservation of momentum (p. 276)
momentum (p. 276)
motion (p. 272)
newton (p. 282)
reaction force (p. 284)
speed (p. 272)
velocity (p. 274)

MATCHING Write the Key Term from above that best matches each description.

1. speed and direction
2. change in velocity
3. mass × velocity
4. unit of force
5. change in position
6. tendency to remain at rest
7. distance traveled per unit of time

FILL IN Write the Key Term from above that best completes each statement.

8. An object's _____ does not include direction.
9. A property of all moving objects is _____.
10. The rush of gases from a rocket engine provides the _____ force.
11. Newton's first law deals with _____.
12. A change in position indicates that _____ has taken place.

Teaching Options

PREPARING STUDENTS FOR STANDARDIZED TESTS

Reading Strategy: Remind students to be careful when reading questions that contain Key Terms such as *acceleration*, *velocity*, and *speed* to avoid confusing the words and their meanings.

Writing Strategy: Tell students to double-check that they record proper decimal points and units when they write answers to problems.

Interpreting Visuals: When using a visual on a test, students can ask themselves what information they need to obtain from the visual in order to answer the question.

ESL/ELL STRATEGY

Restating Events English-language learners will benefit from restating laws and properties in their own words. Have pairs of students work together to explain Newton's laws.

Content Challenges TEST PREP

MULTIPLE CHOICE Write the letter of the term or phrase that best completes each statement.

1. When you move from place to place, you are changing your
   a. mass.
   b. inertia.
   c. position.
   d. speed.

2. An unbalanced force causes a moving object to change
   a. speed.
   b. direction.
   c. neither speed nor direction.
   d. either speed or direction.

3. A car's speedometer tells you
   a. average speed.
   b. instantaneous speed.
   c. acceleration.
   d. velocity.

4. Balanced forces are always opposite in
   a. direction.
   b. size.
   c. size and direction.
   d. size or direction.

5. Velocity includes speed and
   a. acceleration.
   b. inertia.
   c. direction.
   d. force.

6. Average speed is equal to total distance divided by
   a. average distance.
   b. average time.
   c. instantaneous speed.
   d. total time.

7. Action forces and reaction forces are described by Newton's
   a. first law of motion.
   b. second law of motion.
   c. third law of motion.
   d. law of gravitation.

8. According to Newton's second law of motion, force is equal to mass times
   a. acceleration.
   b. speed.
   c. velocity.
   d. inertia.

9. The newton is a unit of
   a. speed.
   b. force.
   c. velocity.
   d. acceleration.

10. Inertia is described by Newton's
    a. first law of motion.
    b. second law of motion.
    c. third law of motion.
    d. law of gravitation.

TRUE/FALSE Write *true* if the statement is true. If the statement is false, change the underlined term to make the statement true.

11. Speed is distance traveled in a given <u>direction</u>.

12. <u>Velocity</u> is found by multiplying mass by velocity.

13. <u>Momentum</u> can be transferred but cannot be lost.

14. Newton's <u>third</u> law of motion deals with inertia.

15. <u>Unbalanced</u> forces always result in motion.

Content Challenges

MULTIPLE CHOICE
1. c (13-1)
2. d (13-4, 13-5)
3. b (13-1)
4. a (13-6)
5. c (13-2)
6. d (13-1)
7. c (13-6)
8. a (13-5)
9. b (13-5)
10. a (13-4)

TRUE/FALSE
11. false; time (13-1)
12. false; Momentum (13-3)
13. true (13-3)
14. false; first (13-4)
15. true (13-4, 13-5)

ALTERNATIVE ASSESSMENT

Defining Key Terms Students may write a science log entry to define each Key Term in this chapter. Students can also write a sentence using each Key Term. Then, students can describe Newton's three laws in their own words.

PORTFOLIO ASSESSMENT

Making Student Portfolios Portfolio Assessment is designed to evaluate a student's performance over an extended period of time. Encourage students to select their own work for inclusion in their portfolios. The Chapter Self-Check, the Lab Activity Report, and the Weekly Journal are some of the reproducibles on the Teacher's Resources CD-ROM that they can include in their portfolios. You can use the Portfolio Assessment Rubric also found on the Teacher's Resources CD-ROM to assess students' portfolios.

Concept Challenges

WRITTEN RESPONSE

1. **CONTRAST:** Average speed is the total distance traveled divided by the total time it takes to travel that distance. Instantaneous speed is speed at any given instant. (13-1)

2. **HYPOTHESIZE:** An object has zero acceleration when it is not changing speed or direction because acceleration is any change in speed or direction. (13-2)

3. **EXPLAIN:** the first car, because it has an acceleration of 15 m/s/s, while the second car has an acceleration of 7.5 m/s/s (13-2)

4. **ANALYZE:** The unbalanced force is acting in the opposite direction of the moving object. Possible answer: The object slows down; If the force was in the same direction, the object would speed up. (13-5)

INTERPRETING A DIAGRAM (13-2)

5. Velocity; It shows both speed and direction.´
6. West
7. East
8. 90 km/h; instantaneous speed
9. 180 km
10. 360 km

Chapter Project Wrap-Up

NEWTON'S LAWS OF MOTION EXPERIMENT BOOKLET

Students' booklets can be exhibited around the classroom. Students can demonstrate their experiments and explain how they prove theories of motion. You can use the Group Activity Rubric found on the Teacher's Resources CD-ROM to assess students' projects. Fill in the rubric with the additional information below. For this project, students should have:

- included three experiments, including diagrams that accurately explain motion, in their booklets.

- organized a logical and neat overall presentation.

Concept Challenges TEST PREP

WRITTEN RESPONSE Complete the exercises and answer each of the following questions in complete sentences.

1. **CONTRAST:** What is the difference between average speed and instantaneous speed?

2. **HYPOTHESIZE:** When does an object have zero acceleration? Explain.

3. **EXPLAIN:** Two cars are stopped at a red light. When the light turns green, both cars accelerate to a speed of 150 m/s. The first car takes 10 seconds to reach this speed. The second car takes 20 seconds. Which car has the greater acceleration?

4. **ANALYZE:** An unbalanced force acts on a moving object. The object slows down. In what direction is the unbalanced force acting? How do you know?

INTERPRETING A DIAGRAM Use Figure 13-23 to answer the following questions.

5. Does this diagram illustrate speed or velocity? Explain.
6. In what direction is the blue car traveling?
7. In what direction is the red car traveling?
8. What speed limit is shown in the diagram? Is this an average speed or an instantaneous speed?
9. If each car continues moving at an average speed of 90 km/h for 2 hours, how far will each car travel?
10. How much distance will separate the cars after 2 hours?

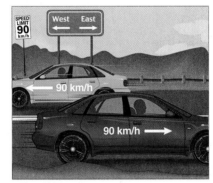

▲ Figure 13-23

Teaching Options

PLANNING GUIDE

◆ **TEACHING THE CHAPTER** This chapter should take approximately 6–9 days to complete instruction and assessment.

	Skills and Features	Projects and Activities	Achieve Science Literacy	Meet Individual Needs
Chapter 14 Opener p. T291	OBSERVE	• Chapter Project		
Lesson 14-1 **What is energy?** pp. T292–T293 Standards: B2a, B3a	ANALYZE, DEFINE, IDENTIFY • Building Math Skills • Integrating Earth Science	• Cooperative Learning • Extending the Lesson • More on the Web	• Study Hint • Reading Strategy	CD-ROM Enrichment Activity
Lesson 14-2 **What are different forms of energy?** pp. T294–T295 Standards: B3a, B3e	LIST, ANALYZE, COMPARE • Designing an Experiment • Science and Technology	• Cooperative Learning • More on the Web	• Study Hint • Reading Strategy • Ongoing Assessment	• ESL/ELL Strategy CD-ROM Enrichment Activity Designing an Experiment
Lesson 14-3 **How does energy change form?** pp. T296–T297 Standard: B3a	ANALYZE, IDENTIFY, DEFINE • Investigate • Interpreting Visuals	• Cooperative Learning • Extending the Lesson • More on the Web	• Study Hint • Reading Strategy	• Reteach CD-ROM Enrichment Activity
Big Idea **What are alternative forms of energy?** pp. T298–T299 Standards: B3a, B3f	RESEARCH, COMMUNICATE, ANALYZE • Science Log: Writing Activity	• Big Idea Online • Close Activity	• Tips for Using Technology	CD-ROM Big Idea Planner
Lesson 14-4 **What is work?** pp. T300–T301 Standard: B3a	HYPOTHESIZE, DESCRIBE, EXPLAIN • Health and Safety Tip • Real-Life Science	• More on the Web	• Study Hint • Writing Hint • Ongoing Assessment	CD-ROM Writing Activity Outline
Lesson 14-5 **How can work be measured?** pp. T302–T303	CALCULATE, LIST, IDENTIFY • Web InfoSearch • Hands-On Activity	• Cooperative Learning • Extending the Lesson • Lab Challenge	• Study Hint • Reading Strategy • Writing Hint • Ongoing Assessment	CD-ROM Enrichment Activity Laboratory Video

Planning Guide continues on next page.

	Skills and Features	Projects and Activities	Achieve Science Literacy	Meet Individual Needs
Lesson 14-6 **What is power?** pp. T304–T305	CALCULATE, DEFINE, IDENTIFY • Designing an Experiment • How Do They Know That?	• Extending the Lesson • More on the Web	• Study Hint • Ongoing Assessment	• Reteach ◉ CD-ROM Enrichment Activity Designing an Experiment
Lab Activity **Studying Energy Changes in a Roller Coaster** pp. T306–T307 Standard: B3a	OBSERVE, ANALYZE, INFER • Set-Up Time: 15 min • Lab Time: 45 min	• Extend the Lab Activity	• Tips for Using Technology	◉ CD-ROM Lab Activity Report
Chapter 14 Challenges pp. T308–T310	• Chapter Summary • Key Term Challenges • Content Challenges • Concept Challenges	• Chapter Project Wrap-Up • Unit Challenge Online	• Study Hint • Preparing Students for Standardized Tests	• ESL/ELL Strategy ◉ CD-ROM Chapter Self-Check Weekly Journal

Teacher Notes

_____

_____

_____

_____

_____

_____

_____

_____

_____

_____

_____

_____

_____

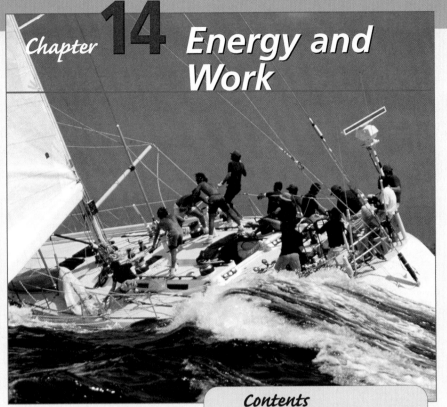

Chapter 14 Energy and Work

▲ **Figure 14-1** A sailboat race is hard work for everyone.

Say the word "sailing" and most people will think about a relaxed afternoon on the water. However, racing sailboats is a different story. This sport involves energy and work. From the minute the boat crosses the starting line until it crosses the finish line, nobody relaxes. The work involves turning cranks and pulling lines, raising and lowering sails. Crew members rush back and forth, straining to get every bit of speed possible from the boat.

▶ What outside force helps to move the sailboat?

Contents

Teaching Options

ASSESSMENT PLANNER

For assessment in the Student Edition, see the following pages:

Content Assessment
Checking Concepts: pp. 293, 295, 297, 301, 303, 305
Thinking Critically: pp. 293, 295, 297, 301, 303, 305
Interpreting Visuals: p. 297
Chapter Challenges: pp. 308–310

Alternative Assessment
Building Skills: p. 293
Web InfoSearch: p. 303
Science Log: p. 299

Performance-Based Assessment
Hands-On Activity: p. 303
Designing an Experiment: pp. 295, 305
Lab Activity: pp. 306–307

• TEACHING RESOURCES •

Teacher's Resources CD-ROM
Lesson Review: Ch. 14, pp. 2, 4, 6, 10, 11, 13
Enrichment: Ch. 14, pp. 3, 5, 7, 8, 12, 14
Key Term Review: Ch. 14, p. 15
Chapter 14 Test: pp. 16–17
Laboratory Manual: pp. 73–76

Laboratory Video
Segment 14: Calculating Work

Chapter 14

Energy and Work

Chapter Overview

In this chapter, students will learn that the two basic kinds of energy are potential energy and kinetic energy. They will recognize the six forms of energy and identify energy conversions. Students will relate work, force, and distance. Finally, students will measure and express work and power, using the proper units, and they will calculate work and power.

About Figure 14-1 Sailboat races may last for a few hours or several days. In October 2001, the 38-m (125-ft) catamaran *Playstation* raced with its 10-member crew from New York City to Lizard Point in Cornwall, England, a distance of 4,600 km (2,900 mi) in a record time of 4 days, 17 hours, 28 minutes, and 6 seconds. The crew maneuvered the sailboat to average a record-shattering speed of almost 26 knots (48 km/h; 30 mi/h).

Answer Possible answer: the force of the wind

Linking Prior Knowledge

For this chapter students should recall:
• the concept of force (Lesson 12-1).
• the nature of speed and velocity (Lesson 13-2).

Chapter Project

SNAIL RUN

MATERIALS: marble, 1-m length of flexible rubber tubing

Divide students into groups of three or four. As students read this chapter, have each group design and build a track on which a marble released at one end will roll down the track at the slowest possible speed. Have groups time the rate at which their marble moved. Allow time for students to observe the motion of the marble on other groups' tracks.
learning styles: visual, tactile

14-1 (pp. 292–293)

1 Introduce

STUDY HINT As students read the lesson, have them list examples of potential energy and kinetic energy in their notebooks.

Linking Prior Knowledge Have students recall the relationship between speed and velocity (Lesson 13-2). Ask students: *How is velocity related to speed?* (Velocity is speed in a given direction.)

2 Teach

Demonstration Demonstrate how potential energy can be stored in a spring. Compress a spring and tie the coils in place with a piece of thread. Place the spring between two balls. Release the spring by cutting the thread. Have students observe that the balls are pushed apart. Ask: *What happened to the balls when the spring was released?* (The balls began to move.) Explain to students that the tied spring had stored energy. The spring had the ability to make something happen because it made the balls move when released. **learning styles: visual, auditory**

Demonstration Make a pendulum by tying a small weight to one end of a piece of string and attaching the opposite end of the string to a ring stand. Gently pull the weight to one side. Hold it so that it remains suspended. Explain that the weight has gravitational energy. Place an object close by. Let go of the weight so that it knocks the object over. Explain how the weight had kinetic energy.
learning styles: visual, tactile

Answers to questions

1 DEFINE: the ability to make something happen

2 IDENTIFY: heat energy and light energy

3 LIST: mass and velocity

READING STRATEGY Some students may not easily grasp the terms *potential* and *kinetic*. To help students better understand the meanings of these two basic kinds of energy, have them use a dictionary to look up the definitions.
learning styles: visual, linguistic

14-1 What is energy?

Objective
Compare potential energy and kinetic energy.

Key Terms
energy: ability to make something happen
potential (poh-TEHN-shuhl) **energy:** stored energy
kinetic (kih-NEHT-ihk) **energy:** energy of motion

Energy Look at the picture of the dam in Figure 14-2. If you have ever taken a shower or stood out in the rain, you know that falling water has energy. The energy of the water falling through the spillways of a dam can be used to generate electricity. However, did you know that the quiet water in the lake behind the dam also has energy?

Energy is the ability to make something happen. There are two general kinds of energy. These are potential energy and kinetic energy.

1 DEFINE: What is energy?

Potential Energy Potential energy is stored energy. The energy of the water in the lake behind the dam in Figure 14-2 is potential energy. The water has energy because of its position. Gravity can cause it to fall to the river below the dam. This kind of stored energy is called gravitational potential energy.

▲ **Figure 14-2** The water above this dam has gravitational potential energy.

292

The gravitational potential energy stored in a sample of matter depends on two factors. These factors are weight and height. The more weight an object has, the more potential energy it has. Potential energy also depends on height. The farther an object has to fall, the more potential energy it has.

The fireworks in Figure 14-3 have a different kind of potential energy called chemical potential energy. This potential energy is stored in the chemicals in the fireworks. When the fireworks are set off, the potential energy stored in the chemicals is released as heat, light, and sound.

▲ **Figure 14-3** Fireworks have chemical potential energy.

2 IDENTIFY: What kind of energy is released when you strike a match?

Kinetic Energy Kinetic energy is energy of motion. Anything that is moving has kinetic energy. When you walk or run, you have kinetic energy. Like potential energy, kinetic energy also depends on two factors. With kinetic energy, the factors are mass and velocity. The faster you move, the more kinetic energy you have. The more mass a moving object has, the more kinetic energy it has.

Think about a car and a truck moving at 30 mph. The truck has the greater mass. So, even though both vehicles are traveling at the same speed, the truck will have more kinetic energy than the car.

Teaching Options

COOPERATIVE LEARNING

Solving Potential Energy Problems Have students work in small groups to answer the Building Math Skills questions on page 293. Suggest that students take turns sketching the situation described in each question, labeling the sketch with the given values, and calculating the answer. **learning styles: visual, logical/mathematical**

EXTENDING THE LESSON

Understanding Potential and Kinetic Energy To help students understand the difference between kinetic energy and potential energy, give them examples of situations where potential energy turns into kinetic energy. (potential energy: a sled at the top of a hill; kinetic energy: a sled sliding down a hill) **learning style: auditory**

◄ **Figure 14-4** Both runners are moving at the same speed. Because the runner on the left has more mass, he also has more kinetic energy than the runner on the right.

▶ **LIST:** What two factors determine how much kinetic energy a moving object has?

✓ CHECKING CONCEPTS

1. The ability to make something happen is _____ .

2. Two kinds of energy are potential energy and _____ energy.

3. Stored energy is _____ energy.

4. Kinetic energy is energy of _____ .

5. A diver on a diving board has _____ potential energy.

THINKING CRITICALLY

6. **COMPARE:** What is the difference between potential energy and kinetic energy?

7. **ANALYZE:** A rock on the edge of a cliff has what kind of energy? When could the rock have both kinetic and potential energy? Explain.

BUILDING MATH SKILLS

If you know the weight of an object and know how high it is above the ground, you can use the formula shown here to find its gravitational potential energy (*PE*).

$$PE = \text{weight} \times \text{height}$$

Remember that weight is a measure of the pull of gravity on a mass. Weight is measured in newtons (N). Height is measured in meters (m). Therefore, potential energy is expressed in units called newton-meters, or N-m. Use the formula to find the gravitational potential energy of each of the following objects.

- a 50-N brick on top of a 4-m ladder
- a 780-N diver standing on a diving board 10 m above the water

---

◆ **Integrating Earth Science**

TOPIC: erosion

SCULPTING EARTH'S SURFACE

Forces can produce change. Over time, forces such as wind, moving water, and ice change the appearance of Earth's surface. The wearing away of Earth's surface in one place and building it up in another place is called erosion.

Moving water can pick up and carry sediments such as soil and gravel. When it is moving fast enough, water can even roll large rocks along the bed of a river. When these materials drag and bounce along a streambed, they carve new channels. Over millions of years, the Grand Canyon in Arizona was carved out by materials carried in the waters of the Colorado River.

▲ **Figure 14-5** These canyons were carved by the moving water of a river.

Ocean waves carve the shoreline. They wear away rocks, making cliffs and terraces. Sediments carried by the water scrape against rocky shorelines. Sometimes this carves out caves and arches. Wind and moving ice, called glaciers, are other agents of erosion.

Thinking Critically What part does kinetic energy play in sculpting Earth's surface?

✓ CHECKING CONCEPTS ANSWERS

1. energy
2. kinetic
3. potential
4. motion
5. gravitational

THINKING CRITICALLY ANSWERS

6. **COMPARE:** Potential energy is stored energy. Kinetic energy is energy of motion.

7. **ANALYZE:** Gravitational potential energy; While the rock is falling from the cliff to the ground, it has both gravitational potential energy (because it is above the ground) and kinetic energy (because it is moving).

4 Close

BUILDING MATH SKILLS ANSWERS

200 N-m; 7,800 N-m

◆ **Integrating Earth Science**

TOPIC: erosion

SCULPTING EARTH'S SURFACE

Real-Life Connection Wind is one of the forces that can cause erosion. It can be very destructive. Wind can pick up the lightest parts of the soil, which are the most fertile. This action can damage crop production. Wind erosion can also create pollution as the dust from this topsoil enters the air. This makes the air unhealthy to breathe and impairs vision. Many governments and other organizations are studying ways to prevent the harmful effects of wind erosion.

Discussion Fill a baking pan with about 3 cm (1 in.) of sand. Have students wear safety goggles and observe the sand as you use a drinking straw to blow across it gently. Ask students: *What happened to the sand?* (The sand moved.) *Why?* (The air pushed it). *What property did the air have that gave it the ability to push the grains of sand and move them?* (energy)

Thinking Critically Answer
The kinetic energy of moving water, wind, and ice supplies the energy required to cause erosion.

MORE ON THE WEB

Simulating Potential and Kinetic Energy Have students visit www.conceptsand challenges.com to use an interactive energy simulation to see how much kinetic energy occurs in each bounce of a ball.

• *TEACHING RESOURCES* •

 Teacher's Resources CD-ROM
Lesson Review: Chapter 14, p. 2
Enrichment: Chapter 14, p. 3

QUICK CONVERSIONS

Gravitational Potential Energy	Metric/SI	English
Brick	50 N	11 lb
Diver	780 N	175 lb
Ladder	4 m	13 ft
Above water	10 m	33 ft

1 Introduce

 STUDY HINT Have students make a six-column chart in their notebooks. As they read this lesson, have students write a form of energy, its definition, and an example in each column.

Linking Prior Knowledge Write the terms *eye*, *ear*, and *skin* on the board. Ask students to identify the energy that each organ senses. (light, sound, and heat)

2 Teach

Discussion Have students picture themselves in Figure 14-6. Ask them what they might be seeing, hearing, or feeling. Explain that visible light is a form of electromagnetic energy. Sound energy is a form of mechanical energy. Expand the discussion by mentioning the other forms of energy: electrical, chemical, and nuclear. Ask students to identify where these forms of energy might be found in the picture. (The light in the tent may be coming from an electric lantern. If so, the lantern uses batteries to supply energy to the bulb in the form of electrical energy. The compounds in wood contain energy in the form of chemical energy, which is released as the wood burns. The particles in the nuclei of atoms in all the materials shown in the picture are held together by energy in the form of nuclear energy.)
learning styles: visual, auditory

READING STRATEGY For students who are visual learners, have them make a drawing of an example of each form of energy. Make sure that they label each drawing with the appropriate form of energy. **learning styles: visual, tactile**

Answers to questions

▶ **LIST:** mechanical energy, electrical energy, electromagnetic energy, heat energy, chemical energy, and nuclear energy

▶ **COMPARE:** Possible answer: They are similar because they can be converted from one form to another. Differences will occur, depending on forms chosen.

14-2 What are different forms of energy?

Objectives
Identify and describe the different forms of energy.

Forms of Energy Your body gets energy from the food you eat. An automobile uses the energy in gasoline to make it move. A clock spring stores energy to turn the hands of the clock. These are some examples of different forms of energy. There are six main forms of energy. They are mechanical energy, electrical energy, electromagnetic energy, heat energy, chemical energy, and nuclear energy.

▶ **LIST:** What are six main forms of energy?

Using Forms of Energy You use the different forms of energy without ever noticing them. If energy came only in one form, the campers in Figure 14-6 might have light to see by but no heat for cooking. Each form of energy has its own characteristics and uses.

Mechanical Energy The energy in moving things is mechanical energy. This type of energy can occur as potential or kinetic energy, or both. For example, when you wind the spring on a toy car, you are storing mechanical energy in the spring. When the toy is turned on, the spring unwinds and the mechanical energy of the spring is seen as the toy car moves. Until the spring winds down completely, it has both potential and kinetic energy.

Electrical Energy The energy that flows through wires and powers the lights and appliances in your house is electrical energy. This energy is in the form of moving electric charges.

Electromagnetic Energy Electromagnetic energy is a form of energy that can travel through a vacuum. Visible light, also called radiant energy, is the most familiar form of electromagnetic energy. Other forms of this energy include X-rays, radio waves, and microwaves.

Heat Energy If you rub your hands together, they become warm. Heat energy, also called thermal energy, is the energy of the moving particles that make up matter. The faster the particles move, the more heat energy they have. All forms of matter contain some heat energy.

Chemical Energy The energy that holds particles of matter together is chemical energy. The energy stored in the head of a match is chemical energy. The energy stored in food and in fuels such as wood and coal is chemical energy.

▲ **Figure 14-6** Several forms of energy can be seen at this campsite.

294

Teaching Options

! FAST FACTS *Medical Imaging Devices*

X-ray machines, CT (computed tomography) scanners, and MRI (magnetic resonance imaging) machines function because materials in the body transmit, absorb, and reflect energy. For example, when X-raying an arm, the soft tissues of the arm will transmit X-rays, while bone tissue absorbs them. The X-rays cast a shadow of the two bones of the lower arm on the film sheet. When the film is developed, the shadow will appear as an image of the ulna and radius bones.

COOPERATIVE LEARNING

Comparing Forms of Energy
Divide the class into six groups. Assign each group a different form of energy. Have groups compare the advantages and disadvantages of the assigned form of energy.

ESL/ELL STRATEGY

Communicating by Brainstorming
Working with peers encourages English-language learners to communicate. Have students work in pairs to brainstorm examples of each of the six main forms of energy.

Nuclear Energy Nuclear energy is the energy stored in the nucleus of an atom. Normally this energy is used to keep the protons and neutrons tightly bound together in the nucleus. However, when the nucleus of a large atom is split, as in a nuclear reactor, some of that energy is released as heat and light. Nuclear energy can also be released when nuclei of light atoms combine. The heat and light from the Sun are produced from this type of nuclear reaction.

COMPARE: Choose two forms of energy. How are they alike? How are they different?

✓ CHECKING CONCEPTS

1. Where does your body get energy from?
2. How many main forms of energy are there?
3. What is mechanical energy?
4. What is the most familiar form of electromagnetic energy?
5. What kind of energy is stored in wood?
6. What is nuclear energy?

Science and Technology

ENERGY IN MEDICINE

Throughout history, medicine has benefited greatly from advances in technology. Much of this technology uses energy. One of the most familiar medical devices is the X-ray machine. X-rays are forms of electromagnetic energy. Like light, X-rays can produce photographs, not of scenery but of bones inside the human body.

Computerized axial tomography is the tongue-twisting name for an advanced X-ray machine known as a CAT scanner. This device includes an X-ray tube. It rotates around a patient producing a three-dimensional image of the internal parts of the body on a computer screen.

Magnetic energy and sound energy are also used in medicine. Magnetic resonance imaging (MRI) machines use magnetic energy to study soft tissues of the body. Ultrasound devices use the energy of sound waves to monitor the health of a developing fetus.

Thinking Critically Explain why energy is important to medical science.

▲ **Figure 14-7** An MRI machine uses magnetic energy.

💡 THINKING CRITICALLY

7. **CLASSIFY:** Of the six main forms of energy, which forms are potential energy? Which are kinetic energy? Explain your answers.

8. **ANALYZE:** Identify each of the following objects as a source of mechanical, electromagnetic, heat, chemical, or nuclear energy. Some of the objects may be sources of more than one form of energy. Explain your answers.

   a. gasoline   d. river
   b. dynamite explosion   e. lightning
   c. burning wood   f. the Sun

DESIGNING AN EXPERIMENT

Design an experiment to solve the following problem. Include a hypothesis, variables, a procedure, and a type of data to study.

PROBLEM: How can you show that sound is a form of mechanical energy?

---

3 Assess

✓ CHECKING CONCEPTS ANSWERS

1. food
2. six
3. energy in moving things
4. visible light
5. chemical
6. energy stored in the nucleus of an atom

💡 THINKING CRITICALLY ANSWERS

7. **CLASSIFY:** potential energy: mechanical, electrical, chemical, nuclear; kinetic energy: mechanical, electromagnetic, heat. Accept all logical explanations.

8. **ANALYZE: a.** chemical **b.** chemical, heat (and mechanical, electromagnetic) **c.** chemical, heat, electromagnetic **d.** mechanical **e.** electrical, electromagnetic (and heat) **f.** electromagnetic, heat, nuclear Accept all logical explanations.

---

4 Close

DESIGNING AN EXPERIMENT

Use the Designing an Experiment Rubric on the Teacher's Resources CD-ROM to assess students' experiments. Fill in the rubric with the additional information below. For this assignment, students should have:

- formed a hypothesis that states that sound is a form of moving energy.
- included data that showed that sound travels from one point to another.

Science and Technology

ENERGY IN MEDICINE

Real-Life Connection The electromagnetic energy produced in MRI scanners and the mechanical energy of sound produced in ultrasound devices do not affect film. Instead, this energy is detected by devices called transducers, which change the incoming electromagnetic or mechanical energy into electrical energy. The electrical energy from the transducers is used to produce images on a monitor screen for viewing.

Thinking Critically Answer
Energy allows doctors to observe body parts without performing surgery.

MORE ON THE WEB

Ion Propulsion Have students learn more about ion propulsion by visiting www.conceptsand challenges.com. Have them write a short report explaining ion propulsion and its benefits.

ONGOING ASSESSMENT

Identifying Energy Bring in pictures representing the six main forms of energy. Display the pictures in front of the classroom in random order. Have students classify each picture according to the energy forms shown. **learning styles: visual, auditory**

• TEACHING RESOURCES •

Teacher's Resources CD-ROM
Lesson Review: Chapter 14, p. 4
Enrichment: Chapter 14, p. 5
Designing an Experiment: Study Tools, p. 14
Designing an Experiment Rubric: Teaching Tools, p. 7

1 Introduce

⚲ INVESTIGATE

TIME: 15 minutes

PURPOSE: Student will infer that potential energy is being converted to kinetic energy through the spring of a windup toy.

MATERIALS: windup toy

PROCEDURE: Have students work in pairs to complete this activity. You might have students vary the amount of potential energy in the spring by winding the spring to different degrees of tension. (The potential energy of the spring increases with tension). Then, have students compare the distance the toy traveled based on the spring tension.

THINK ABOUT IT: Potential energy; The potential energy of the spring changed into the kinetic energy of the moving toy. **learning styles: visual, tactile**

📝 **STUDY HINT** Have students draw Figure 14-8 in their notebooks. As they read the lesson, have them draw arrows to indicate when the bouncing ball has the greatest amount of potential energy and when it has the greatest amount of kinetic energy.

Linking Prior Knowledge Ask students to state the law of conservation of mass (Lesson 8-1). Inform students that this law can also be applied to energy. Have students restate the law, substituting the word *energy* for the word *mass*.

2 Teach

Demonstration Turn on a lamp (without a shade) in front of students. Hold your hand a few inches away from the bulb. Ask: *What is happening to my hand?* (It is being warmed by the light.) Tell students that a light bulb is designed to change electrical energy into electromagnetic energy—visible light. Ask students: *Why does the bulb feel warm?* (It is giving off heat.) *Where did this energy come from?* (The bulb changed some of the electrical energy into heat energy.) Identify this unwanted energy as waste heat.
learning styles: visual, tactile

14-3 How does energy change form?

INVESTIGATE ⚲
Observing Energy Change
HANDS-ON ACTIVITY

1. Place a windup toy on a flat surface.
2. Give the toy a little push and observe what happens.
3. Now, wind the spring of the toy. Pay attention to how the "feel" of the spring changes as you wind it.
4. Place the toy on a flat surface and release the spring.

THINK ABOUT IT: What kind of energy did the spring have after you wound it? How did this energy change?

STEP 3

Objective
Identify examples of energy changing form.

Key Terms
thermal (THUR-muhl) **pollution:** damage that occurs when waste heat enters the environment

law of conservation of energy: energy cannot be made or destroyed, but only changed in form

Changing Potential and Kinetic Energy Energy can change from one form to another. Potential energy and kinetic energy often change form. Look at the bouncing ball in Figure 14-8. As the ball falls, potential energy is changed into kinetic energy and back into potential energy as it bounces to a higher position.

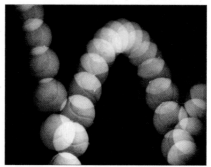

▲ **Figure 14-8** The energy of the bouncing ball is always changing form.

296

The ball in Figure 14-8 has the greatest amount of potential energy at its highest point. It has the greatest amount of kinetic energy just before it hits the ground.

▶ **ANALYZE:** When does a bouncing ball have the least amount of kinetic energy?

Changing Forms of Energy You can observe many examples of changing forms of energy all around you. When you turn on an electric light, electrical energy is changed into light energy and heat energy. When you start an automobile, the engine changes the chemical energy in gasoline into mechanical energy. Nuclear reactors change nuclear energy into heat that is used to generate steam. Your muscles change the chemical energy in food into mechanical energy.

▲ **Figure 14-9** The light energy from the bulb is captured by the solar cells on the calculator. It is changed to electrical energy that powers the calculator.

▶ **IDENTIFY:** What energy change takes place when you turn on an electric light?

Teaching Options

EXTENDING THE LESSON

Understanding Energy Have students look at the bouncing ball in Figure 14-8. Explain that the total energy of the ball (the sum of its gravitational potential energy and kinetic energy at any moment) is decreasing because some of the energy is changing into sound and heat as the ball bounces. Knowing that the total energy of the ball is decreasing as time passes, have students explain in what direction the ball is bouncing. (The height of each bounce is decreasing from right to left. Therefore, the ball is moving from right to left because its total energy is decreasing from right to left.) **learning styles: visual, auditory**

RETEACH

Changing Energy Tell students to rub their hands together. Ask students: *How do your hands feel?* (warm) *What form of energy do your moving hands have?* (mechanical energy) *What form of energy causes your hands to feel warm?* (heat energy) Explain that rubbing your hands together changes mechanical energy to heat energy.
learning styles: tactile, auditory

Waste Heat When energy changes form, some of the energy is always changed into heat. Most of this heat energy is wasted. When waste heat energy escapes into the environment, it causes **thermal pollution**. For example, the water in lakes and rivers is used to remove waste heat from power plants. The waste heat makes the water warmer. The water may become too warm for living things. If the water gets too warm, fish in the lakes and rivers may die.

▶ DEFINE: What is thermal pollution?

Conservation of Energy You know that energy can change from one form to another. Energy also can move from place to place. However, energy can never be lost. Energy can never be created or destroyed. Energy can only be changed in form. This is the **law of conservation of energy.**

Before 1905, the law of conservation of energy did not seem to apply to nuclear energy. In the Sun, nuclear energy is changed into heat energy and light energy. The sun seemed to be producing too much energy for its mass. In 1905, Albert Einstein showed that matter and energy are two forms of the same thing.

▲ **Figure 14-10** The Sun's energy gave Einstein (inset) the inspiration for his theory about matter and energy.

Einstein concluded that matter can be changed into energy, and energy can be changed into matter. The total amount of matter and energy in the universe does not change. Einstein stated this idea in the following equation.

$$E = mc^2$$

In this equation, E is energy, m is matter, or mass, and c is the speed of light. Einstein's equation showed that a small amount of matter could be changed into a huge amount of energy. This is what happens in the Sun.

▶ DEFINE: What is the law of conservation of energy?

✔ CHECKING CONCEPTS

1. A bouncing ball has the greatest amount of _____ energy at the top of its bounce.
2. When a bouncing ball is at the _____ of its bounce, it has the greatest amount of kinetic energy.
3. When you turn on a light, electrical energy is changed into light and _____.
4. An automobile engine changes _____ energy into mechanical energy.
5. The _____ energy in food is changed into mechanical energy by your muscles.
6. A nuclear reactor changes nuclear energy into _____ energy.

💡 THINKING CRITICALLY

7. SYNTHESIZE: Think of a thunderstorm. Describe the forms of energy that occur and the effects they have. Explain each time energy changes from one form to another.

INTERPRETING VISUALS

Study the drawings in Figure 14-11 and answer the following questions.

8. What two forms of energy make item A function?
9. How many forms of energy are shown in B? What are they?

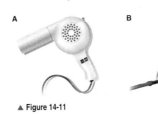

▲ Figure 14-11

Discussion Students are probably aware that water, land, and air pollution are considered major problems. Point out that thermal pollution is also a problem. Describe how thermal pollution occurs and how it may harm living things.
learning style: auditory

Answers to questions

▶ ANALYZE: at the top of its bounce

▶ IDENTIFY: Electrical energy is changed into electromagnetic energy and heat energy.

▶ DEFINE: waste heat that enters the environment

▶ DEFINE: Energy cannot be created or destroyed. It can only be changed in form.

📖 READING STRATEGY A good strategy to use with struggling readers is making connections. Tell students that *therm* comes from a Greek word that means "heat." Ask students to think of words dealing with heat that begin with *therm*. (thermometer, thermal, thermostat)

3 Assess

✔ CHECKING CONCEPTS ANSWERS

1. potential
2. bottom
3. heat
4. chemical
5. chemical
6. electrical

💡 THINKING CRITICALLY ANSWER

7. SYNTHESIZE: Electrical energy is changed into mechanical energy, electromagnetic energy, and heat energy. The mechanical energy we sense as sound, and the electromagnetic energy we sense as visible light.

4 Close

INTERPRETING VISUALS ANSWERS

8. electrical and mechanical
9. 3; electromagnetic, heat, and chemical

MORE ON THE WEB

Thermal Pollution Have students answer questions about thermal pollution at www.conceptsandchallenges.com.

COOPERATIVE LEARNING

Forms of Energy in Sports Have pairs of students pick a sport and identify the changing forms of energy that take place during the playing of that sport.
learning style: interpersonal

• *TEACHING RESOURCES* •

💿 **Teacher's Resources CD-ROM**
Lesson Review: Chapter 14, p. 6
Enrichment: Chapter 14, pp. 7, 8

The Big Idea

(pp. 298–299)

1 Introduce

Objective Students will list several alternative sources of energy and create a model home that uses renewable energy for power.

Linking Prior Knowledge Ask students to name the six forms of energy. List these on the board. Then, have volunteers name the forms of energy used in most homes for heating, cooling, and running appliances. (chemical energy and electrical energy)

2 Teach

Discussion List on the board some of the alternative sources of energy mentioned in the text. Have students name the forms of energy that each source supplies (Sun: electromagnetic energy; wind: mechanical energy; rivers: mechanical energy) Have students discuss how these types of energy can be used directly or changed into other forms of energy used in homes. For example, mechanical energy of the wind can be changed by using a wind turbine and generator to provide electrical energy to operate electrical appliances in the home.

Use the following information in the article, captions, and Fast Facts to help guide students in choosing a topic for their Science Logs.

THE BIG IDEA ONLINE

What are alternative sources of energy? Have students research their Science Log Writing Activity at www.conceptsandchallenges.com. You can have students organize their log by completing the Big Idea activity online. Students may post their work in the Online Classroom Database for others to read.

Reinforcement Students can also use the Big Idea Planner or Big Idea Science Log Entry found on the Teacher's Resources CD-ROM.

◈ *Environmental Science*

THE Big IDEA

What are alternative sources of energy?

Think of the many ways people use energy every day. We use energy to heat and light our homes. Think of the hundreds of different ways we use electricity. Energy is also needed to run all forms of transportation.

Most of the energy people use today comes from burning fossil fuels—oil, coal, and natural gas. However, there are problems with this. Burning fossil fuels creates pollution and increases the greenhouse effect. Also, fossil fuels are not renewable. Once you burn a liter of fuel oil, it is gone forever. So someday, Earth's supply of fossil fuels will run out. It is time to develop some alternative sources of energy.

The Sun is a great energy source. Solar energy is free, and it will be available for billions of years. Drying clothes on a clothesline and using rooftop water heaters are simple ways to use solar energy. Solar panels can capture solar energy and convert it to heat, which can be used to heat our homes.

Wind is another form of "free" energy. This energy source has been used for thousands of years to sail ships, pump water, and grind grain in windmills. Wind can also be used to generate electricity.

The moving water in rivers and tidal basins and heat from below Earth's surface are other natural energy sources. In the future, each of these alternative energy sources may be developed to help replace the energy being produced from fossil fuels today. Look at the pictures on these pages. Then, follow the instructions in the Science Log to find out more about "the big idea."✦

298

Geothermal Power Generator

In places with lots of volcanic activity, heat energy inside Earth can be tapped to make electricity or heat buildings. Iceland plans to use geothermal and other energy sources to be free of fossil fuels by 2030.

Wind Farm

The energy of the wind can be used to spin an electric generator. In windy places, this is a great renewable energy source.

Teaching Options

❗ FAST FACTS   *Solar Energy Comes Home*

Solar energy, electromagnetic energy from the Sun, can be used to heat homes as well as to produce electricity.

Solar heating can be either passive or active. Passive solar heating uses solar energy directly to warm indoor temperatures. Methods for using passive solar heating may include orienting the home to take advantage of sunlight falling on windows and using flooring materials that absorb solar energy and later release it as heat to the room. Active solar heating uses rooftop panels that collect and store solar energy. The solar energy heats water that passes through the panels. The heated water may be used directly, passed through the home to warm it, or stored in insulated containers for later use.

An electric current can be produced by solar energy with the use of photovoltaic cells. A photovoltaic cell, or solar cell, consists of a semiconductor material sandwiched between two conducting materials. As light falls on the surface of the cell, electrons flow between the two conductors. If the conductors are in a circuit, electrons flow through the circuit as an electric current. This electric current carries electrical energy that can be used to operate household devices.

Energy From Water

For hundreds of years, moving water has turned water wheels to grind grain. Today, moving water is used in hydroelectric plants (above right) to generate electricity.

Solar-Powered Highway Emergency Phone

Some emergency phones on the highway are powered with photoelectric cells. In the daytime the sun charges a battery so the phone can work at night.

Science Log:

WRITING ACTIVITY

What alternative energy sources are available where you live? Find out about local renewable energy sources. Think about all the ways you use electricity and other forms of energy in your home. Then, design a house that uses renewable alternatives to fossil fuels to make its energy. Start your search at www.conceptsandchallenges.com.

CHAPTER 14: Energy and Work **299**

3 *Assess*

Use the Writing Activity Rubric in the Teacher's Resources CD-ROM to assess students' Science Logs. Fill in the rubric with the additional information below. For this assignment, students should have:

* listed several alternative sources of energy that are locally available.
* communicated descriptions of a house that uses alternative sources of energy to meet its energy needs.

4 *Close*

Presenting an Idea Have students act as household energy consultants and present their designs to the class. Students' designs might be grouped according to the type of energy used to supply the house. After the presentations, have students discuss similarities and differences in their designs.

Tips for Using Technology

Creating Graphics and Illustrations Students can use graphics to illustrate their house designs. Most graphics creation software has similar tools to create graphics and illustrations. Some of these tools include shape creation tools, text tools, and pencil tools.

Shape tools, such as an oval or a square, allow students to create different types of shapes in their illustration. The text tool allows students to enter text into their illustration. The pencil or drawing tool allows students to draw freehand in an illustration.

• TEACHING RESOURCES •

Teacher's Resources CD-ROM

Big Idea: Chapter 14, p. 9

Big Idea Planner: Study Tools, pp. 11–12

Big Idea Science Log Entry: Study Tools, p. 13

Individual Activity Rubric: Teaching Tools, p. 5

14-4 (pp. 300–301)

1 Introduce

STUDY HINT Before beginning this lesson, have students copy the title of each section in their notebooks, using an outline format. As students read each section, they should write the main idea of each section in their notebooks. Students can also use the Writing Activity Outline found on the Teacher's Resources CD-ROM.

Linking Prior Knowledge Have students recall that a force is a push or pull that tends to change the motion of an object and has direction (Lesson 12-1). Have students explain how the force of gravity shows each of these three characteristics. (The force of gravity is pull, and it can change the velocity of an object and pull objects downward.)

2 Teach

Demonstration Ask students to walk to the wall and try to move it by pushing against it. Then, have them return to their desks and push a book across their desktops. Tell students that in the scientific sense of the word *work*, they did no work on the wall but they did do work on the books. Have them compare and contrast the two situations. Lead students to realize that work is done on an object when a force causes an object to move.
learning styles: tactile, kinesthetic

Discussion Have students look at Figure 14-12. Explain that when the girl lifts the backpack, she does work on the backpack because she changes its mechanical energy. In this situation, she increased its gravitational potential energy. Explain that when she holds the backpack still, she is not changing its mechanical energy. Have students conclude that no work is being done on the backpack because there is no change in its mechanical energy. Discuss other possible examples of work.
learning styles: visual, auditory

Answers to questions

1 DESCRIBE: Work is force multiplied by distance.

2 EXPLAIN: It can make something happen, such as knocking over pins.

T300   UNIT 5: Force, Motion, and Energy

14-4   What is work?

Objective
Relate work, force, and distance.

Key Term
work: force exerted through a distance

Work   When are you doing work? **Work** is done when a force moves an object a certain distance. This relationship can be shown in the following equation.

work = force × distance

Suppose two boys push a car stuck in the mud. No matter how hard they push, they are not able to move the car. They are very tired afterward. Did the boys do any work?

The answer is no. For work to be done, something must be moved. The boys used a great deal of energy, but the car did not move. Work was not done.

1 DESCRIBE: What is the relationship between work, force, and distance?

Work and Energy   Energy has been defined as the ability to make something happen. Energy is also often defined as the ability to do work. When a force moves an object, work is done.

Anything that can make something else move has energy. A moving bowling ball has energy. When the ball hits the pins, the pins move. The energy stored in gasoline can do work. It can make a car move. However, energy can be changed in form without any work being done. If you hold a heavy bag of groceries, your arms will get tired. Chemical energy in your muscles is changed to other forms of energy. However, because this energy is not being used to move the bag of groceries, you are not doing work.

2 EXPLAIN: How do you know a moving bowling ball has energy?

Direction of Motion   For work to be done, a force must make an object move in the same direction as the force. Look at the three pictures in Figure 14-12. In the first picture, the girl is picking up a backpack. The backpack is moving in the direction of the force she used on it. She is doing work. In the middle picture, she is standing still with the pack on her back. She is using force, but no work is being done. In the third picture, she is moving the backpack as she begins to walk. Because she is causing the backpack to accelerate, she is doing work again.

3 EXPLAIN: Why is work done when you lift an object from the floor?

◄ **Figure 14-12**
Work is being done in the first and last pictures but not the middle picture.

300

Teaching Options

! FAST FACTS   *Work and Energy Transfer*

One way of stating the relationship between work and energy is that energy is the ability to do work. Another statement of this relationship is that work transfers energy. The work done on an object equals the change in the object's energy. The latter relationship is often used to estimate the force that causes these changes in energy, a force that is often very difficult to measure. For example, you can estimate the average force that a hockey stick exerts on a hockey puck. When the stick strikes a motionless hockey puck, the puck will begin sliding across the ice at a high speed. Its kinetic energy has increased. By calculating the kinetic energy of the puck from its mass and velocity ($KE = 1/2\ mv^2$), you can calculate the change in its kinetic energy. This change equals the work done on the puck by the stick. By measuring the distance over which the puck and stick were in contact, you can calculate the average force that the stick exerts on the puck from the equation work = force × distance.

Natural Forces at Work Nature supplies the energy to do all kinds of work. Wind pushes sailboats across water and helps kites to fly. Wind energy turns windmills, which in turn generate electricity. The moving water of a river carries barges and pleasure boats. In the past, moving water turned water wheels that ran machinery in factories. Hurricanes, tornadoes, floods, and earthquakes provide the most dramatic examples of nature's ability to do work.

▶ **HYPOTHESIZE:** What role does gravity play as a natural force doing work?

 **CHECKING CONCEPTS**

1. Work = force × _____.
2. Work is not done unless something is _____.
3. The ability to do work is _____.
4. For work to be done, the direction of the _____ must be the same as the direction of motion.

 *Real-Life Science*

SPORTS AND WORK

Athletes pride themselves on their ability to do work. Most sports involve forces that produce movement. Kicking a football is an example. The force applied to the ball causes it to move downfield in the direction of the force. A field-hockey ball is sent on its way when struck by a hockey stick. A push against a basketball sends the ball in the direction of the basket.

Perhaps the most obvious work done in sports is carried out by weight lifters. The goal of weight lifters is to move heavy objects. Some events involve lifting a heavy barbell from the floor and raising it vertically above the head. Then, the barbell has to be slowly lowered back to the floor. The lowering of the barbell requires a great deal of energy, with the muscles acting against the force of gravity.

Thinking Critically Does the losing team in a tug-of-war contest do any useful work? Explain.

▲ Figure 14-13 Work is done when the barbell is lifted.

5. The stored _____ in gasoline can make a car move.

💡 **THINKING CRITICALLY**

6. **ANALYZE:** Is work being done in each of the following examples? Explain your answers.
   a. Someone holds a heavy package for one hour.
   b. A football player kicks a field goal.
   c. A tennis player hits a tennis ball over the net.

HEALTH AND SAFETY TIP

Always be careful when picking up any heavy object from the floor. You should bend your knees and use your leg muscles, not your back muscles, to lift the object. Use library references to find out other ways to prevent back injuries.

---

3 ▶ **EXPLAIN:** Work is done because you apply force over a certain distance.

4 ▶ **HYPOTHESIZE:** Possible answer: Gravity causes objects to fall to the ground.

✏️ **WRITING HINT** Students can improve their writing skills by restating a formula as a sentence. For example, you might have students write a sentence that restates the formula for work without the term *times*.

3 *Assess*

✓ **CHECKING CONCEPTS ANSWERS**

1. distance
2. moved
3. energy
4. force
5. chemical energy

💡 **THINKING CRITICALLY ANSWERS**

6. **a.** no; because the mechanical energy is not changed **b.** yes; because the mechanical energy of the ball changes **c.** yes; because the mechanical energy of the ball changes

4 *Close*

HEALTH AND SAFETY TIP

Explain to students that strong leg and stomach muscles help prevent back injuries.

Real-Life Science

SPORTS AND WORK

Real-Life Connection The work performed on a football by the kicker's foot is done only during the time the foot is in contact with the ball. Even though the distance the ball moves during this time is very small, the average force exerted on the ball by the kicker's foot is tremendously large. As a result, there is a large increase in the kinetic energy of the ball and it begins to soar down the field.

Thinking Critically Answer
Possible answer: They do work on the rope if they moved it in the direction of their pull at any point during the contest.

MORE ON THE WEB

Simulating Hurricanes Have students visit www.concepts andchallenges.com to learn more about the natural forces in hurricanes. Have students take an online hurricane tour.

ONGOING ASSESSMENT

Classifying Work Have students make a list of things that they do that they consider work. As a class, go through the lists to see which of the items a scientist would classify as work.

• TEACHING RESOURCES •

💿 **Teacher's Resources CD-ROM**
Lesson Review: Chapter 14, p. 10

Writing Activity Outline: Study Tools, pp. 20–21

14-5 (pp. 302–303)

1 Introduce

✎ **STUDY HINT** Before beginning this lesson, have students study Figure 14-14. After reading the caption, ask them if they can deduce the formula for finding work. (W = F × d)

Linking Prior Knowledge Have students recall that the basic units of force and distance in SI units are the newton and the meter. Ask students: *What are the abbreviations for* newton *and* meter? (N, m)

2 Teach

Discussion Explain that there is no device that can measure work directly. There is no "workometer" to measure work as there is a speedometer to measure speed. Work must be calculated. Ask students: *What is the formula to calculate work?* (work = force × distance) Write the units for the work formula on the board:

    newton-meter = newton × meter

Explain that work can be measured in newton-meters and that 1 newton-meter is also equal to a joule. The joule is the SI unit of work. **learning styles: visual, auditory**

📖 **READING STRATEGY** Some students may find it difficult to read the passages and then relate them to the diagram. Instead, have them draw their own diagrams as they read each passage. They should include arrows and labels in their diagrams to clearly show the direction and size of each force and the work being done.

Answers to questions

▶ **LIST:** force and distance

▶ **IDENTIFY:** joule

▶ **CALCULATE:** 15 J

✎ **WRITING HINT** When making calculations according to a formula, tell students to make sure that they use the correct units of measurement.

T302 UNIT 5: Force, Motion, and Energy

14-5 How can work be measured?

Objective
Use the proper units to measure and express work.

Key Term
joule (JOOL): SI unit of work; equal to 1 N-m (newton-meter)

Measuring Work To measure work, you must know two things. First, you must know the amount of force used to move an object. The SI unit of force is the newton (N). Second, you must know the distance that the object moves. Distance is usually measured in meters (m).

Work is measured in newton-meters (N-m). Work is equal to force times distance. This can be written as a formula.

$$W = F \times d$$

In this equation, W is work, F is force, and d is distance. Suppose you lift an object weighing 50 N. Remember that weight is a force. You move the object a distance of 2 m. To calculate the amount of work done, multiply the force times the distance.

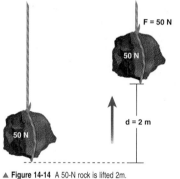

▲ **Figure 14-14** A 50-N rock is lifted 2m. The work done equals 100 N-m.

$$W = F \times d$$
$$W = 50 \text{ N} \times 2 \text{ m}$$
$$W = 100 \text{ N-m}$$

▶ **LIST:** What two things must you know in order to measure work?

Unit of Work Scientists use a unit called a **joule** (J) to measure work. One joule of work is done when a force of 1 N moves an object a distance of 1 m. One joule is equal to 1 N-m of work.

▶ **IDENTIFY:** What unit is used to measure work?

Direction of Force To measure work, you must measure the force applied in the direction of motion. This idea is illustrated in Figures 14-14 and 14-15. To lift a rock that weighs 50 N, you have to overcome gravity. You must apply a force of 50 N in an upward direction. Now, instead of lifting the rock, suppose you pulled the same 50-N rock a distance of 2 m along the ground. How much work have you done? Because you are overcoming friction instead of gravity, you will use less force—about 20 N. You must multiply this force times the distance moved. The work done equals 20 N × 2 m = 40 N-m, or 40 J.

▲ **Figure 14-15** A 50-N rock is dragged 2 m using a force of 20 N. The work done equals 40 N-m or 40 J.

▶ **CALCULATE:** How much work is done if you use 5 N of force to push a 20-N object 3 m across the floor?

302

Teaching Options

EXTENDING THE LESSON

Transferring Energy Read the following situation to the class: A cat weighing 25 newtons carrying a rubber toy weighing 2 newtons climbs a tree to a branch 3 m above the ground. Ask students: *How much work does the cat do on the toy, carrying it to the branch?* (2 N × 3 m = 6 J) *How much work does the cat do on itself climbing to the branch?* (25 N × 3 m = 75 J) *What is the total work done by the cat?* (81 J)
learning styles: auditory, logical/mathematical

COOPERATIVE LEARNING

Calculating Work Have students make flash cards showing various values for force (in newtons), distance (in meters), and work (in newton-meters). Each student should make at least two flash cards for each unit of measure. Then, have students work in groups of three. Instruct two students in each group to hold up a flash card with a different value, and the third student to calculate the missing value. Have students switch roles. If any student is having difficulty determining the missing value, encourage group members to work together on the calculations.

✓ CHECKING CONCEPTS

1. The SI unit of force is the _____.
2. To measure work, you must know both force and _____.
3. Work can be measured in newton- _____.
4. The SI unit of work is the _____.
5. One joule is equal to 1 _____ .
6. To measure work, you must know the amount of force applied in the direction of _____.

THINKING CRITICALLY

7. CALCULATE: How much work is done in each of the following examples? Show all of your calculations.
   a. A child uses 4 N of force to pull a wagon a distance of 2 m along a sidewalk.
   b. A construction worker uses 30 N of force to drag a toolbox a distance of 3 m.

8. COMPARE: In which case is more work done? Explain your answer.
   a. You lift a 40-N object 2 m straight up.
   b. You use 10 N of force to pull the same 40-N object 2 m across the floor.

Web InfoSearch

James Prescott Joule The metric unit of work, the joule, is named after James Prescott Joule. Joule was a physicist. He was born in England in 1818. Joule was one of the four scientists who helped state the law of conservation of energy. Joule's law is also named after him.

SEARCH: Write a short biography about James Prescott Joule and the scientific law named after him. Use the Internet to find out more. Start your search at www.conceptsandchallenges.com. Some key search words are **James Prescott Joule's Law.**

Hands-On Activity

MEASURING WORK

You will need a book, string, a spring scale, and a meter stick.

1. Tie a piece of string around a book.
2. Attach a spring scale to the book using the string.
3. Using the spring scale, lift the book a distance of 1 m. Record the amount of force shown on the spring scale. Calculate the amount of work done in joules.
4. Using the spring scale, pull the book at a constant velocity for a distance of 1 m across your desk or tabletop. Record the amount of force shown on the spring scale. Calculate and record the amount of work done in joules.

▲ STEP 4 Pull the book with the spring scale.

Practicing Your Skills

5. CALCULATE: How much work did you do when you lifted the book?
6. CALCULATE: How much work did you do when you pulled the book across your desk?
7. ANALYZE: Based on your calculations, does it require more work to lift an object or to drag it?

ONGOING ASSESSMENT

Increasing Work Tell students that you do 10 J of work by lifting an object 1 m from the ground. Ask how you could do 20 J of work on lifting the object with the same force. (Lift it to a height of 2 m from the ground.) **learning styles: auditory, logical/mathematical**

QUICK CONVERSIONS		
	Metric/SI	English
Work	1.36 J	1 ft-lb
Energy	1055 J	1 BTU

• TEACHING RESOURCES •

Teacher's Resources CD-ROM
Lesson Review: Chapter 14, p. 11
Enrichment: Chapter 14, p. 12

Laboratory Manual
Lab. Challenge: How is work calculated? pp. 73–76

Laboratory Video
Segment 14: Calculating Work

3 Assess

✓ CHECKING CONCEPTS ANSWERS

1. newton
2. distance
3. meters
4. joule
5. newton-meter
6. motion

THINKING CRITICALLY ANSWERS

7. CALCULATE:
   a. W = F × d; W = 4 N × 2 m;
      W = 8 N-m = 8 J
   b. W = F × d; W = 30 N × 3 m;
      W = 90 N-m = 90 J
8. COMPARE: More work is done in case **a** because a greater force (40 N) is exerted over the same distance (2 m).

4 Close

Web InfoSearch

James Prescott Joule Have students visit www.conceptsand challenges.com to find out more about this scientist. Some key search words are **James Prescott Joule** and **Joule's Law.**

Hands-On Activity

MEASURING WORK

TIME: 15 minutes

PURPOSE: calculating, analyzing

ALTERNATIVE MATERIALS: Blocks of wood may be substituted for the books.

COOPERATIVE LEARNING: Have students work in groups of three. Have one student measure the distance and read the spring scale as the second student lifts or pulls the book. Have the third student construct a data table and record the measurements.

Practicing Your Skills Answers

5. CALCULATE: Answers will vary.
6. CALCULATE: Answers will vary.
7. ANALYZE: In most cases, more work is done by lifting the book than by sliding it the same distance because the weight of the book is greater than the frictional force encountered when sliding the book.

14-6 *(pp. 304–305)*

1 Introduce

✏️ **STUDY HINT** Have students read the captions that appear under the photographs in this lesson. This will allow them to preview what is to come as well as focus on the most important ideas in the lesson.

Linking Prior Knowledge Have students recall that speed is the rate of motion (Lesson 13-1). Ask students: *What is the SI unit of speed?* (meter per second, m/s) *What unit always appears in a unit that measures a rate of time?* (second)

2 Teach

Discussion Have students look at Figure 14-18. Inform them that an electric meter has a disk that rotates like a CD. Tell students that the speed at which the disk rotates indicates the rate at which electrical energy is being supplied to the house. Ask students: *If the electricity to the house was turned off, what would happen to the motion of the disk?* (It would stop.) *Why?* (No electrical energy is being supplied to the house.) Tell students that power is not only the rate of doing work but also the rate at which energy is being supplied. The meter indicates how much electrical energy has been supplied to the house in the units of kilowatt-hours (kWh).
learning styles: visual, auditory

Answers to questions

▶ **DEFINE:** rate of doing work

▶ **IDENTIFY:** power = work ÷ time

▶ **HYPOTHESIZE:** The 60-watt light bulb converts 60 J of electrical energy each second into light and heat, while a 100-watt light bulb converts 100 J of electrical energy each second.

3 Assess

☑ **CHECKING CONCEPTS ANSWERS**

1. power
2. time
3. work
4. distance
5. watt
6. kilowatt
7. joule or J
8. Watt

T304 UNIT 5: Force, Motion, and Energy

14-6 What is power?

Objective
Explain how to measure power.

Key Terms
power: amount of work done per unit of time
watt: SI unit of power; equal to 1 J/s

Power The amount of work done per unit of time is called **power.** The term *power* describes the rate at which you do work. Suppose you took 30 minutes to shovel snow from a sidewalk. Your neighbor used a snowblower to clear a sidewalk of the same size in 10 minutes. If you both did the same amount of work, which one of you used more power? Your neighbor who did the work in less time used more power.

▲ **Figure 14-16** Shoveling snow is hard work and takes a long time.

▲ **Figure 14-17** The power of a snowblower helps a person do the same amount of work in less time.

▶ **DEFINE:** What is power?

304

Measuring Power To measure power, you must measure two things. First, you must measure the amount of work done. Second, you must measure the time needed to do the work. The formula used to measure power is as follows:

$$\text{power} = \text{work} \div \text{time}$$

Recall that work is equal to force times distance. The formula for power can also be written as

$$\text{power} = (\text{force} \times \text{distance}) \div \text{time}.$$

▶ **IDENTIFY:** What is the formula used to measure power?

Unit of Power The SI unit of power is the watt (W). Power is equal to work divided by time. The unit of work is the newton-meter, or joule. The unit of time is the second. Therefore, one watt (1 W) is equal to 1 N-m/s, or 1 J/s. The watt is named after James Watt. Watt was a Scottish engineer who built the first useful steam engine.

Large amounts of power are measured in kilowatts (kW). One kilowatt (1 kW) is equal to 1,000 W. You are probably familiar with watts and kilowatts as units of electric power. For example, light bulbs can be rated as 60 W, 100 W, or 250 W.

Electricity is not free. You have to pay for the electricity you use. How does the electric company know how much electricity your family uses? The electricity used in your house is measured by a meter like the one shown in Figure 14-18. The meter shows how many kilowatt-hours of electricity have been used.

▲ **Figure 14-18** An electric meter

▶ **HYPOTHESIZE:** How does a 60-W light bulb differ from a 100-W light bulb?

Teaching Options

RETEACH

Comparing Work and Power
Have students calculate their weight in newtons. (Multiply pounds by 4.5.) Then, measure the height of a small flight of stairs to the nearest meter. Have students time how long it takes them to walk up the stairs. Calculate the work needed for walking up the stairs. (work = weight × height) Then, calculate the power by dividing the work by the time. Ask students: *Is there a difference between the work and the power in walking up the stairs?* (There is more work than power.) **learning styles: kinesthetic, logical/mathematical**

EXTENDING THE LESSON

Researching James Watt Have interested students research the Scottish engineer James Watt. Have them write a report about his contributions to science. Encourage them to share their reports with the class. **learning style: linguistic**

ONGOING ASSESSMENT

Reviewing Units of Measurement
Ask students: *What is the SI unit of power?* (the watt) *What is the unit of work?* (the newton-meter or joule) *What is 1 kilowatt equal to?* (1,000 watts)

✓ CHECKING CONCEPTS

1. The rate at which work is done is _____.

2. Power is the amount of work done per unit of _____.

3. To measure power, you must find the amount of _____ and the time needed.

4. Power = (force × _____)/time.

5. The SI unit of power is the _____.

6. One _____ is equal to 1,000 W.

7. One watt is equal to 1 N-m/s, or 1 _____ /s.

8. The unit of power is named after James _____.

THINKING CRITICALLY

9. CALCULATE: How much more power is used to move a weight of 500 N a distance of 20 m in 5 s than is used to move a weight of 1,000 N a distance of 30 m in 30 sec?

10. CALCULATE: Find the amount of power used in each of the following examples. Show your calculations.

   a. You use a force of 10 N to move a box 100 m in 10 seconds.

   b. An athlete lifting weights does 900 J of work in 1 second.

   c. A truck does 30,000 J of work in 15 seconds.

   d. A furniture mover uses a force of 150 N to push a large trunk 5 m across the floor in 5 seconds.

DESIGNING AN EXPERIMENT

Design an experiment to solve the following problem. Include a hypothesis, variables, a procedure, and a type of data to collect and study.

PROBLEM: How much power, in watts, do you use when you climb a flight of stairs?

▲ Figure 14-19 Measuring the power of one horse

How Do They Know That?

HORSEPOWER

You are probably familiar with the term *horsepower*. Engines and motors are commonly rated in horsepower. An automobile engine, for example, may have about 100 horsepower. Where does this unit of power come from?

James Watt was the first person to use the term *horsepower*. Watt was a Scottish engineer and inventor. In the 1760s, he built the first practical steam engine. Watt wanted to use a unit of power for his engine that would be familiar to most people. He decided to use the power of a horse as the standard unit of power for the steam engine. Watt found that a strong horse could lift a 746-N load a distance of 1 m in 1 second. In other words, a horse produced 746 J/s of power. Watt defined this amount of power as 1 horsepower (hp).

Today, the unit of power is the watt (W). It is named in honor of James Watt. One watt is equal to 1 J/s. Therefore, 1 hp is equal to 746 W. Real horses are no longer used as a standard of power.

Thinking Critically What types of machinery are still rated in horsepower?

THINKING CRITICALLY ANSWERS

9. CALCULATE: 1,000 W

10. CALCULATE:

   a. power = work ÷ time;
   power = (force × distance) ÷ time;
   power = 10 N × 100 m ÷ 10 s;
   power = 100 N-m/s = 100 J/s;
   power = 100 W

   b. power = work ÷ time;
   power = 900 J ÷ 1 s;
   power = 900 J/s;
   power = 900 W

   c. power = work ÷ time;
   power = 30,000 J ÷ 15 s;
   power = 2,000 J/s;
   power = 2,000 W = 2 kW

   d. power = work ÷ time;
   power = (force × distance) ÷ time;
   power = 150 N × 5 m ÷ 5 s;
   power = 150 N-m/s = 150 J/s;
   power = 150 W

4 Close

DESIGNING AN EXPERIMENT

Use the Designing an Experiment Rubric on the Teacher's Resources CD-ROM to assess students' experiments. Fill in the rubric with the additional information below. For this assignment, students should have:

- mentioned, in forming the hypothesis, that power equals the rate of doing work.

- included, in the procedure, a measurement of their weight, height of the flight of stairs, and time necessary to climb the stairs.

How Do They Know That?

HORSEPOWER

Real-Life Connection By observing that a horse could lift a 746-N load a distance of 1 m in 1 s, Watt determined that the horse could lift the 746-N load at a speed of 1 m/s. Power is sometimes defined as force times speed. For example, 100 W of power is needed to lift a 100-N load at a speed of 1 m/s. If 200 W of power is supplied to lift the same 100-N load, the load can be lifted at a speed of 2 m/s—twice as fast as before.

Thinking Critically Answer
engines and motors

• *TEACHING RESOURCES* •

Teacher's Resources CD-ROM
Lesson Review: Chapter 14, p. 13

Enrichment: Chapter 14, p. 14

Designing an Experiment: Study Tools, p. 14

Designing an Experiment Rubric: Teaching Tools, p. 7

Lab Activity

(pp. 306–307)

1 Prepare the Lab

Studying Energy Changes in a Roller Coaster

SET-UP TIME: ⏰   **LAB TIME:** 🕐

BACKGROUND: Roller coasters are potential and kinetic energy machines. Work is done moving the cars to the top of the first hill. The work transfers gravitational potential energy to the cars. When the cars crest the top of the hill, potential energy converts into kinetic energy and the ride begins. The kinetic energy carries the cars through a series of loops, turns, and hills until the end is reached.

PURPOSE: Students will investigate the relationship between potential energy and kinetic energy.

SCIENCE SKILLS: Students will **model** a roller coaster track, **measure** the height of its hills, and **communicate** results. They will use this experiment to **infer** how kinetic energy and potential energy are related.

ADVANCE PLANNING: Obtain plastic tubing (whose inner diameter is at least 3/4 in.) from a hardware store. Cut the tubing into 1.5-m lengths.

2 Guide the Lab

PROCEDURE: Divide students into groups of three. Discuss the procedure for the activity. Ask students for their ideas of what they might use to support the tubing to make the roller-coaster hills. Remind students that for the first hill, the end of the tubing must be elevated to a height of at least 1 m above the floor or tabletop. Provide students with a copy of the Lab Activity Report found on the Teacher's Resources CD-ROM to record their observations and conclusions.

TROUBLESHOOTING: Tell students that the roller-coaster track must be straight. Any lateral movements will reduce some of the kinetic energy of the marble.

EXPECTED OUTCOME: Students will discover that to keep the marble rolling to the end of the track, each successive hill must be smaller than the one before.

LAB ACTIVITY
Studying Energy Changes in a Roller Coaster

BACKGROUND

Have you ever ridden a roller coaster? If you have, you were probably more concerned with fun than the science behind its operation. Roller coasters are machines that use potential and kinetic energy.

PURPOSE

In this activity, you will experiment with how roller coasters change potential energy into kinetic energy and back again several times.

PROCEDURE

1. Raise one end of the plastic tubing about $1\frac{1}{2}$ m above the floor. Tape this end to a bookcase or some other object so that it stays put. The tubing will serve as a roller-coaster track.

2. Use furniture, books, or other objects to make hills for your model roller coaster. Keep the track with its hills in a straight line. Do not include any turns. Tape the track securely so that it does not move.

Materials
Clear plastic tubing
Masking tape
Small ball bearing or glass bead
Meter stick
Pencil and paper

▲ **STEP 1** Tape one end of the track.

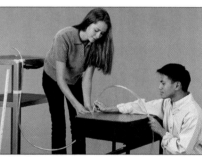

▲ **STEP 2** Create hills and valleys along one track.

Teaching Options

❗ FAST FACTS   *A Roller Coaster's First Hill*

The design of a roller coaster's first hill sets the stage for the rest of the ride. Height, drop, and angle of the first hill are important factors in generating a fast and exciting ride. For example, the first hill of the *Millennium Force* roller coaster at Cedar Point Amusement Park in Sandusky, Ohio, has a height of 94.5 m (310 ft), a drop of 91.4 m (300 ft), and an angle of descent of 80°. At the bottom of the first plunge, the roller coaster has a speed of about 150 km/h (93 mi/h). If the first hill had a shallower angle of descent, the frictional force on the car would be increased and the car would be traveling at a slower speed. The mechanical energy of the car at the top of the first hill carries it along the entire length of the roller-coaster ride, which is 2,010 m (6,595 ft).

3. Measure and record the height of the hills. Draw a sketch of your model roller coaster. Include your measurements.

4. Insert a ball bearing into the tubing at the high end. Test your model. Does the ball bearing reach the end of the track? Explain why. If necessary, adjust your design so that the ball bearing travels the entire length of the track.

5. After testing your roller coaster, take it apart and make a new design for your track. You may wish to add curves or even some loops. Draw a sketch of your new design and test it. Record your observations.

▲ STEP 4 Test your roller coaster

CONCLUSIONS

1. OBSERVE AND DESCRIBE: What happened to the marble as you released it at the top of your roller-coaster track?

2. ANALYZE: Why does the first hill of a roller coaster have to be the highest hill?

3. OBSERVE: Compare the height of the hills as you move from the top to the bottom of the roller coaster.

4. ANALYZE: Why must the pattern of the hills be set up as it is?

5. INFER: Where on your roller coaster does the ball bearing have potential energy changing to kinetic energy? Where is kinetic energy changing to potential energy?

6. INFER: Where on your roller coaster does the ball bearing have the greatest potential energy? The least potential energy?

7. INFER: Where on your roller coaster does the ball bearing have the greatest kinetic energy? The least kinetic energy?

▲ STEP 5 Make a new design for your track.

Tips for Using Technology

Word Processing Software

Have students use word processing software to write about their observations. A simple word processing program allows students to do basic tasks such as entering and editing text. A more complex word processing program allows students to make tables, draw pictures, do math, and make graphs. Remind students to use the spelling and grammar check. Students can print out their word processing document to share with the class.

• TEACHING RESOURCES •

Teacher's Resources CD-ROM
Lab Activity Report: Study Tools, pp. 16–17

Laboratory Activity Rubric: Teaching Tools, p. 8

3 Conclude the Lab

1. **OBSERVE AND DESCRIBE:** Possible observations may include that the marble's speed increases and decreases as it rolls down and up hills, respectively; moves fastest along the level surface; and moves slowest at the crest of hills.

2. **ANALYZE:** The first hill has to be the highest so that the marble has enough gravitational potential energy to overcome friction.

3. **OBSERVE:** The heights of the hills become successively smaller.

4. **ANALYZE:** Since the total energy decreases as energy is expended on friction, the maximum gravitational potential energy of locations along the track must also decrease. The gravitational potential energy depends on the heights of the hills. Therefore, the heights of the hills must decrease along the track so that the marble can crest each hill.

5. **INFER:** Potential energy is changing to kinetic energy when the marble is rolling down a hill. Kinetic energy is changing to potential energy when the marble is rolling up a hill.

6. **INFER:** The marble has the greatest potential energy at the top of the first hill (starting point). It has the least potential energy when it is rolling along the floor or tabletop.

7. **INFER:** The marble has its greatest kinetic energy at the bottom of the first hill. It has its least kinetic energy at the top of the first hill (starting point).

Use the Laboratory Activity Rubric on the Teacher's Resources CD-ROM to assess students' lab activities. Fill in the rubric with the additional information below. For this activity, students should have:

• performed the activity according to the procedure and made sketches of the model roller coasters made during the activity.

• correctly answered the questions in complete sentences.

4 Extend the Lab

Challenge student groups to create the greatest number of hills from start to finish. Permit groups to string their roller-coaster tracks together so that they can redesign their roller coasters to include loops and lateral bends.

Challenges (pp. 308–310)

Chapter Summary

Review Before students begin the Challenges, review the summary with them. Have each student read a bulleted statement and then paraphrase it.

✎ **STUDY HINT** Have students use index cards to create study questions for each Chapter Summary statement. Have students write a Chapter Summary statement on one side of the index card and then a question based on the statement on the other. Have students work in pairs to review the chapter.

Key Term Challenges

MATCHING

1. potential energy (14-1)
2. energy (14-1)
3. work (14-4)
4. kinetic energy (14-1)
5. joule (14-5)
6. watt (14-6)
7. power (14-6)

FILL IN

8. kinetic energy (14-1)
9. energy (14-1)
10. kinetic energy (14-1)
11. thermal pollution (14-3)
12. law of conservation of energy (14-3)
13. work (14-4)
14. joule (14-5)
15. power (14-6)
16. watt (14-6)

Chapter Summary

Lesson 14-1
- **Energy** is the ability to make something happen.
- There are two basic kinds of energy—potential energy and kinetic energy
- **Potential energy** is stored energy. **Kinetic energy** is energy of motion.

Lesson 14-2
- There are six main forms of energy: mechanical energy, electrical energy, electromagnetic energy, heat energy, chemical energy, and nuclear energy.

Lesson 14-3
- Energy can change from one form to another.
- When energy changes form, some of the energy is always changed into heat energy.
- The **law of conservation of energy** states that energy can never be created or destroyed but only changed in form.
- The total amount of matter and energy in the universe never changes.

Lesson 14-4
- **Work** is done when a force moves an object.
- For work to be done, the direction of the applied force must be the same as the direction of motion.

Lesson 14-5
- Work can be measured in newton-meters (N-m).
- The unit of work is the **joule** (J); 1 J = 1 N-m.
- When measuring work, you must measure the force applied in the direction of motion.

Lesson 14-6
- **Power** is the amount of work done per unit of time.
- Power = work/time, or (force × distance)/time.
- The SI unit of power is the **watt** (W).

Key Term Challenges

energy (p. 292)	potential energy (p. 292)
joule (p. 302)	power (p. 304)
kinetic energy (p. 292)	thermal pollution (p. 296)
law of conservation of	watt (p. 304)
energy (p. 296)	work (p. 300)

MATCHING Write the Key Term from above that best matches each description.

1. stored energy
2. ability to make something happen
3. force times distance
4. energy of motion
5. metric unit of work
6. metric unit of power
7. work done per unit time

FILL IN Write the Key Term from above that best completes each statement.

8. The moving water in a waterfall has _____.
9. The _____ in a match is stored in the chemicals in the match head.
10. The faster you run, the more _____ you have.
11. Waste heat that escapes into the environment can cause _____.
12. The _____ states that energy cannot be made or destroyed but only changed in form.
13. When you use force to move an object, you are doing _____.
14. The _____ is the unit used to measure work.
15. The rate at which you do work is called _____.
16. The unit of power is the _____.

Teaching Options

PREPARING STUDENTS FOR STANDARDIZED TESTS

Reading Strategy: Tell students to identify the keywords in the question and then locate those words in the paragraph. This strategy will help them quickly find the information they need to answer the question.

Writing Strategy: Remind students that complete sentences should have a subject and a predicate. Their answers should match the subject and predicate in the question asked.

Interpreting Visuals: Tell students to read all of the questions before studying the visual. Knowing the questions helps them to focus on the parts of the diagram where they will find the answers.

ESL/ELL STRATEGY

Understanding Work Guide students in understanding that work can be done by things as well as by people. For example, falling water does work. People can also do work. Have pairs of students write two sentences that illustrate the different meanings of the word.

Content Challenges TEST PREP

MULTIPLE CHOICE Write the letter of the term or phrase that best completes each statement.

1. An object that is raised above the ground has
   a. heat energy.
   b. kinetic energy.
   c. potential energy.
   d. nuclear energy.

2. All moving objects have
   a. heat energy.
   b. kinetic energy.
   c. potential energy.
   d. nuclear energy.

3. Sound is a form of
   a. nuclear energy.
   b. electromagnetic energy.
   c. chemical energy.
   d. mechanical energy.

4. Electromagnetic energy includes X-rays and
   a. light.
   b. sound.
   c. chemicals.
   d. atoms.

5. An automobile engine changes chemical energy into
   a. electricity.
   b. nuclear energy.
   c. mechanical energy.
   d. light.

6. In the Sun, nuclear energy is changed into light energy and
   a. sound energy.
   b. chemical energy.
   c. electrical energy.
   d. heat energy.

7. Work = force times
   a. distance.
   b. mass.
   c. power.
   d. energy.

8. Work is measured in units called
   a. watts.
   b. meters.
   c. joules.
   d. newtons.

9. One watt is equal to
   a. 1 m/s.
   b. 1 J/s.
   c. 1 N/s.
   d. 1 kW/s.

TRUE/FALSE Write *true* if the statement is true. If the statement is false, change the underlined term to make the statement true.

10. Energy is the ability to do <u>work</u>.

11. Stored energy is <u>kinetic</u> energy.

12. <u>Potential</u> energy is energy of motion.

13. There are <u>six</u> main forms of energy.

14. The energy that holds atomic particles together is <u>nuclear</u> energy.

15. When energy changes form, some energy is always wasted as <u>sound</u>.

16. Energy <u>cannot</u> be made or destroyed.

17. Energy <u>cannot</u> be changed in form without work being done.

18. To measure work, you must know force and <u>time</u>.

19. For work to be done, an object must move in the <u>opposite</u> direction of the force applied to it.

20. In a light bulb, electrical energy is changed to light and <u>sound</u>.

Content Challenges

MULTIPLE CHOICE

1. c (14-1)
2. b (14-1)
3. d (14-2)
4. a (14-2)
5. c (14-3)
6. d (14-2, 14-3)
7. a (14-4)
8. c (14-5)
9. b (14-6)

TRUE/FALSE

10. true (14-1)
11. false; potential (14-1)
12. false; Kinetic (14-1)
13. true (14-2)
14. true (14-2)
15. false; heat (14-3)
16. true (14-3)
17. false; can (14-4)
18. false; distance (14-4)
19. false; same (14-4)
20. false; heat (14-3)

ALTERNATIVE ASSESSMENT

Identifying Energy Tape two meter sticks to a wall, one on top of the other, to show a height of 2 m. Have a volunteer hold a book at the 1.0-m height. Ask: *What kind of energy does the book have?* (gravitational potential energy) *What form of energy does the book have?* (mechanical energy) Tell the volunteer to hold the book at a position where it has more gravitational potential energy. (above 1.0 m) Ask: *If you drop the book, what kind of energy will the book have just before it hits the floor?* (kinetic energy) *What energy change took place when the book was falling?* (Gravitational potential energy changed into kinetic energy.)

PORTFOLIO ASSESSMENT

Making Student Portfolios
Portfolio Assessment is designed to evaluate a student's performance over an extended period of time. Students can demonstrate their comprehension of the concepts in this chapter by making a portfolio. The Chapter Self-Check, the Big Idea Planner, and the Weekly Journal are some of the reproducibles on the Teacher's Resources CD-ROM that they can include in their portfolios. You can use the Portfolio Assessment Rubric also found on the Teacher's Resources CD-ROM to assess students' portfolios.

Content Challenges

WRITTEN RESPONSE

1. **COMPARE:** Potential energy is stored energy. Kinetic energy is energy of motion. (14-1)
2. **ANALYZE:** When a pendulum is at the top of its swing, it has only potential energy. As the pendulum swings, its potential energy changes to kinetic energy. (14-1)
3. **EXPLAIN:** Possible answer: The equation shows that a small amount of matter can be changed to a huge amount of energy. (14-3)
4. **INFER:** A person can use chemical energy to move muscles while pushing on an object that does not move. (14-4)
5. **RELATE:** power = work ÷ time (14-6)
6. **INFER:** because the position of the object determines its gravitational potential energy (14-1)

INTERPRETING A DIAGRAM (14-5)

7. 10 N
8. 2 m
9. 10 N
10. 20 J
11. 10 N
12. 2 m
13. 4 N
14. 8 J
15. Different; More work is being done in lifting the object 2 m than by sliding it 2 m because lifting it requires more force than sliding it.

Chapter Project Wrap-Up

SNAIL RUN

Projects can be exhibited around the classroom. Have students launch their marbles simultaneously and compare the relative speed of each marble. You can use the Individual Activity Rubric found on the Teacher's Resources CD-ROM to assess students' projects. Fill in the rubric with the additional information below. For this project, students should have:

- designed and built a ramp so that a marble rolls down slowly.
- measured times to show the slow rate at which the marble moved.

Content Challenges <u>TEST PREP</u>

WRITTEN RESPONSE Complete the exercises and answer each of the following questions in complete sentences.

1. **COMPARE:** Explain the difference between potential energy and kinetic energy.
2. **ANALYZE:** Describe the changes in potential and kinetic energy that take place in a swinging pendulum.
3. **EXPLAIN:** How does Einstein's equation, $E = mc^2$, support the law of conservation of energy?
4. **INFER:** How is it possible for energy to change form without any work being done?
5. **RELATE:** What is the relationship between work and power?
6. **INFER:** Why is gravitational potential energy called energy of position?

INTERPRETING A DIAGRAM Use Figures 14-20 and 14-21 to answer the following questions.

7. What is the weight of the object in Figure 14-20?
8. What distance is this object being lifted?
9. How much force is needed to lift this object?
10. How much work is being done to lift this object?
11. What is the weight of the object in Figure 14-21?
12. What distance is this object being pulled?
13. How much force is needed to pull this object?
14. How much work is being done to pull this object?
15. Is the amount of work being done in the two diagrams the same or different? Explain.

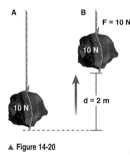

▲ Figure 14-20

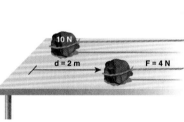

▲ Figure 14-21

310

Teaching Options

UNIT CHALLENGE ONLINE

Renewable Energy You may wish to have students begin the Unit Challenge Online activity described on page T356 of this book.

• *TEACHING RESOURCES* •

Teacher's Resources CD-ROM

Key Term Review: Chapter 14, p. 15

Chapter 14 Test: pp. 16–17

Individual Activity Rubric: Teaching Tools, p. 5

Chapter Self-Check: Teaching Tools, p. 11

Big Idea Planner: Study Tools, pp. 11–12

Weekly Journal: Study Tools, p. 19

Portfolio Assessment Rubric: Teaching Tools, p. 10

Chapter **15** Machines

PLANNING GUIDE

◆ **TEACHING THE CHAPTER** This chapter should take approximately 6–9 days to complete instruction and assessment.

	Skills and Features	Projects and Activities	Achieve Science Literacy	Meet Individual Needs
Chapter 15 Opener p. T311	DESIGN	• Chapter Project		
Lesson 15-1 **What is a simple machine?** pp. T312–T313 Standard: B2c	DESCRIBE, ANALYZE, INFER • Investigate • Building Math Skills	• Cooperative Learning • Extending the Lesson • More on the Web • Lab Skills Worksheet	• Study Hint • Reading Strategy • Ongoing Assessment	CD-ROM Enrichment Activity Concept Map Six Simple Machines
Lesson 15-2 **What is efficiency?** pp. T314–T315 Standard: B2c	ANALYZE, NAME, INFER • Building Math Skills • Real-Life Science	• More on the Web • Lab Challenge	• Study Hint • Reading Strategy • Ongoing Assessment	• ESL/ELL Strategy CD-ROM Enrichment Activity
Lesson 15-3 **How does a lever work?** pp. T316–T317 Standard: B2c	EXPLAIN, HYPOTHESIZE, IDENTIFY • Investigate • Web InfoSearch	• Cooperative Learning • Extending the Lesson	• Study Hint • Reading Strategy • Writing Hint • Ongoing Assessment	CD-ROM Enrichment Activity Six Simple Machines Laboratory Videos
Lesson 15-4 **How do pulleys work?** pp. T318–T319 Standard: B2c	ANALYZE, INFER, MODEL • Building Science Skills • Hands-On Activity	• Extending the Lesson • More on the Web	• Study Hint • Reading Strategy • Ongoing Assessment	• Reteach CD-ROM Enrichment Activity Venn Diagram Six Simple Machines
Lab Activity **Pulley Advantage** pp. T320–T321 Standard: B2c	OBSERVE, ANALYZE, INFER • Set-Up Time: 30 min • Lab Time: 45 min	• Cooperative Learning • Lab Skills Worksheet • Extend the Lab Activity	• Tips for Using Technology	CD-ROM Lab Activity Report Spreadsheet
Lesson 15-5 **What are inclined planes?** pp. T322–T323 Standard: B2c	ANALYZE, DEFINE, EXPLAIN • Hands-On Activity • Interpreting Visuals	• More on the Web	• Study Hint • Writing Hint • Ongoing Assessment	• ESL/ELL Strategy • Reteach CD-ROM Enrichment Activity Six Simple Machines

Planning Guide continues on next page.

Standards: For details on the correlation to National Science Standards see pages *xx–xxi*.

	Skills and Features	Projects and Activities	Achieve Science Literacy	Meet Individual Needs
Big Idea **How did the Egyptians build the Great Pyramid?** pp. T324–T325 Standard: B2c	RESEARCH, COMMUNICATE, ANALYZE • Science Log: Writing Activity	• Big Idea Online • Close Activity	• Tips for Using Technology	• ESL/ELL Strategy ⊙ CD-ROM Big Idea Planner Project Sketch
Lesson 15-6 **What is a compound machine?** pp. T326–T327	COMPARE, DEFINE, NAME • Health and Safety Tip • Science and Technology	• Extending the Lesson • More on the Web	• Study Hint • Reading Strategy • Ongoing Assessment	• Reteach ⊙ CD-ROM Enrichment Activity Writing Activity Outline Six Simple Machines
Chapter 15 Challenges pp. T328–T330	• Chapter Summary • Key Term Challenges • Content Challenges • Concept Challenges	• Chapter Project Wrap-Up	• Study Hint • Preparing Students for Standardized Tests	• ESL/ELL Strategy ⊙ CD-ROM Chapter Self-Check Venn Diagram Concept Map

Teacher Notes

Chapter 15 · Machines

▲ **Figure 15-1** The Guggenheim Museum in New York City

The walkway around the inside walls of the Guggenheim Museum is one continuous ramp. The ramp is an inclined plane, a type of simple machine. You can walk along the ramp and view exhibits from the ground level to the top level without using stairs or an elevator.

▶ Is walking up a ramp easier than walking up a staircase? Explain.

Contents

UNIT 5: Force, Motion, and Energy   **311**

Teaching Options

ASSESSMENT PLANNER

For assessment in the Student Edition, see the following pages:

Content Assessment
Checking Concepts: pp. 313, 315, 317, 319, 323, 327
Thinking Critically: pp. 313, 315, 317, 319, 323, 327
Interpreting Visuals: pp. 319, 323
Chapter Challenges: pp. 328–330

Alternative Assessment
Building Skills: pp. 313, 315, 319
Web InfoSearch: p. 317
Science Log: p. 325

Performance-Based Assessment
Hands-On Activity: pp. 319, 323
Lab Activity: pp. 320–321

• TEACHING RESOURCES •

Teacher's Resources CD-ROM
Lesson Review: Ch. 15, pp. 2, 3, 4, 5, 6, 9
Enrichment: Ch. 15, pp. 7, 10
Key Term Review: Ch. 15, p. 11
Chapter 15 Test: pp. 12–13
Laboratory Manual: pp. 13–14, 77–80

Laboratory Videos
Segment 15: Using First-Class Levers
Segment 16: Using Second-Class Levers

Chapter 15
Machines

Chapter Overview

In this chapter, students will discover that a simple machine is a device that makes work easier. They will determine a machine's efficiency and explore the structure of levers, pulleys, and inclined planes. Students will also realize that a compound machine is made up of simple machines.

About Figure 15-1 This ramp at the Guggenheim Museum is more than just a uniquely designed inclined plane. It is the museum. Most patrons take an elevator to the top floor and then slowly make their way down the ramp while viewing the art on display. Since an inclined plane reduces the amount of work needed, yet increases distance, this is the perfect combination for displaying a lot of art in a small amount of space. In addition, it does not cause the viewers to get too tired from walking up and down stairs.

Answer Possible answer: Yes. Instead of lifting your legs straight up against gravity, you lift them up at an angle, thus reducing work.

Linking Prior Knowledge

For this chapter, students should recall:
- the definition of *friction* (Lesson 12-4).
- the definition of *work* (Lesson 14-4).
- how to measure *work* (Lesson 14-5).

Chapter Project

INVENTING A COMPOUND MACHINE

MATERIALS: posterboard, markers, reference materials

Divide students into small groups. After students have read the lesson, each group should brainstorm ideas on inventing a compound machine that uses all six simple machines. Students do not have to actually build the machine. They should design it, draw what it would look like, and write a description on what it would do and how it would do it. **learning styles: visual, linguistic**

15-1 *(pp. 312–313)*

1 Introduce

🔍 INVESTIGATE

TIME: 10–15 minutes

PURPOSE: Students will identify common machines.

MATERIALS: paper, pencil

PROCEDURE: You might want to start the activity by having volunteers name different machines in the classroom. Have students record these responses in their charts and then complete their charts independently. **learning styles: visual, auditory**

THINK ABOUT IT: Students should identify the parts of their chosen machine and realize that using a machine reduces the amount of energy needed to complete a task.

🖊 **STUDY HINT** Before beginning this lesson, have students review the Key Terms and their definitions.

Linking Prior Knowledge Invite a volunteer to read the lesson objective aloud. Ask students to draw upon their knowledge of work (Lessons 14-4 and 14-5) and their reading of the Key Terms to predict how simple machines make work easier.

2 Teach

Demonstration Bring a variety of machines to class, such as a can opener, a pencil sharpener, a screwdriver, and an eggbeater. Demonstrate how each machine makes work easier by changing the size of the effort force, the direction of a force, or the speed of a force.
learning styles: visual, auditory

Discussion Ask students to observe Figure 15-2 and describe how the six simple machines are alike and how they are different. **learning style: visual**

📖 **READING STRATEGY** To help students understand effort force, have them copy the illustrations in Figure 15-2. They should label the arrows that show where the effort force is applied in each of the examples.

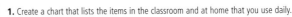

15-1 What is a simple machine?

🔍 INVESTIGATE
Using Machines
HANDS-ON ACTIVITY

1. Create a chart that lists the items in the classroom and at home that you use daily.
2. Check off each item you believe to be a machine.
3. Choose an item from your list. Tell a partner how it works as a machine.

THINK ABOUT IT: What are the different parts of your machine? How does it make your life easier?

STEP 3

Objective
Describe how machines make work easier.

Key Terms

machine: device that makes work easier

wheel and axle: two different-sized wheels that turn together around the same point

effort force: force applied to a machine

resistance force: force that opposes the effort force

mechanical advantage: number of times a machine multiplies the effort force

ideal mechanical advantage: mechanical advantage a machine would have with no friction

Simple Machines People use machines to make work easier. Did you ever try to take the lid off a can of paint using only your hands? If the lid is on very tight, your fingers cannot supply enough force to remove the lid. However, you can use a screwdriver as a lever to help you pry off the lid. A lever is an example of a simple machine. A **machine** is a device that makes work easier. Machines make work easier by changing the size, direction, or speed of a force.

Most machines are made up of two or more of the six simple machines shown in Figure 15-2. They are the lever, the pulley, the inclined plane, the screw, the wheel and axle, and the wedge.

▶ **NAME:** What are the six simple machines?

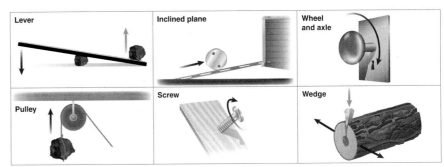

▲ **Figure 15-2** There are six simple machines.

312

Teaching Options

EXTENDING THE LESSON

Making Concept Maps Write the head *Simple Machines* on the board. Draw arrows from this head to each of the following heads: *Lever, Pulley, Inclined Plane, Wedge, Screw,* and *Wheel and Axle.* Have students copy the concept map into their notebooks. Have students include examples of each type of simple machine. Students can also use the Concept Map found on the Teacher's Resources CD-ROM.
learning style: visual

COOPERATIVE LEARNING

Classifying Machines Have students work in pairs to classify the following machines: a knife (wedge), a crowbar (lever), an axe (wedge), a staircase (inclined plane), a steering wheel (wheel and axle), and a clothesline (pulley).

QUICK CONVERSIONS

Metric/SI	English	Metric/SI	English
160 N	36 lb	1,500 N	337 lb
200 N	45 lb	1,600 N	360 lb
300 N	67 lb	3,000 N	675 lb
1,000 N	225 lb		

Wheel and Axle The next time you open a door by turning a doorknob, stop for a minute and think. You have just used a simple machine called a wheel and axle. A **wheel and axle** is two different-sized wheels that turn together around the same point.

A wheel and axle is like a lever that moves in a circle. Many wheel-and-axle machines do not look like a wheel and axle. Figure 15-3 shows how a simple wrench can be a wheel and axle.

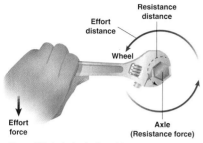

Resistance distance
Effort distance
Wheel
Effort force
Axle (Resistance force)

▲ **Figure 15-3** A wheel and axle machine

What makes a wheel and axle a simple machine? It makes work easier. It takes less force to turn the handle than it would to turn the axle by itself. You exert a small force on the handle, which exerts a larger force on the axle.

2 EXPLAIN: What makes a wheel and axle a simple machine?

Effort Force and Resistance Force The force you apply to a machine is called the **effort force.** For example, the force you apply to a wrench is the effort force. The force that opposes the effort force is called the **resistance force.** The nut is the resistance force you are trying to overcome when you turn the handle. A machine like the wrench lets you use a small force to overcome a large force.

Machines make work easier but they do not change the *amount* of work you do. When you use a machine, you often sacrifice distance to multiply your effort force. Look again at the wrench in Figure 15-3. You can see that the effort force applied to the wrench has to move a greater distance then does the resistance force you overcome when you turn the nut.

3 INFER: Does a wheel and axle change the size, direction, or speed of a force?

Mechanical Advantage Most machines help you do work by multiplying the effort force you apply to the machine. The number of times a machine multiplies the effort force is called the **mechanical advantage (MA)** of that machine. To find the mechanical advantage of a machine, divide the resistance force by the effort force. Use the example below to find the MA if you apply a force of 100 N to a machine to move a 1,500-N object.

$$MA = \text{resistance force} \div \text{effort force}$$
$$MA = 1{,}500 \text{ N} \div 100 \text{ N}$$
$$MA = 15$$

4 DEFINE: What is mechanical advantage?

Ideal Mechanical Advantage The MA that a machine would have with no friction is known as the **ideal mechanical advantage (IMA)** of that machine. For example, the IMA of a single moveable pulley is 2. Such a pulley should multiply your effort force by 2. However, because of friction, and the weight of the pulley, the actual MA of the pulley will be less than 2.

5 DESCRIBE: What is the IMA of a machine?

☑ **CHECKING CONCEPTS**

1. How can you find the IMA of a machine?
2. What is resistance force?
3. What is force effort?

💡 **THINKING CRITICALLY**

4. INFER: How does friction affect the IMA of a machine?
5. ANALYZE: Can the actual MA of a machine ever be greater than its IMA? Explain.

BUILDING MATH SKILLS

Calculating Use the data in Figure 15-4 to find the MA of each simple machine.

	Effort force	Resistance force
a.	300 N	3,000 N
b.	160 N	1,600 N

▲ **Figure 15-4**

Answers to questions

1 NAME: lever, pulley, inclined plane, wedge, screw, and wheel and axle

2 EXPLAIN: It makes work easier.

3 INFER: size

4 DEFINE: the number of times a machine multiplies an effort force

5 DESCRIBE: the mechanical advantage that a machine would have with no friction

Reinforcement Make sure that students understand that machines make work easier by changing the size, direction, or speed of a force. The force that goes into the machine is called the effort force. The force that opposes the effort force is the resistance force. Machines do not, however, increase the work that is put into them. Often, distance is sacrificed. For example, if you use a wrench to turn a nut, the distance that you turn the handle through is greater than the distance that the nut moves.

3 Assess

☑ **CHECKING CONCEPTS ANSWERS**

1. Divide resistance force by effort force.
2. force that opposes the effort force
3. force applied to a machine

💡 **THINKING CRITICALLY ANSWERS**

4. INFER: Friction does not affect the IMA; it affects the MA.
5. ANALYZE: No, the MA of a machine is always less because of friction.

4 Close

BUILDING MATH SKILLS ANSWERS

Calculating

a. 10 N
b. 10 N

ONGOING ASSESSMENT

Classifying Simple Machines Have students list simple machines that they use every day. Write students' responses on the board. As a class, classify each simple machine.
learning styles: auditory, linguistic

• TEACHING RESOURCES •

Teacher's Resources CD-ROM
Lesson Review: Chapter 15, p. 2
Enrichment: Chapter 15, p. 10
Concept Map: Study Tools, p. 4
Six Simple Machines: Visuals, p. 10
Laboratory Manual
Lab. Skills Worksheet 4: Organizing and Analyzing Data, pp. 13–14

1 Introduce

STUDY HINT Before beginning this lesson, have students study Figure 15-6. Ask them to name the eight simple machines. (The eight oars act as levers.)

Linking Prior Knowledge Ask students to recall what they learned about friction (Lesson 12-4). Then, ask them to give examples of friction causing something to get hot.

2 Teach

Discussion To help students understand efficiency as a percentage, compare it with a score on a test. Remind students that the score that they receive on a test can be expressed as a percentage. The percentage is found by dividing the number of questions answered correctly by the number of questions on the test, and then multiplying by 100. Efficiency as a percentage is found by dividing the work done on a machine by the work done by the machine, and then multiplying by 100. **learning styles: auditory, logical/mathematical**

Demonstration Show students how using a longer lever can reduce the needed effort force by prying open a can of paint with a small screwdriver and then another can of paint with a longer screwdriver. Students should observe that it is much easier to open the lid, using the longer screwdriver. **learning style: visual**

READING STRATEGY Write *efficient* on the board. Ask students to describe situations in which they have heard this term. Have students draw upon these real-life experiences to define the term. (producing a desired effect with a minimum amount of waste)

15-2 What is efficiency?

Objective
Explain how to find the efficiency of a machine.

Key Terms
work output: work done by a machine
work input: work done on a machine
efficiency (eh-FIHSH-uhn-see): ratio of work output to work input

Work Input and Work Output The work done by a machine is **work output.** Work output is equal to the resistance force times the distance through which the resistance force moves.

work output = resistance force × resistance distance

The work done on a machine is **work input.** The work input equals the effort force times the effort distance. The effort distance is the distance through which the force moves.

work input = effort force × effort distance

Machines cannot increase the amount of work done. As a result, the work output of a machine is never greater than the work input.

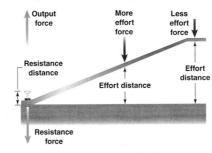

▲ **Figure 15-5** The longer the lever, the greater the effort distance. This reduces the needed effort force.

1 NAME: What is the work done by a machine called?

314

Efficiency Not all of the work put into a machine is changed into useful work. Some of the work input is used to overcome friction. This work is lost as heat energy. The **efficiency** of a machine is the ratio of work output to work input. It is usually expressed as a percentage.

You can find the percentage efficiency of a machine by dividing the work output by the work input and multiplying by 100.

percentage efficiency = work output ÷ work input × 100

Remember, the work done by a machine is always less than the work put into it. So, the efficiency of a machine is always less than 100%.

2 INFER: Why is the efficiency of a machine always less than 100%?

Increasing Efficiency The boat shown in Figure 15-6 is a racing shell. The oars used to move the shell through the water are levers. Each rower exerts an effort force on one end of an oar. As the oar moves through the water, it overcomes a resistance. The boat resists moving through the water because of the force of friction between the boat and the water.

Suppose some way could be found to reduce the force of friction between the boat and the water. This would decrease the resistance. Then, if each crew

▲ **Figure 15-6** Work is being done on the boat by eight simple machines.

Teaching Options

FAST FACTS Law of Conservation of Energy

Since the efficiency of a machine is always less than 100 percent, it would seem that some energy put into a machine is lost. However, just like matter, energy can never be created or destroyed. It can only change form. The difference between a machine's efficiency percentage and 100 percent is the amount of energy that has been changed to heat energy through friction. The efficiency of a car engine can be as low as 30 percent. The remaining 70 percent of the energy put into the engine changes to heat energy.

ESL/ELL STRATEGY

Explaining in- and out- as Prefixes Explain that *in-* and *out-* are prefixes. Tell students that knowing the meaning of a prefix often helps decode an unknown word. Tell students that *in-* commonly means "within," and *out-* commonly means "beyond." Then, write the following terms on the board and have students define each one: *indoors, outdoors, inland,* and *outfield.* **learning styles: auditory, linguistic**

member applies the same effort to the oars, the boat will move farther with each pull on the oars. In other words, the work input would remain the same, but the work output would be greater. This means that the efficiency has been increased.

3 ANALYZE: What is another way to increase efficiency besides decreasing the resistance force?

✓ CHECKING CONCEPTS

1. The work put out by a machine is _____ than the work put into a machine.
2. The efficiency of a machine is usually expressed as a _____.
3. Some of the work you put into a machine is always used to overcome _____.
4. The work put into a machine is equal to the effort force multiplied by the effort _____.
5. The efficiency of a machine always is less than _____.

Real-Life Science

BICYCLING

The first successful bicycle was built by Baron Karl Von Drais de Sauerbrun in Karlsruhe, Germany, in 1817. This early bicycle had no pedals. Riders moved the bicycle forward by pushing backward against the ground with their feet. By 1839, a Scottish blacksmith, Kirkpatrick Macmillan, had added pedals. The modern bicycle began to be developed.

In Europe and Asia, bicycles are major means of transportation. In the United States, bicycles are used mainly for recreation and exercise. Streets in many cities and towns have specially marked bicycle lanes. Bike paths are set aside in parks and in rural areas. All cyclists should be aware of traffic and safety rules before riding their bicycles in any of these areas.

Special bicycles have been developed for racing. These bicycles are made of strong, lightweight materials, such as alloys of titanium and carbon. Racing tires are very narrow to reduce weight and frictional drag. To further reduce friction, cyclists wear tight, specially designed clothing and streamlined helmets. These people take their sport very seriously.

Thinking Critically What features might a bicycle designed for off-road trails have?

▲ Figure 15-8 Modern bicycles are made to be more efficient.

💡 THINKING CRITICALLY

6. ANALYZE: Why can a machine not produce more work than is put into it?
7. HYPOTHESIZE: Why do you think many complex machines have very low efficiencies?

BUILDING MATH SKILLS

Calculating Complete the table in Figure 15-7 by calculating the missing value.

Work input	Work output	Efficiency
10 J	5 J	
20 J		40%
	30 J	60%
45 J	9 J	
	9 J	90%

▲ Figure 15-7

Answers to questions

1 NAME: work output
2 INFER: Some of the work input is used to overcome friction.
3 ANALYZE: reduce the force of friction

3 Assess

✓ CHECKING CONCEPTS ANSWERS

1. less
2. percentage
3. friction
4. distance
5. 100%

💡 THINKING CRITICALLY ANSWERS

6. ANALYZE: because some of the work input is used to overcome friction
7. HYPOTHESIZE: Possible answer: Complex machines have many moving parts that cause friction.

4 Close

BUILDING MATH SKILLS ANSWERS

Calculating

Row 1: 50%, Row 2: 8 J; Row 3: 50 J
Row 4: 20%; Row 5: 10 J

Real-Life Science
BICYCLING

Real-Life Connection Bicycles should be maintained regularly to keep riders safe from injury. Air pressure in the tires should be kept at the recommended level. Moving parts, such as gears and chains, should be cleaned and lubricated. (Lubricants can cut down on friction.) Broken reflectors should be replaced. Failure to maintain these parts may result in accidents.

Thinking Critically Answer
Possible answer: a thick seat and wide tires with deep treads

---

MORE ON THE WEB

Efficient Lighting Have students visit www.concepts andchallenges.com to learn more about the inefficiency of incandescent lightbulbs.

ONGOING ASSESSMENT

Classifying Work Have students classify the following actions as examples of work input or work output: pushing down on a bicycle pedal (work input), blades of a pencil sharpener slicing a pencil (work output), a car moving upward by a jack (work output), turning a screwdriver handle (work input).

• TEACHING RESOURCES •

Teacher's Resources CD-ROM
Lesson Review: Chapter 15, p. 3
Enrichment: Chapter 15, p. 10
Laboratory Manual
Lab. Challenge: How can you find the efficiency of a machine? pp. 77–80

15-3 (pp. 316–317)

1 Introduce

🔍 INVESTIGATE

TIME: 10–15 minutes

PURPOSE: Students will explore the structure of a lever.

MATERIALS: meter stick, wood block, 1-lb weight, spring scale

PROCEDURE: Start the activity with a review of how to use a spring scale. Then, provide students with the materials listed above. Have a volunteer indicate the 50-cm mark on a meter stick. Make sure that all students place the weight at the 100-cm end of the stick and the spring scale at the 0-cm end.

THINK ABOUT IT: closer; when the wood block was at the 45-cm mark **learning styles: visual, tactile**

📝 **STUDY HINT** Before beginning this lesson, have students make a three-column chart in their notebooks with the heads *First-class lever*, *Second-class lever*, and *Third-class lever*. As students read the lesson, have them describe each type of lever and give examples.

Linking Prior Knowledge Ask students to name tools that they have used to pry something open. Record all responses on the board. Explain that the tools they named are types of simple machines called levers.

2 Teach

Demonstration Display a car jack to students. Show the various parts of the jack. Be sure that students understand that the handle of the jack acts as a lever. Then, measure its effort arm and resistance arm to find its ideal mechanical advantage.
learning styles: visual, logical/mathematical

Discussion Copy Figure 15-9 on the board. Point out and describe the resistance force, effort force, and fulcrum. Then, have students look at the diagrams of second- and third-class levers shown on page 317. Ask students how all levers are alike. (They all have an effort arm, a resistance arm, and a fulcrum.) Then, discuss how they are different. (the position of the fulcrum)
learning styles: visual, auditory

15-3 How does a lever work?

🔍 INVESTIGATE

Using a Lever
HANDS-ON ACTIVITY

1. Balance a meter stick on a wood block at the 50-cm mark.
2. Place a 5 N weight on one end of the meter stick. Attach a spring scale to the other end as shown in the picture.
3. Pull down on the spring scale. Record the effort force needed to lift the weight.
4. Repeat Step 3 with the wood block at the 45-cm mark and again with the block at the 55-cm mark.

THINK ABOUT IT: Is it easier to lift the weight when the wood block is closer to the weight or farther from it? In which case did the resistance move farthest?

STEP 3

Objectives

Explain how a lever makes work easier. Describe the three classes of levers.

Key Terms

lever (LEHV-uhr)**:** bar that is free to turn around a fixed point

fulcrum (FOOL-kruhm)**:** fixed point around which a lever pivots or turns

Levers Have you ever used a shovel or a crowbar? If so, then you have used a lever. A **lever** is a bar that is free to turn around a fixed point. The fixed point on which a lever turns is called the **fulcrum.** A lever can make work easier by increasing force. Levers also change the direction of a force and the distance over which a force acts.

A lever has two parts—an effort arm and a resistance arm. The effort arm is the distance from the effort force to the fulcrum. The resistance arm is the distance from the resistance force to the fulcrum.

You can find the IMA of a lever by dividing the length of the effort arm by the length of the resistance arm.

IMA = effort arm length ÷ resistance arm length

▶ **EXPLAIN:** How can you find the ideal mechanical advantage of a lever?

316

Classes of Levers There are three classes, or kinds, of levers. The classes of levers are based on the position of the resistance force, the effort force, and the fulcrum.

In a first-class lever, the fulcrum is between the effort force and the resistance force. These levers multiply force. The direction of the effort force is changed. Examples of first-class levers include crowbars, seesaws, and car jacks.

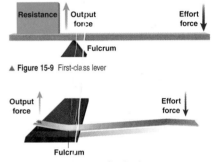

▲ **Figure 15-9** First-class lever

▲ **Figure 15-10** A crowbar is a first-class lever.

A second-class lever has the resistance between the effort force and the fulcrum. Second-class levers always multiply force. The direction of the effort force is not changed. Examples of second-class levers include wheelbarrows and nutcrackers.

Teaching Options

COOPERATIVE LEARNING

Classifying Levers Have pairs of students scan magazines for pictures of a first-, second-, and third-class lever. Then have them glue the pictures on posterboard, labeling each lever's effort arm, resistance arm, and fulcrum. Display the posters around the classroom to reinforce understanding of the three classes of levers.
learning styles: visual, tactile

EXTENDING THE LESSON

Making a Third-Class Lever Have students use a sheet of paper to make a fan. Have them hold one end of the fan and cool themselves with it. Ask: *What type of lever are your fans an example of?* (third-class lever) *How do you know?* (The part of the fan closest to their faces moves a greater distance than the part that they are holding in their hands. The fan is multiplying the distance the resistance force moves.)
learning styles: kinesthetic, tactile

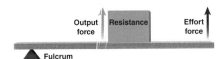

Output force / Resistance / Effort force

Fulcrum

▲ **Figure 15-11** Second-class lever

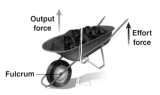

Output force / Effort force

Fulcrum

▲ **Figure 15-12** A wheelbarrow is a second-class lever.

In a third-class lever, the effort force is between the fulcrum and the resistance force. These levers multiply the distance the resistance force moves, but the direction of the effort force is not changed. In third-class levers, the effort arm is always shorter than the resistance arm. Examples of third-class levers include shovels, baseball bats, and brooms.

Effort force / Output force / Resistance

Fulcrum

▲ **Figure 15-13** Third-class lever

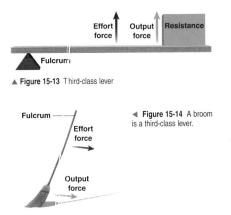

Fulcrum

Effort force

Output force

◀ **Figure 15-14** A broom is a third-class lever.

▶ IDENTIFY: In what class of lever is the effort force between the fulcrum and the resistance force?

☑ CHECKING CONCEPTS

1. The fixed point around which a lever turns is called the _____.
2. There are _____ classes of levers.
3. The ideal mechanical advantage of a lever is equal to the length of the effort arm divided by the length of the _____ arm.
4. In a _____-class lever, the effort force is between the fulcrum and the resistance force.
5. The resistance arm is the distance from the resistance force to the _____.

💡 THINKING CRITICALLY

6. **CALCULATE:** What is the IMA of a lever with an effort arm 2 m long and a resistance arm 0.5 m long?
7. **HYPOTHESIZE:** How could you increase the IMA of a lever?
8. **CLASSIFY:** Classify each of the following as a first-, second-, or third-class lever: nutcracker, bottle opener, hammer, and hockey stick.

Web InfoSearch

Levers in Your Body Different parts of the human body act as levers. Your arm is a third-class lever. Suppose you hold a book in your hand. The book is the resistance. Your elbow is the fulcrum. The muscles in your forearms provide the effort force to lift the book.

SEARCH: Use the Internet to find what other parts of your body act as levers. Create a chart and draw a picture of the body part and an example of the lever action. Start your search at www.conceptsandchallenges.com. Some key search words are **human body levers** and **human body simple machine.**

📖 **READING STRATEGY** Recommend to students that as they study Figures 15-9 and 15-10, they should sketch other first-class levers and label the output force, the effort force, the fulcrum, and the resistance. They should also make sketches for second- and third-class levers.

Answers to questions

▶ **EXPLAIN:** Divide the length of the effort arm by the length of the resistance arm.

▶ **IDENTIFY:** third-class lever

---

3 Assess

☑ CHECKING CONCEPTS ANSWERS

1. fulcrum
2. three
3. resistance
4. third
5. fulcrum

💡 THINKING CRITICALLY ANSWERS

6. **CALCULATE:** 4
7. **HYPOTHESIZE:** Increase the effort arm length or decrease the resistance arm length.
8. **CLASSIFY:** first-class lever: hammer; second-class lever: nutcracker, bottle opener; third-class lever: hockey stick

✏️ **WRITING HINT** Suggest that students write answers to questions in complete sentences. This improves the quality of their thinking as well as their writing.

---

4 Close

Web InfoSearch

Levers in Your Body Have students use the Internet to find out what other parts of the body act as levers. Then, have students create a chart and draw a picture of the body part and an example of the lever action. Some key search words are **human body levers** and **human body simple machine.** Students should begin their search at www.conceptsandchallenges.com.

ONGOING ASSESSMENT

Drawing and Labeling Levers Have students draw examples of each type of lever. Make sure that they correctly label the parts of each lever. **learning styles: visual, tactile**

QUICK CONVERSIONS		
	Metric/SI	English
Resistance weight	5 N	1 lb

• TEACHING RESOURCES •

💿 **Teacher's Resources CD-ROM**
Lesson Review: Chapter 15, p. 4
Enrichment: Chapter 15, p. 10
Six Simple Machines: Visuals, p. 10

📼 **Laboratory Videos**
Segment 15: Using First-Class Levers
Segment 16: Using Second-Class Levers

1 Introduce

✏️ **STUDY HINT** Before beginning this lesson, have students read the captions and art labels in the lesson. This will allow students to preview the different types of pulleys.

Linking Prior Knowledge Ask students to think about how a flag is raised along a flagpole or how water is raised from a well. Inform them that both devices are a type of pulley.

2 Teach

Demonstration Bring a variety of pulleys to class. Set up and show the operation of a single fixed pulley and a simple movable pulley. You can use a spring scale to compare the mechanical advantage of each pulley. **learning styles: visual, auditory**

Discussion Refer students to the diagrams of pulleys on page 318. Explain the difference between a fixed pulley and a movable pulley. Be sure that students understand that the ideal mechanical advantage of a fixed pulley is 1 because a fixed pulley changes the direction of the effort force without increasing the effort force. The ideal mechanical advantage of a movable pulley depends on the number of supporting rope segments that lift the resistance. **learning styles: visual, auditory**

📖 **READING STRATEGY** Tell students that authors often use a main idea with supporting details to present information in text. Refer to the paragraph entitled *Fixed Pulleys* on page 318. Explain that the first sentence of the paragraph states the main idea. The remaining sentences identify details that support this main idea. Reinforce understanding by having students read the paragraph titled *Pulley Systems*. Have them identify its main idea and supporting details.
learning styles: visual, auditory

15-4 How do pulleys work?

Objectives
Explain how pulleys make work easier. Compare fixed and movable pulleys.

Key Term
pulley: rope wrapped around a wheel

Pulleys Look at Figure 15-15. A pulley is being used to raise a bucket. A **pulley** is a rope wrapped around a wheel. Pulleys can change the direction of a force, the size of a force, or both. The pulley in Figure 15-15 changes the direction of a force. When the rope is pulled down, the bucket moves up.

▶ **1 DEFINE:** What is a pulley?

Fixed Pulleys A fixed pulley is attached to something that does not move. The pulley shown in Figure 15-15 is a fixed pulley. Fixed pulleys change the direction of the effort force. They do not increase the effort force. In a fixed pulley, the effort force is equal to the resistance force. As a result, the IMA of a fixed pulley is equal to 1.

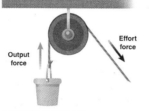
▲ **Figure 15-15** Fixed pulley

▶ **2 EXPLAIN:** Why is the IMA of a fixed pulley equal to 1?

Movable Pulleys Unlike a fixed pulley, a movable pulley can move as the rope is pulled through it. Figure 15-16 shows a single movable pulley. As the free end of the rope is pulled up, the pulley and its load also move up. A movable pulley does not change the direction of the effort

force. It does increase, or multiply, the size of the effort force. The IMA of a single movable pulley is equal to the number of supporting rope segments that lift the resistance. The IMA of a single movable pulley is 2. The effort distance is always twice the resistance distance.

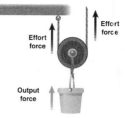
▲ **Figure 15-16** Movable pulley

▶ **3 ANALYZE:** What is the IMA of the movable pulley in Figure 15-16? Why?

Pulley Systems A block and tackle is a pulley system. A pulley system is made up of both fixed and movable pulleys. The pulleys act together to increase the MA of the system. The IMA of a pulley system is equal to the number of supporting ropes. The rope attached to the fixed pulley is not counted. A block and tackle may have a large mechanical advantage, depending on the number of pulleys in the system.

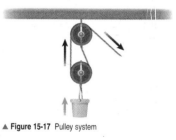
▲ **Figure 15-17** Pulley system

▶ **4 INFER:** Why is the actual MA of a pulley system a lot smaller than its IMA?

318

Teaching Options

EXTENDING THE LESSON

Comparing a Fixed Pulley and a Movable Pulley Have students compare Figures 15-15 and 15-16 by answering the following questions: *With a fixed pulley, in which direction is the effort force moving?* (down) *With a movable pulley, in which direction is the effort force moving?* (up) *Describe the difference between a fixed pulley and a movable pulley.* (A fixed pulley does not move. A movable pulley is attached to the object and can move with the rope.)
learning styles: auditory, linguistic

RETEACH

Understanding Pulleys Display pictures showing the uses of pulleys, such as a person hanging clothes on a clothesline or a person raising a flag on a flagpole. Guide students in recognizing that pulleys help people do work.
learning styles: visual, auditory

✓ CHECKING CONCEPTS

1. A _____ pulley can increase the effort force.
2. The IMA of a fixed pulley is _____.
3. A _____ is an example of a pulley system.
4. The IMA of a pulley system with four supporting ropes is _____.
5. A _____ pulley can change only the direction of a force.

💡 THINKING CRITICALLY

6. EXPLAIN: Why is the IMA of a single movable pulley greater than that of a single fixed pulley?
7. ANALYZE: What kind of pulley is used to raise a flag to the top of a flagpole?
8. INFER: What happens to the actual mechanical advantage of a pulley system as more pulleys are added?

INTERPRETING VISUALS

Figure 15-18 shows a block and tackle.

9. What is the IMA of the block and tackle?

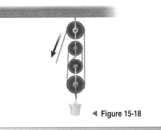

◀ Figure 15-18

BUILDING SCIENCE SKILLS

Modeling Design a machine that uses at least two types of pulleys. Your machine should have a practical use. Draw a diagram or build a working model of your machine. Label each pulley type. Explain how your machine works.

⚛ Hands-On Activity

USING A MOVABLE PULLEY

You will need a spring scale, string, a movable pulley, a book, and tape.

1. Tie the string around the book. Attach the book to the spring scale.
2. Use the spring scale to lift the book. Record the effort force needed to lift the book.
3. Attach the movable pulley to the book and spring scale as shown.
4. Use the pulley to lift the book again. Record the effort force needed to lift the book.

Practicing Your Skills

5. OBSERVE: How much force was needed to lift the book without the pulley?
6. OBSERVE: How much force was needed to lift the book with the pulley?
7. CALCULATE: What is the actual MA of the movable pulley?

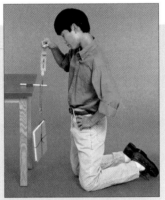

▲ **STEP 3** Attach the pulley to the book and spring scale.

Answers to questions

▶ **1** DEFINE: a rope wrapped around a wheel

▶ **2** EXPLAIN: The effort force is always equal to the resistance force.

▶ **3** ANALYZE: 2; The effort distance is always twice the resistance distance.

▶ **4** INFER: because there is a lot of friction created in a pulley system

3 Assess

✓ CHECKING CONCEPTS ANSWERS

1. movable
2. one
3. block and tackle
4. 4
5. fixed

💡 THINKING CRITICALLY ANSWERS

6. EXPLAIN: because the movable pulley can increase the effort force
7. ANALYZE: fixed
8. INFER: It increases.

INTERPRETING VISUALS ANSWER

9. 4

4 Close

BUILDING SCIENCE SKILLS

Modeling Students should identify the pulley systems in their design and clearly explain how their machine works.

Hands-On Activity

USING A MOVABLE PULLEY

TIME: 15–20 minutes

PURPOSE: comparing, calculating

COOPERATIVE LEARNING: Have pairs of students compare their data and explain any differences.

Practicing Your Skills Answers

5. OBSERVE: Answers will vary, depending on the book used.
6. OBSERVE: Answers will vary, depending on the book used. However, answers should be less than those noted in answer 5.
7. CALCULATE: 2

ONGOING ASSESSMENT

Comparing Pulleys Have students make a Venn diagram to show how fixed and movable pulleys are alike and how they are different. Students can use the Venn Diagram on the Teacher's Resources CD-ROM.
learning styles: visual, tactile

• TEACHING RESOURCES •

🔘 **Teacher's Resources CD-ROM**
Lesson Review: Chapter 15, p. 5
Enrichment: Chapter 15, p. 10
Venn Diagram: Study Tools, p. 10
Six Simple Machines: Visuals, p. 10

Lab Activity

(pp. 320–321)

1 Prepare the Lab

Pulley Advantage

SET-UP TIME: 🕐 **LAB TIME:** 🕐

BACKGROUND: Simple machines make it easier to do work because mechanical advantage reduces force by dividing it over a greater distance. Pulleys provide an excellent model of mechanical advantage. When a single pulley is mounted to the ceiling, a mass can be raised. Pulling down on the rope raises the mass. Since only one rope supports the mass, the mechanical advantage is 1. If the rope is pulled 1 m, the mass rises 1 m. The mechanical advantage changes if the mass is supported by more than one rope. If two ropes are used to support the mass, the mechanical advantage is 2. While two pulleys result in half as much force needed to raise the mass, the ropes must be pulled twice as far.

PURPOSE: Students will investigate the relationship between force and distance in pulley systems.

ALTERNATIVE MATERIALS: A soft-drink can filled with sand or water can be used as the lifting mass.

SCIENCE SKILLS: Students will **measure** the force exerted lifting a mass with various pulley systems and **compare** the distances they had to pull the scale. Students will **record** all data.

ADVANCE PLANNING: Set up laboratory ring stands for students to elevate their pulley systems. Cut cords for the various pulley setups that the students will be using. You might organize this activity as stations, each with different pulleys, for groups to rotate through.

2 Guide the Lab

PROCEDURE: Divide the class into groups of three. Discuss the procedure. Demonstrate how to mount the pulleys and string the cord through them. Discuss how to measure force expended and the distance the force is exerted. Explain that the mechanical advantage of each pulley setup will be determined by the number of cords supporting the mass. Provide students with

---

LAB ACTIVITY
Pulley Advantage

Materials
Ring stand and ring
Pulleys
Cord
Lifting mass
Spring scale – 250 g/5 N
Metric ruler
Calculator

▲ **STEP 2** Set up the pulley.

▲ **STEP 4** Measure the distances.

BACKGROUND

Simple machines like levers, inclined planes, and pulleys make it seem like you get something for nothing. A difficult job becomes easier to do. What is really happening is a trade-off. The job is easier to do but it takes longer to do it. You can see this relationship with pulleys.

PURPOSE

In this activity, you will lift various masses with pulleys. You will then compare the effort forces and the distances the forces have to be exerted.

PROCEDURE

1. Copy the data table in Figure 15-19.

2. Make a single fixed pulley by attaching one pulley to the ring stand. Tie the cord to the mass and run it through the pulley. Tie a loop to the other end of the cord for hooking the spring scale.

3. Lift the weight off the tabletop slightly by pulling on the spring scale. Measure the force on the scale and record it in your data table.

4. Raise the weight 10 cm. Now, measure how far you had to pull the scale to raise the weight that distance. Record your answers in the data table.

5. Set up new pulley arrangements as shown in the picture labeled Step 5. Measure the forces and the distances as before.

320

Teaching Options

❗ FAST FACTS

Belt Drives

The belt drive in different kinds of machinery, such as a car, a motorcycle, or a clothes dryer, is an example of a pulley. Two different-sized wheels are joined together by a belt made of leather, rubber, or another type of material. The larger wheel will rotate with greater force than the smaller wheel but at a slower speed. Tightness in the belt can cause friction. The belt has to be tight enough to prevent it from slipping but not so tight that it causes friction.

COOPERATIVE LEARNING

Dealing With Friction Have small groups of students research ways of reducing the friction of a pulley system. Encourage students to find out what type of materials cause the least amount of friction. Students should also explore how parts of the system are treated so as to reduce friction. Have students share their findings in an oral report to the class.
learning styles: auditory, linguistic

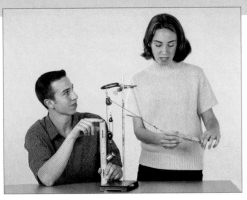

◀ STEP 5
Set up a pulley system.

Pulley Advantage						
Setup	Number of Cords Holding Mass (mechanical advantage)	Lifting Mass	Lifting Force	Lifting Distance	Pulling Distance
1				10 cm	
2				10 cm	
3				10 cm	
4				10 cm	

▲ **Figure 15-19** Copy this chart and use it to record your observations.

CONCLUSIONS

1. OBSERVE: When you increased the number of supporting cords, what happened to the amount of force needed to lift the weight?

2. OBSERVE: When you increased the number of cords supporting the mass, what happened to the distance you had to exert the effort force?

3. ANALYZE: What is the relationship between force and distance when you increase the number of cords to two?

4. INFER: If you want to lift a very heavy mass with a pulley system, what should you do?

---

a copy of the Lab Activity Report found on the Teacher's Resources CD-ROM for students to record their observations and conclusions.

TROUBLESHOOTING: Students may have trouble keeping the cord in the grooves of the sheaves. Maintaining constant force should keep the cord in the grooves. Because of friction, measurements of the lifting force will be somewhat greater than predicted. When used upside down, the spring scales will have to be adjusted for their own mass.

EXPECTED OUTCOME: Students will discover that additional cords supporting the masses reduce the force that must be applied to the cord but that the force must be exerted through a greater distance.

LAB HINT: Use a wide-diameter cord for stringing the pulleys. It will be less likely to slip out of the groove of the sheaves than will string.

3 Conclude the Lab

1. OBSERVE: It decreased.
2. OBSERVE: It increased.
3. ANALYZE: The force is half as much, but the distance is twice as much.
4. INFER: Use as many pulleys and cords as possible.

Use the Laboratory Activity Rubric on the Teacher's Resources CD-ROM to assess students' lab activities. Fill in the rubric with the additional information below. For this activity, students should have:

• performed the activity according to the procedure and filled in the chart with data collected during the activity.

• correctly answered the questions in complete sentences.

4 Extend the Lab

Obtain a block and tackle from a hardware store. Attach each end to short lengths of broom handles. Have two students hold the handles and try to keep them apart while a third student pulls the cord and draws them together. Discuss various uses of pulleys such as cranes, elevators, and window-washing platforms.

Tips for Using Technology

Spreadsheets Have students use spreadsheet software to record the observations from their experiments. Spreadsheets are tables that display data such as numbers, text, dates, or a combination of all three. Students can use spreadsheets to do math to analyze numerical data, and make graphs and charts to present data in a colorful way. Students can use spreadsheet software to present their data to the class. Have students use the Spreadsheet on the Teacher's Resources CD-ROM to plan their spreadsheets.

• TEACHING RESOURCES •

Teacher's Resources CD-ROM
Lab Activity Report: Study Tools, pp. 16–17

Laboratory Activity Rubric: Teaching Tools, p. 8

Spreadsheet: Study Tools, p. 23

Laboratory Manual
Lab. Skills Worksheet 4: Organizing and Analyzing Data, pp. 13–14

1 Introduce

STUDY HINT Have students write the lesson title and objective in their notebooks. As students read the lesson, tell them to write sentences that provide information that meets the objective.

Linking Prior Knowledge Have students describe situations where they have observed or used ramps. Ask what the ramps were used for. Explain that ramps are examples of simple machines called inclined planes.

2 Teach

Demonstration Using a wooden plank, set up a ramp. Illustrate the mechanical advantage of the ramp by loading masses into a small wheeled cart. Make sure that the masses are secure in the cart. Using a spring scale, lift the cart straight up. On the board, write the reading on the spring scale. Then, pull the cart up the ramp by using the spring scale. Also, note this reading on the board. Students will see that less force is needed to pull the cart up the ramp. **learning styles: visual, auditory**

Discussion Be sure that students understand that using an inclined plane results in a reduction in the amount of force needed but an increase in distance. Ask students to identify the formula for determining the IMA of an inclined plane. (length ÷ height)
learning styles: auditory, mathematical

Reinforcement Have students make a screw by cutting a sheet of paper diagonally from one corner to the opposite corner. Have students examine one of the resulting triangles. Ask: *Which edge is an inclined plane?* (the diagonal edge) Next, have students place one of the nondiagonal edges against the barrel of a pencil and wrap the entire triangle around the pencil. Ask: *What simple machine have you just made?* (a screw)
learning styles: auditory, kinesthetic

15-5 What are inclined planes?

Objective
Describe how an inclined plane makes work easier.

Key Term
inclined plane: slanted surface, or ramp

Inclined Planes A ramp is often used to help load barrels onto a truck. The barrels are rolled up the ramp onto the truck. The ramp is an inclined plane. The word *inclined* means "slanted." A plane is a flat surface. Therefore, an **inclined plane** is a slanted surface, or ramp. Inclined planes are simple machines that help make work easier.

▶ **DEFINE:** What is an inclined plane?

MA of an Inclined Plane An inclined plane makes work easier by changing the angle at which you have to exert force to lift resistance. Instead of lifting an object straight up against gravity, you push or pull the object up at an angle. Look at Figure 15-20 showing a man moving a box up an inclined plane. He is raising a 300-N box using only 100 N of effort force. In effect, the ramp has multiplied his effort force by 3. The MA of this ramp is 3.

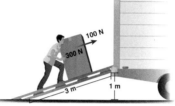
▲ **Figure 15-20** An inclined plane makes work easier.

You can find the IMA of an inclined plane by dividing its length by its height.

$$IMA = length \div height$$
$$IMA = 3\ m \div 1\ m$$
$$IMA = 3$$

▶ **EXPLAIN:** How can you find the approximate MA of an inclined plane?

Wedges and Screws A wedge is a kind of inclined plane. A wedge is most often made of two inclined planes back-to-back. A knife blade and an axe are examples of wedges.

◀ **Figure 15-21** A wedge is two inclined planes back-to-back.

A screw is an inclined plane wrapped around a cylinder. A screw is like the steps wrapped around the center of a spiral staircase. Bolts are examples of screws.

▲ **Figure 15-22** A screw is an inclined plane wrapped around a cylinder.

▲ **Figure 15-23** Screws are simple machines.

▶ **LIST:** What are two examples of wedges?

Teaching Options

RETEACH

Reviewing Mechanical Advantage
Display finely threaded and coarse-threaded screws. Explain that a screw is a combination of an inclined plane and a cylinder. As a screw is turned, material moves up or down the length of the screw. The distance that the material moves is determined by the threads. The smaller the distance between the threads, the greater is the effort distance. Therefore, finely threaded screws have a greater mechanical advantage than coarse-threaded screws. **learning styles: visual, auditory**

ESL/ELL STRATEGY

Explaining Homophones Write *plane* and *plain* on the board. Explain that these terms are homophones, or words that sound alike but have different spellings and meanings. Then, have students use dictionaries to identify the meaning of each term. **learning styles: visual, linguistic**

✓ CHECKING CONCEPTS

1. A _____ is an inclined plane wrapped around a cylinder.
2. The IMA of an inclined plane is equal to its length divided by its _____.
3. A plane is a _____ surface.
4. Bolts are examples of _____.
5. An inclined plane _____ the size of the effort force.
6. A wedge is made up of _____ inclined planes.

💡 THINKING CRITICALLY

7. HYPOTHESIZE: How could you increase the IMA of an inclined plane?
8. ANALYZE: What happens to the IMA of an inclined plane if you increase the height?

INTERPRETING VISUALS

Figure 15-24 shows three ramps: A, B, and C.
9. Which ramp has the smallest IMA? Explain.

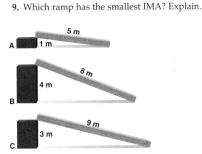

▲ Figure 15-24

🔬 Hands-On Activity

FINDING THE MA OF AN INCLINED PLANE

You will need a wooden board, a spring scale, string, a metric ruler, and three books.

1. Stack two books one on top of the other. Place one end of the wooden board on top of the books to make an inclined plane.
2. Use the metric ruler to measure the length and height of the inclined plane. Record your measurements.
3. Tie one end of the string around the third book. Tie the other end to the spring scale. Measure and record the weight of the book in newtons. The weight of the book is the resistance force, when no ramp is being used.
4. Use the spring scale to pull the book up the inclined plane. Record the effort force shown on the scale.

▲ STEP 4 Use the spring scale to record the effort force.

Practicing Your Skills

5. ANALYZE: Find the IMA of the inclined plane using the formula IMA = length/height.
6. CALCULATE: Find the actual MA of the inclined plane using the formula IMA = resistance force/effort force.
7. HYPOTHESIZE: Why is the actual MA less than the IMA?

CHAPTER 15: Machines **323**

MORE ON THE WEB

Building the Pyramids Have students use the Internet to learn about a pyramid at Meidium. Have students answer the questions at www.conceptsandchallenges.com.

ONGOING ASSESSMENT

Classifying Inclined Planes Have students classify the following devices: zipper (wedge), jar lid (screw), clamp (screw), and key (wedge).

• TEACHING RESOURCES •

Teacher's Resources CD-ROM
Lesson Review: Chapter 15, p. 6
Enrichment: Chapter 15, pp. 7, 10
Six Simple Machines: Visuals, p. 10

Answers to questions

1 DEFINE: slanted surface, or ramp

2 EXPLAIN: divide its length by its height

3 LIST: knife blade and axe

✏️ **WRITING HINT** Remind students to always reread a written response to a question and to check for errors in spelling, subject-verb agreement, capitalization, and punctuation.

3 Assess

✓ CHECKING CONCEPTS ANSWERS

1. screw
2. height
3. flat
4. screws
5. changes
6. two

💡 THINKING CRITICALLY ANSWERS

7. HYPOTHESIZE: Increase its length or lower its height.
8. ANALYZE: It decreases.

INTERPRETING VISUALS ANSWER

9. B; Its length divided by its height results in the smallest of the three IMAs.

4 Close

Hands-On Activity

FINDING THE MA OF AN INCLINED PLANE

TIME: 15–20 minutes

PURPOSE: measuring, analyzing, hypothesizing

COOPERATIVE LEARNING: Have pairs of students share their results and discuss any discrepancies.

Practicing Your Skills Answers

5. ANALYZE: Answers will vary, depending on the setup.
6. CALCULATE: Answers will vary, depending on setup.
7. HYPOTHESIZE: because of friction

The Big Idea

(pp. 324–325)

1 Introduce

Objective Students will apply their knowledge of simple machines to describe how these tools were used to build the Great Pyramid of Khufu.

Linking Prior Knowledge Ask students to recall how a wedge, inclined plane, and lever make work easier as described in Lessons 15-3 and 15-5.

2 Teach

Discussion After students have read the article and call outs, provide real-life examples of the measures described. For example, the Great Pyramid is 137 m tall today, which equals about 445 ft (137 m × 39 in. × 12 in./ft). Invite students to describe models of 445 ft such as 89 five-foot-tall students, each standing on top of one another's shoulders.

Use the information in the articles and captions to help guide students in choosing a topic for their Science Logs.

THE BIG IDEA ONLINE

How did the Egyptians build the Great Pyramid? Have students research their Science Log Writing Activity at www.conceptsandchallenges.com. You can have students organize their log by completing the Big Idea activity online. Students may post their work in the Online Classroom Database for others to read.

Reinforcement Students can also use the Big Idea Planner or Big Idea Science Log Entry found on the Teacher's Resources CD-ROM.

◆ *Integrating History*

THE Big IDEA

How did the Egyptians build the Great Pyramid?

Is it possible to build something 480 ft tall using only simple machines? That is exactly what Khufu did, with a lot of help. The Egyptian Pharaoh Khufu had the Great Pyramid built at Giza 4,500 years ago. For most of recorded history, Khufu's pyramid was the world's largest building. It has a mass of almost 6 billion kilograms. It was originally 147 m tall; it covers an area of about ten football fields. Using only levers, wedges, inclined planes, muscle power, and engineering genius, Egyptian workers put more than 2 million huge blocks precisely in place to construct Khufu's monument.

Archeologists do not agree on exactly how the Great Pyramid and the other pyramids of Giza were constructed. However, they do agree that these structures were built with the simplest of machines. The workers may not even have had the wheel.

Copper wedges were used to cut the huge stone blocks. The stones were probably dragged to the construction site on greased sleds. They were moved up the pyramid on inclined planes. Some historians believe a single ramp was used to move the stones to the top. Others suggest that spiral ramps were built around the sides of the pyramid.

Positioning the top stones and the huge stones that form the inside chambers of the pyramid must have been very tricky. Expert use of levers and wedges was needed to set these stones. Look at the illustrations and text on these two pages. Then, follow the directions in the Science Log to learn more about "the big idea." ◆

324

Wheels and Levers
Did the Egyptians have the wheel? Did they use levers? An ancient painting shows soldiers climbing a ladder on wheels. Others are using levers to move the structure. This is the only known image of a wheel from those times.

Wedges
Stonecutters used chisels made of bronze and copper. These wedge-shaped tools were used to carve fine details in the stone.

Teaching Options

! FAST FACTS *More on the Great Pyramid of Khufu*

The Great Pyramid is the largest of ten pyramids that stand along the west bank of the Nile River in Giza. According to the ancient Greek historian Herodotus, about 100,000 laborers worked on the structures. Construction was limited to about 3 or 4 months a year because of flooding of the Nile. The Egyptians used their understanding of geometry, a field of math that they invented, to plan the pyramids. Because of their calculations, the corner angles of the Great Pyramid are accurate to 1/3,000 of a degree.

ESL/ELL STRATEGY

Working With Peers Working with students who are proficient in English can help English-language learners to communicate. Pair an English-language learner with an English-proficient student. Have both students explain the article and the captions in their own words to each other.

Inclined Planes
Scientists agree that the inclined plane was an important machine used to build the pyramids. They do not agree how they were built. Some experts think the stones were dragged up spiral ramps such as these. Other scientists think that a single, straight ramp was built from the bottom up to the top. Either way, we know they used inclined planes.

Figure 15-25
The Great Pyramid at Giza

science Log

WRITING ACTIVITY

Research the process of cutting a stone for the Great Pyramid and putting it in place. In your science log, draw or describe the process in as much detail as you can. Be sure to explain which simple machines were probably used. Start your search at www.conceptsandchallenges.com.

3 Assess

Use the Writing Activity Rubric on the Teacher's Resources CD-ROM to assess students' Science Logs. Fill in the rubric with the additional information below. For this assignment, students should have:

- described how stones for the Great Pyramid were cut and moved into place.
- communicated, in paragraph form, accurate information on how simple machines were used in this process.

4 Close

Writing a Newspaper Article Have small groups of students work together to write a newspaper article describing the construction of the Great Pyramid. The article should be written for the *Giza Gazetteer*, a local paper of the time. It should explain why the pyramid is being built, as well as how it is being constructed. Allow groups to read their articles aloud to the class.

Tips for Using Technology

Creating a Newspaper Have students use desktop publishing software to make a newspaper that includes their articles describing the construction of the Great Pyramid. Desktop publishing software allows students to combine text and art on a page. Most word processing software programs include tools for desktop publishing. Have students use the Project Sketch on the Teacher's Resources CD-ROM to plan their desktop publishing layouts.

• TEACHING RESOURCES •

Teacher's Resources CD-ROM
Big Idea: Chapter 15, p. 8
Big Idea Planner: Study Tools, pp. 11–12
Big Idea Science Log Entry: Study Tools, p. 13
Individual Activity Rubric: Teaching Tools, p. 5
Project Sketch: Study Tools, p. 18

15-6 (pp. 326–327)

1 Introduce

STUDY HINT Before beginning this lesson, write the title of each section on the board. Have students copy the titles in their notebooks, using an outline format. As students read each section, they should write the topic sentence for each section in their notebooks. Students can also use the Writing Activity Outline found on the Teacher's Resources CD-ROM.

Linking Prior Knowledge Ask students to define the term *compound*. (made up of more than one item) Have students hypothesize what a compound machine is.

2 Teach

Demonstration Display a pair of scissors to the class and point out the three types of simple machines it contains. (two levers, a screw, and two wedges)
learning styles: visual, auditory

Discussion Point out that most machines are compound machines. Ask students to define a compound machine. (machine that combines two or more simple machines) Refer students to Figure 15-27. Have them identify the simple machines that the bike contains. **learning styles: visual, auditory**

READING STRATEGY Relate the concept of compound machines with compound words. Remind students that joining two or more smaller words forms a compound word. Have students scan the lesson for examples of compound words. (handlebars, gearshift, anyplace)

Answers to questions

▶ **DEFINE:** machine that combines two or more simple machines

▶ **IDENTIFY:** wheels and axles, levers, pulleys

▶ **NAME:** fossil fuels and nuclear energy

15-6 What is a compound machine?

Objective
Name some compound machines.

Key Term
compound machine: machine that combines two simple machines or more

Compound Machines Most machines are made up of a combination of simple machines. Machines that combine two simple machines or more are called **compound machines.** Compound machines can do more complicated jobs than simple machines can. They also can have large MAs. The actual MA of a compound machine equals the product of the actual MAs of all of the simple machines that make it up.

▶ **DEFINE:** What is a compound machine?

Examples of Compound Machines Most of the machines you use every day are compound machines. For example, a pair of scissors is a compound machine. A pair of scissors is made up of two levers joined by a screw. The screw is the fulcrum of the levers. Each blade of a pair of scissors is a wedge.

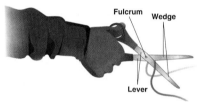

Fulcrum   Wedge

Lever

▲ **Figure 15-26** Scissors are compound machines.

A bicycle is another compound machine. What simple machines make up a bicycle? The wheels and pedals are wheels and axles. The pedals are

▲ **Figure 15-27** A bicycle is a compound machine.

▶ **IDENTIFY:** What are some simple machines in a bicycle?

People and Machines Humans have been using machines for hundreds of thousands of years. Early humans made simple tools from stone. Centuries later, agricultural societies used machines to water their crops, crush grain into flour, and cut wood to build homes.

During the Industrial Revolution, steam began to replace animals as a source of energy for machines. Many inventions during those years, such as the telephone and the telegraph, helped improve communication. We also learned how to heat our homes and power our machinery.

Today, fossil fuels and nuclear energy are used to operate modern machines. Modern machines take us anyplace in the world and to the Moon. In the future, new technology may make even more complex machines possible.

326

Teaching Options

RETEACH

Researching the Industrial Revolution Have students research and choose a compound machine that was invented or used during the Industrial Revolution. Have them write a report that describes the uses of the compound machine and names the types of simple machines involved in its operation. Allow students to read their reports to the class.
learning styles: visual, linguistic

EXTENDING THE LESSON

Listing Simple Machines in a Car Have students list some simple machines that make up a car. (wheel and axle in the tires, brake lever, ignition key is a wedge)

▲ Figure 15-28 The wheels of this train travel on a single track.

3 ► NAME: What are two sources of energy for modern machines?

✓ CHECKING CONCEPTS

1. What are two simple machines that make up a pair of scissors?
2. What is a compound machine?
3. What type of simple machine are the wheels and handlebars of a bicycle?
4. On what does the MA of a compound machine depend?

💡 THINKING CRITICALLY

5. **COMPARE:** How does the MA of a compound machine compare with the MA of each of its simple machines?
6. **ANALYZE:** How does a bicycle make work easier?
7. **MODEL:** Draw a diagram of a pair of scissors. Label the simple machines that make up a pair of scissors on your diagram.

HEALTH AND SAFETY TIP

Machines are very helpful to people. However, if machines are not used properly, they can cause serious injury. It is important to use proper safety precautions when you use any kind of machine. Helmets, kneepads, and goggles are all safety items you might need. Different machines require different precautions. Choose a machine you are interested in and find out the safety precautions and safety equipment needed to use it. Make a poster that illustrates "Machine Safety."

⚛ Science and Technology

ROBOTIC MACHINES

Robots are mechanical workers. Most robots are built to do special jobs. Using robots instead of human workers has some advantages. Robots can work 24 hours a day without resting. They can do the same job over and over without getting tired or bored.

More importantly, robots can work under conditions that would not be safe for humans. The Sewer Access Module robot, or SAM, was designed to do maintenance work in sewers. Today, it is also used to lay fiber-optic cable lines in the sewer.

Robots are used in a wide variety of places. Some surgeons use robots in the operating room to perform open-heart surgeries. The robot can grip, cut, and sew arteries and valves. Surgeons view the heart on a video monitor. They control the robot's movements with joysticks and foot pedals. Because robotic surgery requires a smaller incision, a patient's recovery time is faster.

Thinking Critically For what other types of jobs could robots be used?

▲ Figure 15-29 This robot is used to clean sewers.

---

3 Assess

✓ CHECKING CONCEPTS ANSWERS

1. Accept any two of the following: lever, wedge, and screw.
2. machine that combines two or more simple machines
3. The wheels are wheels and axles, while the handlebars are levers.
4. the mechanical advantage of all its simple machines

💡 THINKING CRITICALLY ANSWERS

5. **COMPARE:** It is greater.
6. **ANALYZE:** A bicycle makes it easier to travel long distances.
7. **MODEL:** Diagrams should show two levers joined by a screw. Each lever should also be a wedge.

HEALTH AND SAFETY TIP

Allow volunteers to present their posters to the class. You may wish to display students' posters in the classroom.

4 Close

Science and Technology

ROBOTIC MACHINES

Real-Life Connection For years, robots have been used by NASA scientists to gather information about space. Archaeologists also use robots to explore regions unfit for humans. Recently, archaeologists exploring the Western Desert of Egypt used robots to collect data. The robots moved through the sand, creating three-dimensional images of the region below. The archaeologists then analyzed the images to determine where to locate their dig.

Discussion Guide students to recognize that a robotic machine can only do what it has been programmed to do. Robotic machines cannot make decisions or react to unanticipated events that crop up.

Thinking Critically Answer
Possible answer: handling products dangerous to humans such as hazardous wastes

---

MORE ON THE WEB

Identifying Simple Machines
Have students use the Internet to review simple machines. Then, have students visit www.conceptsandchallenges.com to view an image gallery of complex machines. Have students identify the different simple machines that exist within the complex machines.

ONGOING ASSESSMENT

Recognizing Machines Have students choose a compound machine that they use every day and list the different simple machines that form it. **learning style: linguistic**

• TEACHING RESOURCES •

💿 **Teacher's Resources CD-ROM**

Lesson Review: Chapter 15, p. 9

Enrichment: Chapter 15, p. 10

Writing Activity Outline: Study Tools, pp. 20–21

Six Simple Machines: Visuals, p. 10

Challenges (pp. 328–330)

Chapter Summary

Review Before students begin the Challenges, review the summary with them. If time permits, have students work in pairs. Give each pair of students one summary point to describe in their own words.

STUDY HINT Have students use index cards to create flash cards for each Key Term. Have students write the Key Term on one side of the index card and the definition on the other side. Then, have students work in pairs to review the Key Terms.

Key Term Challenges

MATCHING

1. effort force (15-1)
2. pulley (15-4)
3. inclined plane (15-5)
4. work output (15-2)
5. resistance force (15-1)
6. work input (15-2)
7. fulcrum (15-3)

APPLYING DEFINITIONS

8. The fixed point on which a lever turns is the fulcrum. (15-3)
9. A compound machine is made up of two or more simple machines. (15-6)
10. The ideal mechanical advantage of a machine describes a machine with 100 percent efficiency. (15-1, 15-2)
11. Work done by a machine is the work output, while work done to a machine is the work input. (15-2)
12. Resistance force is a force that opposes the force applied to a machine or the effort force. (15-1)

Chapter Summary

Lesson 15-1
- **Machines** make work easier by changing the size, direction, or speed of a force.
- The force you apply to a machine is the **effort force,** and the force that opposes the effort force is the **resistance force.**
- **Mechanical advantage** is the number of times a machine multiplies the effort force. It is equal to the resistance force divided by the effort force.
- There are six kinds of simple machines.

Lesson 15-2
- The work done by a machine is **work output.** The work done on a machine is **work input.** The **efficiency** of a machine is a ratio of work output to work input.

Lesson 15-3
- A **lever** is a bar that is free to turn around a fixed point. A lever has two parts called an effort arm and a resistance arm. The IMA of a lever is equal to the length of the effort arm divided by the length of the resistance arm.
- Levers are divided into three classes according to the position of the effort force, the resistance force, and the **fulcrum.**

Lesson 15-4
- A **pulley** is a rope wrapped around a wheel.
- Fixed pulleys change the direction of the effort force. Movable pulleys increase the size of the effort force. A pulley system is made up of fixed and movable pulleys.

Lesson 15-5
- An **inclined plane** is a slanted surface, or ramp.
- The IMA of an inclined plane is equal to its length divided by its height.
- A wedge is often two inclined planes back-to-back. A screw is an inclined plane wrapped around a cylinder.

Lesson 15-6
- A **compound machine** is composed of two or more simple machines.

328

Key Term Challenges

compound machine (p. 326)
efficiency (p. 314)
effort force (p. 312)
fulcrum (p. 316)
ideal mechanical advantage (p. 312)
inclined plane (p. 322)
lever (p. 316)
machine (p. 312)
mechanical advantage (p. 312)
pulley (p. 318)
resistance force (p. 312)
wheel and axle (p. 312)
work input (p. 314)
work output (p. 314)

MATCHING Write the Key Term from above that best matches each description.

1. force applied to a machine
2. rope wrapped around a wheel
3. slanted surface
4. work done by a machine
5. force that opposes the effort force
6. work done on a machine
7. point that a lever turns around

APPLYING DEFINITIONS Explain the difference between the words in each pair. Write your answers in complete sentences.

8. lever, fulcrum
9. simple machine, compound machine
10. mechanical advantage, efficiency
11. work input, work output
12. effort force, resistance force

Teaching Options

PREPARING STUDENTS FOR STANDARDIZED TESTS

Reading Strategy: Tell students that if they have trouble understanding a question, they should try putting it in their own words. This can help them see where the problem is. It may also help them to recall important science content.

Writing Strategy: Remind students to check punctuation and grammar in their sentences as they reread their answers.

Interpreting Visuals: Remind students that the first step in reading a diagram is to identify the subject or topic of the diagram. Often this information is presented in the title. Sometimes knowing the title is all students need to answer a question.

ESL/ELL STRATEGY

Word Bank Have students add Key Terms from this chapter to their word banks. Suggest that students make note of compound words in the list. Have them write definitions for the individual words. Then, have them explain how the meaning of each word relates to the meaning of the compound word.

Content Challenges TEST PREP

MULTIPLE CHOICE Write the letter of the term or phrase that best completes each statement.

1. Machines make work easier by changing a force's
   a. size.
   b. direction.
   c. speed.
   d. size, direction, or speed.

2. A machine with an actual MA of 10 multiplies the effort force
   a. 15 times.
   b. 10 times.
   c. 10%.
   d. 15%.

3. The efficiency of a machine is always less than
   a. 100%.
   b. the mechanical advantage.
   c. work output.
   d. work input.

4. If the percentage efficiency of a machine is 60% and the work input is 50 N-m, what will be the work output?
   a. 160 N-m.
   b. 60 N-m.
   c. 30 N-m.
   d. 100 N-m.

5. In a first-class lever, the fulcrum is between the effort force and
   a. the effort arm.
   b. the resistance arm.
   c. the resistance force.
   d. none of these

6. A wheelbarrow is an example of a
   a. first-class lever.
   b. second-class lever.
   c. third-class lever.
   d. wheel and axle.

7. A block and tackle is an example of a
   a. lever.
   b. pulley.
   c. pulley system.
   d. wheel and axle.

8. The IMA of a pulley system with six ropes supporting the load is
   a. 6.
   b. 3.
   c. 60%.
   d. 1.

9. An inclined plane makes work easier by increasing a force's
   a. direction.
   b. speed.
   c. MA.
   d. size.

10. If you use 50 N of force to push a box weighing 200 N up an inclined plane, the MA of the inclined plane is
    a. 50.
    b. 150.
    c. 4.
    d. 0.215.

FILL IN Write the term or phrase that best completes each statement.

11. People use _____ to make work easier.

12. The efficiency of a machine is equal to the _____ divided by the work input.

13. Some of the work put into a machine is used to overcome _____.

14. The _____ of a lever is the distance from the resistance force to the fulcrum.

15. A pulley can change either the size or the _____ of a force.

Content Challenges

MULTIPLE CHOICE

1. d (15-1)
2. b (15-1)
3. a (15-2)
4. c (15-2)
5. c (15-3)
6. b (15-3)
7. c (15-4)
8. a (15-4)
9. d (15-5)
10. c (15-1, 15-5)

FILL IN

11. simple machines (15-1) or compound machines (15-6)
12. work output (15-2)
13. friction (15-2)
14. resistance arm (15-3)
15. direction (15-4)

ALTERNATIVE ASSESSMENT

Relating Information Students may create a chart in their Science Logs that list the six simple machines. Students can define each type of machine and draw an illustration for each one. Students can also define a compound machine and draw an example.

PORTFOLIO ASSESSMENT

Making Student Portfolios
Encourage students to select their own work for inclusion in their portfolios. Students can demonstrate their comprehension of the concepts in this chapter by making a portfolio. The Venn Diagram and the Concept Map are some of the reproducibles on the Teacher's Resources CD-ROM that they can include in their portfolios. You can use the Portfolio Assessment Rubric also found on the Teacher's Resources CD-ROM to assess students' portfolios.

Concept Challenges

WRITTEN RESPONSE

1. **RELATE:** The effort force must act over a distance. (15-2)
2. **HYPOTHESIZE:** Possible answer: A compound machine is a combination of simple machines. *Complex* can mean two or more related parts. (15-6)
3. **HYPOTHESIZE:** No; Because machines must overcome friction, they cannot have 100 percent or more efficiency. (15-6)
4. **EVALUATE:** Block and tackle; They need to increase both the size and direction of the effort force. (15-4)

INTERPRETING A DIAGRAM (15-3)

5. 30 cm
6. 5 cm
7. 6
8. 3 N
9. .5 N
10. First-class lever; The fulcrum is between the effort force and the resistance force.

Chapter Project Wrap-Up

INVENTING A COMPOUND MACHINE

Allow students to present the drawings of their inventions to the class. You can use the Group Activity Rubric found on the Teacher's Resources CD-ROM to assess students' projects. Fill in the rubric with the additional information below. For this project, students should have:

- invented a compound machine made up of all six simple machines.
- designed, drawn, and included a written description of what the machine would do and how it would do it.

Concept Challenges TEST PREP

WRITTEN RESPONSE **Complete the exercises and answer each of the following questions in complete sentences.**

1. **RELATE:** Why is work input equal to the effort force times the effort distance?
2. **HYPOTHESIZE:** Why do you think compound machines are sometimes called complex machines?
3. **HYPOTHESIZE:** A perpetual motion machine would have more than 100% efficiency. Could such a machine ever be built? Explain your answer.
4. **EVALUATE:** Two piano movers want to raise a piano to the fifth floor of an apartment building. Should they use a fixed pulley, a movable pulley, or a block and tackle to make the work easier? Explain.

INTERPRETING A DIAGRAM **Use Figure 15-30 to answer the following questions.**

5. What is the length of the effort arm of this lever?
6. What is the length of the resistance arm?
7. What is the IMA of this lever?
8. What is the output force in this diagram?
9. How much effort force would be needed to produce the output force?
10. Is this lever a first-, second-, or third-class lever? Explain.

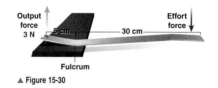
▲ Figure 15-30

Teaching Options

Chapter 16 Heat

PLANNING GUIDE

◆ **TEACHING THE CHAPTER** This chapter should take approximately 9–12 days to complete instruction and assessment.

	Skills and Features	Projects and Activities	Achieve Science Literacy	Meet Individual Needs
Chapter 16 Opener p. T331	HYPOTHESIZE	• Chapter Project		
Lesson 16-1 **What is heat?** pp. T332–T333 Standards: B3a, B3b	INFER, ANALYZE, EXPLAIN • Investigate • Web InfoSearch	• Cooperative Learning	• Study Hint • Reading Strategy • Ongoing Assessment	• Reteach • ESL/ELL Strategy ◉ CD-ROM Writing Activity Outline
Lesson 16-2 **What is temperature?** pp. T334–T335 Standards: B3a, B3b	COMPARE, PREDICT, DEFINE • Investigate • Designing an Experiment • How Do They Know That?	• More on the Web	• Study Hint • Ongoing Assessment	◉ CD-ROM Enrichment Activity Designing an Experiment Temperature Scale
Lesson 16-3 **What is freezing point?** pp. T336–T337 Standards: B1a, B3a, B3b	STATE, INFER, HYPOTHESIZE • Interpreting Visuals • Science and Technology	• Extending the Lesson • More on the Web	• Study Hint • Reading Strategy • Writing Hint • Ongoing Assessment	◉ CD-ROM Temperature Scale
Lesson 16-4 **What is boiling point?** pp. T338–T339 Standards: B1a, B3a, B3b	DEFINE, ANALYZE, INFER • Web InfoSearch • Hands-On Activity	• Cooperative Learning	• Study Hint • Reading Strategy • Ongoing Assessment	• Reteach ◉ CD-ROM Enrichment Activity Temperature Scale
Lesson 16-5 **What is conduction?** pp. T340–T341 Standards: B3a, B3b	RESEARCH, DEFINE, INFER • Investigate • Building Science Skills • Real-Life Science	• More on the Web	• Study Hint • Writing Hint • Ongoing Assessment	• ESL/ELL Strategy • Reteach ▦ Laboratory Videos
Lesson 16-6 **What is convection?** pp. T342–T343 Standards: B1a, B3a, B3b, B3f	ANALYZE, EXPLAIN, IDENTIFY • Health and Safety Tip • Integrating Earth Science	• Extending the Lesson • More on the Web	• Study Hint • Ongoing Assessment	• Reteach ◉ CD-ROM Cause-and-Effect Diagram

Planning Guide continues on next page.

Standards: For details on the correlation to National Science Standards see pages *xx–xxi*.

	Skills and Features	Projects and Activities	Achieve Science Literacy	Meet Individual Needs
Lab Activity **Creating Convection Currents** pp. T344–T345 Standards: B1a, B3a	INFER, ANALYZE, OBSERVE • Set-Up Time: 30 min • Lab Time: 30 min	• Integrating Earth Science • Extend the Lab Activity • Lab Skills Worksheet	• Tips for Using Technology	CD-ROM Lab Activity Report Database Planner
Lesson 16-7 **What is radiation?** pp. T346–T347 Standards: B3a, B3b, B3f	EXPLAIN, IDENTIFY, EXPLAIN • Interpreting Visuals • Hands-On Activity	• More on the Web	• Study Hint • Reading Strategy • Ongoing Assessment	CD-ROM Enrichment Activity
Lesson 16-8 **What is specific heat?** pp. T348–T349 Standards: B1a, B3b	PREDICT, INFER, HYPOTHESIZE • Designing an Experiment • Hands-On Activity	• Extending the Lesson • More on the Web	• Study Hint • Ongoing Assessment	• Reteach CD-ROM Enrichment Activity Designing an Experiment
Lesson 16-9 **What is thermal expansion?** pp. T350–T351 Standard: B1a	EXPLAIN, ANALYZE, COMPARE • Interpreting Visuals • Science and Technology	• More on the Web • Lab Challenge	• Study Hint • Ongoing Assessment	• Reteach Laboratory Video
Big Idea **How do animals control their body temperatures?** pp. T352–353 Standard: B3f	RESEARCH, COMMUNICATE, ANALYZE • Science Log: Writing Activity	• Big Idea Online • Close Activity	• Tips for Using Technology	CD-ROM Big Idea Planner Thumbnail Sketch
Chapter 16 Challenges pp. T354–T356	• Chapter Summary • Key Term Challenges • Content Challenges • Concept Challenges	• Chapter Project Wrap-Up • Unit Challenge Online	• Study Hint • Preparing Students for Standardized Tests	• ESL/ELL Strategy CD-ROM Chapter Self-Check Concept Map Weekly Journal

Chapter 16 Heat

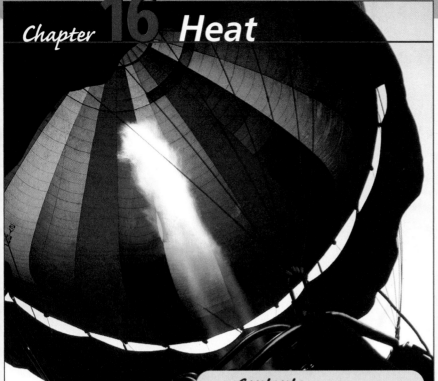

▲ Figure 16-1 Because hot air rises, this balloon can fly.

Imagine floating high above Earth's surface in a hot-air balloon like the one in Figure 16-1. In order to keep the balloon high above the ground, air in the balloon must be heated. Heat energy from the flames causes the particles that make up air to gain energy. The particles move faster and spread farther apart. As a result, the balloon expands and rises high above Earth's surface.

▶ What do you think would happen if the air in the balloon was cooled?

Contents

UNIT 5: Force, Motion, and Energy **331**

Teaching Options

ASSESSMENT PLANNER

For assessment in the Student Edition, see the following pages:

Content Assessment
Checking Concepts: pp. 333, 335, 337, 339, 341, 343, 347, 349, 351
Thinking Critically: pp. 333, 335, 337, 339, 341, 343, 347, 349, 351
Interpreting Visuals: pp. 337, 347, 351
Chapter Challenges: pp. 354–356

Alternative Assessment
Building Skills: p. 341
Web InfoSearch: pp. 333, 339
Science Log: p. 353

Performance-Based Assessment
Hands-On Activity: pp. 339, 347, 349
Designing an Experiment: pp. 335, 349
Lab Activity: pp. 344–345

• TEACHING RESOURCES •

Teacher's Resources CD-ROM
Lesson Review: Ch. 16, pp. 2, 3, 5, 6, 9, 10, 11, 14, 16
Enrichment: Ch. 16, pp. 4, 7, 8, 12, 13, 15
Key Term Review: Ch. 16, p. 18
Chapter 16 Test: pp. 19–20
Laboratory Manual: pp. 13–14, 81–84

Laboratory Videos
Segments 17, 18, 19

Chapter Overview

In this chapter, students will learn that heat is a form of energy and they will identify the freezing, melting, and boiling points of a substance. Students will also learn how heat is transferred by conduction, convection, and radiation. Finally, students will define the specific heat of a substance, and they will learn about thermal expansion of solids, liquids, and gases.

About Figure 16-1 The pilot of a hot-air balloon can control the height of the balloon by regulating the temperature of the air inside the balloon. Heating the air makes the balloon fly higher. Turning off the heater allows the air to cool, which causes the balloon to descend. The pilot can hasten the descent by opening a valve at the top of the balloon, allowing some of the hot air inside to escape.

Answer Possible answer: The air in the balloon would become more dense, and the balloon would descend to Earth's surface.

Linking Prior Knowledge

For this chapter, students should recall:
- how matter changes phase (Lesson 1-4).
- the definition of *density* (Lesson 2-1).
- various forms of energy (Lesson 14-2).

Chapter Project

INVESTIGATING INSULATING ABILITY

MATERIALS: cups of similar size made of various materials such as glass, metal, plastic foam, paper, and plastic; cardboard squares to cover the cups; ice cubes; thermometer, clock

Pairs of students will design and conduct an experiment comparing the insulating ability of various materials. Students will formulate a hypothesis and develop a procedure to collect data that will test the hypothesis. Students can use the Lab Activity Report and other reproducibles found on the Teacher's Resources CD-ROM to summarize their results.
learning styles: visual, tactile

16-1 (pp. 332–333)

1 Introduce

🔍 INVESTIGATE

TIME: 10 minutes

PURPOSE: Students will observe how heat does work.

MATERIALS: pinwheel, light source

PROCEDURE: Have students work in pairs to complete this activity. **learning styles: visual, tactile**

THINK ABOUT IT: The pinwheel rotated in Step 2 but not in Step 1. Turning on the light source caused the pinwheel to rotate. Light and heat are coming from the light source.

📝 **STUDY HINT** Have students copy the titles of each section into their notebooks in an outline format. As they read this lesson, they should write the main idea of each section. Students can also use the Writing Activity Outline found on the Teacher's Resources CD-ROM.

Linking Prior Knowledge Before beginning this lesson, have students recall the different forms of energy (Lesson 14-2). **learning style: linguistic**

2 Teach

Discussion Inform students that all matter has heat. However, the amount of heat in an object may not cause it to feel hot. For example, an ice cube has heat because the molecules in it move back and forth. However, it is not a great amount of heat. Therefore, the ice cube does not feel hot.

Demonstration Measure the temperature of a cup half filled with room-temperature water. Add an ice cube to the cup. Inform students that the temperature of the ice cube is 0°C. Ask students what they think is happening to the temperature of the water. (It is falling.) Ask students what is happening to the temperature of the ice cube. (It is rising.) Measure the temperature of the water. Ask students how they can tell that the temperature of the ice cube is falling. (It is melting.) Inform students that heat moves from a warmer object to a cooler object. In this demonstration, heat moves from the water into the ice cube. As a result, the temperature of the water falls and the temperature of the ice cube rises.

16-1 What is heat?

🔍 INVESTIGATE

Observing Heat
HANDS-ON ACTIVITY

STEP 1

1. Hold a pinwheel over a light source that is not lit. Observe the action of the pinwheel for a full minute.

2. Turn on the light source and hold the pinwheel over it. Observe the action of the pinwheel for a full minute.

THINK ABOUT IT: Compare the action of the pinwheel in Steps 1 and 2. Did the light have any effect on the pinwheel? What type of energy is coming from the light?

Objective
Explain how heat is a form of energy.

Key Term
heat: energy of particles moving from warmer regions to cooler regions

Caloric Have you ever walked on a sandy beach on a hot, summer day? If you have, you probably know that the burning feeling in your feet was caused by the heat in the sand. At one time, people thought that heat was a physical substance. They called this substance caloric (kuh-LAWR-ihk). Caloric was thought to flow like a liquid. Today, we know that heat is not a substance. It is a form of energy. The heat in the sand actually comes from energy absorbed from the Sun.

▶ **EXPLAIN:** What is caloric?

Moving Particles You have learned that matter is made up of tiny particles called atoms and molecules. These tiny particles are always in motion. For example, a brick within a wall is motionless, but the tiny particles that make up the brick are constantly moving. The motion of these particles results in heat, or thermal energy.

◀ **Figure 16-2** The tiny particles that make up a brick are constantly moving.

Heat is the energy of particles moving from a warmer region to a cooler region. All matter has heat. Even an ice cube contains heat, because the molecules of water that make up the ice are moving back and forth. If heat energy is added to the ice cube, the molecules move faster and farther apart. If enough heat energy is added to the ice, the molecules will gain enough energy to leave the solid state and become a liquid. With continued heating, the molecules will gain enough energy to break away from the liquid state and become a gas.

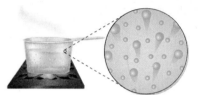

▲ **Figure 16-3** Adding heat energy to water makes the water molecules move faster and farther apart.

▶ **DEFINE:** What is heat?

Movement of Heat What happens when you hold a glass of ice water in your hand? You may notice that after a few minutes, the ice in the water begins to melt. At the same time, your hand gets cold. This happens because heat energy moves from a warmer object to a cooler object. Your hand

332

Teaching Options

RETEACH

Explaining Heat Movement Have students touch a metal object that is at room temperature. Ask them whether it feels warm or cool to the touch. (cool) Then, ask students if they have ever touched the top of a car on a warm, sunny day. Ask how the car felt. (warm) Lead students to conclude that their hands are warmer than a metal object at room temperature, so heat flows from their hands to the metal object. Their hands are cooler than the top of the warm car, so heat flows from the car to their hands. **learning styles: tactile, auditory**

ESL/ELL STRATEGY

Working With Peers Working with English-proficient students can help English-language learners to communicate. Have students work in pairs. One partner should write a question about heat and read it aloud to the other person, who tries to answer the question. Then the other partner should write a question, with the first partner trying to answer it. Both partners should check each other's answers for accuracy.

is warmer than the ice water. Heat from your hand moved into the glass. As heat entered the glass, the water and the ice absorbed the heat and became warmer. Your hand lost some heat energy so it began to feel cooler.

▶ **DESCRIBE:** In what direction does heat move?

Heat and Work How do scientists know that heat is a form of energy? Energy can do work. Remember that something must be moved for work to be done. When you boil water, you can see the water bubbling and moving inside the container. Heat is doing work.

Heat does work when it causes a rocket to be lifted into the air. Heat causes the fuel in a rocket engine to explode, producing hot gases. These hot gases expand rapidly. The expanding gases rush out of the rocket engine. As they do, they push against the rocket, forcing it upward. The moving rocket shows that heat is a form of energy that can do work.

▲ **Figure 16-4** Expanding hot gases cause the rocket to move upward.

▶ **INFER:** How do scientists know that heat is a form of energy?

✔ **CHECKING CONCEPTS**

1. At one time, people thought that heat was a substance called _____.
2. Moving particles have _____ energy.
3. The energy of particles moving from warmer regions to cooler regions is _____.

4. Adding heat energy makes particles of matter move _____.
5. For work to be done, something must be _____.

💡 **THINKING CRITICALLY**

6. **INFER:** Explain how a piece of wood has kinetic energy.
7. **ANALYZE:** Suppose you hit a piece of metal several times with a hammer. When you touch the piece of metal, it feels hot. Explain why the metal gets hot after being hit with the hammer.
8. **HYPOTHESIZE:** Explain what will happen when you place an ice cube in a cup of hot coffee.

Web InfoSearch

Seeing Heat Because heat is energy, you usually cannot see it. Sometimes, however, you can see evidence of it. For example, when steam rises over a pot of boiling water, you can "see" the motion of the heat. Also, wavy air over a hot road is caused by heat. Scientists have invented a technology to see heat. Thermograms show the heat coming from a person or an object. This information is used in many ways.

▲ **Figure 16-5** This thermogram shows the heat coming off a human hand.

SEARCH: Use the Internet to find out more about thermograms. What information might a thermogram of a house or office building tell you? Start your search at www.conceptsandchallenges.com. Some key search words are **thermogram heat loss, energy audit thermogram,** and **thermogram building envelope.**

COOPERATIVE LEARNING

Explaining Figure 16-4 Have students explain Figure 16-4 to other students. Their explanations should describe how the figure illustrates that heat is a form of energy that can do work. learning styles: linguistic, auditory

ONGOING ASSESSMENT

Explaining Heat and Work Ask students: *How do you know that heat is doing work when water boils?* (Work happens when something is moved. Bubbles move inside boiling water.)

• TEACHING RESOURCES •

⊙ **Teacher's Resources CD-ROM**
Lesson Review: Chapter 16, p. 2
Writing Activity Outline: Study Tools, pp. 20–21

📖 **READING STRATEGY** Ask students to think of any words that are similar to *caloric*. Students will probably think of the word *calorie*. Tell students that a calorie is a unit or quantity of heat. You might also introduce them to the meanings of the words *calorific* and *calorimeter*. *Calorific* means "producing heat," and a calorimeter is an apparatus for measuring the quantity of heat.

Answers to questions

▶ **EXPLAIN:** Possible answer: At one time, heat was incorrectly believed to be a physical substance. People called this substance caloric.

▶ **DEFINE:** the energy of particles moving from warmer regions to cooler regions

▶ **DESCRIBE:** from a warmer region to a cooler region

▶ **INFER:** Heat can do work.

---

3 Assess

✔ **CHECKING CONCEPTS ANSWERS**

1. caloric
2. kinetic
3. heat
4. faster
5. moved

💡 **THINKING CRITICALLY ANSWERS**

6. **INFER:** When heat is added to wood, the particles of matter in the wood move faster and faster, and eventually the wood catches fire.
7. **ANALYZE:** Mechanical energy is changed into heat energy.
8. **HYPOTHESIZE:** Heat will move from the cup of hot coffee to the ice cube, causing it to melt.

---

4 Close

Web InfoSearch

Seeing Heat Have students use the Internet to find out more about thermograms. Ask them to find what information a thermogram of a house or an office building might tell. Some key search words are **thermogram heat loss** and **thermogram building envelope.** Students should begin their search at www.conceptsandchallenges.com.

1 Introduce

⌕ INVESTIGATE

TIME: 10–15 minutes

PURPOSE: Students will experiment to find out how their hands are affected by different temperatures.

MATERIALS: 3 shallow pans; paper towels; cold water, warm water, and hot water (not boiling)

PROCEDURE: Have students work in pairs to complete this activity. Explain that after Steps 2 and 3, each pair should discuss how their hands feel.
learning styles: tactile, linguistic

THINK ABOUT IT: No, the hand that was in the cold water feels warmer. The hand that was in the hot water feels cooler.

✎ STUDY HINT Before beginning this lesson, have students study Figure 16-6. Ask them to compare the movement of the particles in both illustrations.
learning style: linguistic

Linking Prior Knowledge Students are familiar with the Fahrenheit temperature scale, which is commonly used in the United States. Remind students that the Celsius temperature scale is normally used when making scientific measurements.
learning style: auditory

2 Teach

Discussion Show students a beaker containing 100 mL of water and another beaker containing 500 mL of water. Use a thermometer to show that the water in both beakers is at the same temperature. Ask students if the two beakers of water have the same amount of heat. Tell students that the temperature is the same in each beaker, so the average kinetic energy of the water particles in each beaker is the same. Then, explain to students that the larger quantity of water has more heat because heat is the total kinetic energy of all the particles in a sample of matter, and the larger quantity of water has more particles.
learning styles: visual, auditory

16-2 What is temperature?

⌕ INVESTIGATE

Observing Temperature Differences
HANDS-ON ACTIVITY

1. Fill a pan with cold water. Fill a second pan with warm water. Fill a third pan with hot but not boiling water.
2. Put both of your hands in the warm water. Observe how your hands feel. Dry your hands. Put one hand into the cold water and the other hand into the hot water.
3. After 1 minute, put both of your hands into the warm water.

THINK ABOUT IT: Did the temperature of the warm water feel the same in both of your hands?

STEP 2

Objective
Differentiate between heat and temperature.

Key Terms
temperature: measure of the average kinetic energy of the particles in a sample of matter
calorie: unit of heat; amount of heat needed to raise the temperature of 1 g of water 1°C

Temperature The measure of the average kinetic energy of all the particles in a sample of matter is called **temperature.** If you compared a bowl of hot soup to a bowl of ice cream, you would find that the average kinetic energy of the soup's particles is greater than the average kinetic energy of the ice cream's particles. The temperature of the soup is higher than the temperature of the ice cream.

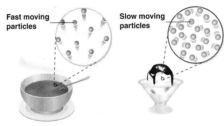

Fast moving particles   **Slow moving particles**

▲ **Figure 16-6** The average kinetic energy of the particles in the soup is greater than the average kinetic energy of the particles in the ice cream.

▷ **DEFINE:** What is temperature?

334

Heat and Temperature Heat is related to temperature, but they are not the same. Heat is the *total* kinetic energy of all the particles in a sample of matter. Temperature is the measure of the *average* kinetic energy of all the particles in a sample of matter.

Two samples of the same material may have the same temperature but not the same amount of heat. For example, a pail of ocean water may have a temperature of 27°C. The ocean water near the beach may also have a temperature of 27°C. However, because there are fewer particles of ocean water in the pail, the amount of heat in it is less than the amount of heat in the nearby ocean.

▲ **Figure 16-7** The pail of ocean water has fewer particles in it than the ocean does. So, at the same temperature, the pail of ocean water has less heat than the ocean.

▷ **COMPARE:** At the same temperature, which has more heat, the water in a bucket or the water in an ocean?

Teaching Options

❗ FAST FACTS

More Units of Heat

The calorie is not the only unit of heat that is used in science. Students are probably familiar with the food Calorie, which is actually a kilocalorie, or 1,000 calories. A food Calorie can raise the temperature of 1,000 g of water 1°C. The metric unit of heat is the joule, which is even smaller than a calorie. One joule is approximately one-quarter of a calorie. The British thermal unit, or Btu, is the amount of heat that will raise the temperature of 1 pound of water 1°F. One Btu equals 252 calories.

ONGOING ASSESSMENT

Explaining the Difference Between Heat and Temperature Ask students: *At the same temperature, which has more heat—a cup of soup or a pot of stew? Why?* (the pot of stew, because it has more particles in it) *Which has greater average kinetic energy? Why?* (neither, because average kinetic energy is temperature, and both samples are at the same temperature)
learning styles: auditory, linguistic

Measuring Heat Heat is directly related to the temperature of a sample of matter. When heat is added to a sample of matter, the average kinetic energy of the particles of matter increases. So, the temperature of the sample goes up. The opposite is also true. When heat is removed from a sample of matter, the average kinetic energy of the particles of matter decreases. The temperature of the sample goes down.

The terms "hot" and "cold" are often used to describe how much heat energy a sample of matter contains. It is important to understand that these terms are not measures of heat energy. They are used to compare the temperature of one sample of matter to that of another.

Heat is measured by describing the temperature change it causes. Heat is measured in units called calories. A **calorie** is the amount of heat needed to raise the temperature of 1 gram of water 1°C. One gram of water is a small amount of water. So, a calorie is a small amount of heat.

▶ **PREDICT:** What happens when you add heat energy to a substance?

✓ CHECKING CONCEPTS

1. Two samples of the same substance may have the same temperature but not contain the same amount of _____.

2. When heat is removed from water, its temperature _____.

3. Heat affects the _____ of a substance.

4. A _____ is a unit of heat.

💡 THINKING CRITICALLY

5. **COMPARE:** Compare the average kinetic energy of the particles in a cup of hot tea to the particles in a glass of iced tea.

DESIGNING AN EXPERIMENT

Design an experiment to solve the following problem. Include a hypothesis, variables, a procedure, and a type of data to study.

PROBLEM: Many people think that coldness can be added to a substance. How can you demonstrate that coldness is an absence of heat?

How Do They Know That?

HEAT IS A FORM OF ENERGY

▲ **Figure 16-8** Benjamin Thompson showed that heat is not a flow of caloric.

Benjamin Thompson was born in Woburn, Massachusetts. During the Revolutionary War, Thompson remained loyal to Great Britain and acted as a spy for the British. During the war, Thompson fled the colonies to live in Great Britain. He was knighted by King George III in 1784. Seven years later, Thompson was made a count of the Holy Roman Empire.

Thompson was also a scientist. Around 1798, Thompson was in charge of a factory that made cannons. The machines used to drill the cannons were turned by horses. Thompson observed that the cannons became very hot as they were drilled. He decided to try an experiment. He surrounded a cannon with a box filled with water. As the cannon was drilled, the water began to boil. The water continued boiling as long as the drilling went on. At that time, people believed that heat was a substance called caloric. Thompson concluded that the heat was produced by the motion of the drill, not a flow of caloric. This was the first step in showing that heat is a form of energy and not a substance.

Thinking Critically What do you think happened to the water once the drilling stopped?

• TEACHING RESOURCES •

💿 **Teacher's Resources CD-ROM**

Lesson Review: Chapter 16, p. 3

Enrichment: Chapter 16, p. 4

Designing an Experiment: Study Tools, p. 14

Designing an Experiment Rubric: Teaching Tools, p. 7

Temperature Scales: Visuals, p. 2

Answers to questions

▶ DEFINE: the measure of the average kinetic energy of the particles in a sample of matter

▶ COMPARE: in an ocean, because the ocean contains more particles

▶ PREDICT: Possible answer: The temperature of the substance increases.

3 Assess

✓ CHECKING CONCEPTS ANSWERS

1. heat
2. falls
3. temperature
4. calorie

💡 THINKING CRITICALLY ANSWER

5. **COMPARE:** The average kinetic energy of the hot-tea particles is greater than that of the cold-tea particles because the temperature of the hot tea is higher than the temperature of the cold tea.

4 Close

DESIGNING AN EXPERIMENT

Use the Designing an Experiment Rubric on the Teacher's Resources CD-ROM to assess students' experiments. Fill in the rubric with the additional information below. For this assignment, students should have:

- mentioned that heat moves from a warmer object to a cooler object.
- included temperature as a variable in the procedure.

How Do They Know That?

HEAT IS A FORM OF ENERGY

Technology Connection In addition to performing fundamental research on the nature of heat, Benjamin Thompson was also an inventor. He invented a kitchen range, a double boiler, and a drip coffee pot. He was one of the first people in Europe to promote the use of James Watt's steam engine. His work also led to improvements in various types of heating and cooking equipment.

Thinking Critically Answer
Possible answer: Heat would no longer be produced, and the water would stop boiling.

16-3 (pp. 336–337)

1 Introduce

STUDY HINT Before beginning this lesson, have students review the Key Terms and their definitions. Ask students how freezing point and melting point are related. (The states of matter are opposite.) **learning style: linguistic**

Linking Prior Knowledge Have students review ways in which matter can change from one state to another (Lesson 1-4). **learning style: linguistic**

2 Teach

Demonstration To introduce this lesson, bring three glasses of water to class, one containing water right from the tap, one containing water that has been in the freezer long enough to begin to freeze, and one containing water that has been in the freezer overnight. Make sure that a thermometer is inserted into each of the two beakers and then placed in the freezer. Measure the temperature of the water in each glass. Write the temperatures on the board. Have students note that as liquid water becomes a solid, the temperature reaches the freezing point of water. Once the liquid completely changes to ice, the temperature of the ice can decrease until it reaches the temperature at which the freezer is set. **learning style: visual**

READING STRATEGY Ask students what they think of when they hear the word *absolute*. Ask how they can apply this to the meaning of *absolute zero*. (Students may associate the word *absolute* with words such as *pure*, *total*, or *ultimate*. These associations may help them to understand that absolute zero is the lowest possible temperature.)

Answers to questions

1 DEFINE: the temperature at which water changes to ice, 0°C

2 STATE: −117°C

3 DESCRIBE: Particle motion slows until it almost stops.

4 STATE: 0°C

16-3 What is freezing point?

Objective
Identify the freezing point and melting point of a substance.

Key Terms
freezing point: temperature at which a liquid changes to a solid

melting point: temperature at which a solid changes to a liquid

Freezing Water When water freezes, it changes to ice. Suppose you put a beaker of water into a freezer whose temperature is set at –10°C. As the water loses heat, its temperature will drop. When the temperature reaches 0°C, the water will begin to freeze. At this point, the temperature of the water stops going down. As the water changes to ice, more heat is lost. After a while, the water will completely change to ice.

The temperature at which a liquid turns to ice is called its **freezing point.** The freezing point of water is 0°C. Once the water has completely changed to ice, the temperature of the ice can drop below 0°C. Figure 16-9 shows how the temperature of water changes as it freezes.

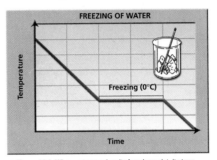

FREEZING OF WATER

Temperature / Time

Freezing (0°C)

▲ **Figure 16-9** When water reaches its freezing point, it stays at 0°C until it completely changes to ice. Its temperature can then fall below 0°C. The temperature will stop falling once it equals its surroundings.

1 DEFINE: What is the freezing point of water?

336

Freezing Points of Other Liquids When heat is removed from a liquid, its temperature goes down. Removing heat from a liquid at its freezing point changes the liquid into a solid. Every liquid has its own freezing point. Figure 16-10 shows the freezing points of some liquids.

FREEZING POINTS OF SOME LIQUIDS	
Liquid	**Freezing point**
Acetic acid	17°C
Acetone	−95°C
Benzene	6°C
Ethyl alcohol	−117°C
Glycerine	18°C
Mercury	−39°C
Water	0°C

▲ Figure 16-10

2 STATE: What is the freezing point of ethyl alcohol?

Absolute Zero As you remove heat from a sample of matter, the particles of the matter slow down. The temperature of the sample falls. If you continue to remove heat from the sample, you might expect to reach a point at which the particles of matter stop moving. At such a point, no more heat could be removed from the sample of matter. The temperature of the sample would be absolute zero.

Absolute zero is described as the coldest temperature possible. Its value is about –273°C! In order to lower the temperature of something, its heat must be transferred to something colder. Because absolute zero is the coldest possible temperature, it will never be reached.

3 DESCRIBE: What happens to the particles of a substance as the temperature nears absolute zero?

Melting Point The temperature at which a solid changes to a liquid is called its **melting point.** The freezing point and the melting point of a substance can be the same. When heat is removed from a liquid, it changes to a solid. When heat is added to

---

Teaching Options

EXTENDING THE LESSON

Using a Table Tell students that the lowest temperature recorded on Earth was −89°C (−129°F) in Antarctica. Write this temperature on the board. Ask students which of the substances in Figure 16-10 would be liquids at this temperature. (acetone and ethyl alcohol) **learning styles: visual, logical/mathematical**

QUICK CONVERSIONS

Freezing Point		
	Metric/SI	**English**
Acetic acid	17°C	62.6°F
Acetone	−95°C	−139°F
Benzene	6°C	42.8°F
Ethyl alcohol	−117°C	−178.6°F
Glycerine	18°C	64.4°F
Mercury	−39°C	−38.2°F
Water	0°C	32°F

a solid, it changes back to a liquid. The melting point of ice is 0°C—the same as its freezing point.

▲ **Figure 16-11** The freezing point and the melting point of water are the same, 0°C.

◀ **STATE:** What is the melting point of water?

✓ CHECKING CONCEPTS

1. What happens when water freezes?
2. At what temperature does water begin to freeze?

3. What is the temperature called at which all particle motion almost stops?
4. What is the melting point of ice?

💡 THINKING CRITICALLY

5. **HYPOTHESIZE:** The water in a lake has just reached 0°C. Explain why it may not be safe to go ice skating on the lake.
6. **COMPARE:** How are melting point and freezing point different? How are they alike?

INTERPRETING VISUALS

Look back at Figure 16-9 to answer the following questions.

7. **INFER:** What does the red part of the graph indicate?
8. **ANALYZE:** What happens to the temperature of water as time passes?
9. **STATE:** What happens to the temperature of water after it reaches the freezing point?

Science and Technology
CRYOGENICS

When heat energy is removed from a substance, the temperature of the substance goes down. When all of the available heat has been removed from a substance, its temperature cannot go down any further. At this temperature, all the particles of the substance almost stop moving. This is the lowest possible temperature that can be reached. It is called absolute zero. This temperature has never been reached. However, scientists have been able to cool substances to within 0.01°C of absolute zero. The study of such very low temperatures is called cryogenics (kriy-oh-JEHN-ihks).

Cryogenics is important in the refrigeration of food, in space technology, and in medicine. In cryogenic surgery, a surgeon uses an extremely cold probe instead of a scalpel. Cryogenic surgery reduces bleeding. It can also reduce much of the pain felt after the surgery. Many cryogenic operations can be done in a doctor's office.

Cryogenics may help the automobile industry. Hydrogen and oxygen are gases at normal temperatures. However, at very low temperatures, they become liquids. Liquid hydrogen and liquid oxygen are used as fuels in some rockets. In the future, liquid hydrogen may replace gasoline as a fuel for automobiles.

Thinking Critically How has cryogenics helped different industries?

▲ **Figure 16-12** In a cryogenics laboratory, substances are cooled to very low temperatures.

✓ CHECKING CONCEPTS ANSWERS

1. It changes to ice.
2. 0°C
3. absolute zero
4. 0°C

💡 THINKING CRITICALLY ANSWERS

5. **HYPOTHESIZE:** All of the water may not have turned into ice.
6. **COMPARE:** Melting point is the temperature at which a solid changes to a liquid. Freezing point is the temperature at which a liquid changes to a solid. For a pure substance, the melting point and freezing point are the same.

INTERPRETING VISUALS ANSWERS

7. **INFER:** The water loses heat and the temperature drops.
8. **ANALYZE:** It decreases.
9. **STATE:** It remains at the freezing point for a while, then it continues to decrease.

✐ **WRITING HINT** As students write responses to the Interpreting Visuals questions, remind them that each answer should have a subject and a predicate. The subject and verb should agree.

4 Close

Science and Technology
CRYOGENICS

Technology Connection Some substances behave in unusual ways when they are cooled to very low temperatures. For example, some materials are able to conduct electric current with no resistance at temperatures near absolute zero. This phenomenon is known as superconductivity. Superconducting magnets cooled with liquid helium are used in magnetic resonance imaging (MRI) devices, which produce images of internal organs. Superconducting magnets are also used in particle accelerators, fusion energy research, and special high-speed trains.

Thinking Critically Answer
Cryogenic surgery can help to reduce pain and bleeding. Cryogenics is also useful in refrigeration and in space technology, and it may help the automobile industry.

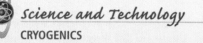

MORE ON THE WEB

Cold as Ice Have students use the Internet to read more about absolute zero and the three temperature scales. Then, have students answer the questions at www.conceptsand challenges.com.

• TEACHING RESOURCES •

💿 **Teacher's Resources CD-ROM**
Lesson Review: Chapter 16, p. 5
Temperature Scales: Visuals, p. 2

ONGOING ASSESSMENT

Identifying Melting Points Ask students what would be the melting point of solid forms of the substances listed in Figure 16-10. (the same as their freezing points)
learning style: logical/mathematical

16-4 (pp. 338–339)

1 Introduce

✏️ **STUDY HINT** Have students write the lesson title and objectives in their notebooks. As students read the lesson, tell them to write the sentences that provide the information that meets the objective.

Linking Prior Knowledge Ask students to share any experiences they have had with boiling water. Ask them how they know when water is boiling.

2 Teach

Demonstration Heat a beaker of water. Record the temperature every 20 seconds. Have students observe that once the water begins to boil, the temperature stabilizes at 100°C. Point out the small bubbles that appear in the water, which show that a gas is being formed. The gas is water vapor. Water vapor turns into steam. As liquid water turns into water vapor at 100°C, the water absorbs a great amount of heat energy. In fact, water vapor contains more potential energy than liquid water at 100°C. This is why a burn from steam can be more serious than a burn from boiling water. **learning style: visual**

Discussion Use Figure 16-15 to discuss the difference between evaporation and boiling. Point out that evaporation occurs at the surface of a liquid, while boiling occurs throughout the liquid. Also, explain that boiling occurs at the liquid's boiling point, while evaporation can occur at a lower temperature.
learning styles: auditory, visual

Answers to questions

▶1 DEFINE: temperature at which a liquid changes to a gas

▶2 ANALYZE: mercury

▶3 DEFINE: the change of a liquid to a gas at the surface of the liquid

📖 **READING STRATEGY** Ask students if the word *evaporation* provides a clue to its meaning. Point out that *evaporation* contains the word *vapor*, which is the gaseous form of a substance.

What is boiling point?

Objectives

Identify the boiling point of a liquid. Differentiate between boiling and evaporation.

Key Terms

boiling point: temperature at which a liquid changes to a gas

evaporation (ee-vap-uh-RAY-shuhn)**:** change from a liquid to a gas at the surface of the liquid

Boiling Water When water boils, it changes to steam. Steam is water in the form of a gas. As you heat water, the temperature of the water rises. As the temperature of the water rises, small bubbles appear in the water. These bubbles show that a gas, steam, is being formed. As you continue to heat the water, more and more bubbles are formed. At 100°C, the bubbles start to leave the container. However, the temperature of the water stays at 100°C. The temperature remains at 100°C until all of the water has changed to steam.

The temperature at which a liquid changes to a gas is called its **boiling point.** The boiling point of water is 100°C. After all the water turns into steam, its temperature can then rise above 100°C. Figure 16-13 shows how the temperature of water changes as it boils.

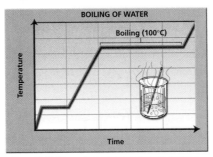

BOILING OF WATER

Boiling (100°C)

Temperature

Time

▲ **Figure 16-13** When water reaches its boiling point, it stays at 100°C until it completely changes to steam. The temperature of the steam can then rise above 100°C.

▶1 DEFINE: What is boiling point?

338

Boiling Points of Other Liquids When heat is added to a liquid, the temperature of the liquid rises. When the liquid reaches its boiling point, it begins to form a gas. Every liquid has its own boiling point. Figure 16-14 shows the boiling points of some liquids.

BOILING POINTS OF SOME LIQUIDS	
Liquid	**Boiling point**
Acetic acid	118°C
Acetone	57°C
Benzene	80°C
Ethyl alcohol	78°C
Glycerine	290°C
Mercury	357°C
Water	100°C

▲ **Figure 16-14**

▶2 ANALYZE: Which liquid listed in Figure 16-14 has the highest boiling point?

Evaporation When a liquid is allowed to stand uncovered at room temperature, it slowly changes to a gas. This change is called **evaporation.** Evaporation happens only at the surface of a liquid and can occur at temperatures below the boiling point. When a liquid evaporates, some particles at the surface of the liquid gain enough energy to escape into the air. This is different from when a liquid boils. When a liquid boils, bubbles form throughout the liquid and rise out of the liquid.

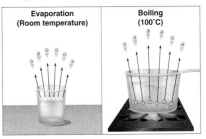

Evaporation (Room temperature)

Boiling (100°C)

▲ **Figure 16-15** Evaporation occurs at the surface of a liquid (left). When a liquid boils, gas bubbles form throughout the liquid and then rise out of the liquid (right).

▶3 DEFINE: What is evaporation?

Teaching Options

RETEACH

Demonstrating Evaporation Put 20 mL of water into both a test tube and a 100-mL beaker. Each day, show students how much water remains in the test tube and in the beaker. Point out that the water in the beaker evaporates faster because it has a larger surface area, and evaporation occurs at the surface of a liquid. **learning styles: visual, auditory**

QUICK CONVERSIONS		
Boiling Point		
	Metric/SI	**English**
Acetic acid	118°C	244.4°F
Acetone	57°C	134.6°F
Benzene	80°C	176°F
Ethyl alcohol	78°C	172.4°F
Glycerine	290°C	554°F
Mercury	357°C	674.6°F
Water	100°C	212°F

1. When water _____, it changes to steam.
2. The temperature at which water changes to steam is its _____.
3. The boiling point of water is _____°C.
4. When a liquid reaches its boiling point, it begins to change to a _____.
5. An uncovered liquid changes to a gas at room temperature by the process of _____.
6. Evaporation occurs only at the _____ of a liquid.

THINKING CRITICALLY

7. COMPARE: In your own words, explain the difference between boiling and evaporation.
8. HYPOTHESIZE: Why is it possible to get a more serious burn from steam than from boiling water?

9. EXPLAIN: As water is heated, what evidence is there that a gas is forming?
10. INFER: When does the temperature of boiling water rise above 100°C?

Web InfoSearch

Boiling Point and Elevation The boiling point of liquids can change depending upon elevation above or below sea level. At elevations above sea level, the boiling point is lower. At elevations below sea level, the boiling point is higher.

SEARCH: Use the Internet to find the boiling point of water at different elevations above and below sea level. Why does elevation affect the boiling point of water? Start your search at www.conceptsandchallenges.com. Some key search words are **water boiling point altitude** and **water boiling point elevation**.

Hands-On Activity

CHANGING THE BOILING POINT OF WATER

You will need three beakers, water, a measuring cup, a balance, salt, a stirrer, a thermometer, and a hot plate.

1. Pour 100 mL of water into each beaker.
2. Add 10 g of salt to the first beaker. Add 20 g of salt to the second beaker. Do not add any salt to the third beaker. Stir the salt in the first and second beakers.
3. Heat the water in each beaker until it boils. Record the temperature of the water in each beaker as it boils.

Practicing Your Skills

4. OBSERVE: What is the boiling point of the water in the first beaker? The second beaker? The third beaker?
5. INFER: How does adding 10 g of salt affect the boiling point of water?
6. INFER: How does adding 20 g of salt affect the boiling point of water?

▲ STEP 3 Record the temperature of the water as it boils.

---

3 Assess

✓ CHECKING CONCEPTS ANSWERS

1. boils
2. boiling point
3. 100
4. gas
5. evaporation
6. surface

THINKING CRITICALLY ANSWERS

7. COMPARE: Boiling occurs throughout a liquid. Evaporation occurs only at the surface of a liquid.
8. HYPOTHESIZE: Steam contains more heat energy than boiling water does, so steam can transmit more heat when it comes in contact with skin.
9. EXPLAIN: Bubbles appear in the water.
10. INFER: after all the water turns into steam

4 Close

Web InfoSearch

Boiling Point and Elevation Have students use the Internet to find out why elevation affects the boiling point of water. Some key search words are **water boiling point altitude** and **water boiling point elevation**. Students should begin their search at www.conceptsand challenges.com.

Hands-On Activity

CHANGING THE BOILING POINT OF WATER

TIME: 15–30 minutes
PURPOSE: observing, inferring
SAFETY TIP: Caution students to stay a safe distance away from boiling water when they record its boiling point.

Practicing Your Skills Answers

4. OBSERVE: about 100°C; Possible answer: 102°C; Possible answer: 104°C
5. INFER: It raises the boiling point of the water.
6. INFER: It raises the boiling point of the water even more.

ONGOING ASSESSMENT

Comparing Graphs Have students compare Figure 16-13 to Figure 16-9 on page 336. Ask students how the two figures are similar and how they differ. (Both graphs have similar curves, but their slopes are opposite.)
learning style: logical/mathematical

COOPERATIVE LEARNING

Making a Chart After students complete the Web InfoSearch activity, have them work in pairs to create a chart that shows the boiling points of water at different levels above and below sea level.
learning styles: interpersonal, visual

• TEACHING RESOURCES •

Teacher's Resources CD-ROM
Lesson Review: Chapter 16, p. 6
Enrichment: Chapter 16, pp. 7, 8
Temperature Scales: Visuals, p. 2

1 Introduce

INVESTIGATE

TIME: 10–15 minutes

PURPOSE: Students will experiment to find out how well different materials conduct heat.

MATERIALS: hot water (not boiling), jar, metal spoon, plastic spoon, wooden spoon

PROCEDURE: Have students work in pairs to complete this activity. Explain that after Step 2, each pair should discuss how the handle of each spoon feels. **learning styles: tactile, linguistic**

THINK ABOUT IT: No; Some materials conduct heat better than others do.

STUDY HINT Remind students that contrasting means telling how two things are different. As students read this lesson, encourage them to contrast good conductors of heat and poor conductors of heat.

Linking Prior Knowledge Ask students to recall the properties of metals and nonmetals (Lesson 3-8).

2 Teach

Demonstration Attach plastic buttons to the underside of a metal ruler at 6-cm intervals by using margarine or wax. Ask students what they think will happen if you heat one end of the ruler. Hold one end of the ruler with a glove or mitt and heat the other end over a Bunsen burner. Students will note that the buttons fall off in order as heat is conducted along the ruler. **learning style: visual**

Reinforcement To show students that wood and wax are two examples of insulators, hold up a lighted candle and a lighted match. Ask students why your fingers are not burned. (Heat is not conducted.) **learning style: visual**

Answers to questions

1. DEFINE: the process of heat transfer in solids

2. IDENTIFY: metals, especially copper and silver

3. EXPLAIN: to help keep them warm in winter and cool in summer

---

16-5 What is conduction?

INVESTIGATE

Observing Heat Transfer
HANDS-ON ACTIVITY

1. Half-fill a jar with hot water. Place a wooden spoon, a metal spoon, and a plastic spoon into the jar. Do not allow the spoons to touch each other.

2. After a full minute, touch the handle of each spoon.

THINK ABOUT IT: Did the handles of all three spoons feel the same? If not, how can you explain the difference?

STEP 1

Objective
Describe how heat is transferred through solids.

Key Terms
conduction (kuhn-DUK-shuhn): process of heat transfer in solids

conductor: material that conducts heat easily

insulator: material that does not conduct heat easily

Heat Transfer in Solids A blacksmith hammers a piece of iron to make horseshoes. When a blacksmith places a piece of iron into a flame, the iron gets very hot. The heat energy causes the particles in the iron to bump into each other. After a while, the iron gets hot enough so that it becomes soft. The piece of iron can then be hammered into shape.

▲ **Figure 16-16** As the iron gets hot, the particles within it bump into each other.

340

Heat is transferred through solids by **conduction.** You learned that heat moves from an object with a higher temperature to an object with a lower temperature. When fast-moving particles in a sample of matter bump into slow-moving particles, heat energy passes from the fast-moving particles to the slow-moving particles. As a piece of iron is heated, heat energy is transferred from the fast-moving particles to the slow-moving particles. The slow-moving particles gain energy and bump into other particles. In this way, heat energy is transferred throughout the sample of matter.

▶ **DEFINE:** What is conduction?

Conductors of Heat All metals are good conductors of heat. A **conductor** is a material that allows heat to move through it easily. Copper, gold, silver, iron, aluminum, and steel are all good conductors of heat. Copper and silver are two of the best conductors of heat. Heat will travel faster through items made of copper and silver than it will through items made of iron or steel.

▶ **IDENTIFY:** What substances are good conductors of heat?

Poor Conductors of Heat Many materials are poor conductors of heat. Materials that do not conduct heat easily are called **insulators.** Wood, paper, wax, and air are poor conductors of heat. These materials are insulators.

Insulators prevent heat from moving from place to place. Houses are insulated to keep them warm in winter and cool in summer. To insulate houses, spaces are left between the inside and

---

Teaching Options

ESL/ELL STRATEGY

Building Vocabulary Skills Tell students that the root *duc* comes from the Latin word *ductus*, which means "act of leading." Have students work in small groups to brainstorm words (other than *conductor* and *conduction*) that contain this root. Then, create a class list of these words. (Possible answers: *duct, induct, deduct, aqueduct*)
learning styles: auditory, linguistic

RETEACH

Comparing Heat Loss Fill a metal container and a plastic-foam container of similar size with equal amounts of boiling water. Place thermometers in each container and periodically compare the temperatures. Students will note that the temperature of the water in the metal container drops faster than the temperature of the water in the plastic-foam container. Identify metals as good conductors and plastic foam as a good insulator.
learning style: visual

outside walls of the house. The spaces are filled with an insulating material. During winter, this insulation helps keep heat from escaping to the outside. During the summer, insulation helps keep heat from getting into the house.

▲ **Figure 16-17** Pots made of copper are good conductors of heat. Handles made of plastic are good insulators.

3 EXPLAIN: Why are insulators used in houses?

✓ CHECKING CONCEPTS

1. How does heat travel by conduction?
2. Name two materials that are good conductors of heat.
3. What is an insulator?
4. Name two materials that are good insulators.

THINKING CRITICALLY

5. INFER: Explain how food in a pot gets heated by conduction.
6. EXPLAIN: How is a blanket an insulator?

BUILDING SCIENCE SKILLS

Researching Insulators do not allow heat to move easily through them. Look throughout your home to find examples of insulators. Make a list of them and describe what kind of material they are made of. Explain how each one of them acts as an insulator.

Real-Life Science
HOME INSULATION

In many parts of the United States, winters are cold and summers are hot. In these parts of the country, houses must be insulated. Home insulation keeps houses warm in winter and cool in summer. Home insulation can help reduce the amount of fuel needed to heat or cool a home. Good insulation can cut fuel use by as much as 50%.

▲ **Figure 16-18** Home insulation keeps houses warm in winter and cool in summer.

Insulation is needed in those parts of a house where the most heat is usually lost. In most homes, heat loss occurs through the attic floor, the ceiling of an unheated basement, and the side walls. Different types of insulation can be used in these places. For example, blankets of fiberglass can be inserted between beams in floors and ceilings. Liquid plastic foam can be sprayed into the spaces between the inside and outside walls.

A number called an R-value is used to grade insulating materials. An insulating material with a high R-value is best at preventing heat loss. Choosing insulation with the highest R-value can greatly reduce fuel costs.

Thinking Critically How does insulation keep a house cool in summer?

MORE ON THE WEB

Home Insulation Have students use the Internet to learn about home insulation. Then, have students answer the questions at www.conceptsandchallenges.com.

ONGOING ASSESSMENT

Explaining Burning Ask students: *Explain how a burning log heats up.* (As the log is heated by a flame, heat energy passes from the fast-moving particles in the log to the slow-moving particles. The slow-moving particles gain energy and bump into other particles.)

• TEACHING RESOURCES •

Teacher's Resources CD-ROM
Lesson Review: Chapter 16, p. 9

Laboratory Videos
Segment 17: Observing Conduction

Segment 18: How Does Heat Travel by Conduction?

3 *Assess*

✓ CHECKING CONCEPTS ANSWERS

1. Particles of matter bump into one another.
2. Possible answers: copper and silver
3. a substance that does not conduct heat easily
4. Possible answers: wood, paper, wax, air, foam, and plastic

THINKING CRITICALLY ANSWERS

5. **INFER:** Heat travels by conduction from the heat source into the pot, and then from the pot into the food.
6. **EXPLAIN:** A blanket helps keep body heat from escaping.

4 *Close*

BUILDING SCIENCE SKILLS

Researching Check students' lists. Accept all logical responses.

WRITING HINT As students conduct their research on insulators in their homes, suggest that they record their findings in a three-column chart. Draw the chart on the board for students to copy. The columns could be entitled: *Type of insulator*, *Material(s) it is made of*, and *How it acts as an insulator*. Tell students that they can add as many rows as necessary to the chart. **learning styles: visual, linguistic**

Real-Life Science
HOME INSULATION

Real-Life Connection The R-value of a material is a measure of its resistance to heat flow. Many insulating materials, such as fiberglass and cellulose, have R-values between 2.0 and 4.0 per inch of thickness. Other materials do not insulate as well, and so they have lower R-values. For example, the R-value of a single-pane glass window is 0.9.

Discussion Ask students: *What are some ways to reduce heat transfer through windows?* (using double-pane windows or storm windows)

Thinking Critically Answer
During the summer, insulation helps keep heat from getting into the house.

16-6 (pp. 342–343)

1 Introduce

STUDY HINT Before beginning this lesson, have students read the captions and art labels that appear in the lesson. This will allow them to preview what is to come as well as to focus on the most important ideas in the lesson.

Linking Prior Knowledge Have students review the definition of *density* (Lesson 2-1).

2 Teach

Demonstration Demonstrate convection in liquids. Place shredded pieces of paper into a beaker. Fill the beaker with water. Allow the paper to settle to the bottom. Heat the beaker, and have students observe the movement of the paper.
learning style: visual

Discussion Describe how home heating makes use of convection. Typically, heat is supplied near the floor of a room. The warm air rises toward the ceiling, then it cools and sinks toward the floor as more heated air rises to replace it. The result is an endless cycle of rising and sinking air.
learning style: auditory

Reinforcement Be sure that students understand that convection currents happen because of differences in density. Point out that warm air is less dense than cold air because the particles in warm air are farther apart. Therefore, warm air rises and cold air sinks. **learning style: auditory**

Answers to questions

▶ **DEFINE:** the process of heat transfer in gases and liquids

▶ **EXPLAIN:** Warmer liquid rises to the surface, carrying heat upward. Cooler liquid sinks to the bottom.

▶ **IDENTIFY:** convection

16-6 What is convection?

Objective
Describe how heat travels through gases and liquids.

Key Terms
convection (kuhn-VEHK-shuhn): transfer of heat in gases and liquids

convection current: movement of gases or liquids caused by differences in density

Heat Transfer in Gases and Liquids The transfer of heat in gases and liquids is called **convection.** When gases and liquids are heated, the particles gain energy and move faster and farther apart. Because these particles are farther apart, the heated gas or liquid becomes less dense than the cooler, surrounding gas or liquid. This makes the less-dense gas or liquid rise and the cooler, denser gas or liquid moves in to take its place. As it rises, the gas or liquid carries heat with it.

▶ **DEFINE:** What is convection?

Convection Currents Heat is carried in gases and liquids by means of convection currents. **Convection currents** are movements of gases or liquids caused by differences in density. Convection currents transfer heat. Air is a gas. Air at Earth's surface is warmed by the Sun and then rises. Cool air above the North Pole and the South Pole sinks. The rising of warm air and the sinking of cool air cause convection currents. Certain birds, such as eagles and hawks, use rising warm air in convection currents to soar above Earth's surface.

▲ **Figure 16-19** An eagle uses convection currents to soar.

342

Convection currents are found in liquids as well as in air. In bodies of water, warmer water rises to the surface and carries heat with it. Cooler water sinks to the bottom. Convection currents cause heat to be transferred through bodies of water. When water is heated in a pot, convection currents form. Figure 16-20 shows convection currents in a pot of boiling water.

◀ **Figure 16-20** Convection currents transfer heat in a liquid.

Just below Earth's crust is a layer of rock called the mantle. The mantle is heated from below by heat from Earth's core. Rock in the upper part of the mantle behaves like a very thick liquid. Scientists believe that convection currents traveling through the upper mantle are responsible for the very slow movement of large sections of Earth's crust. This concept is known as the theory of plate tectonics.

▶ **EXPLAIN:** How do convection currents transfer heat in liquids?

Uses of Convection Heat transfer by convection is used in some home heating systems. In a hot-water heating system, water is heated in a hot-water heater. The hot water is then pumped through pipes to each room in the house. The hot water flows through heaters near the floor of each room. The hot water warms the air near the floor by conduction. The warm air rises, carrying heat through each room by means of convection currents. Heat circulates through each room in this way. After the water loses some of its heat, it returns to the hot-water heater to repeat the process.

Teaching Options

RETEACH

Explaining How Convection Affects Ocean Currents Explain to students how convection currents cause surface currents and deep ocean currents in large bodies of water. Water at the surface evaporates. In many bodies of water, the surface water that is left behind becomes saltier and more dense. Because of its increased density, the water sinks to the ocean floor and flows as deep ocean currents. Less salty water, which is less dense, rises and flows at the surface of the water as surface currents.
learning style: auditory

EXTENDING THE LESSON

Demonstrating Convection Use a liquid motion lamp, or lava lamp, to demonstrate convection. Explain to students that the lamp contains two liquids of similar densities that do not dissolve in each other. When the lamp is turned on, the heavier liquid at the bottom of the lamp is heated, so it expands and its density decreases, causing blobs of the liquid to rise to the top of the lamp. As the blobs cool, their density increases and they fall to the bottom where they are heated again, and the cycle repeats.
learning styles: visual, auditory

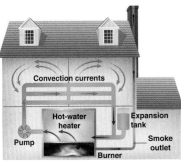

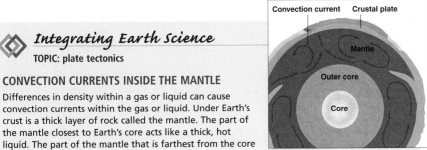

▲ **Figure 16-21** In a hot-water heating system, heated water travels through a system of pipes to heat a home.

▶ **IDENTIFY:** What method of heat transfer is used in a hot-water heating system?

CHECKING CONCEPTS

1. Heat travels through gases by _____.
2. Warm air is _____ dense than cold air.

3. Warm water rises and cool water _____.
4. Convection takes place in gases and _____.

✓ THINKING CRITICALLY

5. **ANALYZE:** To cool a room, should an air conditioner be placed at the bottom of a wall or at the top of a wall? Explain your answer.
6. **INFER:** Is heat transferred through solids by convection? Explain.

HEALTH AND SAFETY TIP

Smoke and gases from the burners of hot-water heaters contain pollutants. These pollutants are sent through an exhaust pipe that runs out through a chimney or vent in the roof. Hot air containing the pollutants rises up the chimney. Cool, clean air moves in from outside to take its place. Why do you think these pollutants need to be removed from a house?

Convection current · · · Crustal plate

Mantle

Outer core

Core

▲ **Figure 16-22** Convection currents in the mantle

◆ Integrating Earth Science

TOPIC: plate tectonics

CONVECTION CURRENTS INSIDE THE MANTLE

Differences in density within a gas or liquid can cause convection currents within the gas or liquid. Under Earth's crust is a thick layer of rock called the mantle. The part of the mantle closest to Earth's core acts like a thick, hot liquid. The part of the mantle that is farthest from the core has the properties of a thick, cooler liquid. Scientists believe that the differences in the density in the mantle cause convection currents. The thick, hot liquid of the mantle rises and cools. The cooler liquid of the mantle sinks. As the cooler liquid gets closer to the core, it heats up and rises. The process repeats over and over again.

Scientists also believe that these convection currents cause the plates that make up the crust to continuously move. The crust floats on top of the mantle. The convection currents in the mantle carry the plates along so that the continents that sit on top of the plates slowly move, too. This concept supports the theory of plate tectonics. The theory of plate tectonics explains how Earth has changed over time.

Thinking Critically How do convection currents support the theory of plate tectonics?

---

3 Assess

✓ CHECKING CONCEPTS ANSWERS

1. convection
2. less
3. sinks
4. liquids

💡 THINKING CRITICALLY ANSWERS

5. **ANALYZE:** Because cool air sinks, the air conditioner should be placed high on a wall.
6. **INFER:** No; Convection currents cannot form in solids.

4 Close

HEALTH AND SAFETY TIP ANSWER

The pollutants would be hazardous if they remained in the house.

◆ Integrating Earth Science

TOPIC: plate tectonics

CONVECTION CURRENTS INSIDE THE MANTLE

Earth-Science Connection According to the theory of plate tectonics, Earth's crust is broken into seven large plates and several smaller ones. The movement of these plates causes the continents to slowly move. About 200 million years ago, there was only one continent, a giant landmass now called Pangaea. Over time, this landmass separated into the continents that we know today. Some scientists believe that in about 250 million years, most of today's continents will rejoin to form another giant continent.

Discussion Ask students to think of possible evidence that would support the theory that one giant continent existed millions of years ago. (Possible answers: the discovery of similar fossils on different continents, the fact that the shapes of the coastlines of South America and Africa appear to fit together like pieces of a jigsaw puzzle)

Thinking Critically Answer
Scientists believe that convection currents in Earth's mantle carry along the plates that make up Earth's crust. This concept explains how the continents move and supports the theory of plate tectonics.

MORE ON THE WEB

Convection Fireplaces Have students visit www.concepts andchallenges.com to learn about convection fireplaces. Have students write a short report about the differences between a convection fireplace and a regular fireplace.

• TEACHING RESOURCES •

💿 **Teacher's Resources CD-ROM**
Lesson Review: Chapter 16, p. 10
Cause-and-Effect Diagram: Study Tools, p. 3

ONGOING ASSESSMENT

Making Cause-and-Effect Diagrams
Have students make a cause-and-effect diagram for convection currents.

Lab Activity

(pp. 344–345)

1 Prepare the Lab

Creating Convection Currents

SET-UP TIME: 🕐 LAB TIME: 🕐

BACKGROUND: Convection is one of three main ways that heat energy is transferred from place to place. It primarily operates in fluids such as liquids and gases. Convection also operates in slow-moving plastic materials such as the rock in Earth's mantle. The material being heated expands in volume, reducing its density. This causes the heated material to become buoyant and it rises, carrying the heat with it. A classic example of convection is a pot of soup on a stove. Soup at the bottom of the pot is heated from below, and the soup becomes less dense and rises. Cooler soup at the top of the pot falls and becomes heated as well. This process produces vertical circular convection currents within the pot. Eventually, the boiling point is reached and all the soup is heated evenly.

PURPOSE: Students will create convection currents in deep storage containers filled with water.

ALTERNATIVE MATERIALS: Small vials can be used in place of the test tubes. Large beakers or canning jars can be used in place of the deep storage containers.

SCIENCE SKILLS: Students will **observe** how samples of water at different temperatures circulate because of convection.

ADVANCE PLANNING: Obtain the materials needed before class. The test tubes should be less than 10 mL in size.

2 Guide the Lab

PROCEDURE: Divide students into small groups. Demonstrate how to add food coloring to the test tubes and how to lower the test tubes into the storage containers. Discuss the kinds of observations that students will be making. Provide students with a copy of the Lab Activity Report found on the Teacher's Resources CD-ROM to record their observations and conclusions.

LAB ACTIVITY
Creating Convection Currents

Materials
Safety goggles
Apron
Deep storage container
Small test tube
Warm water
Cold water
Food coloring (red, blue)

BACKGROUND
How does an entire pot of soup on a stove get hot when only the bottom of the pot touches the stove? Heat travels through the metal pot to the soup by conduction. Then another process takes over. In this activity, you will study heat transfer by convection currents.

PURPOSE
In this activity, you will create convection currents in liquids.

PROCEDURE 🔪✂️🔒

1. Copy the chart shown in Figure 16-23 onto a sheet of paper. Put on safety goggles and an apron.

2. Fill the storage container almost to the top with cold water. If you need to move the box to your table, snap the lid on before carrying it.

3. Fill the test tube with very warm water almost to the top. Add a few drops of red food coloring to the water. Gently shake the test tube from side to side to mix the food coloring and water together.

4. Place your thumb or pointer finger over the mouth of the test tube. Very gently, lower the test tube into the storage container until the test tube reaches the bottom and settles over on its side.

5. Remove your finger from the mouth of the test tube. Observe what happens to the colored water.

▲ **STEP 3** Add red food coloring to the warm water in the test tube.

▲ **STEP 4** Gently lower the test tube to the bottom of the container.

Teaching Options

◈ INTEGRATING EARTH SCIENCE

Lake Turnover Lake turnover occurs when seasonal temperature changes cause the density of surface water to change.

During warm summer months, a lake forms layers. The water near the surface is warmed by contact with the air. Because warm water is less dense than cool water, the lighter surface water forms the lake's top layer. The deepest water in the lake is colder and its density is high.

In the fall, the surface air and water become colder. As the water temperature drops, its density increases. Eventually the surface water becomes colder and denser than the water below. The surface water sinks and forces the deeper water toward the surface, resulting in the fall turnover.

A similar process occurs in the spring. During cold winter months, a layer of ice may form on the lake. The deeper water is more dense. As the surface water warms in spring, the temperature at the surface increases to 4°C, where water's density is highest. The surface water sinks and the deeper water rises toward the surface, resulting in the spring turnover.
Have students make diagrams showing what occurs in a lake during the spring and fall turnovers.

▲ **STEP 5** Observe what happens to the warm (red) water.

▲ **STEP 6** Remove your finger from the test tube near the surface of the water.

6. Repeat the experiment, this time using very warm water in the container and cold water, colored blue, in the test tube. Also, remove your finger from the test tube near the surface of the water. Observe what happens to the blue colored water.

Creating Convection Currents

Observations of container with cold water and test tube with warm water	Observations of container with warm water and test tube with cold water

▲ **Figure 16-23** Copy this chart and use it to record your observations.

CONCLUSIONS

1. **OBSERVE:** What happened to the red, warm water in the test tube when you placed it in the cold water?

2. **OBSERVE:** What happened to the blue, cold water in the test tube when you placed it in the warm water?

3. **ANALYZE:** What caused the colored water to move in both experiments?

4. **INFER:** What would happen if, in the first experiment, you held the test tube at the surface of the cold water?

5. **INFER:** What would happen in the second experiment if you lowered the test tube to the bottom of the box?

Tips for Using Technology

Databases Have students use database software to record their observations about convection currents. Databases allow students to enter and edit information, store and organize a lot of information easily, and search for specific information. Databases also allow students to arrange information by putting it in a specific order and to present information by using special layouts. Students can use database software to share their data with the class. Students can also use the Database Planner found on the Teacher's Resources CD-ROM.

• TEACHING RESOURCES •

Teacher's Resources CD-ROM
Lab Activity Report: Study Tools, pp. 16–17

Laboratory Activity Rubric: Teaching Tools, p. 8

Database Planner: Study Tools, p. 22

Laboratory Manual
Lab. Skills Worksheet 4: Organizing and Analyzing Data, pp. 13–14

TROUBLESHOOTING: It is important that the water in the storage containers be very still before inserting the test tubes. Swirling water in the containers will interfere with the convection currents and make them difficult to study.

EXPECTED OUTCOME: Students will learn about convection by observing that colored warm water rises in cold water and colored cold water sinks in warm water.

LAB HINT: Although convection will take place when the temperature difference between the warm and cold water is just one or two degrees Celsius, the effects of convection will be greater if the temperature difference is about 20 degrees Celsius. Use dark food coloring such as blue or green.

3 Conclude the Lab

1. **OBSERVE:** The warm water rose to the top and spread out.
2. **OBSERVE:** The cold water sank to the bottom and spread out.
3. **ANALYZE:** convection resulting from the different densities of warm and cold water
4. **INFER:** The colored water would stay at the top and spread out.
5. **INFER:** The colored water would stay at the bottom and spread out.

Use the Laboratory Activity Rubric on the Teacher's Resources CD-ROM to assess students' lab activities. Fill in the rubric with the additional information below. For this activity, students should have:

- performed the activity according to the procedure and filled in the chart with data collected during the activity.
- correctly answered the questions in complete sentences.

4 Extend the Lab

Ask students to think of examples of convection in nature. Point out that convection creates wind on Earth's surface and currents in the oceans. Discuss how hot-air balloons and fireplaces work.

16-7 (pp. 346–347)

1 Introduce

STUDY HINT Before beginning this lesson, have students scan the lesson for unfamiliar words. Have students work in pairs or small groups to define each of the words on their lists.
learning styles: auditory, linguistic

Linking Prior Knowledge Students are familiar with heat from the Sun, and they may also have experienced heat from an open fire a few feet away. Ask students how they think the heat travels from the Sun or the fire to them. Tell students that they will learn the answer in this lesson.
learning style: linguistic

2 Teach

Demonstration Use an electric heater to illustrate how heat travels by conduction, convection, and radiation. Convection currents of hot air rising from the glowing heater coil warm the case of the heater. Heat travels through the case by conduction. Heat is transmitted to the room by convection and radiation. Heat from convection can be felt above the heater. Heat from radiation is projected from the front of the heater. Most electric heaters have a reflective surface behind the heating coils, which reflects radiant energy out into the room. **learning styles: visual, tactile**

Reinforcement Make sure that students understand that active solar-heating systems use all three methods of heat transfer. (radiation: Energy from the Sun is captured by solar collectors; conduction: Heat in the solar collectors is used to heat water or air; convection: Convection currents in water or air circulate throughout the home, heating it.)
learning style: auditory

READING STRATEGY Explain to students that in a diagram, arrows are very important. They point from one process to the next. Make sure that students follow the arrows in Figure 16-26. Reading the labels next to the arrows further explains how an active solar-heating systems works.

16-7 What is radiation?

Objective
Describe how heat travels through empty space.

Key Terms
vacuum: region where no matter exists
radiation (ray-dee-AY-shuhn)**:** transfer of energy through space

Heat from the Sun The Sun is about 150 million kilometers from Earth. Yet, Earth's surface is heated by energy from the Sun. In order for Earth to receive this energy, the energy must travel through the vacuum that exists in space between the Sun and Earth. You learned that a **vacuum** is a region where no matter exists. Because there are no particles of matter in a vacuum, the energy that reaches Earth cannot be transferred by conduction or convection.

▶ **DEFINE:** What is a vacuum?

Heat Transfer Through Space Energy from the Sun is transferred to Earth by radiation. **Radiation** is the transfer of energy through space. Particles of matter are not needed for the transfer of heat energy by radiation. The heat is in the form of electromagnetic waves.

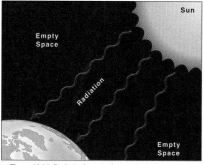

▲ **Figure 16-24** Radiation from the Sun travels through empty space.

▶ **IDENTIFY:** What is radiation?

346

Another Source of Radiation The Sun is not the only source of radiation on Earth. Hot objects also radiate heat. For example, food is kept warm under hot lights in some restaurants, and an electric heater can heat a room. Have you ever toasted a marshmallow over an open fire? You do not have to put the marshmallow directly into the fire. If the marshmallow is close enough to the flame, heat radiates from the fire to the marshmallow and melts it.

▲ **Figure 16-25** Radiation from the fire heats the marshmallow.

▶ **IDENTIFY:** List some sources of radiation.

Radiation in Home Heating Radiation from the Sun is used in some home heating systems. One type of heating system is called a passive solar-heating system. In this type of system, energy from the Sun heats a building directly. Large windows are usually placed where they will receive the maximum amount of sunlight. Energy from the Sun is absorbed by the walls and floors of the building and changed to heat. Shades covering the windows prevent heat loss at night.

Another type of heating system is an active solar-heating system. In an active solar-heating system, energy from the Sun is captured by solar collectors. Solar collectors are made of materials that absorb radiation from the Sun. They are usually installed on the roof or on the side of the house that faces the Sun. The energy captured by the solar collectors is used to heat water or air. The heated water or air is then circulated through the building. Because the amount of energy received from the Sun

Teaching Options

! FAST FACTS   *The Greenhouse Effect*

Background Earth's atmosphere plays an important role in the warming of Earth by the Sun. Some of the solar radiation that reaches Earth's surface is absorbed by the surface and then reradiated as heat. Much of this reradiated energy is absorbed by certain gases in the atmosphere, such as carbon dioxide, methane, and water vapor. These gases, in turn, radiate heat in all directions. About half of the heat radiated by atmospheric gases is directed back at Earth's surface, keeping the surface warm. Atmospheric gases act like the glass panels in a greenhouse, which trap heat, keeping the plants inside warm. Therefore, the warming effect of atmospheric gases is called the greenhouse effect.

Over the past century, the amount of carbon dioxide in the atmosphere has increased by 28 percent. Most scientists attribute this increase to the burning of fossil fuels, such as petroleum and coal. If the carbon dioxide concentration in the atmosphere continues to increase at this rate, Earth's average surface temperature could rise about one to four degrees in the next 100 years. While such a rise may seem small, it would be large enough to change climates, affect agriculture, and raise sea levels.

varies, backup heating systems are used in both passive and active solar-heating systems.

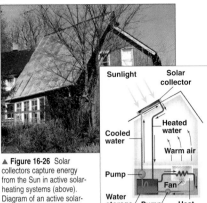

▲ Figure 16-26 Solar collectors capture energy from the Sun in active solar-heating systems (above). Diagram of an active solar-heating system (right).

4 NAME: What are two kinds of heating systems that use radiation?

✓ CHECKING CONCEPTS

1. Earth receives heat from the _____.
2. Space where no matter exists is called a _____.
3. Heat cannot travel from the Sun by _____ or convection.
4. The transfer of energy through empty space is called _____.
5. Two kinds of solar heating systems are active and _____ solar heating.

💡 THINKING CRITICALLY

6. **INFER:** Why does your face get warm when you turn it toward the Sun?

INTERPRETING VISUALS

Use the diagram in Figure 16-26 to answer the question.

7. **EXPLAIN:** How does the heat exchanger help create convection currents in the house?

Hands-On Activity

MEASURING THE EFFECT OF PASSIVE SOLAR HEATING

You will need two cardboard boxes, black construction paper, white paper, two thermometers, plastic wrap, scissors, and tape.

▲ STEP 4 Place each box in direct sunlight.

1. Cut a large hole, or "window" in one side of each cardboard box. ⚠ CAUTION: Be careful when using scissors.
2. Completely line the inside of one box with black construction paper. Completely line the inside of the other box with white paper. Place a thermometer inside each box.
3. Cover each window with plastic wrap. Tape the plastic wrap tightly to the box.
4. Place each box in direct sunlight. Make sure that the window of each box fully faces the sunlight.
5. After about 20 minutes, open the boxes and read the temperature on each thermometer.

Practicing Your Skills

6. **MEASURE:** Which box got warmer?
7. **INFER:** Why did one box get warmer than the other?
8. **ANALYZE:** How does the box that got warmer model a passive solar heating system?

CHAPTER 16: Heat **347**

Answers to questions

1 DEFINE: a space where no matter exists

2 IDENTIFY: the transfer of energy through space

3 IDENTIFY: Possible answers: hot objects such as an electric heater, a hot light, and an open fire

4 NAME: passive solar-heating system and active solar-heating system

3 Assess

✓ CHECKING CONCEPTS ANSWERS

1. Sun
2. vacuum
3. conduction
4. radiation
5. passive

💡 THINKING CRITICALLY ANSWER

6. **INFER:** Energy from the Sun heats your face directly. Your face absorbs heat energy from the Sun.

INTERPRETING VISUALS ANSWER

7. **EXPLAIN:** The heat exchanger transfers heat from the liquid to the surrounding air. The heated air rises, forming convection currents.

4 Close

Hands-On Activity

MEASURING THE EFFECT OF PASSIVE SOLAR HEATING

TIME: 30 minutes

PURPOSE: modeling, comparing, analyzing

SAFETY TIP: Caution students to be careful when handling scissors.

ALTERNATIVE MATERIALS: Use black and white paint to paint the inside of the boxes instead of lining them with black and white construction paper.

Practicing Your Skills Answers

6. **MEASURE:** the box lined with black construction paper
7. **INFER:** The box lined with black paper absorbed more radiation from the Sun than the other box.
8. **ANALYZE:** Energy from the Sun heated the box directly as occurs in a passive solar-heating system.

MORE ON THE WEB

Ultraviolet Radiation Have students visit www.concepts andchallenges.com to learn more about ultraviolet radiation from the Sun. Then, have students design a Sun safety flyer.

ONGOING ASSESSMENT

Demonstrating Heat Transfer Have students work in pairs to make a poster demonstrating heat transfer by conduction, convection, and radiation. Students' posters should summarize these methods of heat transfer and provide examples of each. **learning styles: visual, auditory**

• TEACHING RESOURCES •

💿 **Teacher's Resources CD-ROM**
Lesson Review: Chapter 16, p. 11
Enrichment: Chapter 16, pp. 12, 13

1 Introduce

STUDY HINT Have students create word webs in their notebooks. The main topic should be *specific heat*. As student read this lesson, they can add arms to their webs on which they record information about specific heat.

Linking Prior Knowledge Ask students if they have ever heated a large pot of water on a stove. Ask how long it took for the water to boil. Students will probably say that the water heated up rather slowly.

2 Teach

Demonstration Put 100 mL of water in a beaker and 100 g of sand in an identical beaker. Measure the temperature of the contents in each beaker to be sure that they are the same. Warm the beakers on low heat on a hot plate for 2 minutes, stirring frequently to create an even temperature in each beaker. Do not overheat the sand. Then, remove the beakers and measure the temperature of their contents. Students will note that the temperature of the sand is higher than the temperature of the water. Tell students that the sand becomes warm more quickly because the amount of heat needed to raise the temperature of the sand is lower than the amount of heat needed to raise the temperature of the same amount of water. **learning styles: visual, auditory**

Discussion Tell students that in the early 1900s, many homes did not have efficient heating systems, so people often placed bottles of hot water at the foot of their beds to help keep them warm during cold nights. Ask students if they can think of any properties of water that make it particularly useful for this purpose. (Water's high specific heat allows it to store a large amount of heat that is released gradually as the water cools.)

16-8 What is specific heat?

Objective
Describe the physical property of specific heat.

Key Term
specific heat: amount of heat needed to raise the temperature of 1 g of a substance 1°C.

Sand and Water Imagine a hot summer day at the beach. The sand is burning hot under your feet. You run into the water and it is "freezing" cold. How can the sand be so hot while the water is so cold? The answer is that different materials require a different amount of heat to raise their temperatures. Sand requires less heat to raise its temperature than water does. This is why the sand is so hot. However, water needs a much greater amount of heat to raise it to the same temperature as the sand. This is why the water is so much colder than the sand.

▶ **1** **INFER:** Which needs a greater amount of heat to raise its temperature, water or sand?

Specific Heat Adding heat to a substance increases its temperature. However, the rise in temperature for different types of substances is not the same, even if you have the same amount of each substance. For example, if you have equal amounts of sand and water, adding the same amount of heat to both samples will not give you the same temperature in both samples. The temperature of the sand will always be higher than the temperature of the water. The amount of heat needed to raise the temperature of any substance depends on the chemical makeup of the substance.

▲ **Figure 16-27** When heat is added to equal samples of sand and water, the temperature of the sand will always be higher than the temperature of the water.

348

The ability of a substance to absorb heat is called its specific heat. **Specific heat** is the amount of heat needed to raise the temperature of 1 g of a substance 1°C. For example, it takes 0.09 calories of heat to raise the temperature of 1 g of copper 1°C. Specific heat is a physical property. Every pure substance has its own specific heat. Figure 16-28 shows the specific heats of some substances.

SPECIFIC HEATS OF SOME SUBSTANCES	
Substance	Specific heat (cal /g°C)
Aluminum	0.22
Copper	0.09
Gold	0.03
Iron	0.11
Lead	0.03
Water	1.00

▲ **Figure 16-28**

▶ **2** **INFER:** If the same amount of heat is added to equal samples of gold and aluminum, which sample will have a higher temperature?

Applications of Low Specific Heat A substance with a low specific heat gets hot easily. Not only are metals such as copper and aluminum good conductors of heat, they also have low specific heats. This means that it does not take much heat energy to raise these metals to high temperatures.

▶ **3** **PREDICT:** Do substances with high specific heats get hot quickly or slowly?

Water Is Unique Water can take in or give off a lot of heat energy without a large change in temperature. Its specific heat is much higher than other earth materials, such as those that make up air and soil. That is why in winter, the air temperature around a lake can be as low as −20°C, but the water temperature may be 20°C. In summer, the air near the same lake can warm up to 25°C, whereas the water temperature remains a comfortable 12°C.

Teaching Options

RETEACH

Comparing Specific Heats Heat a 100-g piece of iron to 100°C in a beaker of boiling water. Put 100 mL of room-temperature water in a second beaker. Measure the temperature and write it on the board. Write *100°C* next to it. Transfer the piece of iron to the second beaker. Stir the water and measure the temperature frequently until the temperature stabilizes. Write the final temperature on the board, then calculate the temperature change of the water and of the piece of iron. The iron should have a larger temperature change than the water because iron has a lower specific heat than water.

EXTENDING THE LESSON

Predicting Temperature Change Ask students: *When 1 calorie of heat is added to 1 gram of aluminum, what is the temperature increase of the aluminum?* Use Figure 16-28 to show students that the specific heat of water is $\frac{1.00}{0.22}$ or 4.5 times greater than the specific heat of aluminum. Therefore, 1 calorie of heat raises the temperature of 1 gram of aluminum by 4.5°C. **learning style: logical/mathematical**

Water has an unusually high specific heat. One calorie of heat energy only raises the temperature of 1 g of water 1°C. Water's specific heat is about ten times greater than that of iron. This means that one calorie of heat raises the temperature of 1 g of iron about 10°C.

▶ **HYPOTHESIZE:** On a very cold day, which is apt to be warmer, water in a lake or the air around the lake?

✓ CHECKING CONCEPTS

1. Specific heat is the amount of heat needed to increase the temperature of _____ of a substance 1°C.
2. If a material has a _____ specific heat, it gets hot easily.
3. Iron gets _____ times hotter than water does when the same amount of heat is applied to both.
4. Specific heat is a _____ property.

🔆 THINKING CRITICALLY

5. **PREDICT:** Which would you expect to be hotter in the summer, a city near a large lake or a city that is far from any body of water? Explain your answer.
6. **ANALYZE:** A silver spoon and a stainless steel spoon are both placed in a cup of hot tea. The silver spoon becomes too hot to handle within minutes. The stainless steel spoon is warm. Explain the difference in the two substances.

DESIGNING AN EXPERIMENT

Design an experiment to solve the following problem. Include a hypothesis, variables, a procedure, and a type of data to study.

PROBLEM: Does ocean water have the same specific heat as pure water? If not, which has the higher specific heat?

Hands-On Activity

COMPARING THE SPECIFIC HEATS OF TWO METALS

You will need safety goggles, plastic gloves, an apron, two blocks of paraffin wax, a strip of copper, a strip of aluminum, a pencil, a beaker, water, a hot plate, tongs, and a timer.

1. Put on safety goggles, an apron, and plastic gloves.
2. Half-fill the beaker with water. Heat the beaker on a hot plate. ⚠ CAUTION: Hot plates and hot water can cause burns.
3. When the water boils, drop both metal strips into the beaker. Boil gently for 5 minutes.
4. Using the tongs, remove the copper strip from the beaker. Place it on top of one paraffin block.
5. Using the tongs, remove the aluminum strip from the beaker. Place it on top of the other paraffin block.
6. Observe the blocks of paraffin for 5 minutes.

▲ STEP 6 Place the heated metal strips on blocks of paraffin wax. Observe for 5 minutes.

Practicing Your Skills

7. IDENTIFY: Which metal strip melted the most wax?
8. INFER: Which metal has the lower specific heat?

Answers to questions

▶ **1** INFER: water

▶ **2** INFER: gold, because its specific heat is lower

▶ **3** PREDICT: slowly, because more heat is needed to raise the temperature

▶ **4** HYPOTHESIZE: water in the lake

3 Assess

✓ CHECKING CONCEPTS ANSWERS

1. 1 gram
2. low
3. about ten
4. physical

🔆 THINKING CRITICALLY ANSWERS

5. **PREDICT:** The city that is far from a lake is probably hotter because the lake is cooler than the surrounding air and it tends to reduce the temperature of the city near the lake.
6. **ANALYZE:** The silver spoon gets hot faster because the specific heat of silver is lower than the specific heat of stainless steel.

4 Close

DESIGNING AN EXPERIMENT

Use the Designing an Experiment Rubric on the Teacher's Resources CD-ROM to assess students' experiments. Fill in the rubric with the additional information below. For this assignment, students should have:

- included temperature change as a variable in the experiment.
- designed a procedure that uses equal masses of pure water and ocean water.

Hands-On Activity

COMPARING THE SPECIFIC HEATS OF TWO METALS

TIME: 15–20 minutes
PURPOSE: comparing, inferring

Practicing Your Skills Answers

7. IDENTIFY: copper strip
8. INFER: copper

ONGOING ASSESSMENT

Graphing Specific Heats Have students make a bar graph that shows the data in Figure 16-28.
learning styles: linguistic, logical/mathematical

• TEACHING RESOURCES •

💿 **Teacher's Resources CD-ROM**
Lesson Review: Chapter 16, p. 14
Enrichment: Chapter 16, p. 15
Designing an Experiment: Study Tools, p. 14
Designing an Experiment Rubric: Teaching Tools, p. 7

16-9 (pp. 350–351)

1 Introduce

STUDY HINT Have students write the lesson title and objective in their notebooks. As students read the lesson, tell them to write the information that meets the objective. **learning style: linguistic**

Linking Prior Knowledge Students are familiar with thermometers that contain alcohol or mercury. Ask students how these thermometers work. (The liquid in the thermometer expands when it is heated and contracts when it is cooled.) **learning style: auditory**

2 Teach

Demonstration To show students the thermal expansion of gases, stretch a balloon over the mouth of a flask. Gently heat the flask. Students will observe that the balloon inflates. Point out that the balloon inflates as heated air expands. **learning style: visual**

Discussion Show students a spray can such as an air-freshener container. The label probably states that the can should not be stored at a temperature above 120°F. Ask students why the label has this warning. Point out that gases expand when heated. Adding heat to a gas in a closed container causes the gas particles to move faster and to collide more frequently with the container walls. An explosion can occur if the pressure inside the container becomes too high. **learning styles: visual, auditory**

Answers to questions

1 DEFINE: expansion of a substance caused by heating

2 EXPLAIN: They expand.

3 STATE: It expands.

4 EXPLAIN: As the gas expands, its density decreases. The air in the balloon becomes lighter than the surrounding air, and the balloon rises.

16-9 What is thermal expansion?

Objective
Describe what happens to solids, liquids, and gases when they are heated.

Key Term
thermal expansion: expansion of a matter caused by heating

Heat and Expansion The expansion of matter caused by heating is called **thermal expansion.** Most materials expand, or get larger, when they are heated. You have learned that when heat energy is applied to a material, the particles of matter gain kinetic energy. The particles move faster and spread farther apart. As a result, the material expands. This happens even when the material does not change its state of matter.

What happens to a material as it cools? The particles move closer together. The material contracts, or gets smaller. Most solids contract when they are cooled.

1 DEFINE: What is thermal expansion?

Expansion in Solids Have you ever seen the spaces between the joints on a bridge? The spaces are there because they allow the metals in the bridge to expand. Metals, like most solids, expand when the weather gets hot. Without the spaces, the bridge could be badly damaged.

▲ **Figure 16-29** Spaces between the joints allow the metals in the bridge to expand.

350

Spaces are built into concrete sidewalks, railroad tracks, and other structures for the same reason. You may be familiar with expansion in solids, too. If you have ever placed the lid of a jar under hot water, you know that the heat from the water can make the lid expand enough to loosen it.

2 EXPLAIN: What happens to most solids when they are heated?

Expansion in Liquids Most liquids expand when they are heated. The particles of the liquid move farther apart as the liquid is heated. The opposite is usually true, too. When a liquid is cooled, the particles move closer together. The substance contracts, or gets smaller. However, water is an exception. Water contracts until it reaches a temperature of 4°C. Then it expands instead of contracting. The freezing point of water is 0°C. When water is cooled from 4°C to 0°C, it expands and its volume increases. As the volume of water increases, the density decreases. As a result, ice is less dense than water. This is why ice floats.

▲ **Figure 16-30** Ice floats because it is less dense than water.

3 STATE: What happens to water as it is cooled from 4°C to 0°C?

Expansion in Gases Gases also expand when they are heated and contract when they are cooled. Hot-air balloons rise because of the expansion of heated air.

Teaching Options

RETEACH

Demonstrating Ice Formation To show that water expands when it freezes, fill a plastic container to the top with water. Cover the container and place it in a freezer. Have students note that when the water froze, it cracked the container. Point out that water is unusual because it expands when it freezes, whereas other substances contract. **learning style: visual**

RETEACH

Demonstrating Expansion of a Gas Put the cap on an empty 2-L plastic bottle and place it in a refrigerator. As the bottle cools, it will probably become indented and its volume will decrease. Show the cold bottle to students and ask them what happened to it. Point out that the air inside the bottle contracted as it cooled. Leave the bottle at room temperature, and it will expand again. **learning styles: visual, auditory**

Thermal expansion of a gas within a container can be dramatic. The particles in a gas are farther apart and move faster than the particles in a solid or a liquid. Adding heat to a gas will cause its particles to collide with one another and the sides of their container. If a gas in a container becomes too hot, the increased pressure can cause the container to burst. This is the reason why food should not be heated in a tightly sealed container.

4 EXPLAIN: How does the expansion of gas cause a hot-air balloon to rise?

✓ **CHECKING CONCEPTS**

1. What is the expansion of materials caused by heating called?
2. What happens to most solids when they are cooled?
3. What happens to most liquids when they are heated?
4. What can happen if a gas in a container is heated?
5. What happens to gases when they are cooled?

Science and Technology
BIMETALLIC THERMOSTATS

Thermal expansion can be used to help control how a home is heated and cooled. A device called a thermostat regulates the temperature in most homes. Inside the thermostat is a strip made of two metals. The device is called a bimetallic thermostat. The prefix *bi-* means "two."

The two metals in the thermostat expand when they are heated. However, they expand at different rates. One of the metals will expand faster than the other. It will also contract faster when cooled. As a result, the bimetallic strip bends when it is heated. It straightens out when it is cooled. This bending and unbending controls a switch.

The switch controls an electric circuit, which turns the home heating system on and off. For example, when the temperature in a room gets too high, the thermostat switches off the electric current. The heating system goes off, and the temperature drops. When the temperature gets too low, the thermostat switches the current back on. The heating system goes on, and the temperature rises.

Thinking Critically Why do you think the metal strip needs to be made of two different metals?

---

6. COMPARE: What happens to the particles of most solids when they are heated? What happens to the particles in most solids when they are cooled?
7. HYPOTHESIZE: What would happen to a sidewalk on a hot day if there were no cracks between the squares in the sidewalk?

INTERPRETING VISUALS

Look at Figure 16-31 to answer the following question.

8. ANALYZE: Explain how the drawings illustrate thermal expansion.

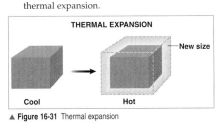

THERMAL EXPANSION

Cool ___ Hot ___ New size

▲ **Figure 16-31** Thermal expansion

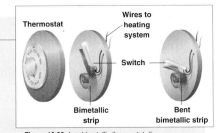

Thermostat — Wires to heating system — Switch — Bimetallic strip — Bent bimetallic strip

▲ **Figure 16-32** In a bimetallic thermostat, the bending and unbending of the bimetallic strip controls a switch.

---

3 Assess

✓ **CHECKING CONCEPTS ANSWERS**

1. thermal expansion
2. They contract.
3. They expand.
4. The gas expands. The expanding gas might cause the container to burst.
5. They contract.

THINKING CRITICALLY ANSWERS

6. COMPARE: The particles gain kinetic energy when they are heated, so they move faster and spread farther apart. When they are cooled, the particles lose kinetic energy, so they move closer together.
7. HYPOTHESIZE: The concrete in the sidewalk would expand, causing the sidewalk to buckle and become damaged.

INTERPRETING VISUALS ANSWER

8. ANALYZE: When a solid is heated, it expands, or gets larger.

4 Close

Science and Technology
BIMETALLIC THERMOSTATS

Technology Connection A bimetallic thermostat makes use of thermal expansion despite the fact that in percentage terms, thermal expansion of solids is quite small. When the temperature of a 1-m steel bar is increased by 80°C, the bar's length increases by only about 1 mm, or 0.1 percent of the bar's original length.

Liquids usually expand more than solids when they are heated. As water's temperature increases from 10°C to 90°C, its volume increases by about 3.5 percent, and its density decreases by a similar amount. Thermal expansion is largest in gases. When air is heated from 10°C to 90°C at constant pressure, its volume increases by 28 percent.

Thinking Critically Answer
The two metals expand at different rates, so the metal strip bends when it is heated and straightens out when it is cooled. In this way, the metal strip acts as a switch that turns the heating system on and off.

MORE ON THE WEB

Rising Sea Level Have students visit www.concepts andchallenges.com to learn why the sea level is rising. Have students write a short report about their findings.

ONGOING ASSESSMENT

Illustrating Thermal Expansion Have students make a drawing showing how the joints on the bridge in Figure 16-29 might look on a very hot day. (The spaces between the joints would be smaller because of thermal expansion.)
learning style: logical/mathematical

• TEACHING RESOURCES •

Teacher's Resources CD-ROM
Lesson Review: Chapter 16, p. 16

Laboratory Manual
Lab. Challenge: What happens to liquids when they are heated? pp. 81–84

Laboratory Video
Segment 19: Heating Liquids

The Big Idea

(pp. 352–353)

1 Introduce

Objective Students will learn about the characteristics and behaviors of endotherms and ectotherms. Students will classify in their Science Logs various animals of a particular region as either endotherms or ectotherms and describe the behaviors of these animals that help them survive.

Linking Prior Knowledge Ask students to recall some examples of heat transfer by radiation (Lesson 16-7). Then, have students locate any examples of radiation in the Big Idea. (the lizard absorbing heat from the Sun)

Also, have students review the properties of insulators (Lesson 16-5). Ask students to name some types of insulation used by endotherms to help regulate their body temperatures. (Walruses have a thick layer of blubber.)

2 Teach

Discussion After students have read the article and call outs, encourage them to use reference materials to learn about the climates of two or three of the locations on the map before choosing the region that they will write about in their Science Logs.

Use the information in the article, captions, and Fast Facts to help guide students in choosing a topic for their Science Logs.

THE BIG IDEA ONLINE

How do animals control their body temperatures? Have students research their Science Log Writing Activity at www.conceptsand challenges.com. You can have students organize their log by completing the Big Idea activity online. Students may post their work in the Online Classroom Database for others to read.

Integrating Life Science

THE Big IDEA

How do animals control their body temperatures?

Many animals are able to live in areas where the climate is extremely hot or extremely cold. The abilities of these animals to regulate their body temperatures and to behave in certain ways help them to live under extreme weather conditions.

Animals are classified into two groups—warm-blooded animals and cold-blooded animals. These terms are a bit confusing because both kinds of animals can be warm. Therefore, many scientists call warm-blooded animals endotherms (ehn-doh-thurms) and cold-blooded animals ectotherms (ehk-toh-thurms).

An endotherm regulates its body temperature to maintain a constant internal temperature. The endotherm has no control over this process. For example, when an endotherm is in cold surroundings, its body shivers to keep warm. When it is in hot surroundings, its body perspires or "sweats" to cool off.

The body temperature of an ectotherm can adjust to the temperature of the environment outside of its body. For example, the body temperature of an ectotherm that lives in water can decrease to better adapt to the temperature of the water. An ectotherm can also increase its body temperature by lying in the Sun. An ectotherm has some control over its body temperature because it can move from colder environments to warmer environments and vice versa.

Read about the endotherms and ectotherms that appear on these two pages. Then, follow the directions in the Science Log to find out more about "the big idea."◆

352

Walruses
Endotherms that live in cold environments have adaptations that help them to keep from losing heat. Sea mammals, such as these walruses, have a thick layer of insulating fat called blubber that retains body heat.

Lizards
A lizard is an ectotherm. It lies out in the Sun to absorb heat. Absorbing heat increases its body temperature.

Figure 16-33 Endotherms and ectotherms are found around the world.

Teaching Options

! FAST FACTS *More on Body Temperature Regulation*

Ectotherms Ectotherms have poorly insulated bodies, and they regulate their body temperatures mainly by adjusting their behavior. A lizard increases its body temperature by sitting in the Sun or basking on a warm rock. If it becomes too warm, it moves into the shade. On a cold night, a lizard's body temperature drops significantly, and it becomes very sluggish. Before this happens, the lizard seeks out a safe place to avoid predators. Ectotherms such as reptiles are most common in the tropics because they cannot adjust to very cold temperatures.

Endotherms Endotherms can regulate their body temperatures in several ways. Mammals that live in cold climates are typically insulated with fur and fat. A less dramatic but more familiar example of heat conservation is the behavior of some cats and dogs who curl up into a ball on a cold night.

During hot weather, endotherms have methods to avoid overheating. Humans and some other animals perspire, which uses evaporation to allow heat to leave the body. A dog's panting cools its body by increasing evaporation from the mouth and nose.

Polar Bears
Polar bears are endotherms that maintain the same body temperature even when swimming in freezing water.

Elephants
Some endotherms have to work to keep cool. Elephants enjoy baths to keep cool. Also, their large ears increase the surface area to radiate more heat out of their bodies.

WRITING ACTIVITY

Science Log
On a map, look at the regions that are very cold or very hot. Pick a region and research what kinds of animals can be found there. In your science log, list the animals and classify them as either endotherms or ectotherms. Describe the behaviors that the animals have that help them live in their environments. Start your search at www.conceptsandchallenges.com.

Fishes
Ocean water can drop below freezing. The Arctic charr is an ectotherm that has a special protein in its blood that keeps its tissues from freezing.

Reinforcement Students can also use the Big Idea Planner or Big Idea Science Log Entry found on the Teacher's Resources CD-ROM.

3 Assess

Use the Writing Activity Rubric on the Teacher's Resources CD-ROM to assess students' Science Logs. Fill in the rubric with the additional information below. For this assignment, students should have:

- classified animals in the region they wrote about as either endotherms or ectotherms.
- described how the behaviors of these animals help them to live in their environments.

4 Close

Writing Travel Brochures Have students work in pairs to create a travel brochure for the region they picked in their Science Log Writing Activity. Their brochures should encourage tourism by including descriptions of some of the interesting animals that live in the region. Have students present their completed brochures to the class.

Tips for Using Technology

Travel Brochure Have students use desktop publishing software to create their travel brochures. Desktop publishing software allows students to combine text and art on a page. Most word processing software programs include tools for desktop publishing. Students can use these tools to give text special formats, make a special border around the text, and plan a page layout. Have students use the Thumbnail Sketch on the Teacher's Resources CD-ROM to plan their desktop publishing layouts.

• TEACHING RESOURCES •

Teacher's Resources CD-ROM
Big Idea: Chapter 16, p. 17
Big Idea Planner: Study Tools, pp. 11–12
Big Idea Science Log Entry: Study Tools, p. 13
Writing Activity Rubric: Teaching Tools, p. 9
Thumbnail Sketch: Study Tools, p. 24

Challenges *(pp. 354–356)*

Chapter Summary

Review Before students begin the Challenges, review the summary with them. If time permits, divide students into groups of three. Have students in each group describe the summary points from one of the lessons in their own words.

🖉 **STUDY HINT** Have students work in pairs to review the Key Terms. Students can alternate, with one student reading a definition of a Key Term and the other student identifying the Key Term.

Key Term Challenges

MATCHING

1. evaporation (16-4)
2. heat (16-1)
3. vacuum (16-7)
4. radiation (16-7)
5. melting point (16-3)
6. convection (16-6)
7. temperature (16-2)
8. thermal expansion (16-9)

FILL IN

9. freezing point (16-3)
10. conduction (16-5)
11. insulators (16-5)
12. convection currents (16-6)
13. calorie (16-2)
14. specific heats (16-8)

Chapter Summary

Lesson 16-1
- **Heat** is energy of particles moving from warmer to cooler regions.
- All matter has heat.
- Heat energy moves from a warmer object to a cooler object.

Lesson 16-2
- **Temperature** is a measure of the average kinetic energy of the particles of a substance.
- Heat affects the temperature of a substance.

Lesson 16-3
- The temperature at which a liquid changes to a solid is its **freezing point.**
- The temperature at which a solid changes to a liquid is its **melting point.**

Lesson 16-4
- The temperature at which a liquid changes to a gas is its **boiling point.**

Lesson 16-5
- Heat moves through solids by **conduction.**
- Heat travels by conduction when moving particles of matter bump into one another.

Lesson 16-6
- Heat is transferred in gases and liquids by **convection.**
- **Convection currents** are found in liquids and gases.

Lesson 16-7
- Energy from the Sun travels through empty space.
- Transfer of energy through space is called **radiation.**

Lesson 16-8
- **Specific heat** is the amount of heat needed to raise the temperature of 1 g of a substance 1°C.

Lesson 16-9
- **Thermal expansion** is the expansion of a material caused by heating.

354

Key Term Challenges

boiling point (p. 338)	heat (p. 332)
calorie (p. 334)	insulator (p. 340)
conduction (p. 340)	melting point (p. 336)
conductor (p. 340)	radiation (p. 346)
convection (p. 342)	specific heat (p. 348)
convection	temperature (p. 334)
current (p. 342)	thermal
evaporation (p. 338)	expansion (p. 350)
freezing point (p. 336)	vacuum (p. 346)

MATCHING Write the Key Term from above that best matches each description.

1. change from a liquid to a gas at the surface of the liquid
2. total kinetic energy of all the particles in a sample of matter
3. region where no matter exists
4. transfer of heat through space
5. temperature at which a solid changes to a liquid
6. transfer of heat through a gas or liquid
7. measure of the average kinetic energy of the particles in a sample of matter
8. expansion of a material caused by heating

FILL IN Write the Key Term from above that best completes each statement.

9. The temperature at which a liquid changes to a solid is called the _____.
10. The heat transfer in solids is called _____.
11. Materials that do not conduct heat easily are called _____.
12. The up and down movements of gases or liquids that cause heat to be transferred is called _____.
13. A _____ is a unit of heat.
14. Substances with low _____ get hot easily.

Teaching Options

PREPARING STUDENTS FOR STANDARDIZED TESTS

Reading Strategy: Tell students to look for keywords to help them choose the best answer to each question. Some examples of keywords are *all, most, none, not, never,* and *always.*

Writing Strategy: Tell students to read the directions carefully before they begin to write. This will help them to provide all the necessary information in their answers.

Interpreting Visuals: Remind students that when they are viewing a table, they should carefully read the title and the column heads to fully understand the information that the table provides.

ESL/ELL STRATEGY

Peer Tutoring Peer-tutored hands-on activities help English-language learners in two ways. Working with peers encourages students to communicate, while hands-on activities help make scientific concepts easier to understand without the barriers of difficult scientific language.

Content Challenges TEST PREP

MULTIPLE CHOICE **Write the letter of the term or phrase that best completes each statement.**

1. Before Benjamin Thompson's experiment, people thought that heat was a
   a. force.
   b. gas.
   c. form of energy.
   d. substance.

2. A unit used to measure heat is the
   a. calorie.
   b. gram.
   c. degree Celsius.
   d. liter.

3. When water freezes, it changes to
   a. heat.
   b. ice.
   c. caloric.
   d. absolute zero.

4. Scientists now know that heat is a
   a. force.
   b. liquid.
   c. form of energy.
   d. substance.

5. When you add or remove heat from a material, you change its
   a. mass.
   b. weight.
   c. potential energy.
   d. temperature.

6. When water boils, it changes to
   a. ice.
   b. small particles.
   c. a solid.
   d. steam.

7. Water changes to ice at
   a. 0°C.
   b. 22°C.
   c. 100°C.
   d. 212°F.

8. Warm air
   a. floats.
   b. sinks.
   c. rises.
   d. turns into steam.

9. The freezing point of a substance is the same as its
   a. boiling point.
   b. elevation point.
   c. dew point.
   d. melting point.

10. Energy moves through a vacuum by
    a. conduction.
    b. convection.
    c. radiation.
    d. evaporation.

TRUE/FALSE **Write *true* if the statement is true. If the statement is false, change the underlined term to make the statement true.**

11. Adding heat energy makes particles of matter move <u>slower</u>.

12. Most solids <u>expand</u> as they freeze.

13. Absolute zero is about <u>–273°C</u>.

14. Particles of matter are always <u>moving</u>.

Content Challenges

MULTIPLE CHOICE

1. d (16-2)
2. a (16-2)
3. b (16-3)
4. c (16-1)
5. d (16-2)
6. d (16-4)
7. a (16-3)
8. c (16-6)
9. d (16-3)
10. c (16-7)

TRUE/FALSE

11. false; faster (16-1)
12. false; contract (16-9)
13. true (16-3)
14. true (16-1)

ALTERNATIVE ASSESSMENT

Describing Properties Students may write a science log entry describing some properties of water. In their descriptions, students should discuss how heat is transferred in water by convection currents and state the freezing point and boiling point of water. They should also refer to the unusual properties of water such as its specific heat and thermal expansion. **learning style: linguistic**

PORTFOLIO ASSESSMENT

Making Student Portfolios Portfolio Assessment is designed to evaluate a student's performance over an extended period of time. It is important that students include work that they are proud of or that they have put great effort into completing. The Chapter Self-Check, the Concept Map, and the Weekly Journal are some of the reproducibles on the Teacher's Resources CD-ROM that they can include in their portfolios. You can use the Portfolio Assessment Rubric also found on the Teacher's Resources CD-ROM to assess students' portfolios.

Concept Challenges

WRITTEN RESPONSE

1. **COMPARE:** Temperature is a measure of the average kinetic energy of the particles in a sample of matter, and heat is the total kinetic energy of all the particles in a sample of matter. (16-2)
2. **EXPLAIN:** Liquid in a thermometer expands when it is heated and contracts when it cools. (16-9)
3. **HYPOTHESIZE:** Possible answer: It is not possible to reach absolute zero in a laboratory. Some heat would always move from the laboratory into the substance that is being cooled. (16-3)
4. **COMPARE:** Conduction is heat transfer in solids. Convection is the process of heat transfer in gases and liquids. Radiation is the transfer of heat through empty space. (16-5, 16-6, 16-7)
5. **EXPLAIN:** It showed that heat is not a substance. It is a form of energy. (16-2)

INTERPRETING A TABLE (16-8)

6. water
7. gold and lead
8. aluminum
9. copper
10. aluminum

Chapter Project Wrap-Up

INVESTIGATING INSULATING ABILITY

Students can use the Lab Activity Report and other reproducibles found on the Teacher's Resources CD-ROM to summarize their results. Students can use graphic organizers and charts to present their results to the class. You can use the Laboratory Activity Rubric found on the Teacher's Resources CD-ROM to assess students' projects.

Fill in the rubric with the additional information below. For this project, students should have:

- designed and conducted an experiment that compared the insulating ability of different materials.
- formulated a hypothesis and developed a procedure to collect data.

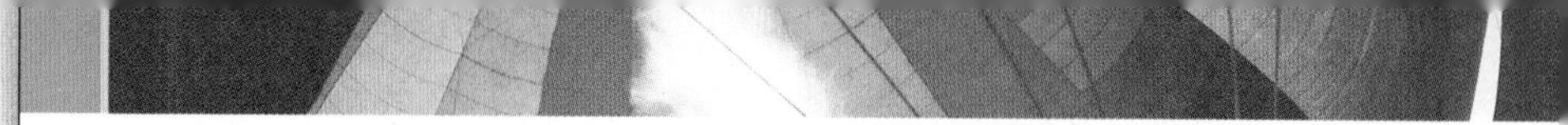

Concept Challenges TEST PREP

WRITTEN RESPONSE **Complete the exercises and answer each of the following questions in complete sentences.**

1. **COMPARE:** What is the difference between temperature and heat?
2. **EXPLAIN:** How is thermal expansion applied in a thermometer?
3. **HYPOTHESIZE:** Do you think it is possible to reach absolute zero in a laboratory? Why or why not?
4. **COMPARE:** Describe the differences between the transfer of heat by conduction, convection, and radiation.
5. **EXPLAIN:** How did Benjamin Thompson's experiment disprove the caloric theory?

INTERPRETING A TABLE **Use Figure 16-34 to answer the following questions.**

6. Which substance has the highest specific heat?
7. Which substance has the lowest specific heat?
8. Which substance has a specific heat of 0.22 cal/g °C?
9. Which substance heats up faster, copper or iron?
10. Which substance heats up slower, gold or aluminum?

SPECIFIC HEATS OF SOME SUBSTANCES	
Substance	**Specific heat (cal /g°C)**
Aluminum	0.22
Copper	0.09
Gold	0.03
Iron	0.11
Lead	0.03
Water	1.00

▲ Figure 16-34

356

Teaching Options

UNIT CHALLENGE ONLINE

Renewable Energy Send students to www.conceptsandchallenges.com. Have them complete the online activity for Unit 5. Students will learn about five sources of renewable energy and explore one source in detail. Have students post their results on the Online Classroom Database.

• *TEACHING RESOURCES* •

Teacher's Resources CD-ROM

Key Term Review: Ch. 16, p. 18

Chapter 16 Test: pp. 19–20

Lab Activity Report: Study Tools, pp. 16–17

Laboratory Activity Rubric: Teaching Tools, p. 8

Chapter Self-Check: Teaching Tools, p. 11

Concept Map: Study Tools, p. 4

Weekly Journal: Study Tools, p. 19

Portfolio Assessment Rubric: Teaching Tools, p. 10

PLANNING GUIDE

◆ **TEACHING THE CHAPTER** This chapter should take approximately 5–8 days to complete instruction and assessment.

	Skills and Features	Projects and Activities	Achieve Science Literacy	Meet Individual Needs
Chapter 17 Opener p. T357	MODEL	• Chapter Project		
Lesson 17-1 What is a wave? pp. T358–T359 Standards: B2a, B3a	DEFINE, ANALYZE, EXPLAIN • Investigate • Health and Safety Tip	• More on the Web	• Study Hint • Reading Strategy • Ongoing Assessment	• ESL/ELL Strategy • Reteach
Lesson 17-2 How do waves travel through matter? pp. T360–T361 Standards: B2a, B3a	INFER, LIST, CLASSIFY • Investigate • Integrating Earth Science	• Extending the Lesson • More on the Web	• Study Hint • Reading Strategy	• Reteach CD-ROM Enrichment Activity Features of a Transverse Wave
Lesson 17-3 What are the features of a wave? pp. T362–T363 Standards: B2a, B3a	COMPARE, IDENTIFY, COMPARE • Building Math Skills • How Do They Know That?	• Cooperative Learning • Extending the Lesson • More on the Web • Lab Challenge	• Study Hint • Reading Strategy • Ongoing Assessment	CD-ROM Enrichment Activity Venn Diagram Features of a Transverse Wave
Lab Activity Making Waves pp. T364–T365 Standards: B2a, B3a	INFER, ANALYZE, OBSERVE • Set-Up Time: 10 min • Lab Time: 20 min	• Integrating the Sciences • Lab Skills Worksheet • Extend the Lab Activity	• Tips for Using Technology	CD-ROM Lab Activity Report Database Planner Features of a Transverse Wave
Lesson 17-4 How are waves reflected? pp. T366–T367 Standards: B2a, B3a	CONTRAST, STATE, DEFINE • Web InfoSearch • Hands-On Activity	• Cooperative Learning	• Study Hint • Reading Strategy • Writing Hint • Ongoing Assessment	• ESL/ELL Strategy CD-ROM Enrichment Activity Writing Activity Outline

Planning Guide continues on next page.

Standards: For details on the correlation to National Science Standards see pages *xx–xxi*.

	Skills and Features	Projects and Activities	Achieve Science Literacy	Meet Individual Needs
Lesson 17-5 **How are waves refracted?** pp. T368–T69 Standard: B2a	HYPOTHESIZE, DESCRIBE, DEFINE • Web InfoSearch • Hands-On Activity	• Cooperative Learning	• Study Hint	• ESL/ELL Strategy • Reteach Laboratory Video
Big Idea **Tsunami: How big can a wave get?** pp. T370–T371 Standards: B2a, B3a	RESEARCH, COMMUNICATE, ANALYZE • Science Log: Writing Activity,	• Big Idea Online • Close Activity	• Tips for Using Technology	CD-ROM Big Idea Planner Web Page Planner
Chapter 17 Challenges pp. T372–T374	• Chapter Summary • Key Term Challenges • Content Challenges • Concept Challenges	• Chapter Project Wrap-Up	• Study Hint • Preparing Students for Standardized Tests	• ESL/ELL Strategy CD-ROM Chapter Self-Check Weekly Journal

Teacher Notes

Chapter 17 Waves

▲ **Figure 17-1** A pebble dropped in a pond creates waves in a circular pattern.

A pebble falls and disturbs the smooth, calm surface of a pond. The energy of the falling pebble is transferred to the water. Small waves called ripples move out in all directions from the place where the pebble entered the water. These waves carry the energy to the edges of the pond.

▶ What will happen when the water drops from the splash fall back to the pond's surface?

Contents

Chapter 17 Waves

Chapter Overview

In this chapter, students will classify waves as electromagnetic or mechanical, explain the difference between transverse and longitudinal waves, describe wave speed, frequency, wavelength, and amplitude, and learn and apply the law of reflection. Students will also study refraction of waves.

About Figure 17-1 As a pebble drops into a pond of water, the waves form concentric circles that move outward, away from the pebble. The circles grow larger, but the waves grow weaker the farther away from the pebble they are. The weaker waves produce smaller ripples.

Answer The drops will cause their own ripples on the surface of the pond.

Linking Prior Knowledge

For this chapter, students should recall:

• the characteristics of motion and speed (Lesson 13-1).

• the definition of *energy* (Lesson 14-1).

• the law of conservation of energy (Lesson 14-3).

Chapter Project

WAVE DIAGRAMS

MATERIALS: construction paper, markers

Students can create diagrams illustrating the features and behavior of transverse waves and longitudinal waves. Using Figures 17-9, 17-10, and 17-14 as models, have students make one illustration showing a transverse wave hitting and reflecting off a barrier and another illustration showing a longitudinal wave doing the same. Have students assign each diagram an appropriate title and label the following features on each diagram: amplitude, frequency, wavelength, crest, trough, compression, rarefaction, incident wave, angle of incidence, normal, angle of reflection, and reflected wave.

learning styles: tactile, visual

Teaching Options

ASSESSMENT PLANNER

For assessment in the Student Edition, see the following pages:

Content Assessment
Checking Concepts: pp. 359, 361, 363, 367, 369
Thinking Critically: pp. 359, 361, 363, 367, 369
Chapter Challenges: pp. 372–374

Alternative Assessment
Building Skills: p. 363
Web InfoSearch: pp. 367, 369
Science Log: p. 371

Performance-Based Assessment
Hands-On Activity: pp. 367, 369
Lab Activity: pp. 364–365

• TEACHING RESOURCES •

Teacher's Resources CD-ROM
Lesson Review: Ch. 17, pp. 2, 3, 5, 7, 9
Enrichment: Ch. 17, pp. 4, 6, 8
Key Term Review: Ch. 17, p. 11
Chapter 17 Test: pp. 12–13
Laboratory Manual: pp. 13–14, 85–88

Laboratory Video
Segment 20: How Is Light Refracted?

1 Introduce

🔍 INVESTIGATE

TIME: 5–10 minutes

PURPOSE: Students will create waves and observe how waves move through water.

MATERIALS: shallow pan, water, pencil or ruler, cork

PROCEDURE: Have students record their observations as the waves move through the water. Have students predict how the cork will move, then make notes or drawings to document what they observe.

THINK ABOUT IT: The waves move forward through the water, but the water only moves up and down.

STUDY HINT Have students scan the pages, reading the subtitles and looking at the illustrations. Have them write questions they would like to answer during their reading. Encourage students to write the answers to their questions as they read.

Linking Prior Knowledge Before beginning this lesson, have students recall the definition of *energy* (Lesson 14-1).

2 Teach

Demonstration Drop a small stone into a pan of water. Have students observe the small circular waves that move outward. Define waves as disturbances that transfer energy from place to place. Be sure that students understand that in addition to ocean waves, there are other types of waves, such as sound waves and light waves. **learning styles: visual, auditory**

Discussion The movement of particles in a wave may be difficult for students to grasp. Many students think that the medium travels forward with a wave. Emphasize that only the energy in a wave moves forward. The particles in a medium only move in small circles. Refer students to Figure 17-4 showing the movement of water particles in a wave to illustrate your description. Have students notice that the cork bobs up and down, but travels very little. **learning styles: auditory, visual**

17-1 What is a wave?

🔍 INVESTIGATE *Observing How Waves Travel*
HANDS-ON ACTIVITY

1. Fill a shallow pan with water to a depth of 3 cm.
2. Using a pencil or ruler, repeatedly touch the surface of the water at one end of the pan for about 1 minute. Sketch what you see happening to the water's surface.
3. Place a cork in the middle of the pan. Predict how it will move with the waves.
4. Repeat Step 2 to test your prediction.

THINK ABOUT IT: What does the motion of the cork tell you about the movement of waves?

STEP 4

Objective
Identify a wave as energy traveling through a medium.

Key Terms
wave: disturbance that transfers energy from place to place

mechanical wave: wave that transfers energy through matter

electromagnetic wave (ee-lehk-troh-mag-NEHT-ihk): wave that transfers energy through empty space

medium: material through which mechanical waves can travel

Waves and Energy If you have ever stood in heavy surf, like that shown in Figure 17-2, you know that water waves have a lot of energy. **Waves** are disturbances that transfer energy from place to place.

▼ **Figure 17-2** There is a great amount of energy in heavy surf.

Mechanical waves transfer energy through some form of matter. **Electromagnetic waves,** such as light and radio waves, do not need matter. They can transfer energy through empty space. You will learn more about this type of wave in a later chapter.

▲ **Figure 17-3** The swimmer and his feathered friends create V-shaped waves as they move through the water. These waves transfer energy supplied by the swimmers.

1 DEFINE: What are waves?

Mechanical Waves Mechanical waves can travel only through some kinds of matter. Any material through which mechanical waves travel is called a **medium.** The picture in Figure 17-3 shows how water can serve as a medium. Air serves as a medium for sound waves.

Teaching Options

RETEACH
Identifying Mediums That Waves Travel Through Draw two columns on the board. Label one column *Mechanical* and the other *Electromagnetic*. Name a variety of waves. Have volunteers list the wave in the correct column. If the waves are mechanical, students should also name the type of medium that the wave travels through. Examples of waves: mechanical—sound (through air), ocean (through water), earthquake (through land or water); electromagnetic—laser, radio, electricity, magnets, radiation **learning styles: auditory, visual**

ONGOING ASSESSMENT
Explaining How Different Mediums Transmit Waves Tell students to think about different liquid mediums. Ask: *How would you compare sweeping a spoon across a container of water to sweeping a spoon across a container of honey?* Students should recognize the difference in the quality of waves. In the first example, a wave and splash would occur. In the second example, the wave would be negligible. **learning styles: auditory, linguistic**

When a wave travels through a medium, only energy moves from place to place. The particles of the medium do not move forward with the wave. Think of a bottle floating on water as shown in Figure 17-4. What happens as a wave moves past the bottle? The bottle moves up and down. It does not move forward in the same direction as the wave. The wave moves through the water.

▶ **STATE:** Do all mechanical waves need a medium?

Particle Motion in a Medium When a wave travels through a medium such as water, the particles of the medium do not move forward with the wave. Figure 17-4 shows a wave moving through water. As described earlier, the bottle does not travel with the wave. It bobs up and down. This up-and-down motion of the bottle is caused by the motion of the water particles.

As a wave moves through the water, each water particle follows a circular path. The size of the circles is greatest at the surface of the water and decreases with depth. The water does not move forward with the wave. The energy of the wave is transferred forward to the next group of water particles, which also move in circles.

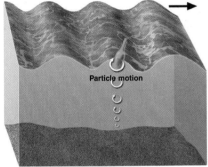

Direction of wave movement

Particle motion

▲ **Figure 17-4** As a wave passes, a bottle will bob up and down but will not move forward.

▶ **DESCRIBE:** What happens to water particles as a wave moves through the water?

CHAPTER 17: Waves   359

✔ CHECKING CONCEPTS

1. Water waves carry _____.
2. Water is a _____ for waves.
3. Particles move in _____ as wave energy moves forward.
4. Some waves, such as _____ waves, do not require a medium.
5. Light waves can travel through _____.
6. When a wave moves through a medium, only _____ moves from place to place.

💡 THINKING CRITICALLY

7. **EXPLAIN:** You are sitting in a rowboat in the middle of a lake when a motorboat passes by, making waves that hit your boat. Describe what happens to your boat.
8. **ANALYZE:** Does the engine of a space shuttle produce sound as it orbits Earth?

HEALTH AND SAFETY TIP

During a hurricane or other large storm, a great deal of energy is carried by ocean waves. Storm waves can cause serious damage when they hit the shore. You should stay away from the shore during a hurricane. Look at Figure 17-5 for a safety checklist. Check with your local Red Cross for anything specific in your area.

HURRICANE SAFETY TIPS	
What You Need	**What You Have to Do**
☐ A full gas tank in your car	☐ Tape windows
☐ Necessary medications	☐ Close shutters
☐ First-aid kit	☐ Stay inside or evacuate
☐ Canned goods	☐ Fill tub with water
☐ Fresh batteries	☐ Tie down movable items outside
☐ Flashlight	☐ Stay on the side of the house away from the wind
☐ Portable radio	☐ Beware of downed power lines and broken gas mains

▲ **Figure 17-5**

Answers to questions

▶ **DEFINE:** disturbances that transfer energy from place to place

▶ **STATE:** Yes, mechanical waves can only travel through 2 mediums.

▶ **DESCRIBE:** The particles move in small circles.

📖 **READING STRATEGY** Tell students that they can often improve comprehension of reading materials by reviewing the questions at the end of a section before they read the section. In this instance, students can read the Checking Concepts questions on page 359 before reading pages 358 and 359. The questions will let students know what information to look for and what concepts will be stressed on these pages.

3 Assess

✔ CHECKING CONCEPTS ANSWERS

1. energy
2. medium
3. circles
4. Possible answers: electromagnetic, light, or radio
5. empty space
6. energy

💡 THINKING CRITICALLY ANSWERS

7. **EXPLAIN:** The boat moves up and down as the waves pass by.
8. **ANALYZE:** No, sound waves are mechanical and need a medium. Space is empty and has no medium.

4 Close

HEALTH AND SAFETY TIP

Point out to students that hurricanes have caused millions of dollars in damage and killed thousands of people. Those most at risk live along the coastline in areas prone to hurricanes, though hurricane tracking and predicting has helped reduce the number of fatalities and injuries. Have students discuss ways that coastal communities might prepare for a disaster such as a hurricane in order to keep people and property safe.
learning styles: auditory, linguistic

MORE ON THE WEB

Reviewing Waves Students can view an online movie, do activities, and listen to summaries about waves at www.conceptsandchallenges.com.

ESL/ELL STRATEGY

More Than One Meaning Explain to students that many words have more than one meaning. For example, the word *medium* can refer to a size or a middle position. In this lesson, *medium* refers to matter through which a wave moves.

• TEACHING RESOURCES •

💿 **Teacher's Resources CD-ROM**
Lesson Review: Chapter 17, p. 2

17-2 (pp. 360–361)

1 Introduce

🔍 INVESTIGATE

TIME: 5–10 minutes

PURPOSE: Students will model speed, wavelength, and the troughs and crests of waves.

MATERIALS: colored ribbon, rope

PROCEDURE: Have students observe the way the ribbon moves in relation to the waves made by the rope. Have students make notes or drawings to reinforce what they observe.

THINK ABOUT IT: a. The ribbon moved up and down, but in the opposite direction of the rope. **b.** The waves did not move up and down as much. **c.** The wavelengths were shorter.
learning styles: visual, tactile

✏️ **STUDY HINT** Have students draw a diagram showing the difference between a transverse wave and a longitudinal wave.

Linking Prior Knowledge Ask students to define a right angle. Have a volunteer draw a right angle on the board.

2 Teach

Demonstration Use a coil spring to illustrate the difference between transverse and longitudinal waves. Have a student hold one end of the spring while another student moves the other end up and down. Explain that this up-and-down motion is created by a transverse wave. Create more transverse waves, and have a third student point out the crests and troughs of the waves.

Next, stretch the spring out, and then squeeze some of the coils together. Release the coils. This back-and-forth motion shows a longitudinal wave. Create more longitudinal waves, asking for volunteers to describe the compression and rarefaction of the waves. **learning styles: visual, tactile**

Answers to questions

▶ **LIST:** the crest and the trough

▶ **DEFINE:** parts of a longitudinal wave where the particles of the medium are far apart

---

17-2 How do waves travel through matter?

🔍 INVESTIGATE

Observing Waves in a Rope
HANDS-ON ACTIVITY

1. Tie a colored ribbon to the middle of a 3-m length of rope.
2. Tie one end of the rope to a doorknob. Hold the other end of the rope and stand opposite the door.
3. Quickly move your end of the rope up and down. Observe the ribbon's motion.
4. Increase the speed at which you move the end of the rope up and down. Observe the resulting waves.

STEP 3

THINK ABOUT IT: a. What happened to the ribbon when you moved the rope?
b. What happened when you increased the speed of your movements? **c.** What happened to the wavelength?

Objective
Classify waves as transverse or longitudinal.

Key Terms

transverse (trans-VUHRS) **wave:** wave in which the particles of the medium move up and down at right angles to the direction of the wave motion

crest: high point of a transverse wave

trough (TRAWF): low point of a transverse wave

longitudinal (lahn-juh-TOOD-uhn-uhl) **wave:** wave in which the particles of the medium move back and forth in the direction of the wave motion

compression (kuhm-PRESH-uhn): part of a medium where the particles are close together

rarefaction (rer-uh-FAK-shuhn): part of a medium where the particles are far apart

Transverse Waves There are two types of mechanical waves, transverse and longitudinal. The difference between the two kinds of waves is the way the particles of the medium move. In a **transverse wave,** the particles of the medium move at right angles, or perpendicular, to the direction of the wave motion. Water waves are transverse waves.

There are two parts to a transverse wave. The **crest** is the high point of a transverse wave. The **trough** is the low point of the wave.

You can demonstrate a transverse wave by tying one end of a rope to a doorknob and jerking the other end with a sharp up-and-down motion as shown in Figure 17-6.

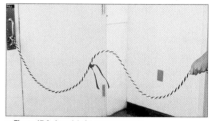

▲ **Figure 17-6** A model of a transverse wave

▶ **LIST:** What are the two parts of a transverse wave?

Longitudinal Waves The sound of thunder moves in a series of longitudinal waves. A **longitudinal wave** is a wave in which particles of the medium move back and forth, parallel to the direction of the wave motion. The air is the medium that carries the energy of the thunder clap.

360

Teaching Options

RETEACH

Modeling Mechanical Waves
Have students line up shoulder to shoulder. Have the first student bob up and down once, and then the next student does the same, and so on. Ask students what kind of wave they have just modeled. (transverse) Have all students lean to their right and then lean to their left. Ask students what kind of wave they modeled. (longitudinal)
learning styles: auditory, kinesthetic

EXTENDING THE LESSON

Discussing Examples of Waves
Explain to students that there are many examples of waves in everyday life. Ask students to consider an ocean wave, which is a transverse wave. In an ocean wave, the crest can be visible, but the trough would be underwater. Explain that thunder is an example of a longitudinal wave. The sound of the thunder comes from the expansion and contraction, or rarefaction and compression, of air.
learning styles: auditory, linguistic

A longitudinal wave has two parts. A clap of thunder pushes the particles of air close together. This part of the wave is called a **compression**. The compressed particles move forward in the direction of the wave motion. As the particles move forward, they leave behind part of the wave where the particles are far apart. This part of the wave is called a **rarefaction**. The rarefaction also moves forward.

Direction of wave ⟶

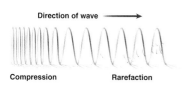

Compression   Rarefaction

▲ **Figure 17-7** A model of a longitudinal wave

▶ DEFINE: What are rarefactions?

✔ CHECKING CONCEPTS

1. All waves carry _____.
2. The difference between waves depends on how the _____ of the medium move.
3. The particles of the medium move up and down in a _____ wave.
4. The particles of the medium move back and forth in a _____ wave.
5. The parts of a transverse wave are the crest and the _____.

💡 THINKING CRITICALLY

6. INFER: Are ocean waves transverse waves or longitudinal waves? How do you know?
7. CLASSIFY: Clap your hands together. What kind of wave did you make?
8. INFER: Have you ever seen fans do "the wave" at a baseball or football game? What kind of wave did they make?

◈ *Integrating Earth Science*

TOPICS: earthquakes, seismic waves

EARTHQUAKE WAVES

In October 1989, a large earthquake struck San Francisco and Oakland, California. The earthquake registered 7.1 on the Richter scale. The Richter scale is a measure of how much energy an earthquake releases. The California earthquake of 1989 was very powerful.

The energy of an earthquake produces waves that travel through the Earth. All earthquakes produce three main types of waves. These waves are called primary waves (P-waves), secondary waves (S-waves), and long waves (L-waves). L-waves are also called surface waves. They cause the surface of the Earth to rise and fall. L-waves cause the greatest damage during an earthquake.

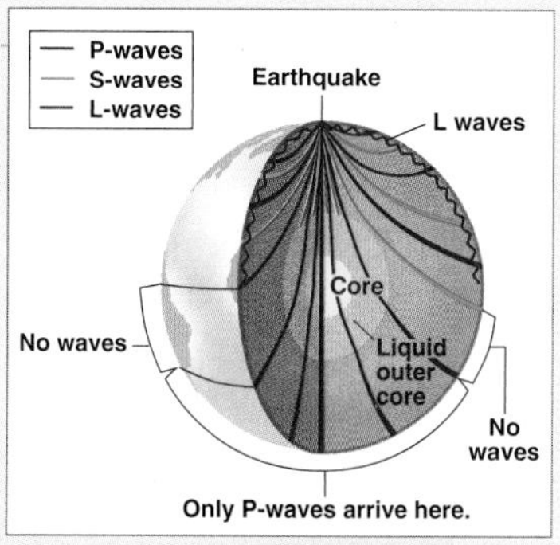

Scientists record earthquake waves on an instrument called a seismograph. P-waves, S-waves, and L-waves travel at different speeds. Scientists calculate the difference in arrival times of the three waves. They use this information to locate the area of Earth's surface directly above the earthquake's origin.

Thinking Critically Which waves cause the most damage? Explain your answer.

▲ **Figure 17-8** A diagram of three kinds of seismic waves

— P-waves
— S-waves
— L-waves

Earthquake
L waves
Core
No waves
Liquid outer core
No waves
Only P-waves arrive here.

MORE ON THE WEB

Viewing Wave Animations
Have students visit www.conceptsandchallenges.com to view animations of mechanical wave movement. Have students write a short report detailing the different types of mechanical waves.

• TEACHING RESOURCES •

💿 **Teacher's Resources CD-ROM**

Lesson Review: Chapter 17, p. 3

Enrichment: Chapter 17, p. 4

Features of a Transverse Wave: Visuals, p. 11

📖 **READING STRATEGY** Students can improve their comprehension and retention of the text by practicing three simple steps. First, students read the paragraph. Next, students ask themselves what the main idea and supporting details of the paragraph are. Finally, students paraphrase the paragraph.

---

3 Assess

✔ CHECKING CONCEPTS ANSWERS

1. energy
2. particles
3. transverse
4. longitudinal
5. trough

💡 THINKING CRITICALLY ANSWERS

6. INFER: transverse; because water waves are transverse waves
7. CLASSIFY: longitudinal
8. INFER: transverse

---

4 Close

◈ *Integrating Earth Science*

TOPICS: earthquakes, seismic waves

EARTHQUAKE WAVES

Earth-Science Connection The area of Earth's surface above an earthquake's origin, or focus, is called the epicenter. Scientists need seismographs from three stations to locate an epicenter. A circle is drawn on a map around each station. Each station is at the center of its circle. There is only one point where all three circles cross. The epicenter is near this point.

Demonstration Make a model of a simple seismograph. Set up a four-legged chair on a desk. Tie strings around the legs so that a felt-tip marker can be suspended in the center between all four legs. The marker should be suspended low enough so that the point barely touches a sheet of paper lying on the desk top right beneath it. Demonstrate how the seismograph records wave motions by gently moving the desk. As the chair moves with the desk, the pen will record the motions. Ask students what the desk represents. (Earth's surface) **learning styles: visual, tactile**

Thinking Critically Answer
L waves cause the most damage because they impact the surface of Earth.

1 Introduce

📝 STUDY HINT Before beginning this lesson, have students copy the titles of each section in their notebooks, using an outline format. As students read each section, they should write the main idea of the section in their notebooks.

Linking Prior Knowledge Ask students to think back to the scientific definition of *speed* (Lesson 13-1). Ask: *What ratio does speed represent?* (distance per unit of time) *Can this ratio be applied to waves? Why?* (Yes; This ratio is similar to the ratio that describes frequency, which is the number of waves that pass a point per second.)

2 Teach

Demonstration Students may have a hard time grasping the frequency, amplitude, and wavelength of a longitudinal wave. Use a coil spring to help illustrate the concepts. Have students create a longitudinal wave on the spring and point out the three features on the spring.
learning styles: visual, tactile

Discussion Draw a transverse wave on the board or on an overhead projector. Help students locate and define the frequency, wavelength, and amplitude of the wave.
learning styles: visual, linguistic

Reinforcement To make sure that students understand the differences between transverse waves and longitudinal waves, have them make Venn diagrams to compare and contrast the properties of both types of waves. Students should indicate that wavelength, frequency, and amplitude are the properties that both types of waves have in common.
learning styles: linguistic, visual

📖 READING STRATEGY To focus on the main concepts of the lesson, ask students to preview the three questions on this page. This will help them focus their attention on the reading and prepare them to look for the most important details.

17-3 What are the features of a wave?

Objectives
Describe the features of a wave. Relate wave speed, frequency, and wavelength.

Key Terms
wavelength: distance between two neighboring crests or troughs

frequency (FREE-kwuhn-see): number of complete waves passing a point in a given time

amplitude (AM-pluh-tood): height of a transverse wave

speed: distance a wave travels in one unit of time

hertz (HURTS): unit used to measure the frequency of a wave

Features of Transverse Waves All waves have some basic features. These features are wavelength, frequency, and amplitude. Figure 17-9 shows these features in a transverse wave.

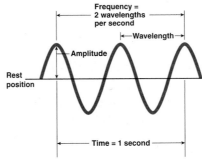

▲ **Figure 17-9** Features of a transverse wave

All waves have a certain length. The distance from the crest or trough of one wave to the crest or trough of the next wave is the **wavelength.** Wavelength can be measured in meters or centimeters.

A certain number of waves pass a point in a given amount of time. The number of complete waves per unit of time is called **frequency.** Frequency is expressed in waves per second.

362

When a wave moves through a medium, the particles of the medium are moved from their rest position. The height the particles are moved is called the **amplitude** of the wave.

1 ▶ LIST: What are some basic features of a wave?

Features of Longitudinal Waves Longitudinal waves have the same features as transverse waves. The distance from one compression to another or from one rarefaction to another is the wavelength. The number of waves that pass a certain point each second is the frequency. The amplitude of a longitudinal wave depends on the amount of energy in the wave. This is shown by how tightly or loosely compressed the particles are.

2 ▶ DEFINE: What is the amplitude of a longitudinal wave?

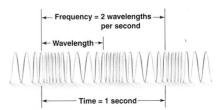

▲ **Figure 17-10** Features of a longitudinal wave

Speed of a Wave All waves move. Their speed of movement is related to their frequency and wavelength. **Speed** is the distance a wave travels in one unit of time. Wave speed is equal to frequency times wavelength.

$$\text{speed} = \text{frequency} \times \text{wavelength}$$

Scientists use a unit called a **hertz** to measure frequency. One hertz (Hz) is equal to one wave per second. When frequency is measured in hertz and wavelength is measured in meters, speed is measured in meters per second (m/s).

3 ▶ IDENTIFY: What is the equation used to find the speed of a wave?

Teaching Options

EXTENDING THE LESSON

Discussing How Density Affects Speed Inform students that the speed of a wave depends on the medium in which the wave travels through. The density of a medium is a property that affects the speed of waves traveling through it. For example, a thick liquid such as honey is denser than water. If you stirred a spoon in honey, you would find that the spoon moves slower than it would in water. Have students create a list of mediums that are denser than water. (Possible answers: molasses, mud, ketchup)
learning styles: auditory, linguistic

COOPERATIVE LEARNING

Finding Wavelengths Have students research frequency of other technologies that resulted from Hertz's discovery. Students should find the wavelengths of televisions, short-wave radios, X-rays, microwaves, cell phones, radio telescopes, radar, remote controls, satellites, and light bulbs. Students can then take the frequencies and create a bulletin-board display, putting the different items in order of their frequencies.
learning styles: visual, tactile

1. All waves have amplitude, _____, and frequency.
2. Amplitude is the _____ of a transverse wave.
3. Wavelength can be measured in _____ or centimeters.
4. The number of _____ passing a point in a given time is called frequency.
5. The speed of a wave is equal to _____ multiplied by wavelength.
6. The _____ is the unit used to measure frequency.
7. One hertz is equal to one _____ per second.

THINKING CRITICALLY

8. LIST: Name the parts of a transverse wave and the corresponding parts of a longitudinal wave.
9. COMPARE: What is the difference between amplitude in a transverse wave and amplitude in a longitudinal wave?

BUILDING MATHEMATICS SKILLS

Use the equation to complete the following questions:

speed = frequency × wavelength

a. A wave has a frequency of 50 Hz and a wavelength of 10 m. What is the speed of the wave?
b. The speed of a wave is 5 m/s. Its wavelength is 2 m. What is the frequency of the wave?
c. The frequency of a wave is 20 Hz. Its speed is 100 m/s. What is the wavelength of the wave?

How Do They Know That?

HEINRICH HERTZ

During the 1800s, the physicist James Clerk Maxwell developed a theory of electromagnetism. Using Maxwell's findings, Henrich Hertz, a physics professor, sought to perfect Maxwell's theory. Hertz conducted a series of experiments in which he proved that electricity can be transmitted in electromagnetic waves. He set up a condenser using two metal rods. He placed the rods end to end, leaving space between them small enough for a spark. When charged, the rods produced a spark that traveled back and forth between them. Thus, Hertz proved that the velocity of radio waves can be timed. Their velocity is the same as that of light. He was also able to solve the problem of how to free the waves from electric and magnetic fields.

A young inventor used Hertz's findings to develop both the telegraph and the radio. Radar is also based on Hertz's work.

The unit used to measure frequency of waves, Hertz (Hz), is named after this great physicist.

▲ Figure 17-11 Heinrich Hertz

Thinking Critically What important discovery concerning electricity was made by Hertz?

MORE ON THE WEB

Reviewing Wave Features
Have students use the Internet to review waves. Have students answer the questions at www.conceptsandchallenges.com.

ONGOING ASSESSMENT

Calculating Speed Ask students to find the speed of a wave whose frequency is 3 Hz and wavelength is 2 m. (6 m/s; 3 waves/second × 2 meters/wave)
learning style: logical/mathematical

• TEACHING RESOURCES •

Teacher's Resources CD-ROM
Lesson Review: Chapter 17, p. 5
Enrichment: Chapter 17, p. 6
Venn Diagram: Study Tools, p. 10
Features of a Transverse Wave: Visuals, p. 11

Laboratory Manual
Lab. Challenge: What factors affect the transfer of energy by waves? pp. 85–88

Answers to questions

▶ 1 LIST: amplitude, wavelength, and frequency

▶ 2 DEFINE: how tightly or loosely compressed the particles are

▶ 3 IDENTIFY: speed = frequency × wavelength

3 Assess

✓ CHECKING CONCEPTS ANSWERS

1. wavelength
2. height
3. meters
4. complete waves
5. frequency
6. hertz
7. wave

THINKING CRITICALLY ANSWERS

8. LIST: wavelength, frequency, and amplitude; wavelength, frequency, and amplitude
9. COMPARE: The amplitude is the height of a transverse wave and the amount of energy in a longitudinal wave.

BUILDING MATH SKILLS ANSWERS

a. 500 m
b. 2.5 Hz
c. 5 m

4 Close

How Do They Know That?

HEINRICH HERTZ

Technology Connection Hertz's studies led to the development of many technological advances, including radio, television, microwaves, X-rays, and cell phones. Students may be familiar with Hertz's name from their familiarity with the radio. AM radio is broadcast between 535 kHz (kilohertz) to 1.7 MHz (megahertz), which means the waves are between 3 km and 300 m long. By contrast, FM radio waves between 88 MHz to 108 MHz are around 3 m long. The numbers of the wavelengths of AM and FM frequencies match the call numbers of the radio stations.

Thinking Critically Answer
Electricity can be transmitted in electromagnetic waves.

Lab Activity

(pp. 364–365)

1 Prepare the Lab

Making Waves

SET-UP TIME: **LAB TIME:**

BACKGROUND: The basic properties of waves are easily demonstrated through the use of coil springs.

PURPOSE: Students will create and study waves, using a coil spring.

ALTERNATIVE MATERIALS: Metal coil springs work best for this activity but plastic coil springs also work.

SCIENCE SKILLS: Students will **observe** the relationships between wavelength, frequency, and energy in waves. They will also **infer** how the pitch of a sound relates to frequency.

ADVANCE PLANNING: Obtain the materials needed before class. Make sure that open areas are available to stretch the springs. Narrow, metal coil springs can be stretched through the air or along the floor. Plastic coil springs may need support and should be stretched across several adjoining level worktables or along the floor.

2 Guide the Lab

PROCEDURE: Divide students into small groups. During the wave making, only two students should work the spring and the rest of the group should observe. Have students rotate positions so that each one gets to create waves and to be an observer. Demonstrate how to make waves with the springs. With coil springs stretched across the air, move one end of the spring side to side. Moving the end faster changes the frequency and wavelengths. Make sure that students understand how to measure frequency and wavelength. Provide students with a copy of the Lab Activity Report found on the Teacher's Resources CD-ROM for students to record their observations and conclusions.

LAB ACTIVITY
Making Waves

Materials
Safety goggles
Coil spring
Meter stick
Clock with second hand
Stopwatch

BACKGROUND

One of the ways energy is transmitted is through waves. Water waves carry kinetic energy across oceans to pound on distant shorelines. Sound is carried in waves that cause the eardrums in our ears to vibrate. How do waves carry energy?

PURPOSE

You will create waves in a spring and observe their properties.

PROCEDURE

1. Select an area in which to conduct your experiment. The test area should be 3 to 4 meters long.

2. Copy the chart in Figure 17-12 onto a sheet of paper. Put on safety goggles.

3. Select two members of your group to operate the springs for the first tests.

4. Stretch the spring the length of the test area.

5. Begin making waves in the spring by moving just one end of the spring side to side. The movement should be slow and easy.

6. Measure the length of the waves produced. Then, use the stopwatch to count how many waves arrive at the other end of the spring each second (frequency). Record your observations.

7. Increase the number of waves by moving one end of the spring faster. Again, measure the wavelength and the number of waves arriving at the other end each second.

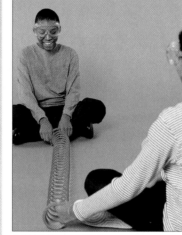

▲ **STEP 4** Stretch the spring.

364

Teaching Options

◇ INTEGRATING THE SCIENCES

Medicine Ultrasound technology allows doctors to use sound waves to study and examine different parts of the body without surgery. Obstetricians can examine unborn babies to check their development and to look for potential birth defects. Cardiologists can look at the heart for defects. Ultrasound can also be used to break up kidney stones so that surgery is not needed.

Meteorology Weather forecasters use radar, or radio detection and ranging, to show weather patterns around the world. Radar waves are waves similar in frequency to microwaves. Satellites around the world send and receive the waves. The information from the radar waves can indicate the types of weather experienced around the world. The satellite sends the information back to Earth, where meteorologists use computers and other instruments to interpret the information.

Ask students to use reference materials to locate other practical uses of ultrasound and radar. Students can generate a list on a piece of butcher paper on a wall and continue to add to the list as the unit progresses.

learning styles: visual, tactile

▲ STEP 5 Move one end side to side to make waves.

▲ STEP 7 Move the spring faster to increase the wave frequency.

8. Increase the number of waves again and make the same observations as before.

9. Switch jobs in your group and repeat the tests.

Wavelengths, Frequency, and Energy

	Wavelength (length between crests)	Frequency (waves per second)	Energy Needed (small, medium, or large)
Test 1			
Test 2			
Test 3			

▲ **Figure 17-12** Copy this chart and use it to record your observations.

CONCLUSIONS

1. OBSERVE: When the wavelengths are long, is the frequency low or high?

2. OBSERVE: When the wavelengths are short, is the frequency low or high?

3. ANALYZE: Which waves are easier to make, short waves or long waves?

4. INFER: If you hear a low sound, what can you infer about its frequency?

5. INFER: If you hear a high sound, does it have a low frequency or a high frequency?

Tips for Using Technology

Databases Have students use database software to record wavelength, frequency, and energy. Databases allow students to enter and edit information, store and organize a lot of information easily, and search for specific information. Databases also allow students to arrange information by putting it in a specific order and to present information in special layouts. Students can use databases to share their data. Have students use the Database Planner on the Teacher's Resources CD-ROM to plan their databases.

• TEACHING RESOURCES •

Teacher's Resources CD-ROM
Lab Activity Report: Study Tools, pp. 16–17

Laboratory Activity Rubric: Teaching Tools, p. 8

Database Planner: Study Tools, p. 22

Features of a Transverse Wave: Visuals, p. 11

Laboratory Manual
Lab. Skills Worksheet 4: Organizing and Analyzing Data, pp. 13–14

TROUBLESHOOTING: Make sure that only one student is making waves at a time. Two students producing vibrations will counteract each other.

SAFETY TIP: If using a narrow coil spring, attach short rope loops to the ends. Have students slip the loops around their wrists before stretching the springs. The loops will reduce the chance of the spring slipping.

EXPECTED OUTCOME: Students will observe that long waves have low frequencies and short waves have high frequencies. Furthermore, they will observe that lower frequency, long wavelength waves take less energy to produce than higher frequency, short wavelength waves.

3 Conclude the Lab

1. OBSERVE: low
2. OBSERVE: high
3. ANALYZE: short waves
4. INFER: that its frequency is low
5. INFER: high

Use the Laboratory Activity Rubric on the Teacher's Resources CD-ROM to assess students' lab activities. Fill in the rubric with the additional information below. For this activity, students should have:

- performed the activity according to the procedure and filled in the chart with data collected during the activity.

- correctly answered the questions in complete sentences.

4 Extend the Lab

Display a stringed instrument. Compare the movement and pitch of thinner strings to thicker strings.

1 Introduce

STUDY HINT Before beginning this lesson, have students study Figure 17-14. Ask students to explain what the red arrows are showing. As they read the lesson, have students define each term in the diagram.

Linking Prior Knowledge Ask students to recall the law of conservation of energy (Lesson 14-3). Ask a volunteer to explain it.

2 Teach

Demonstration Bounce a ball against a wall. Have students observe how the ball hits the wall and then bounces back. Ask students what they think happens when the ball hits the wall. (Energy from the ball is absorbed by the wall, but energy that does not get absorbed gets reflected back in the ball.) Remind students that the total amount of energy is never lost. It gets transferred between the ball and the wall.

Throw the ball so that it hits the wall at an angle. Have students observe how the ball bounces back. Ask students if they notice anything special about the way the ball bounced off the wall. (It bounced off the wall at the same angle that it hit the wall.) Explain angles of incidence and reflection.
learning styles: auditory, visual

Answers to questions

1. **DESCRIBE:** The wave bounces back from the barrier.

2. **DEFINE:** wave that bounces back from a barrier

3. **STATE:** The angle of incidence is equal to the angle of reflection.

READING STRATEGY Explain to students that in a diagram, arrows are very important. They show how one step or process follows another. Make sure that students follow the arrows in Figure 17-14. Reading the labels next to the arrows further explains how the angle of incidence equals the angle of reflection.

17-4 How are waves reflected?

Objectives
Describe what happens when a wave strikes a barrier. State the law of reflection.

Key Terms
reflection: bouncing of a wave after striking a barrier
incident wave: wave that strikes a barrier
reflected wave: wave that bounces off a barrier
normal: line at right angles to a barrier

Waves and Barriers What happens when a wave hits a barrier like the rocks in Figure 17-13? Remember that all waves carry energy. Some of the wave's energy may be absorbed by the barrier. If the barrier does not absorb the wave's energy, the wave bounces off the barrier. This bouncing of a wave from a barrier is called **reflection.**

▲ **Figure 17-13** An incident wave strikes a barrier and is reflected.

1. **DESCRIBE:** What happens when a wave strikes a barrier that does not absorb all of its energy?

366

Reflection Some familiar examples of reflections include a ball bouncing off a wall, your image coming from a mirror, and an echo in an empty room. Figure 17-14 shows what happens when a wave strikes a barrier. The red arrows show the direction of the wave. The wave that strikes the barrier is called the **incident wave.** The wave that bounces off the barrier is called the **reflected wave.**

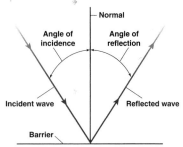

▲ **Figure 17-14** The angle of incidence equals the angle of reflection.

2. **DEFINE:** What is a reflected wave?

Law of Reflection The law of reflection describes what happens when a wave is reflected from a barrier. The angle at which an incident wave strikes a barrier is called the angle of incidence, or i. The angle at which the wave is reflected is called the angle of reflection, or r. These angles are measured from a line called the normal. The **normal** is a line at a right angle to the barrier. A right angle is equal to 90°. The law of reflection states that the angle of incidence is equal to the angle of reflection. Suppose a wave strikes a barrier at a 45° angle. The reflected wave will bounce off the barrier at a 45° angle.

3. **STATE:** What is the law of reflection?

Teaching Options

FAST FACTS
Uses for Lasers

Lasers are used in many types of technology, including CDs, dental equipment, and high-tech saws. Part of what makes a laser work is the law of reflection. A laser uses two mirrors to reflect light back and forth inside a tube. As the light reflects back and forth between the two mirrors, the light becomes very intense. One of the mirrors is designed to let some of the light pass through instead of reflecting it. This ray of escaped light is the laser beam.

COOPERATIVE LEARNING

Modeling Incidence and Reflection Using pencils and a mirror, have pairs of students model the angle of incidence and the angle of reflection. Set up the mirror vertically on a desk or table. One partner should line the pencil up with the point touching the barrier. The pencil can be placed at any angle to the barrier. The other partner should then take a pencil and show the reflected wave.
learning styles: tactile, visual

1. What happens when a wave strikes a barrier?
2. What is reflection?
3. What is a wave that strikes a barrier called?
4. What is a wave that bounces back from a barrier called?
5. What is the normal?
6. What is the angle formed by the normal and the barrier?

Web InfoSearch

Standing Waves Use the Internet to find out what standing waves are and how they are formed. Write a report of your findings. Include a diagram of standing waves in a rope. Start your search at www.conceptsandchallenges.com. Some key search words are **standing waves** and **reflected waves**.

💡 THINKING CRITICALLY

Use Figure 17-15 to answer the following questions.

7. CONTRAST: What is the difference between the angle of incidence and the angle of reflection?
8. ANALYZE: Which arrow represents the incident wave?
9. ANALYZE: Which arrow represents the reflected wave?
10. ANALYZE: Which angle is the angle of incidence?
11. ANALYZE: Which angle is the angle of reflection?

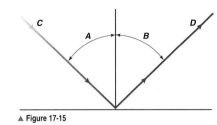

▲ Figure 17-15

⚛ Hands-On Activity

MEASURING THE ANGLE OF INCIDENCE AND THE ANGLE OF REFLECTION

You will need a small rubber ball, dark construction paper, a protractor, ruler, a small amount of talcum powder, and a marking pen.

1. Fold the construction paper in half lengthwise. Open the paper and lay it on the floor with the short side against the wall. The line of the fold represents the normal.
2. Measure an angle of 45° between the wall and the normal and mark it. Spread a small amount of talcum powder on this side of the normal.
3. Lay a ruler along the marked angle as shown. Slowly roll the ball along the edge of the ruler.
4. Observe the ball as it bounces off the wall. It should leave a light path of powder. Mark the angle of this path from the wall and measure it.
5. Label the angles of incidence and reflection.

Practicing Your Skills

6. MEASURE: What is the size of the angle of incidence?
7. MEASURE: What is the size of the angle of reflection?

▲ **STEP 3** Using the ruler as a guide, roll the ball toward the wall.

CHAPTER 17: Waves **367**

---

3 Assess

✓ CHECKING CONCEPTS ANSWERS

1. It bounces back.
2. the bouncing back of a wave from a barrier
3. incident wave
4. reflected wave
5. line at right angles to a barrier
6. 90°

💡 THINKING CRITICALLY ANSWERS

7. CONTRAST: The angle of incidence is the angle at which an incident wave strikes a barrier. The angle of reflection is the angle at which the wave is reflected from the barrier. The angle measures are equal.
8. ANALYZE: *C*
9. ANALYZE: *D*
10. ANALYZE: *A*
11. ANALYZE: *B*

4 Close

Web InfoSearch

Standing Waves Have students visit www.conceptsandchallenges.com to find out what standing waves are and how they are formed.

✎ **WRITING HINT** Suggest that students develop an outline to organize the information about standing waves that they find on Internet sites. They should refine the outline as new information is found. Then, they should use the refined outline to write their reports.

Hands-On Activity

MEASURING THE ANGLE OF INCIDENCE AND THE ANGLE OF REFLECTION

TIME: 10–15 minutes

PURPOSE: measuring

SAFETY TIP: Caution students not to breathe in any talcum powder.

COOPERATIVE LEARNING: Organize students into pairs or small groups for this activity.

Practicing Your Skills Answers

6. MEASURE: 45°
7. MEASURE: 45°

ESL/ELL STRATEGY

Explaining Science Terms Explain to students that many words have more than one meaning and that certain words have a meaning that is unique to science. For example, the word *normal* can mean something that is natural or regular. However, in this lesson, *normal* refers to a line at a right angle to a barrier.

ONGOING ASSESSMENT

Identifying Variables Ask students what the variables *i* and *r* stand for. (the angle of incidence and the angle of reflection)

• TEACHING RESOURCES •

💿 **Teacher's Resources CD-ROM**

Lesson Review: Chapter 17, p. 7

Enrichment: Chapter 17, p. 8

Writing Activity Outline: Study Tools, pp. 20–21

17-5 (pp. 368–369)

1 Introduce

✎ **STUDY HINT** Before beginning this lesson, have students read the captions and art labels. This will allow them to preview what is to come as well as to focus on the most important ideas in the lesson.

Linking Prior Knowledge Before beginning this lesson, have students recall how *density* is defined (Lesson 2-1). Ask them which is denser—air or water. (water)

2 Teach

Demonstration Place a pencil at an angle in a glass of water. Ask students to describe how the pencil appears. Students should notice that the pencil appears broken where it enters the water. Explain that the pencil looks broken because the light waves are refracted, or bent, when they move from air into water. **learning styles: visual, auditory**

Discussion Explain to students that waves travel in straight lines until they travel from one medium to another. When waves travel from one medium to another, their speed changes. Instead of traveling in straight lines, the waves bend. The bending of waves is called refraction. Different types of waves travel through different mediums at different speeds.

Refer students to Figure 17–18. Describe the three laws of refraction.
learning styles: visual, auditory

Reinforcement Have students study Figure 17-17. Ask: *Are the waves traveling from a more dense medium to a less dense medium or from a less dense medium to a more dense medium?* (less dense to more dense) *Are the waves bent toward the normal or away from the normal?* (toward the normal)
learning styles: visual, auditory

Answers to questions

▶ **DEFINE:** bending of a wave as it moves at an angle from one medium to another

▶ **EXPLAIN:** change in speed

▶ **DESCRIBE:** away from the normal

Objective
Describe what happens to a wave when it moves from one medium to another.

Key Term
refraction: bending of a wave as it moves from one medium to another

Changing the Medium Waves travel in straight lines through a medium. What happens to a wave when it moves from one medium to another? Suppose a wave moves from air into water. If the wave enters the water at an angle other than 90°, the wave bends. This bending of a wave as it moves from one medium to another is called **refraction.**

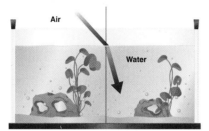

▲ **Figure 17-16** As the wave leaves the air and enters the water, it is refracted.

▶ **DEFINE:** What is refraction?

Refraction and Wave Speed Waves bend when they go from one medium to another because they change speed. Water is denser than air. When a light wave moves from air into water, it slows down. When a light wave moves from water into air, it speeds up. This change in speed causes the wave to be refracted, or bent.

You can see the results of refraction by performing a simple experiment. Place a pencil into a glass of water at an angle. The pencil appears to be broken where it enters the water. As light waves move from air into water, they slow down. This change in speed causes the light waves to be refracted. As a result, the pencil appears broken.

368

◀ **Figure 17-17** A pencil placed in water at an angle appears broken.

▶ **EXPLAIN:** What causes refraction as waves move from one medium to another?

Laws of Refraction The three laws of refraction describe how waves are refracted when they move from one medium to another.

- When a wave moves at an angle from a less dense medium to a more dense medium, it is bent toward the normal.

- When a wave moves at an angle from a more dense medium to a less dense medium, it is bent away from the normal.

- When a wave moves from one medium to another along the normal, it is not bent.

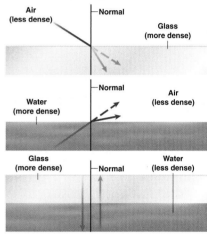

▲ **Figure 17-18** These diagrams illustrate the three laws of refraction.

▶ **DESCRIBE:** In what direction is a wave bent when it moves at an angle from a more dense medium to a less dense medium?

Teaching Options

RETEACH

Comparing Moving Rates Through Different Mediums Students should remember that the reason the waves refract is the change in speed as the wave travels from one medium to another. Ask students to describe how fast they could run on a track. Then, have them describe how fast they could run in sand. Finally, have students describe how fast they could run through mud. The medium that they are running in impacts the speed. The change in running speed is similar to the way light travels through different mediums. Encourage students to make an illustration of running through different mediums in order to remember that the medium can impact speed. **learning styles: linguistic, tactile**

ESL/ELL STRATEGY

Explaining Refraction Have an English-language learner work together with a student who is proficient in English to explain the three laws of refraction.

✓ CHECKING CONCEPTS

1. Waves travel through a medium in _____ lines.
2. When a wave moves at an angle from one medium to another, it _____.
3. The bending of a wave is called _____.
4. Refraction is caused by a change in _____.
5. The speed of a light wave _____ when it moves from water into air.
6. When a wave moves at an angle from a less dense medium to a more dense medium, it is bent _____ the normal.

💡 THINKING CRITICALLY

Use Figure 17-19 to answer question 7.

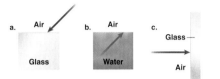

a. Air / Glass   b. Air / Water   c. Glass — Air

▲ Figure 17-19

7. **ANALYZE:** Copy the diagrams onto a separate sheet of paper. Draw arrows to show how the light waves will be refracted in each example.
8. **HYPOTHESIZE:** Have you ever tried to pick up an object underwater? Why do you think the object appeared closer to the surface of the water than it really was?

Web InfoSearch

Ocean Waves Ocean waves change direction as they come close to a shoreline. Waves almost always approach the shore at an angle. However, they usually hit the shore straight on. As waves approach the shallow water near shore, they slow down. This change in speed causes the waves to change direction.

SEARCH: Use the Internet to find out more about the direction of ocean waves. Start your search at www.conceptsandchallenges.com. Some key search words are **ocean waves, wave,** and **ocean wave refraction.**

⚛ *Hands-On Activity*

OBSERVING THE EFFECTS OF REFRACTION

You will need safety goggles, a small bowl, water, and a penny.

1. Place a penny into a small bowl.
2. Move away from the bowl until you can no longer see the penny.
3. Without changing your position, have a partner add water to the bowl until you can see the penny again.

Practicing Your Skills

4. **ANALYZE:** Why could you not see the penny when you moved away from the bowl?
5. **HYPOTHESIZE:** Why could you see the penny again after water was added to the bowl?
6. **MODEL:** Draw a diagram showing how light waves reflected from the penny were refracted as they moved from the water into the air.

▲ STEP 3 Add water until your partner can see the penny.

CHAPTER 17: Waves **369**

---

3 Assess

✓ CHECKING CONCEPTS ANSWERS

1. straight
2. Possible answers: bends or refracts
3. refraction
4. Possible answers: speed or density
5. Possible answers: changes or increases
6. toward

💡 THINKING CRITICALLY ANSWERS

7. **ANALYZE: a.** toward the normal **b.** away from the normal **c.** along the normal
8. **HYPOTHESIZE:** because the light was refracted

4 Close

Web InfoSearch

Ocean Waves Have students use the Internet to find out more about the direction of waves. Some key search words are **ocean waves, wave refraction,** and **ocean wave refraction.** Students should begin their search at www.conceptsandchallenges.com.

Hands-On Activity

OBSERVING THE EFFECTS OF REFRACTION

TIME: 10–15 minutes

PURPOSE: observing, diagramming

SAFETY TIP: Water can be dispensed from prefilled pitchers to eliminate the risk of spills.

COOPERATIVE LEARNING: Have partners change roles and then repeat the activity.

Practicing Your Skills Answers

4. **ANALYZE:** The penny lies flat on the bottom of the bowl, so it becomes hard to see.
5. **HYPOTHESIZE:** Possible answer: The light waves refracted as light moved from the penny to our eyes, so it appeared as if the penny was lying higher than it actually was.
6. **MODEL:** Diagrams should show the refraction away from the normal as light moves from the penny to students' eyes.

COOPERATIVE LEARNING

Modeling Refraction To model wave refraction, have pairs of students draw a straight line on a sheet of paper to represent the normal and use a pipe cleaner (or other thin, bendable object) to represent the wave. Instruct students to take turns showing the refraction of a wave moving between mediums with differing densities by bending the pipe cleaner and placing it on the normal. **learning styles: tactile, visual**

• *TEACHING RESOURCES* •

💿 **Teacher's Resources CD-ROM**
Lesson Review: Chapter 17, p. 9

📼 **Laboratory Video**
Segment 20: How Is Light Refracted?

The Big Idea

(pp. 370–371)

1 Introduce

Objective Students will identify the approach of a tsunami and create a system to warn potential victims of the dangers of one. Students will research tsunami warning systems and write about them in their Science Logs.

Linking Prior Knowledge Ask students to recall how waves move and transfer energy (Lesson 17-1). Also, have students review the information explained regarding waves produced by earthquakes (Lesson 17-2).

2 Teach

Discussion After students have read the article and the call outs, ask why Hawaii is prone to tsunamis. Students might choose to use encyclopedias or the Internet to answer this question. Students should also explain why the origin for the word *tsunami* is Japanese. Have students bring their findings back to the class for the entire group to share and discuss. Using the information located, students should be able to choose potential warning systems and preparation recommendations for communities at risk for a tsunami.
learning styles: auditory, linguistic

Use the information in the article and captions to help guide students in choosing a topic for their Science Logs.

THE BIG IDEA ONLINE

Tsunami: How big can a wave get?
Have students research their Science Log Writing Activity at www.conceptsandchallenges.com. You can have students organize their log by completing the Big Idea activity online. Students may post their work in the Online Classroom Database for others to read.

Reinforcement Students can also use the Big Idea Planner or Big Idea Science Log Entry found on the Teacher's Resources CD-ROM.

Integrating Earth Science

THE Big IDEA

Tsunami: How big can a wave get?

How big can an ocean wave get? Think about a wave 18 m taller than average that is traveling at 800 km/h (480 mph). Does it sound like a horror movie? Such waves actually exist. They are called seismic sea waves or *tsunamis*, a Japanese word meaning "harbor wave." They occur most commonly in the Pacific.

Tsunamis are fast, high-energy waves related to earthquakes or volcanic eruptions on the seafloor. Sometimes people call them tidal waves. However, they are not caused by tides. A tsunami is caused by seismic activity, which is the movement of the Earth's crust. Energy from violent seismic movement on the ocean floor is transmitted into the water as a waveform. The high-energy wave can travel thousands of kilometers from its source.

In the deep open ocean, a tsunami might be only 1 m high, but when it reaches shore, watch out. The wave crest might be 18 m higher than normal waves.

The two worst tsunamis in this century struck Hawaii in 1946 and 1960. The port of Hilo on the Big Island of Hawaii was hit the worst. The 1960 tsunami killed 61 people.

Now, Hawaii has a tsunami warning system to protect people. When seismographs (earthquake detectors) detect a seafloor earthquake starting a tsunami, loud alarms go off along the coast warning people to head for the hills. Surprisingly, it is also safe to be out at sea. In the open ocean, a passing tsunami would just feel like a large wave. Its awesome power is only revealed when the tsunami moves into the shallow water near the shore.

Look at the illustrations and photos that appear on these two pages. Then, follow the directions in the Science Log to find out more about "the big idea." ✦

Figure 17-20 Woodcut by Japanese artist Hokusai

Tsunami Damage
Out at sea a tsunami doesn't appear much larger than other waves. However, when the high energy of the tsunami hits the shore, it can be very destructive. In 1960, the port of Hilo in Hawaii suffered great damage.

370

Teaching Options

! FAST FACTS *More About Tsunamis*

Earthquakes often cause tsunamis. However, many tsunamis can come from volcanic eruptions, landslides, and the impact of very large meteorites. One of the most deadly tsunamis came in 1883, caused by the eruption of the Indonesian volcano, Krakatoa. The tsunamis that followed the eruption killed over 30,000 people.

Tsunamis travel so fast and for such great distances that an event on one continent can lead to disaster for another continent. An earthquake near Chile in 1960 caused a tsunami that traveled as far as Japan, killing 150 people. The tsunami traveled 16,000 km (10,000 mi) in less than a day. Not only do tsunamis travel at amazingly fast speeds, but because they are waves, once they come in contact with a barrier, they reflect back and travel out to the ocean again. Tsunamis can travel back and forth across the ocean many times before dissipating.

Science Log

Find out how the tsunami warning system in Hawaii works. Your job is running part of the warning system. What data do you need to collect? How will you analyze the data? What do you think are the best ways to warn people? How will you make sure the people of your island are prepared to respond to a potential tsunami? To research a warning system, visit www.conceptsandchallenges.com.

Seismograph
Seismographs detect the seafloor earthquakes that start a tsunami. That is the key to the early warning system.

Evacuation Map
This map can be found in local Hawaiian phone books. It shows which areas must be evacuated when a tsunami is detected.

EVACUATE ALL SHADED AREAS

Warning Signal
Although tsunamis move very fast, warning sirens like this give people time to get to the safety of higher ground.

CHAPTER 17: Waves **371**

3 Assess

Use the Writing Activity Rubric on the Teacher's Resources CD-ROM to assess students' Science Logs. Fill in the rubric with the additional information below. For this assignment, students should have:

- explained how the tsunami warning system in Hawaii works and given examples of data that could be collected.
- listed ways that people living in tsunami-prone communities can prepare for a tsunami.

4 Close

Create a Public Service Announcement
Have students work in small groups to write and perform a public service announcement informing a coastal community about the hazards of a tsunami. The announcement should explain the dangers posed by a tsunami, what people should and should not do when a warning occurs, and preparations that can be made. The announcement should be performed for the class.
learning styles: auditory, linguistic

Tips for Using Technology

Developing Student Web Pages: The Basics of HTML After students research a warning system, have them create a Web page that contains safety information. Developing basic student Web pages can be an easy task even if you are not familiar with HTML. Web sites such as www.Geocities.com, www.Angelfire.com, and www.Tripod.Lycos.com offer free Web site hosting and tools that make creating a Web page easier. Students can also use the Web Page Planner found on the Teacher's Resources CD-ROM.

• TEACHING RESOURCES •

Teacher's Resources CD-ROM
Big Idea: Chapter 17, p. 10
Big Idea Planner: Study Tools, pp. 11–12
Big Idea Science Log Entry: Study Tools, p. 13
Writing Activity Rubric: Teaching Tools, p. 9
Web Page Planner: Study Tools, p. 25

Challenges (pp. 372–374)

Chapter Summary

Review Before students begin the Challenges, review the summary with them. Have students make a set of index cards, each with a boldface term written on it. Review each section, and have students hold up the term referred to as it is discussed.

✎ **STUDY HINT** Have students use main concepts in each section to create an outline. Students should be sure that all Key Terms and concepts are included.

Key Terms Challenges

MATCHING

1. medium (17-1)
2. crest (17-2)
3. amplitude (17-3)
4. hertz (17-3)
5. incident wave (17-4)
6. normal (17-4)
7. waves (17-1)

FILL IN

8. transverse wave (17-2)
9. longitudinal wave (17-2)
10. compression (17-2)
11. wavelength (17-3)
12. Reflection (17-4)

Chapter Summary

Lesson 17-1
- **Waves** are disturbances that transfer energy from place to place.
- Any substance through which waves can travel is called a **medium**.
- The particles of a medium do not move in the same direction as a wave but in small circles.

Lesson 17-2
- In a **transverse wave**, the particles of the medium move up and down at right angles to the direction of the wave motion. Its parts are the **crest** and the **trough**.
- In a **longitudinal wave**, the particles of the medium move back and forth in the same direction as the wave motion. Its parts are the **compression** and the **rarefaction**.

Lesson 17-3
- **Wavelength** is the distance from crest to crest or from trough to trough.
- **Frequency** is the number of complete waves passing a point in a given amount of time.
- **Amplitude** is the height of a wave.
- The **speed** of a wave is equal to the frequency multiplied by the wavelength.

Lesson 17-4
- A wave that strikes a barrier is called the **incident wave**.
- A wave that bounces off a barrier is called the **reflected wave**.
- The law of **reflection** states that the angle of incidence is equal to the angle of reflection.

Lesson 17-5
- The laws of **refraction** describe how waves are refracted, or bent, when they move from one medium to another.

Key Term Challenges

amplitude (p. 362)
compression (p. 360)
crest (p. 360)
electromagnetic wave (p. 358)
frequency (p. 362)
hertz (p. 362)
incident wave (p. 366)
longitudinal wave (p. 360)
mechanical wave (p. 358)
medium (p. 358)

normal (p. 366)
rarefaction (p. 360)
reflected wave (p. 366)
reflection (p. 366)
refraction (p. 368)
speed (p. 362)
transverse wave (p. 360)
trough (p. 360)
wavelength (p. 362)
wave (p. 358)

MATCHING Write the Key Term from above that best matches each description.

1. substance through which waves can travel
2. high point of a wave
3. height of a wave
4. unit used to measure frequency
5. wave that strikes a barrier
6. line at 90° to a barrier
7. disturbances in a medium

FILL IN Write the Key Term from above that best completes each statement.

8. In a _____, the particles of the medium move up and down at right angles to the direction of the wave motion.
9. In a _____, the particles of the medium move back and forth in the direction of the wave motion.
10. The two parts of a longitudinal wave are the _____ and the rarefaction.
11. The basic features of all waves are amplitude, _____, and frequency.
12. _____ occurs when a barrier does not absorb all of a wave's energy.

Teaching Options

PREPARING STUDENTS FOR STANDARDIZED TESTS

Reading Strategy: Tell students that it is important to consider every choice in a multiple-choice test, even if they are sure they know the answer.

Writing Strategy: Tell students to make a quick outline or organizer before writing. This will help them stay on topic and present an organized response.

Interpreting Visuals: Tell students to read all the questions before studying the visual. Knowing the questions helps them to focus on the parts of the diagram where they will find the answers.

ESL/ELL STRATEGY

Improving Communications Skills Working with peers encourages English-language learners to communicate. Have students work in pairs. One student should make up three questions about the chapter and read them aloud to the other student. The partner should answer the questions. Then, partners should reverse roles. Each pair should check each other's answers to make sure that the correct answers were given.

Content Challenges TEST PREP

MULTIPLE CHOICE Write the letter of the term or phrase that best completes each statement.

1. Waves are caused by
   a. potential energy.
   b. kinetic energy.
   c. heat energy.
   d. nuclear energy.

2. Mechanical waves cannot travel through
   a. air.
   b. water.
   c. metal.
   d. empty space.

3. When a longitudinal wave moves through a medium, the particles of the medium move
   a. in circles.
   b. up and down.
   c. back and forth.
   d. in the direction of the wave motion.

4. The two kinds of waves are transverse and
   a. circular.
   b. normal.
   c. longitudinal.
   d. compression.

5. The crest of a wave is the wave's
   a. low point.
   b. length.
   c. speed.
   d. high point.

6. In a transverse wave, the particles of the medium move
   a. at right angles to the direction of wave motion.
   b. back and forth to the direction of wave motion.
   c. at opposite angles to the wave motion.
   d. backward against the wave motion.

7. In a rarefaction, the particles are
   a. squeezed together.
   b. lined up.
   c. spread apart.
   d. not moving.

8. Wavelength can be measured in
   a. meters.
   b. hertz.
   c. angles.
   d. number of waves.

9. The wave's speed is equal to the frequency of the wave multiplied by the
   a. amplitude.
   b. wavelength.
   c. height.
   d. medium.

10. The angle between the normal and a barrier is equal to
    a. 45°.
    b. 90°.
    c. 180°.
    d. 360°.

TRUE/FALSE Write *true* if the statement is true. If the statement is false, change the underlined term to make the statement true.

11. The angle of incidence is equal to the angle of refraction.

12. When a wave is refracted, it is bent.

13. In a rarefaction, the particles are spread apart.

14. Mechanical waves do not need a medium to transfer energy.

Concept Challenges

MULTIPLE CHOICE

1. b (17-1)
2. d (17-1)
3. d (17-2)
4. c (17-2)
5. d (17-2)
6. a (17-2)
7. c (17-2)
8. a (17-3)
9. b (17-3)
10. b (17-4)

TRUE/FALSE

11. false; reflection (17-4)
12. true (17-5)
13. true (17-2)
14. false; Electromagnetic (17-1)

ALTERNATIVE ASSESSMENT

Relating Information Students may write a science log entry explaining the difference between mechanical waves and electromagnetic waves. Students can then give detailed descriptions of the features of transverse waves and longitudinal waves. Finally, students can explain the processes of reflection and refraction in detail.
learning style: linguistic

PORTFOLIO ASSESSMENT

Making Student Portfolios Portfolio Assessment provides an opportunity for students who are generally not good test-takers to demonstrate their learning in another way. Students can demonstrate their comprehension of the concepts in this chapter by making a portfolio. The Chapter Self-Check, the Big Idea Planner, and the Weekly Journal are some of the reproducibles on the Teacher's Resources CD-ROM that they can include in their portfolios. You can use the Portfolio Assessment Rubric also found on the Teacher's Resources CD-ROM to assess students' portfolios.

Concept Challenges

WRITTEN RESPONSE

1. **HYPOTHESIZE:** The waves will reflect off the barrier, the doorknob. (17-2)
2. **COMPARE:** Possible answer: The crest or trough is used to find the amplitude. The compression or rarefaction is also used to calculate amplitude. (17-2)
3. **HYPOTHESIZE:** Light from the Sun would not be able to travel through space to Earth. (17-2)

INTERPRETING A DIAGRAM (17-3)

4. c
5. a
6. b
7. speed = wavelength × frequency
8. It decreases.
9. It decreases.

Chapter Project Wrap-Up

WAVE DIAGRAMS

Students' diagrams can be exhibited around the classroom. Students can present their diagrams and describe similarities and differences between transverse and longitudinal waves. You can use the Individual Activity Rubric found on the Teacher's Resources CD-ROM to assess students' projects. Fill in the rubric with the additional information below. For this project, students should have:

- drawn two diagrams showing the features of transverse and longitudinal waves and their reflective behavior.
- titled and labeled each diagram appropriately.

Concept Challenges TEST PREP

WRITTEN RESPONSE Answer each of the following questions in complete sentences.

1. **HYPOTHESIZE:** You can make transverse waves in a rope tied to a doorknob. What happens to the waves when they reach the door?
2. **COMPARE:** How are the crests and troughs of a transverse wave like the compressions and rarefactions of a longitudinal wave?
3. **HYPOTHESIZE:** Suppose that light waves needed a medium through which to travel. How do you think the world would be different?

INTERPRETING A DIAGRAM Use Figure 17-21 to answer the following questions.

4. Which letter represents the wavelength of the wave?
5. Which letter represents the amplitude?
6. Which letter represents the frequency?
7. What is the relationship between speed, wavelength, and frequency?
8. If the frequency of a wave increases and the speed stays the same, what happens to the wavelength?
9. If the speed of a wave does not change but the wavelength increases, what happens to the frequency?

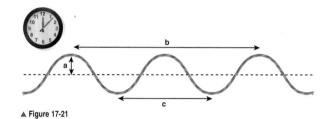

▲ **Figure 17-21**

Teaching Options

• *TEACHING RESOURCES* •

Teacher's Resources CD-ROM

Key Term Review: Chapter 17, p. 11

Chapter 17 Test: pp. 12–13

Individual Activity Rubric: Teaching Tools, p. 5

Chapter Self-Check: Teaching Tools, p. 11

Big Idea Planner: Study Tools, pp. 11–12

Weekly Journal: Study Tools, p. 19

Portfolio Assessment Rubric: Teaching Tools, p. 10

PLANNING GUIDE

◆ **TEACHING THE CHAPTER** This chapter should take approximately 8–11 days to complete instruction and assessment.

	Skills and Features	Projects and Activities	Achieve Science Literacy	Meet Individual Needs
Chapter 18 Opener p. T375	EXPLAIN	• Chapter Project		
Lesson 18-1 **What is sound?** pp. T376–T377 Standards: B2a, B3a	OBSERVE, DEFINE, DESCRIBE • Designing an Experiment • Hands-On Activity	• Cooperative Learning • More on the Web	• Study Hint • Reading Strategy	• ESL/ELL Strategy • Reteach CD-ROM Designing an Experiment Spider Map
Lab Activity **Experimenting With Vibrations** pp. T378–T379	OBSERVE, INFER • Set-Up Time: 10 min • Lab Time: 20 min	• Extend the Lab Activity • Lab Skills Worksheet	• Tips for Using Technology	CD-ROM Lab Activity Report Spreadsheet
Lesson 18-2 **How do sound waves travel?** pp. T380–T381 Standard: B3a	INFER, EXPLAIN, DESCRIBE • Investigate • Web InfoSearch • Science and Technology	• Extending the Lesson	• Study Hint • Reading Strategy	• Reteach
Lesson 18-3 **What is the speed of sound?** pp. T382–T383 Standard: B2a	DEFINE, HYPOTHESIZE, COMPARE • Building Math Skills • Science and Technology	• Cooperative Learning • Extending the Lesson • More on the Web	• Study Hint • Reading Strategy	CD-ROM Enrichment Activity
Lesson 18-4 **What is intensity?** pp. T384–T385 Standard: B3a	HYPOTHESIZE, ANALYZE, DEFINE • Health and Safety Tip • Integrating Environmental Science	• Extending the Lesson • More on the Web • Lab Challenge	• Study Hint • Reading Strategy • Writing Hint • Ongoing Assessment	CD-ROM Writing Activity Outline
Lesson 18-5 **What are frequency and pitch?** pp. T386–T387 Standard: B3a	OBSERVE, DEFINE, IDENTIFY • Web InfoSearch • Hands-On Activity	• Cooperative Learning • Extending the Lesson	• Study Hint	• ESL/ELL Strategy

Planning Guide continues on next page.

Standards: For details on the correlation to National Science Standards see pages *xx–xxi*.

	Skills and Features	Projects and Activities	Achieve Science Literacy	Meet Individual Needs
Big Idea How do animals use sound? pp. T388–T389	RESEARCH, COMMUNICATE, ANALYZE • Science Log: Writing Activity	• Big Idea Online • Close Activity	• Tips for Using Technology	CD-ROM Big Idea Planner Thumbnail Sketch
Lesson 18-6 What is sound quality? pp. T390–T391	NAME, DEFINE, IDENTIFY • Investigate • Web InfoSearch	• Extending the Lesson	• Study Hint	• Reteach CD-ROM Enrichment Activity Concept Map
Lesson 18-7 What is the Doppler effect? pp. T392–T393	RESEARCH, COMPARE, EXPLAIN • Building Science Skills • Integrating Earth Science	• Extending the Lesson • More on the Web	• Study Hint • Reading Strategy • Writing Hint • Ongoing Assessment	• Reteach CD-ROM Enrichment Activity
Lesson 18-8 How do you hear? pp. T394–T395	SEQUENCE, NAME, INFER • Interpreting Visuals • Real-Life Science	• More on the Web • Integrating Life Science	• Study Hint • Reading Strategy • Ongoing Assessment	• Reteach CD-ROM The Eye/The Ear KWL Chart
Chapter 18 Challenges pp. T396–T398	• Chapter Summary • Key Term Challenges • Content Challenges • Concept Challenges	• Chapter Project Wrap-Up	• Study Hint • Preparing Students for Standardized Tests	• ESL/ELL Strategy CD-ROM Chapter Self-Check KWL Chart

Teacher Notes

Chapter 18 Sound

▲ **Figure 18-1** The instruments in this band make very recognizable sounds.

Sounds are all around you. When you hear a sound, most of the time you will recognize its source. For example, you would be able to tell the difference between the sound made by a bagpipe and one made by a bass drum. Although sounds are different, they all have something in common. All sounds are produced by objects that are moving back and forth rapidly.

▶How does striking a drum produce a sound?

Contents

UNIT 6: Waves, Sound, and Light   **375**

Teaching Options

ASSESSMENT PLANNER

For assessment in the Student Edition, see the following pages:

Content Assessment
Checking Concepts: pp. 377, 381, 383, 385, 387, 391, 393, 395
Thinking Critically: pp. 377, 381, 383, 385, 387, 391, 393, 395
Interpreting Visuals: p. 395
Chapter Challenges: pp. 396–398

Alternative Assessment
Building Skills: pp. 383, 393
Web InfoSearch: pp. 381, 387, 391
Science Log: p. 389

Performance-Based Assessment
Hands-On Activity: pp. 377, 387
Designing an Experiment: p. 377
Lab Activity: pp. 378–379

• TEACHING RESOURCES •

Teacher's Resources CD-ROM
Lesson Review: Ch. 18, pp. 2, 3, 4, 7, 8, 10, 13, 15
Enrichment: Ch. 18, pp. 5, 6, 11, 12, 14
Key Term Review: Ch. 18, p. 16
Chapter 18 Test: pp. 17–18
Laboratory Manual: pp. 13–14, 89–92

Chapter 18
Sound

Chapter Overview

In this chapter, students will describe how sound waves travel through a medium, explain the relationship between the intensity and loudness of a sound, explain the relationship between frequency and pitch, and explain the Doppler effect. Students will also trace the path of sound waves through the ear to the brain.

About Figure 18-1 To play a bagpipe, a player inflates the bag with air, either by blowing air into the bag or pumping it in with bellows. Once the bag is full, the sounding pipes constantly play notes. The pipes contain reeds, and the vibration of the reeds caused by the air produces music.

Answer When a drum is struck, the drumhead vibrates and causes the air around it to vibrate.

Linking Prior Knowledge

For this chapter, students should recall:
• the characteristics of motion and speed (Lesson 13-1).
• the definition of *wave* (Lesson 17-2).

Chapter Project

MUSEUM OF MUSIC

MATERIALS: construction paper, markers, reference materials, posterboard, materials to make musical instruments (boxes, rubber bands, drinking glasses)

Students can work in small groups to create displays for a museum of music. As a class, brainstorm ideas for museum displays. Spark students' thinking with suggestions such as a diagram showing the ear and what happens inside the ear as it hears music; an experiment showing how the music made by a rubber band changes with different lengths, widths, and tension; or a demonstration showing how to use water glasses to make music (including what happens when the liquid is something other than water). Students' displays should include explanatory notes on posterboard that include what items they used for the display and what scientific principles are at work.
learning styles: tactile, visual

18-1 (pp. 376–377)

1 Introduce

✎ **STUDY HINT** Before beginning this lesson, have students copy the title of each section in an outline format in their notebooks. As they read the lesson, students should write the main ideas under each section.

Linking Prior Knowledge Ask students to name the two kinds of mechanical waves (Lesson 17-2). (transverse and longitudinal) Ask students which type of wave is created by thunder. (longitudinal)

2 Teach

Discussion To introduce this lesson, ask students to sit quietly for 3 minutes and listen to all the sounds that can be heard in the classroom. Have them describe the sounds. List their responses on the board. Explain to students that sound is a form of energy that travels in the form of waves. All sounds are caused by vibrations. Have students read the responses on the board. For each sound listed, have students describe the objects that vibrated in order to produce the sounds that they heard.
learning style: auditory

📖 **READING STRATEGY** Remind students that context clues, or surrounding words and sentences, can help them understand the meanings of words that they do not know. Refer to the sentence under *Forming Sound* that contains the word *compression*. Point out the words *squeezed together*, and tell students that *compression* means "squeezing together."

Answers to questions

▶1 DEFINE: a form of energy that travels as waves

▶2 DEFINE: a rapid back-and-forth movement

▶3 DESCRIBE: compressions and rarefactions

▶4 DESCRIBE: Answers will vary.

18-1 What is sound?

Objective
Identify sound as a form of energy caused by vibrations.

Key Terms
sound: form of energy that travels as waves
vibration: rapid back-and-forth movement

Sound and Energy There are sounds all around you. Some sounds are loud and others are very faint. Walking in a park, you may hear the sounds of birds singing and dogs barking. In a quiet room, you may hear the sound of an alarm clock ticking. Sound is a form of energy. **Sound** energy travels in the form of waves.

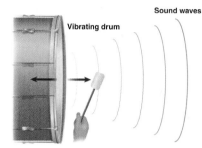
▲ **Figure 18-2** When a drum is struck, it vibrates and causes the air around it to vibrate.

▶1 DEFINE: What is sound?

Vibrations All sounds are caused by vibrations. A **vibration** is a rapid back-and-forth movement. Suppose you are listening to the sound from a stereo speaker. If you place your hand on the speaker, you will feel a vibration.

Objects that vibrate produce sound. Place your fingers on the front of your throat. When you speak, you can feel something vibrate. That something is your vocal cords (see Figure 18-3). The sound of your voice is produced when your vocal cords cause the air around them to vibrate.

376

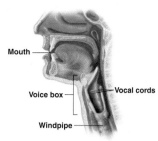
▲ **Figure 18-3** The sound of your voice is caused by the vibrations of your vocal cords.

▶2 DEFINE: What is a vibration?

Forming Sound For every sound that you hear, some object is vibrating. Strum a guitar. The guitar strings vibrate. When a string vibrates in one direction, it pushes on the air on that side of it. Air particles are squeezed together. The squeezed-together particles form a compression. When the string moves back, those air particles spread apart. The spread-out particles form a rarefaction. As the string continues to vibrate, compressions and rarefactions move away from the string. They form a sound wave.

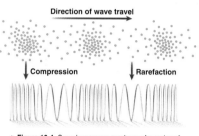
▲ **Figure 18-4** Sound waves are made up of a series of compressions and rarefactions.

▶3 DESCRIBE: What forms a sound wave?

Teaching Options

RETEACH

Modeling Compressions When describing sound waves, remind students that a rarefaction is part of a medium where the particles are far apart, and a compression is part of a medium where the particles are close together. Demonstrate pressing your hands together as you say *compression* to help students create a visual cue for remembering the definition of the word.
learning styles: visual, auditory

COOPERATIVE LEARNING

Making Word Webs Students can work with partners to make word webs to explore the concept of sound. Their webs can include arms that focus on the definition of sound, how sound is produced, and various sounds and the vibrations that make those sounds. Allow time for students to share their word webs with the class. Students can also use the Spider Map found on the Teacher's Resources CD-ROM.
learning styles: visual, interpersonal

Sources of Sounds You now know that when you hear a sound, something is vibrating to produce it. Different sounds can come from different sources. Figure 18-5 shows sources of a few of the sounds you might hear every day.

SOURCES OF SOUNDS	
Sound	**Vibration Source**
Violin	Strings
Drum beat	Drum skin and sticks
Human voice	Vocal cords
Knocking door	Door
Car revving	Engine
Pencil scratching	Lead and paper

▲ Figure 18-5

▶ DESCRIBE: How many other sounds and sources can you add to the list in Figure 18-5?

✓ CHECKING CONCEPTS

1. A sound is caused by a _____.
2. Sound is a form of _____ that travels as waves.

3. A _____ is a rapid back-and-forth movement.
4. All vibrating objects produce _____.
5. Sound waves are formed by compressions and _____.
6. If you place your fingers on your windpipe while you are speaking, you will feel a _____.
7. When you strum a guitar, the _____ vibrate.

💡 THINKING CRITICALLY

8. **PREDICT:** What will happen if you place a glass of water on a stereo speaker?
9. **HYPOTHESIZE:** Is it possible to make a sound without causing a vibration? Why or why not?
10. **OBSERVE:** Sit by an open window. What sounds do you hear? What is causing each sound?

DESIGNING AN EXPERIMENT

Design an experiment to solve the following problem. Include a hypothesis, variables, a procedure, and a type of data to study.

PROBLEM: Can sound travel through solid objects?

Hands-On Activity

OBSERVING VIBRATIONS IN A TUNING FORK

You will need a tuning fork and a glass of water.

1. Place the glass of water on a flat surface. Let the glass sit for a few seconds until the water is still.
2. Gently strike the tuning fork against the edge of a table. Observe what happens.
3. Strike the edge of the table again with the tuning fork. Touch the ends of the tuning fork onto the surface of the water. Observe what happens to the water in the glass.

Practicing Your Skills

4. **OBSERVE:** What happened to the tuning fork when you struck it against the table? Did you hear a sound?
5. **OBSERVE:** What happened when you put the tuning fork into the glass of water?

▲ **STEP 3** Put the ends of the vibrating tuning fork in the water.

CHAPTER 18: Sound **377**

---

3 Assess

✓ CHECKING CONCEPTS ANSWERS

1. vibration
2. energy
3. vibration
4. sound
5. rarefactions
6. vibration
7. strings

💡 THINKING CRITICALLY ANSWERS

8. **PREDICT:** The vibration from the speaker will cause the water to vibrate.
9. **HYPOTHESIZE:** No; All sounds are caused by vibrations.
10. **OBSERVE:** Answers will vary but might include traffic noises or people talking. Students should explain what vibrations cause each of the sounds.

4 Close

DESIGNING AN EXPERIMENT

Use the Designing an Experiment Rubric on the Teacher's Resources CD-ROM to assess students' experiments. Fill in the rubric with the additional information below. For this assignment, students should have:

• hypothesized as to whether sound travels through solid objects.
• written a step-by-step procedure and designed and drawn a data table.

Hands-On Activity

OBSERVING VIBRATIONS IN A TUNING FORK

TIME: 10–15 minutes

PURPOSE: observing

DISCUSSION: In order to get a good splash from the water, be sure to use a 128-hertz tuning fork. Before you place the tuning fork in the water, ask students to predict what will happen. Encourage them to compare and contrast their predictions with their results.

Practicing Your Skills Answers

4. **OBSERVE:** The tuning fork vibrated; yes
5. **OBSERVE:** The vibrating tuning fork caused water to vibrate and splash out of the glass.

MORE ON THE WEB

Reviewing Sound Have students view an online movie, do activities, and take an online quiz about sound at www.conceptsandchallenges.com.

ESL/ELL STRATEGY

Feeling Vibrations Have students lightly place their hands on their windpipes and speak. They should feel the vibrations from the sounds of their voices. Relate this exercise to Figure 18-3 to help students understand how vibrations play a part in speech. **learning style: tactile**

• TEACHING RESOURCES •

Teacher's Resources CD-ROM
Lesson Review: Chapter 18, p. 2
Designing an Experiment: Study Tools, p. 14
Designing an Experiment Rubric: Teaching Tools, p. 7
Spider Map: Study Tools, p. 9

Lab Activity

(pp. 378–379)

1 Prepare the Lab

Experimenting With Vibrations

SET-UP TIME: ⏱   **LAB TIME:** 🕐

BACKGROUND: Vibration produces sound. The air surrounding a vibrating object is set into motion. Waves, traveling outward, reach our eardrums, which begin to vibrate. They transmit this motion through tiny bones in the inner ear to the nervous system. Electrical signals sent to the brain interpret this motion as sound.

The speed or frequency of the vibration determines the pitch of the sound. The higher the frequency of the waves, the higher is the pitch. This relationship is easily seen and heard by watching vibrating strings in instruments such as guitars and flat springs as they are plucked. In this activity, students use slightly stiff plastic rulers as flat springs. When the rulers are plucked, vibrations create sound. The vibration speed (slow, medium, fast) is easy to observe, and the accompanying sound changes with the frequency.

PURPOSE: Students will investigate frequency and pitch by adjusting the length of a vibrating ruler.

SCIENCE SKILLS: Students will **investigate** and **observe** how the pitch of a sound changes with changes in the frequency of vibrations.

ADVANCE PLANNING: Obtain the materials needed before class. Bring a stringed instrument, such as a guitar or a violin, to class for comparison.

2 Guide the Lab

PROCEDURE: Have students work in pairs. Discuss the instructions and demonstrate the placement of fingers on the ruler. Show how to pluck the rulers. Make sure that students understand that the length of the ruler used is not just the part sticking over the end of the table. The length begins from the place where the finger is pressing down on it. The tapping of the ruler on the table surface creates the sound. Provide students with a copy of the Lab Activity Report found on the Teacher's Resources CD-ROM for students to record their observations and conclusions.

LAB ACTIVITY
Experimenting With Vibrations

Materials
Plastic metric ruler (15-cm)
Pencil and paper

BACKGROUND

Sound is created when an object vibrates. The vibrations are converted to waves that travel through the air. Different speeds of vibration produce different sounds. What is the relationship between the rate of vibration and the highness or lowness of the sound you hear?

PURPOSE

You will experiment with vibrations and sound, and create a simple musical instrument.

PROCEDURE

1. Copy the chart in Figure 18-6 on a separate sheet of paper.

2. Place a plastic ruler on a table so that the end of the ruler extends 5 cm past the edge of the table. Hold the ruler on the table with one finger at the 10-cm mark.

3. With your other hand pull up on the end of the ruler and release it. This action will cause the ruler to vibrate. Listen to the sound it produces. Record your observations in the chart.

4. Press down on the ruler at the 9-cm mark with a second finger. Again, pull up and release the end of the ruler and listen to the sound. Watch how fast the ruler vibrates.

5. Move the second finger to the 8-cm mark and again pull up and release the ruler. Repeat with your finger on the 7-cm and the 6-cm marks.

▲ STEP 2 Hold a ruler near the edge of a table.

▲ STEP 3 Make the ruler vibrate.

378

Teaching Options

❗ FAST FACTS   *Noise or Music?*

Both noise and music are forms of sound, but what makes them different? Noise is usually described as an unpleasant mixture of random, unrelated frequencies, or tones. Music is made up of either pure tones (tones composed of a single frequency) or combinations of tones that are related harmonically. *Harmonics* is the term for the set of vibrations of various frequencies that make up a single musical tone.

Tones are related harmonically when their frequencies are multiples of one another. For example, when a musician plucks a harp string, it vibrates along its entire length, producing a particular harmonic, called the first harmonic. But the string also vibrates in sections that are fractions (one-half, one-third, or one-fourth) of the string. Each of these vibrating sections produces a different harmonic, also called an overtone, with a different frequency. Because these overtones are related mathematically to the first harmonic, they combine to produce a pleasant sound.

When overtones are not related in this way, the sounds are not pleasant and are usually considered noise. Machinery, explosions, and the sound of a badly played musical instrument are a few examples of noise.

6. Try other positions with the ruler to make different sounds. Extend the ruler out further over the edge or bring it closer.

7. Use the data in your chart to write the "finger positions" as your "musical notes." Have a partner try to play your "song" from your written notes. See if you can play someone else's "song."

▲ STEP 7 Play someone else's song.

Changing Sound			
Trial	Finger Position in Centimeters	Speed of Vibration (very slow, medium, very fast, etc.)	Highness or Lowness of Sound (lowest, medium, highest, etc.)
1	10		
2	9		
3	8		
4	7		
5	6		
6			
7			
8			

▲ Figure 18-6 Copy this chart and use it to record your observations.

CONCLUSIONS

1. OBSERVE: When the part of the ruler that vibrates is long, are the vibrations slow or fast?

2. OBSERVE: When the part of the ruler that vibrates is short, are the vibrations slow or fast?

3. INFER: If you hear a low sound, such as the sound produced by a foghorn, is it caused by slow vibrations or fast vibrations?

4. INFER: What kind of sound is produced by an object that vibrates fast?

Tips for Using Technology

Spreadsheets Have students use spreadsheet software to record the observations from their experiments. Spreadsheets are tables that display data such as numbers, text, dates, or a combination of all three. Students can use spreadsheets to make their data look special by using formats, do math to analyze numerical data, and make graphs and charts to present data in a colorful way. Have students use the Spreadsheet on the Teacher's Resources CD-ROM to plan their spreadsheets.

• TEACHING RESOURCES •

Teacher's Resources CD-ROM
Lab Activity Report: Study Tools, pp. 16–17

Laboratory Activity Rubric: Teaching Tools, p. 8

Spreadsheet: Study Tools, p. 23

Laboratory Manual
Lab. Skills Worksheet 4: Organizing and Analyzing Data, pp. 13–14

TROUBLESHOOTING: Make sure that students press the ruler down firmly in order to produce a clear sound.

EXPECTED OUTCOME: Students will observe that longer lengths of the ruler will vibrate slower and will produce sounds with lower pitches.

LAB HINT: Test the rulers that you are using before having students do the experiment. The distance the ruler extends over the table and the placement of the fingers may have to be adjusted depending on the stiffness of the rulers.

3 Conclude the Lab

1. OBSERVE: slow
2. OBSERVE: fast
3. INFER: slow vibrations
4. INFER: high

Use the Laboratory Activity Rubric on the Teacher's Resources CD-ROM to assess students' lab activities. Fill in the rubric with the additional information below. For this activity, students should have:

• performed the activity according to the procedure and filled in the chart with data collected during the activity.

• correctly answered the questions in complete sentences.

4 Extend the Lab

Have students combine several rulers along one edge of a table like keys of a piano. While several students press the rulers to the tabletop at different places, another student plays the keys. Relate the length of the vibrating portion of the ruler to sound produced by a trombone. Pulling out the slide lengthens the air path and produces a low note, and pulling in the slide produces a high note. Encourage students to find out about other musical instruments and how they work. Students can share their findings with the class. You might want to integrate the results of this lab with the Chapter Project.

1 Introduce

🔍 INVESTIGATE

TIME: 5–10 minutes

PURPOSE: Students will create a telephone with paper cups and string to demonstrate the way in which sound travels.

MATERIALS: paper cups, string

PROCEDURE: Students should work in pairs. They can poke holes in the cups with the tip of a sharpened pencil. Be sure that they hold the cups so that the strings are stretched tightly.

THINK ABOUT IT: The sound travels through vibrations in the string.
learning styles: auditory, tactile

✎ **STUDY HINT** Before beginning this lesson, have students write the objective in their notebooks. As they read the lesson, have them write information that supports the objective.

Linking Prior Knowledge Remind students that waves carry energy, but they do not carry materials in a forward motion. Also, review reflection of waves (Lesson 17-4).

2 Teach

Demonstration Ask a few students to put their ears against the wall of the classroom. Ask them to describe what they hear in the next room. Use this activity to show students that sound waves can travel through solids. **learning style: auditory**

📖 **READING STRATEGY** Remind students that an effect is something that happens, and a cause is something that makes the effect happen. Point out that paying attention to these relationships can help them remember main ideas. Draw two boxes on the board and label them *Cause* and *Effect*. Draw an arrow from the *Cause* box to the *Effect* box. Model a sample cause and effect. (*Cause:* There is no air on the Moon. *Effect:* Sound waves cannot be produced.) Encourage students to add other cause-and-effect relationships as they read.

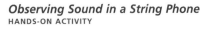

18-2 How do sound waves travel?

INVESTIGATE 🔍

Observing Sound in a String Phone
HANDS-ON ACTIVITY

1. Make a small hole in the bottom of each of two paper cups.
2. Insert one end of a 10-m piece of string through the hole in each cup and tie a large knot at each end of the string.
3. Take one of the cups and give your partner the other. Move apart until the string is tight.
4. Have your partner speak into one cup while you hold the other cup to your ear. Take turns speaking into the cups.

THINK ABOUT IT: How does the sound travel from one cup to the other?

STEP 4

Objective
Describe how sound waves travel.

Key Terms
longitudinal (lahn-juh-TOOD-uhn-uhl) **wave:** wave in which the particles of the medium move back and forth in the direction of the wave motion

medium: material through which mechanical waves can travel

echo: reflected sound waves

Sound Waves Sound waves are longitudinal waves. In a **longitudinal wave,** the particles of the medium move back and forth in the direction of the wave motion. Figure 18-7 shows how a sound wave moves through the air. Compressions and rarefactions of air particles move in the same direction as the sound waves.

▶ **DESCRIBE:** Why are sound waves longitudinal waves?

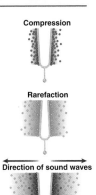

Compression

Rarefaction

Direction of sound waves

▲ Figure 18-7 Parts of a sound wave.

Medium for Sound A **medium** is a material through which mechanical waves can travel. Air is a medium for sound waves. All sound waves need a medium through which they can travel. Sound waves can travel through gases, liquids, and solids. In each medium, the sound waves are made up of compressions and rarefactions of the particles that make up the medium.

Dolphins and whales use sound to communicate with each other. They can do this because sounds travel faster through water. Sounds also travel faster through solids. If you put your ear against a wall, you may hear sounds in the next room.

▶ **EXPLAIN:** Why is water a good medium for communication between dolphins?

No Sound in a Vacuum On the Moon, astronauts cannot use sound to communicate. There is no air on the Moon. In a vacuum, there are no particles of a medium to compress. This means sound waves cannot be produced.

▶ **INFER:** Would astronauts on the Moon be able to hear a rocket engine?

▲ Figure 18-8 There is no sound on the Moon.

380

Teaching Options

‼ FAST FACTS *Mapping the Ocean Floor*

Sonar is only one of the technologies used to map the ocean floor. Ships with sonar technology generally travel slowly, so only a small part of the ocean's floor has been mapped with depth measurements from sonar. Even with the most sophisticated sonar, it would take 125 years to map the ocean floor, using this method alone.

Satellites gather information to measure the level of the ocean surface. These measurements help scientists determine the shape (the peaks and valleys) of the ocean floor. Two different satellites, launched in 1978 and 1985, used microwave radiation to measure the level of the ocean surface. The mountains and valleys underwater change Earth's gravity. The strong gravity near an underwater mountain, for example, attracts more water and slightly raises the level of the ocean. Data from these satellites allowed mapmakers to map the ocean floor in about 2 years.

Reflected Waves Reflection is the bouncing back of a wave from a barrier that does not absorb its energy. If you clap your hands in a carpeted room, the sound will be absorbed by the carpeting. Suppose you clap your hands in an empty room with a wooden floor. You will hear the sound of the clap reflected from the floor and the walls. When a sound wave is reflected, the reflected sound wave is called an **echo.**

▶ **IDENTIFY:** What is a reflected sound wave called?

✓ CHECKING CONCEPTS

1. In a _____ wave, the particles of the medium move in the same direction as the wave motion.

2. A sound wave needs a _____ in which to travel.

3. Sound waves are made up of moving compressions and _____.

4. Whales can use sounds to communicate because sound waves can travel through _____.

5. Sound cannot be heard in a vacuum because there is no _____ for the sound waves.

6. Sound can travel through liquids such as water, gases such as air, and _____ such as walls.

7. Sound waves that are reflected from a surface are called _____.

8. When a sound wave is not reflected, the energy of the sound has been _____ by the surroundings.

THINKING CRITICALLY

9. **INFER:** If you clapped your hands on the Moon, would you hear the sound? Explain.

Web InfoSearch

Echolocation The biggest difference between bats and other animals is the way that they see. Most animals see by using their eyes. However, most bats "see" by using a system called echolocation.

SEARCH: Use the Internet to find out more about echolocation. Then, create a poster showing how echolocation in animals works. Start your search at www.conceptsandchallenges.com. Some key search words are **echolocation, bat sonar,** and **bat sight.**

Science and Technology
SONAR

Echoes can be used to measure distances under water. This method of using echoes is called sonar. The word *sonar* stands for **so**und **na**vigation and **r**anging. Sound waves are sent from a transmitter on a ship to the bottom of the ocean. The time it takes for the sound wave to reach the bottom and bounce back as an echo is measured. This time is then divided in half to find out how long the sound took to go one way. Suppose sound waves were sent out and returned in 4 seconds. The time for the sound waves to go one way is 2 seconds. The speed of sound in water is about 1,500 m/s. Therefore, the water is about 3,000 m deep. Sonar can be used to make maps of the ocean floor. It is also used to locate objects, such as boats and fish.

Thinking Critically How do you think sonar can be used to find schools of fish?

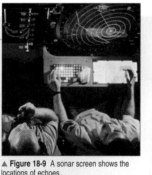
▲ **Figure 18-9** A sonar screen shows the locations of echoes.

Answers to questions

▶1 **DESCRIBE:** The particles in the air move back and forth in the direction of the wave motion.

▶2 **EXPLAIN:** Sound waves travel easily through water.

▶3 **INFER:** no, because there is no air on the Moon

▶4 **IDENTIFY:** an echo

3 Assess

✓ CHECKING CONCEPTS ANSWERS

1. longitudinal
2. medium
3. rarefactions
4. a liquid
5. medium
6. solids
7. echoes or reflected sound waves
8. absorbed

THINKING CRITICALLY ANSWER

9. **INFER:** There would be no sound. Because there is no air, there is no medium through which sound waves can travel.

4 Close

Web InfoSearch

Echolocation Have students visit www.conceptsandchallenges.com to find out more about echolocation. Some key search words are **echolocation** and **bats sight.**

Science and Technology
SONAR

Discussion Relate sonar to radar. Point out to students that radar is based on the reflection of radio waves in the air, while sonar is based on the reflection of underwater sound waves. Submarines use sonar to detect obstacles in the ocean in order to navigate safely. Sonar devices contained in floating buoys can be monitored by radio.

Thinking Critically Answer
When the time for sound waves to return suddenly becomes much smaller, some object is in the way of the ocean floor. If this object passes quickly through the space, it may be a school of fish.

RETEACH

Demonstrating Longitudinal Waves Use a coil spring to demonstrate the longitudinal nature of sound waves. One student can hold one end while you move the other end to create the wave. Ask students what would happen if they tried to make a wave with the spring in another medium, such as a thick liquid. Use the discussion to help students understand that the medium affects how quickly the wave will travel.
learning styles: visual, interpersonal

• TEACHING RESOURCES •

⊚ **Teacher's Resources CD-ROM**
Lesson Review: Chapter 18, p. 3

EXTENDING THE LESSON

Investigating Dolphin Communication Interested students may want to use reference sources to find out more about dolphin communication. Guide students to find out the dolphin sounds that scientists have classified and what those sounds might mean.

1 Introduce

📝 **STUDY HINT** Ask students to create a word web about the speed of sound. They should start by writing *speed of sound* in the middle of a sheet of paper and circling the words. As they read, they can add arms to the web to note details about the speed of sound.

Linking Prior Knowledge Ask students what they notice when they see and hear a bat strike a baseball. Students may note that they can see the bat strike the ball before they can hear the crack. Explain that light travels faster than sound, such as when lightning is seen before thunder is heard. You might also discuss the concept of speed (Lesson 13-1).

2 Teach

Discussion Have students recall their experiences with fireworks. Students may recall that the burst of color from fireworks can be seen before the sound of the explosion is heard. Ask students to explain this occurrence. Then, point out that differences in the speed of light and the speed of sound account for the time lapse. Follow up the discussion of fireworks with a discussion of thunder and lightning. **learning style: auditory**

Demonstration To demonstrate that sound travels at different speeds through different materials, knock on various surfaces in the classroom, such as the top of a desk, a book, a door, and a window. Students will notice that sometimes the noise seems muffled. Explain that the muffling effect is caused by the speed at which sound travels through the material. **learning style: auditory**

📖 **READING STRATEGY** Inform students that the word *sonic* means "having to do with sound." Ask students to define the words *supersonic* and *sonic boom*.

Answers to questions

▶ **STATE:** about 340 m/sec

▶ **ANALYZE:** steel

▶ **DEFINE:** any speed faster than the speed of sound

18-3 What is the speed of sound?

Objective
Describe how the speed of sound changes in different materials.

Key Terms
supersonic: faster than the speed of sound for that medium

sonic boom: loud noise caused by breaking the sound barrier

Speed of Sound The speed of sound in air is about 340 m/s. This speed is much slower than the speed of light. In a thunderstorm, a flash of lightning is seen before the sound of thunder is heard. The light from the lightning flash travels much faster than the sound of the thunder produced by the lightning.

▲ **Figure 18-10** Lightning causes thunder.

You can use the speed of sound to estimate how far away a lightning flash is from your location. Start counting the seconds as soon as you see a flash of lightning. Stop counting when you hear the thunder. Sound travels about 1 km in 3 seconds. If it takes 3 seconds for the sound of the thunder to reach you, the lightning is about 1 km away.

▶ **STATE:** What is the speed of sound in air?

Speed of Sound in Different Materials Sound travels at different speeds in different materials and at different temperatures. In water, sound travels at about 1,500 m/s. Figure 18-11 lists the approximate speeds of sound in some different materials.

SPEEDS OF SOUNDS AT 25°C	
Material	**Speed (m/sec)**
Air	346
Cork	500
Fresh water	1,498
Steel	5,200
Rubber	60
Glass	4,540
Wood (oak)	1,850

▲ **Figure 18-11**

▶ **ANALYZE:** In which of the materials listed in Figure 18-11 does sound travel fastest?

Faster than Sound Many jet airplanes can travel faster than the speed of sound. Some airplanes can travel two or three times the speed of sound. Any speed faster than the speed of sound is said to be **supersonic.** When an airplane travels at supersonic speeds, it moves faster than the sound produced by its engines. When a plane traveling at supersonic speed passes overhead, it will be some distance away before you hear the sound of its engines. Figure 18-12 shows the first airplane, the Glamorous Glennis, to travel faster than the speed of sound. When something moves through air at speeds faster than the speed of sound, a loud noise is created. This noise is called a **sonic boom.**

▲ **Figure 18-12** Chuck Yeager piloted the first plane to travel at supersonic speeds.

Teaching Options

EXTENDING THE LESSON

Calculations With the Speed of Sound Encourage students to use the value for the speed of sound in air (340 m/sec) to do mathematical calculations. Students could, for example, convert the speed of sound into km/h (1,224 km/h) or mph (760 mph). Students could also calculate the speed of sound in water at 20°C (68°F), which is 1,480 m/s, to km/s (1.48 km/s), to km/h (5,328 km/h), to ft/s (4,856 ft/s) and to mph (3,310 mph).

COOPERATIVE LEARNING

Comparing Speeds Students can work in small groups to design experiments that would solve the following problem: How can you show that the speed of sound is faster in steel than in air? Students' experiments should include a materials list, safety precautions, step-by-step instructions, and a method of recording data. If it is possible to carry out the experiments in class, allow time for students to conduct their experiments and share the results. **learning styles: tactile, interpersonal**

In 1997, Andy Green broke the sound barrier on land with his car named Thrust. He did so exactly fifty years after the sound barrier was broken by Captain Chuck Yeager. Figure 18-13 shows the supersonic car that Green used to accomplish this feat.

▲ Figure 18-13 Andy Green's supersonic car

▶ DEFINE: What is supersonic speed?

✓ CHECKING CONCEPTS

1. The speed of sound in air is about _____.

2. You can see a _____ airplane before you hear it because it is moving faster than sound.

3. Light travels _____ than sound.

4. A flash of lightning can be seen _____ the sound of thunder it produces can be heard.

💡 THINKING CRITICALLY

Use the information in Figure 18-11 to answer the following questions.

5. COMPARE: Would the sound of an approaching train travel faster through the metal railroad tracks or through the air? Explain.

6. HYPOTHESIZE: **a.** Why do you think rubber is sometimes used for soundproofing a room? **b.** What other materials in the table would be good for soundproofing? Explain.

BUILDING MATH SKILLS

Calculating Find out how long it would take sound to travel through 2 m of the following materials.

a. air   e. glass

b. water   f. wood

c. steel   g. cork

d. rubber

🔬 *Science and Technology*

SUPERSONIC AIRPLANES

The speed of sound in air is called Mach 1. Before October 14, 1947, no airplane had ever reached the speed of Mach 1. On that day, Chuck Yeager became the first person to fly faster than the speed of sound. He had broken the sound barrier.

Today, supersonic planes can fly at speeds of Mach 2 or even Mach 3. For example, the supersonic *Concorde* crosses the Atlantic Ocean in much less time than other passenger airplanes.

▲ Figure 18-14 The *Concorde* is an airliner that can travel at supersonic speeds.

One disadvantage of planes that travel at supersonic speeds is that they produce loud noises called sonic booms. A sonic boom is caused when a plane breaks the sound barrier. Sonic booms can be so loud that they break windows and knock pictures off walls. To avoid the problem of sonic booms, supersonic planes are not allowed to fly over heavily populated areas.

Thinking Critically The Concorde only travels at supersonic speeds over the ocean. Why do you think this is so?

---

3 *Assess*

✓ CHECKING CONCEPTS ANSWERS

1. 340 m/sec
2. supersonic
3. faster
4. before

💡 THINKING CRITICALLY ANSWERS

5. COMPARE: The sound would be faster on metal tracks because sound travels faster through steel than through the air.
6. HYPOTHESIZE: **a.** The speed of sound is slow in rubber. **b.** Cork; The speed of sound in cork is not as fast as in other solids.

4 *Close*

BUILDING MATH SKILLS ANSWERS

Calculating

a. 0.0058 sec
b. 0.0013 sec
c. 0.00038 sec
d. 0.033 sec
e. 0.00044 sec
f. 0.0011 sec
g. 0.0040 sec

Science and Technology

SUPERSONIC AIRPLANES

Real-Life Connection Introduced in 1976, the *Concorde* is the world's only supersonic passenger aircraft. The *Concorde* completes the flight from New York to London in less than 4 hours. The *Concorde's* takeoff speed is about 402 km/h (250 mph), but the aircraft can reach a cruising speed of Mach 2 (about 2,150 km/h; 1,336 mph). When people fly overseas on the *Concorde,* the time change allows them to "arrive before they leave."

Thinking Critically Answer
Sonic booms can break windows and cause other damage to buildings. No damage occurs over the ocean because there are no buildings in the ocean.

• *TEACHING RESOURCES* •

💿 **Teacher's Resources CD-ROM**
Lesson Review: Chapter 18, p. 4
Enrichment: Chapter 18, pp. 5, 6

QUICK CONVERSIONS

Metric/SI	English
346 m/sec	1,135 ft/sec
1,498 m/sec	4,915 ft/sec
5,200 m/sec	17,061 ft/sec
60 m/sec	197 ft/sec
4,540 m/sec	14,896 ft/sec
1,850 m/sec	6,070 ft/sec

1 Introduce

📝 **STUDY HINT** Have students study Figures 18-15 and 18-16. Ask them to compare the two illustrations.

Linking Prior Knowledge Ask students how their ears feel when they listen to loud music or when they hear a siren. Ask: *What do you think accounts for the loudness of these sounds?* You might also review the definition of *energy* (Lesson 14-1) and the features of a wave (Lesson 17-3).

2 Teach

Discussion To introduce the lesson, begin class by whispering. Gradually increase the loudness until you are speaking loudly. Point out that increasing the amount of energy increased the loudness of the sound. Describe the link between amplitude and loudness. **learning style: auditory**

Demonstration To demonstrate that loud sounds have more energy than soft sounds, slap a meter stick on your desk, using varying amounts of energy. Students should notice that, when you do not use a lot of energy to slap the meter stick, the sound is softer than when you use more energy. **learning style: auditory**

📖 **READING STRATEGY** Suggest that students look at the comprehension questions on page 385 before they begin reading. Students can rephrase the Checking Concepts statements as questions to guide their reading. The first statement, for example, would become "When you raise the volume on a radio, what part of the sound waves are you increasing?"

Answers to questions

▶1 **DEFINE:** the amount of energy in a sound wave

▶2 **ANALYZE:** 115–120 decibels

18-4 What is intensity?

Objective
Explain the relationship between the intensity and the loudness of a sound.

Key Terms
intensity: amount of energy in a sound wave
decibel: unit used to measure the intensity or loudness of a sound

Intensity Sound energy travels in the form of waves. Some sounds are loud. Others are soft. Figures 18-15 and 18-16 show wave patterns for a soft sound and a loud sound.

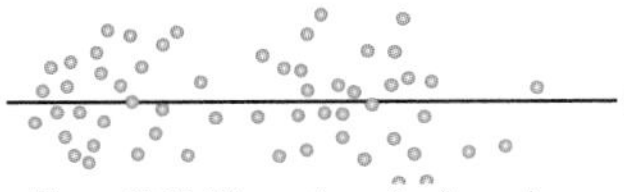

▲ **Figure 18-15** Wave pattern of soft sound

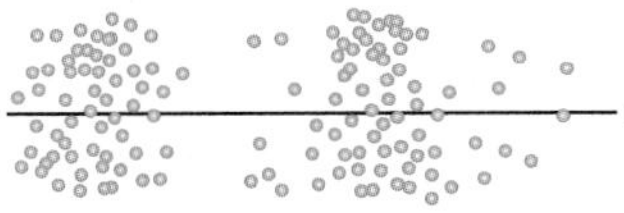

▲ **Figure 18-16** Wave pattern of loud sound

The amount of energy a sound has is called the **intensity** of the sound. As Figures 18-15 and 18-16 show, a wave carrying a loud sound has a greater amplitude than that of a wave carrying a soft sound. So, molecules in a wave carrying a loud sound travel farther than do the molecules in a wave carrying a soft sound. The molecules in the loud wave have more energy.

▲ **Figure 18-17** Which instrument will produce sounds of greater intensity?

▶1 **DEFINE:** What is intensity?

Measuring Intensity Intensity is measured in units called **decibels** (dB). The sound of people talking has an intensity of about 65 decibels. The softest sound a human can hear is about 20 decibels. The sound of a train going by may have an intensity of 95 decibels. Sounds louder than 120 decibels can be dangerous. They can damage your ears. Figure 18-18 shows the intensity of different sounds measured in decibels.

INTENSITY OF SOUND	
Sound	**Intensity (dB)**
Cat purring	10–20
Soft music	30
Average home	40–50
Conversation	60–70
Heavy traffic	70–80
Loud music	80–100
Thunder	110
Rock concert	115–120
Jet engine	170
Rocket engine	200

▲ **Figure 18-18**

▶2 **ANALYZE:** What is the intensity of the sound at a rock concert?

Teaching Options

❗ FAST FACTS
Mastering Acoustics

Acoustics is the science of sound. Many acoustics engineers work on the design of concert halls. The sound of music in a concert hall has to be clear enough for everyone in the hall to be able to hear. Many concert halls have dead spots where it is hard to hear the music clearly. An acoustics engineer tries to decrease the number of echoes from the walls of a concert hall and makes sure that not too much sound is absorbed.

EXTENDING THE LESSON

Classifying Intensities Interested students can use simple reference sources to find out the intensities of sounds other than those listed in Figure 18-18. Encourage students to classify the sounds as *dangerous* or *not dangerous*, including the items already listed in Figure 18-18.

1. When you raise the volume on a radio, you are increasing the _____ of the sound waves.
2. The _____ in a sound wave determines the amplitude of the wave.
3. The _____ of a sound wave is the amount of energy it has.
4. The unit used to measure intensity is the _____.
5. The more intensity a sound wave has the _____ the sound.

THINKING CRITICALLY

6. INFER: Which is more dangerous to your ears, heavy traffic noise or a rock concert? Explain.

7. HYPOTHESIZE: Two people hear a loud sound. One person is 10 m from the source of the sound. The other person is 50 m from the source. The sound does not seem as loud to the person 50 m from the source as it does to the person standing closer. What does this tell you about the intensity of a sound wave?

HEALTH AND SAFETY TIP

Your ears are very sensitive to sound. Loud sounds can damage your hearing. An intensity of 120 db is called the threshold of pain. This means that a sound louder than 120 dB is so loud that it will hurt your ears. You should keep this in mind when listening to live music or when using earphones to listen to a recording. Use library references to find out how to protect yourself from dangerously loud sounds. Write a short report on your findings.

Integrating Environmental Science

TOPIC: noise pollution

TOO MUCH SOUND

The world is full of sounds. There are many sources of sound. Some of the loudest sounds come from machines. These loud machine sounds may cause noise pollution. Any loud, unwanted sound is called noise. In cities, the sounds of street traffic, of machines at construction sites, and of airplanes all combine to cause noise pollution.

Noise pollution is a nuisance but it can also be a hazard. Too much noise can damage the ears by destroying the delicate hairs and tiny muscles in the ears. Noise can also cause stress. People who live or work around too much noise may develop high blood pressure or a stress-related illness.

There are ways to decrease noise pollution. People are encouraged to use mass transit to decrease the amount of traffic on city streets. Laws have been passed to keep people from playing radios too loudly in public places. You are encouraged to use ear protection when exposed to loud noises over an extended period of time.

Thinking Critically What can you do to help prevent noise pollution?

▲ Figure 18-19 Construction work contributes to noise pollution.

MORE ON THE WEB

Noise Pollution Have students write a short report about noise pollution by following the guidelines at www.conceptsandchallenges.com.

ONGOING ASSESSMENT

Explaining a Diagram Ask students to explain the diagrams in Figures 18-15 and 18-16, using the words *amplitude* and *intensity*. Ask them to choose two different sounds from Figure 18-18 that might coincide with the two diagrams.

• **TEACHING RESOURCES** •

Teacher's Resources CD-ROM
Lesson Review: Chapter 18, p. 7

Writing Activity Outline: Study Tools, pp. 20–21

Laboratory Manual
Lab. Challenge: How can the speed of sound through air be measured? pp. 89–92

---

3 Assess

✓ CHECKING CONCEPTS ANSWERS

1. amplitude
2. energy
3. intensity
4. decibel
5. louder

THINKING CRITICALLY ANSWERS

6. INFER: A rock concert; A rock concert is more intense. (115–120 decibels)
7. HYPOTHESIZE: As distance increases, the intensity of sound decreases.

4 Close

HEALTH AND SAFETY TIP

Encourage students to share their findings with the class. They might create public service announcements about sound safety.

✐ WRITING HINT Suggest that students develop an outline to organize the information that they gather in writing their reports. They should refine the outline as new information is found. Then, they should use their outlines to help them write their reports.

Integrating Environmental Science

TOPIC: noise pollution

TOO MUCH SOUND

Real-Life Connection When students think of pollution, they may picture an open garbage dump, a dirty river, or smoke pouring out of a factory. Point out that pollution can be invisible, tasteless, and odorless. Noise, for example, is pollution because it can harm the hearing of people and other animals.

Discussion Spark discussion on why noise pollution is a more prominent problem in large cities than places away from populated areas. Ask if students have experienced noise pollution and what they do to lessen their exposure and prevent harm to their hearing.

Thinking Critically Answer
Answers will vary. Students may respond with safety measures, such as wearing earplugs, or measures that they can take to help the problem, such as turning down loud music.

1 Introduce

✏️ **STUDY HINT** Have students preview the material by reading the heads and boldface words and studying the graphics. Ask students to write questions that they would like answered, and then answer them as they read.

Linking Prior Knowledge Ask students if they have ever seen a whistle that makes dogs react even though humans cannot hear any sound. Ask: *Why can dogs hear the whistle while people cannot?* Allow time for students to share their ideas.

2 Teach

Discussion Bring a dog whistle to class and blow it. Students will observe that they cannot hear the sound. Use this fact as a springboard for a discussion on ultrasonic frequencies and the relationship between frequency and pitch. **learning style: auditory**

Demonstration Review the fact that sound may differ in loudness. Demonstrate this fact by using two tuning forks of the same pitch. Strike one tuning fork gently to produce a soft sound. Strike the other more forcefully to produce a louder sound.

You may want to bring in a guitar to demonstrate to students how tightening the strings changes the pitch of the sound produced. Inform students that a fret is a strip of metal that runs across the fingerboard of the guitar. Strum the strings of the guitar. Then, press your finger on a string so that it comes in contact with a fret and strum the strings again. Students should notice that holding down the string, or shortening it, changed the pitch of the sound. **learning style: auditory**

Answers to questions

1️⃣ IDENTIFY: number of complete waves that pass a point each second

2️⃣ DESCRIBE: A high-frequency sound has a high pitch, while a low-frequency sound has a low pitch.

3️⃣ HYPOTHESIZE: The string vibrates more slowly or more quickly, resulting in many different pitches.

18-5 What are frequency and pitch?

Objective
Explain how frequency and pitch are related.

Key Terms
pitch: how high or low a sound is
ultrasonic (uhl-truh-SAHN-ihk): sound above 20,000 Hz frequency
infrasonic: sound below 20 Hz frequency

Frequency of a Sound Different sounds have different frequencies. The frequency of a wave is the number of complete waves that pass a point each second. Each pair of compressions and rarefactions is a complete sound wave. The frequency of a sound wave is the number of compressions and rarefactions produced per second. Frequency is measured in hertz (Hz). One hertz is equal to one wave per second.

1️⃣ IDENTIFY: What is frequency?

Frequency and Pitch Frequency and pitch are related. A sound's **pitch** tells how high or low a sound is. A high-frequency sound has a high pitch. A low-frequency sound has a low pitch. A toy whistle has a frequency of about 1,000 Hz. This is a high-pitched sound. Thunder, a low-pitched sound, has a frequency of about 50 Hz.

▲ **Figure 18-20** These instruments can make both high- and low-pitched sounds.

2️⃣ DESCRIBE: How are the frequency and the pitch of a sound related?

386

Changing Pitch A guitar can make sounds of many different pitches. If you look at the strings of the guitar in Figure 18-21, you will see that some are thick and some are thin. The thick strings make low-pitched sounds. The thin strings make high-pitched sounds. A guitar has tuning pegs that tighten or loosen the strings. Changing the tightness of the strings also changes the pitch. Placing your fingers on the frets across the neck of the guitar changes the length of the string. This action changes the pitch of the sound produced.

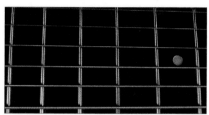

▲ **Figure 18-21** The different strings on a guitar make sounds of different pitch.

3️⃣ HYPOTHESIZE: How does changing the tightness of a string affect the sound it produces?

Range of Hearing Humans can hear sounds with frequencies between 20 Hz and 20,000 Hz. This is called the range of human hearing. Sounds that have frequencies higher than 20,000 Hz are called **ultrasonic**. The prefix *ultra-* means "above." Ultrasonic sounds have too high a pitch to be heard by humans. The range of human hearing decreases as a person gets older. Children can hear higher-frequency sounds better than adults can.

Some animals can hear ultrasonic sounds. Dogs can hear sounds with frequencies up to about 50,000 Hz. Often, dogs are trained using ultrasonic whistles. The dogs hear it but people do not.

4️⃣ DEFINE: What is an ultrasonic sound?

Infrasonic Sound Sound that is too low for humans to hear is called **infrasonic**. The prefix *infra-* means "below." Infrasonic is any sound below 20 Hz.

Teaching Options

COOPERATIVE LEARNING

Sorting Musical Pitches Have students create posters to show musical instruments sorted by pitch. Encourage them to use reference materials to find the names of various musical instruments and whether those instruments are considered high-pitched, low-pitched, or somewhere in between. Students can work in small groups to create posters with the lowest-pitched instruments (such as the tuba) on one end, the highest-pitched instruments (such as the piccolo) on the other end, and instruments with medium pitches placed in the appropriate places. Students can draw the instruments or cut out pictures of the instruments to glue on their posters. **learning styles: tactile, visual**

ESL/ELL STRATEGY

Dictionary of Terms This lesson contains many terms that may be new to students. Work with students in small groups to create dictionaries of terms. Write the words on the board (*frequency, pitch, hertz, ultrasonic, range of hearing*, and so on). Students can each define one or two of the terms in their own words and share the meanings with the group. Be sure that students understand how the terms apply to sound. **learning style: linguistic**

Elephants communicate distress with infrasonic sound at about 6 Hz. They stamp on the ground with their feet. The sound produces waves that travel many miles to other elephants.

◄ **Figure 18-22** Elephants communicate with infrasonic sounds.

▶ DEFINE: What is an infrasonic sound?

✔ CHECKING CONCEPTS

1. The unit used to measure frequency is the _____.

2. Sounds that humans can hear are between 20 and _____ Hz.

3. Even if two sounds have the same intensity, they can have different _____.

4. One hertz is equal to one _____ per second.

Hands-On Activity

OBSERVING CHANGES IN PITCH

You will need 5 test tubes, a test-tube rack, a metric ruler, and a container of water.

1. Place the test tubes in the test-tube rack.

2. Pour different amounts of water into each test tube. Use the metric ruler to measure the height of the column of air above the water in each test tube. The heights should be as follows: 2 cm, 4 cm, 6 cm, 8 cm, and 10 cm.

3. Blow across the top of each test tube. Observe the pitch of the sound you hear from each tube.

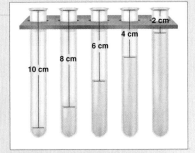

▲ STEP 2 Set up the test tubes so each has a different amount of air above the water.

Practicing Your Skills

4. INFER: How does the height of the column of air affect the pitch of the sound?

5. OBSERVE: Which test tube produced the highest pitch?

6. OBSERVE: Which test tube produced the lowest pitch?

CHAPTER 18: Sound **387**

THINKING CRITICALLY

5. COMPARE: Which sound has a lower pitch, a sound with a frequency of 20 Hz or one with a frequency of 20,000 Hz? How do you know?

6. HYPOTHESIZE: The sound of a siren coming toward you has a higher pitch than the sound of a siren that is standing still. What does this tell you about the frequency of a sound that is moving toward you?

Web InfoSearch

Ultrasound A technique called ultrasound can be used to see inside solid objects. Ultrasound uses very high-pitched sounds. Most of the sound waves pass through the object, but some are reflected. The reflected waves produce an image on a screen. Ultrasound images are similar to X-rays.

SEARCH: Use the Internet to find out how ultrasound is used in the fields of medicine, engineering, and construction. Start your search at www.conceptsandchallenges.com. Some key search words are **ultrasound, medicine, engineering,** and **construction.**

EXTENDING THE LESSON

Classifying Sounds Bring to class recordings of various sounds and play them one at a time. Ask students to classify the sounds as high-pitched or low-pitched. You can also ask whether these sounds are high-frequency or low-frequency. Remind students that sounds that are low in pitch are also low in frequency.
learning style: auditory

• TEACHING RESOURCES •

Teacher's Resources CD-ROM
Lesson Review: Chapter 18, p. 8

▶ DEFINE: sound with a frequency higher than 20,000 Hz

▶ DEFINE: sound below 20 Hz frequency

3 Assess

✔ CHECKING CONCEPTS ANSWERS

1. hertz (Hz)
2. 20,000
3. frequencies or pitches
4. wave

THINKING CRITICALLY ANSWERS

5. COMPARE: 20 Hz; Frequency and pitch are directly proportional.

6. HYPOTHESIZE: The frequency increases as the source of the sound moves closer.

4 Close

Web InfoSearch

Ultrasound Have students visit www.conceptsandchallenges.com to find out how ultrasound is used in different fields and industries. Some key search words are **ultrasound, medicine, engineering,** and **construction.**

Hands-On Activity

OBSERVING CHANGES IN PITCH

TIME: 10–15 minutes

PURPOSE: comparing, observing

DISCUSSION: Elicit from students that the height of the column of air determines the pitch. Point out that if small plastic soft-drink bottles were used instead of test tubes or some other liquid was used instead of water, the relative results would be the same.

Practicing Your Skills Answers

4. INFER: The pitch changes as the height of the air column above the water changes.

5. OBSERVE: The test tube with the 2-cm column of air produced the highest pitch.

6. OBSERVE: The test tube with the 10-cm column of air produced the lowest pitch.

The Big Idea

(pp. 388–389)

1 Introduce

Objective Students will locate an animal sound on the Internet, listen to the sound, and hypothesize what that sound means to the animal. They will devise ways to test their hypotheses.

Linking Prior Knowledge Ask students to review the definitions of *ultrasonic* and *infrasonic*. Ask: *What sounds do you know of that animals can hear but humans cannot?*

2 Teach

Discussion After students read the article and the call outs, ask them to classify the various animal sounds as infrasonic or ultrasonic. You might play audio recordings of some of the sounds. Point out the caption for the wolves' sounds. Ask students how they think researchers discovered that a certain wolf call signals loneliness. **learning style: auditory**

Use the information in the article, captions, and Fast Facts to help guide students in choosing a topic for their Science Logs.

THE BIG IDEA ONLINE

How do animals use sound? Have students research their Science Log Writing Activity at www.conceptsandchallenges.com. You can have students organize their log by completing the Big Idea activity online. Students may post their work in the Online Classroom Database for others to read.

Reinforcement Students can also use the Big Idea Planner or Big Idea Science Log Entry found on the Teacher's Resources CD-ROM.

◆ *Integrating Life Science*

THE Big IDEA

How do animals use sound?

Listen to the world around you. Vibrations in the air make your eardrum move. Tiny bones in your middle ear amplify the vibrations. Then, your inner ear changes the vibrations into messages for your brain. Human ears work in the range of about 20 to 20,000 vibrations per second or hertz.

Some animals make sounds that are too high- or too low-pitched for our ears to detect. Sounds above the range of human hearing are called ultrasonic and sounds below the range of human hearing are called infrasonic.

Bats make ultrasonic chirps with a wide range of frequencies. They use the echoes of their chirps to locate food with sonar. Dolphins and other sea mammals also use ultrasound for communication and sonar.

Humpback whales are amazing vocalists. They sing mostly in the autumn before migrating to tropical feeding grounds. Each group's song changes from season to season. Humpback songs can last for 30 minutes and range from 20 to 9,000 Hz.

Elephants communicate with infrasonic sounds that travel many kilometers. When some family groups of elephants come together, they flap their ears and exchange greetings in the range of 5 to 50 Hz, a very low-pitched way of saying hello.

Look at the illustrations that appear on these two pages. Then, follow the directions in the Science Log to find out more about "the big idea." ◆

388

Elephants
When elephants greet each other they stand side by side and exchange rumbling infrasonic hellos that vary from 5 to 50 Hz.

Whales
Humpback Whales sing complex eerie sounding songs that range from 20 to 9,000 Hz. Long ago sailors believed the songs were the cries of sailors' ghosts.

Teaching Options

! FAST FACTS *More About Animal Sounds*

Whales
Humpback whales are known for singing songs that are sometimes more than 20 minutes long. The songs, which are most likely part of a mating ritual, are each a series of phrases. All of the whales in a particular migrating group sing a song that sounds nearly the same. A group's song will change a little every year, resulting in a song that sounds almost completely different every 4 or 5 years.

Dolphins
Dolphins are almost constantly whistling, or making clicking sounds. The clicks are short sounds; dolphins can click 300 times a second. Dolphins use the clicks for echolocation, enabling them to locate fish, squid, and small shrimp. The whistles are used to communicate emotions, such as fear. Scientists are unsure whether dolphin communications are complex enough to be a true language.

Bats

Bats are so good at using ultrasound to locate that they can catch moths and mosquitoes even when they are flying at full speed. Bat chirps have a frequency from 10,000 to over 100,000 Hz.

Science Log

WRITING ACTIVITY

On the Web find the sound of any animal. Listen carefully to it. Write a hypothesis predicting what the sound means for the animal. How could you test your hypothesis? Write down a procedure for an observation or an experiment that would help you test your hypothesis on animal sounds. For additional information for your experiment, visit www.conceptsandchallenges.com.

Wolves

Some researchers believe that wolves can hear sounds all the way up to 80,000 Hz. Wolves have many calls. The wolf's "lonesome" call ranges from 200 to 2,200 Hz.

Dolphins

Bottlenose dolphins make sounds for echolocation and communication. Each task has a different range of sound, varying from about 250 Hz to 150,000 Hz. The frequency during echolocation is about 100,000 Hz. Many people wonder if they have languages like humans.

3 Assess

Use the Writing Activity Rubric on the Teacher's Resources CD-ROM to assess students' Science Logs. Fill in the rubric with the additional information below. For this assignment, students should have:

- identified the animal sounds that they heard and hypothesized what the animal sounds mean.
- written experiments for testing their hypotheses about the animals' sounds.

4 Close

Creating a Park Service Guide Ask students to imagine that they are tour guides at a national park in which visitors will see one of the animals discussed on pages 388 and 389 or one of the animals researched during this activity. Students should develop guides for park visitors. The guides should include a description of the animal, what to listen for if a person sees the animal, and an explanation of what those sounds mean. Encourage students to make drawings of the animals and use vivid words that describe the animals' sounds. **learning styles: visual, linguistic**

Tips for Using Technology

Creating Guides for Park Visitors Have students use desktop publishing software to make a guide about animals in a national park. Desktop publishing software allows students to combine text and art on a page. Most word processing software programs include tools for desktop publishing. Students can use these tools to give text special formats, to make a special border around the text, and to plan a page layout. Have students use the Thumbnail Sketch on the Teacher's Resources CD-ROM to plan their desktop publishing layouts.

• TEACHING RESOURCES •

Teacher's Resources CD-ROM

Big Idea: Chapter 18, p. 9

Big Idea Planner: Study Tools, pp. 11–12

Big Idea Science Log Entry: Study Tools, p. 13

Writing Activity Rubric: Teaching Tools, p. 9

Thumbnail Sketch: Study Tools, p. 24

1 Introduce

INVESTIGATE

TIME: 5–10 minutes

PURPOSE: Students will pluck the string on a stringed instrument in several different places to link the pitch and loudness to the sound quality of the instrument.

MATERIALS: stringed instrument, such as a guitar or violin

PROCEDURE: Be sure to demonstrate proper handling of the instrument, and lead students through the steps, one step at a time.

THINK ABOUT IT: Answers will vary. Students may detect overtones with the higher-pitched note on the string. **learning styles: tactile, auditory**

STUDY HINT To focus on the main concepts of the lesson, ask students to create an outline or other graphic organizer as they read the lesson. Suggest that they use the heads as main topics and write supporting details for each head as they read.

Linking Prior Knowledge Ask students to think about two different musicians, such as a tuba player and a flute player, both playing the same note. Even though the note is the same, the note sounds very different played by the two instruments. Ask students to speculate what makes the note sound different. Also, encourage students to share their knowledge of the types of musical instruments.

2 Teach

Demonstration If any students play stringed instruments, ask them to demonstrate a fundamental tone and overtones. Emphasize that musical instruments have different sound qualities. If instruments are not available, play sound recordings instead. **learning style: auditory**

Answers to questions

1 DEFINE: sound quality

2 DEFINE: the lowest-pitched sound produced when a whole string vibrates

3 DEFINE: sounds that have a higher pitch than the fundamental tone

T390 UNIT 6: Waves, Sound, and Light

18-6 What is sound quality?

INVESTIGATE

Listening to a String Instrument
HANDS-ON ACTIVITY

1. Pluck the lowest-pitched string of a violin or guitar.
2. Lightly touch the string in the center to change its vibrations. LIsten for the higher note.
3. Pluck the same string again. Touch it one-third of the way along its length to get the next highest note.

THINK ABOUT IT: How does the pitch and loudness of these sounds affect the quality of the sound heard?

STEP 3

Objective
Explain how overtones affect sound quality.

Key Terms
timbre (TAM-buhr)**:** sound quality

fundamental tone: lowest pitched sound produced when an object vibrates

overtones: sounds that have a higher pitch than the fundamental tone

music: a pleasing combination of sounds

noise: unpleasant combination of sounds with irregular patterns of vibration

Sound Quality Suppose a trumpet player and a clarinet player play the same note. The sounds they make have the same frequency and the same intensity. Can you hear a difference between the two sounds? The sounds are different even though the frequency and the intensity are the same. The sounds differ because of their **timbre,** or sound quality. The sounds of a trumpet and a clarinet have different timbres.

1 DEFINE: What is timbre?

Fundamental Tone When an object vibrates, it produces a sound with a certain frequency. Figure 18-23 shows a vibrating string. Notice that the whole string is vibrating. When the whole string vibrates, it produces the lowest possible frequency and pitch. The lowest-pitched sound produced is called the **fundamental tone.**

String

▲ **Figure 18-23** Fundamental tone

2 DEFINE: What is a fundamental tone?

Overtones Parts of the string shown in Figure 18-24 can vibrate faster than the whole string. When parts of the string are vibrating, the string produces sounds with a higher pitch than the fundamental tone. The high-pitched sounds produced when different parts of a string vibrate are called **overtones.**

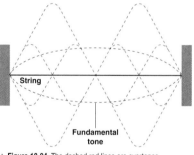
String

Fundamental tone

▲ **Figure 18-24** The dashed red lines are overtones.

390

Teaching Options

FAST FACTS

Thomas Edison and Sound Recordings

Most students listen to music on CDs. In the past, people used phonographs to listen to music. American inventor Thomas Edison (1847–1931) helped to develop the first phonograph. He was the first person to record a human voice.

The earliest phonograph was called a gramophone. It could reproduce sounds, but the quality of the sound was poor. Today, digital phonographs can reproduce sounds with a great deal of accuracy.

RETEACH

Understanding Diagrams If students are still having difficulty understanding the difference between tones and overtones, point out Figures 18-23 and 18-24. Discuss the figures in terms of amplitude and frequency, and ask students how the two diagrams are different from each other. Point out that Figure 18-24 has extra wave action that causes the overtones.

The sounds produced by a musical instrument or a human voice also have overtones. The quality of a sound is a result of these overtones. Without overtones, all vibrations of the same frequency would have the same quality.

▶ 3 DEFINE: What are overtones?

Music Different musical instruments have different sound qualities. How do the different instruments in an orchestra combine to make music? **Music** is a pleasing combination of sounds. Some elements of music are rhythm, melody, and harmony.

- **Rhythm** The basic beat in music is known as the rhythm. When you listen to music, the rhythm you hear might come from drums or a bass guitar. If you clap your hands to the beat of the music, you are adding rhythm.
- **Melody** The combination of musical notes is called the tune or the melody. If you hum or sing a song, you are repeating the melody.
- **Harmony** In an orchestra or chorus, different instruments or voices perform together. Many different notes are heard at the same time. Combining the different notes is called harmony. Good harmony makes music sound better.

▶ 4 IDENTIFY: What are three elements of music?

Musical Instruments Musical instruments can be divided into three main groups.

- **Percussion Instruments** These instruments include drums, pianos, and any instrument that is played by being tapped or hit.
- **String Instruments** These instruments make music from the sound of vibrating strings. Examples include guitars, violins, and cellos.
- **Wind Instruments** These instruments make music when air is blown through them. Examples include trumpets, clarinets, and flutes.

▶ 5 NAME: What are the three main groups of musical instruments?

Noise **Noise** is an unpleasant combination of sounds with irregular patterns of vibration. Unlike music, noise has no agreeable quality.

▶ 6 DEFINE: What is noise?

✓ CHECKING CONCEPTS

1. The quality of a sound is its _____.
2. When a whole string vibrates, it produces a _____.
3. All sounds are a combination of fundamental tones and _____.
4. Two sounds can have the same _____ and intensity but still sound different.
5. Higher-pitched sounds produced when parts of a string vibrate are called _____.
6. Unpleasant sounds are _____.
7. Rhythm, melody, and harmony combine to make _____.

💡 THINKING CRITICALLY

8. **INFER:** What would human voices sound like without overtones?
9. **INFER:** A violin and a piano are playing the same musical note with the same frequency and the same intensity. Why do they sound different?
10. **CLASSIFY:** Identify each of the following instruments as percussion, string, or wind instruments.
    a. tuba   c. harp
    b. kettle drum   d. trumpet

Web InfoSearch

The Musical Scale Our musical scale is made up of eight notes. Each musical note has its own pitch. Each note is represented by a letter of the alphabet. A set of eight notes is called an octave. The last note in an octave has twice the frequency of the first note. The human ear can hear a total of about 10 octaves.

SEARCH: Use the Internet to find out what a musical scale looks like. Draw a scale with all the notes placed properly. Start your search at www.conceptsandchallenges.com. Some key search words are **music** and **musical scale**.

▶ 4 IDENTIFY: rhythm, melody, and harmony

▶ 5 NAME: percussion, string, and wind instruments

▶ 6 DEFINE: a combination of unpleasant sounds with irregular patterns of vibration

Reinforcement Students may not understand why they are discussing such terms as *rhythm, melody,* and *harmony* in a science text. Point out that although music, science, and mathematics are different areas of study, music and the sciences have much in common. Encourage students to link music with science and explain how they are related. You might apply their explanations to the Chapter Project. **learning styles: auditory, logical/mathematical**

3 Assess

✓ CHECKING CONCEPTS ANSWERS

1. timbre
2. fundamental tone
3. overtones
4. frequency
5. overtones
6. noise
7. music

💡 THINKING CRITICALLY ANSWERS

8. **INFER:** All voices would sound the same.
9. **INFER:** They have different timbre.
10. **CLASSIFY:** **a.** wind **b.** percussion **c.** string **d.** wind

4 Close

Web InfoSearch

The Musical Scale Have students use the Internet to find out what a musical scale looks like. Then, have students draw a scale with all the notes placed properly. Some key search words are **musical scale, treble clef notes,** and **musical scale note names.** Students should begin their search at www.conceptsandchallenges.com.

EXTENDING THE LESSON

Speaking Sounds Let students know that the bulge at the top of their windpipe is called the larynx. The vocal cords are inside the larynx. When a person speaks, the vocal cords tighten. Air passes over the vocal cords and makes them vibrate. Ask students: *Why do some people have lower voices than others?* (Vocal cords differ in length and thickness.) *What makes a voice change?* Have students use reference sources to answer the questions. (Vocal cords can change in length and thickness, such as during puberty.)

• TEACHING RESOURCES •

Teacher's Resources CD-ROM
Lesson Review: Chapter 18, p. 10
Enrichment: Chapter 18, pp. 11, 12
Concept Map: Study Tools, p. 4

1 Introduce

✎ **STUDY HINT** Ask students to write the objective for the lesson in their notebooks. As they read, they can write an explanation of the Doppler effect in their own words.

Linking Prior Knowledge Discuss the example of the Doppler effect described in the first section of the text. Ask students to give real-life examples, both from the lesson and from their own experiences.

2 Teach

Discussion Before discussing the Doppler effect, remind students that frequency is the number of complete waves that pass a point each second. As you describe the Doppler effect with the examples in the text, be sure that students understand that the Doppler effect applies to all waves, not just sound waves. **learning style: auditory**

Demonstration Bring a portable radio to class. Turn on the radio at a low volume. Holding the radio, stand in the middle of the room. Tell students to listen to the radio. Then, walk toward the front of the room. For students in the back of the room, the sound waves will appear to have a lower frequency. For students in the front of the room, the sound waves will appear to have a higher frequency. Point out that this apparent change in the frequency of waves is the Doppler effect. **learning style: auditory**

📖 **READING STRATEGY** Students can improve their comprehension and retention of the text by practicing three simple steps. First, students read the paragraph. Next, students ask themselves what the main idea and supporting details of the paragraph are. Last, students paraphrase the paragraph.

Answers to questions

▶**1** COMPARE: approaching

▶**2** DEFINE: an apparent change in the frequency of waves

▶**3** COMPARE: higher as it comes toward you

18-7 What is the Doppler effect?

Objective
Explain what is meant by the Doppler effect.

Key Term
Doppler effect: apparent change in the frequency of waves

Changing Frequency The frequency of a wave sometimes changes. Remember that frequency is the number of complete waves that pass a point in a given time. Frequency seems to change when a wave source moves toward you or away from you. Imagine you are sitting on a dock. You can count the number of waves hitting the dock. As a motorboat passes you, many waves hit the dock. The frequency of the waves is high. As the boat continues on, fewer waves hit the dock. The frequency returns to what it was before the boat passed.

▲ **Figure 18-25** The frequency of waves changes as a boat passes.

▶**1** COMPARE: Will you be able to count more waves when a boat is approaching or heading away from a dock?

Doppler Effect An apparent change in the frequency of waves is called the **Doppler effect.** The Doppler effect occurs when there is relative motion between the source of the waves and an observer. The frequency of waves appears to change when the observer is moving toward or away from the source of the waves. The frequency also seems to change when the source of the waves is moving and the observer is standing still. For the Doppler effect to take place, either the source or the observer must be moving.

▶**2** DEFINE: What is the Doppler effect?

Doppler Effect and Sound You are probably most familiar with the Doppler effect in sound waves. The frequency of sound waves seems to change as the source of the waves moves toward or away from you. Suppose you are waiting for a train to pass a crossing. You can hear the train whistle as the train approaches the crossing. The waves are pushed closer together by the motion of the train. The pitch of the sound seems to get higher as more and more waves per second reach your ears. As the train passes you, the sound waves spread out. Fewer waves reach your ear every second. The pitch of one sound seems to get lower.

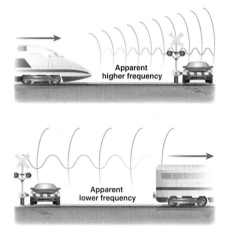

▲ **Figure 18-26** The Doppler effect causes the sound of a train whistle to change as it passes.

▶**3** COMPARE: Does the frequency of sound waves from a train whistle become higher or lower as the train comes toward you?

392

Teaching Options

✔ CHECKING CONCEPTS

1. The apparent change in the frequency of waves is called the _____.

2. Waves hit a dock more often when a boat is moving _____ the dock.

3. The Doppler effect is caused by _____.

4. The frequency of waves appears to change when either the source of the waves or the _____ is moving.

5. The frequency of sound waves is _____ when the source of the waves is moving away from you.

6. As a boat moves toward you, the frequency of the water waves appears _____ than if the boat was moving away from you.

💡 THINKING CRITICALLY

7. EXPLAIN: Describe how the sound of a car horn changes as the car approaches you and then passes you.

8. PREDICT: Will the pitch of the sound of the fire engine's siren seem higher to a person standing at point A or point B? Explain.

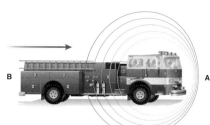

▲ Figure 18-27

BUILDING SCIENCE SKILLS

Researching Visit your local police station. Many police forces use Doppler radar to measure the speed of passing cars. Find out how Doppler radar works. How do radar detectors in cars work? How is Doppler radar used to track the path of fast-moving storms? What are other uses of Doppler radar? Describe your findings to the class.

◇ **Integrating Earth Science**

TOPICS: stars, universe

RED SHIFT

Astronomers study the wavelength of light from the stars to find out about the universe. The wavelength of light determines the color of the light. Red light has a long wavelength. Blue light has a short wavelength.

The Doppler effect causes an apparent change in the frequency of a wave. It also causes an apparent change in wavelength. If a light source is moving away from an observer, the wavelength of the light appears to change. The light appears redder than it would if the source were not moving. This change in wavelength is called the red shift.

Astronomers have studied the red shifts of many different galaxies. They found that all of the galaxies are moving away from Earth. Each galaxy is also moving away from every other galaxy. This suggests that the universe is expanding, or getting bigger.

Thinking Critically What would astronomers see if the universe were shrinking?

▲ Figure 18-28 Galaxies are moving apart.

CHAPTER 18: Sound **393**

---

3 Assess

✔ CHECKING CONCEPTS ANSWERS

1. Doppler effect
2. toward
3. relative motion
4. observer
5. low
6. higher

💡 THINKING CRITICALLY ANSWERS

7. EXPLAIN: As the car approaches, the pitch of the horn becomes higher. As the car passes and moves away, the pitch becomes lower.

8. PREDICT: Point A; The pitch becomes higher as the fire truck approaches point A.

4 Close

BUILDING SCIENCE SKILLS

Researching If students are unable to visit a police station, you might invite a guest speaker or provide reference sources for students to use to find the answers to the questions. Have students draw posters to illustrate how Doppler radar works.

✏ WRITING HINT Before students visit the police station, make sure that they prepare a list of questions that they would like answered.

◇ **Integrating Earth Science**

TOPICS: stars, universe

RED SHIFT

Earth-Science Connection To help students understand red shift, describe the relationship between frequency and wavelength. Frequency increases as wavelength decreases. This accounts for the red shift. As frequency apparently becomes lower, wavelength appears to change and become longer.

Discussion Ask: *What determines the color of light?* (the wavelength) *What did astronomers find out by studying the red shifts of galaxies?* (All of the galaxies are moving away from Earth and from one another.)

Thinking Critically Answer
The astronomers would see a blue shift.

MORE ON THE WEB

Simulating the Doppler Effect Students can adjust the properties of sound waves and see how they interfere with one other by visiting www.conceptsandchallenges.com.

• TEACHING RESOURCES •

◎ **Teacher's Resources CD-ROM**
Lesson Review: Chapter 18, p. 13
Enrichment: Chapter 18, p. 14

ONGOING ASSESSMENT

Explaining Figure 18-26 Ask students to explain what is happening in Figure 18-26. Be sure that they use the terms *waves* and *frequency* to tell why the sound of the train whistle seems to change.

1 Introduce

✎ **STUDY HINT** Ask students to write the lesson title in their notebooks. As they read, they can answer the question *How do you hear?* by listing the processes that occur when sound travels into the ear.

Linking Prior Knowledge Ask students to tell what they know about the ear and the process of hearing. Write their ideas in the K (know) column of a KWL chart.

2 Teach

Discussion Refer students to Figure 18-29. As students read *How the Ear Hears*, they can trace and discuss the path of sound waves through the ear.

Ask students if they have ever had an ear infection. For those who have, ask them what it felt like. (ear ached, felt like there was fluid inside the ear, felt dizzy, had a fever) Inform students that ear infections are caused by irritation of the tiny hair cells inside the ear. Ear infections can make a person feel dizzy because the irritated ear cells send mixed messages to the brain. Make sure that students understand that ear infections do not necessarily affect a person's hearing.
learning styles: visual, auditory

Demonstration If possible, obtain a model of the human ear so that students can see the ear in three dimensions. Relate the parts of the model to Figure 18-29.
learning styles: tactile, visual

📖 **READING STRATEGY** Continue the KWL chart with students. Have them write in the *W* (want to know) column any questions that they would like to have answered as they read the material. As they read, they can answer the questions in the *L* (learned) column.

Answers to questions

▶ **NAME:** outer, middle, and inner ear

▶ **NAME:** eardrum, hammer, anvil, stirrup, cochlea

▶ **INFER:** When you are dizzy, you could fall and injure yourself.

18-8 How do you hear?

Objective
Trace the path of sound waves through the ear to the brain.

Key Terms
hearing: one of the five human senses

ear: sense organ that detects sound

eardrum: thin sheet of tissue that vibrates when sound waves strike it

cochlea (KAHK-lee-uh)**:** organ that changes sound vibrations into nerve signals

Hearing Sounds One of the five human senses is **hearing.** What happens when you hear a sound? For a sound to be heard, three things are needed: a source of the sound, a medium to transmit the sound, and a sense organ to detect the sound.

In humans, the sense organ that detects sound is the **ear.** Look at the diagram of the human ear in Figure 18-29. There are three main parts to the ear: the outer ear, the middle ear, and the inner ear.

▶ **NAME:** What are the three main parts of the human ear?

How the Ear Hears A sound wave first enters the outer ear. The outer ear funnels the sound wave into the ear. The sound wave moves through the ear canal to the eardrum. The **eardrum** is a thin sheet of tissue that vibrates when sound waves strike it. The vibrating air particles in the sound wave make the eardrum vibrate.

The vibrations from the eardrum are transferred to the middle ear. There are three small bones in the middle ear. They are the hammer, the anvil, and the stirrup. The vibrations are transferred from the hammer, to the anvil, and then to the stirrup.

The vibrations are then transmitted to the inner ear. In the inner ear, the vibrations are transferred to the cochlea. The **cochlea** is the organ that changes sound vibrations into nerve impulses. The cochlea is filled with liquid and is attached to nerve fibers. The nerve fibers join to form one nerve. The nerve transmits the impulses to the brain. In the brain, the nerve impulses are interpreted as sound.

▶ **NAME:** Which parts of the ear vibrate when a sound is heard?

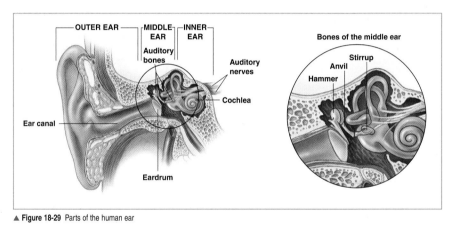

▲ **Figure 18-29** Parts of the human ear

394

Teaching Options

◈ **INTEGRATING LIFE SCIENCE**

Describing the Ear Help students to understand how their ears function. The part of the ear that people can see—the outer ear—is called the pinna or auricle. The outer ear, shaped like a cup, collects sounds. After a sound comes in, it travels in the outer ear canal toward the middle ear. The job of the outer ear canal is to protect the other parts of the ear. Earwax plays a big part in this job. Special chemicals in earwax ward off infections that could hurt the skin inside the ear canal. Ask students why they think earwax is sticky. (because part of its job is to collect dirt and keep the ear canal clean)

RETEACH

Tracing Sound If students are still having trouble identifying the parts of the ear and following the path of sound, copy the Ear Visual on the Teacher's Resources CD-ROM onto a transparency to display for the class. Have students take turns coming up to the transparency and pointing out steps in the detection of sound. They can use a wax pencil to label with a *V* the parts of the ear that vibrate.
learning styles: tactile, visual

Dizziness The inner ear has another important role that has nothing to do with hearing. The inner ear maintains balance. After you ride a roller coaster, you may feel dizzy. Dizziness is a temporary loss of balance. It is often caused by an ear infection. The infection irritates the tiny hair cells that project into fluid-filled canals in the inner ear's balance center. When irritated, these hair cells send mixed-up messages to the brain, tricking the brain into thinking you are spinning.

▶ **INFER:** Why is it important to maintain balance?

✓ CHECKING CONCEPTS

1. The _____ is the organ that detects sound.
2. Of the five senses, the one that is involved with sound is _____.
3. Sound waves travel from the outer ear, to the _____, and then to the inner ear.
4. The part of the ear that vibrates first is the _____.
5. The _____ converts the sound vibrations into nerve impulses.

💡 THINKING CRITICALLY

6. **SEQUENCE:** Arrange the following steps in the correct order.
   a. The vibrations are transferred to the hammer, anvil, and stirrup. **b.** The vibrations of air particles in the sound wave cause the eardrum to vibrate. **c.** The vibrations are transferred to the cochlea. **d.** The brain interprets the electrical impulses as sounds. **e.** A sound wave is transmitted by the source. **f.** The vibrations are converted to electrical impulses along a nerve that goes to the brain. **g.** The sound waves travel through the medium. **h.** The sound waves enter the outer ear and go into the ear canal.

INTERPRETING VISUALS

Look at Figure 18-29 to help you answer the following questions.

7. Where is the liquid that helps you maintain balance located?
8. Which parts of the ear have a liquid medium for sound to travel?
9. Which parts of the ear have a solid medium?
10. Which parts of the ear have a gaseous medium?

 Real-Life Science

THE CHANGING TELEPHONE

In 1876, Alexander Graham Bell received a patent for the first working telephone. Two years later, telephone service began in the United States. Since that time, the telephone has undergone many changes and improvements.

In 1977, communications companies began testing mobile, or cellular, telephones. By 1987, more than one million people had subscribed to cellular phone systems. Today, personal computers can be used to connect to regular telephones and can be used to make video phone calls.

The next dramatic change in the telephone will likely be disposable cellular telephones. Prototypes of these telephones have already been produced. They are as thin as a credit card and can be recycled.

THINKING CRITICALLY: What are some advantages of disposable phones?

▲ **Figure 18-30** Alexander Graham Bell testing his phone

---

3 Assess

✓ CHECKING CONCEPTS ANSWERS

1. ear
2. hearing
3. middle ear
4. eardrum
5. cochlea

💡 THINKING CRITICALLY ANSWER

6. **SEQUENCE: e, g, h, b, a, c, f, d**

INTERPRETING VISUALS ANSWERS

7. inner ear
8. cochlea or inner ear
9. outer and middle ear
10. outer ear

4 Close

Real-Life Science

THE CHANGING TELEPHONE

Background Although Alexander Graham Bell is best known for his invention of the telephone, he also worked on other inventions and was a teacher of deaf students. Born in Scotland in 1847, he immigrated to Canada and then the United States, where he began teaching deaf students in 1871 with a system called visible speech. This system shows how the lips, tongue, and throat are used to make sound. Bell started a school to train other teachers of deaf students.

Bell's ideas for the telephone came when he was working on a multiple telegraph in 1875. His first successful experiment with the telephone came in 1876, when he said to his assistant via the telephone, "Watson, come here; I want to see you."

Discussion Spark discussion on the effects of the telephone on people's daily lives. Ask what life would be like without the telephone. Ask: *What advances in telephone technology do you think may take place in the future?*

Thinking Critically Answer
Possible answer: They are easy to carry, and they can be recycled.

MORE ON THE WEB

The Bionic Ear Have students visit www.conceptsand challenges.com to learn about cochlear implants. Then, have students write a short report on the bionic ear.

• TEACHING RESOURCES •

Teacher's Resources CD-ROM
Lesson Review: Chapter 18, p. 15
The Eye/The Ear: Visuals, p. 12
KWL Chart: Study Tools, p. 7

ONGOING ASSESSMENT

Reviewing the Parts of the Ear Ask students: *Which part of the ear is a thin sheet of tissue?* (the eardrum) *What are the three small bones in the inner ear called?* (hammer, anvil, and stirrup) *Which part of the ear changes sound vibrations into nerve impulses?* (the cochlea)

Challenges (pp. 396–398)

Chapter Summary

Review Before students begin the Challenges, review the summary with them. You might copy the summary on a transparency, leaving out the Key Terms. Create a word bank with the Key Terms on the board, and ask volunteers to choose the words from the word bank that complete the summary. You can record the words on the transparency.

✏️ **STUDY HINT** Have students use the main concepts in each section to create an outline. Students should be sure that all Key Terms and concepts are included.

Key Terms Challenges

MATCHING

1. pitch (18-5)
2. supersonic (18-3)
3. vibration (18-1)
4. overtones (18-6)
5. timbre (18-6)
6. ear (18-8)
7. music (18-6)
8. hearing (18-8)
9. sound (18-1)
10. decibel (18-4)

FILL IN

11. medium (18-2)
12. echo (18-2)
13. amplitude (18-4)
14. ultrasonic (18-5)
15. fundamental tone (18-6)

Chapter Summary

Lesson 18-1
* **Sound** is a form of energy that travels as waves. All sounds are caused by **vibrations.**

Lesson 18-2
* Sound waves are **longitudinal waves.** All sound waves need a **medium** through which to travel. A reflected sound wave is called an **echo.**

Lesson 18-3
* The speed of sound is much slower than the speed of light. Sound travels at different speeds in different materials. Jet airplanes can reach supersonic speeds.

Lesson 18-4
* Loud sounds have more energy than soft sounds do. The **intensity** of a sound wave determines the loudness of the sound. Intensity is measured in **decibels** (dB).

Lesson 18-5
* Different sounds have different frequencies. A high-frequency sound has a high pitch. A low-frequency sound has a low pitch.
* Some animals can hear **ultrasonic** or **infrasonic** sounds.

Lesson 18-6
* The sounds of a trumpet and a clarinet differ because of their sound quality, or **timbre.**
* When a string vibrates as a whole, it produces a **fundamental tone.**
* When different parts of a string vibrate, they produce **overtones.**
* **Music** is a combination of rhythm, melody, and harmony. **Noise** is an unpleasant combination of sounds with no regular pattern of vibrations.

Lesson 18-7
* The **Doppler effect** is caused by motion of the observer or of the source of the waves.

Lesson 18-8
* The **ear** is the human sense organ that detects sound.

396

Key Term Challenges

cochlea (p. 394)	medium (p. 380)
decibel (p. 384)	music (p. 390)
Doppler effect (p. 392)	noise (p. 390)
ear (p. 394)	overtone (p. 390)
eardrum (p. 394)	pitch (p. 386)
echo (p. 380)	sonic boom (p. 382)
fundamental tone (p. 390)	sound (p. 376)
hearing (p. 394)	supersonic (p. 382)
infrasonic (p. 386)	timbre (p. 390)
intensity (p. 384)	ultrasonic (p. 386)
longitudinal wave (p. 380)	vibration (p. 376)

MATCHING Write the Key Term from above that best matches each description.

1. how high or low a sound is
2. speed faster than sound
3. rapid back-and-forth movement
4. frequency above the fundamental tone
5. sound quality
6. sense organ that detects sound
7. includes rhythm, melody, and harmony
8. one of the human senses
9. form of energy that travels as waves
10. unit of intensity

FILL IN Write the Key Term from above that best completes each statement.

11. A sound wave needs a _____ in which to travel.
12. A reflected sound wave is an _____.
13. The amount of energy in a sound wave is the _____ of the wave.
14. Sound with a frequency greater than 20,000 Hz is _____.
15. The _____ is the lowest-pitched sound produced when a whole string vibrates.

Teaching Options

PREPARING STUDENTS FOR STANDARDIZED TESTS

Reading Strategy: Tell students to look for words such as *always* and *never*. These words usually signal a wrong answer.

Writing Strategy: Tell students to organize their thoughts in an outline or other graphic organizer and to write important terms that they want to be sure to include.

Interpreting Visuals: Remind students to carefully read titles, captions, and labels in visuals and to put into their own words the information contained in visuals to be sure that they understand what is being pictured.

ESL/ELL STRATEGY

Defining Key Terms To help students define unfamiliar terms, have them write each word on one side of an index card. On the other side of the card, have students define the word. English-proficient students can help English-language learners study the words and their definitions.

Content Challenges <u>TEST PREP</u>

MULTIPLE CHOICE Write the letter of the term or phrase that best completes each statement.

1. To find their way in the dark, bats use
   a. overtones.
   b. ultrasound.
   c. echolocation.
   d. timbre.

2. A high-pitched sound has a
   a. low frequency.
   b. fundamental tone.
   c. high frequency.
   d. low intensity.

3. Two sounds with the same frequency and intensity will sound different because of
   a. timbre.
   b. pitch.
   c. vibrations.
   d. wavelength.

4. The speed of sound in air is
   a. 125 m/s.
   b. 340 m/s.
   c. 430 m/s.
   d. 540 m/s.

5. The unit of frequency is the
   a. hertz.
   b. decibel.
   c. m/s.
   d. pitch.

6. Sound travels fastest in
   a. liquids.
   b. solids.
   c. gases.
   d. a vacuum.

7. Dolphins communicate by making
   a. low-frequency sounds.
   b. high-intensity sounds.
   c. high-frequency sounds.
   d. low-intensity sounds.

8. Music consists of rhythm, melody, and
   a. intensity.
   b. harmony.
   c. percussion.
   d. frequency.

9. Before your eardrum vibrates, the sound wave has to travel through the
   a. anvil.
   b. ear canal.
   c. inner ear.
   d. cochlea.

10. A sound wave consists of compressions and
    a. overtones.
    b. fundamental tones.
    c. rarefactions.
    d. frequencies.

TRUE/FALSE Write *true* if the statement is true. If the statement is false, change the underlined term to make the statement true.

11. Sound cannot travel through a <u>vacuum</u>.

12. A high-intensity sound wave has a lot of <u>energy</u>.

13. Sound waves cause the <u>ear canal</u> to vibrate.

14. An echo is a sound wave that has been <u>made louder</u>.

15. One hertz is equal to one <u>compression</u> per second.

16. A drum is an example of a <u>percussion</u> instrument.

17. The beat of the music is the <u>melody</u>.

18. There are <u>three</u> main types of musical instruments.

19. Vibrations from the eardrum enter the <u>outer</u> ear.

20. Humans can hear sounds between <u>20 Hz</u> and 20,000 Hz.

Content Challenges

MULTIPLE CHOICE

1. c (18-2)
2. c (18-5)
3. a (18-6)
4. b (18-3)
5. a (18-5)
6. b (18-3)
7. c (18-2)
8. b (18-7)
9. b (18-8)
10. c (18-1)

TRUE/FALSE

11. true (18-1)
12. true (18-4)
13. false; eardrum (18-8)
14. false; reflected (18-2)
15. false; wave (18-5)
16. true (18-7)
17. false; rhythm (18-7)
18. true (18-7)
19. false; middle (18-8)
20. true (18-5)

ALTERNATIVE ASSESSMENT

Relating Information Students may write a Science Log entry explaining the relationship between frequency and pitch. Students can then explain how intensity and pitch are related. Finally, students can explain the processes of hearing, describing how the parts of the ear work together to allow hearing to take place.

PORTFOLIO ASSESSMENT

Making Student Portfolios
Students can demonstrate their comprehension of the concepts in this chapter by making a portfolio. The KWL Chart and the Big Idea Planner are some of the reproducibles on the Teacher's Resources CD-ROM that they can include in their portfolios. You can use the Portfolio Assessment Rubric also found on the Teacher's Resources CD-ROM to assess students' portfolios.

Concept Challenges

WRITTEN RESPONSE

1. **HYPOTHESIZE:** The particles in a solid are closer together. (18-2)
2. **PREDICT:** Vibrations are transferred to the bones of the middle ear. (18-8)
3. **INFER:** It pushes on the air in front of it, causing it to vibrate. (18-1)
4. **EXPLAIN:** A 50 Db sound wave has a larger amplitude than a 20 Db sound wave, because loudness increases with amplitude. (18-4)
5. **PREDICT:** You might have a loss of hearing. (18-4)

INTERPRETING VISUALS (18-8)

6. eardrum
7. cochlea and auditory nerve
8. cochlea
9. They are shaped like these objects.
10. Cupping the hand helps funnel the sound waves into the ear canal.

Chapter Project Wrap-Up

MUSEUM OF MUSIC

Students' displays can be exhibited around the classroom. Allow groups to present their displays to the class. You can use the Individual Activity Rubric found on the Teacher's Resources CD-ROM to assess students' projects. Fill in the rubric with the additional information below. For this project, students should have:

- prepared a display appropriate for a museum of music.
- indicated how science principles apply to music in their displays.

Content Challenges TEST PREP

WRITTEN RESPONSE Answer each of the following questions in complete sentences.

1. **HYPOTHESIZE:** Why does sound travel faster in a solid than in a gas?
2. **PREDICT:** What happens after a sound wave makes the eardrum vibrate?
3. **INFER:** What does a vibrating guitar string do to the air around it?
4. **EXPLAIN:** Which sound wave has a larger amplitude, a 20-dB sound or a 50-dB sound? How do you know?
5. **PREDICT:** What might happen to your sense of hearing if you were exposed to loud noises over a long period of time?

INTERPRETING VISUALS Use Figure 18-31 to answer the following questions.

6. When a sound is heard, what part of the ear vibrates first?
7. Which parts make up the inner ear?
8. Where is the energy of a sound wave converted to electrical impulses?
9. Why do you think the bones in the middle ear are called the hammer, the anvil, and the stirrup?
10. Cupping your hand to your ear helps you to hear sounds more clearly. Why?

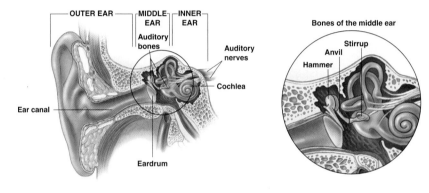

▲ **Figure 18-31** The human ear

398

Teaching Options

• TEACHING RESOURCES •

Teacher's Resources CD-ROM

Key Term Review: Chapter 18, p. 16

Chapter 18 Test: pp. 17–18

Individual Activity Rubric: Teaching Tools, p. 5

KWL Chart: Study Tools, p. 7

Big Idea Planner: Study Tools, pp. 11–12

Portfolio Assessment Rubric: Teaching Tools, p. 10

Chapter Self-Check: Teaching Tools, p. 11

PLANNING GUIDE

◆ **TEACHING THE CHAPTER** This chapter should take approximately 10–13 days to complete instruction and assessment.

	Skills and Features	Projects and Activities	Achieve Science Literacy	Meet Individual Needs
Chapter 19 Opener p. T399	RESEARCH	• Chapter Project		
Lesson 19-1 **What is the electromagnetic spectrum?** pp. T400–T401 Standard: B3a	HYPOTHESIZE, LIST, COMPARE • Health and Safety Tip • Science and Technology	• More on the Web • Extending the Lesson	• Study Hint • Reading Strategy • Ongoing Assessment	• Reteach CD-ROM Writing Activity Outline Features of a Transverse Wave
Lesson 19-2 **What is light?** pp. T402–T403 Standards: B3a, B3c	EXPLAIN, INFER, CLASSIFY • Investigate • Web InfoSearch • How Do They Know That?	• Cooperative Learning • Extending the Lesson	• Study Hint	• Reteach CD-ROM Enrichment Activity Spider Map
Lesson 19-3 **How do light waves travel?** pp. T404–T405 Standards: B3a, B3c	RELATE, CLASSIFY, CONTRAST • Interpreting Visuals • Real-Life Science	• Extending the Lesson • More on the Web	• Study Hint • Writing Hint • Ongoing Assessment	• Reteach CD-ROM Enrichment Activity Venn Diagram Features of a Transverse Wave
Lesson 19-4 **What are sources of light?** pp. T406–T407 Standard: B3c	INFER, DEFINE, CLASSIFY • Designing an Experiment • Integrating Earth Science	• Cooperative Learning • More on the Web	• Study Hint • Reading Strategy • Ongoing Assessment	• ESL/ELL Strategy CD-ROM Enrichment Activity Designing an Experiment
Lesson 19-5 **What is photosynthesis?** pp. T408–T409 Standards: B3a, B3c, B3e, B3f	INFER, HYPOTHESIZE, IDENTIFY • Web InfoSearch	• Extending the Lesson • Integrating Earth Science	• Study Hint • Reading Strategy	• ESL/ELL Strategy CD-ROM Cause-and-Effect Diagram
Lesson 19-6 **How do lenses refract light?** pp. T410–T411 Standard: B3c	HYPOTHESIZE, DEFINE, PREDICT • Web InfoSearch • People in Science	• Lab Challenge	• Study Hint	• Reteach Laboratory Video

Planning Guide continues on next page.

Standards: For details on the correlation to National Science Standards see pages *xx–xxi*.

	Skills and Features	Projects and Activities	Achieve Science Literacy	Meet Individual Needs
Lesson 19-7 How do you see? pp. T412–T413 Standard: B3c	INFER, SYNTHESIZE, NAME • Investigate • Interpreting Visuals • Science and Technology	• Cooperative Learning • More on the Web	• Study Hint • Reading Strategy • Ongoing Assessment	• Reteach CD-ROM Flowchart The Eye/The Ear
Lab Activity Comparing Convex and Concave Lenses pp. T414–T415 Standard: B3c	OBSERVE, ANALYZE, SYNTHESIZE • Set-Up Time: 15 min • Lab Time: 20 min	• Lab Skills Worksheet • Extend the Lab Activity	• Tips for Using Technology	• ESL/ELL Strategy CD-ROM Lab Activity Report
Lesson 19-8 How do mirrors reflect light? pp. T416–T417 Standard: B3c	INFER, PREDICT, APPLY • Building Math Skills • Hands-On Activity	• Extending the Lesson • More on the Web	• Study Hint • Reading Strategy • Ongoing Assessment	• Reteach CD-ROM Enrichment Activity
Lesson 19-9 What is color? pp. T418–T419 Standard: B3c	INFER, COMPARE, DESCRIBE • Web InfoSearch • Integrating Life Science	• Cooperative Learning • Integrating Life Science	• Study Hint • Reading Strategy	• Reteach CD-ROM KWL Chart
Lesson 19-10 How can light be used? pp. T420–T421 Standards: B3c, B3d	INFER, CONCLUDE, EXPLAIN • Building Science Skills • Science and Technology	• Extending the Lesson • More on the Web	• Study Hint • Reading Strategy • Ongoing Assessment	• Reteach
Big Idea How is light used in the home? pp. T422–423 Standards: B3a, B3b, B3c, B3f	RESEARCH, COMMUNICATE, ANALYZE • Science Log: Writing Activity	• Big Idea Online • Close Activity	• Tips for Using Technology	CD-ROM Big Idea Planner Thumbnail Sketch
Chapter 19 Challenges pp. T424–T426	• Chapter Summary • Key Term Challenges • Content Challenges • Concept Challenges	• Chapter Project Wrap-Up • Unit Challenge Online	• Study Hint • Preparing Students for Standardized Tests	• ESL/ELL Strategy CD-ROM Chapter Self-Check Spider Map

Chapter 19 Light

▲ **Figure 19-1** A bundle of optical fibers

Light is a form of energy. Much of our information comes to us in the form of light images. Light can travel through empty space. It can also travel through other materials, such as glass, water, and air. Many technologies that use light, such as fiber optics, have been developed. In fiber optics, light is carried through thin cables of a glasslike material. Fiber optics are used in many areas of life, particularly communications.

▶ Name something you use daily that works by fiber optics.

Contents

Chapter 19
Light

Chapter Overview

In this chapter, students will identify the parts of the electromagnetic spectrum, recognize that light is a form of electromagnetic energy, explain the process of photosynthesis, and contrast how light rays are bent by a concave lens and a convex lens. Students will also describe how the eye senses light and forms images, and describe the images formed by mirrors. Finally, students will learn more about color and describe several modern uses of light.

About Figure 19-1 The simplest use of fiber optics is the transmitting of light to locations that would be hard to reach any other way. Optical fibers are often used to transmit images in medical instruments for viewing the inside of the human body and for laser surgery. Fiber-optic communication systems link people around the world much more quickly than traditional phone systems.

Answer Possible answers: telephones, computers, and printers

Linking Prior Knowledge

For this chapter, students should recall:

- the composition of organic compounds for photosynthesis (Lesson 4-7).
- the classifications and features of waves (Lessons 17-1 and 17-2).

Chapter Project
CREATING BIG IDEAS

MATERIALS: paper, markers, research materials

Have students create their own Big Idea two-page spread based on lessons in this chapter. First, they will need to pick another science discipline that they will be making a connection to. They can choose from life science or Earth science. The following are possible ideas: What are the similarities between a camera and the human eye? How is the Moon an illuminated object? Students can also make up an idea of their own. You may wish to have students work in pairs. They should research the subject, gather pictures, draw diagrams, and come up with a Science Log idea.

Teaching Options

ASSESSMENT PLANNER

For assessment in the Student Edition, see the following pages:

Content Assessment
Checking Concepts: pp. 401, 403, 405, 407, 409, 411, 413, 417, 419, 421
Thinking Critically: pp. 401, 403, 405, 407, 409, 411, 413, 417, 419, 421
Interpreting Visuals: pp. 405, 413
Chapter Challenges: pp. 424–426

Alternative Assessment
Building Skills: pp. 417, 421
Web InfoSearch: pp. 403, 409, 411, 419
Science Log: p. 423

Performance-Based Assessment
Hands-On Activity: p. 417
Designing an Experiment: p. 407
Lab Activity: pp. 414–415

• TEACHING RESOURCES •

Teacher's Resources CD-ROM
Lesson Review: Ch. 19, pp. 2, 3, 5, 7, 9, 10, 11, 12, 14, 15
Enrichment: Ch. 19, pp. 4, 6, 8, 13
Key Term Review: Ch. 19, p. 17
Chapter 19 Test: pp. 18–19
Laboratory Manual: pp. 13–14, 93–96

Laboratory Video
Segment 21: What Kinds of Images Are Formed by Lenses?

1 Introduce

✏️ **STUDY HINT** Before beginning this lesson, write the title of each section on the board. Have students copy the titles in their notebooks, using an outline format. As students read each section, they should write the main idea in their notebooks. Students can also use the Writing Activity Outline found on the Teacher's Resources CD-ROM.

Linking Prior Knowledge Ask students to recall what they know about the frequency and wavelengths of waves. Have them review the properties of electromagnetic waves (Lesson 17-2).

2 Teach

Discussion Refer students to Figure 19-3 as you discuss the different types of electromagnetic waves. Be sure that students understand that wavelength and frequency are inversely proportional. The longer the wavelength is, the lower the frequency. Ask students which type of waves have a longer wavelength: gamma rays or radio waves. (radio waves) Then, ask which waves have a higher frequency: gamma rays or radio waves. (gamma waves) **learning styles: auditory, visual**

Demonstration Copy the wavelengths from Figure 19-3 on the board. Point out to students how each type of wave has a different wavelength and frequency from the other types of wavelengths. Explain to students that visible light also has different wavelengths. The different wavelengths determine the color of the light. There are seven colors of light that make up visible light: red, orange, yellow, green, blue, indigo, and violet. Red light has the longest wavelength, and violet light has the shortest wavelength. **learning style: visual**

Answers to questions

▶ **COMPARE:** Unlike mechanical waves, electromagnetic waves can travel through empty space.

▶ **LIST:** radio waves, microwaves, infrared waves, visible light, ultraviolet light, X-rays, and gamma rays

19-1 What is the electromagnetic spectrum?

Objective
Identify the parts of the electromagnetic spectrum.

Key Terms
electromagnetic (ee-lehk-troh-mag-NEHT-ihk)
spectrum: range of electromagnetic waves
visible spectrum: seven colors that make up white light

Electromagnetic Waves Light is a form of energy. Sometimes light behaves as if it is made up of tiny particles of energy called photons. Unless disturbed, photons travel in straight lines. Other times, light behaves as an electromagnetic wave. Unlike mechanical waves, electromagnetic waves can travel through empty space.

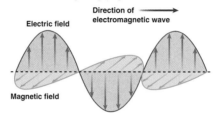

▲ Figure 19-2 Electromagnetic waves are made up of two transverse waves.

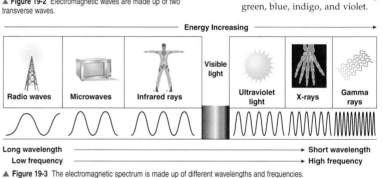

▲ Figure 19-3 The electromagnetic spectrum is made up of different wavelengths and frequencies.

400

Electromagnetic waves have both electrical properties and magnetic properties. These waves are made up of two transverse waves that vibrate at right angles to each other.

▶ **COMPARE:** How are electromagnetic waves different from mechanical waves?

The Electromagnetic Spectrum Light that you can see is called visible light, or white light. Visible light waves make up a small part of a much larger band of waves called the **electromagnetic spectrum**. Figure 19-3 shows the different types of waves that make up the electromagnetic spectrum. As the figure shows, the energy of a wave is related to its wavelength and its frequency.

- **Radio waves** Radio waves have the longest wavelength and the lowest frequency. They are used for radio, television, and radar signals.

- **Microwaves** Microwaves are used for wireless communications and microwave ovens.

- **Infrared rays** All objects give off infrared rays. You cannot see infrared rays, but you can feel them as heat.

- **Visible spectrum** The only part of the electromagnetic spectrum that can be seen by the human eye is the **visible spectrum**. It is made up of the colors red, orange, yellow, green, blue, indigo, and violet.

Teaching Options

RETEACH

Understanding the Electromagnetic Spectrum Help students understand that the visible spectrum is the only part of the electromagnetic spectrum that can actually be seen by the human eye. (*Visible* means "can be seen.") Help students differentiate between the parts of the spectrum by playing the game Who am I? Give a statement such as *I am used for wireless communication*. Students would answer *microwaves*. Continue play, allowing students to make up clues if time permits. **learning styles: auditory, linguistic**

EXTENDING THE LESSON

Comparing the Waves of the Electromagnetic Spectrum Write true/false statements on the board, underlining a keyword in each statement. Students should tell whether the statements are true or false. For each false statement, students should change the underlined word to make the statement true. Use examples such as the following: *Gamma rays have the <u>lowest</u> frequency of all the waves on the electromagnetic spectrum.* (false; highest) *You can feel <u>infrared</u> rays as heat.* (true) **learning styles: visual, linguistic**

- **Ultraviolet rays** Ultraviolet rays can cause sunburn. Ultraviolet light is used to kill bacteria.
- **X-rays** X-rays have a very short wavelength and a high frequency. X-rays are used in medicine to form images of bones and internal organs.
- **Gamma rays** Gamma rays have a shorter wavelength and a higher frequency than X-rays do. They are given off during nuclear reactions.

LIST: What are the electromagnetic waves that make up the electromagnetic spectrum?

✓ CHECKING CONCEPTS

1. Waves with the longest wavelength and the lowest frequency are _____.
2. Waves usually given off during nuclear reactions are _____.
3. Only those waves in the _____ can be seen by the human eye.

4. Waves with wavelengths slightly longer than visible light are _____.
5. Rays usually felt as heat are _____.

💡 THINKING CRITICALLY

6. **HYPOTHESIZE:** Microwaves are high-frequency radio waves. Microwave ovens can be used to cook food quickly. The microwaves are absorbed by the food. Why do you think that food in a microwave oven gets hot, but a glass dish does not?

HEALTH AND SAFETY TIP

High-frequency electromagnetic waves are dangerous. Too much exposure to X-rays is harmful. Find out why X-ray technicians wear lead aprons or stand behind a lead screen when taking X-ray pictures. Why are pregnant women advised not to have X-rays taken?

Science and Technology

CELL PHONES

Cellular or cell phones have helped change the way we communicate. These phones are small radio transmitters and receivers. One of hundreds of antennae receives radio signals when you make a call. These radio signals are transmitted on a radio frequency to a local cell site. A mobile telephone switching office (MTSO) picks up the signals and sends them through regular wired phones. The MTSO tracks and transfers your calls as you move from area to area. It reverses when you get a call.

Two kinds of wireless phone networks are analog and digital. In analog, voices are carried on radio waves with limitations. This service is easy to steal, and busy signals and static are common. Conversations can be picked up on radio scanners.

Digital service is newer. Voices convert to computer language and then change back to voices on the receiving end. Busy signals and static are less common. Your conversation can not be heard on a scanner. This service is hard to steal. The newest technology is PCS (personal communication service). Computer language is transmitted on a range of frequencies that are always changing. This technology allows you to access the Internet, and have paging and text messaging capabilities.

Thinking Critically How have cell phones changed the way we communicate?

▲ **Figure 19-4** Cell phones receive and transmit radio waves.

ONGOING ASSESSMENT

Explaining Light Waves Ask students: *Do light waves need a medium to travel through? How do you know?* (no; because light travels through space, which is a vacuum)

• TEACHING RESOURCES •

Teacher's Resources CD-ROM
Lesson Review: Chapter 19, p. 2

Writing Activity Outline: Study Tools, pp. 20–21

Features of a Transverse Wave: Visuals, p. 11

📖 **READING STRATEGY** Remind students that paraphrasing can help them self-monitor as they read. After you read the first paragraph, demonstrate paraphrasing, or restating the material in your own words. Remind students that, if they are unable to paraphrase, they most likely need to reread to be sure that they understand what they have read.

3 Assess

✓ CHECKING CONCEPTS ANSWERS

1. radio waves
2. gamma rays
3. visible spectrum
4. infrared rays
5. infrared rays

💡 THINKING CRITICALLY ANSWER

6. **HYPOTHESIZE:** Microwaves are not absorbed by glass.

HEALTH AND SAFETY TIP

X-rays cannot penetrate lead, so lead blocks the rays from entering the body. Pregnant women should not have X-rays taken because X-rays may cause birth defects in unborn babies.

4 Close

Science and Technology

CELL PHONES

Technology Connection Although cell phones seem like a recent invention, the idea for cell phones was published in 1947. At first, they were used by businesses and in the military. They were not available commercially until 1981. A study conducted in the United States in 2001 found that 30 percent of teenagers 15–17 years old own a cell phone. Cell phones are even more popular in Europe than in the United States. In Europe, about two-thirds of the people own cell phones.

Discussion Ask students what type of waves from the electromagnetic spectrum are used in cell phone technology. (radio waves) Lead students to compare and contrast analog and digital wireless phone networks.

Thinking Critically Answer Wireless phones allow people instant access to communication, and they keep people in touch in case of an emergency.

1 Introduce

🔍 INVESTIGATE

TIME: 10 minutes

PURPOSE: Students will observe how light travels.

MATERIALS: index cards, flashlight, hole punch

PROCEDURE: Students can work in small groups to complete the experiment. Consider punching the holes in the cards yourself so that the size of the hole is the same in each card. Be sure that students do not shine bright flashlights directly into other students' eyes. **learning styles: visual, tactile**

THINK ABOUT IT: You can see the light through the holes, but the light cannot be seen when the card is moved. Light travels in a straight line.

✏️ **STUDY HINT** Have students make word webs focusing on the word *light* as they read. They can include such details as the definition of light, how light is made, and how light travels. Allow time for students to share their word webs with the class. Students can also use the Spider Map found on the Teacher's Resources CD-ROM.

Linking Prior Knowledge Light is a form of electromagnetic energy that is transmitted by waves. Remind students that waves carry energy, not matter.

2 Teach

Demonstration Obtain a piece of rubber hose. Bend it in the middle and point one end toward a light source. Have students take turns looking through the other end. Students will not be able to see the light source because light travels in straight lines. Then, straighten out the hose. Again, have students take turns looking through the hose. This time students will be able to see the light. **learning styles: visual, tactile**

Discussion Use a radiometer to demonstrate that light is a form of energy. Show that the vanes of the instrument turn when exposed to light. When the light source is removed, they stop. Review the concept that energy is the ability to do work and that, since light can do work, it is a form of energy.
learning styles: visual, auditory

19-2 What is light?

19-2

🔍 INVESTIGATE

Observing How Light Travels
HANDS-ON ACTIVITY

1. Stack three index cards one on top of the other and make a hole in the center.
2. Fold one edge of each card vertically. The folded edge should be about 4 cm wide.
3. Stand the cards in a row as shown. Line them up so that you can see through the holes.
4. Have a classmate shine a flashlight through the holes in the cards. Move the center card a few centimeters to the left or right. Observe what happens.

THINK ABOUT IT: Can you see the light when the cards are lined up? Can you still see the light when you move the center card? What do these results tell you about the way light travels?

STEP 4

Objective
Describe light as a form of electromagnetic energy.

Key Terms
light: form of electromagnetic energy made up of streams of photons

photon (FOH-tahn): tiny bundle of energy

ray: straight line that shows the direction of light

Light Energy When you sit in bright sunlight, you can feel your skin get warm. Objects warm up in sunlight. **Light** is a form of electromagnetic energy. Light energy can be changed into heat, electricity, and other forms of energy.

▶ **CLASSIFY:** What is light?

Particles of Light Light sometimes behaves as if it is made up of small bundles of energy called **photons**. Photons are such small particles that a single photon cannot be seen. A beam of light is made up of a stream of many photons. Each photon carries a certain amount of energy. Some photons have more energy than others.

▶ **DESCRIBE:** Of what is a light beam made?

Rays of Light When you turn on a flashlight, you see a beam of light. The beam of light from the flashlight looks like a straight line. Light travels in straight lines. A **ray** of light is a straight line that shows the direction of a light beam. A ray of light will continue to travel in a straight line unless its direction is changed. There are many ways to model light. Scientists model light in different ways, depending on the question they want to answer.

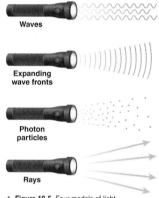

Waves

Expanding wave fronts

Photon particles

Rays

▲ **Figure 19-5** Four models of light

▶ **DESCRIBE:** What does a ray of light look like?

402

Teaching Options

EXTENDING THE LESSON

Researching Transformation of Light Energy Encourage students to find out more about the ways in which light energy is changed into other types of energy. Students can make illustrated posters showing some of the processes they find. In a solar calculator, for example, light energy is transformed into electrical energy. When the Sun shines on a plant, light energy changes into chemical energy. Display students' posters in the room. **learning styles: linguistic, tactile**

RETEACH

Modeling Light Copy Figure 19-5 onto the board. Omit the labels and put the figures in a different order. Ask students to match the terms (*waves, expanding wave fronts, photon particles,* and *rays*) to the drawings. Explain that each one of these figures is correct. Light behaves in all of these ways, not just one.
learning styles: visual, auditory

✔ CHECKING CONCEPTS

1. You cannot see individual _____ of light because they are very small.
2. Light travels in _____ lines.
3. A stream of photons makes up a _____ beam.
4. Light is a form of _____ energy.
5. A _____ of light shows the direction of a light beam.

💡 THINKING CRITICALLY

6. INFER: Turn on a lamp and hold your hand near the light bulb. Do you feel heat? What is the source of the heat?
7. EXPLAIN: Give two common examples to show that light travels in straight lines.

⚛ How Do They Know That?

PHOTONS AND THE THEORY OF LIGHT

Research for hundreds of years supports the idea that light is made up of particles of energy called photons.

In the late 1600s, Sir Isaac Newton studied how light acts as it meets objects in its path. Newton noticed that light could not travel around objects like other waves could. For example, sound can travel around a corner, but light cannot. He suggested that light was made up of tiny streams of energy particles.

In 1887, Heinrich Hertz found that some frequencies of light, such as violet, would cause metals to give off their electrons. When he used red light, no matter how strong, nothing happened. This experiment showed that the particles in violet light were more energetic than those in red light. This is called the photoelectric effect.

In 1900, Max Planck published a theory on electromagnetic radiation. Albert Einstein used this theory to help explain his theory on photons. He said that a photon's energy depends on the frequency of the light. This theory won Einstein the Nobel Prize.

The photoelectric effect has many everyday uses. Light meters in cameras, soundtracks in films, and automatic street lights all work because of the photoelectric effect. The photons in a light source make an electric current that controls these light-sensitive machines.

Thinking Critically Why do you think it is important to understand the nature of light?

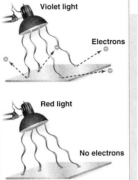

Violet light

Electrons

Red light

No electrons

▲ **Figure 19-6** Hertz's experiment

CHAPTER 19: Light **403**

Answers to questions

1️⃣ CLASSIFY: Light is a form of electromagnetic energy that is made up of streams of photons.

2️⃣ DESCRIBE: a stream of many photons

3️⃣ DESCRIBE: a straight line

3 Assess

✔ CHECKING CONCEPTS ANSWERS

1. photons
2. straight
3. light
4. electromagnetic
5. ray

💡 THINKING CRITICALLY ANSWERS

6. INFER: yes; the electrical energy in the lamp, which can be converted into both light and heat
7. EXPLAIN: Possible answer: a searchlight or headlights on a car

---

COOPERATIVE LEARNING

Illustrating Models of Light Have students work in groups of four. Ask each group member to choose a different model of light described in the lesson and draw a diagram that illustrates the model. Have each student use the diagram to explain the model to the other group members.
learning styles: visual, linguistic

• TEACHING RESOURCES •

💿 **Teacher's Resources CD-ROM**
Lesson Review: Chapter 19, p. 3
Enrichment: Chapter 19, p. 4
Spider Map: Study Tools, p. 9

4 Close

How Do They Know That?

PHOTONS AND THE THEORY OF LIGHT

Real-Life Connection The photoelectric effect is also used to generate electricity from sunlight. In this application, electricity is produced when light strikes a photovoltaic cell, or solar cell. Many handheld calculators, satellites, and emergency telephones along highways run on electricity from photovoltaic cells.

Thinking Critically Answer
Possible answer: Light is very useful to people. People should find out all they can in order to use it more effectively.

1 Introduce

✎ **STUDY HINT** Ask students to create a chart with two columns and three rows. Have students use the title of the lesson as the title for their charts. In the first column, they should write each of the section titles, one title per box. As they read, students can fill in the second column with pertinent facts relating to the section titles.

Linking Prior Knowledge Ask students whether light travels slower or faster than sound. (faster) Ask them for an example. (Possible answer: You see lightning before you hear the thunder it produces.) Then, ask them to recall the way in which sound travels (Lesson 18-2). Let students know that light also travels in waves, but that light waves and sound waves have some important differences.

2 Teach

Demonstration Using a piece of wire, make a rigid model of several wavelengths of a transverse wave. Use the model to demonstrate amplitude and wavelength. Move the model past a fixed point to illustrate frequency. **learning style: visual**

Discussion Draw Figure 19-7 on the board, omitting the labels. Add the labels as you discuss each of the terms in the text. Include in your discussion a comparison of light waves to sound waves, making sure that students understand how the waves are alike and how they are different. **learning styles: auditory, visual**

Answers to questions

▶ **CONTRAST:** Light wave are transverse, while sound waves are longitudinal. Unlike sound waves, light waves do not need a medium in which to travel.

▶ **DESCRIBE:** Sometimes they act as if they are made up of particles, and other times they act as if they are made of waves.

▶ **LIST:** speed, wavelength, frequency, and amplitude

19-3 How do light waves travel?

Objective

Describe how light travels as transverse waves.

Key Term

transverse (trans-VURS) **wave:** wave in which the particles of the medium move up and down at right angles to the direction of the wave motion

Light Waves Light is made up of streams of photons. However, light also behaves like a wave. Light is a type of electromagnetic wave. Electromagnetic waves are different from sound waves. Sound is a longitudinal wave. A sound wave needs a medium in which to travel. Sound cannot be heard in a vacuum, or empty space.

Light waves are different from sound waves in two ways. Light travels in transverse waves. In transverse waves, the particles move up and down at right angles to the direction of wave motions. Also, light waves do not need a medium in which to travel. Light can travel through a vacuum.

▶ **CONTRAST:** How do light waves differ from sound waves?

Photons and Light Waves Some experiments with light show that it is made up of photons. Other experiments show that light acts as a wave. Scientists have learned that some waves act as if they are made up of particles.

▶ **DESCRIBE:** How do light waves act?

Properties of Light Waves Like all waves, light waves have four properties. They are speed, wavelength, frequency, and amplitude.

- The speed of light is 300,000 km/s in a vacuum. Light and all other electromagnetic waves travel at this speed. The speed of light in a vacuum is the fastest possible speed.

- The wavelength of light is the distance from the crest or trough of one wave to the crest or trough of the next wave.

- The number of light waves that pass by a point each second is the frequency.

- The amplitude is the height of a wave. A bright light has a greater amplitude than a dim light does.

▶ **LIST:** What are the four properties of a light wave?

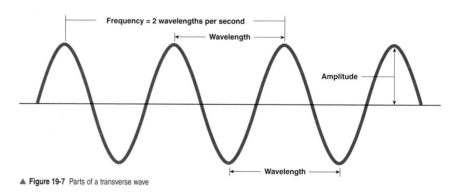

▲ **Figure 19-7** Parts of a transverse wave

404

Teaching Options

✓ CHECKING CONCEPTS

1. In a _____ wave, the particles of the medium move at right angles to the direction of the wave motion.

2. A light wave is a moving stream of _____.

3. The properties of light waves include speed, _____, frequency, and amplitude.

4. Light waves travel fastest in a _____.

5. Light waves do not need a _____ in which to travel.

THINKING CRITICALLY

6. CLASSIFY: Identify each of the following as a sound wave or a light wave.
   a. longitudinal wave
   b. does not travel through a vacuum
   c. waves seem to be made up of particles
   d. transverse waves
   e. can travel in a vacuum

7. RELATE: Light waves with very high frequencies are called ultraviolet light. Ultraviolet light cannot be seen by the human eye. How is ultraviolet light similar to ultrasonic sound?

INTERPRETING VISUALS

Look at Figure 19-8. Compare the two waves by discussing wavelength, frequency, amplitude, and speed.

Wave A

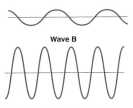

Wave B

▲ **Figure 19-8** Compare the waves.

Real-Life Science

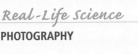

PHOTOGRAPHY

Photography is a popular activity that can teach you a lot about light. The word *photography* means "writing with light." To take a photograph, you need a camera, film, and a good source of light.

A camera has a lens and an opening for light to enter. This opening is called an aperture. When you take a picture, the aperture is open for only a short period of time. The light goes through the lens and onto the film. Film is very sensitive to light. Too much light will cause the photograph to be too bright, or overexposed. If there is not enough light, the photograph will be too dark, or underexposed. This is because the chemical on the film changes whenever a photon hits it.

Many schools have amateur photography clubs. Joining a photography club is a good way to learn more about taking photographs.

Thinking Critically How is film underexposed or overexposed?

▲ **Figure 19-9** The varied light made parts of this photo brighter and darker.

---

3 Assess

✓ CHECKING CONCEPTS ANSWERS

1. transverse
2. photons
3. wavelength
4. vacuum
5. medium

THINKING CRITICALLY ANSWERS

6. **CLASSIFY:** sound wave: a, b; light wave: c, d, e

7. **RELATE:** Ultrasonic sound cannot be heard by the human ear, and ultraviolet light cannot be seen by the human eye.

INTERPRETING VISUALS ANSWER

Wave A has a longer wavelength, lower frequency, smaller amplitude, fewer waves, and slower speed than **Wave B.**

✎ **WRITING HINT** As students respond to the Interpreting Visuals question, remind them that they can use words that signal contrasts. Examples: The wavelength of Wave A is short, *while* the wavelength of Wave B is long. The frequency of Wave B is relatively high *compared* to the frequency of Wave A. **learning style: linguistic**

4 Close

Real-Life Science
PHOTOGRAPHY

Technology Connection To control the amount of light that travels through the aperture, cameras have a set of overlapping metal plates. These plates open or close to expand or reduce the diameter of the lens. The shutter speed determines the length of exposure to light. Many cameras have two metal plates between the lens and film. Before someone takes a picture, the first plate is closed. When the picture is taken, this plate slides open. Then, when the exposure time is complete, the second plate slides across to cover the lens. The ideal amount of time for exposing the film to light depends on the speed of the film.

Thinking Critically Answer
Film is underexposed if it is exposed to light for too short a time period. It is overexposed if the film is exposed to light for too long.

ONGOING ASSESSMENT

Making Venn Diagrams Students can make Venn diagrams comparing and contrasting sound waves and light waves. They might review Chapter 17 to find out properties that all waves have in common and Chapter 18 to find out the properties of sound waves.

• TEACHING RESOURCES •

◉ **Teacher's Resources CD-ROM**
Lesson Review: Chapter 19, p. 5
Enrichment: Chapter 19, p. 6
Venn Diagram: Study Tools, p. 10
Features of a Transverse Wave: Visuals, p. 11

19-4 *(pp. 406–407)*

1 Introduce

✏️ **STUDY HINT** Have students read the Key Terms and their definitions. Then, have them brainstorm examples of each Key Term.

Linking Prior Knowledge Ask students to picture a full Moon in a dark night sky. Ask them to describe how the Moon looks. Students may say that the Moon glows. Ask students if they think that the Moon is a glowing object. Guide students to realize that the Moon itself does not give off light. Elicit students' ideas about the source of the light that shines from the Moon.

2 Teach

Discussion Discuss the difference between a luminous object and an illuminated object. Use the Sun, a classroom light, or other light source as an example of a luminous object. Point out that any object that is visible and is not luminous must be illuminated. **learning styles: auditory, visual**

Demonstration Differentiate between opaque, translucent, and transparent materials. Show students examples of objects that are opaque, objects that are translucent, and objects that are transparent. Point out to students that objects that are opaque create shadows when light falls on them. Translucent objects allow some light to pass through but you still cannot see anything through them. **learning styles: visual, auditory**

Answers to questions

▶1 **DEFINE:** an object that gives off its own light

▶2 **IDENTIFY:** an illuminated object

▶3 **NAME:** opaque, transparent, or translucent

📖 **READING STRATEGY** Remind students that the main idea of a piece of writing is the most important idea. Supporting details tell more about the main idea. Encourage students to identify the main idea of each of the sections on the page.

T406 UNIT 6: Waves, Sound, and Light

19-4 What are sources of light?

Objectives
Differentiate between luminous and illuminated objects. Describe what happens when light strikes different materials.

Key Terms
luminous (LOO-muh-nuhs) **object:** object that gives off its own light

illuminated (ih-LOO-muh-nayt-uhd) **object:** object that reflects light

opaque (oh-PAYK): material that blocks light

transparent (trans-PEHR-uhnt): material that transmits light easily

translucent (trans-LOO-suhnt): material that transmits some light

Luminous Objects A flashlight, a candle, and a light bulb are sources of light. Objects that give off their own light are called **luminous objects**. The Sun is a luminous object. It is the source of light for Earth and other planets in the solar system.

▶1 **DEFINE:** What is a luminous object?

Illuminated Objects What happens when the light from a luminous object strikes another object? The light may be reflected. An object that reflects light is called an **illuminated object**.

Opaque   Translucent   Transparent

406

The Moon is an illuminated object. The Moon is not the source of its own light. Sunlight strikes the Moon and is reflected from its surface. You see the Moon by reflected sunlight.

▶2 **IDENTIFY:** What is an object that reflects light called?

Opaque, Transparent, and Translucent Materials When light shines on a material, one of three things can happen. The material may block the light and form a shadow. Material that blocks light is called an **opaque** object. When you place your hand in front of a light source, you will see a shadow. Your hand is opaque.

A material may allow light to pass through unchanged. This kind of material is called **transparent**. A sheet of clear glass allows light and images to pass through. The glass is transparent.

A material may allow some of the light to pass through. This kind of material is called **translucent**. A stained glass window will allow some light to pass through, but no details of images are visible. The stained glass is translucent.

▶3 **NAME:** What are three types of materials that affect light differently?

◀ **Figure 19-10** You cannot see the stem of the flower through the opaque vase. A blurry view of the stem is seen through the translucent vase. The entire stem can clearly be seen through the transparent vase.

Teaching Options

COOPERATIVE LEARNING

Illustrating Luminous and Illuminated Objects Students can work in groups to create collages. Assign each group one word to illustrate: *luminous, illuminated, opaque, transparent,* or *translucent*. Students in each group can cut out magazine pictures of items that correspond to their word and use the pictures to create a collage. Allow time for students to share their work with the class. **learning styles: visual, tactile**

ONGOING ASSESSMENT

Defining and Providing Examples of Key Terms Write the words *luminous* and *illuminated* on the board. Ask volunteers to define the terms in their own words. Then, name several objects, one object at a time. Ask students to give a thumbs up sign if the named object is *luminous*. Then, write the words *opaque, transparent,* and *translucent* on the board. Have volunteers define the terms and give examples for each category. **learning style: linguistic**

1. When you shine a flashlight on objects in a dark room, the objects that you see are _____ objects.
2. An object that blocks light and casts a shadow is an _____ object.
3. The Moon is an _____ object.
4. A sheet of clear glass is _____ because it allows light to pass through easily.
5. A sheet of stained glass is _____ because it only allows some light to pass through.
6. An illuminated object _____ the light from another source.
7. The Sun is a _____ because it gives off light.

THINKING CRITICALLY

8. **INFER:** You cannot see the Sun on a cloudy day even though sunlight can still illuminate objects. Are clouds transparent or translucent?
9. **CLASSIFY:** Which of the following objects are luminous and which are illuminated?
   a. the flame of a candle
   b. Earth
   c. a star
   d. a campfire
   e. a sheet of paper

DESIGNING AN EXPERIMENT

Design an experiment to solve the following problem. Include a hypothesis, variables, a procedure, and a type of data to study.

PROBLEM: Do transparent objects allow more light to pass through than translucent objects do?

Integrating Earth Science

Topic: lunar eclipse

ASTRONOMICAL SHADOWS

Opaque objects cast shadows by blocking the light shining on them. Your body is opaque. It blocks the Sun's light. You have probably seen your shadow on a sunny afternoon.

During a lunar eclipse, Earth blocks the light from the Sun. The Moon passes through Earth's shadow. Like most shadows, Earth's shadow consists of both an umbra (UM-bruh) and a penumbra (pih-NUM-bruh). The umbra is a sharp, black inner part of a shadow. The penumbra is the gray, outer part of the shadow.

When a point source shines directly on an object, the shadow will only have an umbra. A spotlight is an example of a point source of light. Most light comes from sources of light that spread out. A fluorescent light is an example of a source of light that spreads out.

Thinking Critically Why do most shadows have penumbras?

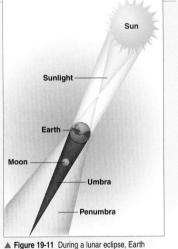

▲ **Figure 19-11** During a lunar eclipse, Earth hides the Moon from the Sun.

ESL/ELL STRATEGY

Drawing Opaque, Transparent, and Translucent Objects English-language learners may understand how light falls on objects better if they draw examples of opaque, transparent, and translucent objects. Make sure that students label each drawing correctly.

• TEACHING RESOURCES •

Teacher's Resources CD-ROM
Lesson Review: Chapter 19, p. 7
Enrichment: Chapter 19, p. 8
Designing an Experiment: Study Tools, p. 14
Designing an Experiment Rubric: Teaching Tools, p. 7

3 Assess

✓ CHECKING CONCEPTS ANSWERS

1. illuminated
2. opaque
3. illuminated
4. transparent
5. translucent
6. reflects
7. luminous object

THINKING CRITICALLY ANSWERS

8. **INFER:** translucent
9. **CLASSIFY:** luminous objects: a, c, d; illuminated objects: b, e

DESIGNING AN EXPERIMENT

Use the Designing an Experiment Rubric on the Teacher's Resources CD-ROM to assess students' experiments. Fill in the rubric with the additional information below. For this assignment, students should have:

• in forming the hypothesis, mentioned characteristics of transparent and translucent objects.

• realized, in the procedure, that they will need transparent objects, translucent objects, a source of light, and a way to measure or observe the amount of light that passes through each object.

4 Close

Integrating Earth Science

TOPIC: lunar eclipse

ASTRONOMICAL SHADOWS

Earth-Science Connection Lunar eclipses are not the only kinds of eclipses visible from Earth. In a solar eclipse, the new Moon passes directly between the Sun and Earth. As the shadow of the Moon crosses Earth, daytime turns to darkness for a few moments and the Sun's corona (the ring of gases surrounding the Sun) is visible as the Moon totally covers the bright Sun.

Safety Tip Remind students to never look directly at a solar eclipse.

Thinking Critically Answer
Most shadows have penumbras because the light causing the shadows comes from a source that spreads the light rays out.

1 Introduce

STUDY HINT As students read this lesson, have them describe the cause-and-effect relationship between sunlight and green plants. Students can also use the Cause-and-Effect Diagram found on the Teacher's Resources CD-ROM.

Linking Prior Knowledge Ask students to describe what would happen if they took a green plant and put the plant in a dark closet. Ask why plants need sunlight. You might review the composition of organic compounds (Lesson 4-7) and the description of a chemical reaction (Lesson 8-1).

2 Teach

Demonstration One week before beginning this lesson, place a plant in the classroom with its leaves facing away from the Sun. Ask students to observe the plant for the next week. You might have students draw the plant as it appears each day. Ask students to describe how the leaves responded to sunlight. (The leaves turned toward the Sun.)
learning styles: visual, linguistic

Discussion Remind students of the importance of photosynthesis. Photosynthesis is the food-making process in plants. The leaves of plants take in carbon dioxide from air. The roots of plants take in water from soil. The chemical substance chlorophyll, found in the cells of leaves, helps plants use energy from sunlight to make sugar. The process of photosynthesis produces sugar and oxygen. This process is also a source of food for the organisms that eat plants and the organisms that, in turn, eat the plant-eating organisms. In fact, photosynthesis is the main source of oxygen on Earth. **learning style: auditory**

Answers to questions

▶ **INFER:** They use the energy to make their own food.

▶ **IDENTIFY:** photosynthesis

▶ **PREDICT:** blue

19-5 What is photosynthesis?

Objective
Explain how plants use the energy of the Sun to make food.

Key Terms
photosynthesis (foht-oh-SIHN-thuh-sihs): process by which plants use energy from the Sun to make food

chlorophyll (KLAWR-uh-fihl): substance in plants that absorbs the Sun's light and gives plants their green color

chloroplast: part of green plant cells where photosynthesis takes place

Light and Energy Any form of energy can be converted to another form of energy. Light energy can be changed into heat energy, electrical energy, chemical energy, or other forms of energy. Plants convert the electromagnetic energy of sunlight into the chemical energy stored in food. The plants use the chemical energy to make their own food.

▶ **INFER:** Why do plants need sunlight?

Photosynthesis The process by which a plant uses sunlight to make food is called **photosynthesis**. The leaves of a plant absorb the most sunlight. The flat part of a leaf always tries to face the Sun. As the Sun moves across the sky, the leaves respond by moving to continue facing the Sun. The food that plants make is sugar. Plants can change this sugar into starch, fats, and proteins. These nutrients are stored in the plants as chemical energy. This energy can be used at a later time.

Photosynthesis is a chemical process. During this process, water, carbon dioxide and energy from the Sun are used to make the sugar. Roots absorb the needed water from the soil. Veins carry the water up the stem and into the leaves. Carbon dioxide enters the plant through openings called stomata. Sunlight supplies the energy the plant needs to make the sugar. During photosynthesis, oxygen is given off as a by-product. The formula for photosynthesis is shown below.

$$6CO_2 + 6H_2O \xrightarrow[\text{Sunlight}]{\text{Energy}} C_6H_{12}O_6 + 6O_2$$

Carbon dioxide, Water, Sugar, Oxygen

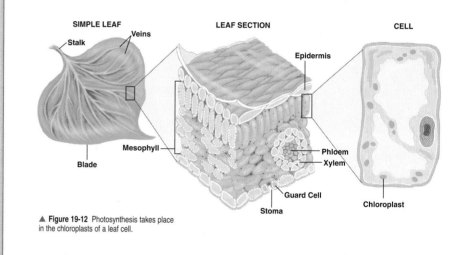

SIMPLE LEAF — Stalk, Veins, Blade, Mesophyll
LEAF SECTION — Epidermis, Phloem, Xylem, Guard Cell, Stoma
CELL — Chloroplast

▲ **Figure 19-12** Photosynthesis takes place in the chloroplasts of a leaf cell.

Teaching Options

◈ INTEGRATING EARTH SCIENCE

Oxygen in the Atmosphere Oxygen makes up about 21 percent of Earth's atmosphere. Most of the oxygen in Earth's atmosphere comes from photosynthetic organisms. Earth's atmosphere, however, did not always contain this important gas. It is believed that about 4 billion years ago, Earth's atmosphere contained mainly oxidants such as carbon dioxide and nitrogen. One of the earliest life forms, cyanobacteria, appeared about a billion years later. These types of organisms were the first photosynthetic organisms to put oxygen into the air. In time, green plants and other photosynthetic organisms evolved to add more and more oxygen into the air. The amount of oxygen in the atmosphere began to level off around 600 million years ago and has stayed fairly constant since. Have interested students use the Internet or other resources to research what other types of organisms put oxygen into the air (Possible organisms: lichens, diatoms, euglenoids, red algae, and brown algae). Have students share the results of their research with the class.

▲ Figure 19-13 A rain-forest ecosystem

Most organisms depend on plants and photosynthesis for survival. When animals eat plants, they take in food that has stored chemical energy. Animals that only eat other animals still depend on plants because the animals that they eat, eat plants. Plants are an important part of most ecosystems, such as the rain forest shown in Figure 19-13.

2▶ IDENTIFY: What is the process by which plants use sunlight to make food?

Chlorophyll The substance in a leaf that absorbs sunlight is called **chlorophyll**. Chlorophyll is a chemical pigment, or coloring, needed for photosynthesis. It absorbs all the colors of the visible spectrum except green, which it reflects. As a result, leaves look green. Without chlorophyll, photosynthesis could not take place. Wherever there is chlorophyll, photosynthesis can occur.

The chlorophyll is located inside special parts of plant cells. The cell parts that contain chlorophyll are called **chloroplasts**. The cells in the upper layer of the leaf contain many chloroplasts. Therefore, most photosynthesis takes place in this layer.

3▶ PREDICT: What color would leaves appear if chlorophyll reflected only blue light?

✔ CHECKING CONCEPTS

1. In photosynthesis, electromagnetic energy is turned into _____ energy.
2. The food that a plant makes is _____.
3. Food is a form of _____ energy.
4. The substance that gives plants their green color is _____.
5. A plant's _____ always face the Sun in order to get the most amount of sunlight.
6. Chlorophyll absorbs all the Sun's light except _____ light.

THINKING CRITICALLY

7. INFER: Plants always make more food than they need. The extra food is stored in the plant. What happens when an animal eats a plant?
8. HYPOTHESIZE: What happens to the energy that plants do not store as food?

Web InfoSearch

Photoelectric Cells A process that can be compared to photosynthesis is used to produce electricity from solar energy. Sunlight is absorbed by photoelectric cells. Photoelectric cells convert sunlight into electrical energy. The electrical energy is stored in batteries. This process is similar to what a plant does, except that the plant stores the energy as food. Many photoelectric cells are put together to make solar panels. Solar panels are used on homes, office buildings, and satellites.

SEARCH: Use the Internet to write a report on how a solar panel works. Start your search at www.conceptsandchallenges.com. Some key search words are **solar panels, photoelectric cells, photovoltaic panels,** and **solar power.**

📖 READING STRATEGY Students sometimes have trouble making connections as they read. Remind students that they should think back to what they have read before and to their own prior knowledge as they read to make connections. Draw students' attention to the chemical equation. Ask students what they notice about the products. (One of the products is an organic compound.) Ask what they remember about organic compounds. (They contain carbon.)

Reinforcement Write the chemical equation for photosynthesis on the board. Point out the part of the process that corresponds to each part of the equation. The products are the substances that a plant uses, along with the Sun's energy, to make the sugar that it uses for food. Oxygen is given off as a waste product.
learning styles: auditory, visual

3 Assess

✔ CHECKING CONCEPTS ANSWERS

1. chemical
2. sugar
3. chemical
4. chlorophyll
5. leaves
6. green

THINKING CRITICALLY ANSWERS

7. INFER: The stored energy in the plant is used by the animal.
8. HYPOTHESIZE: Possible answer: The plants use the energy to grow and reproduce.

4 Close

Web InfoSearch

Photoelectric Cells Have students use the Internet to write a report on how a solar panel works. Some key search words are **solar panels, photoelectric cells, photovoltaic panels,** and **solar power.** Students should begin their search at www.conceptsandchallenges.com.

EXTENDING THE LESSON

Observing Plant Cells Have students observe prepared slides of plant cells under a microscope. Tell students to sketch what they see. Have students identify the chloroplasts.
learning styles: visual, auditory

ESL/ELL STRATEGY

Putting Together Photosynthesis Inform students that *photo-* means "light" and *synthesis* means "a combining of parts into a whole." Ask students to define the word *photosynthesis.*

• TEACHING RESOURCES •

◉ Teacher's Resources CD-ROM
Lesson Review: Chapter 19, p. 9
Cause-and-Effect Diagram: Study Tools, p. 3

19-6 (pp. 410–411)

1 Introduce

✏️ **STUDY HINT** Have students write the lesson objective in their notebooks. As they read this lesson, they should write the information that meets the objective.

Linking Prior Knowledge Ask students to picture a side-mounted rearview mirror on a car. Remind students that many of these mirrors have "Objects in mirror are closer than they appear" printed on them. Ask students if they can explain why this phenomenon occurs. (The curve of the mirror affects the reflection.)

2 Teach

Demonstration Show students how light is refracted as it passes into water. Fill a beaker with water. Dim the lights. From above the water at an angle less than 90°, shine a ray of light from a strong penlight into the water. Students will see that the ray of light is bent. Then, stand a ruler in a vertical position in the water to serve as the normal. Shine the penlight into the water again. Students will observe that as light passes from air to water, it is bent toward the normal. **learning style: visual**

Discussion Remind students that when light moves from one medium to another, it is bent, or refracted. Bring a variety of concave, convex, double convex, double concave, and convex-concave lenses to class for students to observe. They should note the curves of each type of lens and should see how light is refracted differently by each type of lens.
learning styles: tactile, visual

Answers to questions

▶ **PREDICT:** It is refracted.

▶ **HYPOTHESIZE:** Light needs to pass through the lens.

▶ **DEFINE:** an image that can be projected onto a screen

▶ **IDENTIFY:** the distance between the lens and the focal point

▶ **DESCRIBE:** They spread apart.

19-6 How do lenses refract light?

Objective
Compare and contrast how light rays are bent by a concave lens and a convex lens.

Key Terms
lens: transparent material that bends light
real image: image that can be projected onto a screen
virtual image: image that cannot be projected onto a screen
convex lens: lens that curves outward
concave lens: lens that curves inward

Refraction of Light Light rays travel in straight lines. When light moves from one medium into another at an angle other than 90°, the direction of the light changes. Suppose a beam of light passes from air into another material, such as glass. The path of light will be bent, or refracted. Light rays passing through the lenses in Figures 19-14 and 19-15 are refracted.

▶ **PREDICT:** What happens to a beam of light when it passes from air into water?

Lenses A **lens** is a transparent material that bends, or refracts, light. All lenses have either one or two curved surfaces. There are two main types of lenses. They are convex and concave lenses.

▶ **HYPOTHESIZE:** Why is a lens made of a transparent material?

Real and Virtual Images A lens can form a real image. A **real image** is an image that can be projected onto a screen.

The image you see when you look into a mirror is a **virtual image**. It is always right-side up. This image is called virtual because the image does not really exist, even though you see it. A virtual image cannot be projected onto a screen.

▶ **DEFINE:** What is a real image?

Convex Lenses A **convex lens** curves outward. Figure 19-14 shows a convex lens. Light that passes through a convex lens is bent inward. When a convex lens refracts light, the light rays are brought together at a point called the focal point. The distance between the lens and the focal point is the focal length.

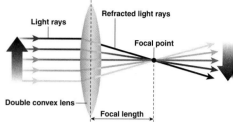

▲ **Figure 19-14** A double convex lens forms a real image.

Light is refracted as it enters the lens. It also is refracted as it leaves the lens. The amount of refraction depends on how curved the lens is.

▶ **IDENTIFY:** What is the focal length of a convex lens?

Concave Lenses A **concave lens** curves inward. Light that passes through a concave lens is bent away from the lens. The light rays are spread apart. Figure 19-15 shows a concave lens.

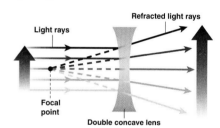

▲ **Figure 19-15** A double concave lens forms a virtual image.

▶ **DESCRIBE:** What happens to light rays as they pass through a concave lens?

410

Teaching Options

❗ FAST FACTS *Making the Universe Seem Closer*

A telescope is a device that makes objects that are far away appear to be close. Telescopes come in all shapes and sizes. A telescope that is only 15 cm long allows a person to read the writing on a dime that is 55 m away. The basic principle of a telescope is to gather enough light to form a bright image inside the telescope and then magnify that image. In a simple design, a telescope has an objective lens or primary mirror that collects light from a distant object and brings that light to a focal point. The eyepiece lens takes the bright light from the focal point and magnifies the light so that the viewer can see the image.

✓ CHECKING CONCEPTS

1. A _____ image cannot be projected onto a screen.

2. A _____ lens curves inward.

3. A _____ can be projected onto a screen.

4. A _____ lens curves outward.

5. The _____ is where rays of light are brought together by a convex lens.

6. The _____ is the distance from the focal point to the lens.

7. A _____ image will be right-side up.

💡 THINKING CRITICALLY

8. COMPARE: Explain the difference between a real image and a virtual image.

9. ANALYZE: How are light rays brought together after passing through a convex lens?

Web InfoSearch

Telescopes A telescope is a device that allows you to see objects at great distances. From the giant Hubble Space Telescope, which orbits Earth, to the personal telescope used at home or at school, telescopes come in many sizes and strengths.

SEARCH: Use the Internet to find out more about telescopes. How do they work? Why do some telescopes show an upside-down image? Start your search at www.conceptsandchallenges.com. Some key search words are **refractor telescopes**, **how telescopes work**, and **telescopes' refractor lenses**.

⚛ People in Science

ASTRONOMERS

Astronomy is the study of stars, planets, and the solar system. Astronomers are the scientists who study how these objects originated, what they are made of, and how and where they move. Astronomers may choose from many different jobs. Some study the formation of galaxies, solar astronomy, the origins of stars, or planetary science. Some astronomers design programs to observe the universe; others observe just our solar system.

Astronomers have a very hard job because they cannot see, touch, smell, weigh, or perform experiments on the objects they are studying. Instead they need to observe the light given off or reflected by objects. The motion of objects is also measured. In order to become an astronomer, a solid background in physics is necessary. You also need to know how to work a computer. Good math, observation, reasoning, and communication skills are necessary.

Astronomers do not spend all day looking through a telescope. They study the data recorded by a telescope and sent to a computer. Then, they have to put that information into readable form. Astronomers also give lectures, teach, and write articles.

Thinking Critically Why is an astronomer's job difficult?

▲ **Figure 19-16** This is the telescope and data recording area of the Lowell Telescope at Perth Observatory in Australia.

---

3 Assess

✓ CHECKING CONCEPTS ANSWERS

1. virtual
2. concave
3. real image
4. convex
5. focal point
6. focal length
7. virtual

💡 THINKING CRITICALLY ANSWERS

8. COMPARE: A real image is upside down and can be projected onto a screen, while a virtual image is always right side up and cannot be projected onto a screen.

9. ANALYZE: Light rays are bent inward toward the focal point.

4 Close

Web InfoSearch

Telescopes Have students use the Internet to find out how telescopes work. Some key search words are **refractor telescopes** and **how telescopes work.** Students should begin their search at www.conceptsandchallenges.com.

People in Science

ASTRONOMERS

Technology Connection Modern astronomers realized that ground-based telescopes were limiting clear views of the universe because Earth's atmosphere blocked or distorted some of the light given off or reflected by distant objects. An astrophysicist came up with the idea of putting a telescope in space. The Hubble Space Telescope, named for the American astronomer Edwin Hubble, took 8 years to build. The telescope went into orbit in 1990. Astronomers soon discovered that there was a problem with Hubble's mirror, and they could not focus the telescope. In 1993, space shuttle astronauts fixed the problem, and Hubble began sending clear images back to Earth.

Thinking Critically Answers
Possible answer: They need to possess knowledge of many different fields.

RETEACH

Understanding Diagrams If students are still having difficulty understanding how convex and concave lenses refract light, draw attention to Figures 19-14 and 19-15. Show that light rays enter both types of lenses, but only a convex lens brings rays together to a focal point. Light rays spread apart after entering a concave lens. Encourage students to trace the paths of the light rays with their fingers. **learning styles: visual, tactile**

• TEACHING RESOURCES •

💿 **Teacher's Resources CD-ROM**
Lesson Review: Chapter 19, p. 10

Laboratory Manual
Lab. Challenge: How is light refracted? pp. 93–96

📼 **Laboratory Video**
Segment 21: What Kinds of Images Are Formed by Lenses?

19-7 (pp. 412–413)

1 Introduce

🔍 INVESTIGATE

TIME: 5–10 minutes

PURPOSE: Students will observe how the eye reacts to light and darkness.

MATERIALS: penlight, paper, pencil

PROCEDURE: Before students begin the experiment, demonstrate with a volunteer. Show students that they do not need to shine the light for a long time in order to observe results.

learning styles: visual, tactile

THINK ABOUT IT: In bright light, the iris expands and the pupil gets smaller.

📝 **STUDY HINT** Have students write the title of each section in their notebooks. As students read each section, they should write the topic sentence under the correct title.

Linking Prior Knowledge Students may already have some idea of how the eye works. Encourage them to list what they know as you write their ideas on the board.

2 Teach

Demonstration If possible, bring in a three-dimensional model of the eye. Have students locate the parts of the eye shown in Figure 19-17. As students point out a part of the eye, they can discuss its function. **learning styles: tactile, visual**

📖 **READING STRATEGY** Because the process of using the eye to see is described in steps in the text, some students may benefit from creating flowcharts as they read to show the process.

Answers to questions

▶ **RELATE:** The eye is the organ of the body that is used for sight.

▶ **NAME:** cornea, pupil, iris, lens, and retina

▶ **RELATE:** The lens forms an image on the retina. The retina converts the image into electrical impulses that travel along the optic nerve to the brain.

19-7 How do you see?

INVESTIGATE

How Does the Eye React to Light?
HANDS-ON ACTIVITY

STEP 4

1. Work with a partner. You need a penlight, a sheet of paper, and a pencil.
2. Stand face-to-face.
3. Darken the room. Record what you observe about each other's eyes.
4. Now, shine the penlight into the eye of your partner. Record what you observe in your partner's eye.
5. Alternate roles so you each get a chance to observe what happens.

THINK ABOUT IT: In dim light, your iris contracts and the pupil gets bigger. What happens in bright light?

Objectives
Identify the parts of the eye. Describe how the eye senses light.

Key Terms
eye: sense organ that detects light
sight: one of the five human senses
image: picture formed by the eye

Observing Light You see an object when light from the object enters your eye. The **eye** is the human organ that detects light. **Sight** is one of the five human senses.

▶ **RELATE:** How is the eye related to sight?

Parts of the Eye The eye is made up of parts that work together to help you see. Look at Figure 19-17. The front of the eye is covered with a clear layer called the **cornea**. The cornea is a protective layer that keeps dirt and bacteria from damaging the inner eye. The cornea covers the **pupil**. The pupil is the opening through which light enters the eye.

The amount of light that enters the eye is controlled by the **iris**. The iris is a muscle that contracts or expands, depending on the amount of light available. When there is too much light, the iris contracts. When there is not enough light, the iris expands.

After light enters the eye, it is focused by the **lens**. It is the clear part behind the pupil. The lens can change shape so that the eye can concentrate on an object. The lens works like the autofocus on a camera.

▶ **NAME:** What are the parts of the eye involved in sight?

The Retina Light entering the eye is focused by the lens onto the retina. The lens, a convex lens, focuses light on the retina, producing an image. An **image** is a picture that is formed by the eye.

The retina converts the image into electrical impulses. The impulses travel along the optic nerve to the brain. The brain interprets the electrical impulses as a right-side-up image.

▶ **RELATE:** How do the lens and the retina work together?

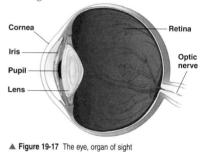

▲ **Figure 19-17** The eye, organ of sight

412

Teaching Options

RETEACH

Identifying the Parts of the Eye Draw Figure 19-17 on the board or on a transparency, leaving out the labels. Ask volunteers to label the various parts that you describe. You might instruct a volunteer to name and label the part of the eye that expands and contracts to adjust the light. (pupil) Continue until all the parts have been named and described. **learning styles: visual, linguistic**

COOPERATIVE LEARNING

Matching Eye Parts With Functions Have students work in groups to make cards for a memory game. On index cards, they can write each of the parts of the eye, one part per card. On another set of cards, they can write what those parts do, one function per card. Students should shuffle the cards and lay them facedown. They can then use the cards to play Concentration. Students must match the parts of the eyes to their functions. **learning styles: linguistic, visual**

1. Electrical impulses travel along the _____ to the brain.

2. The _____ is the opening that lets light into the eye.

3. The _____ controls the amount of light that can enter the eye.

4. The _____ is a clear protective layer over the eye.

5. The eye is a sense organ that detects _____.

6. An image formed on the _____ is upside down.

THINKING CRITICALLY

7. INFER: What energy changes take place when you see an image?

8. SYNTHESIZE: Suppose you walk into a dark room after being out in bright sunlight.

Several minutes pass before you can see objects in the room clearly. What happened to your eyes during that time?

INTERPRETING VISUALS

Use Figure 19-18 to answer the following questions.

9. What type of corrective lens is used to correct nearsightedness?

10. What type of corrective lens is used to correct farsightedness?

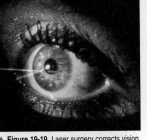

Nearsightedness (eyeball too long)

Farsightedness (eyeball too short)

▲ **Figure 19-18** Identify the lenses.

Science and Technology

LASIK EYE SURGERY

Laser is an acronym for light amplification by the stimulated emission of radiation. Lasik (LAY-sik) is an acronym for laser in situ keratomileusis. Lasik eye surgery corrects some vision problems using lasers.

Lasik has been practiced in the United States since 1996. It was invented in Colombia by Drs. Virgilio Galvis and Luis Ruiz. The laser used and approved in the United States is called the VISX. It can correct nearsightedness and some other eye problems. During lasik eye surgery, a flap of the cornea is cut and folded over. A laser beam then takes away some of the tissue from the inside of the cornea. A metal ring is used with an infrared tracking device to make sure that the laser points to the right spot. The laser reshapes that part of the cornea. Then, the flap is put back.

There are benefits if you can have the surgery. It is same-day surgery. You have it done in the doctor's office and can leave after a short stay. However, not everyone with poor vision can be helped by this surgery. Also, like any surgery, lasik surgery does have some risk involved, such as infection. It is very important to seek medical advice before allowing any surgery to be done.

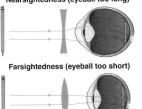

▲ **Figure 19-19** Laser surgery corrects vision by reshaping the cornea.

Thinking Critically Why do you think recovery from lasik surgery is so quick?

CHAPTER 19: Light **413**

---

3 Assess

✓ CHECKING CONCEPTS ANSWERS

1. optic nerve
2. pupil
3. iris
4. cornea
5. light
6. retina

THINKING CRITICALLY ANSWERS

7. INFER: Light is converted to electrical energy.

8. SYNTHESIZE: The iris contracts and the pupil expands to let more light into your eye.

INTERPRETING VISUALS ANSWERS

9. concave
10. convex

4 Close

Science and Technology

LASIK EYE SURGERY

Technology Connection Inform students that lasik eye surgery is most successful when used to correct myopia, or nearsightedness. In nearsightedness, the light from distant objects gets focused in front of the retina rather than on the retina. The eyeball may be too long. A person with myopia can see close-up objects well, but faraway objects are blurry. In lasik eye surgery, the cornea can easily be shortened or flattened out to help the eye focus images on the retina.

Discussion Share with students that lasik eye surgery has potential side effects, which include undercorrection (not removing enough tissue), overcorrection (removing too much tissue), wrinkling of the cornea, halos around lights, blurred vision, and increased sensitivity to light. Ask students why people might still want to have lasik eye surgery given the potential side effects and who might benefit from such a procedure.

Thinking Critically Answer
Possible response: The cornea is quick to heal. Because the flap is closed, the area that has been reshaped is protected from things that might contaminate or hurt the eye.

MORE ON THE WEB

Night Vision Have students visit www.conceptsand challenges.com to learn how night vision technology works.

ONGOING ASSESSMENT

Giving Clues to Identify Eye Parts
Give clues and ask students to identify the parts of the eyes described by your clues. If time allows, give students a term related to the eye and ask them to make clues of their own.

• TEACHING RESOURCES •

Teacher's Resources CD-ROM
Lesson Review: Chapter 19, p. 11
Flowchart: Study Tools, p. 6
The Ear/The Eye: Visuals, p. 12

Lab Activity

(pp. 414–415)

1 Prepare the Lab

Comparing Convex and Concave Lenses

SET-UP TIME: ⏲ **LAB TIME:** ⏰

BACKGROUND: Light rays travel in straight lines. When light moves from one medium into another at an angle other than 90°, the direction of the light changes. When light passes through a lens that is curved, the path of light will be bent, or refracted. A convex lens forms a real image that can be projected onto a screen. A concave lens forms a virtual image that is projected right side up and cannot be projected onto a screen.

PURPOSE: Students will use concave and convex lenses to create images. They will compare and contrast those images.

ALTERNATIVE MATERIALS: Students can make their screens by taping the white paper onto the wall rather than on a book.

SCIENCE SKILLS: Students will investigate and observe how each type of lens affects the image that is formed.

ADVANCE PLANNING: Obtain the materials needed before class. You might cut out the shape shown in Figure 19-20 for students beforehand.

2 Guide the Lab

PROCEDURE: Divide students into pairs or small groups. Lead them through the steps so that you can model the procedure. Provide students with a copy of the Lab Activity Report found on the Teacher's Resources CD-ROM for students to record their observations and conclusions.

LAB ACTIVITY
Comparing Convex and Concave Lenses

Materials
Convex lens (10-cm focal length),
Concave lens (10-cm focal length),
Flashlight,
Metric ruler,
Dark construction paper or cardboard,
1 sheet of white paper,
Notebook paper,
Tape, scissors, pencil
Hardcover book

▲ **STEP 3** Hold the lens over your name.

▲ **STEP 5** Set up a projection screen.

BACKGROUND

A lens is an object that bends, or refracts, light. When light passes through a lens, an image is created. Images can be real or virtual. A real image will be inverted, or upside down. A virtual image will be right-side up. Real images can be projected; virtual ones cannot. There are two types of lenses, convex and concave. Convex lenses curve outward in the center. Concave lenses curve inward in the center.

PURPOSE

In this activity, you will compare the images formed by convex and concave lenses.

PROCEDURE

1. Copy the chart shown in Figure 19-20 onto a sheet of paper.

2. Write your name on a sheet of notebook paper. Write it as you normally write it—not too big and not too small.

3. Hold the convex lens over your name and look through it. Slowly lift the lens toward your eye. Observe your name through the lens. You may have to move the lens back and forth to focus the image of your name. Record your observations on your chart.

4. Repeat Step 3 using the concave lens.

5. Create a "projection screen" as shown in the Step 5 photo. Tape a sheet of white paper onto a large hardcover book. Then, stand the book upright so that the "screen" is at one end of your desk or table.

6. Now, make a "projector." Lay the construction paper flat on a table. Place the head of the flashlight onto the paper and trace it to make a circle. Cut out the circle. Fold the circle in half. In the center, draw

414

Teaching Options

⚠ FAST FACTS *What Is a Fresnel Lens?*

Sometimes there is a thin piece of plastic on the back window of a van or recreational vehicle that magnifies objects for the driver. This thin piece of plastic, which does the job of a magnifying glass, is called a fresnel lens. It is flat on one side and ridged on the other. In the 1800s, such lenses focused the beam of lighthouse lamps. A fresnel lens works something like this: If a magnifying glass could be sliced into hundreds of rings, each smaller than the next, and the rings were made flat on one side and stacked, the rings would focus light toward the center. Fresnel lenses can be made in many different sizes.

ESL/ELL STRATEGY

Pairing Students English-language learners may have difficulty following the procedure. Pair an English-language learner with an English-proficient student during this lab. The English-proficient student can help the English-language learner in carrying out the procedure, as well as help in interpreting the results.

a triangle connected to a rectangle along the folded edge of the paper, as shown in Figure 19-20. Now, cut out the shape and unfold the paper. You should have an arrow-shaped hole in the middle of the circle. Tape the circle over the head of the flashlight. Be careful not to put tape over the cutout arrow.

◀ **Figure 19-20** Draw and cut out this shape.

7. Hold the flashlight about 50 cm from the "screen." Turn on the flashlight and point it at the screen. Hold the convex lens in front of the lighted flashlight. Move the lens back and forth to focus the image of the arrow on the screen. You may have a partner hold the light steady while you focus. You also may need to turn the lens slightly until you see the arrow clearly. Record your observations.

8. Now, repeat Step 7 using the concave lens. Record your observations. Remember, only real images can be projected.

▲ **STEP 7** Focus the lens so you see an image on the screen.

Comparison of Convex and Concave Lenses

	Eye	Flashlight
Convex		
Concave		

▲ **Figure 19-21** Copy this chart and use it to record your observations.

CONCLUSIONS

1. OBSERVE: What did the convex lens do to your name?

2. OBSERVE: What did the concave lens do to your name?

3. ANALYZE: Which lens allowed you to see real images? How do you know?

4. INFER: Which type of lens do you think would be used in a magnifying glass?

5. SYNTHESIZE: How are different lenses used to correct people's vision?

Tips for Using Technology

Searching the Internet Have students use the Internet to research devices that use convex and concave lenses. Remind students that one important tool for finding information on the Internet is a search engine. A search engine allows the user to type in a keyword or phrase. The engine then searches thousands of sites on the Internet for those that contain the keyword or phrase. After a few seconds, the search engine returns many addresses for other sites related to the topic.

• TEACHING RESOURCES •

Teacher's Resources CD-ROM
Lab Activity Report: Study Tools, pp. 16–17

Laboratory Activity Rubric: Teaching Tools, p. 8

Laboratory Manual
Lab. Skills Worksheet 4: Organizing and Analyzing Data, pp. 13–14

TROUBLESHOOTING: If students have trouble focusing the images, remind them to move the lenses back and forth to focus the image. They may also need to tilt the lens from top to bottom depending on the angle of light in order to get a sharp image.

SAFETY TIP: Lenses may have rough edges. If the edges are rough or flaking, you might sand the edges with fine sandpaper.

EXPECTED OUTCOME: Students will observe that the convex lens forms a small, real image, and a concave lens forms a larger, virtual image.

3 Conclude the Lab

1. **OBSERVE:** made it appear smaller
2. **OBSERVE:** made it appear larger
3. **ANALYZE:** The convex lens; images appeared upside down.
4. **INFER:** concave
5. **SYNTHESIZE:** Concave lenses are used to correct nearsightedness. Convex lenses are used to correct farsightedness.

Use the Laboratory Activity Rubric on the Teacher's Resources CD-ROM to assess students' lab activities. Fill in the rubric with the additional information below. For this activity, students should have:

- performed the activity according to the procedure and filled in the chart with data collected during the activity.

- correctly answered the questions in complete sentences.

4 Extend the Lab

Students can do research to find out about devices that use convex and concave lenses, such as telescopes, microscopes, cameras, and film projectors. As students do their research, they should relate their findings to their lab experiments. Have students find out what types of lenses are at work in these devices and what the lenses do.

1 Introduce

STUDY HINT Ask students to write the Key Terms in their notebooks, leaving space between each of the terms. As students read, encourage them to take notes about each of the Key Terms, including real-life examples.

Linking Prior Knowledge Ask students to recall what happens when sound waves hit a surface. (They reflect, or cause an echo. Lesson 18-2) Let students know that in this lesson, they will find out what happens when light reflects from the surface of a mirror. **learning styles: linguistic, auditory**

2 Teach

Demonstration Use a smooth piece and a crumpled piece of aluminum foil to show students regular and diffuse reflection. Circulate both samples around the class so that students can see the differences in their reflections when they look at the shiny side of both samples. Students should realize that the smooth piece of foil gives a somewhat regular reflection and the crumpled piece of foil gives a diffuse reflection. **learning styles: tactile, visual**

Discussion Encourage students to identify different objects that act as mirrors and to describe the appearance of objects that are reflected in them.
learning styles: linguistic, auditory

READING STRATEGY The text in the *Plane Mirrors* section may seem technical and much like jargon to students. Suggest that as they read the sentences, students refer to the diagram, tracing their fingers along the path of light.
learning styles: linguistic, tactile

Answers to questions

▶1 IDENTIFY: diffuse reflection and regular reflection

▶2 INFER: because it has a smooth surface

▶3 APPLY: because the images they form are always right side up

---

19-8 How do mirrors reflect light?

Objective
Describe how mirrors form clear images.

Key Terms
regular reflection: reflection that forms a clear image
diffuse reflection: reflection that forms a fuzzy image
plane mirror: smooth surface that reflects light and forms images

Reflected Light Light not completely absorbed or transmitted by an object will be reflected. The type of surface affects the type of reflection. There are two types of reflection. They are regular reflection and diffuse reflection.

When a beam of light strikes a smooth surface, the light is reflected from that surface at the same angle. A **regular reflection** forms a clear image. For example, the light reflected from the surface of a still pond will form clear images of the objects around the pond. A regular reflection only occurs when a surface is completely smooth and even, as shown in Figure 19-22.

▲ Figure 19-22
Regular reflection

▲ Figure 19-23
Diffuse reflection

416

When light strikes a rough surface, it will be reflected at different angles. The reflected light from a **diffuse reflection** forms a fuzzy image because light is scattered in many directions. On a windy day, the surface of a pond is not smooth. The light reflected from the surface of the pond will form fuzzy images as shown in Figure 19-23. It is by diffuse reflection that we are able to see nonluminous objects.

▶1 IDENTIFY: What are the two types of reflection called?

Plane Mirrors Mirrors form regular reflections. A **plane mirror** is a smooth surface that reflects light and forms images. The light from an object striking a mirror at an angle will be reflected from the mirror at the same angle. Figure 19-24 shows a a baseball reflected in a mirror at a 70° angle. This is the angle of incidence. The reflected beam bounces off the mirror at a 70° angle. This is the angle of reflection. According to the law of reflection, the angle of incidence is equal to the angle of reflection. The image formed by the mirror is the same distance behind the reflecting surface as the object is in front of it. Figure 19-24 shows that distances *A* and *B* are equal.

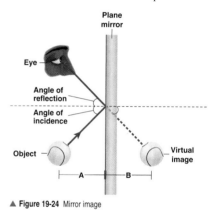

▲ Figure 19-24 Mirror image

▶2 INFER: Why does a mirror form a clear image?

Teaching Options

EXTENDING THE LESSON

Observing Mirror Images Have students observe how images are reflected in flat mirrored surfaces. Student should place a ruler in front of a mirror so that the 1-cm mark is closest to the mirror. Next, they should touch the 3-cm mark on the ruler and observe the image in the mirror. Have them move a hand to the 6-cm mark and observe the image. Finally, they should place a book in front of the mirror so that the title is facing the mirror. Observe the image. Have students draw conclusions about how objects are reflected in mirrors.

RETEACH

Identifying Different Kinds of Reflections Show students photographs such as those in Figures 19-22 and 19-23 and ask them to identify whether the reflections are regular or diffuse reflections. Then, ask volunteers to explain Figure 19-24, describing the path that light takes when it reflects off a plane mirror.
learning styles: visual, linguistic

Convex and Concave Mirrors Not all mirrors are flat, or plane. Some have curved surfaces. A mirror with a surface that curves outward is called a convex mirror. The images reflected in a convex mirror appear to be smaller and farther away. These images are always virtual. Convex mirrors are used in car side-view mirrors and for security in stores.

A mirror with a surface that curves inward is called a concave mirror. Images can be real or virtual, depending on the position of the object. Sometimes images reflected in a concave mirror will appear magnified. Concave mirrors are used in makeup mirrors and as headlight reflectors.

❸ APPLY: Why do you think a car's side-view mirror would be convex?

✓ CHECKING CONCEPTS

1. On a windy day, the surface of a pond will form a _____ reflection.
2. A plane mirror forms _____ images.
3. The angle of incidence is equal to the angle of _____.

Hands-On Activity

HOW TO MAKE A PERISCOPE

You will need scissors, heavy oak tag, rubber cement, and two round pocket mirrors.

1. Draw solid lines on your oak tag like the lines in Figure 19-25.
2. Cut along the solid lines to make the frame and slits for the mirrors. ⚠ CAUTION: Be careful when using scissors.
3. Fold the oak tag by following the dotted lines in the pattern. Glue or tape the long edges together.
4. Place mirrors at opposite ends of this box. One mirror should be angled toward the middle of the box; the other should be angled toward its nearest end opening. Glue the mirrors in place. Then, glue the top and bottom.
5. Now, test your periscope.

Practicing Your Skills

6. IDENTIFY: What parts in the periscope help you see around corners?
7. EXPLAIN: How is this possible?

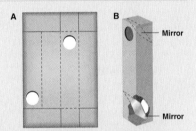

▲ Figure 19-25

4. If an incident ray is at a 45° angle, the _____ ray will also be at a 45° angle.
5. A _____ is a smooth surface that reflects light and forms images.
6. A _____ mirror has a surface that curves inward.

💡 THINKING CRITICALLY

7. INFER: How does reflection help us see nonluminous objects?
8. PREDICT: A bathroom mirror is covered with steam. Will the mirror produce a diffuse reflection or a regular reflection? Explain.

BUILDING MATH SKILLS

Measuring the Difference Look at Figure 19-24. Measure the distance from the object to the mirror. Compare this distance with the distance from the image to the mirror. Now, compare the height of the object and the height of the image. What does this tell you about the image formed by a flat mirror?

---

3 Assess

✓ CHECKING CONCEPTS ANSWERS

1. diffuse
2. clear
3. reflection
4. reflected
5. mirror
6. concave

💡 THINKING CRITICALLY ANSWERS

7. INFER: Light rays encounter many surfaces of nonluminous objects facing in all directions, so they are reflected in all directions. Thus, we can see the diffusely reflected light from any direction or position.
8. PREDICT: Diffuse reflection; Water droplets make the mirror a rough surface.

BUILDING MATH SKILLS ANSWER

Measuring the Difference The distance from the object to the mirror is the same as the distance from the image to the mirror. The heights of the object and the image are the same. The image formed by a flat mirror is the same distance behind the mirror as the object is in front of the mirror, and it is the same size as the object.

4 Close

Hands-On Activity

HOW TO MAKE A PERISCOPE

TIME: 20 minutes

PURPOSE: modeling, experimenting

ALTERNATIVE MATERIALS: If the oak tag proves difficult for students to use, they could use stiff, heavy cardboard instead.

COOPERATIVE LEARNING: Allow pairs of students time to experiment with the periscopes.

Practicing Your Skills Answers

6. IDENTIFY: the mirrors
7. EXPLAIN: The light from an object striking a mirror at an angle will be reflected from the mirror at the same angle. The light is then reflected at an angle from the second mirror, making the object visible to the person using the periscope.

• TEACHING RESOURCES •

💿 **Teacher's Resources CD-ROM**
Lesson Review: Chapter 19, p. 12
Enrichment: Chapter 19, p. 13

ONGOING ASSESSMENT

Determining Where Mirrors Are Used Ask students to give examples of where convex mirrors and concave mirrors are used. (convex: as side-view mirrors on cars; concave: headlight reflectors)

1 Introduce

✏️ **STUDY HINT** Before beginning this lesson, have students read the captions and art labels that appear in the lesson. This will allow them to preview what is to come as well as to focus on the most important ideas in the lesson.

Linking Prior Knowledge Read the lesson title and the objectives and ask students what they already know about this topic. List their ideas on the board. Then, ask what further questions they have. Record their questions on the board and have students answer them after reading the lesson. Students can also use the KWL chart found on the Teacher's Resources CD-ROM.

2 Teach

Demonstration Use a prism to disperse white light into the seven basic colors of light. Have students compare the spectrum with the one shown in Figure 19-26.
learning styles: tactile, visual

Discussion Be sure that students understand that white light is composed of seven colors of light. Bring in a picture of a rainbow. Explain that rainbows are formed when raindrops act as natural prisms. Have students identify the seven colors that make up a rainbow.
learning styles: visual, auditory

📖 **READING STRATEGY** Remind students that the main idea of a paragraph is usually stated in its topic sentence. Encourage students to look for main ideas and supporting details as they read each paragraph. **learning style: auditory**

Answers to questions

▶ **DESCRIBE:** The wavelength of light determines its color. Red light has the longest wavelength, while violet has the shortest.

▶ **PREDICT:** green

19-9 What is color?

Objectives
Describe how a prism forms a visible spectrum. Explain why different objects have different colors.

Key Terms
prism (PRIZ-uhm): triangular piece of transparent glass that separates white light into a band of colors

dispersion (di-SPUR-shun): separation of white light into its component colors

Visible Spectrum Visible light, or white light, is made up of seven different colors. These colors, which combine to make up the visible spectrum, are red, orange, yellow, green, blue, indigo, and violet. Each of these colors of light has its own wavelength. Red light has the longest wavelength. Violet light has the shortest wavelength.

DISPERSION OF WHITE LIGHT

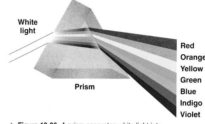

White light

Prism

Red
Orange
Yellow
Green
Blue
Indigo
Violet

▲ **Figure 19-26** A prism separates white light into the colors of the visible spectrum.

A triangular piece of clear glass called a **prism** can be used to separate white light into its colored spectrum. Light is bent, or refracted, as it enters the prism and again as it leaves the prism. Each color of light is refracted by a slightly different amount, causing the white light to break up into its individual colors. This process of separating white light into its individual colors is called **dispersion**.

▶ **DESCRIBE:** How does wavelength affect the color of light?

418

Color of Objects When white light reflects from an object, the object may appear to have a color. The object absorbs all the colors of the spectrum except the color it reflects. When white light shines on a red object, all colors except red are absorbed. The red light is reflected, and the object appears red.

White light

▲ **Figure 19-27** An object appears red because it absorbs all colors except red.

Some objects absorb all of the light and do not reflect any color. These objects appear black. Other objects reflect all of the light. They do not absorb any of the colors. These objects appear white. Others absorb all colors but one. The color you see is the color reflected by the object.

White light

▲ **Figure 19-28** A black object absorbs all light. None is reflected.

White light

▲ **Figure 19-29** A white object reflects all colors.

▶ **PREDICT:** What color will an object appear if it reflects only green light?

Teaching Options

◈ INTEGRATING LIFE SCIENCE

Perceiving Colors Tell students that a prism refracts white light into various colors, but the human eye does not have to see pure light to perceive a color. When red and green light are mixed together, they appear yellow to the human eye, even though the color was mixed and is not pure. Any color can be made by mixing different quantities of red, blue, and green, so these three colors are known as primary colors. Some pairs of colors are called complementary colors. If these pairs are mixed, they produce the color white.

RETEACH

Identifying Observed and Reflected Colors To help students understand the concept of light absorption and reflection, hold up different objects that are red, orange, yellow, green, blue, indigo, violet, white, or black. For each object, ask what colors of light are observed and what colors are reflected. Refer students to Figures 19-27, 19-28, and 19-29 if they need reinforcement.
learning styles: visual, linguistic

✓ CHECKING CONCEPTS

1. A blue object absorbs all the colors of the visible spectrum except _____.
2. A _____ separates white light into the colors of the visible spectrum.
3. Red has the _____ wavelength of all the colors of the visible spectrum.
4. An object appears _____ because it absorbs all the colors of the visible spectrum.

THINKING CRITICALLY

5. **INFER:** The frequency of a wave increases as its wavelength decreases. Which color of light has the highest frequency? Which has the lowest?
6. **COMPARE:** How is a rainbow like a visible spectrum?

Web InfoSearch

Colorblindness The inability to see the color red, green, or blue is called colorblindness. A colorblind person sees these colors as gray. Colorblindness is a genetic disorder. It is inherited from a person's parents. Men are colorblind more often than are women.

SEARCH: Use the Internet to find out more about colorblindness. Explain why men have this disorder more often than women do. Start your search at www.conceptsandchallenges.com. Some key search words are **colorblindness, color receptors,** and **colorblind genes.**

◆ *Integrating Life Science*

TOPICS: animals, ecology, adaptations, camouflage

COLOR IN ANIMALS

A pigment is a substance found in living things that absorbs light. Different pigments absorb different wavelengths of light and reflect others.

Animals contain pigments in their skin that cause them to be a certain color. These pigments are contained in special cells called chromatophores. Many animals have colors that help them blend into their surroundings. This is called camouflage. Camouflage is an adaptation that allows the animal to hide itself from predators. For example, the flounder has coloring that closely matches the color of the sea floor.

Not all animals try to blend in. Sometimes organisms do just the opposite. Some animals, especially those that are poisonous, have very bright colors. These colors are called warning colors. Poison dart frogs from the South American rain forest have been found in a wide array of colors and patterns. These frogs can be found in blue, yellow, orange, and even purple. These colors warn predators, "Don't eat me. I'm poisonous!"

Thinking Critically Some frogs of the rain forest are brightly colored but are not poisonous. What do you think is the reason for this?

▲ **Figure 19-30** A green tree frog is well hidden in the leaves.

---

3 Assess

✓ CHECKING CONCEPTS ANSWERS

1. blue
2. prism
3. longest
4. black

THINKING CRITICALLY ANSWERS

5. **INFER:** violet; red
6. **COMPARE:** In a rainbow, sunlight is separated into the colors of the visible spectrum.

---

4 Close

Web InfoSearch

Colorblindness Have students use the Internet to learn more about colorblindness. Students should explain why men have this disorder more often than women do. Some key search words are **colorblindness, color receptors,** and **colorblind genes.** Students should begin their search at www.conceptsandchallenges.com.

◆ *Integrating Life Science*

TOPICS: animals, ecology, adaptations, camouflage

COLOR IN ANIMALS

Life-Science Connection Many insects exhibit the color protection described in this article. Some insects, for example, are the same color as the leaves on which they live. Caterpillars often rely on camouflage because they are too slow to outrun predators. The bright colors of some caterpillars warn predators that they are distasteful or poisonous. Instead of hiding, caterpillars with warning coloration feed out in the open.

Discussion Ask students to name other animals that rely on camouflage or warning coloration to protect themselves from predators. You might have students locate photographs in science books to share with the class.

Thinking Critically Answer
Even if the animals are not poisonous, their bright colors will convince predators that they are poisonous and protect the animals from harm.

COOPERATIVE LEARNING

Creating a Mnemonic Device
Students can work in small groups to create a mnemonic, or memory device, to help them remember the order of the colors in the visible spectrum. Write the names of the colors in a horizontal row on the board. Then, encourage students to think of a sentence to write below the colors in which each word begins with the same letter as the corresponding color in the visible spectrum. **learning styles: visual, linguistic**

• TEACHING RESOURCES •

◉ **Teacher's Resources CD-ROM**
Lesson Review: Chapter 19, p. 14
KWL Chart: Study Tools, p. 7

19-10 (pp. 420–421)

1 Introduce

✐ **STUDY HINT** Before beginning this lesson, have students scan the lesson for unfamiliar words and make a list of them. Then, have students work in pairs to define each of the words on their lists.

Linking Prior Knowledge Read the title of the lesson and ask students to contribute their ideas about the uses of light. Have students make a list of their ideas and encourage them to add more ideas to their list as they read.

2 Teach

Demonstration If you have a laser in your school, demonstrate it as part of this lesson. Show the interference effects and the high energy of the laser beam. **learning styles: visual, tactile**

Discussion To begin the lesson, bring in a CD and display it for the class. You might also show students the bar codes on supermarket products. Tell students that these items illustrate different uses of lasers. Have any students who have seen a laser show describe it to the rest of the class. **learning styles: auditory, visual**

📖 **READING STRATEGY** This lesson lists many uses of light. Encourage students to connect information about the uses of light in this lesson with that presented in previous lessons. (Lasik eye surgery, for example, was in Lesson 19-7.)

Answers to questions

▶ **DEFINE:** Laser light has only one color and does not spread out.

▶ **EXPLAIN:** The heat of a laser beam sticks the retina back into place.

▶ **DESCRIBE:** It reflects repeatedly within the glass.

▶ **EXPLAIN:** Doctors can see inside the body, so they can operate with small incisions. Patients are able to recover more quickly from surgery.

19-10 How can light be used?

Objective
Identify uses of light in different areas of life.

Key Terms
laser: device that produces a powerful beam of light

total internal reflection: occurs when light is repeatedly reflected within a given material

fiber optics: use of optical fibers

Lasers Have you ever heard of a powerful beam of light that can cut through a steel plate? This kind of light is different from white light. This light comes from a laser. A **laser** is a device that produces a very powerful beam of light.

The difference between white light and laser light is their wavelengths and energy content. White light is made up of many different wavelengths. It includes all the visible colors. Laser light is made up of only one wavelength. As a result, laser light is only one color. Unlike the light waves in white light, the waves in laser light are all in step. A beam of laser light can travel long distances in a straight line. It does not spread out as a beam of white light does.

▶ **DEFINE:** How is laser light different from normal white light?

Uses of Lasers Lasers have many uses. In medicine, lasers can be used to repair a detached retina and prevent blindness. A detached retina results when the retina comes loose from the back of the eye. The heat of a laser beam can attach the retina back into place. Lasers are also used to treat skin tumors, birthmarks, and some cancers.

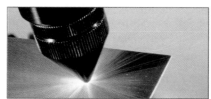

▲ **Figure 19-31** A laser beam cutting metal

420

In industry, lasers can be used for cutting, welding, and drilling. For example, a laser beam can make a clean cut through thick layers of cloth. You are probably familiar with the use of lasers in CDs and DVDs. Lasers are also used in supermarkets to read the bar codes on many different products.

▶ **EXPLAIN:** How can a laser repair a detached retina?

Optical Fibers Glasslike fibers that can transmit information in the form of light pulses are called optical fibers. These fibers are able to send information much more quickly and clearly than copper wire or radio waves can.

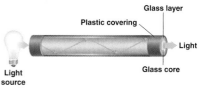

▲ **Figure 19-32** Total internal reflection

The reason light travels through optical fibers so quickly is because it reflects within the glass. If light is reflected at a great enough angle, the light does not refract through the glass. Instead, it reflects repeatedly within the optical fiber. This is called **total internal reflection**.

▶ **DESCRIBE:** How does light travel so quickly through an optical fiber?

Uses of Fiber Optics The use of optical fibers is called **fiber optics**. Fiber optics is used in many industries. One industry using fiber optics more and more is the communications industry.

Phone companies use fiber optics in most of their new wiring. They also are replacing their remaining copper wiring with fiber optics. Cable television companies have also begun to use fiber optics. Television signals are sent to entire communities using optical fibers. Then, the signal is split into regular cable wiring, which is sent to each home.

Teaching Options

EXTENDING THE LESSON

Tracking Lasers and Fiber Optics Have students keep a diary for several days to list examples in their daily lives in which lasers or fiber optics play a part. Students may note activities such as listening to a CD, having a price scanned in a supermarket, or visiting a dentist who is using a laser light to see inside the mouth. Allow time for students to share their lists with the class. **learning styles: visual, linguistic**

RETEACH

Playing a "Light" Game Write several uses of light mentioned in the lesson on the board. Include some descriptions that are uses of sound rather than light, such as echolocation. Small groups of students can work together to pick out the words or phrases that do not describe a job done with light. Groups can race against the clock or each other to complete the activity. Allow time to check students' responses. **learning style: linguistic**

The computer industry is also using fiber optics. Many universities and businesses use fiber optics in their local area networks. A local area network, or LAN, is a group of connected computers that share data, software, and hardware.

Fiber optics is used in medicine. Doctors can attach cameras to optical fibers. The optical fibers are then inserted into the body through a small incision, such as in the knee. This allows doctors to see within the body so they can operate making small incisions. This allows patients to recover more quickly from surgery.

▶ **EXPLAIN:** How do fiber optics help patients and doctors?

☑ CHECKING CONCEPTS

1. What is a laser?
2. What can lasers be used for in industry?
3. In what form do optical fibers transmit information?
4. What is fiber optics?

Science and Technology
HOLOGRAMS

There is a special kind of photography that uses laser light. This process is known as holography (huh-LAHG-ruh-fee). Laser light is used to produce a three-dimensional image. The image is known as a hologram (HAHL-uh-gram).

With the invention of the laser in 1960, Dennis Gabor, the hologram inventor, was finally able to produce crisp holographic images. He was awarded the Nobel Prize in 1971 for his work.

To make a hologram, two pictures of an object are taken. Each picture is taken from a slightly different angle. Then, the two pictures are combined into one hologram.

When you look at a hologram, you can view the original object from different angles. It is as if the object were in front of you, even though you are seeing only an image of the object.

There are several practical uses for holograms. Architects can use holograms to show three-dimensional views of buildings. Structural engineers can use holograms to test the sturdiness of a solid object.

Thinking Critically How did the invention of the laser help Gabor complete his design of the hologram?

▲ **Figure 19-33** Holograms use laser light to create a three-dimensional effect.

☑ THINKING CRITICALLY

5. **CONCLUDE:** How does total internal reflection help make optical fibers work so well?
6. **INFER:** Why can the light from a laser travel a greater distance than light from a normal source of white light?

BUILDING SCIENCE SKILLS

Inferring One major difference between optical fibers and copper wiring is the way that they send and receive information. Optical fibers transmit information using pulses of light. Copper wiring uses pulses of electricity. This difference makes optical fibers less sensitive to power surges and electrical interference. Why do you think this makes optical fibers more useful in computers and computer networks?

---

3 Assess

☑ CHECKING CONCEPTS ANSWERS

1. A laser is a tool that produces a very powerful beam of light.
2. Lasers can be used for cutting, welding, and drilling.
3. in the form of light pulses
4. the use of optical fibers in many industries, such as medicine

THINKING CRITICALLY ANSWERS

5. **CONCLUDE:** The light reflects repeatedly within the optical fiber, allowing the light to travel quickly.
6. **INFER:** Light from a normal source will diffuse. Light from a laser is concentrated.

BUILDING SCIENCE SKILLS ANSWER

Inferring Optical fibers are more useful in computers and computer networks than copper wiring because optical fibers are less sensitive to power surges and electrical interference. These occurrences in copper wiring could cause a loss of information.

4 Close

Science and Technology
HOLOGRAMS

Technology Connection Consider bringing holograms to class for students to examine. They are inexpensive and available from many scientific supply houses. Many holograms can be viewed with monochromatic light. Students will note the three-dimensional feature of the image, permitting the viewer to get a different perspective by changing the angle of view. The appearance of a hologram may be offered as additional evidence of the wave nature of light.

Discussion Ask students to describe holograms that they have seen. Some students may be familiar with holograms on credit cards, which prevent the cards from being easily duplicated.

Thinking Critically Answer
The laser provided a more intense light source, providing for crisper images.

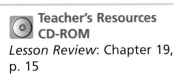

• TEACHING RESOURCES •

Teacher's Resources CD-ROM
Lesson Review: Chapter 19, p. 15

ONGOING ASSESSMENT

Using Fiber Optics Ask students: *What types of industries are using fiber optics? How are they using them?* (communication industry: wiring of phones; computer industry: sharing information; medicine: attaching to cameras and then inserting into the body)

The Big Idea

(pp. 422–423)

1 Introduce

Objective Students will name some of the ways in which light is used in homes. They will do research to find out how light is used in a particular technology and include a model of the technology being used in homes.

Linking Prior Knowledge Ask students to recall the uses of light that they learned (Lesson 19-10). Ask if any of those uses of light are at work in their own homes. Ask if they know how light plays a part in making the devices work.

2 Teach

Discussion After students read the article and the call outs, ask them to tell how light plays a part in the various devices. Ask students if they know how recently these technologies were developed for consumer use. Have students think of any uses of light in their own homes that are not reflected on the diagram.
learning styles: visual, linguistic

Use the information in the article, call outs, and Fast Facts to help guide students in choosing a topic for their Science Logs.

THE BIG IDEA ONLINE

How is light used in the home?
Have students research their Science Log Writing Activity at www.conceptsandchallenges.com. You can have students organize their log by completing the Big Idea activity online. Students may post their work in the Online Classroom Database for others to read.

Reinforcement Students can also use the Big Idea Planner or Big Idea Science Log Entry found on the Teacher's Resources CD-ROM.

⬥ Integrating Technology

THE Big IDEA

How is light used in the home?

Technology is the practical application of knowledge. Beginning with the first stone tools, people have used technology to accomplish tasks. A new technology often improves on older methods. It may be faster, save energy, and produce better results. Society must always weigh the risks of new technologies against their benefits. They must always be environmentally friendly.

Advances in technology have expanded our choices at home. We can chop with a knife or a food processor. We can cook with fire, electricity, or microwaves. Newer "flash bake" ovens use light to cook foods rapidly.

We also have more forms of entertainment and communication. Music on CDs sounds clearer than music on records or tapes. Besides broadcast television, choices today include cable, satellites, videotapes, and digital versatile discs (DVDs). Fiber-optic cable makes long-distance phone calls clearer. The Internet has created another way to communicate with friends and family far away.

Like lamps and mirrors, many types of technology at home use light. Look at the boxes of text that appear on this page and the next. They point out devices that are typical in homes today and some that may become common in the future. Then, follow the directions in the Science Log to learn more about "the big idea."⬥

Grow Lights
Fluorescent grow lights mix blue and red wavelengths. Blue light promotes leaf growth. A combination of red and blue lights encourages flowering.

Speed Cook Oven
A combination of intense visible light and infrared energy cooks food in one-fourth the time of conventional ovens. First used in restaurants, "flash bake" ovens are now sold for homes.

▲ **Figure 19-34** Inside a house

422

Teaching Options

! FAST FACTS More About Light-Using Devices

Solar Energy Storage
One of the problems with solar energy is that it is not always available. Solar energy has to be stored in order to meet demands on cloudy days. Therefore, water- and rock-storage systems use these substances to retain the heat of the Sun. Batteries can also serve as storage devices for solar energy.

Sound Recording
The laser on a CD player retrieves digital information from a CD and converts that information into an electrical signal.

Television Camera
Not only do televisions use light, but television cameras, used to produce television programs, also employ light. A television camera has a fixed lens to focus the scene onto the front of the pickup device. A camera has a system of prisms and mirrors that separate light from a scene into the three primary colors. Each beam of light is directed to a pickup device that picks up only that primary color. The colors are then combined in the correct proportions to create an image.

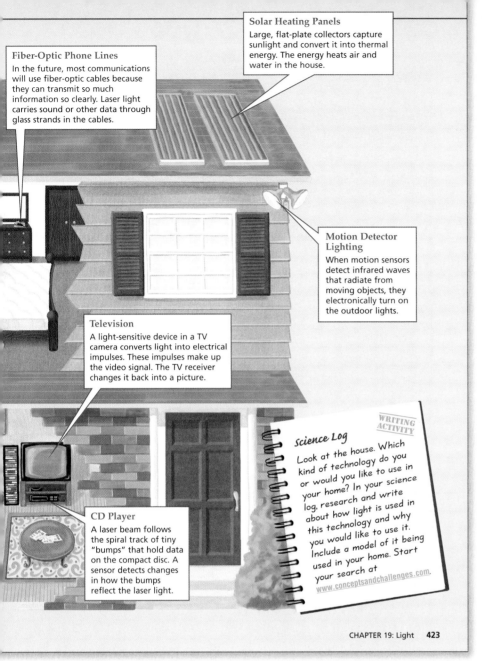

Solar Heating Panels
Large, flat-plate collectors capture sunlight and convert it into thermal energy. The energy heats air and water in the house.

Fiber-Optic Phone Lines
In the future, most communications will use fiber-optic cables because they can transmit so much information so clearly. Laser light carries sound or other data through glass strands in the cables.

Motion Detector Lighting
When motion sensors detect infrared waves that radiate from moving objects, they electronically turn on the outdoor lights.

Television
A light-sensitive device in a TV camera converts light into electrical impulses. These impulses make up the video signal. The TV receiver changes it back into a picture.

CD Player
A laser beam follows the spiral track of tiny "bumps" that hold data on the compact disc. A sensor detects changes in how the bumps reflect the laser light.

WRITING ACTIVITY

Science Log
Look at the house. Which kind of technology do you or would you like to use in your home? In your science log, research and write about how light is used in this technology and why you would like to use it. Include a model of it being used in your home. Start your search at www.conceptsandchallenges.com.

3 Assess

Use the Writing Activity Rubric on the Teacher's Resources CD-ROM to assess students' Science Logs. Fill in the rubric with the additional information below. For this assignment, students should have:

- identified a light-using technology that they use or would like to use, conducted research on it, wrote about how light is used in this technology, and explained why they would like to use it.
- included a model of the practical applications of the technology.

4 Close

Create Advertisements Ask students to write advertisements for the devices that they researched. Their advertisements should show the devices, tell how they are used, and explain why the devices should be purchased. Remind students to include facts about the devices as well as colorful and persuasive words that would entice readers to buy the light-using devices.
learning styles: linguistic, visual

Tips for Using Technology

Presenting Light-Using Technology Have students use presentation software to present their research and model. Presentation software allows them to use a computer to put text and art together in a slide show. They can use a scanner to incorporate their own art in their slide show. Students can then print their slide show and use it as a handout. Students can also use presentation software to share their data with the class. Have students use the Thumbnail Sketch on the Teacher's Resources CD-ROM to plan their presentations.

• *TEACHING RESOURCES* •

Teacher's Resources CD-ROM
Big Idea: Chapter 19, p. 16
Big Idea Planner: Study Tools, pp. 11–12
Big Idea Science Log Entry: Study Tools, p. 13
Writing Activity Rubric: Teaching Tools, p. 9
Thumbnail Sketch: Study Tools, p. 24

Challenges (pp. 424–426)

Chapter Summary

Review Before students begin the Challenges, review the summary with them. You might rephrase the summary statements as questions for students to answer. For example, the summary for Lesson 19-5 would become "What substance in plants absorbs the Sun's light and allows photosynthesis to occur?"

STUDY HINT Have students copy the summaries onto a sheet of paper that they have folded in half vertically. The summaries should break apart the sentences at places that make sense for review (Light is a form of/electromagnetic energy. A convex lens curves/outward.) Students can fold their papers so that one half is not visible. They can say the first part of a sentence, attempt to complete the sentence, and then unfold the paper to check the answer.

Key Terms Challenges

MATCHING

1. eye (19-7)
2. ray (19-2)
3. real image (19-6)
4. visible spectrum (19-9)
5. photon (19-2)
6. transparent (19-4)
7. laser (19-10)
8. electromagnetic spectrum (19-1)
9. diffuse reflection (19-8)

FILL IN

10. photosynthesis (19-5)
11. illuminated (19-4)
12. image (19-7)
13. luminous objects (19-4)
14. plane mirror (19-8)

Chapter Summary

Lesson 19-1
- The **electromagnetic spectrum** includes radio waves, microwaves, infrared waves, visible light, ultraviolet rays, X-rays, and gamma rays.

Lesson 19-2
- **Light** is a form of electromagnetic energy.

Lesson 19-3
- Light travels in **transverse waves**. Light does not need a medium in which to travel.

Lesson 19-4
- **Luminous objects** give off their own light. **Illuminated objects** reflect light.
- **Opaque**, **transparent**, and **translucent** are three types of objects that affect light differently.

Lesson 19-5
- **Chlorophyll** is a substance in plants that absorbs the Sun's light and allows **photosynthesis** to occur.

Lesson 19-6
- A **convex lens** curves outward, whereas a **concave lens** curves inward.
- A convex lens is used to form **real images**. A concave lens can form **virtual images**.

Lesson 19-7
- The parts of the **eye** are the cornea, pupil, iris, lens, retina, and optic nerve.
- Light is focused onto the retina by the lens. The brain interprets the **image** on the retina to make it look right-side up.

Lesson 19-8
- A **plane mirror** is a smooth surface that reflects light and forms images.
- **Regular reflection** produces a clear image. **Diffuse reflection** produces a fuzzy image.

Lesson 19-9
- A **prism** can separate white light into the colors of the spectrum.
- The color of an object depends on what part of the spectrum it reflects or absorbs.

Lesson 19-10
- A **laser** produces a powerful beam of light.
- Optical fibers are glass fibers that can quickly transmit information in the form of light pulses.

424

Key Term Challenges

chlorophyll (p. 408)
chloroplast (p. 408)
concave lens (p. 410)
convex lens (p. 410)
diffuse reflection (p. 416)
electromagnetic spectrum (p. 400)
eye (p. 412)
fiber optics (p. 420)
illuminated objects (p. 406)
image (p. 412)
laser (p. 420)
lens (p. 410)
light (p. 402)
luminous object (p. 406)
opaque (p. 406)
photon (p. 402)
photosynthesis (p. 408)
plane mirror (p. 416)
prism (p. 418)
ray (p. 402)
real image (p. 410)
regular reflection (p. 416)
refraction (p. 418)
sight (p. 412)
total internal reflection (p. 420)
translucent (p. 406)
transparent (p. 406)
transverse wave (p. 404)
virtual image (p. 410)
visible spectrum (p. 400)

MATCHING Write the Key Term from above that best matches each description.

1. organ used for sight
2. straight line that shows the direction of light travel
3. image that can be projected
4. seven colors that make up white light
5. small bundle of energy
6. material that allows light to pass through easily
7. device that produces a powerful beam of light
8. range of electromagnetic waves
9. reflection that forms a fuzzy image

FILL IN Write the Key Term from above that best completes each statement.

10. By the process of _____, a plant makes its own food from the Sun's light.
11. When you shine a light in a dark room, the objects that you see are _____.
12. An _____ forms on the retina.
13. Lamps are _____ because they give off their own light.
14. A _____ is a smooth surface that reflects and refracts images.

Teaching Options

PREPARING STUDENTS FOR STANDARDIZED TESTS

Reading Strategy: Tell students to try out each of the answers, placing each of the answers in the sentence. The wrong answers may definitely sound wrong, helping students narrow their choices.

Writing Strategy: Tell students to organize their thoughts before writing by creating an outline, word web, or other appropriate graphic organizer.

Interpreting Visuals: Tell students that tables, charts, and graphs often compare information, so it is important to understand what is being compared. That information can be found directly above or below the title along the horizontal and vertical lines at the sides, called axes.

ESL/ELL STRATEGY

Tell students to look for keywords such as *all*, *always*, *never*, *none*, or *not* in questions. For example, in multiple-choice question 3, a keyword to note is *not*.

Content Challenges TEST PREP

MULTIPLE CHOICE **Write the letter of the term or phrase that best completes each statement.**

1. Chlorophyll absorbs all the colors of the visible spectrum except
   a. red.
   b. green.
   c. blue.
   d. violet.

2. The refracted image from a convex lens is
   a. right-side up.
   b. reversed.
   c. upside down.
   d. none of the above.

3. The color that is not one of the seven colors of the visible spectrum is
   a. red.
   b. blue.
   c. indigo.
   d. brown.

4. The type of electromagnetic wave that can be felt as heat is
   a. gamma rays.
   b. infrared rays.
   c. X-rays.
   d. ultraviolet rays.

5. The part of the eye that controls the amount of light entering the eye is the
   a. pupil.
   b. cornea.
   c. iris.
   d. retina.

6. In photosynthesis, electromagnetic energy is converted to
   a. electrical energy.
   b. nuclear energy.
   c. chemical energy.
   d. mechanical energy.

7. Unlike a beam of white light, a laser beam has
   a. no color.
   b. one wavelength.
   c. two colors.
   d. no wavelength.

8. The point where the light that passes through a lens is brought together is called the
   a. focal length.
   b. refraction point.
   c. focal point.
   d. retina.

9. Light reflects completely within a fiber-optic cable because of
   a. gravity.
   b. total internal reflection.
   c. photosynthesis.
   d. regular reflection.

10. An object that absorbs all colors of light and does not reflect any appears
    a. green.
    b. white.
    c. black.
    d. blue.

TRUE/FALSE **Write** *true* **if the statement is true. If the statement is false, change the underlined term to make the statement true.**

11. According to the law of <u>refraction</u>, the angle of incidence is equal to the angle of reflection.

12. Illuminated objects, such as the <u>Sun</u>, reflect light.

13. The reason light travels through optical fibers so quickly is because it <u>refracts</u> within the glass.

14. The parts of a cell where photosynthesis takes place are called <u>chloroplasts</u>.

15. All electromagnetic waves are streams of <u>photons</u>.

Content Challenges

MULTIPLE CHOICE

1. b (19-5)
2. c (19-7)
3. d (19-9)
4. b (19-1)
5. c (19-7)
6. c (19-5)
7. b (19-10)
8. c (19-6)
9. b (19-10)
10. c (19-9)

TRUE/FALSE

11. false; reflection (19-8)
12. false; Moon (19-4)
13. false; reflects (19-10)
14. true (19-5)
15. true (19-3)

ALTERNATIVE ASSESSMENT

Relating Information Students may write a Science Log entry describing the parts of the electromagnetic and visible spectrums. They should relate the four different models of light and explain the behavior that light exhibits in each model. Finally, students should describe reflection and refraction and how the shape of a lens influences refraction.
learning style: linguistic

PORTFOLIO ASSESSMENT

Making Student Portfolios Portfolio Assessment is designed to evaluate a student's performance over an extended period of time. Encourage students to select their own work for inclusion in their portfolios. The Lab Activity Report and the Spider Map are some of the reproducibles on the Teacher's Resources CD-ROM that they can include in their portfolios. You can use the Portfolio Assessment Rubric also found on the Teacher's Resources CD-ROM to assess students' portfolios.

Concept Challenges

WRITTEN RESPONSE

1. **COMPARE:** Possible answer: Photons reflect from a surface in a similar way that a particle would. Like moving particles, photons have energy. (19-2)
2. **EXPLAIN:** A prism bends, or refracts, white light, separating it into different wavelengths. (19-9)
3. **INFER:** In a vacuum, there is no interference. (19-3)
4. **EXPLAIN:** A laser beam is made up of only one wavelength. (19-10)
5. **HYPOTHESIZE:** Possible answer: Yes; Some animals have abilities that humans do not have. (19-7)
6. **MODEL:** The pupil is like the aperture. The retina is similar to the film, and the lens of the eye is similar to the camera lens. (19-7)

INTERPRETING A DIAGRAM (19-6)

7. convex
8. A
9. B
10. The light rays will converge at B.
11. brought together
12. a real image or an upside-down image

Chapter Project Wrap-Up

CREATING BIG IDEAS

Students' Big Ideas can be put on posterboard or construction paper and exhibited around the classroom. Students can present their findings on the topics they chose to research. You can use the Group Activity Rubric found on the Teacher's Resources CD-ROM to assess students' projects. Fill in the rubric with the additional information below. For this project, students should have:

- chosen a science discipline to connect ideas from this chapter to, performed research on their topic, and displayed information using pictures or diagrams.
- developed a Science Log idea.

Concept Challenges TEST PREP

WRITTEN RESPONSE **Answer each of the following questions in complete sentences.**

1. **COMPARE:** What are two ways that a photon is similar to a particle?
2. **EXPLAIN:** How does a prism separate white light into a spectrum?
3. **INFER:** Why do electromagnetic waves travel best in a vacuum?
4. **EXPLAIN:** Why does a laser beam not spread out over long distances?
5. **HYPOTHESIZE:** Some animals can hear ultrasonic sounds, even though humans cannot. Do you think that some animals can see ultraviolet light, even though humans cannot? Why or why not?
6. **MODEL:** Think of your eye as a camera. A camera has an opening for light to enter called an aperture. Which part of the eye is similar to the camera's aperture? Which part is similar to the film in the camera? Which part is similar to the camera lens?

INTERPRETING A DIAGRAM **Use Figure 19-35 to answer the following questions and to complete the exercise.**

7. What type of lens is shown?
8. Which letter on the diagram represents the focal length of the lens?
9. Which letter represents the focal point?
10. Copy the diagram on a sheet of paper. Show the path of light rays passing through the lens.
11. Are the light rays brought together or spread apart by the lens?
12. What kind of image would be formed at point C?

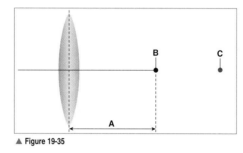
▲ Figure 19-35

Teaching Options

• TEACHING RESOURCES •

Teacher's Resources CD-ROM

Key Term Review: Chapter 19, p. 17

Chapter 19 Test: pp. 18–19

Group Activity Rubric: Teaching Tools, p. 6

Lab Activity Report: Study Tools, pp. 16–17

Spider Map: Study Tools, p. 9

Portfolio Assessment Rubric: Teaching Tools, p. 10

Chapter Self-Check: Teaching Tools, p. 11

PLANNING GUIDE

◆ **TEACHING THE CHAPTER** This chapter should take approximately 9–11 days to complete instruction and assessment.

	Skills and Features	Projects and Activities	Achieve Science Literacy	Meet Individual Needs
Chapter 20 Opener p. T427	LABEL	• Chapter Project		
Lesson 20-1 **What is electric charge?** pp. T428–T429 Standard: B2c	EXPLAIN, NAME, INFER • Interpreting Visuals • Investigate	• More on the Web	• Study Hint • Ongoing Assessment	CD-ROM Model of an Atom
Lab Activity **Observing Static Electricity** pp. T430–T431 Standard: B3a	HYPOTHESIZE, INFER, ANALYZE • Set-Up Time: 15 min • Lab Time: 45 min	• Extending the Lesson • Lab Skills Worksheet • Extend the Lab Activity	• Tips for Using Technology	CD-ROM Lab Activity Report
Lesson 20-2 **What is a battery?** pp. T432–T433 Standards: B1b, B3a, B3d	DEFINE, IDENTIFY, ANALYZE • Investigate • Web InfoSearch • Real-Life Science	• Integrating Life Science	• Study Hint • Ongoing Assessment	CD-ROM Wet Cell and Dry Cell
Lesson 20-3 **What are insulators and conductors?** pp. T434–T435 Standards: B1b, B3a, B3d	INFER, APPLY, COMPARE • Health and Safety Tip • People in Science	• More on the Web • Lab Challenge	• Study Hint • Reading Strategy • Ongoing Assessment	• Reteach Laboratory Video
Lesson 20-4 **What are two kinds of electric current?** pp. T436–T437 Standards: B3a, B3d	ANALYZE, DEFINE, EXPLAIN • Designing an Experiment • Integrating Life Science	• Extending the Lesson • More on the Web	• Study Hint • Writing Hint	CD-ROM Designing an Experiment
Lesson 20-5 **What is a series circuit?** pp. T438–T439 Standards: B3a, B3d	IDENTIFY, DEFINE, HYPOTHESIZE • Interpreting Visuals • Investigate • Science and Technology	• More on the Web	• Study Hint • Ongoing Assessment	• ESL/ELL Strategy • Reteach CD-ROM Enrichment Activity

Planning Guide continues on next page.

Standards: For details on the correlation to National Science Standards, see pages *xx–xxi*.

	Skills and Features	Projects and Activities	Achieve Science Literacy	Meet Individual Needs
Lesson 20-6 What is a parallel circuit? pp. T440–T441 Standards: B3a, B3d	LABEL, DEFINE, DESCRIBE • Investigate • Building Science Skills • People in Science	• Extending the Lesson • More on the Web • Cooperative Learning	• Study Hint • Reading Strategy • Ongoing Assessment	• Reteach
Lesson 20-7 How is electricity measured? pp. T442–T443 Standards: B3a, B3d	EXPLAIN, IDENTIFY, DEFINE • Web InfoSearch • Science and Technology	• Cooperative Learning	• Study Hint	• ESL/ELL Strategy CD-ROM Enrichment Activity Temperature Scale
Lesson 20-8 What is Ohm's law? pp. T444–T445 Standards: B3a, B3d	INFER, CALCULATE, NAME • Building Math Skills • Science and Technology	• More on the Web	• Study Hint • Reading Strategy • Writing Hint • Ongoing Assessment	• Reteach
Lesson 20-9 How can you use electricity safely? pp. T446–T447 Standards: B3a, B3d	ANALYZE, DESCRIBE, INFER • Health and Safety Tip • Science and Technology	• Cooperative Learning • More on the Web	• Study Hint	
Big Idea How have electrical inventions changed history? pp. T448–T449 Standard: B3a	RESEARCH, COMMUNICATE, ANALYZE • Science Log: Writing Activity	• Big Idea Online • Close Activity	• Tips for Using Technology	• ESL/ELL Strategy CD-ROM Big Idea Planner
Chapter 20 Challenges pp. T450–T452	• Chapter Summary • Key Term Challenges • Content Challenges • Concept Challenges	• Chapter Project Wrap-Up • Unit Challenge Online	• Study Hint • Preparing Students for Standardized Tests	• ESL/ELL Strategy CD-ROM Chapter Self-Check Venn Diagram

Chapter 20 Electricity

▲ **Figure 20-1** The skyline at night in Seattle, Washington

Electricity provides the energy that lights up the skyline of the city in Figure 20-1. Electricity can make a city look beautiful at night, but it also plays a very important role in your life. From providing power to the appliances in your home to helping your body function properly, you rely on electricity. Although it is a very useful source of energy, electricity can be dangerous. Safety rules must be followed when using electricity.

▶ Can you name some safety rules to follow when using electricity?

Contents

Teaching Options

ASSESSMENT PLANNER

For assessment in the Student Edition, see the following pages:

Content Assessment
Checking Concepts: pp. 429, 433, 435, 437, 439, 441, 443, 445, 447
Thinking Critically: pp. 429, 433, 435, 437, 439, 441, 443, 445, 447
Interpreting Visuals: pp. 429, 439
Chapter Challenges: pp. 450–452

Alternative Assessment
Building Skills: pp. 441, 445
Web InfoSearch: pp. 433, 443
Science Log: p. 449

Performance-Based Assessment
Designing an Experiment: p. 437
Lab Activity: pp. 430–431

• TEACHING RESOURCES •

◉ **Teacher's Resources CD-ROM**
Lesson Review: Ch. 20, pp. 2, 3, 4, 5, 6, 8, 9, 11, 12
Enrichment: Ch. 20, pp. 7, 10
Key Term Review: Ch. 20, p. 14
Chapter 20 Test: pp. 15–16
Laboratory Manual: pp. 13–14, 97–100

📼 **Laboratory Video**
Segment 22: Comparing Electrical Conductors and Insulators

Chapter 20 Electricity

Chapter Overview

In this chapter, students will learn about electricity, differentiate between direct current and alternating current, and compare a series circuit and a parallel circuit. They will also use the correct units to measure voltage, current, and resistance. Finally, students will describe ways to use electricity safely.

About Figure 20-1 In Seattle, Washington, electricity is needed to operate the three elevators in the Space Needle in the foreground of the picture. Near the top of the Space Needle, electricity is needed for the revolving restaurant. Although you cannot see them in the picture, 24 rooftop lightning rods protect the building from being damaged by lightning.

Answer Possible answers: Do not use appliances near water and do not plug too many appliances into one outlet.

Linking Prior Knowledge

For this chapter, students should recall:

• the parts of an atom (Lesson 3-3).

• the properties of metals and nonmetals (Lessons 3-8, 11-1).

Chapter Project

DEMONSTRATING CIRCUITS

MATERIALS: various materials including batteries, wire, bulbs, switches, index cards, masking tape, posterboard, pens

As students read the chapter, they will make a series circuit and a parallel circuit and compare the two. Have students make labels for each circuit that identifies the kind of circuit, the source of electric current, the wire, the switches, and the load. Encourage students to add other information such as voltage, resistance, and electric current. Encourage students to make their circuits different in some way, such as using different kinds of loads or inventing a device with their circuits. You might want to give students the option of drawing and labeling diagrams instead of building the circuits.

1 Introduce

🔍 INVESTIGATE

TIME: 10–15 minutes

PURPOSE: Students will observe a spark, or electric charge.

MATERIALS: rubber balloon, piece of wool or nylon, safety goggles

PROCEDURE: Have students blow up balloons and tie the ends into knots. Then, have them rub their balloons with a piece of wool or nylon. After a few minutes, dim the lights and have students slowly move a finger near the balloon and observe what happens. If the humidity in the classroom is high, students may have difficulty building up a charge and seeing a spark.
learning styles: visual, tactile

THINK ABOUT IT: Students should see a spark and will probably say that this has happened to them before. **learning styles: visual, tactile**

📝 **STUDY HINT** Have students write the lesson title and the title of each section in their notebooks. As students read the lesson, tell them to write the sentence that provides the main idea of each section.

Linking Prior Knowledge Have students review the parts of an atom (Lesson 3-3). Ask: *What are the three main parts of an atom, and what charge does each part have?* (Protons have a positive charge, neutrons have no charge, and electrons have a negative charge.)

2 Teach

Demonstration Tear a sheet of paper into small pieces. Form a small mound with the pieces of paper. Rub a plastic comb with a piece of silk. Next, hold the comb about an inch above the mound of paper. The comb should attract the pieces of paper. Ask students why the paper is attracted to the comb. (Rubbing the comb gave it a charge. There must be an opposite charge in the paper. Opposite charges caused the paper to be attracted to the comb.)

20-1 What is electric charge?

🔍 INVESTIGATE

Observing Electric Charges
HANDS-ON ACTIVITY

1. Blow up a rubber balloon. Tie the end into a knot.
2. Rub the balloon with a piece of wool or nylon.
3. Dim the lights in your classroom. Bring your finger near the balloon. Observe what happens between the balloon and your finger.

THINK ABOUT IT: What did you observe between your finger and the balloon? Has something like this ever happened to you before?

STEP 3

Objective
Explain how objects become electrically charged.

Key Terms
proton: atomic particle with a positive electric charge

electron: atomic particle with a negative electric charge

neutron: atomic particle with neither a negative nor a positive electric charge

static electricity: buildup of electric charges in an object

Atoms You have learned that all matter is made up of atoms. The three basic parts of an atom are protons, neutrons, and electrons. Protons and neutrons are found in the nucleus of an atom, and electrons are found in the electron cloud that surrounds the nucleus.

▶ **NAME:** What are the three main parts of an atom?

Electric Charge Protons and electrons have a property called electric charge. **Protons** have positive electric charge (+). **Electrons** have negative electric charge (–). The strength of the positive electric charge on a proton is the same as the strength of the negative electric charge on an electron. **Neutrons** do not have charge. They are neutral.

Electric charge is not a physical property that can be seen or touched. However, electric charge exerts a force that affects the behavior of matter. Matter that is electrically charged follows these rules:

* Objects with like charges repel, or push away, from each other.

* Objects with unlike charges attract each other.

Because they have opposite charges, protons and electrons attract each other. However, because they have the same electric charge, protons do not attract each other. They repel, or push away, from each other. Electrons also repel each other.

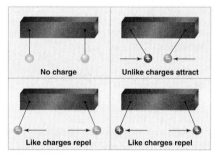

No charge | Unlike charges attract
Like charges repel | Like charges repel

▲ **Figure 20-2** How electric charges behave

▶ **EXPLAIN:** How do protons and electrons affect each other?

Teaching Options

❗ FAST FACTS *The Sound of Hot Air*

The static discharge of lightning briefly heats the air along its path to about 20,000°C (36,000°F). This is about three times the temperature of the surface of the Sun. The sudden heating of the air causes it to expand rapidly. This expansion causes the surrounding air to compress. The result is heard as thunder. Although thunder and lightning occur at almost the same time, people usually see the lightning before they hear the thunder because light travels faster than sound. You can estimate how far away the lightning is by first counting the length of time between the flash of lightning and the sound of the thunder. Then, to find the distance in miles, divide the number of seconds between the flash of lightning and the sound of thunder by 5. To find the distance in kilometers, divide the number of seconds by 3.

Neutral Objects Although an atom is made up of electrically charged particles, the atom as a whole has no electric charge. The number of protons and the number of electrons in an atom is always the same. Therefore, the electric charges cancel each other. The atom is neutral.

Most matter is electrically neutral. However, neutral objects can become electrically charged. An object becomes electrically charged when its atoms lose or gain electrons. The electrons in the atoms of some matter are held loosely to the atoms. If these electrons are separated from their atoms, the atoms become electrically charged. For example, when you walk across a carpet, your feet can rub off and pick up electrons from the carpet. Your body then gets a small electric charge. If you then touch a metal doorknob, electrons jump from your hand to the doorknob. You can see a spark.

3 ▶ **DESCRIBE:** Why are atoms usually neutral?

Static Electricity Protons are held tightly in the nucleus of all atoms. However, electrons are free to move from a region of negative electric charge to a region of positive electric charge. The buildup of electric charges on an object is called **static electricity**. The word *static* means "not moving." In static electricity, electrons do not flow. They remain at rest for a time but will eventually leave the object.

Static electricity can be produced when different materials rub against each other. For example, if a sock and a shirt rub against each other in a clothes dryer, electrons may be transferred between both items. The sock may lose some of its electrons to the shirt and become positively charged. The shirt gains these electrons and becomes negatively charged. Because the sock and the shirt have opposite charges, they stick to each other. This attraction is called static cling.

4 ▶ **INFER:** Why can a sock stick to a shirt after coming out of a clothes dryer?

Static Discharge Objects that have static electricity will eventually lose their charge. The extra electrons will move onto other objects, and the original object will return to its neutral condition. The loss of static electricity is called static discharge.

A dramatic example of static discharge is lightning. During a storm, water particles in clouds swirl around and rub against each other. This friction produces electric charges in different areas of the clouds. The negative area of the cloud repels the negatively charged electrons on the surface of the ground below. The surface of the ground then becomes positively charged. An attraction develops between the negatively charged area of the cloud and the positively charged ground. If the force of attraction becomes great enough, electrons from the cloud will jump to the ground. When this happens, a spark of lightning is produced.

▲ **Figure 20-3** The force of attraction between charges in clouds and the ground can produce lightning.

5 ▶ **EXPLAIN:** How does lightning occur?

✓ CHECKING CONCEPTS

1. An electron has a _____ charge.
2. A _____ object has neither a positive nor a negative charge.
3. Static electricity is the buildup of _____ on an object.
4. Two electrons will _____ each other.

💡 THINKING CRITICALLY

5. **EXPLAIN:** What can happen if you walk across a carpet and then touch a metal doorknob?
6. **INFER:** Why is the buildup of electric charge on an object called static electricity?

INTERPRETING VISUALS

Use Figure 20-2 to answer the following questions.

7. **INFER:** How do like charges behave?
8. **EXPLAIN:** How do objects without a charge behave?

CHAPTER 20: Electricity **429**

Discussion Ask volunteers to describe experiences they have had with static electricity. Tell students that the plastics and synthetic fabrics in wide use today easily become electrically charged. This accounts for their clinging quality. Crackling sounds and sometimes visible discharges can be noticed when handling these fabrics in dry air. The self-adhering quality of plastic food wrap is also a result of static charge.
learning styles: auditory, linguistic

Answers to questions

1 ▶ **NAME:** protons, neutrons, and electrons

2 ▶ **EXPLAIN:** They attract each other.

3 ▶ **DESCRIBE:** The number of protons and electrons are usually the same, and their charges cancel each other.

4 ▶ **INFER:** because they have opposite charges

5 ▶ **EXPLAIN:** Electrons from a cloud are attracted to the positively charged ground below. If the force of attraction becomes great enough, charges will move between the cloud and the ground.

3 Assess

✓ CHECKING CONCEPTS ANSWERS

1. negative
2. neutral
3. electric charges
4. repel

💡 THINKING CRITICALLY ANSWERS

5. **EXPLAIN:** The body picks up electrons from the carpet and has an electric charge. The electrons jump from the hand to the doorknob, causing a spark.
6. **INFER:** because *static* means "not moving," and the electrons do not flow

4 Close

INTERPRETING VISUALS ANSWERS

7. **INFER:** They repel each other.
8. **EXPLAIN:** Possible answer: They have no effect on each other.

• *TEACHING RESOURCES* •

💿 **Teacher's Resources CD-ROM**
Lesson Review: Chapter 20, p. 2
Model of an Atom: Visuals, p. 5

ONGOING ASSESSMENT

Recognizing Charges Tell students that a certain atom has eight electrons and eight protons. Ask students what charge the atom would have if it had seven electrons and eight protons. (positive) Ask students what charge the atom would have if it had nine electrons and eight protons. (negative)

Lab Activity

(pp. 430–431)

1 Prepare the Lab

Observing Static Electricity

SET-UP TIME: ⏱ **LAB TIME:** ⏱

BACKGROUND: When two objects are rubbed together, they become charged only if electrons move from one object to the other. The object that gains the electrons gains a negative charge. The object that loses electrons gains a positive charge. Which object loses electrons and which object gains electrons depends on how tightly the objects hold electrons. When a wool sweater rubs against cotton, the wool loses electrons. When a wool sweater rubs against hair, the hair loses electrons. When plastic is rubbed with silk in this activity, the silk tends to give up electrons and the plastic becomes negatively charged.

PURPOSE: Students will observe static electricity by giving a plastic pen a charge and using it to pick up a sheet of spiral-shaped tracing paper.

SCIENCE SKILLS: Students will **record** observations about what happens when a plastic pen is first placed above tracing paper and then what happens after the pen is rubbed with silk and placed above the paper. They will **analyze** the different results. Students will **infer** the purpose of rubbing the pen with silk and the reason tracing paper was used instead of regular paper. Students will also **hypothesize** what eventually happens to the spiral tracing paper.

ADVANCE PLANNING: Gather the materials you will need for the lab. A cardboard template of a circle with a 20-cm diameter can be made ahead of time. Students can trace the template instead of using a compass.

2 Guide the Lab

PROCEDURE: Divide students into pairs. Discuss the procedures. Emphasize the importance of using care when working with the tracing paper because it tears easily. Make sure that students understand that the pen should be placed slightly above the center of the spiral but should not touch it. Have students copy the chart before

---

LAB ACTIVITY
Observing Static Electricity

Materials
Sheet of tracing paper
Compass
Ruler
Scissors
Plastic pen
Metal pie plate
Piece of silk

BACKGROUND
Static electricity is produced when different materials rub against each other. Electrons from one object may be gained by another object. The object that loses electrons becomes positively charged. The object that gains electrons becomes negatively charged. The opposite charges cause the two objects to stick to each other.

PURPOSE
In this activity, you will observe how static electricity can attract an object.

PROCEDURE

1. Copy the chart in Figure 20-4 onto a sheet of paper.

2. Use a compass to lightly draw a large circle on a sheet of tracing paper. The circle should be about 20 cm in diameter. Be careful not to tear the tracing paper.

3. Use scissors to cut the circle out of the tracing paper. Place the tip of a pen in the center of the circle. Draw a spiral that goes all the way to the very edge of the circle. Again, draw carefully so that you do not tear the tracing paper.

4. Carefully cut along the spiral line that you drew. When you are finished, you should have one long continuous piece of tracing paper. Lay the spiral in a metal pie plate.

5. Place the end of your pen above the center of the spiral without touching the tracing paper. Observe what happens. Record your observations on the chart.

6. Rub your pen with a piece of silk a few times. Again, place the end of the pen slightly above the center of the spiral. Do not touch the tracing paper. Slowly lift your pen up. Observe what happens. Record your observations.

▲ STEP 2 Draw a 20-cm-wide circle on tracing paper.

▲ STEP 4 Cut along the spiral line.

430

Teaching Options

❗ FAST FACTS *Materials Likely to Give Up Electrons*

Scientists have developed a list that ranks some common materials from ones that are the most likely to lose electrons to those that are the most likely to gain electrons. If two materials on the list are rubbed together, the material that is higher on the list is more likely to give up electrons. The human hand and human hair are high on the list and tend to give up electrons. Plastic wrap and polyester are low on the list.

EXTENDING THE LESSON

Increasing and Decreasing the Imbalance of Charges Rubbing does not actually cause electrons to move from one object to another. The amount of surface area that comes in contact with the object affects the number of electrons that are gained or lost. Rubbing objects together increases the imbalance of charges by increasing the surface area that has contact. Have volunteers describe what might decrease the imbalance of charges. (Moisture in the air and on objects carries extra electrons away from objects.)

▲ STEP 5 Place your pen above the center of the spiral.

▲ STEP 6 Rub your pen with a piece of silk.

Observing Static Electricity

Experiment	Observations
Pen above spiral	
Pen above spiral after rubbing with a piece of silk	

▲ **Figure 20-4** Copy this chart and use it to record your observations.

CONCLUSIONS

1. OBSERVE: What happened the first time you placed your pen above the spiral tracing paper? What happened after you rubbed the pen with the piece of silk?

2. ANALYZE: Why was there a different result?

3. INFER: What was the purpose of rubbing the pen with the piece of silk?

4. INFER: Why did you use tracing paper instead of regular paper?

5. HYPOTHESIZE: After Step 6, what eventually happened to the spiral tracing paper?

Tips for Using Technology

Word Processing Software
Have students use word processing software to write a short description of their lab observations. A simple word processing program allows them to do basic tasks such as entering and editing text. A more complex word processing program allows students to make tables, draw pictures, do math, and make graphs. Remind students to use the spell check before printing their word processing documents to share with the class.

• TEACHING RESOURCES •

Teacher's Resources CD-ROM
Lab Activity Report: Study Tools, pp. 16–17

Laboratory Activity Rubric: Teaching Tools, p. 8

Laboratory Manual
Lab. Skills Worksheet 4: Organizing and Analyzing Data, pp. 13–14

beginning the activity. Provide students with a copy of the Lab Activity Report found on the Teacher's Resources CD-ROM to record their observations and conclusions.

TROUBLESHOOTING: This activity works best when the humidity in the classroom is low. If the humidity is high, try placing the tracing paper in an air-conditioned room overnight and bringing it into the classroom when students are ready to use it. If the charged pen is not picking up the spiral, encourage students to rub it more with the silk cloth.

EXPECTED OUTCOME: The pen should have no effect on the spiral before it is rubbed. After being rubbed with silk, the pen should attract the spiral, and students should be able to lift the spiral off the pie tin.

3 Conclude the Lab

1. OBSERVE: Nothing; The pen attracted the tracing paper and picked it up.
2. ANALYZE: The pen was neutral the first time, but became electrically charged after being rubbed with silk.
3. INFER: to give the pen a charge
4. INFER: Tracing paper is more easily attracted to a charged object because it is thinner and lighter.
5. HYPOTHESIZE: Possible answers: The paper and pen lost their charges, the spiral was no longer attracted to the pen, or the spiral fell back to the pie plate.

Use the Laboratory Activity Rubric on the Teacher's Resources CD-ROM to assess students' lab activities. Fill in the rubric with the additional information below. For this activity, students should have:

- performed the activity according to the procedure and filled in the chart with data collected during the activity.
- correctly answered the questions in complete sentences.

4 Extend the Lab

Ask volunteers to comb their hair with a rubber comb. Tell them that they are rubbing electrons off each strand of hair. Ask students to predict what this will do. (Hair has a positive charge and will be attracted by the negatively charged comb. The strands of hair have the same charge and will repel each other.)

1 Introduce

INVESTIGATE

TIME: 15–20 minutes

PURPOSE: Students will make a wet cell from a lemon.

MATERIALS: two 25-cm pieces of copper wire, strip of copper, strip of zinc, lemon, magnetic compass

PROCEDURE: Have students wrap an end of a wire around one end of a copper strip. Then, have them wrap an end of the other wire around one end of a zinc strip. Tell students to make sure that bare wire is touching the metal strips. Have students gently push and roll the lemon on a table to release more juice inside the lemon. Then, have students insert the free end of the copper strip into one end of the lemon and the free end of the zinc strip into the other end, making sure that the strips do not touch. Have students wrap the free ends of the wires around the compass.

THINK ABOUT IT: It moves. Possible answers: An electric current or a magnetic field was produced.

✎ **STUDY HINT** Before beginning this lesson, read the lesson objectives and the Key Terms aloud so that students can hear their pronunciations.

Linking Prior Knowledge Have students review how ions in solution conduct electricity (Lesson 9-6). Ask students if distilled water will conduct electricity. (no)

2 Teach

Discussion Bring a variety of dry cells to class. Show students the negative and positive terminals. Then, refer students to Figure 20-6 and ask a volunteer to describe the electrodes and electrolyte of a dry cell. **learning styles: visual, auditory**

Answers to questions

1▶ DEFINE: Possible answer: A series of devices that change chemical energy into electrical energy

2▶ IDENTIFY: a negative pole, a positive pole, and an electrolyte

3▶ CONTRAST: In a dry cell, the electrolyte is a moist paste. In a wet cell, the electrolyte is an acid or a base in a solution.

20-2 What is a battery?

INVESTIGATE

Making a Lemon Wet Cell
HANDS-ON ACTIVITY

1. Wrap several turns of wire around a magnetic compass.
2. Wrap one end of the wire around the end of a strip of copper. Wrap the other end of the wire around the end of a strip of zinc.
3. Insert the free end of the copper strip into the side of a lemon. Insert the free end of the zinc strip next to the copper strip. Make sure that the strips do not touch each other.

THINK ABOUT IT: What happens to the needle of the compass? What do you think takes place?

STEP 3

Objectives

Identify a battery as a series of electrochemical cells that are connected together. Compare a wet cell and a dry cell.

Key Terms

electrochemical cell: device that changes chemical energy to electrical energy

battery: a series of electrochemical cells that are connected to each other

electrolyte: substance that forms ions when melted or dissolved in water

Electrochemical Cell Under certain conditions, chemical energy can be converted to electrical energy. A device that changes chemical energy to electrical energy is called an **electrochemical cell**. A series of two or more electrochemical cells that are connected to each other is called a **battery**.

1▶ DEFINE: What is a battery?

Wet Cell The simplest type of electrochemical cell is called a wet cell. A wet cell is made up of a negative pole, a positive pole, and an electrolyte. An **electrolyte** is a substance that forms ions when melted or dissolved in water. The electrolyte in most wet cells is an acid or a base. The negative and positive poles of a wet cell are called electrodes. The ions transfer the negative charge between the electrodes in a cell. Zinc can be used

as a negative electrode. Copper can be used as a positive electrode.

A chemical reaction in a wet cell causes electrons to move from the copper electrode to the zinc electrode. As Figure 20-5 shows, when the two electrodes are connected to each other by a metal wire, electrons flow from the zinc electrode through the wire to the copper electrode.

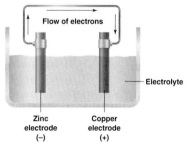

Flow of electrons

Electrolyte

Zinc electrode (−) Copper electrode (+)

▲ **Figure 20-5** Outside a wet cell, electrons flow through a wire from the negative electrode to the positive electrode.

2▶ IDENTIFY: What are the three parts of a wet cell?

Dry Cell A dry cell is used as a source of electrical energy in flashlights and portable electronic devices. A dry cell works in the same way that a wet cell does. The electrolyte is a moist paste inside the cell. The zinc casing of the cell is the negative electrode. The positive electrode runs down the center of the battery and is usually made of carbon.

Teaching Options

⚠ FAST FACTS Different Parts for Batteries

Although all batteries contain two electrodes and an electrolyte, the materials they are composed of can differ. The dry-cell battery in Figure 20-6 is a zinc-carbon battery. The electrodes are zinc and carbon, and the electrolyte is an acidic paste. The electrodes in alkaline batteries are zinc and manganese oxide. The electrolyte is an alkaline paste. Rechargeable lead-acid batteries have lead and lead-oxide electrodes with a very acidic electrolyte. Rechargeable nickel-cadmium batteries have electrodes that are made of nickel hydroxide and cadmium, and their electrolyte is potassium hydroxide.

◈ INTEGRATING LIFE SCIENCE

Replacing Batteries in Medical Devices Pacemakers are devices that can be implanted in a person's body to help the heart beat normally. A tiny generator contains a computer and a battery that runs it. The battery usually lasts for 5 to 8 years. When it is time for the battery to be replaced, the whole generator is replaced in a simple surgical procedure. Have interested students search library or Internet sources to find out what kinds of batteries are used in pacemakers. Have them report their findings to the class.

When the two electrodes are connected by a conductor, electrons flow through the conductor from the carbon to the zinc.

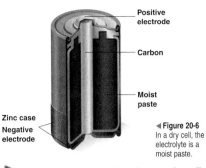

Positive electrode

Carbon

Moist paste

Zinc case
Negative electrode

◄ **Figure 20-6**
In a dry cell, the electrolyte is a moist paste.

3 CONTRAST: How is the electrolyte in a dry cell different from that in a wet cell?

✓ CHECKING CONCEPTS

1. A series of electrochemical cells that are connected to each other makes up a _____.

2. A _____ cell is used in a flashlight.

3. An electrochemical cell converts chemical energy into _____ energy.

4. The negative electrode of a wet cell is usually made of _____.

💡 THINKING CRITICALLY

5. ANALYZE: In a wet cell, the electrons flow from the zinc electrode to the copper electrode. Why do they not flow from the copper to the zinc?

Web InfoSearch

Rechargeable Batteries Batteries that can be used over and over again are called rechargeable batteries. Two types of rechargeable batteries are lithium batteries and nickel-cadmium batteries. These types of batteries can be used in cellular phones, laptop computers, and digital cameras.

SEARCH: Use the Internet to find out how they work. Start your search at www.conceptsandchallenges.com. Some key search words are **batteries** and **rechargeable**.

Real-Life Science

DISPOSAL OF BATTERIES

Every year, Americans use billions of batteries. When used up, most of these batteries are thrown into the trash. These batteries are then buried in landfills or they are burned in incinerators. However, batteries often contain poisonous metals that can leak into the groundwater through landfills. They can also be released into the air when batteries are incinerated, or burned. Two of these metals, mercury and cadmium, are very dangerous. Mercury can cause harm to the nervous systems in humans and in fish. Cadmium can cause cancer.

Batteries should be separated from ordinary trash and disposed of in special hazardous-waste landfills. Such landfills are built on top of clay to stop poisons from leaking into groundwater. Many cities now have special sites for the collection of batteries. To prevent the release of dangerous materials into the environment, we must dispose of batteries safely.

Thinking Critically Why is the proper disposal of batteries so important?

▲ **Figure 20-7** The proper disposal of batteries is an important environmental concern.

ONGOING ASSESSMENT

Explaining Batteries Ask a volunteer to use Figure 20-5 to explain the parts of a wet-cell battery and how it works. Then, ask another volunteer to use Figure 20-6 to explain the parts of a dry-cell battery and how it works. Ask other volunteers to explain what the two kinds of batteries have in common and how they are different.
learning styles: visual, linguistic

• TEACHING RESOURCES •

Teacher's Resources CD-ROM
Lesson Review: Chapter 20, p. 3
Wet Cell and Dry Cell: Visuals, p. 13

Reinforcement Have students look at Figure 20-5. Explain that in both a wet cell and a dry cell, electrons move from a negative electrode to a positive electrode. learning styles: visual, auditory

3 Assess

✓ CHECKING CONCEPTS ANSWERS

1. battery
2. dry
3. electrical
4. zinc

💡 THINKING CRITICALLY ANSWER

5. ANALYZE: Electrons flow from the negative electrode (zinc) to the positive electrode (copper), not from positive to negative.

4 Close

Web InfoSearch

Rechargeable Batteries Have students use the Internet to find out how rechargeable batteries work. Some key search words are **rechargeable batteries** and **types of batteries**. Students should begin their search at www.conceptsand challenges.com.

Real-Life Science

DISPOSAL OF BATTERIES

Real-Life Connection Many of the batteries that students use are alkaline batteries. If an alkaline battery is damaged, the potassium hydroxide it contains can leak out and cause severe chemical burns to the skin or eyes. If potassium hydroxide gets on the skin or in the eyes, it should be quickly washed off with large amounts of water. The potassium hydroxide can also leak out of an old or damaged battery in a flashlight or other devices and cause damage.

Thinking Critically Answer
Possible answer: They contain poisonous metals that can leak into groundwater or be released into the air.

1 Introduce

STUDY HINT Before beginning this lesson, have students write the title of each section in outline format in their notebooks. As they read this lesson, have them write the main idea of each section.

Linking Prior Knowledge Have students review the properties of metals and nonmetals (Lessons 3-8, 11-1). Ask student to compare the ability of metals and nonmetals to conduct electricity. (Most metals are good conductors of electricity. Nonmetals generally are poor conductors of electricity.)

2 Teach

Discussion Most students probably are aware that copper is used for electrical wiring. Ask students why metals, such as copper, are good conductors of electricity. (They allow electric charges or electrons to flow through them easily.) Ask a volunteer to explain why the copper wires in electrical cords are covered with a nonmetal, such as rubber. (The rubber is not a good conductor of electricity and keeps the electric charges from leaving the wire.) **learning styles: auditory, linguistic**

Answers to questions

▶ **DEFINE:** a material that allows electric charges to flow through it easily

▶ **INFER:** Electrons will not flow.

▶ **EXPLAIN:** to prevent electric charges from leaving the wire

READING STRATEGY *Conduct* comes from a word that means "to escort or lead." *Insulate* comes from a word that means "island." Have students find the definitions of *conduct* and *insulate* in a dictionary. Tell them to look for words in the definition that can help them remember that a conductor allows electricity to flow through it easily and an insulator prevents electricity from flowing through it easily. (conduct: transmit, convey, lead; insulate: isolate, separate from)

20-3 What are insulators and conductors?

Objective
List some examples of conductors and insulators.

Key Terms
conductor: material through which electric charge can flow easily

insulator: material through which electric charge does not flow easily

Conductors A material through which electric charge can flow easily is called a **conductor**. Most metals are good conductors of electricity.

If a metal wire is placed between the positive and negative poles of a battery, a path is created so that electrons can flow. Suppose metal wires are used to attach a light source to the positive and negative poles of a battery. Electrons will flow through the wire and the light bulb will light up. If a piece of rubber is used instead of metal wires, electrons will not flow. The light bulb will not light up.

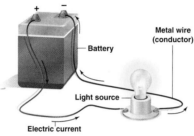

▲ **Figure 20-8** Electrons will flow if a metal wire is attached to both poles of a battery.

Some conductors are better than others. Wire made of copper is one of the best conductors of electricity. Wire made of aluminum is lighter and is less expensive than wire made of copper. However, aluminum is not as good a conductor of electricity.

▶ **DEFINE:** What is a conductor?

434

Insulators A material through which electric charge does not flow easily is called an **insulator**. Rubber is an insulator. When a piece of rubber is placed between two oppositely charged objects, charges will not flow. Electrons in the atoms of rubber are held tightly together so that they cannot move freely throughout the material. Other insulators are cork, wood, cloth, plastic, and air.

▶ **INFER:** What happens when a piece of rubber is placed between two oppositely charged objects?

Insulated Wires Electrical cords use both insulators and conductors. The conductor is usually made of copper. The copper wire is covered with an insulator, such as rubber. The rubber prevents electric charges from leaving the bare wire.

The rubber insulation of electric cords may become cracked or worn. Such electric cords are dangerous because they can cause a short circuit. A short circuit results when two uninsulated wires touch, allowing a large amount of electric charge to jump between them. Wires carrying too much charge can become very hot, perhaps causing a fire.

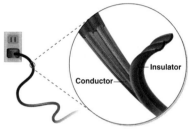

▲ **Figure 20-9** Most household cords have two wires covered with rubber insulation to prevent electric charges from leaving the wire.

▶ **EXPLAIN:** Why are electric cords often covered with rubber?

Teaching Options

RETEACH

Demonstration Display examples of insulators, such as rubber, cork, and plastic, and conductors, such as a copper wire, a metal paper clip, aluminum foil, and a coin. Place the items into two groups by asking students to tell if each item is a conductor or an insulator. If possible, use a conductivity tester to test the items for conductivity. Ask students what kind of materials are insulators. (nonmetals) Ask what kind of materials are conductors. (metals) **learning styles: visual, auditory**

ONGOING ASSESSMENT

Identifying Problems With Electrical Cords Ask students to explain what can happen if the insulation covering an electrical cord is worn off, cracked, or damaged in some way that exposed the wire inside the cord. Have a volunteer explain to the class what a short circuit is. **learning styles: auditory, linguistic**

1. A _____ allows current to flow easily through it.
2. Rubber is an _____ because it does not allow an electric charge to flow easily through it.
3. In an insulated electrical wire, the conductor is often _____.
4. An electric cord is safe to touch because it is covered with _____.
5. If two conducting wires in an electric cord touch, a _____ will result.
6. Cork is a good _____.
7. A copper wire is one of the best _____.
8. A short circuit results when two _____ wires touch, allowing an electric charge to jump between them.

9. INFER: A lightning rod is supposed to keep a bolt of lightning from damaging a house. The rod is placed at the top of the house and is connected to the ground. What material would make a good lightning rod? Explain.
10. COMPARE: How is a conductor different from an insulator? Give an example of each.
11. APPLY: Why is it safe to use an insulated wire but not safe to use an uninsulated wire?

HEALTH AND SAFETY TIP

You should not try to repair or rewire electric appliances yourself. They use large amounts of electricity and can be quite dangerous. Frayed or worn electric wires can cause a bad electric shock. What should you do if wires or appliances in your home need repair?

People in Science
BENJAMIN FRANKLIN (1706–1790)

Benjamin Franklin was a politician, a writer, a businessman, and an inventor. He is probably most famous for an experiment that he performed in the summer of 1752. One night, Benjamin Franklin tied a key to the string of a kite. He then flew the kite during an electrical storm. He was hoping to collect an electric charge from lightning directly onto the key. He wanted to prove that lightning is really an electric charge sent through the air. During the experiment, Franklin was successful in conducting the charge from lightning to the key.

Franklin performed many experiments with lightning during the course of his life. Because he understood the danger of electricity, Franklin invented the lightning rod to protect ships and buildings. He realized that lightning is attracted to tall, pointed objects. So, he invented a pointed metal object that could be mounted on the roof of tall structures. When lightning occurred, lightning bolts would be attracted to the metal rod rather than to the ship or the building.

In addition to being the first person to understand that lightning is a huge electric discharge, Benjamin Franklin also gave the names *positive* and *negative* to opposite electric charges.

Thinking Critically Why is Benjamin Franklin's experiment with the kite considered dangerous?

▲ **Figure 20-10** Benjamin Franklin conducted lightning to the ground by using a kite and a key.

MORE ON THE WEB

Lightning Protection Systems
Have students visit www.conceptsandchallenges.com to view diagrams of homes that have lightning protection systems installed. Have students design a community bulletin board complete with diagrams and an explanation of how the systems work.

• **TEACHING RESOURCES** •

Teacher's Resources CD-ROM
Lesson Review: Chapter 20, p. 4
Laboratory Manual
Lab. Challenge: How are electrical conductors different from insulators? pp. 97–100
Laboratory Video
Segment 22: Comparing Electrical Conductors and Insulators

---

3 Assess

✓ CHECKING CONCEPTS ANSWERS

1. conductor
2. insulator
3. copper
4. Accept any of the following: rubber, insulator, or rubber insulation.
5. short circuit
6. insulator
7. conductors
8. uninsulated

THINKING CRITICALLY ANSWERS

9. INFER: a material that is a conductor because its purpose is to conduct the electric charges to the ground
10. COMPARE: A conductor allows electric charges to flow through it easily, but an insulator does not. Possible conductors include copper or aluminum. Possible insulators include rubber or cork.
11. APPLY: An insulated wire keeps the electric charges from leaking out, but an uninsulated wire allows the electric charges to move out of the wire and can lead to short circuits and fires.

4 Close

HEALTH AND SAFETY TIP

Possible answers: Stop using the wires and appliances that need repair, tell an adult about the problem, have a professional fix the wires and appliances or replace them.

People in Science
BENJAMIN FRANKLIN (1706–1790)

Background Benjamin Franklin most likely flew his kite with the attached metal key during the beginning of a thunderstorm before lightning became dangerous. From the clouds, the kite collected negative charges that traveled down the string to the key. He might have held a piece of silk to keep electric charges from traveling to his body. When he reached his hand toward the key, a spark occurred. He found that clouds can contain electric charges, and he inferred that lightning is an electrical spark.

Thinking Critically Answer
Possible answers: Lightning could have followed the string to Benjamin Franklin's body and electrocuted him.

1 Introduce

STUDY HINT Before beginning this lesson, have students write the lesson title and objective in their notebooks. As students read the lesson, tell them to write the information that meets the objective.

Linking Prior Knowledge Ask volunteers where they have seen huge towers or poles supporting the wires that carry electricity to homes and businesses. Tell students that these wires carry a different kind of electric current than batteries do.

2 Teach

Demonstration Show students a radio that can operate with batteries or by plugging into an outlet. Turn the radio on without plugging it in. Ask students what is supplying the electricity for the radio. (batteries) Tell students that a battery produces a direct current. Then, plug the radio into an outlet. Ask students what is supplying the electricity for the radio. Although students might answer the outlet or the wires in the wall, point out that the source of the electricity is a power plant. Tell students that an alternating current flows through the wires.
learning styles: visual, auditory

Answers to questions

1 EXPLAIN: Static electricity does not flow, and appliances need a flow of electricity.

2 DEFINE: current that always flows in the same direction

3 DEFINE: current that reverses direction at a regular rate

WRITING HINT Before students submit a piece of writing, encourage them to write a draft of what they want to say. Then, have students read the draft to find out if they want to add information and if the information they included makes sense.

20-4 What are two kinds of electric current?

Objective
Differentiate between direct current and alternating current.

Key Terms
electric current: flow of electric charge through a conductor

direct current: current in which electrons always flow in the same direction

alternating current: current in which electrons constantly change direction at a regular rate

Useful Electricity You have learned that the electric charges that build up on objects with static electricity do not flow. Instead, these negative charges can jump between objects. Static electricity cannot be used to run the electrical appliances in your home. In order for electricity to be useful, the electric charges must flow steadily.

When a conductor is connected to an appliance and to the opposite poles of a battery, electrons will flow steadily through the conductor. The flow of electric charge through a conductor is called an **electric current**. An electric current is like a stream of water. However, instead of a flow of water, it is a continuous flow of electrons.

1 EXPLAIN: Why can static electricity not be used to run electrical appliances?

Direct Current An electric current in which charges flow in one direction only is called **direct current (DC)**. The current produced by electrochemical cells, including dry cells, is direct current. Figure 20-11 shows two dry cells in a flashlight. When the flashlight is turned on, the electric current produced by the dry cells keeps the bulb lit. Notice that the current flows in one direction.

436

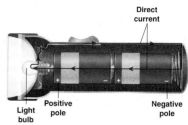
▲ Figure 20-11 The arrows show the path followed by direct current in a flashlight.

2 DEFINE: What is direct current?

Alternating Current A second type of electric current does not flow in one direction only. An **alternating current (AC)** constantly changes direction at a regular rate. Most of the electricity found in homes, schools, and businesses is alternating current.

The main advantage of alternating current over direct current is that alternating current can be transported more easily over long distances. Another advantage is that the voltage of an alternating current can be increased or decreased.

▲ Figure 20-12 Electricity from power plants travels as alternating current to homes.

Teaching Options

! FAST FACTS *Direction of Electrical Currents*

There are two different models used to illustrate current flow in electrical circuit diagrams, both of which are correct. The Conventional Flow model is the popular method. It shows current travelling from positive to negative poles in a circuit. In some nonmetallic substances, positive charges actually do move in this direction. However, the Conventional Flow is opposite to the flow of electrons in metallic substances, which leads to some confusion. The Electron Flow model shows the direction that the electrons flow in a solid metal conductor, such as a wire. With this model, a circuit will show the direction of current flowing from negative to positive. This is the less popular method, although perhaps more scientifically accurate in some cases.

EXTENDING THE LESSON

Evaluating Advantages and Disadvantages Have students brainstorm and list advantages and disadvantages of using alternating current at home. (alternating current: advantage: available at the flip of a switch and does not run out, disadvantage: electricity can go off during storms or other problem)

Alternating current can be changed to direct current. In the home, many electronic devices such as computers, television sets, and CD players use direct current. Converters built into these devices are designed to change the alternating current from the household outlet to direct current.

▶ DEFINE: What is alternating current?

✓ CHECKING CONCEPTS

1. The flow of electric charge through a conductor is called _____.
2. Current that reverses direction at a regular rate is called _____ current.
3. A battery is a source of _____ current.
4. Most of the electricity that is used in everyday life comes from _____ current.
5. The type of electric current supplied by power plants is _____ current.

💡 THINKING CRITICALLY

6. COMPARE: How is alternating current different from direct current?
7. ANALYZE: A toy manufacturer is making an electric toy that plugs into a wall outlet. The toy needs direct current in order to operate. How should the toy be made?

DESIGNING AN EXPERIMENT

Design an experiment to solve the following problem. Include a hypothesis, variables, a procedure, and a type of data to study.

PROBLEM: Will a battery last longer if it is kept in a freezer before it is used?

◈ Integrating Life Science

TOPICS: nervous system, adaptation, predator, prey

ANIMALS THAT USE ELECTRICITY

Electric currents, or impulses, are also found in living things. The nervous system of most organisms uses electric charges. Some organisms, however, have more specialized uses of electricity.

An electric eel can stun or kill its prey with a strong electric charge. The electric eel has special musclelike cells that generate electricity. Eels also use their electric ability for self-defense against predators.

The duck-billed platypus uses electricity to find its food, even in total darkness. Duck-billed platypuses live in streams in Australia. With a special sense that detects electricity, they can find tasty crayfish and other prey, even at night in muddy water. The platypus has a special organ on the end of its soft bill that picks up faint electric signals coming from the muscles of animals swimming nearby.

Animals that produce and use electricity are usually found in water habitats. They are not found on land because water can conduct electricity, whereas air is a good insulator.

Thinking Critically Do you think that an electric eel can produce electricity out of water as well as it does in water? Explain your answer.

▲ **Figure 20-13** An electric eel (top) and a platypus (bottom) both use electricity to survive.

---

3 Assess

✓ CHECKING CONCEPTS ANSWERS

1. electric current
2. alternating
3. direct
4. alternating
5. alternating

💡 THINKING CRITICALLY ANSWERS

6. COMPARE: The charges in alternating current reverse direction at a regular rate, but in direct current, the charges always flow in the same direction.
7. ANALYZE: The toy should be made with a built-in converter that changes alternating current to direct current.

4 Close

DESIGNING AN EXPERIMENT

Use the Designing an Experiment Rubric on the Teacher's Resources CD-ROM to assess students' experiments. Fill in the rubric with the additional information below. For this assignment, students should have:

- written a hypothesis that explained what effect freezing would have on a battery.
- compared, in the procedure, a battery that had been kept in a freezer and a battery that had not been kept in a freezer.

◈ Integrating Life Science

TOPICS: nervous system, adaptation, predator, prey

ANIMALS THAT USE ELECTRICITY

Life-Science Connection Neurons in animals are special cells that transmit electrical signals called nerve impulses. These signals can move through a neuron because of an imbalance of charges inside and outside the neuron's membrane. When the neuron is stimulated, ions move through the membrane, changing the charges. In animals such as mammals, neurons located in the sense organs collect information from the environment and send the information to the brain, which interprets it. The neurons in the brain then send electrical signals with directions back to the body through neurons.

Thinking Critically Answer
no, because water is a better conductor of electricity than are land or air

---

MORE ON THE WEB

Simulating Alternating Current
Have students use the Internet to simulate an alternating current circuit. Students will see how voltage and current directions change with each cycle. Have students visit www.conceptsandchallenges.com for more details.

• TEACHING RESOURCES •

◉ **Teacher's Resources CD-ROM**
Lesson Review: Chapter 20, p. 5

Designing an Experiment: Study Tools, p. 14

Designing an Experiment Rubric: Teaching Tools, p. 7

1 Introduce

⊙ INVESTIGATE

TIME: 10–15 minutes

PURPOSE: Students will make a simple electric circuit.

MATERIALS: D-cell battery, 2 pieces of insulated wire with ends stripped (about 25 cm each), flashlight bulb in a holder

PROCEDURE: Students should connect one end of both wires to the light bulb holder and then touch the other ends of the wires to the two ends of the battery. **learning styles: visual, tactile**

THINK ABOUT IT: The wires allow electricity to flow through them. The three main parts are the battery, the wires, and the bulb.

🖊 **STUDY HINT** Before beginning this lesson, have students compare Figures 20-14 and 20-15. Ask students what parts both figures have in common.

Linking Prior Knowledge Tell students that when they turn on a lamp or a ceiling light, they are using a circuit. Ask students to name some other devices that work because of a circuit.

2 Teach

Demonstration Make a simple series circuit with a light bulb, a 6-volt dry cell, and a switch to show how a series circuit and a closed circuit work. Trace the single path that the electric current follows in the circuit. Ask students what kind of circuit was made. (series) Ask what happens when the switch is on, or closed. (The bulb lights.) **learning styles: visual, auditory**

Discussion Ask students to use Figure 20-16 to describe the path of the electric current in a series circuit that has two light bulbs. Ask what would happen if one of the light bulbs was disconnected. Make sure that students understand that the current flows from the positive terminal of the battery and follows a single path through all the parts of the circuit. If any part of the circuit is removed or does not allow electricity to flow through it, the circuit is not closed and no electric current will flow. **learning styles: visual, auditory**

20-5 What is a series circuit?

INVESTIGATE

Making an Electric Circuit
HANDS-ON ACTIVITY

1. Obtain a dry-cell (size D) battery, two insulated wires, and one light bulb in a holder from your teacher.
2. Connect the light bulb holder to the battery by using the wires. You will know if you have connected everything properly when the light bulb lights up.

THINK ABOUT IT: What purpose do the wires serve? What are the three main parts to this setup?

STEP 2

Objectives
Explain how electricity flows through a closed circuit. Describe a series circuit.

Key Terms
electric circuit: path that an electric current follows

series circuit: circuit in which electric current follows only one path

Circuits An **electric circuit** is the path that an electric current follows. All electric circuits have three parts: a source of electric energy, a load or device that uses the electric energy, and wires. The source of the electric energy can be a battery or a wall outlet. The load can be a light bulb, an appliance, or some other electric device. Wires connect the source to the load.

▲ **Figure 20-14** An electric circuit has three parts: a source, wires, and a load.

▶ **DEFINE:** What is an electric circuit?

438

Open and Closed Circuits What would happen if the only bridge over a river was closed for repair? Vehicles using that bridge would not be able to cross the river. The path that connects both sides of the river would no longer be complete. The same situation occurs in an electric circuit. If the electric circuit is not complete, then the electric charges cannot flow. An electric circuit that is incomplete or has a break in the pathway is called an open circuit. Electric charges cannot flow through an open circuit. Electric charges can flow only through a complete or closed circuit. In a closed circuit, there are no breaks in the path.

A switch is used to control (open and close) an electric circuit. When a switch is in the "off" position, the circuit is open. Electric charges will not flow when a switch is in the off position. When the switch is in the "on" position, the circuit is closed. Electric charges will flow when the switch is in the on position.

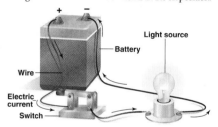

▲ **Figure 20-15** Electric charges flow when a switch is in the closed, or on, position.

▶ **EXPLAIN:** Why is a switch used in an electric circuit?

Teaching Options

RETEACH

Identifying Switches Most electrical devices have a switch as a part of their circuits. Have students work in groups to list all the different kinds of switches in their homes. (Possible answers: thermostat, light switches on walls and lamps, light switch in refrigerator and oven, on/off switches on small appliances, lever on a toaster) Ask students if a circuit is open or closed when one of these switches is on. (closed) Then, have volunteers from each group read their lists as you write the kinds of switches on the board.
learning styles: auditory, linguistic

ONGOING ASSESSMENT

Identifying the Parts of a Circuit Ask volunteers to name the three parts of all electric circuits and to describe each part in Figures 20-14, 20-15, and 20-16. Ask what additional part is in Figures 20-14 and 20-15 but not in Figure 20-16. (on/off switch)
learning styles: visual, linguistic

Series Circuit The simplest type of electric circuit is called a **series circuit**. In a series circuit, the electric charges follow only one path through all elements of the circuit. Figure 20-16 shows a series circuit. In this circuit, a battery is connected to two light sources. The current goes through the first light, then through the second light, and then back to the battery.

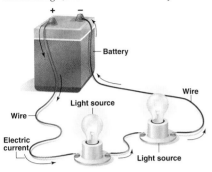

▲ **Figure 20-16** In a series circuit, electric current follows one path.

▶ **DEFINE:** What is a series circuit?

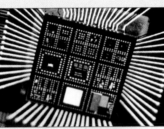
✓ CHECKING CONCEPTS

1. What is the path that an electric current follows called?
2. What are the three parts of an electric circuit?
3. In what kind of electric circuit does electric current follow only one path?
4. In which position will a switch allow electric charges to flow?

💡 THINKING CRITICALLY

5. **HYPOTHESIZE:** In a series circuit with two lamps, what do you think would happen if one of the lamps was not working? Explain your answer.

INTERPRETING VISUALS

Use Figure 20-15 to answer the following questions.

6. **IDENTIFY:** Which object is the load?
7. **HYPOTHESIZE:** What would happen if the switch was in the off position? Explain your answer.

Answers to questions

▶ **1 DEFINE:** the path that an electric current follows

▶ **2 EXPLAIN:** to open and close the circuit

▶ **3 DEFINE:** circuit in which electric current follows only one path

---

3 Assess

✓ CHECKING CONCEPTS ANSWERS

1. an electric circuit
2. source of electric current, a load or device that uses the electric energy, and wires
3. series circuit
4. the "on" position

💡 THINKING CRITICALLY ANSWER

5. **HYPOTHESIZE:** The other lamp would not work either because the circuit would be open.

INTERPRETING VISUALS ANSWERS

6. **IDENTIFY:** the light bulb
7. **HYPOTHESIZE:** The circuit would be open, no current could flow through it, and the bulb would not light.

---

4 Close

Science and Technology

COMPUTER CHIPS—INTEGRATED CIRCUITS

Discussion Without the invention of the integrated circuit, computers would be huge and too expensive for people to have in their homes. In fact, many of the devices used today would not be available. Ask students to name devices that would not exist without integrated circuits. (Some examples include video games, personal computers, digital cameras, telephone answering machines, microwave ovens, calculators, and digital and quartz watches.) Then, discuss how students' lives would be different.

Thinking Critically Answer
Possible answer: They are inexpensive and small.

20-6 (pp. 440-441)

1 Introduce

🔍 INVESTIGATE

TIME: 10–15 minutes

PURPOSE: Students will make a parallel circuit.

MATERIALS: D-cell battery, 4 pieces of insulated wire with ends stripped (about 25 cm each), 2 flashlight bulbs in holders

PROCEDURE: Students can connect the wires to the light bulb holders and then touch the two free ends of the wires to the two ends of the battery. Remind students that if they remove one bulb, the other bulb should stay lit. **learning styles: visual, auditory**

THINK ABOUT IT: The electric current can follow more than one path so that one bulb can be lit while the other one is not. In a series circuit, the electric current follows only one path. If one bulb is not lit, the other bulb cannot be lit either.

✏️ **STUDY HINT** Have students compare both illustrations in Figure 20-18. Ask them how these illustrations differ from each other.

Linking Prior Knowledge Ask volunteers for examples of times when the electricity suddenly went off in only part of their homes. Ask what electrical devices stopped working and what electrical devices kept on working.

2 Teach

Demonstration Construct a parallel circuit containing a 6-volt battery, three small 6-volt lamps, and a switch. Trace the three paths that the electric current may follow. Then, open the switch and replace one of the lamps with a burned-out lamp. Challenge students to predict what will happen when you close the switch. Students will observe that the current is still able to flow through the two remaining paths. **learning styles: visual, auditory**

Answers to questions

▶ **DEFINE:** circuit in which electric current can follow more than one path

▶ **DESCRIBE:** The current stops flowing.

20-6 What is a parallel circuit?

🔍 INVESTIGATE
Making Another Kind of Electric Circuit
HANDS-ON ACTIVITY

1. Obtain a dry-cell (size D) battery, four insulated wires, and two light bulbs in holders from your teacher.
2. Connect the light bulbs to the battery using the wires. Do not make a series circuit. Make sure that you use all four wires to create separate paths. You will know that you have correctly connected the wires when you remove one of the light bulbs and the other stays lit.

THINK ABOUT IT: What is the difference between this type of electric circuit and a series circuit?

STEP 2

Objectives
Describe a parallel circuit. Compare a parallel circuit and a series circuit.

Key Term
parallel circuit: circuit in which an electric current can follow more than one path

Parallel Circuit In a series circuit, there is only one path that an electric current can follow. In a **parallel circuit** an electric current can follow more than one path. The illustration on the right in Figure 20-18 shows a parallel circuit. Two lamps are connected to one battery. Notice how the wires are connected to each lamp. If one lamp goes out, charges can still flow through the other path. The other lamp will remain lit.

▶ **DEFINE:** What is a parallel circuit?

Series Circuits versus Parallel Circuits In a series circuit with two lamps, what would happen if one of the lamps went out? The charges flowing to that lamp would stop. Because there is a break in the path, neither lamp would light. This is a great disadvantage in using a series circuit.

However, if the two lamps were set up in a parallel circuit, this problem could be avoided. In a

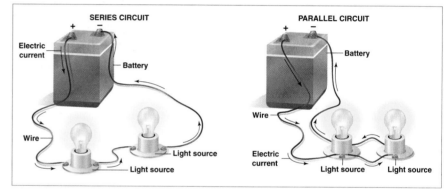

▲ **Figure 20-18** In a series circuit (left), electric current has only one path to follow. In a parallel circuit (right), electric current can follow more than one path.

440

Teaching Options

EXTENDING THE LESSON

Investigating Circuit Symbols Scientists, electricians, and other professionals who work with circuits use symbols to represent the different parts of circuits. Some of the symbols represent open and closed switches, wires, sources of electric current, and loads. Encourage interested students to find out more about the symbols used in circuit diagrams. Ask them to make a chart that shows the symbols and a circuit diagram that uses the symbols. Have volunteers share their chart and diagram with the class. **learning styles: visual, tactile**

RETEACH

Identifying Circuits If possible, bring in a string of holiday lights that are in a series circuit and another string of lights that are in a parallel circuit. Turn on both strings of lights to show students that they work. Then, unscrew a light in each string just enough to break the connection. (Caution: If you remove the lights, replace them with burned-out bulbs instead of leaving an open socket.) Ask students to explain which one is a series circuit and which one is a parallel circuit. **learning styles: visual, linguistic**

parallel circuit, the current can follow more than one path. If the lamps were connected in different paths, one lamp would not stop working if the other lamp went out. Because the charges could follow different paths, electric current could still reach the other lamp. This is the reason why electric circuits in homes and businesses are parallel circuits.

 DESCRIBE: What happens to the current in a series circuit when a lamp goes out?

✓ CHECKING CONCEPTS

1. In a _____ circuit, the current follows only one path.
2. In a _____ circuit, the current can follow more than one path.
3. Homes, offices, and schools use _____ electric circuits.

People in Science
ELECTRICIAN

An electrician is a person who is trained to install and repair electric equipment. An electrician must know how much electricity a building needs. A house with basic appliances such as a refrigerator and a television needs a certain amount of electricity. A high-rise apartment building needs much more electricity.

Most homes have wall outlets that supply a certain amount of electricity. However, different kinds of appliances may need a different amount of electricity. An electrician has to make sure that the correct amount is being used. An electrician must also be familiar with different types of wires. Most houses use copper wiring, but some use aluminum. Older homes may need to have all the wiring replaced. An electrician needs to make sure that the correct type of wiring is used.

Anyone interested in a career as an electrician should take courses in mathematics, physics, and chemistry in high school. They can also participate in apprenticeship programs that take four to five years to complete.

Thinking Critically What are some of the things an electrician must know when installing wiring in a home?

▲ **Figure 20-20** An electrician needs to know how much electricity a building needs.

---

4. **HYPOTHESIZE:** How could you change a series circuit into a parallel circuit?

📖 **BUILDING SCIENCE SKILLS**

Labeling a Diagram Figure 20-19 shows an open series circuit with one lamp connected to the current source. Copy the diagram into your notebook. Identify and label each of the following parts in the diagram: the source of the electric energy, the lamp, the wire, and the switch.

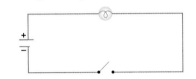

▲ **Figure 20-19** Open series circuit

📖 **READING STRATEGY** Words with double consonants in the middle, such as *parallel*, generally split into two syllables between the two consonants. Have students look for other examples in the text. (current, battery, follow, connect)

3 Assess

✓ CHECKING CONCEPTS ANSWERS

1. series
2. parallel
3. parallel

💡 THINKING CRITICALLY ANSWER

4. **HYPOTHESIZE:** Add wires that are paths for the electric current to follow from the source of the current through each load and back to the source.

4 Close

BUILDING SCIENCE SKILLS

Labeling a Diagram Students should identify and label the source, lamp, wires, and switch.

People in Science
ELECTRICIAN

Real-Life Connection Faulty wiring and the wrong number of amps in circuits can lead to fires and damage appliance motors and electronic devices. When people need electrical work done in their homes, finding a qualified electrician is important. There are two levels of qualified electricians. They both need to have a state license. Master electricians must pass a standardized test and have at least 2 years of experience. They are qualified to plan, design, install, and maintain electrical systems. Journeyman electricians have not yet qualified for master electrician. In some states, they are required to work with a master electrician.

Thinking Critically Answers
Possible answers: how much electricity the home needs, the correct amount of electricity for different appliances, and the correct type of wiring to use

---

MORE ON THE WEB

Design a Parallel Circuit Have students use the Internet to build a virtual parallel circuit. Students can test their circuits by using the simulation. Have students visit www.concepts andchallenges.com for more details.

ONGOING ASSESSMENT

Using Two Batteries Flashlights usually have two or more batteries. Ask students to explain if these batteries are part of a series circuit or a parallel circuit. (series, because the electric current has only one path to follow)

• TEACHING RESOURCES •

💿 **Teacher's Resources CD-ROM**
Lesson Review: Chapter 20, p. 8

COOPERATIVE LEARNING

Making Diagrams Have pairs of students create their own diagrams that show a parallel circuit. Students should label all parts of their diagrams.

1 Introduce

✎ **STUDY HINT** Before beginning this lesson, write the title of the lesson and the Key Terms on the board. Read the Key Terms aloud so that students can hear their pronunciations.

Linking Prior Knowledge Ask students to name some electric devices that cause wires or other materials to glow and give off heat and light. (Possible answers: light bulb, toaster, oven, electric heater, and hair dryer) Tell students that these wires and materials glow because they have more resistance to the flow of electric current than the other wires in the circuit do.

2 Teach

Demonstration If possible, bring a DC voltmeter with several ranges to class. Show students how the voltmeter works and how each range is listed. The higher range of the voltmeter should be used first in making a measurement to avoid a possible overload of the instrument. Use the voltmeter to test the voltage of different batteries, such as a 6-volt battery, a D-cell battery, and a AA-cell battery. Ask students what voltage is. (energy available to move charges through a circuit) Make sure that students understand that batteries with different voltages supply electrons with different amounts of energy to move through a circuit.
learning styles: visual, auditory

Discussion Tell students that even though a battery has a certain number of volts and therefore supplies charges with a certain amount of energy to move through a circuit, the amount of electric current that moves through a circuit with that battery depends on the resistance of the other parts of the circuit. The wires and the load in the circuit have resistance. Ask students what four things affect the resistance of a wire. (length, diameter, material it is made of, and temperature)

Answers to questions

▸ EXPLAIN: energy available to move charges through a circuit

▸ IDENTIFY: electric current

20-7 How is electricity measured?

Objective
Use the correct units to measure voltage, current, and resistance.

Key Terms
voltage: energy available to move charges through a circuit

volt: unit used to measure voltage

ampere: unit used to measure electric current

resistance: opposition to the flow of electric current

ohm: unit used to measure resistance

Voltage Energy is needed to make something move, even something as tiny as an electron. The energy available to move charges through a circuit is called **voltage**. Voltage is measured in units called **volts** and is measured with an instrument called a voltmeter.

▸ EXPLAIN: What is voltage?

Current The amount of electric current depends on the number of charges flowing through a wire. The unit for measuring electric current is the **ampere**, or amp. An ampere is a measure of the number of charges flowing past a point in a circuit in one second. A device used to measure the amount of electric current is called an ammeter.

▸ IDENTIFY: What is an ampere a measure of?

Resistance **Resistance** is the tendency for materials to oppose the flow of electric charges. Some insulating materials, such as rubber and plastic, have very high resistance. Other materials that are good conductors, especially metals, have lower resistance. The unit for measuring resistance is the **ohm.**

Four things affect the resistance of a wire.
- **Length** The longer a wire is, the more resistance it has.
- **Diameter** The thinner a wire is, the more resistance it has.
- **Material** Wires made of poor conductors have more resistance than wires made of good conductors.
- **Temperature** As a wire gets hotter, its resistance increases.

The resistance of a material to the flow of electricity can be useful. For example, a light bulb lights up because of the resistance of the wire inside the bulb. As electric current passes through a light bulb, the wire inside the bulb resists the electric current. Its resistance to the electric current heats up the wire so that it glows.

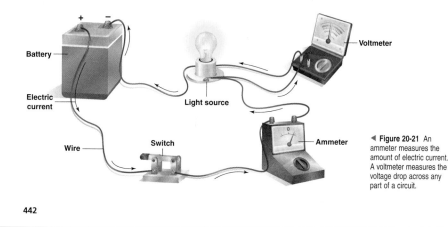

Battery
Electric current
Wire
Switch
Light source
Voltmeter
Ammeter

◂ **Figure 20-21** An ammeter measures the amount of electric current. A voltmeter measures the voltage drop across any part of a circuit.

442

Teaching Options

❗ FAST FACTS *High Voltage Nears Home*

The electric current produced at power plants and transported through wires has a very high voltage. This allows the current to be transported over long distances. The high-voltage current passes through a series of transformers as it nears the homes or businesses where it will be used. A transformer reduces the level of the voltage to 110–120 volts or 220–240 volts just before the current enters a home or business.

COOPERATIVE LEARNING

Reviewing Key Terms Have students work in pairs to explain electromotive force and resistance. Then, ask students to explain what volt, ampere, and ohm measure.
learning styles: auditory, linguistic

QUICK CONVERSIONS		
	Metric/SI	English
Absolute zero/ Zero resistance	−273°C	−459°F
Some superconductors	−250°C	−418°F

◄ Figure 20-22 Resistance to electric current causes the wire in the light bulb to glow.

▶ DEFINE: What is resistance?

✓ CHECKING CONCEPTS

1. Energy available to move charges through a circuit is called _____.
2. Current is measured in _____.
3. The unit for resistance is the _____.
4. A long wire has _____ resistance than a short wire.

Science and Technology

SUPERCONDUCTORS

When a conductor such as a wire carries an electric current, the conductor becomes hot. This causes the resistance of the conductor to increase. However, there are materials that show no resistance to the flow of electrons at temperatures close to absolute zero. Absolute zero is –273°C. Scientists are working to develop materials that have near-zero resistance at temperatures well above absolute zero. Such materials are called superconductors.

▲ Figure 20-23 Liquid nitrogen is used to make superconductors.

Some materials become superconductors at temperatures below –250°C. Liquid helium has been used to cool materials to this temperature. However, liquid helium is very expensive. Scientists have found that some materials become superconductors when cooled with liquid nitrogen. So, researchers are looking to use liquid nitrogen as a coolant. Liquid nitrogen does not reach temperatures as low as liquid helium, but it is much less expensive. However, much research is needed before such "warm" superconductors become part of our daily lives.

Thinking Critically Why do you think finding materials that are superconductors at room temperature can be useful?

CHAPTER 20: Electricity **443**

THINKING CRITICALLY

5. HYPOTHESIZE: Which has more resistance, a conductor or an insulator? Explain.
6. EXPLAIN: How is resistance useful in a toaster?
7. EXPLAIN: How could you measure the amount of electric current running through a circuit?

Web InfoSearch

Volts, Amps, Ohms Volt, ampere, and ohm are units of measurements taken from the names of famous scientists.

SEARCH: Use the Internet to find out about each scientist for whom each unit of measurement is named. Start your search at www.conceptsandchallenges.com. Some key search words are **volt, ampere,** and **ohm.**

▶ DEFINE: the tendency for materials to oppose the flow of electric current

3 Assess

✓ CHECKING CONCEPTS ANSWERS

1. voltage
2. amperes
3. ohm
4. more

💡 THINKING CRITICALLY ANSWERS

5. HYPOTHESIZE: an insulator, because it opposes the flow of electrons
6. EXPLAIN: It causes the wires in the toaster to heat up.
7. EXPLAIN: Make an ammeter part of the circuit.

4 Close

Web InfoSearch

Volts, Amps, Ohms Have pairs of students search the Internet to find out about each scientist for whom these units of measurement were named. Students should begin their search at www.conceptsand challenges.com.

Science and Technology

SUPERCONDUCTORS

Real-Life Connection Although much research needs to be done on superconductors, some superconductors are being used now. The particle accelerators that make the study of subatomic particles possible use superconductors. Maglev trains, trains that float by using electromagnets and that travel at very high speeds, use superconductors. Magnetic resonance imaging (MRI), an important diagnostic medical tool, also uses superconductors. In these uses, the superconductors are part of electromagnets.

Thinking Critically Answer Superconductors can then be used in homes and businesses to conduct electricity without the resistance, heat, and energy loss of wires.

ESL/ELL STRATEGY

Pronouncing Words Named After Scientists Although many words in English follow basic rules of pronunciation, many do not. Sometimes a scientific term is named for the person who discovered it, and students will have to memorize the word or guess at its pronunciation because it does not follow the rules. *Volt, ampere,* and *ohm* are all named after scientists.

learning styles: auditory, linguistic

• TEACHING RESOURCES •

🔘 **Teacher's Resources CD-ROM**

Lesson Review: Chapter 20, p. 9
Enrichment: Chapter 20, p. 10
Temperature Scales: Visuals, p. 2

1 Introduce

STUDY HINT Before beginning this lesson, have students write the lesson title and the objective in their notebooks. As students read the lesson, tell them to write the information that meets the objective.

Linking Prior Knowledge Ask students to list the different voltages of batteries that they have used. List students' answers on the board. Then, ask volunteers what voltage is supplied by electrical outlets in their homes. (mostly 110-volt, some 220-volt) Tell students that voltage is one thing they need to know to calculate the amount of current in a closed circuit.

2 Teach

Discussion Ask students to review what current, voltage, and resistance are and what units are used to measure each of them. Write the terms and their units on the board. Then, tell students that the amount of current in a closed circuit varies. Ask students what two things affect the amount of current in a circuit. (voltage and resistance) Emphasize that Ohm's law is the relationship between current, voltage, and resistance. Write the equation for Ohm's law on the board, using the terms *current*, *voltage*, and *resistance*. Ask students to tell how to write the equation, using units of measurement. (Amperes = Volts ÷ Ohms) **learning styles: visual, auditory**

Answers to questions

1 NAME: current, voltage, and resistance

2 DESCRIBE: The current in a wire is equal to the voltage divided by the resistance.

3 CALCULATE: 11 ohms

READING STRATEGY Tell students that *oh* in *Ohm* gives a clue to its pronunciation.

20-8 What is Ohm's law?

Objective
Explain the relationships between electric current, voltage, and resistance.

Key Term
Ohm's law: current in a wire is equal to the voltage divided by the resistance

I, V, and R Every closed circuit has an electric current (I), voltage (V), and resistance (R). Current, voltage, and resistance vary from circuit to circuit. Different power sources have different amounts of voltage. For example, a D-cell battery has 1.5 volts, while the electricity used in our homes is at 110 volts.

◀ **Figure 20-24** Different power sources have different amounts of voltage.

Resistance in a circuit depends on the kind of wires used and the kind of load through which the current moves. A wire made of copper has less resistance than one made of tin. A toaster will offer more resistance than a mixer. The amount of current in a circuit depends on the voltage and on the total resistance offered by the load.

1 NAME: What do I, V, and R stand for?

Ohm's Law Even though the current, voltage, and resistance vary from circuit to circuit, there is often a simple relationship among them. This relationship is called Ohm's law. **Ohm's law** states that the current (I) in a wire is equal to the voltage (V) divided by the resistance (R).

$$\text{Current} = \text{Voltage} \div \text{Resistance}$$
or
$$I = V \div R$$

444

The units of measurements used would be amperes, which is shown by the following formula.

$$\text{Amperes} = \text{Volts} \div \text{Ohms}$$

2 DESCRIBE: What does Ohm's law state?

Using Ohm's Law Suppose a 12-volt battery is connected to a circuit with a resistance of 6 ohms. What is the current?

$$I = V \div R$$
$$I = 6 \text{ volts} \div 3 \text{ ohms}$$
$$I = 2 \text{ amps}$$

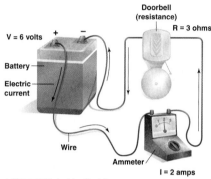

▲ **Figure 20-25** Applying Ohm's law

You can rearrange the formula so that you can find resistance or voltage. To find the voltage (V), multiply the current (I) by the resistance (R). To find the resistance, divide the voltage by the current. As long as you know any two values, you can use Ohm's law to find the remaining value.

Voltage	Resistance
$V = I \times R$	$R = V \div I$

▲ **Figure 20-26**

Teaching Options

! FAST FACTS *Is Battery Size Related to Voltage?*

Batteries come in different sizes, but their size is not necessarily related to their voltage. D-cell batteries are larger than C-cell batteries, which are larger than AA-cell batteries. However, they are all 1.5-volt batteries. A 9-volt battery is smaller than either a D-cell or a C-cell battery even though it has a higher voltage. Batteries used in some cordless phones have a shape that is similar to a 9-volt battery but they are larger than 9-volt batteries and have 3.6 volts. A tiny battery used in hearing aids is 1.4 volts.

ONGOING ASSESSMENT

Practicing Ohm's Law Write the equations for finding current, voltage, and resistance as heads across the top of the board. Give students several practice problems for finding electric current, voltage, and resistance, using Ohm's law. Ask volunteers to write the equations under the correct head on the board. **learning styles: visual, logical/mathematical**

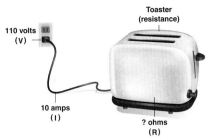

110 volts
(V)

Toaster
(resistance)

10 amps
(I)

? ohms
(R)

▲ **Figure 20-27** Find the resistance at the moment when I = 10 amps and V = 110 volts.

3 ▸ CALCULATE: What is the resistance of the toaster in Figure 20-27?

✓ CHECKING CONCEPTS

1. Every closed circuit has an electric current, voltage, and _____.
2. According to Ohm's law, I = _____ ÷ R.

3. Resistance is measured in _____.
4. Electric current is measured in _____.

💡 THINKING CRITICALLY

5. **INFER:** How is electric current related to resistance and voltage?

📋 BUILDING MATH SKILLS

Calculating Copy the table in Figure 20-28 on a sheet of paper. Use Ohm's law (I = V ÷ R) to complete the chart. Express your answer in whole numbers or decimals.

I (amps)	V (volts)	R (ohms)
?	10	70
15	250	?
5	?	25
5	110	?

▲ **Figure 20-28** Find the missing values.

Science and Technology

ELECTRIC CARS

Today's gasoline-powered cars use up much of America's oil supply. The gases that they give off account for almost half the amount of pollution in the air. However, the supply of oil and other resources are limited, and the increasing pollution in the air is a health concern. As a result, some automakers are looking to make electric cars an alternative to gasoline-powered cars.

Electric cars would reduce the use of gasoline and oil. Because electric cars do not rely on the burning of fuels, they also would create less pollution. Electric cars are also more efficient than gas-powered cars. An electric car does not waste as much of the power it produces as a gas-powered car does.

The electric cars available today use lead-acid batteries. These batteries can be charged using household current from a wall plug. However, these batteries are expensive, and they limit the distance that the car can travel. Instead of relying on batteries, some cars are being built with parts that store large amounts of electricity. Manufacturers are also looking to develop fuel cells that use hydrogen to generate electricity.

Thinking Critically Why are electric cars better for the environment than gas-powered cars?

▲ **Figure 20-29** An electric car

---

3 Assess

4 Close

Science and Technology

ELECTRIC CARS

Real-Life Connection Cars and other motor vehicles cause more air pollution in the Unites States than any other single cause. Some of the pollutants can be harmful to people's health. Other pollutants in exhaust do not become harmful until they react with other substances in the atmosphere. Some of the major air pollutants are ozone, particulate matter, nitrogen oxides, carbon monoxide, and sulfur dioxides. Many of these pollutants can irritate and damage a person's lungs.

Discussion Ask volunteers to share what they know about ozone alerts. During ozone alerts, people are encouraged to stay inside as much as possible and to avoid exercising outside. People are also asked to limit the fuel they burn during this time.

Thinking Critically Answer
They do not create as much pollution.

RETEACH

Illustrating Ohm's Law On the board, draw a simple version of the circuit in Figure 20-25. Leave out the values for voltage, resistance, and amps. Explain that an ammeter is a device that measures electric current in amperes, or amps. Assign various values to two of the different circuit elements and have the class calculate the unknown values. Ask students whether they would be able to calculate the resistance if there was no ammeter attached to the circuit. (No, the ammeter provides the value for the current, which is needed along with the voltage to calculate the resistance in the circuit.)
learning styles: visual, logical/mathematical

20-9 (pp. 446–447)

1 Introduce

STUDY HINT Before beginning this lesson, have students write the lesson title and the title of each section in their notebooks. As students read the lesson, tell them to write the sentence or main idea of each section.

Linking Prior Knowledge Ask students if they know where the fuse box or the circuit breakers are located in their homes. Then, ask students if they know the purpose of fuses or circuit breakers. Make sure that students understand that the fuses and circuit breakers interrupt the electric current if a circuit is overloaded so that the wires do not become too hot and cause a fire.

2 Teach

Demonstration If possible, display a blown fuse, a new fuse, and a circuit breaker. Have students examine the difference between the blown fuse and the new fuse. Show students the on and off positions on the circuit breaker. Ask students how a fuse stops current from flowing. (melts and opens the circuit) Ask students how a circuit breaker stops current from flowing. (switches to the off position and opens the circuit)
learning styles: visual, linguistic

Answers to questions

1. IDENTIFY: Too much current flows through a wire.

2. DEFINE: A thin piece of metal that melts when too much current flows through it, stopping the current.

3. DESCRIBE: It turns off when there is too much current flowing.

4. INFER: Possible answers: to carry out very important life processes, to make the heart beat, and to make nerves and muscles work

5. STATE: Possible answers: Do not plug too many appliances into one outlet, do not allow electric cords to become worn, and do not run electric cords under carpets.

20-9 How can you use electricity safely?

Objective
Describe ways to use electricity safely.

Key Terms
fuse: thin piece of metal that melts and breaks a circuit if too much current is flowing

circuit breaker: switch that opens a circuit if too much current is flowing

Overloaded Circuits Electricity is a wonderful source of energy, but it can also be dangerous. Too many appliances connected to one outlet may cause an overloaded circuit. In an overloaded circuit, too much current flows through a wire. The wire may overheat. It can then melt its insulation and cause a short circuit. Heat and sparks could result in a fire. A frayed wire can also cause a fire.

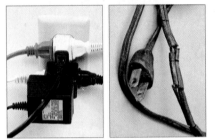

▲ **Figure 20-30** An overloaded circuit or a frayed wire can cause a fire.

1. IDENTIFY: What happens in an overloaded circuit?

Fuses The electricity that comes into your home travels through power lines. The power lines lead to a distribution center. From this center, separate wires go to different circuits in the house or building. These wires are connected to the wall outlets that provide the local power.

Some distribution centers, especially in older homes, have fuses. A **fuse** is a thin piece of metal

446

that melts or "blows" when too much current flows through it. By melting, the fuse stops current from flowing and prevents an overloaded circuit. When you replace the fuse, the current begins moving again. The electrical system in cars and many appliances have fuses to prevent overloaded circuits.

2. DEFINE: What is a fuse?

Circuit Breakers Once a fuse blows, it has to be replaced in order for the current to flow again. In order to avoid having to replace fuses, most newer homes use circuit breakers. A **circuit breaker** is a switch that turns off when there is too much current flowing. A circuit breaker is another way of preventing an overloaded circuit. To start the current flowing again, the breaker must be turned back on.

▲ **Figure 20-31** Circuit breakers prevent overloaded circuits.

3. DESCRIBE: How does a circuit breaker prevent an overloaded circuit?

Electricity in Humans Cells in your body use electricity to carry out very important life processes. For example, the rate at which your heart beats is controlled by electrical signals sent out by certain cells in your body. The muscles that control the movement of your body and your nerves work in a similar manner. This small amount of electricity is produced within your body. It is very dangerous if your body receives an electric current from an outside source. Normal processes within your body can be disrupted by such an electric shock.

4. INFER: List ways in which your body uses electricity.

Teaching Options

! FAST FACTS   *GFCI Outlets Help Prevent Shocks*

Some outlets are called ground fault circuit interrupter (GFCI) outlets. These special outlets have a safety switch that instantly switches off in some situations that could be dangerous. By switching off, they help prevent electric shocks. The switches look like other outlets except that they have two buttons on them. One of the buttons is used to test the outlet. The other button is used to reset the outlet or turn the switch back on. Newer blow dryers have built-in ground fault circuit interrupters. Tell students that GFCI outlets are most often found in bathrooms, kitchens, and outdoors, where the possibility of electric shock is greater.

Electrical Safety Rules Electricity can be dangerous if it is not used carefully. Here are some safety rules to follow when using electricity.

- Do not plug too many appliances into one outlet.
- Do not allow electric cords to become worn.
- Do not run electric cords under carpets.

5▶ STATE: State an electrical safety rule.

✔ **CHECKING CONCEPTS**

1. Too many appliances connected to one outlet may cause an _____ circuit.
2. Heat and sparks from a frayed wire may cause a _____.
3. Power lines that come into your home lead to a _____.
4. A _____ is a thin piece of metal that melts when too much current moves through it.

THINKING CRITICALLY

5. HYPOTHESIZE: Resistance in a wire increases with the length of the wire. Do you think it is a good idea to connect several extension cords to a single outlet? Explain.

6. ANALYZE: What can happen if too many appliances are connected to one wall outlet?

HEALTH AND SAFETY TIP

A bolt of lightning can heat the air around it to a temperature hotter than the surface of the Sun! During a lightning storm, if you cannot go indoors, make sure that you stay away from tall buildings and trees. Avoid metal objects, such as baseball bats and even metal umbrellas. Do not go swimming or play in an open field. Why should you not stand under a tree during a lightning storm?

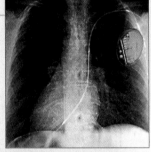

▲ **Figure 20-32** An artificial pacemaker is inserted in the heart.

Science and Technology
PACEMAKERS

Heart muscle responds to electrical signals. These signals are used to control the rate of the heart's rhythm. The natural pacemaker of the heart is a small amount of tissue that generates electric charge. This charge spreads through the chambers of the heart to keep them pumping or beating in a repeated rhythm. If this natural pacemaker stops working properly, the normal functions of the body are interrupted. A surgeon may have to insert an artificial pacemaker to keep the heart pumping normally.

Artificial pacemakers contain a battery. The battery sends electric charges through a wire inserted into a vein that leads to the heart. The heart muscle responds to these weak electrical charges in the same way that it would to a natural pacemaker. Without electric charges to regulate its pumping rhythm, the heart may beat irregularly. An irregular heartbeat can lead to a heart attack.

Thinking Critically How does an artificial pacemaker work?

3 Assess

✔ CHECKING CONCEPTS ANSWERS

1. overloaded
2. fire
3. fuse box or circuit breakers
4. fuse

💡 THINKING CRITICALLY ANSWERS

5. HYPOTHESIZE: no; because the resistance increases, which may cause a fire
6. ANALYZE: The circuit can become overloaded, and the fuse will blow or the circuit breaker will turn off. Too much current can flow through the wire, the wire may overheat and melt its insulation and cause sparks, and the heat and sparks can start a fire.

4 Close

HEALTH AND SAFETY TIP ANSWER

Lightning may strike the tree and travel to your body.

Science and Technology
PACEMAKERS

Life-Science Connection A pacemaker contains a tiny computer that must be programmed for each patient after it is implanted. A doctor can program the pacemaker by using a handheld device that programs the computer through the patient's skin. The patient then has a checkup every month or two. The unusual part of this checkup is that it takes place over the phone. The patient holds a special device over the pacemaker that checks the pacemaker and transmits the information over the phone. Since some other devices can cause a problem with pacemakers, caution and special procedures must be used if the person needs a medical procedure such as an MRI or radiation therapy. Cell phones can cause a problem with pacemakers, but only if they are less than 6 inches from the pacemaker. Appliances, such as microwaves, do not interfere with pacemakers.

Thinking Critically Answer
It sends electrical charges to the heart to regulate the pumping rhythm.

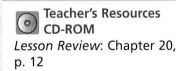

• TEACHING RESOURCES •

Teacher's Resources CD-ROM
Lesson Review: Chapter 20, p. 12

COOPERATIVE LEARNING

Making Electrical Safety Posters
Have small groups make posters illustrating electrical safety rules. Display the posters throughout the school so all students will be reminded of electrical safety rules.
learning styles: visual, interpersonal

The Big Idea

(pp. 448–449)

1 Introduce

Objective Students will brainstorm devices that they think people need. Students will design one of these devices, describe it, and make labeled drawings. Students also will research how they would have this device patented.

Linking Prior Knowledge Ask students to recall how electronic devices that use direct current can be powered by the alternating current from an outlet (Lesson 20-4).

2 Teach

Discussion After students have read the article, ask them to name some of Thomas Edison's inventions. Ask volunteers to describe Edison's inventions and tell how they changed history.
learning styles: visual, linguistic

Use the information in the article and captions to help guide students in choosing a topic for their Science Logs.

Reinforcement Students can also use the Big Idea Planner or Big Idea Science Log Entry found on the Teacher's Resources CD-ROM.

◆ *Integrating History*

THE Big IDEA

Figure 20-33 ▶
Thomas Alva Edison (1847–1931) This American inventor applied for a patent every two weeks during his working career.

How have electrical inventions changed history?

If you have ever switched on a light bulb, listened to recorded music, or watched a movie, you have used a device that runs on electricity. Benjamin Franklin first investigated electricity in the mid 1700s. Now, electricity is a very important source of energy.

The use of electricity has changed history throughout the world. Homes, businesses, and schools all depend on appliances that are powered by electricity. Many of the inventions that use electricity are the products of a famous inventor, Thomas Alva Edison.

Thomas Edison received over 1,000 patents. Some of these patents were for his own inventions, such as the phonograph, the first practical electric light bulb, motion picture technology, and the alkaline storage battery. The other patents were for devices that he improved upon, such as the telephone, the typewriter, the stock ticker, and the printing telegraph.

These inventions, and many others, have had a lasting influence on the world. Because of these many devices that run on electricity, our lives are made easier and more enjoyable. We are able to communicate faster and more easily. We can do more work and perform it faster. We can enjoy music and movies. We can travel safer and faster, and our homes are also filled with electrical devices that make our lives more comfortable.

Learn about some of Thomas Edison's inventions that appear on these two pages. Then follow the directions in the Science Log to come up with your own invention. ◆

The Printing Telegraph
In 1869, Thomas Edison received a patent for a device that he improved upon, the printing telegraph. This device received messages from great distances and printed them out.

The Phonograph
In 1877, Thomas Edison was the first person to make a machine that recorded sound. This invention led to the development of the phonograph record, and gave birth to the recording industry.

448

Teaching Options

! FAST FACTS *Lower Manhattan Gets Electricity*

The invention of the light bulb was not very useful to most people because they did not have electricity. One of Edison's many achievements was the creation of an electric industry to distribute electricity to the public. In 1882, the people in a small area in Manhattan were the first customers to be supplied with electricity by a commercial power station. Edison continued his work and started a number of electric companies. Eventually, these companies were brought together and became Edison General Electric. Later, this company was merged with another company and the company name became General Electric.

ESL/ELL STRATEGY

Working With Peers Working with students who are proficient in English can help English-language learners to communicate. Pair an English-language learner with an English-proficient student. Have both students explain the article and the captions in their own words to each other.

Science Log

Thomas Edison invented devices that he thought were needed by people. Brainstorm about devices that you think people have a need for. In your science log, design one of these devices. Describe it and make labeled drawings. Research how you would have this device patented. Start your search at www.conceptsandchallenges.com.

The First Practical Light Bulb
In 1879, with the help of skilled assistants, he tested hundreds of materials to create the first practical light bulb. This light bulb used a filament made of carbon.

The Kinetoscope
In 1892, Edison and his staff completed work on a device that showed moving pictures. The moving pictures were seen through a wooden box called a kinetoscope.

CHAPTER 20: Electricity **449**

3 Assess

Use the Individual Activity Rubric on the Teacher's Resources CD-ROM to assess students' Science Logs. Fill in the rubric with the additional information below.

For this assignment, students should have:

- designed and described a device that they think people need.
- created labeled drawings of the device and researched how they would have the device patented.

4 Close

Making a Light Bulb Timeline Edison improved the light bulb and made it practical to use, but he did not invent the first light bulb. Ask students to find out more about the light bulb and its inventors. Encourage students to make a timeline that shows the various stages in the invention of the light bulb. Ask students to share their timelines with the class.
learning styles: visual, tactile

Tips for Using Technology

Using Web-Based E-Mail Services Students can e-mail their requests for patents to you. Two popular types of e-mail are Web-based e-mail and *POP3* e-mail. If you need to create e-mail accounts for your students or yourself, you may want to consider Web-based e-mail first. Web-based e-mail is an e-mail service that allows you to send and receive e-mail using your Web browser software. Companies such as www.Hotmail.com, www.Yahoo.com, and www.MailandNews.com offer these services at no cost.

• TEACHING RESOURCES •

Teacher's Resources CD-ROM
Big Idea: Chapter 20, p. 13

Big Idea Planner: Study Tools, pp. 11–12

Big Idea Science Log Entry: Study Tools, p. 13

Individual Activity Rubric: Teaching Tools, p. 5

Challenges (pp. 450–452)

Chapter Summary

Review Before students begin the Challenges, review the summary with them. If time permits, have students work in pairs. Give each pair of students one summary point to describe in their own words.

✎ **STUDY HINT** Have students use index cards to create flash cards for each Key Term. Have students write the Key Term on one side of the index card and the definition on the other side. Then, have students work in pairs to review the Key Terms.

Key Term Challenges

MATCHING

1. ohm (20-7)
2. battery (20-2)
3. series circuit (20-5)
4. alternating current (20-4)
5. ampere (20-7)
6. circuit breaker (20-9)
7. parallel circuit (20-6)

FILL IN

8. conductor (20-3)
9. direct current (20-4)
10. Ohm's law (20-8)
11. static electricity (20-1)
12. electrodes (20-2)

Chapter Summary

Lesson 20-1
- Atoms have three basic parts: **protons, electrons,** and **neutrons.**

Lesson 20-2
- The two types of **electrochemical cells** are a wet cell and a dry cell.

Lesson 20-3
- A **conductor** allows electric charges to flow easily.
- An **insulator** prevents electric charges from flowing through it easily.

Lesson 20-4
- The flow of charges through a conductor is called **electric current**.
- The two types of electric current are **direct current** (DC) and **alternating current** (AC).

Lesson 20-5
- In a **series circuit,** electric current follows only one path.

Lesson 20-6
- In a **parallel circuit,** the electric current can follow more than one path.

Lesson 20-7
- **Volts, amperes,** and **ohms** are the units used to measure **voltage,** current, and **resistance.**

Lesson 20-8
- **Ohm's law** states that current in a wire is equal to the voltage divided by the resistance.

Lesson 20-9
- Electricity must be used safely.

Key Term Challenges

alternating current (p. 436)
ampere (p. 442)
battery (p. 432)
circuit breaker (p. 446)
conductor (p. 434)
direct current (p. 436)
electric circuit (p. 438)
electric current (p. 436)
electrochemical cell (p. 432)
electrode (p. 432)
electrolyte (p. 432)
electron (p. 428)
fuse (p. 446)
insulator (p. 434)
neutron (p. 428)
ohm (p. 442)
Ohm's law (p. 444)
parallel circuit (p. 440)
proton (p. 428)
resistance (p. 442)
series circuit (p. 438)
static electricity (p. 428)
volt (p. 442)

MATCHING Write the Key Term from above that best matches each description.

1. unit for measuring resistance
2. series of electrochemical cells
3. circuit in which the current follows one path
4. electric current that changes direction at a regular rate
5. unit for measuring electric current
6. emergency switch that opens a circuit if too much current is flowing
7. circuit in which electric current can follow more than one path

FILL IN Write the Key Term from above that best completes each statement.

8. A metal is a good _____ of electricity.
9. Current that flows in the same direction is called _____.
10. According to _____, the current in a closed circuit is equal to the voltage divided by the resistance.
11. The buildup of electrons on an object is called _____.
12. The poles of a wet cell are called _____.

Teaching Options

PREPARING STUDENTS FOR STANDARDIZED TESTS

Reading Strategy: Remind students that carefully reading and thinking about each answer choice will help them avoid making mistakes. Tell them to eliminate answers that are obviously wrong. They should try to recall facts that help them to narrow the choices. They should think about what they know that applies to the question.

Writing Strategy: Remind students to check for correct punctuation and complete sentences as they reread their answers.

Interpreting Visuals: Tell students that the first step in reading a diagram is to identify the subject or topic of the diagram. Often this information is presented in the title. Sometimes knowing the title is all students need to answer a question.

ESL/ELL STRATEGY

Restating Processes English-language learners will benefit from restating how a circuit works in their own words. Have pairs work together to summarize each process in the lessons.

Content Challenges TEST PREP

MULTIPLE CHOICE Write the letter of the term or phrase that best completes each statement.

1. A battery in a flashlight is an example of
   a. a wet cell.
   b. a dry cell.
   c. alternating current.
   d. a parallel circuit.

2. According to Ohm's law, current is equal to
   a. resistance.
   b. voltage divided by resistance.
   c. resistance multiplied by voltage.
   d. voltage plus resistance.

3. One of the best conductors of electric current is a wire made of
   a. brass.
   b. magnesium.
   c. copper.
   d. rubber.

4. Electric current can follow more than one path in
   a. a series circuit.
   b. an alternating circuit.
   c. a direct circuit.
   d. a parallel circuit.

5. The most common type of current used in homes, offices, and schools is
   a. direct current.
   b. alternating current.
   c. both alternating and direct current.
   d. neither alternating nor direct current.

6. The resistance in a wire will increase if
   a. the thickness of the wire is decreased.
   b. the temperature of the wire is increased.
   c. the length of the wire is increased.
   d. all of the above.

7. If several appliances are connected in series circuit and one of the appliances stops working
   a. none of the appliances will work.
   b. the rest of the appliances will continue to work.
   c. there may be a short circuit.
   d. the current needs to be increased.

8. A circuit breaker is useful in case there is
   a. an overloaded circuit.
   b. not enough current.
   c. not enough voltage.
   d. too much static electricity.

9. Electric current is measured in
   a. volts.
   b. ohms.
   c. amps.
   d. electrons.

10. Most of the circuits in the home are
    a. series circuits.
    b. parallel circuits.
    c. electronic circuits.
    d. short circuits.

TRUE/FALSE Write *true* if the statement is true. If the statement is false, change the underlined term to make the statement true.

11. In a dry cell battery, the electrolyte is a <u>dry</u> paste.

12. Current can flow only in a <u>closed</u> circuit.

13. A <u>circuit breaker</u> is used to turn a circuit on or off.

14. In a <u>parallel</u> circuit, the current follows only one path.

Content Challenges

MULTIPLE CHOICE

1. b (20-2)
2. b (20-8)
3. c (20-3)
4. d (20-6)
5. b (20-4)
6. d (20-7)
7. a (20-5)
8. a (20-9)
9. c (20-7)
10. b (20-6)

TRUE/FALSE

11. false; moist (20-2)
12. true (20-4)
13. false; switch (20-5)
14. false; series (20-5)

ALTERNATIVE ASSESSMENT

Defining Key Terms Students may write a science log entry that uses complete sentences to define each Key Term in this chapter. Students may also draw diagrams to illustrate how electric charges behave, the three parts of a circuit, a series circuit, and a parallel circuit.

PORTFOLIO ASSESSMENT

Making Student Portfolios Portfolio Assessment is designed to evaluate a student's performance over an extended period of time. Students can demonstrate their comprehension of the concepts in this chapter by making a portfolio. The Chapter Self-Check, Venn Diagram, and Big Idea Planner are some of the reproducibles on the Teacher's Resources CD-ROM that they can include in their portfolios. You can use the Portfolio Assessment Rubric also found on the Teacher's Resources CD-ROM to assess students' portfolios.

Concept Challenges

WRITTEN RESPONSE

1. **HYPOTHESIZE:** No; It is not safe to touch the wires because the wires still may be carrying a very high voltage. (20-4, 20-9)
2. **ANALYZE:** The lights are connected in a series circuit. If they were connected in a parallel circuit, the electric current would have a separate path to follow for each bulb, and all the bulbs would stay lit. (20-5, 20-6)
3. **CALCULATE:** Circuit **a** has more current. (20-8)
4. **ANALYZE:** Possible answer: Lightning occurs when negative charges in a cloud are attracted to positive charges on the ground and the charges jump to the ground. (20-1)

INTERPRETING VISUALS

5. series circuit (20-5)
6. the battery (or source of electric current), the wires, the bell (or load), and an ammeter (to measure amperes or electric current) (20-5)
7. It would increase. (20-7)
8. 6 amps (20-8)

Chapter Project Wrap-Up

DEMONSTRATING CIRCUITS

Students can present their circuits to the class or students can move around the room to study other students' circuits. You can use the Individual Activity Rubric found on the Teacher's Resources CD-ROM to assess students' projects. Fill in the rubric with the additional information below. For this project, students should have:

- built or drawn diagrams of a series circuit and a parallel circuit.
- accurately labeled the circuits.

Concept Challenges TEST PREP

WRITTEN RESPONSE Answer each of the following questions in complete sentences.

1. **HYPOTHESIZE:** During a storm, a power line falls from its pole. Is it safe to touch the wires? Explain.
2. **ANALYZE:** A string of decorative lights goes out when one bulb stops working. Are the lights connected in a series circuit or a parallel circuit? How do you know?
3. **CALCULATE:** Which circuit has more current? **a.** voltage = 12 volts, resistance = 2 ohms **b.** voltage = 32 volts, resistance = 6 ohms **c.** voltage = 24 volts, resistance = 8 ohms
4. **ANALYZE:** How is lightning an example of static discharge?

INTERPRETING VISUALS Use Figure 20-34 to answer the following questions.

5. What kind of circuit is shown in the diagram?
6. What are the four parts of this circuit?
7. If you were to connect a light bulb in the circuit, what would happen to the resistance of the circuit?
8. If the voltage was increased to 18 volts, what would be the new value for I?

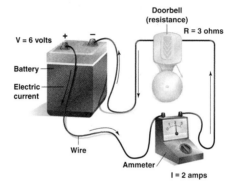

▲ **Figure 20-34** A circuit diagram

452

Teaching Options

UNIT CHALLENGE ONLINE

Standby Power You may wish to have students begin the Unit Challenge Online activity described on page T478 of this book.

• TEACHING RESOURCES •

Teacher's Resources CD-ROM
Key Term Review: Chapter 20, p. 14

Chapter 20 Test: pp. 15–16

Individual Activity Rubric: Teaching Tools, p. 5

Chapter Self-Check: Teaching Tools, p. 11

Venn Diagram: Study Tools, p. 10

Big Idea Planner: Study Tools, pp. 11–12

Portfolio Assessment Rubric: Teaching Tools, p. 10

PLANNING GUIDE

◆ **TEACHING THE CHAPTER** This chapter should take approximately 9–12 days to complete instruction and assessment.

	Skills and Features	Projects and Activities	Achieve Science Literacy	Meet Individual Needs
Chapter 21 Opener p. T453	RESEARCH	• Chapter Project		
Lesson 21-1 **What is a magnet?** pp. T454–T455 Standard: B1a	DESCRIBE, INFER, ANALYZE • Designing an Experiment • How Do They Know That?	• Cooperative Learning • More on the Web	• Study Hint • Reading Strategy	• ESL/ELL Strategy • Reteach CD-ROM Writing Activity Outline Designing an Experiment
Lesson 21-2 **What causes magnetism?** pp. T456–T457	DEFINE, DESCRIBE, COMPARE • Investigate • Interpreting Visuals	• More on the Web • Integrating The Sciences • Lab Challenge	• Study Hint	• Reteach CD-ROM Enrichment Activity Laboratory Video
Lesson 21-3 **How can you make a magnet?** pp. T458–T459 Standard: B1a	CLASSIFY, PREDICT, CONTRAST • Building Social Studies Skills • Hands-On Activity	• More on the Web • Integrating Life Science	• Study Hint • Writing Hint • Ongoing Assessment	
Lesson 21-4 **How is Earth like a magnet?** pp. T460–T461 Standard: B3f	MODEL, CLASSIFY, DEFINE • Building Science Skills • How Do They Know That?	• More on the Web	• Study Hint • Reading Strategy • Ongoing Assessment	• Reteach CD-ROM Enrichment Activity
Lesson 21-5 **How are electricity and magnetism related?** pp. T462–T463 Standards: B3a, B3d	EXPLAIN, DESCRIBE, DEFINE • Investigate • People in Science	• More on the Web	• Study Hint • Ongoing Assessment	
Lesson 21-6 **What is an electromagnet?** pp. T464–T465 Standards: B3a, B3d	LIST, ANALYZE, PREDICT • Interpreting Visuals • Hands-On Activity	• More on the Web	• Study Hint • Ongoing Assessment	CD-ROM Enrichment Activity

Planning Guide continues on next page.

Standards: For details on the correlation to National Science Standards see pages *xx–xxi*.

	Skills and Features	Projects and Activities	Achieve Science Literacy	Meet Individual Needs
Lesson 21-7 What is a transformer? pp. T466–T467 Standards: B3a, B3d	INVESTIGATE, DESCRIBE, INFER • Building Science Skills • Real-Life Science	• Extending the Lesson • More on the Web	• Study Hint • Writing Hint • Ongoing Assessment	• ESL/ELL Strategy
Lesson 21-8 What is an electric motor? pp. T468–T469 Standards: B2a, B3a, B3d	EXPLAIN, INFER, PREDICT • Designing an Experiment • People in Science	• Cooperative Learning • Extending the Lesson • More on the Web	• Study Hint • Reading Strategy	CD-ROM Spider Map Designing an Experiment
Lab Activity Making an Electric Motor pp. T470–T471 Standards: B2a, B3a, B3d	OBSERVE, HYPOTHESIZE, ANALYZE • Set-Up Time: 15 min • Lab Time: 30 min	• Extend the Lab Activity	• Tips for Using Technology	CD-ROM Lab Activity Report Database Planner Electric Motor
Lesson 21-9 What is an electric generator? pp. T472–T473 Standards: B2a, B3a, B3d	NAME, HYPOTHESIZE, IDENTIFY • Web InfoSearch • Science and Technology	• Cooperative Learning • Extending the Lesson	• Study Hint • Reading Strategy • Ongoing Assessment	CD-ROM Enrichment Activity
Big Idea How does a maglev train work? pp. T474–T475 Standards: B2a, B3a	RESEARCH, COMMUNICATE, ANALYZE • Science Log: Writing Activity	• Big Idea Online • Close Activity	• Tips for Using Technology	CD-ROM Big Idea Planner Thumbnail Sketch
Chapter 21 Challenges pp. T476–T478	• Chapter Summary • Key Term Challenges • Content Challenges • Concept Challenges	• Chapter Project Wrap-Up • Unit Challenge Online	• Study Hint • Preparing Students for Standardized Tests	• ESL/ELL Strategy CD-ROM Chapter Self-Check Weekly Journal

Chapter 21 Magnetism

▲ **Figure 21-1** The aurora over the North Pole

The beautiful glow in the sky in Figure 21-1 is not an unusual sight near the North and South poles. The glowing lights are called an aurora. They are caused by particles from the Sun colliding with atoms in Earth's upper atmosphere. Like all objects that have the property of magnetism, Earth has magnetic poles. These magnetic poles produce a magnetic field around Earth. Earth's magnetic field prevents many of the particles from the Sun from entering Earth's atmosphere.

▶ How does the magnetic field around Earth protect it?

Contents

UNIT 7: Electricity and Magnetism   **453**

Teaching Options

ASSESSMENT PLANNER

For assessment in the Student Edition, see the following pages:

Content Assessment
Checking Concepts: pp. 455, 457, 459, 461, 463, 465, 467, 469, 473
Thinking Critically: pp. 455, 457, 459, 461, 463, 465, 467, 469, 473
Interpreting Visuals: pp. 457, 465
Chapter Challenges: pp. 476–478

Alternative Assessment
Building Skills: pp. 459, 461, 467
Web InfoSearch: p. 473
Science Log: p. 475

Performance-Based Assessment
Hands-On Activity: pp. 459, 465
Designing an Experiment: pp. 455, 469
Lab Activity: pp. 470–471

• TEACHING RESOURCES •

Teacher's Resources CD-ROM
Lesson Review: Ch. 21, pp. 2, 3, 5, 6, 8, 9, 11, 12, 13
Enrichment: Ch. 21, pp. 4, 7, 10, 14
Key Term Review: Ch. 21, p. 16
Chapter 21 Test: pp. 17–19
Laboratory Manual: pp. 101–104

Laboratory Video
Segment 23: Observing Magnetic Lines of Force

Chapter 21
Magnetism

Chapter Overview

In this chapter, students will learn the properties of a magnet, explain how materials can be magnetized, compare permanent magnets and temporary magnets, explain how Earth acts like a magnet, and understand the relationship between electricity and magnetism. Students will also describe how to make an electromagnet and explain how transformers, electric motors, and generators work.

About Figure 21-1 Auroras occur at both geographic poles. They can appear in many forms, including arcs across the sky, bright clouds, or a bright, fuzzy glow. Because particles from the Sun cause disturbances in Earth's magnetic field, communication by radio, telephone, and telegraph may be interrupted during this phenomenon. Earth is not the only planet that has auroras. Astronomers have observed auroras in the atmosphere of Jupiter.

Answer The magnetic field prevents many of the Sun's particles from entering Earth's atmosphere.

Linking Prior Knowledge

For this chapter, students should recall:
* the definition of *electricity* (Lesson 20-1).
* the two types of electric current—direct and alternating (Lesson 20-4).
* how energy changes form (Lesson 14-3).

Chapter Project

MAGNET EXPO

MATERIALS: The materials for this project depend on the projects chosen by students. Have available simple reference sources and a variety of magnets.

Students will contribute to a Magnet Expo. Have students research a device that uses a magnet or an electromagnet to operate. If possible, students should build the device or create a labeled diagram of it. They should explain the purpose of the device and how the magnet or electromagnet helps the device work. Remind students that toys are also devices that can be made with magnets. **learning style: tactile**

1 Introduce

✎ **STUDY HINT** Have students write the title of the lesson and the titles of each section in outline format in their notebooks. As they read this lesson, have them write the main idea of each section. Students can also use the Writing Activity Outline found on the Teacher's Resources CD-ROM.

Linking Prior Knowledge Ask students to recall what they know about magnets and their properties. You might refer to the information that students learned about metals (Lesson 10-1).

2 Teach

Discussion Be sure that students understand that for a substance to be magnetic, it must contain a magnetic element, usually iron, nickel, or cobalt. Explain that steel is magnetic because it is a mixture that consists mostly of iron. Students may be familiar with magnetic objects—such as computer diskettes, cassette tapes, and videos—that do not seem to be magnetic. Explain that these objects are magnetic because they contain small particles of iron. **learning style: auditory**

Reinforcement Point out to students that when a magnet is suspended, the end that points to the north pole is labeled *N*. This pole is also called the north-seeking pole. Make sure that students understand that even the smallest piece of a magnet has a north pole and a south pole.
learning styles: visual, auditory

Answers to questions

▶1 **DEFINE:** force of attraction or repulsion by magnetic materials

▶2 **DEFINE:** one of two ends of a magnet where magnetic force is strongest

▶3 **DESCRIBE:** Like poles repel. Unlike poles attract.

▶4 **LIST:** Accept any of the following: in appliances, telephones, doorbells, speakers, electric motors, alarm systems, special trains, and particle research.

21-1 What is a magnet?

Objective
Describe the properties of a magnet.

Key Terms
magnetism: force of attraction or repulsion by magnetic materials
pole: end of a magnet

Magnetism When you hold a magnet close to certain types of metals, the metals move toward the magnet. The metals are pulled toward the magnet by a force called magnetism. **Magnetism** is a force of attraction or repulsion by magnetic materials.

Not all matter is attracted to a magnet. For example, if you hold a magnet near a piece of wood, the wood will not be attracted to the magnet. Copper, aluminum, plastics, and glass are other materials that are not attracted to a magnet. Elements that are attracted to a magnet include iron, nickel, and cobalt. Objects made of steel, which is mostly iron, are also attracted to magnets.

◀ **Figure 21-2**
Materials such as iron and steel are attracted to magnets.

▶ **DEFINE:** What is magnetism?

Magnetic Poles Each end of a magnet is called a magnetic **pole.** The magnetic forces of a magnet are strongest at its poles. Every magnet has two poles—a north pole (N) and a south pole (S). If you hang a magnet by a string, it will turn until its north pole points north and its south pole points south. Thus, the north pole of a magnet is sometimes called the north-seeking pole and the south pole of a magnet

454

is sometimes called the south-seeking pole. Magnets always have two poles. Even if a magnet were broken up into tiny pieces, each tiny piece would still have a north pole and a south pole.

▶ **DEFINE:** What is a pole?

Properties of a Magnet Magnetic poles behave in the same way that electric charges do when like and unlike charges are brought together. If a north pole of one magnet and a south pole of another magnet are brought together, they will attract each other. The unlike poles of any two magnets always attract each other in the same way that unlike electric charges attract each other.

If the north pole of one magnet is brought near the north pole of another magnet, they will repel, or push away from, each other. Two magnetic south poles will also repel each other. The like poles of any two magnets always repel each other in the same way that like electric charges repel each other.

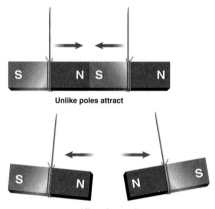

Unlike poles attract

Like poles repel
▲ **Figure 21-3** How magnets behave

▶ **DESCRIBE:** How do the poles of a magnet affect each other?

Uses of Magnets You may not realize it, but magnets play a very important role in your life. They are used in electric can openers, telephones,

Teaching Options

RETEACH

Understanding Poles Help students visualize how poles attract and repel each other by providing a model that simulates Figure 21-3. Use two long blocks and label the ends *north* and *south* as in the illustration. Put the blocks together so that the north and south poles meet. Ask students if the blocks would stay together or push apart if they were magnets. Repeat with other combinations. (S/S and N/N)
learning styles: visual, logical/mathematical

COOPERATIVE LEARNING

Experimenting With Magnets Divide students into small groups. Distribute several bar magnets to each group and allow students to explore the properties of a magnet. Have students bring like poles and unlike poles near each other to observe how unlike poles attract each other and like poles repel each other. Students can write their observations and ideas in their notebooks.
learning styles: visual, tactile

doorbells, stereo speakers, electric motors, and alarm systems. Magnets are also used in high-energy particle research and to run special high-speed trains.

4 LIST: Name some ways in which magnets are used.

✓ CHECKING CONCEPTS

1. Magnetism is a force of _____ or repulsion by magnetic materials.
2. When hung from a string, the north pole of a magnet points _____.
3. The south pole of a magnet is sometimes called the _____.
4. The north pole of one magnet will _____ the south pole of another magnet.
5. Elements attracted to a magnet are iron, _____, and cobalt.
6. If you cut a magnet in half, each half will have a north pole and a _____.

THINKING CRITICALLY

7. **INFER:** Why could the north pole of a magnet be called the north-seeking pole?
8. **DESCRIBE:** Describe what will happen if you bring the north pole of one magnet near the north pole of another magnet.
9. **ANALYZE:** How are magnets similar to electric charges?
10. **INFER:** How do you think a magnet is used in an electric can opener?

DESIGNING AN EXPERIMENT

Design an experiment to solve the following problem. Include a hypothesis, variables, a procedure, and a type of data to study.

PROBLEM: A homeowner has a door that she wants to keep slightly open. How can magnets be used to keep the door from shutting?

How Do They Know That?
MAGNETIC COMPASS

Magnets can be found in nature. Naturally occurring substances with magnetic properties are called natural magnets. The ancient Greeks found natural deposits of magnetic iron ore. They discovered this ore in a region of Turkey known as Magnesia. The ore is called magnetite (MAG-nuh-tyt). Magnetite can also be found in many other parts of the world.

Magnetite was used by sailors and navigators to find directions at sea. Pieces of magnetite were called lodestone because sailors found that a piece of magnetite always pointed toward the North Star. The North Star was called the lodestar, or leading star. Sailors made magnetic compasses with a pointer made of lodestone.

Today, magnetic compasses are often used by hikers and backpackers. The pointer of a magnetic compass always points north. Once you know where north is, you can easily locate the other three directions, or compass points.

Thinking Critically If a hiker is trying to hike in an easterly direction, would a compass be of any help to the hiker? Explain your answer.

▲ **Figure 21-4** Sailors once used a magnetic compass like this one.

MORE ON THE WEB

Simulating Magnets Have students visit www.concepts andchallenges.com to learn about different types of magnets.

ESL/ELL STRATEGY

Determining Magnetism Display several objects that would either be attracted to or not attracted to a magnet. Point to each object one at a time. Ask students to give a thumbs-up sign if the object shown would attract a magnet and a thumbs down sign if it would not. Ask students to explain why each object is or is not attracted to a magnet.

• TEACHING RESOURCES •

Teacher's Resources CD-ROM
Lesson Review: Chapter 21, p. 2
Writing Activity Outline: Study Tools, pp. 20–21
Designing an Experiment: Study Tools, p. 14
Designing an Experiment Rubric: Teaching Tools, p. 7

📖 **READING STRATEGY** Remind students that most words have more than one meaning. The word *pole*, for example, can mean "a limit or an extreme," "a rod or stick," or "an opposite." Ask students to determine which meaning of *pole* is used in this lesson. Have them write it in their notebooks.

3 Assess

✓ CHECKING CONCEPTS ANSWERS

1. attraction
2. north
3. south-seeking pole
4. attract
5. nickel
6. south pole

💡 THINKING CRITICALLY ANSWERS

7. **INFER:** The north pole of a magnet always turns to face north.
8. **DESCRIBE:** The north poles will repel each other.
9. **ANALYZE:** The unlike poles of any two magnets always attract each other in the same way that unlike electric charges attract each other.
10. **INFER:** Possible answers: to hold the lid as the can is being opened and in the electric motor that turns the can

4 Close

DESIGNING AN EXPERIMENT

Use the Designing an Experiment Rubric on the Teacher's Resources CD-ROM to assess students' experiments. Fill in the rubric with the additional information below. For this assignment, students should have:

- mentioned the repulsive property of magnets in forming the hypothesis.
- included magnets in the procedure.

How Do They Know That?
MAGNETIC COMPASS

Discussion Ask students: *Why do you think the Greeks called iron ore magnetite?* (The ore was discovered in Magnesia, Turkey.)

Thinking Critically Answer
Yes; Once you know where north is and face north, you can determine that east is to your right, south is behind you, and west is to your left.

21-2 (pp. 456–457)

1 Introduce

INVESTIGATE

TIME: 10 minutes

PURPOSE: Students will observe the behavior of a magnet in order to determine its north and south poles.

MATERIALS: bar magnets, string, masking tape

PROCEDURE: To be sure that students do not know which pole is which on the hanging magnet, you might cover the ends with tape before students come to class.

THINK ABOUT IT: by observing which poles attracted and which repelled the ends of the covered magnet **learning styles: visual, tactile**

✎ **STUDY HINT** Have students read the captions and art labels that appear in the lesson. This will allow them to preview what is to come as well as to focus on the most important ideas in the lesson.

Linking Prior Knowledge Spark discussion by showing refrigerator magnets or other commonly used magnets. Ask students what happens when they pull a magnet away from the refrigerator and then slowly move the magnet toward the refrigerator. (They can feel a pull as they remove the magnet, and as they move the magnet toward the refrigerator, the magnet suddenly sticks.)

2 Teach

Demonstration To introduce the lesson, place a bar magnet on an overhead projector. Cover the magnet with a clear sheet of plastic. Sprinkle iron filings around the magnet to show students the shape of the magnetic field. **learning style: visual**

Demonstration Place two bar magnets on an overhead projector with the north pole of one magnet pointed toward the south pole of the other magnet. Cover the magnets with a sheet of plastic. Sprinkle iron filings around the magnets. Lightly tap the edge of the plastic sheet. Have students sketch the shape of the magnetic field in their notebooks. Then, repeat the demonstration with like poles pointed toward each other. Again, have students

---

21-2 What causes magnetism?

INVESTIGATE

Finding the Pole of a Magnet
HANDS-ON ACTIVITY

1. Cover the pole markings of a bar magnet with masking tape. Tie one end of a piece of string around the center of the magnet. Tape the other end of the string to the edge of your desk or table. Allow the magnet to hang from your desk or table.

2. Use another bar magnet to determine the poles of the hanging magnet.

THINK ABOUT IT: How did you determine the poles of the hanging magnet?

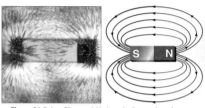

STEP 1

Objective
Demonstrate the shape of a magnetic field.

Key Terms
magnetic field: describes the region of magnetic force around a magnet

magnetic lines of force: lines that show the shape of a magnetic field

magnetic domain: groups of atoms whose magnetic poles are all lined up in the same direction

Magnetic Field If you bring a magnet close to an iron object, the magnetic force will attract the object. The magnet does not need to touch the object in order for the magnetic force to attract it. This attraction happens because every magnet has a magnetic field around it. The **magnetic field** describes the region of magnetic force around a magnet.

The magnetic fields around different magnets are not the same. Some magnets may have a stronger magnetic field than others do. Figure 21-5 shows the magnetic field around a bar magnet. Iron filings have been sprinkled over the bar magnet. The iron filings line up around the magnet showing the shape of the magnet's magnetic field.

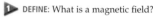

▲ **Figure 21-5** Iron filings sprinkled on plastic covering a bar magnet line up along the magnetic lines of force around the magnet.

▶ **1** DEFINE: What is a magnetic field?

Magnetic Lines of Force A magnetic field is made up of **magnetic lines of force.** When iron filings are sprinkled around a magnet, they will line up along the magnetic lines of force. Magnetic lines of force always begin at one pole and end at the opposite pole. They are also closest together at the poles because the magnetic field is strongest at the poles.

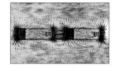

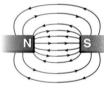

▲ **Figure 21-6** Magnetic lines of force show that unlike poles attract.

456

Teaching Options

◈ INTEGRATING THE SCIENCES

Chemistry A mass spectrometer is a device used by chemists to determine the chemical composition of a sample of matter. Mass spectrometers make use of magnetic fields. In most types of mass spectrometers, a thin beam of positive ions is deflected by an electric field and then deflected in the opposite direction by a magnetic field. The ions are then registered on a photographic plate. The heavier an ion is and the faster it travels, the less it is deflected. The ability to measure the mass and velocity of ions in a substance helps a chemist identify the makeup of a substance. Have students look up the following words and copy the pronunciations and definitions into their notebooks: *spectrometer, matter, ion, deflect, mass,* and *velocity.* **learning style: linguistic**

RETEACH

Interpreting Diagrams Have students refer to Figures 21-5 and 21-6. Be sure that students understand that the lines shown are not visible to the eye. The only way that these lines can be seen is by putting magnetic material, such as iron filings, around a magnet to show the lines of force.
learning style: visual

The magnetic lines of force between two like poles can be seen in Figure 21-7. The lines of force show that two like poles repel each other. The lines of force from the north pole of each magnet are bent away from the north pole of the other magnet.

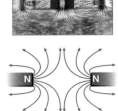
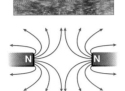

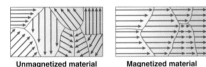

▲ **Figure 21-7** Magnetic lines of force show that like poles repel.

Two unlike poles attract each other. The lines of force from the north pole of one magnet bend toward the south pole of the other magnet.

▶ **DESCRIBE:** What do the magnetic lines of force show?

Magnetic Domains All matter is made up of atoms. The motion of electrons causes all atoms to have magnetic properties. In magnetic materials such as iron, groups of atoms can join together so that the magnetic fields of each atom point in the same direction. The north pole of each atom all point in the same direction. The south pole of each atom all point in the opposite direction. Groups of atoms whose magnetic poles are all lined up in the same direction are called **magnetic domains.**

Most of the magnetic domains of magnetic materials point in the same direction. However, the domains of unmagnetized materials point in different directions. Because the domains point in different directions, their magnetic fields cancel each other.

Unmagnetized material	Magnetized material

▲ **Figure 21-8** The domains of unmagnetized materials point in different directions. The domains of magnetized materials point in the same direction.

▶ **DEFINE:** What is a magnetic domain?

CHAPTER 21: Magnetism **457**

✓ CHECKING CONCEPTS

1. What is a magnetic field?
2. What happens when you bring a magnet near a piece of iron?
3. What are magnetic lines of force?
4. How can iron filings be used to show magnetic lines of force?
5. Why are magnetic lines of force closest together at the poles of a magnet?
6. What causes all atoms to have magnetic properties?

💡 THINKING CRITICALLY

7. **PREDICT:** What will happen to the magnetic lines of force when the north poles of two magnets are placed next to each other?
8. **EXPLAIN:** How can magnetic lines of force show that unlike poles attract each other?
9. **COMPARE:** How are the domains of magnetized and unmagnetized materials different?
10. **INFER:** If an object made of iron is brought near a magnet without actually touching it, how can the magnetic force of the magnet attract the object?

INTERPRETING VISUALS

Use Figure 21-9 to answer the question.

11. **ANALYZE:** Is pole *A* a north pole or a south pole? How do you know?

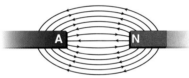

▲ **Figure 21-9** Magnetic lines of force around two magnets

---

sketch the shape of the magnetic field. Tell students to compare their drawings with the diagrams shown in Figures 21-6 and 21-7. **learning style: visual**

Answers to questions

▶1 **DEFINE:** the region of magnetic force around a magnet

▶2 **DESCRIBE:** the shape of the magnetic field

▶3 **DEFINE:** group of atoms whose magnetic fields are all lined up in the same direction

3 Assess

✓ CHECKING CONCEPTS ANSWERS

1. the region of magnetic force around a magnet
2. The magnetic force will attract the iron.
3. lines that show the shape of a magnetic field
4. When iron filings are sprinkled around a magnet, they will line up along the magnetic lines of force.
5. The magnetic field is strongest at the poles.
6. The motions of electrons cause atoms to have magnetic properties.

💡 THINKING CRITICALLY ANSWERS

7. **PREDICT:** They will curve away from each other.
8. **EXPLAIN:** The lines of force from the north pole of one magnet bend toward the south pole of the other magnet.
9. **COMPARE:** The domains of magnetized materials all line up in the same direction. The domains of unmagnetized materials point in different directions.
10. **INFER:** The magnet has a magnetic force around it.

4 Close

INTERPRETING VISUALS ANSWER

11. **ANALYZE:** Pole *A* is a south pole. The magnetic lines of force show that the two poles are attracted to each other.

• TEACHING RESOURCES •

⊚ **Teacher's Resources CD-ROM**
Lesson Review: Chapter 21, p. 3
Enrichment: Chapter 21, p. 4

Laboratory Manual
Lab. Challenge: What is the shape of a magnetic field? pp. 101–104

📼 **Laboratory Video**
Segment 23: Observing Magnetic Lines of Force

1 Introduce

STUDY HINT After students read this lesson, have them make a two-column chart. In the first column, students should list the properties of temporary magnets and in the second column, they should list the properties of permanent magnets.

Linking Prior Knowledge Read aloud the lesson title and ask students if they know any answers to the question. List students' ideas on the board to revisit after reading.

2 Teach

Demonstration Demonstrate magnetic induction. Hold an iron nail over some iron filings. Students will observe that the nail is not a natural magnet. Then, make the nail magnetic by stroking it with a magnet in one direction. Demonstrate the nail's induced magnetism by again holding it over the iron filings. Students will observe that the nail now attracts the filings. **learning style: visual**

Discussion Make sure that students understand the inverse relationship between the ease with which a material is magnetized and the length of time the material stays magnetized. After comparing the magnetic induction of iron and aluminum and identifying the two metals as temporary magnets, ask students whether nickel is a temporary or permanent magnet. (temporary) **learning style: auditory**

Answers to questions

1 NAME: magnetite, or lodestone

2 DEFINE: process by which a material is magnetized

3 CLASSIFY: temporary

4 EXPLAIN: dropping it or heating it

WRITING HINT As students relate the steps involved in making a magnetic compass, remind them to use time order words. Ask students to suggest words such as *first*, *next*, *second*, and *then*. Ask students to use these words to rewrite the directions in the Hands-On Activity in their own words.

21-3 How can you make a magnet?

Objectives
Explain how materials can be magnetized. Compare permanent magnets and temporary magnets.

Key Term
magnetic induction: process by which a material can be made into a magnet

Natural Magnets Some magnets occur in nature. These magnets are called natural magnets. Magnetite, or lodestone, is an example of a natural magnet. Certain materials that are not natural magnets can be made into magnets, or magnetized (MAG-nuh-tyzd). For example, rubbing an iron nail with a magnet in one direction will magnetize the nail. The magnetized nail will have the same properties as a natural magnet.

▲ **Figure 21-10** Magnetite, or lodestone, is a natural magnet.

1 NAME: What is an example of a natural magnet?

Magnetic Induction The process by which a material is magnetized, or made into a magnet, is called **magnetic induction.** In magnetic induction, the domains of certain materials are made to point in the same direction. They become magnetized. Some materials are easier to magnetize than others. Alloys of iron, nickel, and cobalt are easy to magnetize. Rubbing objects made of these materials with a magnet can cause the domains within the objects to point in the same direction. When this happens, these materials become magnetized. Other materials show weak magnetic properties. For example, if an aluminum object is placed in the magnetic field of a strong magnet, the atoms of the metal may be weakly affected by the magnetism. However, when the object is removed from the magnetic field, the domains will go back to pointing in different directions.

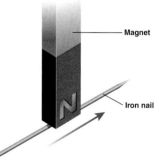

Magnet

Iron nail

▲ **Figure 21-11** Magnetic induction causes the iron nail to become magnetized.

2 DEFINE: What is magnetic induction?

Temporary and Permanent Magnets Once a material is magnetized, it may or may not remain magnetized. Iron is easily magnetized, but the iron loses its magnetism quickly. A material that is easily magnetized tends to lose its magnetism quickly. A magnet made of this kind of material is called a temporary magnet.

Materials that are hard to magnetize can stay magnetized for a long time. A piece of steel is harder to magnetize than a piece of iron. However, the steel will keep its magnetic properties much longer than will a piece of iron. A magnet that is hard to magnetize but tends to keep its magnetism is called a permanent magnet.

3 CLASSIFY: Is an iron magnet a temporary magnet or a permanent magnet?

458

Teaching Options

◈ INTEGRATING LIFE SCIENCE

Using Magnetic Fields in Medicine When doctors need to look inside a person's body, but do not want to perform surgery, they often use technology called MRI (Magnetic Resonance Imaging). In a certain type of MRI machine, a patient lies down and is slid into a tube. The tube is the bore, or center, of a large magnet. The body part to be scanned is then lined up so it is in the center of the magnetic field. The MRI changes the magnetic field around the tissue that is being examined. Normal tissue reacts differently to this alteration than abnormal or diseased tissue. By viewing the image of the scan, doctors can see whether scanned tissue is normal.

An MRI is ideal for diagnosing such problems as tumors, multiple sclerosis, infections in the brain or spine, strokes, and tendonitis. An MRI can help a doctor see torn ligaments or injuries to joints without having to perform invasive surgery. Because the magnets in the machines are so strong, people who have some types of implants (such as pacemakers) in their bodies cannot go into the machine because the magnet might make the devices malfunction. Students can do additional research on how an MRI works and write a summary to share with the class.

Losing Magnetism All magnets, even permanent magnets, can lose their magnetism. If you drop a magnet, you can cause the magnetic domains inside of it to stop pointing in the same direction. When the magnetic domains point in different directions, the magnet loses some or all of its magnetic properties. Heating a magnet can also cause it to become demagnetized. The energy from the heat can cause the atoms to move faster and farther apart. When this happens, the magnetic domains are no longer aligned.

▶ **EXPLAIN:** What are two ways in which a magnet can become demagnetized?

✓ CHECKING CONCEPTS

1. An example of a natural magnet is _____.

2. Rubbing an iron nail in the same direction with a magnet will _____ the nail.

3. When a piece of iron becomes magnetized, the magnetic _____ point in the same direction.

4. A _____ magnet is hard to magnetize.

5. A _____ magnet will not keep its magnetic properties for a long time.

6. All magnets can lose their _____.

7. Dropping a magnet can cause its _____ to point in different directions.

THINKING CRITICALLY

8. **INFER:** An iron nail has been magnetized. Does the magnetized nail have a north pole and a south pole? Explain.

9. **CONTRAST:** What is the difference between a temporary magnet and a permanent magnet?

10. **PREDICT:** Soft iron is very easy to magnetize. Will soft iron make a good permanent magnet? Why or why not?

11. **EXPLAIN:** How does dropping a magnet affect the magnetic domains within the magnet?

BUILDING SOCIAL STUDIES SKILLS

Researching The properties of the ore magnetite have been known for more than 2,000 years. The ancient Chinese may have discovered the properties of magnetite as early as 2600 B.C. Use library references, encyclopedias, and the Internet to find out how the ancient Chinese used magnetite and how they explained its properties in stories and myths.

Hands-On Activity

MAKING A MAGNETIC COMPASS

You will need a sewing needle, a bar magnet, a pushpin, a cork, a small plastic container of water, and a magnetic compass.

1. Insert the pushpin into the bottom of the cork.
2. Float the cork, with the pushpin pointing down, in a container of water.
3. Rub the magnet against the needle about 20 times. Rub in one direction only.
4. Lay the needle on top of the cork. Observe in which directions the needle points when it stops turning. Using a magnetic compass away from your setup, compare the direction of the needle with the direction of the compass pointer.

▲ **STEP 4** Observe in which direction the needle points.

Practicing Your Skills

5. **DESCRIBE:** What effect does rubbing with a magnet have on the needle?

6. **OBSERVE:** In which directions does the floating needle point?

---

3 Assess

✓ CHECKING CONCEPTS ANSWERS

1. magnetite or lodestone
2. magnetize
3. domains
4. permanent
5. temporary
6. magnetism
7. magnetic domains

💡 THINKING CRITICALLY ANSWERS

8. **INFER:** Yes; Any magnet has a north pole and a south pole.

9. **CONTRAST:** A temporary magnet is easily magnetized, but it tends to lose its magnetism quickly. A permanent magnet is hard to magnetize, but it keeps its magnetism.

10. **PREDICT:** No; A material that is easy to magnetize is a temporary magnet.

11. **EXPLAIN:** Dropping a magnet can cause the magnetic domains to point in different directions, which causes the magnet to lose its magnetism.

4 Close

BUILDING SOCIAL STUDIES SKILLS

Researching Suggest that students write questions to guide their research. Students may want to report their findings with illustrated posters, timelines, and so on. learning style: linguistic

Hands-On Activity

MAKING A MAGNETIC COMPASS

TIME: 10–15 minutes

PURPOSE: modeling, observing

Discussion Ask students why rubbing the magnet against the needle in a back-and-forth motion will not magnetize the needle. (The domains within the needle will not point in the same direction.) Ask students whether this needle is a temporary or permanent magnet. (temporary) Ask how they know. (It is easy to magnetize.)

Practicing Your Skills Answers

5. **DESCRIBE:** The needle becomes magnetic.

6. **OBSERVE:** north and south

ONGOING ASSESSMENT

Listing Properties Draw a two-column chart on the board with the heads *Easy to Magnetize* and *Not Easy to Magnetize*. Write phrases, such as *alloys of iron, keeps magnetism permanently*, and *loses magnetism when dropped*, on self-stick notes. Students can place the notes in the appropriate column on the chart. learning styles: auditory, logical/mathematical

• TEACHING RESOURCES •

🔘 **Teacher's Resources CD-ROM**
Lesson Review: Chapter 21, p. 5

MORE ON THE WEB

Magic or Magnetism? Have students visit www.concepts andchallenges.com to read about a scientist who discovered how to make a magnet levitate between his fingertips.

1 Introduce

STUDY HINT Before beginning this lesson, ask students to write the title of the lesson in their notebooks. As they read the lesson, students should write the information that answers the question in the lesson title.

Linking Prior Knowledge Ask students to explain why a needle in a magnetic compass points to the north. Guide students to realize that Earth must have magnetic properties in order to influence the movement of a magnet in a compass.

2 Teach

Demonstration Repeat William Gilbert's experiment for the class. Obtain a bar magnet with its poles labeled. Tie a string around the middle of the magnet and suspend it from a ring stand. Students will observe that the north pole of the magnet points north, and the south pole of the magnet points south. **learning style: visual**

Discussion Ask volunteers to point out and name Earth's geographic poles on a globe or world map. Be sure that students understand that Earth's poles are not named for their magnetic polarity, but for their geographic locations. **learning styles: visual, auditory**

Answers to questions

1 STATE: Earth has north and south poles just like a bar magnet does.

2 EXPLAIN: They are near the geographic poles, but not exactly at those points.

3 INFER: The north pole of a magnet points in that direction. Magnetic poles repel each other, therefore, Earth's geographic North Pole is the magnetic south pole.

4 DEFINE: Earth's magnetic field

READING STRATEGY Remind students that the main idea of a paragraph or other piece of writing is its most important idea. Details support, or tell more about, the main idea. Encourage students to identify the main idea of each of the sections as they read and find the details that support each main idea.

21-4 How is Earth like a magnet?

Objective
Explain how Earth acts like a magnet.

Key Term
magnetosphere (mag-NEET-oh-sfeer): region of Earth's magnetic field

William Gilbert In the early 1600s, a British scientist named William Gilbert made observations about magnetism. Gilbert observed that if you hang a bar magnet from a string, one pole of the magnet always points north and the other pole always points south. William Gilbert was the first person to suggest an explanation for this observation. He proposed that Earth itself is a magnet, and just like any magnet, Earth has a north pole and a south pole.

1 STATE: How did Gilbert's proposal compare Earth to a magnet?

Earth's Magnetic Poles Scientists have discovered that William Gilbert's proposal was correct. Earth does act as if a huge bar magnet is buried deep inside of it. This causes Earth to have two magnetic poles. One of Earth's magnetic poles is near the geographic North Pole in Canada. The other magnetic pole is near the geographic South Pole in Antarctica. The magnetic poles of Earth are not exactly at Earth's geographic poles. In fact, the magnetic pole near Earth's geographic North Pole is about 1,300 kilometers away from it.

2 EXPLAIN: Where are Earth's magnetic poles in relation to Earth's geographic poles?

Earth's Magnetic Poles Are Not Earth's Geographic Poles You have learned that the north pole of a magnet always points north. However, like magnetic poles repel each other. This means that when a magnet points to the geographic North Pole, the North Pole is really Earth's magnetic south pole. It also means that when the south pole of a magnet faces Earth's geographic South Pole, the South Pole must be Earth's magnetic north pole. Figure 20-12 shows Earth's magnetic poles and geographic poles.

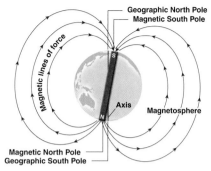

▲ Figure 21-12 Earth's magnetic poles are not the same as Earth's geographic poles.

3 INFER: Why is Earth's geographic North Pole called the magnetic south pole?

The Magnetosphere Like any magnet, Earth is surrounded by a magnetic field. The magnetic field is strongest near the north and south magnetic poles. Earth's magnetic field extends far into space. The magnetic field around Earth is called the **magnetosphere.**

The magnetosphere traps charged particles released by the Sun. Most of these particles are deflected by the magnetosphere. However, some particles do get through it. When these charged particles hit Earth's atmosphere, they interact with other particles, causing the air above Earth's surface to glow. This glowing area is called an aurora (aw-RAWR-uh).

Auroras seen in the Northern Hemisphere near the North Pole are also called the northern lights or aurora borealis. Auroras seen in the Southern Hemisphere near the South Pole are called the southern lights, or aurora australis.

Teaching Options

RETEACH

Clearing Up Misconceptions Some students may still confuse the north and south geographic poles with the north and south magnetic poles. Draw students' attention to Figure 21-12, pointing out that the poles are opposites: the magnetic south pole is the geographic North Pole. Explain why the geographic and magnetic pole names are opposites. (Opposite poles attract each other, while like poles repel. The magnetic north pole of Earth would repel the north pole of a magnet rather than attract it.) Have students write a mnemonic device to help them remember that the poles are opposites. Ask students to share their mnemonic devices with the class. **learning style: linguistic**

▲ Figure 21-13 The southern lights are caused by particles from the Sun interacting with particles in Earth's atmosphere.

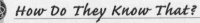

▶ DEFINE: What is the magnetosphere?

✔ **CHECKING CONCEPTS**

1. When a compass points north, it is pointing to Earth's magnetic _____ pole.
2. Earth's magnetic south pole attracts the _____ pole of a magnet.

3. Earth's geographic North Pole is also Earth's magnetic _____ pole.
4. Earth is surrounded by a magnetic field called the _____.

💡 **THINKING CRITICALLY**

5. CLASSIFY: Is Earth a permanent magnet or a temporary magnet? How do you know?
6. INFER: Explain why auroras occur in both the Northern Hemisphere and the Southern Hemisphere.

BUILDING SCIENCE SKILLS

Making a Model The Sun produces a stream of high-energy particles called solar wind. Solar wind causes the magnetosphere to form into a special shape. Find out the shape of the magnetosphere. Then, use markers and poster board to make a model of it. Share your illustration with your class.

How Do They Know That?

THE HISTORY OF EARTH'S MAGNETISM IN ROCKS

Scientists have found that Earth acts like a giant magnet. The magnetism comes from deep within the planet. Earth's center, or core, is surrounded by hot liquid metal. As the liquid metal flows, it produces a magnetic field. The flowing liquid metal around the core changes over time. These changes cause Earth's magnetic field to change with it. In fact, every few thousand years, the magnetic field of the Earth reverses itself. Geologists discovered this fact by studying the magnetic fields in certain rocks.

▲ Figure 21-14 Volcanic rock contains magnetic stripes that can be detected by special instruments.

Rocks containing the metal iron can become permanent magnets when they form. These magnetic rocks can form inside volcanoes. As lava from the volcano cools, Earth's magnetic field pulls on the magnetic materials in the rock. The magnetic materials in the rock line up to match the magnetic field of Earth at the time that the rock formed.

Geologists study the magnetic patterns inside these rocks. Special instruments are used to study these rocks because the magnetic patterns cannot be seen with the naked eye. From the magnetic patterns in many of the rocks, scientists have learned about the reversals of Earth's magnetic field. A reversal of Earth's magnetic field occurs every few thousand years.

Thinking Critically How can magnetic rocks reveal that Earth's magnetic field reverses itself?

---

3 Assess

✔ **CHECKING CONCEPTS ANSWERS**

1. south
2. north
3. south
4. magnetosphere

💡 **THINKING CRITICALLY ANSWERS**

5. CLASSIFY: Earth is a permanent magnet. It has retained its magnetic field.
6. INFER: The magnetosphere that is responsible for the auroras surrounds the entire Earth, so the auroras occur in both hemispheres.

4 Close

BUILDING SCIENCE SKILLS

Making a Model Students can use reference sources to find out more about solar wind. Solar wind not only affects the magnetosphere of Earth, it also extends to other planets in the solar system.

How Do They Know That?

THE HISTORY OF EARTH'S MAGNETISM IN ROCKS

Interdisciplinary Connection Share with students that volcanic rock has not only revealed that Earth's magnetic field reverses every few thousand years but also that Earth's magnetic poles were once located in different places from where they are today. Five hundred million years ago, the north magnetic pole lay south of what is now the state of Hawaii. For the next 300 million years, the magnetic equator was across what is now the United States. Geologists believe that this happened because the axis of the Earth stayed the same while the plates on the Earth's crust gradually shifted.

Discussion Ask students: *What produces the magnetic field inside Earth?* (the flowing liquid metal around Earth's core) *How do magnetic stripes form within the volcanic rocks?* (The magnetic materials in the rock line up to match Earth's magnetic field at the time that the rocks form.)

Thinking Critically Answer
The stripes reveal the direction of Earth's magnetic field at the time the rock hardened.

MORE ON THE WEB

The North Pole Is Moving!
Have students use the Internet to learn more about Earth's geographic and magnetic poles. Have students answer the questions at www.conceptsand challenges.com.

ONGOING ASSESSMENT

Comparing Earth and a Magnet Ask students: *Name two ways in which Earth is like a magnet.* (Earth acts as if a huge bar magnet is buried deep inside of it, and Earth has a magnetic field around it.)

• **TEACHING RESOURCES** •

Teacher's Resources CD-ROM
Lesson Review: Chapter 21, p. 6
Enrichment: Chapter 21, p. 7

21-5 (pp. 462–463)

1 Introduce

🔍 INVESTIGATE

TIME: 10–15 minutes

PURPOSE: Students will set up a simple circuit and then observe how electricity affects a magnetic compass.

MATERIALS: 2 insulated wires, dry cell (size D) battery, light bulb, magnetic compass

PROCEDURE: Have students work in small groups to complete this activity. Remind students that the bulb should be lit before they bring the compass near the wires.

THINK ABOUT IT: The pointer of the compass points in a different direction.

✏️ **STUDY HINT** Before beginning this lesson, have students scan the lesson for unfamiliar words. Have students work in pairs to define each word on their list.

Linking Prior Knowledge Read the lesson title with students and ask them to discuss what they know about electricity. Have students review the definition of *electricity* (Lesson 20-1) and recall what a battery is (Lesson 20-2).

2 Teach

Demonstration Show the effect of moving a magnet near a wire. Use an ordinary bar magnet. Connect the wire directly to a large demonstration galvanometer. A weak current will flow through the wire when the magnet is moved past it. Show that the current stops when the magnet stops moving. **learning style: visual**

Discussion Be sure that students understand the difference between Oersted's and Faraday's discoveries. Oersted discovered that an electric current causes a magnetic field. Farady discovered that a changing magnetic field causes an electric current. **learning style: auditory**

Answers to questions

▶ **DESCRIBE:** An electric current produces a magnetic field.

▶ **DEFINE:** the process by which an electric current is produced when a wire is exposed to a changing magnetic field

T462 UNIT 7: Electricity and Magnetism

21-5 How are electricity and magnetism related?

INVESTIGATE 🔍

Observing Magnetism and Electricity
HANDS-ON ACTIVITY

1. Note in what direction the pointer of a magnetic compass points.
2. Connect two insulated wires to a dry cell (size D) battery and a light bulb in a holder.
3. When the light bulb lights up, carefully bring the compass near the wires. Observe the pointer of the compass.

THINK ABOUT IT: What happens to the pointer of the compass?

STEP 3

Objective

Explain the relationship between electricity and magnetism.

Key Terms

electromagnetism: relationship between electricity and magnetism

electromagnetic induction: process by which an electric current is produced by moving a wire in a magnetic field

Oersted's Discovery Have you ever used a magnetic compass around an electrical device? If you have, you may have noticed that the pointer of the compass gets "confused." The pointer may no longer point north. This happens because of the relationship between electricity and magnetism. This relationship is called **electromagnetism.** The Danish scientist Hans Christian Oersted (UR-sted) was the first person to show that this relationship does exist.

More than 150 years ago, Hans Christian Oersted discovered an important property of electric current. Oersted connected a simple series circuit made up of a battery and a wire. As charges flowed through the wire, Oersted noticed that a nearby compass pointer moved. When the circuit was disconnected, the compass pointer returned to its original position. He also noticed that when the direction of the current was reversed, the pointer moved in the opposite

462

direction. Hans Christian Oersted discovered that an electric current produces a magnetic field.

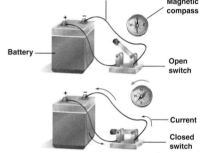

▲ Figure 21-15 When electric current flows through a circuit, a magnetic field is produced.

▶ **DESCRIBE:** What did Hans Christian Oersted discover?

Electromagnetic Induction An electric current produces a magnetic field. Does a magnetic field produce an electric current? A British scientist named Michael Faraday tried to answer this question. He hung a wire that remained still. Then he moved a strong magnet around it. He found that when the magnet was held still, no electric current moved through the wire. However, when he moved the magnet toward and away from the wire continuously, electric charges flowed through

---

Teaching Options

❗ FAST FACTS How much is an amp?

Ask students if they have ever heard or used the word *amps* to describe power. *Amps* is short for *amperes*. An ampere is the SI unit used to measure the rate of flow of an electric current. One ampere, which is one of seven base units in the metric system, is equal to one unit of electric charge flowing past a cross section of an electric circuit in 1 second. Amperes are also defined in terms of magnetic force produced by electric currents. At 100 volts, a 100-watt light bulb requires about 1 ampere of current. Some currents are so tiny (such as those needed to run small calculators) that they are measured in microamperes. French physicist Andre Marie Ampere, for whom the ampere was named, was the first person to show that currents flowing through parallel wires cause magnetic forces between the wires.

the wire. He also noticed that the direction of the current depended upon the direction of the movement of the magnet.

Faraday also tried moving a wire coil around a stationary magnet and got the same results. Thus, Faraday found that electric current will be produced in a wire that is exposed to a changing magnetic field. The process by which an electric current is produced when a wire is exposed to a changing magnetic field is called **electromagnetic induction.** The current is induced, or caused to flow, in a wire when the wire cuts across magnetic lines of force.

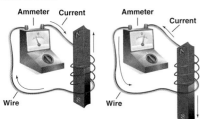

▲ **Figure 21-16** In electromagnetic induction, electric current is produced in a wire by a changing magnetic field.

▶ DEFINE: What is electromagnetic induction?

People in Science

JOSEPH HENRY (1797–1878)

Joseph Henry was an American scientist. He studied electricity and magnetism. He and the British scientist Michael Faraday made similar discoveries at about the same time. Joseph Henry discovered that a changing magnetic field will induce a current in a conductor. However, Faraday is given credit for making the same discovery.

Joseph Henry was born in Albany, New York, on December 17, 1797. He helped Samuel Morse develop the telegraph. In 1831, Henry built a telegraph of his own. He also built one of the most powerful devices known at the time. Joseph Henry's device used electromagnetism to lift more than a ton of weight.

▲ **Figure 21-17** Joseph Henry

In 1846, Joseph Henry was appointed to head the Smithsonian Institution in Washington, D.C. He was also the main organizer of the National Academy of Science and started the U.S. Weather Service. In honor of Joseph Henry, the unit for electromagnetic induction is called the henry.

Thinking Critically Why is the unit for electromagnetism called the henry?

✓ CHECKING CONCEPTS

1. Oersted discovered that an _____ caused a magnetic field.
2. An electric current is produced when a wire is exposed to a _____ magnetic field.
3. Michael Faraday discovered electromagnetic _____.
4. Electromagnetism is the relationship between _____ and magnetism.

💡 THINKING CRITICALLY

5. DESCRIBE: What determines the direction of electric current in a wire when a magnet is moved around the wire?
6. EXPLAIN: What happens to a nearby compass when you disconnect a circuit?
7. EXPLAIN: Why will an electric current not be produced in a wire that is exposed to a stationary magnetic field?

3 Assess

✓ CHECKING CONCEPTS ANSWERS

1. electric current
2. changing
3. induction
4. electricity

💡 THINKING CRITICALLY ANSWERS

5. DESCRIBE: the direction of the movement of the magnet
6. EXPLAIN: The compass point returns to its original position.
7. EXPLAIN: Electromagnetic induction occurs only when a wire is moving in a magnetic field.

4 Close

People in Science

JOSEPH HENRY (1797–1878)

Real-Life Connection Consider demonstrating a telegraph, playing an audio recording of a telegraphed message, or showing students the code used by telegraph operators. To help students understand how codes were used to send messages, you might have students work in small groups to make up their own codes. Tell students to write messages using their secret codes. After each group is finished, try to decipher all the messages as a class.

Discussion Ask students: *How were Henry's discoveries related to Faraday's?* (They both made the same discovery at about the same time—that a changing magnetic field will induce a current in a conductor.)

Ask students to summarize Joseph Henry's accomplishments. List his accomplishments on the board. (He discovered the relationship between magnetism and electricity, helped Morse develop the telegraph, used electromagnetism to make a device that lifted more than a ton of weight, headed the Smithsonian Institution, organized the National Academy of Science, and started the U.S. Weather Service.)

Thinking Critically Answer
because Joseph Henry discovered electromagnetic induction at the same time as Faraday did but was not given credit for it

MORE ON THE WEB

Writing About Electromagnetic Induction Have students visit www.conceptsandchallenges.com to learn about uses for electromagnetic induction. Have students write a short report about their findings.

ONGOING ASSESSMENT

Examining the Diagram Ask students to explain what is happening in Figure 21-16. Be sure that they explain why the arrows are pointed in their particular directions.
learning style: linguistic

• TEACHING RESOURCES •

💿 **Teacher's Resources CD-ROM**
Lesson Review: Chapter 21, p. 8

21-6 *(pp. 464–465)*

1 *Introduce*

✎ **STUDY HINT** Have students study Figure 21-18. Ask them how the magnetic compass differs in the top illustration from the bottom illustration. (The needle moves a greater distance in the top illustration.)

Linking Prior Knowledge Review the forms of energy (Lesson 14-2) and the two types of electric current—direct and alternating (Lesson 20-4).

2 *Teach*

Discussion Draw attention to Figure 21-18 and ask students to explain why the magnetic field is stronger in the first figure. (Coiling the wire causes the magnetic fields around each coil to be added together. The more coils that are added, the stronger is the magnetic field.) Ask students to look at Figure 21-19. Ask them why the setup shown in this figure would create a strong magnetic field. (Wrapping coils of wire around a piece of metal will produce the greatest strength in the magnetic field.) Students should identify iron as a material that is easily magnetized.
learning styles: visual, auditory

Demonstration Tell students that one common use of electromagnets is in devices called relays. Explain that a relay is a switch that can be turned on or off by an electromagnet. Use wires to connect a battery to a lamp. Place a switch in this circuit consisting of a flexible strip of metal cut from a tin can. Attach one end of the strip to a wire from the battery, and allow the other end of the strip to touch a wire to the lamp. The lamp should light up when the circuit is complete. Then, hold an electromagnet (like the kind students will make in the Hands-On Activity on page 465) over the metal strip. The electromagnet should pull the strip away from the wire to the lamp, turning off the lamp. Explain that relays work this way in circuit breakers, which shut off the current in house circuits if the circuits are overloaded.
learning styles: visual, auditory

21-6 What is an electromagnet?

Objective
Describe how to make an electromagnet.

Key Term
electromagnet: temporary magnet made by wrapping a current-carrying wire around a metal core

Magnetic Field Strength A wire carrying an electric current always has a magnetic field around it. The magnetic field around a straight wire is not very strong. If the wire is wound into a coil, the magnetic field becomes much stronger. The magnetic fields around each coil of wire add together. The more turns you add to the coil, the stronger the magnetic field will become. Increasing the amount of current running through the wire will also increase the magnetic field around the wire.

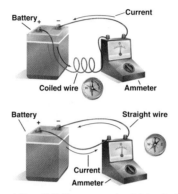

▲ **Figure 21-18** The compasses show that strength of the magnetic field around a coiled wire is stronger than the strength of the magnetic field around a straight wire.

▶ **PREDICT:** Which will have a stronger magnetic field, a wire coil with two turns or a wire coil with four turns?

Electromagnets The strength of the magnetic field around a wire can be increased by adding turns to the wire coil and by increasing the amount

464

of current flowing through the wire. However, wrapping coils of wire around a piece of metal, such as iron, will produce the greatest strength in the magnetic field around the wire. The magnetic field around the wire aligns the magnetic domains within the piece of iron. The strength of the magnetic field around the coiled wire and the strength of the magnetic field around the iron add together.

When electric current flows through a coil of wire that is wrapped around an iron core, a strong magnet is produced. This type of magnet is called an **electromagnet.** The magnetic material in the center of an electromagnet is called a core. An electromagnet is a temporary magnet. As long as current is flowing through the wire, the electromagnet has a strong magnetic field. When the current is turned off, there is no longer a magnetic field.

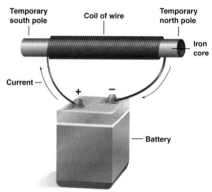

▲ **Figure 21-19** An electromagnet is made up of an energy source, a wire coil, and a metal core.

The strength of an electromagnet can be increased in two ways. Adding more turns to the wire coil around the magnetic core makes an electromagnet stronger. Increasing the current through the wire also makes an electromagnet stronger.

▶ **INFER:** What are two ways to make an electromagnet stronger?

Teaching Options

❗ FAST FACTS

Alnico—A Metal Alloy

The word *alnico* comes from <u>al</u>uminum + <u>ni</u>ckel + <u>co</u>balt. This metal alloy, which also contains iron and may include copper or titanium, is used in making strong permanent magnets. Alnico magnets were first developed in the 1930s. This material is very stable, resistant to corrosion, and able to withstand high temperatures and temperature changes. Alnico magnets can be molded into different shapes, so they are used in many applications, such as sensors in cars and amplifiers.

ONGOING ASSESSMENT

Writing About Electromagnets
Remind students to use the comparative and superlative forms of adjectives as they write about the strengths of electromagnets. Some students may make the mistake of using the comparative form ending in *-er* plus the word *more*, as in *more stronger*. Write *strong*, *stronger*, and *strongest* on the board. Have students use these words to write three sentences about electromagnets.
learning style: linguistic

Uses of Electromagnets Electromagnets have many important uses. They are used in devices, such as radios, telephones, and computers. Large electromagnets are used to lift heavy pieces of metal. Electromagnets are very useful because they can be turned on and off.

▲ Figure 21-20 Electromagnets can be used to lift heavy objects.

 EXPLAIN: Why are electromagnets so useful?

✓ CHECKING CONCEPTS

1. What is an electromagnet?
2. Why is an electromagnet considered to be a temporary magnet?
3. What are two ways to increase the strength of the magnetic field around a wire?
4. Name three devices that use electromagnets.

💡 THINKING CRITICALLY

5. CONTRAST: How is an electromagnet different from a permanent magnet?
6. LIST: What are the materials needed to make an electromagnet?

INTERPRETING VISUALS

Look at Figure 21-19 of an electromagnet to answer the following questions.

7. PREDICT: What would happen if you were to disconnect the wires from the dry cell?
8. ANALYZE: What would happen if there were fewer coils wrapped around the metal core?

🔬 *Hands-On Activity*

MAKING AN ELECTROMAGNET

You will need paper clips, a D-cell battery, a 6-volt battery, insulated wire, and an ungalvanized nail.

1. Wrap 20 turns of wire around an ungalvanized nail. Connect the ends of the wire to the terminals of the D-cell battery.
2. Try to pick up some paper clips.
3. Now, wrap 40 turns of wire around the nail. Connect the ends of the wire to the same battery. See how many paper clips you can pick up.
4. Connect the electromagnet with 40 turns of wire to the 6-volt battery. See how many paper clips you can pick up.

▲ STEP 4 Pick up paper clips with your electromagnet.

Practicing Your Skills

5. OBSERVE: How many paper clips did the electromagnet with 20 turns of wire connected to the D-cell battery pick up? With 40 turns?
6. COMPARE: Were you able to pick up more paper clips when the electromagnet was connected to the D-cell battery or to the 6-volt battery? Explain.

MORE ON THE WEB

Telegraphy Have students use the Internet to read about several inventions in the telegraphy industry that were made possible because of electromagnetics. Have students take the online quiz at www.conceptsandchallenges.com.

• *TEACHING RESOURCES* •

💿 **Teacher's Resources CD-ROM**
Lesson Review: Chapter 21, p. 9
Enrichment: Chapter 21, p. 10

Answers to questions

▶ PREDICT: wire coil with four turns

▶ INFER: add more coils of wire and increase the current through the wire

▶ EXPLAIN: They can be turned on and off.

3 *Assess*

✓ CHECKING CONCEPTS ANSWERS

1. An electromagnet is a temporary magnet made by wrapping a current-carrying wire around an iron core.
2. When the current is turned off, there is no longer a magnetic field.
3. Add more coils and increase the current.
4. Possible answers: radio, telephone, and computer

💡 THINKING CRITICALLY ANSWERS

5. CONTRAST: Possible answer: When the current is turned off, an electromagnet does not have a magnetic field. A permanent magnet always has a magnetic field.
6. LIST: a metal core, an insulated wire, and a source of power, such as a battery

INTERPRETING VISUALS ANSWERS

7. PREDICT: The electromagnet would be turned off.
8. ANALYZE: The strength of the electromagnet would decrease.

4 *Close*

Hands-On Activity

MAKING AN ELECTROMAGNET

TIME: 15–20 minutes

PURPOSE: observing, comparing

SAFETY TIP: Remind students to handle both nails and electricity carefully. Tell students to pick up any paper clips that fall on the floor.

Practicing Your Skills Answers

5. OBSERVE: Students' answers should indicate that the electromagnet with 40 turns picked up more paper clips than the electromagnet with 20 turns.
6. COMPARE: The 6-volt battery allows more paper clips to be picked up. The strength increases as the current increases.

1 Introduce

STUDY HINT Have students write the lesson title and the two objectives in their notebooks. As students read the lesson, tell them to write the information that meets the objectives.

Linking Prior Knowledge Show students a picture of a utility pole with a transformer on top. Ask students if they know what this device at the top of a pole is and what job it performs. Also, ask students to recall the differences between alternating current and direct current (Lesson 20-4).

2 Teach

Discussion Ask students how electrons flow in a direct current (in one direction) and in an alternating current (flow of electrons reverses direction regularly). Refer students to Figures 21-22 and 21-23. Have them compare the number of coils in the primary coil and secondary coil in both figures. Describe to students how step-up transformers increase the voltage of alternating current and how step-down transformers decrease the voltage of alternating current.
learning styles: visual, auditory

Demonstration Demonstrate a transformer that can be taken apart. Show and identify the various parts. Use AC voltmeters and ammeters to demonstrate the change in voltage in step-up and step-down transformer circuits. **learning style: visual**

Answers to questions

1 DEFINE: A transformer is a device that uses alternating current in the primary coil to induce a current in the secondary coil.

2 DESCRIBE: It increases voltage of alternating current.

3 EXPLAIN: It decreases voltage of alternating current.

4 INFER: A step-down transformer is used to decrease voltage before electricity is sent into homes, businesses, and schools.

21-7 What is a transformer?

Objectives
Explain how a transformer works. Compare a step-up and a step-down transformer.

Key Term
transformer: device in which alternating current in one coil of wire induces a current in a second coil of wire

Transformers Suppose you wrap two coils of wire around a nail. You attach one of the coils to a dry cell and a switch. This coil is called the primary coil. You connect the other coil to an ammeter. This is the secondary coil. When you close the switch in the primary coil, the ammeter shows that a current flows in the secondary coil. This current quickly dies out. When you open the switch, current again flows in the secondary coil. Again, it quickly dies out. To keep current flowing to the secondary coil, you must keep opening and closing the switch.

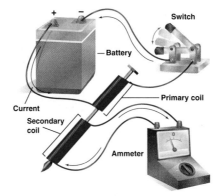

▲ **Figure 21-21** To keep current flowing to the secondary coil, the switch has to be opened and closed over and over again.

A **transformer** is a device that uses alternating current in the primary coil to induce a current in the secondary coil. The primary coil is connected to a source of alternating current.

1 DEFINE: What is a transformer?

466

Step-Up Transformers A transformer can be used to increase the voltage of alternating current. This kind of transformer is called a step-up transformer. A step-up transformer has more turns of wire in the secondary coil than in the primary coil. The more turns of wire there are in the secondary coil, the higher the voltage will be. Power companies use step-up transformers to produce high-voltage electricity to send over long distances.

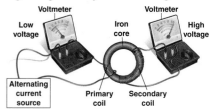

▲ **Figure 21-22** A step-up transformer has fewer coils in the primary coil than in the secondary coil.

2 DESCRIBE: What does a step-up transformer do?

Step-Down Transformers A transformer can also decrease the voltage of alternating current. A transformer that decreases voltage is called a step-down transformer. A step-down transformer has fewer turns of wire in the secondary coil than in the primary coil. The fewer the turns of wire in the secondary coil, the lower the voltage will be. Step-down transformers lower the high voltage carried by power lines.

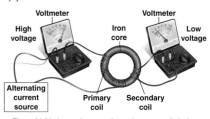

▲ **Figure 21-23** A step-down transformer has more coils in the primary coil than in the secondary coil.

3 EXPLAIN: What does a step-down transformer do?

Teaching Options

EXTENDING THE LESSON

Explaining Transformers Inform students that electricity passes through several transformers between a power plant and a home. At most power plants, electricity is produced at a voltage of 1,000 to 26,000 volts. A step-up transformer raises the voltage to between 138,000 and 765,000 volts for long-distance transmission. As the electricity gets closer to its point of use, it passes through a series of step-down transformers that lower the voltage in stages: first to as low as 69,000 volts, then to between 2,400 and 33,000 volts, and finally to 120 or 240 volts near the home.

ESL/ELL STRATEGY

Using Strategies to Define Words Some students may find it difficult to comprehend the technical terms in this lesson. Encourage them to keep a list of words that are new to them and use strategies to define those words. Reteach strategies as necessary, including using context clues, checking a dictionary, and studying graphic resources.

Transmission of Electricity Power plants use transformers to send electricity to homes, businesses, and schools. Very often, power plants are located in areas far away from where electricity is needed. Electricity has to travel long distances to reach these areas. At power plants, electricity is produced at low voltage. However, when electricity travels long distances, there is a loss of energy. By using a step-up transformer, power companies are able to send high-voltage electricity over long distances without too much loss of energy. Because electricity is usually used at a lower voltage, step-down transformers lower the voltage before the electricity is sent into homes, businesses, and schools.

✏️ **INFER:** When is a step-down transformer used?

✅ **CHECKING CONCEPTS**

1. What is a transformer?
2. Which coil of a transformer is attached to a source of current?

⚛️ *Real-Life Science*

BIRDS ON A WIRE

High-voltage electricity is transmitted through electric power lines. The voltage can range from about 7,200 to 800,000 volts. Electricity that escapes from these lines can do great damage. Sparks from fallen lines can cause fires.

You should never go near power lines. You can be seriously injured if enough electricity passes through your body. Power workers who repair power lines have to wear protective clothing when they work on the lines. Yet, birds can sit on power lines all day long without getting hurt. Why are birds not in danger when they sit on electric power lines?

The answer is that birds do not form a circuit with the electricity in the power lines. Because they are not connected to the ground or another wire, current never flows through their bodies. Electric current stays in the wire. As long as a bird's body is only in contact with a line at the same voltage, it is safe. However, if a bird extends its wing and touches another wire at a different voltage, it would get a shock. Also, if a bird's wing touched a tree while it was sitting on a power line, it would get a shock.

Thinking Critically Why would a bird get shocked if its wing touched another wire at a different voltage?

▲ **Figure 21-24** Birds do not form a circuit with the electricity in a power line.

3. What kind of transformer can be used to increase voltage?
4. What kind of transformer can be used to decrease voltage?

💡 **THINKING CRITICALLY**

5. CONTRAST: What is the difference between a step-up transformer and a step-down transformer?

📋 **BUILDING SCIENCE SKILLS**

Investigating The voltage from a wall outlet in your home is 120 volts. Unplug and look at several appliances around your home. How much voltage do they need to operate? The voltage is usually given on the appliance or in the owner's manual. Which appliances need less than 120 volts? Which need more than 120 volts? Do the appliances use step-down or step-up transformers?

✏️ **WRITING HINT** Suggest that students write answers to questions in complete sentences. This improves the quality of their thinking as well as their writing.

3 Assess

✅ **CHECKING CONCEPTS ANSWERS**

1. A transformer is a device that uses alternating current in one coil of wire to induce a current in a second coil.
2. primary coil
3. step-up transformer
4. step-down transformer

💡 **THINKING CRITICALLY ANSWER**

5. CONTRAST: A step-up transformer increases voltage, while a step-down transformer decreases voltage.

4 Close

📋 **BUILDING SCIENCE SKILLS**

Investigating Allow time for students to share results with the class. If time permits, you might bring small appliances to class for students to examine.

Real-Life Science

BIRDS ON A WIRE

Real-Life Connection Inform students that power lines are a small part of a power distribution grid, the network through which power travels. A power plant produces three different phases of electrical power at once and sends those three phases out on their own wires. Four wires come out of every electrical power plant, one for each of the three phases and one that is neutral. A power company may also use the ground as one of its wires. The earth is a good conductor, so it can be used as a return path for electrons. Usually, the maximum distance that voltage can travel on a wire is about 300 miles. To reduce the loss of electricity, the voltages in the lines are very high—from 155,000 to 765,000 volts.

Thinking Critically Answer
Touching a wire with a different voltage allows the flow of electric current, which would shock the bird.

MORE ON THE WEB

Reviewing Transformers Have students use the Internet to learn more about transformers. Have students take the online quiz at www.concepts andchallenges.com.

ONGOING ASSESSMENT

Explaining Differences Ask volunteers to explain the differences between a step-up transformer and a step-down transformer. Encourage them to describe the major parts of the transformer, tell how the transformer changes electric current, and where these types of transformers are used.

• *TEACHING RESOURCES* •

💿 **Teacher's Resources CD-ROM**
Lesson Review: Chapter 21, p. 11

1 Introduce

✏ **STUDY HINT** Have students create word webs in their notebooks. The topic should be *electric motors*. As students read this lesson, they can add arms to their webs on which they record information about electric motors. Students can also use the Spider Map found on the Teacher's Resources CD-ROM.

Linking Prior Knowledge Ask students if they know how electrical appliances and toys run. Elicit from students that these devices have motors. Ask if students know how motors work. Prompt them to discuss their ideas.

2 Teach

Demonstration To show students that changing the direction of an electric current will reverse the poles of an electromagnet, connect an electromagnet to a dry cell. Use a compass to identify the poles. Then, switch the connections to the dry cell so that the direction of the current is reversed. Again, use a compass to identify the poles. Students will observe that the poles are reversed. **learning style: visual**

Discussion Draw students' attention to Figure 21-25 and ask students to point to each of the parts as you slowly read the caption. Be sure that students understand that an electric motor changes electrical energy from the energy source (battery) into mechanical energy, which can be seen in the rotating electromagnet.
learning styles: visual, auditory

Answers to questions

▶ **PREDICT:** The poles will be reversed.

▶ **INFER:** The changing poles cause the electromagnet to rotate.

▶ **INFER:** to reverse the direction of the current so that the electromagnet will rotate

▶ **EXPLAIN:** to change electrical energy into mechanical energy

---

21-8 What is an electric motor?

Objective
Explain how an electric motor works.

Key Term
electric motor: device that changes electrical energy into mechanical energy

Reversing Magnetic Poles By changing the direction of an electric current running through an electromagnet, you can reverse the poles of the electromagnet. Suppose you connect an electromagnet to a dry cell. As the current flows, one end of the electromagnet becomes a north pole. The other end becomes a south pole. You can use a compass to identify the poles. What will happen if you switch the connections to the dry cell? The direction of the current will be reversed. The magnetic poles of the electromagnet will also be reversed. The compass will indicate the new magnetic poles.

▶ **PREDICT:** What will happen to the poles of an electromagnet if you change the direction of the electric current?

Electric Motor The ability to reverse the poles of an electromagnet explains how an electric motor works. An **electric motor** changes electrical energy into mechanical energy. You learned that mechanical energy is the energy of motion.

An electric motor is made up of an electromagnet, a permanent magnet, and a source of alternating current. The electromagnet is free to rotate. It is attached to a source of alternating current. When current flows, the poles of the electromagnet are attracted to the opposite poles of the permanent magnet. As the direction of the current changes, the poles of the electromagnet are reversed. The poles of the electromagnet are now repelled by the like poles of the permanent magnet. This repulsion causes the electromagnet to rotate.

Attraction and repulsion between the electromagnet and the permanent magnet cause the electromagnet to rotate. As long as alternating current is supplied, the electromagnet rotates continuously. The mechanical energy of the rotating magnet enables the motor to do work. The rotating magnet can be connected to a device such as a fan or a wheel.

▶ **INFER:** How does an electric motor change electrical energy into mechanical energy?

Reversing Direct Current If direct current were used to run an electric motor, the electromagnet would not rotate continuously. Because the direction of the current would not change, the poles of the electromagnet would not reverse.

However, direct current can be used to run an electric motor if a special switch is used. This switch, called a commutator, reverses the direction of the current. Constantly reversing the direction of the current will cause the electromagnet to rotate.

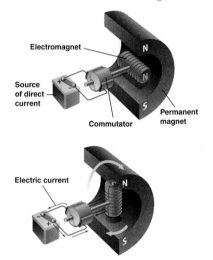

▲ **Figure 21-25** An electric motor at rest (top). When current flows (bottom), attraction and repulsion between the permanent magnet and the electromagnet cause the electromagnet to rotate. A commutator reverses the direct current to keep the electromagnet rotating.

▶ **INFER:** What is the purpose of a commutator?

468

Teaching Options

EXTENDING THE LESSON

Studying Electric Motors in Toys Bring to class several battery-operated cars or other toys that have parts that move when a switch is closed. Such toys contain electric motors. CAUTION: Do not bring devices that are powered by electricity from a wall outlet. Allow students to open up the toys, and ask them to identify the electric motor in each toy. Have them identify the different parts of the motor. Then, have them trace the path of electric current through the battery, switch, and motor. Ask them to explain how rotation of the shaft that extends from the motor causes parts of the toy to move. (The shaft may be coupled to the moving parts through gears or pulleys.) **learning styles: visual, tactile**

Uses of Electric Motors Many electrical appliances have electric motors. Electric fans, food processors, and refrigerators all use electric motors. There are many kinds of electric motors that are designed for specific uses. All electric motors have one thing in common. They all use the force of magnetism to change electrical energy into useful mechanical energy.

▲ **Figure 21-26** Electric toys use electric motors to run.

 EXPLAIN: Why does an electrical appliance need a motor?

People in Science

AUTOMOBILE MECHANIC

An automobile engine is a complex machine. It is made up of a motor, a battery, a generator, and many other electrical parts. Many jobs for automobile mechanics are available in automobile service stations, government installations, or in the service departments of automobile dealerships.

▲ **Figure 21-27** An automobile mechanic maintains and repairs different parts of a car.

Automobile mechanics are trained to inspect, maintain, and repair the mechanical and electrical parts in different types of automobiles. They install and replace parts, adjust brakes, and use computers to check different parts of a car. Beginning mechanics get on-the-job training. Some receive classroom instruction together with hands-on practice. They may also work with an experienced mechanic. Specialty mechanics may work on only one part of a car's engine.

To be an automobile mechanic, you should graduate from high school and then complete a formal training program in automotive repair. Good reading, mathematics, and computer skills are usually required.

Thinking Critically Why do you think an automobile mechanic should have computer skills?

---

3 Assess

4 Close

People in Science

AUTOMOBILE MECHANIC

Lab Activity

(pp. 470–471)

1 Prepare the Lab

Making an Electric Motor

SET-UP TIME: **LAB TIME:**

BACKGROUND: The relationship between electricity and magnetism was discovered in 1820. Danish scientist Hans Christian Oersted observed that an electric current flowing through a wire creates a magnetic field around the wire. Because of this discovery, today we have electric motors and generators that make thousands of practical devices possible.

PURPOSE: Students will use the relationship between magnetism and electricity to construct a simple electric motor.

ALTERNATIVE MATERIALS: A cork can be used in place of the film canister. A sturdy rubber band or electrical tape can be substituted for the duct tape.

SCIENCE SKILLS: Students will **investigate** the relationship between electricity and magnetism and **construct** a motor, using these scientific principles.

ADVANCE PLANNING: Cut wire pieces to the correct length prior to class. You might have a completed motor available so that students have a model to guide them as they work.

2 Guide the Lab

PROCEDURE: Divide students into small groups. Lead them through the directions and model each step of the procedure. The drawing below shows the desired shape of a paper clip after bending. You may wish to copy the drawing on the board for students to use as a guide.

Provide copies of the Lab Activity Report found on the Teacher's Resources CD-ROM for students to record their observations and conclusions. Diagrams depicting various steps of the procedure are also provided on the Teacher's Resources CD-ROM. You may wish to distribute copies of these diagrams to aid students in assembling their motors.

LAB ACTIVITY
Making an Electric Motor

Materials
Safety goggles, apron
D-cell battery
Magnet wire, 1 meter
Small film canister
Fine sandpaper
2 large metal paper clips
Ceramic magnet
Wire cutters
Needle-nose pliers
Duct tape
Modeling clay
Pencil and paper

▲ **STEP 3** Wrap the coil to keep it from unwinding.

▲ **STEP 4** Sand off insulation from half of the wire.

BACKGROUND
Magnetism and electricity are closely related. Many devices you use every day, such as radios, CD players, and vacuum cleaners depend on this relationship. How can this relationship be demonstrated?

PURPOSE
You will construct a simple electric motor.

PROCEDURE

1. Copy the chart shown in Figure 21-28. Put on goggles and an apron.

2. Starting about 8 cm from one end of a piece of magnet wire, wrap the wire around a film canister seven times. Cut the long end of the wire, leaving an 8-cm end free.

3. Slide the coiled wire off the film canister and wrap the two free ends around the coil two or three times to keep the coil from unwinding.

4. Use fine sandpaper to remove all of the insulation from about 3 cm of one end of the wire. Then place the other end of the wire flat on your work surface and sand off the insulation from *half* of the wire for a length of about 3 cm.

5. Using needle-nose pliers, bend two large paper clips to make supports for the coil. Use duct tape to attach the paper clips to the ends of a D-cell battery.

6. Place a ceramic magnet on the side of the battery, then place the battery-magnet setup on a piece of modeling clay.

470

Teaching Options

! FAST FACTS *How a Blow-Dryer Works*

Students know that electricity and magnetism are interrelated. Share with them how an everyday device, such as a blow-dryer, works. Two basic parts in a blow-dryer work together to speed up the evaporation of water from hair: a simple motor-driven fan and a heating coil. When the switch is turned on, current flows through the blow-dryer. The power from the circuit travels to the coiled wire in the heating element. Then, the current makes the small motor spin and the fan turns. The air from the fan is then blown over and through the heating element. The heated air streams out the end of the barrel to dry the hair.

Students may want to draw diagrams of blow-dryers or other simple appliances and label the parts to show how they work.

▲ STEP 5 Bend two large paper clips.

▲ STEP 8 Turn the coil slowly with your hand.

7. Place the coil in the cradle formed by the ends of the paper clip.

8. Turn the coil slowly with your hand. Record your observations.

9. Give the coil a gentle push to spin it. Record how many times the coil spins.

Making an Electric Motor	
Experiment	Observations
Turning the coil by hand	
Spinning the coil	

▲ Figure 21-28 Copy this chart and use it to record your observations.

CONCLUSIONS

1. INFER: What is the purpose of the battery and the magnet?

2. OBSERVE: What did you feel and observe as you moved the coil by hand?

3. INFER: What causes the coil to keep spinning after your initial push?

4. ANALYZE: What would happen if you were to increase the number of turns of wire?

5. HYPOTHESIZE: Is a circle the best shape? Do you think that an oval or square would be better? Give reasons for your answers.

Tips for Using Technology

Databases Have students use database software to record their observations about the effect of the shape of a coil on a motor. Databases allow students to enter and edit information, store and organize a lot of information easily, and search for specific information. Students can use database software to share their data with the class. Have students use the Database Planner on the Teacher's Resources CD-ROM to plan their databases.

• TEACHING RESOURCES •

Teacher's Resources CD-ROM
Lab Activity Report: Study Tools, pp. 16–17

Laboratory Activity Rubric: Teaching Tools, p. 8

Database Planner: Study Tools, p. 22

Electric Motor: Visuals, p.21

SAFETY: Caution students that the magnet wire and paper clips will become very hot if the loop is left in the cradle for several minutes.

TROUBLESHOOTING: If the motor does not work, check the following:

• Make sure that the paper clips are angled so that the wire coil does not touch the magnet as the coil turns.

• Be sure that the coil is fairly level as it sits in the paper-clip cradle.

• Try holding the paper clips against the battery with one hand while giving the coiled wire a gentle push.

• Have students reread each step and check each part of the motor made during a particular step.

EXPECTED OUTCOME: Students' devices should demonstrate the action of an electric motor.

3 Conclude the Lab

1. **INFER:** The battery is the source of direct current. The magnet is the permanent magnet that repels and attracts the electromagnet.
2. **OBSERVE:** the attraction and repulsion between the coil and the magnet
3. **INFER:** The attraction and repulsion results in reversing poles. The reversing poles keep the coil spinning.
4. **ANALYZE:** It would make a stronger electromagnet.
5. **HYPOTHESIZE:** Accept any logical answers.

Use the Laboratory Activity Rubric on the Teacher's Resources CD-ROM to assess students' lab activities. Fill in the rubric with the additional information below. For this activity, students should have:

• built an electric motor according to directions in the activity.

• filled in the data chart with their observations and correctly answered the conclusion questions.

4 Extend the Lab

Have students test the motor using different-shaped coils. Have them determine if the shape changes the way in which the motor works.

1 Introduce

✏️ **STUDY HINT** Have students read the captions and art labels that appear in the lesson. This will allow them to preview what is to come as well as to focus on the most important ideas in the lesson.

Linking Prior Knowledge Review with students the forms of energy (Lesson 14-2) and how energy changes from one form to another (Lesson 14-3).

2 Teach

Discussion Draw students' attention to Figure 21-30, pointing out the various parts of the generator. You might read the lesson text aloud so that students can follow along on the diagrams as you read. Encourage students to compare and contrast electric generators with electric motors. Focus on the type of energy that each produces and converts. **learning styles: auditory, visual**

Answers to questions

▶ **IDENTIFY:** alternating current

▶ **DEFINE:** a device that changes mechanical energy into electrical energy

▶ **NAME:** coal and oil

📖 **READING STRATEGY** Remind students that the topic sentence of a paragraph usually includes the main idea. Encourage students to identify the main idea in each paragraph of the lesson. Tell them to look for details that support these main ideas.

3 Assess

☑️ **CHECKING CONCEPTS ANSWERS**

1. A current is produced in the wire.
2. alternating current
3. a device that changes mechanical energy into electrical energy
4. turbines

21-9 What is an electric generator?

Objective
Explain how an electric generator works.

Key Term
electric generator: device that changes mechanical energy into electrical energy

Induced Current A current can be induced in a loop of wire by spinning the loop inside a magnetic field. Remember that an electric current is induced when a wire cuts across magnetic lines of force. Figure 21-29 shows a loop of wire in a magnetic field. The loop is spinning clockwise. As the wire moves across the magnetic field, it cuts the magnetic lines of force. As a result, current flows through the wire. When the wire moves down through the magnetic field, the current flows in one direction. When the wire moves up, the current flows in the opposite direction. The change in current direction produces an alternating current in the wire.

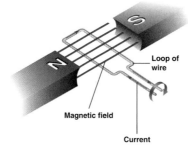

▲ **Figure 21-29** As the loop of wire spins inside the magnetic field of the magnets, alternating current is produced in the wire.

▶ **IDENTIFY:** What kind of current is induced when a loop of wire spins in a magnetic field?

Electric Generators An **electric generator** is a device that changes mechanical energy into electrical energy. It is the opposite of an electric motor, which changes electrical energy to mechanical energy. An electric generator is made up of an insulated coil of wire and a magnet. The

472

coil of wire is attached to a power source that causes the coil to spin. Spinning the coil of wire in the magnetic field of the magnet exposes the wire to a changing magnetic field. When this happens, electric current is produced in the coil of wire. The mechanical energy used to spin the coil of wire is changed into electrical energy. The ends of the coil of wire can be connected to a load, such as a light bulb. When electricity runs through the wires, the bulb will light.

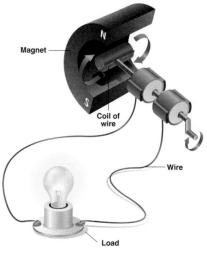

▲ **Figure 21-30** Turning the handle of this generator will cause the coil of wire to spin in the magnetic field of the magnet. An alternating electric current will be produced in the wires. As the current flows through the wires, the light bulb will light up.

▶ **DEFINE:** What is an electric generator?

Uses of Generators Most of the electricity you use every day comes from generators. Power plants use large generators to supply electricity to homes, offices, schools, and other buildings. These large generators use very strong magnets and many coils of wire to produce a great amount of energy. The mechanical energy for these generators is supplied by turbines (TUR-bihnz). A turbine is a large wheel that is turned by steam or

---

Teaching Options

COOPERATIVE LEARNING

Drawing a Diagram Have students work in small groups to create diagrams that show the way in which power comes from a power plant to a home or school. Students' diagrams should include generators and turbines. The way in which the turbines are moved should be included in the diagrams. Students may need to do additional research to create accurate diagrams. Allow time for students to share and display their diagrams.
learning styles: visual, interpersonal

EXTENDING THE LESSON

Saving Energy Use this lesson to emphasize the importance of turning off unnecessary lights and other electrical appliances as a measure of conserving nonrenewable fossil fuels. Students can research different ways to save energy in the home, such as installing insulation, weatherproofing windows, and using light bulbs with different wattage. Students can report their findings in informational pamphlets or posters.
learning style: linguistic

moving water. The water used to turn a turbine may come from a dam or river. Steam is produced by burning fuels, such as coal or oil, or from nuclear energy.

▶ **NAME:** What are two fuels that are burned to make steam for turbines in generators?

☑ CHECKING CONCEPTS

1. What happens when a loop of wire cuts magnetic lines of force?
2. What kind of electric current is induced when a loop of wire turns in a magnetic field?
3. What is a generator?
4. What supplies the mechanical energy in a generator?
5. What is a turbine?
6. Name two sources of energy that are used to make steam for turbines.

🔆 THINKING CRITICALLY

7. **CONTRAST:** Explain how a generator is the opposite of an electric motor.

⚛ *Science and Technology*

ELECTRIC POWER PLANTS

Electric power plants provide electricity for large numbers of people. Electric power plants use generators to produce electricity. Instead of a simple loop of wire spinning in the magnetic field of a magnet, these generators use many coils of wire and strong electromagnets. The spinning wires are connected to a turbine. The energy to spin the turbine comes from steam or moving water.

Some generators use the energy from waterfalls to spin the turbine. These generators are known as hydroelectric (hy-droh-ee-LEHK-trihk) plants. Hydroelectric plants are usually built near dams and reservoirs. Hydroelectric plants provide only a limited amount of power in the United States. The high cost to build them and the damage to the environment that they cause are some reasons why hydroelectric power plants are not a major source of electricity.

Thinking Critically Why are hydroelectric power plants usually built near dams and reservoirs?

▲ **Figure 21-31** Moving water spins turbines in this hydroelectric power plant.

8. **INFER:** What would happen if the coil of wire in a generator stopped spinning?
9. **HYPOTHESIZE:** The mechanical energy used to spin the coil of wire in a generator comes from a turbine. Think of ways in which you could supply the mechanical energy to run a turbine.

Web InfoSearch

Geothermal Energy In some parts of the world, heat inside Earth produces steam and boiling water. This heat is called geothermal (jee-oh-THUR-muhl) energy.

SEARCH: Use the Internet to find out how geothermal power plants use steam and boiling water to spin turbines and generate electricity. Start your search at www.conceptsandchallenges.com. Some key search words are **geothermal energy** and **generators.**

---

5. a large wheel that is turned by steam or moving water
6. burning fuels such as coal or oil and nuclear energy

💡 THINKING CRITICALLY ANSWERS

7. **CONTRAST:** A generator changes mechanical energy into electrical energy. An electric motor changes electrical energy into mechanical energy.
8. **INFER:** The current would no longer be produced.
9. **HYPOTHESIZE:** Possible answer: You could use a hand crank to supply the energy yourself.

4 Close

Web InfoSearch

Geothermal Energy Have students use the Internet to find out how geothermal power plants can use steam and boiling water to spin turbines and generate electricity. Some key search words are **geothermal energy, geothermal generators,** and **geothermal power plants.** Students should begin their search at www.conceptsandchallenges.com.

Science and Technology

ELECTRIC POWER PLANTS

Real-Life Connection Hydroelectric power plants are expensive to build and cause environmental damage. Other types of power plants have similar drawbacks. Ask students to list problems associated with power plants that operate on fossil fuels, such as coal, or on nuclear energy. (Burning of fossil fuels causes air pollution and likely contributes to global warming. Nuclear power plants produce radioactive wastes, are expensive to build, and pose a risk of releasing radioactive material during an accident.) Explain that deciding on a type of power plant to build requires careful weighing all of the advantages and disadvantages of each type.

Discussion Ask students if they know what type of fuel is used to create electricity in local power plants. Ask: *Why can hydroelectric plants provide only a limited supply of electrical energy?* (They are expensive to build and may damage the environment.)

Thinking Critically Answer

They must be built near waterfalls or other sources of falling water.

ONGOING ASSESSMENT

Determining True/False Statements
Give several statements for volunteers to identify as true or false. If the statements are false, students can change them to make them true. Examples might include:

- A direct current is produced when current flows in opposite directions. (False; An alternating current is produced.)
- Steam can be produced by nuclear energy and by burning fuels such as coal and oil. (true)

learning style: auditory

• TEACHING RESOURCES •

💿 **Teacher's Resources CD-ROM**

Lesson Review: Chapter 21, p. 13

Enrichment: Chapter 21, p. 14

The Big Idea

(pp. 474–475)

1 Introduce

Objective Students will be able to explain what maglev trains are and how a German maglev works. They will learn about and describe the advantages and disadvantages of this form of transportation. They will compare maglev technology to other forms of transportation.

Linking Prior Knowledge Ask students to recall properties of magnets (Lesson 21-1) and the relationship between electricity and magnetism (Lesson 21-5). Have students recall what an electromagnet is and what its advantages are (Lesson 21-6).

2 Teach

Discussion After students have read the article and call outs, ask students to explain how the German Transrapid works. Ask: *How are maglev trains different from other types of trains?*
learning styles: visual, auditory

Use the information in the article and captions to help guide students in choosing a topic for their Science Logs.

THE BIG IDEA ONLINE

How does a maglev train work?
Have students research their Science Log Writing Activity at
www.conceptsandchallenges.com.
You can have students organize their log by completing the Big Idea activity online. Students may post their work in the Online Classroom Database for others to read.

Reinforcement Students can also use the Big Idea Planner or Big Idea Science Log Entry found on the Teacher's Resources CD-ROM.

◈ *Integrating Technology*

THE Big IDEA

How does a maglev train work?

Imagine using the power of magnets to make a train float above its tracks. It sounds a lot like science fiction but it is real. Trains that use electromagnets are called magnetic levitation trains, maglevs for short.

Currently, maglevs are an experimental form of transportation. These trains use the properties of magnets to float above their tracks. In some maglevs, electromagnets generate magnetic forces that cause the train and the track to repel each other. These magnetic forces are similar to the forces that cause the like poles of two magnets to repel each other. In other types of maglevs, a force of attraction is generated by electromagnets that lift up the train. This force of attraction is similar to the attraction between the unlike poles of two magnets. In both types of maglevs, the trains run on a cushion of air a few centimeters above their tracks.

There seem to be many advantages to maglev trains compared to conventional trains. Maglevs do not have many moving parts, and could, therefore, require less maintenance. Because maglevs float above their tracks, there is no friction between the train and the track. Without friction, maglevs produce less noise than conventional trains. Maglevs are also expected to be much faster than conventional trains. They can travel up to 500 km/h.

In Germany, engineers have designed a maglev train that uses attractive magnetic forces to lift up the train. Read about the German maglev train, the Transrapid, that appears on these two pages. Find out how this type of train operates. Then, follow the Science Log to learn more about "the big idea." ✦

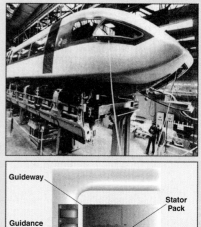

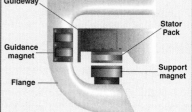

The Flanges
The bottom of the German Transrapid has extensions on both sides. These extensions, called flanges (FLAN-jez), wrap around a special track, called a guideway. The inside of a flange can be seen in the top photo. The diagram below it shows how magnets are used to lift the train. Magnetic attraction between the support magnet and the stator (STAT-uhr) pack, a highly magnetic material, causes the train to float about 10 mm above the guideway. Guidance magnets keep the train on the track.

474

Teaching Options

❗ FAST FACTS *Japanese Maglev Trains*

Along the 42-km (26-mi) Yamanashi Maglev Test Line in the shadow of Mount Fuji, Japanese maglev trains cruise at speeds of about 510 km/h (320 mi/h). The trains move along a U-shaped concrete path called a guideway. Embedded in the walls of the guideway are coils of wire, each shaped like a figure eight. As a train speeds by, a superconducting magnet onboard passes just below the center of the coil. The moving magnetic field of the superconducting magnet induces an electric current in the coil, which causes it to become a temporary electromagnet. Because direction of the induced current in the top and bottom of the coil is in opposite directions, the upper half of the coil attracts the train's superconducting magnet while the bottom of the coils repels it. The train is simultaneously pulled and pushed upward by a magnetic force that balances the train's weight. As a result, the train levitates in the guideway. For levitation to occur, the train must exceed a minimum speed. Below this minimum speed, the train rides on rubber tires along the guideway.

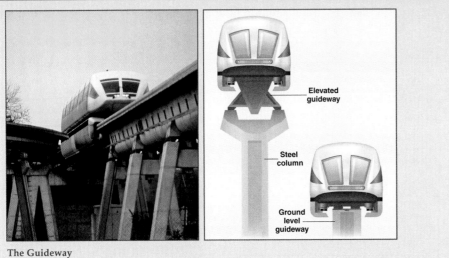

The Guideway
The guideway can be mounted on an elevated steel column (left illustration) or it can be mounted at ground level (right illustration).

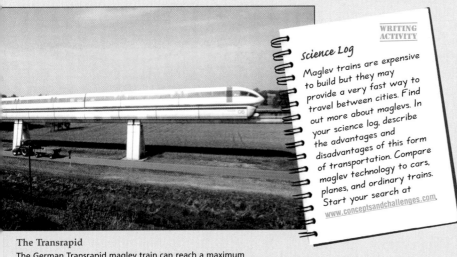

WRITING ACTIVITY

science Log

Maglev trains are expensive to build but they may provide a very fast way to travel between cities. Find out more about maglevs. In your science log, describe the advantages and disadvantages of this form of transportation. Compare maglev technology to cars, planes, and ordinary trains. Start your search at www.conceptsandchallenges.com.

The Transrapid
The German Transrapid maglev train can reach a maximum speed of about 500 km/h. The shape of its front portion helps it to travel fast by allowing it to move efficiently through air. It also cuts down on the amount of noise that the train makes.

CHAPTER 21: Magnetism **475**

3 Assess

Use the Writing Activity Rubric on the Teacher's Resources CD-ROM to assess students' Science Logs. Fill in the rubric with the additional information below. For this assignment, students should have:

- described the advantages and disadvantages of maglev trains.
- compared maglev trains to other forms of transportation.

4 Close

Creating Travel Brochures Ask students to think about a trip that would be made more convenient by traveling via maglev trains. Ask them to create travel brochures describing the destination and also the form of transportation. Their brochures should include facts about maglev trains that interested travelers may want to know. Students should also use colorful, vivid language that would make people excited about traveling to a certain place on a maglev train.
learning styles: visual, linguistic

Tips for Using Technology

Travel Brochures Have students use desktop publishing software to create their travel brochures featuring a maglev train. Desktop publishing software allows students to combine text and art on a page. Most word processing software programs include tools for desktop publishing. Students can use desktop publishing software to create newsletters and brochures to share their data with the class. Have students use the Thumbnail Sketch on the Teacher's Resources CD-ROM to plan their desktop publishing layouts.

• TEACHING RESOURCES •

Teacher's Resources CD-ROM
Big Idea: Chapter 21, p. 15
Big Idea Planner: Study Tools, pp. 11–12
Big Idea Science Log Entry: Study Tools, p. 13
Writing Activity Rubric: Teaching Tools, p. 9
Thumbnail Sketch: Study Tools, p. 24

Challenges (pp. 476–478)

Chapter Summary

Review Hint Before students begin the Challenges, review the summary with them. You might read the sentences aloud, omitting the boldface words and asking students to supply the omitted words. You could also provide two alternative words from which students can choose.

STUDY HINT Have students work in pairs to create an outline of the chapter, using the summaries as a guide. Collect the outlines and compile them into one study guide that you can copy and distribute to students. Use the outlines as the basis for a class review of the material.

Key Term Challenges

MATCHING

1. magnetism (21-1)
2. pole (21-1)
3. electromagnet (21-6)
4. magnetic induction (21-3)

FILL IN

5. electromagnetic induction (21-5)
6. generator (21-9)
7. magnetosphere (21-4)
8. magnetic field (21-2)
9. electromagnetism (21-5)
10. electric motor (21-8)

Chapter Summary

Lesson 21-1
- **Magnetism** is a force of attraction or repulsion by magnetic materials.
- Like **poles** repel. Unlike poles attract.

Lesson 21-2
- A **magnetic field** is the area around a magnet where magnetic forces act.

Lesson 21-3
- The process by which a material is made into a magnet is called **magnetic induction.**
- A temporary magnet tends to lose its magnetism quickly.
- A permanent magnet tends to keep its magnetism.

Lesson 21-4
- Earth has a magnetic north pole and a magnetic south pole.
- The magnetic field around Earth is called the **magnetosphere.**

Lesson 21-5
- The relationship between electricity and magnetism is called **electromagnetism.**

Lesson 21-6
- An **electromagnet** is made by wrapping current-carrying coils of wire around a metal core.

Lesson 21-7
- A **transformer** uses alternating current in the primary coil to induce a current in the secondary coil.
- A step-up transformer increases the voltage of alternating current.
- A step-down transformer decreases the voltage of alternating current.

Lesson 21-8
- An **electric motor** is a device that changes electrical energy into mechanical energy.

Lesson 21-9
- An **electric generator** is a device that uses magnets to change mechanical energy into electrical energy.

476

Key Term Challenges

electric generator (p. 472)
electric motor (p. 468)
electromagnet (p. 464)
electromagnetic induction (p. 462)
electromagnetism (p. 462)
magnetic domain (p. 456)
magnetic field (p. 456)
magnetic induction (p. 458)
magnetic lines of force (p. 456)
magnetism (p. 454)
magnetosphere (p. 460)
pole (p. 454)
transformer (p. 466)

MATCHING Write the Key Term from above that best matches each description.

1. force of attraction or repulsion by magnetic materials
2. end of a magnet
3. temporary magnet formed by wrapping a current-carrying coil of wire around a metal core
4. process of making an object into a magnet

FILL IN Write the Key Term from above that best completes each statement.

5. Because of _____, a current will flow in a wire moving across a magnetic field.
6. A _____ converts mechanical energy into electrical energy.
7. The magnetic field around Earth is also called the _____.
8. The area around a magnet is called the _____.
9. The relationship between electricity and magnetism is called _____.
10. An _____ converts electrical energy into mechanical energy.

Teaching Options

PREPARING STUDENTS FOR STANDARDIZED TESTS

Reading Strategy: Remind students that they should first eliminate answers that they know are wrong. Then, they can try out the remaining answers by reading the first part of the item and each answer as a complete sentence. Encourage students to recheck their answers after they finish a test.

Writing Strategy: Encourage students to identify the type of writing they are asked to do, such as sequence or compare and contrast. Remind them to use words that help organize that type of writing such as *first* and *next* for sequential writing or *but* and *likewise* for comparing and contrasting.

Interpreting Visuals: Remind students to look carefully at captions and labels before they answer questions about a visual.

ESL/ELL STRATEGY

Word Bank Have students create a word bank of Key Terms from this list. Suggest that students classify related words into groups. This can be done by scanning the lessons to see which terms were presented in each lesson.

Content Challenges TEST PREP

MULTIPLE CHOICE **Write the letter of the term or phrase that best completes each statement.**

1. In a step-down transformer,
   a. the secondary coil has more turns.
   b. the primary coil has fewer turns.
   c. the secondary coil has fewer turns.
   d. the primary and secondary coils have the same number of turns.

2. Oersted discovered
   a. that an electric current flows through a compass.
   b. magnetic induction.
   c. the magnetosphere.
   d. that an electric current produces a magnetic field.

3. A temporary magnet
   a. keeps its magnetic properties for a long time.
   b. is hard to magnetize.
   c. loses its magnetic properties quickly.
   d. is a natural magnet.

4. When the north and south poles of two magnets are facing each other, they
   a. attract each other.
   b. repel each other.
   c. have no effect on each other.
   d. magnetize each other.

5. One way to increase the strength of an electromagnet is to
   a. increase the resistance in the wire.
   b. decrease the voltage in the wire.
   c. decrease the current in the wire.
   d. increase the current in the wire.

6. In order for a 9-volt appliance to use the 120 volts from a wall outlet, it needs
   a. a step-up transformer.
   b. a step-down transformer.
   c. a coil.
   d. an electric motor.

7. William Gilbert was one of the first scientists to study
   a. electric motors.
   b. generators.
   c. electromagnetism.
   d. magnetism.

8. Earth's magnetic north pole is located
   a. near the geographic North Pole.
   b. near the geographic South Pole.
   c. at the geographic North Pole.
   d. at the geographic South Pole.

9. An iron bar becoming magnetized is an example of
   a. magnetic induction.
   b. electromagnetic induction.
   c. a transformer.
   d. an electric motor.

10. Electromagnetic induction was studied by
    a. Tesla.
    b. Oersted.
    c. Faraday.
    d. the Ancient Greeks.

TRUE/FALSE **Write** *true* **if the statement is true. If the statement is false, change the underlined term to make the statement true.**

11. In a step-up transformer, the <u>primary</u> coil has fewer turns of wire.

12. An electric <u>motor</u> converts electrical energy into mechanical energy.

13. To increase the strength of an electromagnet, <u>decrease</u> the number of turns of wire around the metal core.

14. Earth's magnetic south pole is the same as the <u>south</u> pole of a bar magnet.

Content Challenges

MULTIPLE CHOICE

1. c (21-7)
2. d (21-5)
3. c (21-3)
4. a (21-1)
5. d (21-6)
6. b (21-7)
7. d (21-4)
8. b (21-4)
9. a (21-3)
10. c (21-5)

TRUE/FALSE

11. true (21-7)
12. true (21-8)
13. false; increase (21-6)
14. true (21-4)

CUMULATIVE ASSESSMENT

Assessing Students' Progress You may wish to administer the final examination found on the Teacher's Resources CD-ROM at this point. Distribute copies of the Scantron Sheet, also found on the Teacher's Resources CD-ROM, for students to record their answers.

PORTFOLIO ASSESSMENT

Making Student Portfolios
Students can demonstrate their comprehension of the concepts in this chapter by making a portfolio. The Chapter Self-Check and the Weekly Journal are two of the reproducibles on the Teacher's Resources CD-ROM that they can include in their portfolios. You can use the Portfolio Assessment Rubric also found on the Teacher's Resources CD-ROM to assess students' portfolios.

Concept Challenges

WRITTEN RESPONSE

1. **COMPARE:** Magnetic induction is the process by which a material can be made into a magnet. Electromagnetic induction is the production of magnetism by an electric current. (21-3, 21-5)

2. **CONTRAST:** In an electric motor, electrical energy is changed into mechanical energy. In an electric generator, mechanical energy is changed into electrical energy. (21-8, 21-9)

3. **DESCRIBE:** The north pole of the compass would point to the south pole of the magnet. (21-1)

4. **ANALYZE:** As the loop moves up and down, the current flows in opposite directions. (21-9)

5. **HYPOTHESIZE:** Possible answer: Resistance might cause this loss of energy. (21-7)

INTERPRETING VISUALS (21-7)

6. the secondary coil

7. the primary coil

8. Diagram A is a step-up transformer. Diagram B is a step-down transformer.

9. Diagram A, the step-up transformer; It can be used to increase voltage.

10. Diagram B, the step-down transformer; It can be used to decrease voltage.

11. Diagram B, the step-down transformer; It lowers the voltage.

Chapter Project Wrap-Up

MAGNET EXPO

Have students give a short presentation of their displays to the class. You can use the Individual Activity Rubric found on the Teacher's Resources CD-ROM to assess students' projects. Fill in the rubric with the additional information below. For this project, students should have:

- researched and built or created a diagram of a device that uses a magnet or an electromagnet.

- explained the purpose of the device and how the magnet or electromagnet helps it work.

Concept Challenges TEST PREP

WRITTEN RESPONSE Answer each of the following questions in complete sentences.

1. **COMPARE:** Explain the difference between magnetic induction and electromagnetic induction.

2. **CONTRAST:** Describe the energy changes that take place in an electric motor and in an electric generator.

3. **DESCRIBE:** How could you use a compass to identify the north and south poles of a magnet?

4. **ANALYZE:** Why does a spinning loop of wire in a magnetic field produce alternating current instead of direct current?

5. **HYPOTHESIZE:** In most transformers, some energy is lost between the primary coil and the secondary coil. What do you think might cause this loss of energy?

INTERPRETING VISUALS Use Figures 21-32 and 21-33 to answer each of the following questions.

6. In Diagram *A*, which coil has more turns of wire?

7. In Diagram *B*, which coil has more turns of wire?

8. Which diagram shows a step-up transformer? Which shows a step-down transformer?

9. Which kind of transformer would you use to change the voltage from 10 volts to 50 volts? Explain.

10. Which kind of transformer would you use to change the voltage from 50 volts to 10 volts? Explain.

11. Which kind of transformer must be used before the electricity from power lines can be used in your home? Explain.

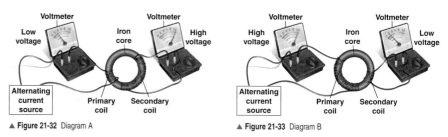

▲ **Figure 21-32** Diagram A   ▲ **Figure 21-33** Diagram B

Teaching Options

• TEACHING RESOURCES •

Teacher's Resources CD-ROM

Key Term Review: Chapter 21, p. 16

Chapter 21 Test: pp. 17–19

Individual Activity Rubric: Teaching Tools, p. 5

Chapter Self-Check: Teaching Tools, p. 11

Weekly Journal: Study Tools, p. 19

Portfolio Assessment Rubric: Teaching Tools, p. 10

Scantron Sheet: Teaching Tools, p. 12

Appendix  Metric System

The Metric System and SI Units

The metric system is an international system of measurement based on units of ten. More than 90% of the nations of the world use the metric system. In the United States, both the English system and the metric system are used.

The *Système International*, or SI, has been used as the international measurement system since 1960. The SI is a modernized version of the metric system. Like the metric system, the SI is a decimal system based on units of ten. When you want to change from one unit in the metric system to another unit, you multiply or divide by a multiple of ten.

- When you change from a smaller unit to a larger unit, you divide.
- When you change from a larger unit to a smaller unit, you multiply.

METRIC UNITS

LENGTH	SYMBOL	RELATIONSHIP
kilometer	km	1 km = 1,000 m
meter	m	1 m = 100 cm
centimeter	cm	1 cm = 10 mm
millimeter	mm	1 mm = 0.1 cm
AREA	**SYMBOL**	
square kilometer	km²	$1 \text{ km}^2 = 1{,}000{,}000 \text{ m}^2$
square meter	m²	$1 \text{ m}^2 = 1{,}000{,}000 \text{ mm}^2$
square centimeter	cm²	$1 \text{ cm}^2 = 0.0001 \text{ m}^2$
square millimeter	mm²	$1 \text{ mm}^2 = 0.000001 \text{ m}^2$
VOLUME	**SYMBOL**	
cubic meter	m³	$1 \text{ m}^3 = 1{,}000{,}000 \text{ cm}^3$
cubic centimeter	cm³	$1 \text{ cm}^3 = 0.000001 \text{ m}^3$
liter	L	1 L = 1,000 mL
milliliter	mL	1 mL = 0.001 L
MASS	**SYMBOL**	
metric ton	t	1 t = 1,000 kg
kilogram	kg	1 kg = 1,000 g
gram	g	1 g = 1,000 mg
centigram	cg	1 cg = 10 mg
milligram	mg	1 mg = 0.001 g
TEMPERATURE	**SYMBOL**	
Kelvin	K	
degree Celsius	°C	

▲ Figure 1

COMMON METRIC PREFIXES

micro-	0.000001 or 1/1,000,000	deka-	10
milli-	0.001 or 1/1,000	hecto-	100
centi-	0.01 or 1/100	kilo-	1,000
deci-	0.1 or 1/10	mega-	1,000,000

▲ Figure 2

METRIC-STANDARD EQUIVALENTS

SI to English	English to SI
LENGTH	
1 kilometer = 0.621 mile (mi)	1 mi = 1.61 km
1 meter = 1.094 yards (yd)	1 yd = 0.914 m
1 meter = 3.28 feet (ft)	1 ft = 0.305 m
1 centimeter = 0.394 inch (in.)	1 in. = 2.54 cm
1 millimeter = 0.039 inch	1 in. = 25.4 mm
AREA	
1 square kilometer = 0.3861 square mile	$1 \text{ mi}^2 = 2.590 \text{ km}^2$
1 square meter = 1.1960 square yards	$1 \text{ yd}^2 = 0.8361 \text{ m}^2$
1 square meter = 10.763 square feet	$1 \text{ ft}^2 = 0.0929 \text{ m}^2$
1 square centimeter = 0.155 square inch	$1 \text{ in.}^2 = 6.452 \text{ cm}^2$
VOLUME	
1 cubic meter = 1.3080 cubic yards	$1 \text{ yd}^3 = 0.7646 \text{ m}^3$
1 cubic meter = 35.315 cubic feet	$1 \text{ ft}^3 = 0.0283 \text{ m}^3$
1 cubic centimeter = 0.0610 cubic inch	$1 \text{ in}^3 = 16.39 \text{ cm}^3$
1 liter = 0.2642 gallon (gal)	1 gal = 3.79 L
1 liter = 1.06 quarts (qt)	1 qt = 0.946 L
1 liter = 2.11 pints (pt)	1 pt = 0.47 L
1 milliliter = 0.034 fluid ounce (fl oz)	1 fl oz = 29.57 mL
MASS	
1 metric ton = 0.984 ton	1 ton = 1.016 t
1 kilogram = 2.205 pounds (lb)	1 lb = 0.4536 kg
1 gram = 0.0353 ounce (oz)	1 oz = 28.35 g
TEMPERATURE	
Celsius = 5/9(°F − 32)	Fahrenheit = 9/5°C + 32
0°C = 32°F (Freezing point of water)	72°F = 22°C (Room temperature)
100°C = 212°F (Boiling point of water)	98.6°F = 37°C (Human body temperature)
Kelvin = (°F + 459.67)/1.8	Fahrenheit = (K × 1.8) − 459.67

▲ Figure 3

Appendix **479**

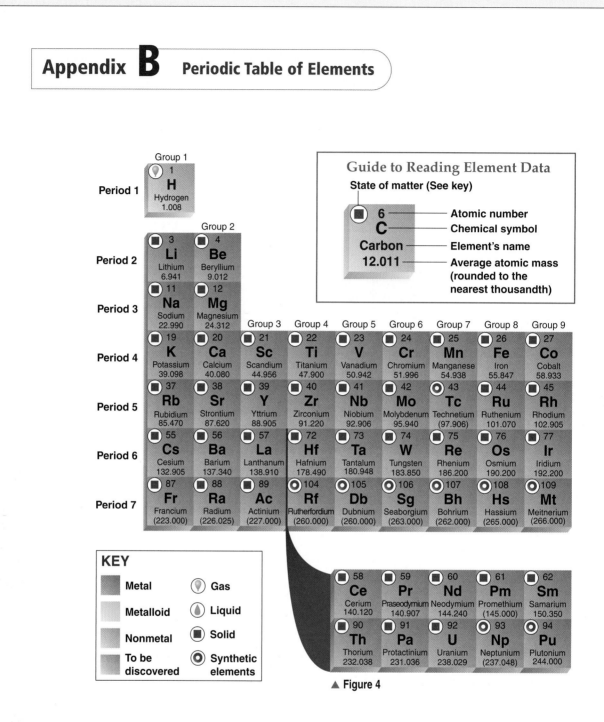

▲ Figure 4

Group 18

| | | | | | | | | 2 **He** Helium 4.003 |

| Group 13 | Group 14 | Group 15 | Group 16 | Group 17 | |

| 5 **B** Boron 10.811 | 6 **C** Carbon 12.011 | 7 **N** Nitrogen 14.007 | 8 **O** Oxygen 15.999 | 9 **F** Fluorine 18.998 | 10 **Ne** Neon 20.183 |

| 13 **Al** Aluminum 26.982 | 14 **Si** Silicon 28.086 | 15 **P** Phosphorus 30.974 | 16 **S** Sulfur 32.064 | 17 **Cl** Chlorine 35.453 | 18 **Ar** Argon 39.948 |

| Group 10 | Group 11 | Group 12 | | | | | |

| 28 **Ni** Nickel 58.710 | 29 **Cu** Copper 63.540 | 30 **Zn** Zinc 65.370 | 31 **Ga** Gallium 69.720 | 32 **Ge** Germanium 72.590 | 33 **As** Arsenic 74.922 | 34 **Se** Selenium 78.960 | 35 **Br** Bromine 79.909 | 36 **Kr** Krypton 83.800 |

| 46 **Pd** Palladium 106.400 | 47 **Ag** Silver 107.870 | 48 **Cd** Cadmium 112.400 | 49 **In** Indium 114.820 | 50 **Sn** Tin 118.690 | 51 **Sb** Antimony 121.750 | 52 **Te** Tellurium 127.600 | 53 **I** Iodine 126.904 | 54 **Xe** Xenon 131.300 |

| 78 **Pt** Platinum 195.090 | 79 **Au** Gold 196.967 | 80 **Hg** Mercury 200.590 | 81 **Tl** Thallium 204.370 | 82 **Pb** Lead 207.200 | 83 **Bi** Bismuth 208.980 | 84 **Po** Polonium (209.000) | 85 **At** Astatine (210.000) | 86 **Rn** Radon (222.000) |

| 110 **Uun** Ununnilium (269) | 111 **Uuu** Unununium (272) | 112 **Uub** Ununbium (272) | | 114 **Uuq** Ununquadium (285) | | | | |

| 63 **Eu** Europium 151.960 | 64 **Gd** Gadolinium 157.250 | 65 **Tb** Terbium 158.924 | 66 **Dy** Dysprosium 162.500 | 67 **Ho** Holmium 164.930 | 68 **Er** Erbium 167.260 | 69 **Tm** Thulium 168.934 | 70 **Yb** Ytterbium 173.040 | 71 **Lu** Lutetium 174.970 |

| 95 **Am** Americium (243.000) | 96 **Cm** Curium (247.000) | 97 **Bk** Berkelium (247.000) | 98 **Cf** Californium (251.000) | 99 **Es** Einsteinium (254.000) | 100 **Fm** Fermium (257.000) | 101 **Md** Mendelevium (258.000) | 102 **No** Nobelium (259.000) | 103 **Lr** Lawrencium (260.000) |

*Atomic masses in parentheses are of the most common form of the atom.

Appendix C Chemical Elements

LIST OF CHEMICAL ELEMENTS		
Element	Atomic Symbol	Atomic Number
Actinium	Ac	89
Aluminum	Al	13
Americium	Am	95
Antimony	Sb	51
Argon	Ar	18
Arsenic	As	33
Astatine	At	85
Barium	Ba	56
Berkelium	Bk	97
Beryllium	Be	4
Bismuth	Bi	83
Bohrium	Bh	107
Boron	B	5
Bromine	Br	35
Cadmium	Cd	48
Calcium	Ca	20
Californium	Cf	98
Carbon	C	6
Cerium	Ce	58
Cesium	Cs	55
Chlorine	Cl	17
Chromium	Cr	24
Cobalt	Co	27
Copper	Cu	29
Curium	Cm	96
Dubnium	Db	105
Dysprosium	Dy	66
Einsteinium	Es	99
Erbium	Er	68
Europium	Eu	63
Fermium	Fm	100
Fluorine	F	9
Francium	Fr	87
Gadolinium	Gd	64
Gallium	Ga	31
Germanium	Ge	32
Gold	Au	79

▲ Figure 5

LIST OF CHEMICAL ELEMENTS		
Element	Atomic Symbol	Atomic Number
Hafnium	Hf	72
Hassium	Hs	108
Helium	He	2
Holmium	Ho	67
Hydrogen	H	1
Indium	In	49
Iodine	I	53
Iridium	Ir	77
Iron	Fe	26
Krypton	Kr	36
Lanthanum	La	57
Lawrencium	Lr	103
Lead	Pb	82
Lithium	Li	3
Lutetium	Lu	71
Magnesium	Mg	12
Manganese	Mn	25
Meitnerium	Mt	109
Mendelevium	Md	101
Mercury	Hg	80
Molybdenum	Mo	42
Neodymium	Nd	60
Neon	Ne	10
Neptunium	Np	93
Nickel	Ni	28
Niobium	Nb	41
Nitrogen	N	7
Nobelium	No	102
Osmium	Os	76
Oxygen	O	8
Palladium	Pd	46
Phosphorus	P	15
Platinum	Pt	78
Plutonium	Pu	94
Polonium	Po	84
Potassium	K	19
Praseodymium	Pr	59
Promethium	Pm	61

LIST OF CHEMICAL ELEMENTS		
Element	Atomic Symbol	Atomic Number
Protactinium	Pa	91
Radium	Ra	88
Radon	Rn	86
Rhenium	Re	75
Rhodium	Rh	45
Rubidium	Rb	37
Ruthenium	Ru	44
Rutherfordium	Rf	104
Samarium	Sm	62
Scandium	Sc	21
Seaborgium	Sg	106
Selenium	Se	34
Silicon	Si	14
Silver	Ag	47
Sodium	Na	11
Strontium	Sr	38
Sulfur	S	16
Tantalum	Ta	73
Technetium	Tc	43
Tellurium	Te	52
Terbium	Tb	65
Thallium	Tl	81
Thorium	Th	90
Thulium	Tm	69
Tin	Sn	50
Titanium	Ti	22
Tungsten	W	74
Ununnilium	Uun	110
Unununium	Uuu	111
Ununbium	Uub	112
Ununquadium	Uuq	114
Uranium	U	92
Vanadium	V	23
Xenon	Xe	54
Ytterbium	Yb	70
Yttrium	Y	39
Zinc	Zn	30
Zirconium	Zr	40

482

Appendix **D**   Science Terms

Analyzing Science Terms

You can often unlock the meaning of an unfamiliar science term by analyzing its word parts. Prefixes and suffixes, for example, each carry a meaning that comes from a word root. This word root usually comes from the Latin or Greek language. The following list of prefixes and suffixes provides clues to the meaning of many science terms.

WORD PART	MEANING	EXAMPLE
-ate	salt of an acid	nitrate
bar-, baro-	weight, pressure	barometer
bi-	two	binary
carbo-	containing carbon	carbonate
co-	with, together	coagulation
de-	remove from	decomposition
electro-	electricity	electrolyte
-graph	write	thermograph
hydro-	water, containing hydrogen	hydrometer, hydrocarbon
-ide	binary compound	sulfide
in-	not	insoluble
-logy	study of	cosmology
-lysis	decomposition	electrolysis
magneto-	magnetism	magnetosphere
-meter	measuring device	manometer
non-	not	nonmetal
photo-	light	photoelectric
poly-	many	polyatomic
re-	again, back	reflection
-sonic	sound	supersonic
-sphere	ball, globe	magnetosphere
sub-	under, beneath	subscript
super-	above, more than	supersonic
therm-, thermo-	heat	thermometer
trans-	across, beyond	transparent
ultra-	beyond	ultrasound
un-	not	unsaturated

▲ Figure 6

Appendix **E** Mathematics Review

Adding Integers

You can add integers with unlike signs on a number line.

Add ⁻5 + ⁺7

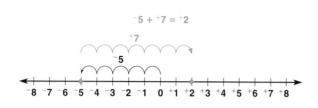

Subtracting Integers

To subtract an integer, add its opposite.

Subtract ⁻6 − ⁺2

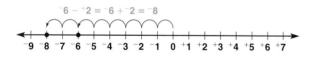

Multiplying Integers

When you multiply integers, you must decide if the answer is positive or negative.

If the signs of the integers are the same, the product is positive.

$$^+5 \times {}^+4 = {}^+20$$
$$^-5 \times {}^-4 = {}^+20$$

If the signs of the integers are different, the product is negative.

$$^+5 \times {}^-4 = {}^-20$$
$$^-5 \times {}^+4 = {}^-20$$

Dividing Integers

The rules for dividing integers are the same as the rules for multiplying integers.

If the signs of the integers are the same, the quotient is positive.

$$^-36 \div {}^-9 = {}^+4$$
$$^+36 \div {}^+9 = {}^+4$$

If the signs of the integers are different, the quotient is negative.

$$^-36 \div {}^+9 = {}^-4$$
$$^+36 \div {}^-9 = {}^-4$$

Solving an Equation

To solve an equation, find the value of the variable that makes the equation true.

Is $b = 3$ the solution to the equation?

$$4b = 12$$

Replace b with 3 in the equation.

$$4 \times 3 = 12$$
$$12 = 12$$

Yes, $b = 3$ is the solution to the equation.

Adding and Subtracting Decimals

When adding or subtracting decimals, always be sure to line up the decimal points correctly.

Add 3.4 km, 20.95 km, and 153.6 km.

```
    3.4
   20.95
 + 153.6
 ───────
  177.95 km
```

Subtract 13.5 mL from 35.75 mL.

```
   35.75
 −  13.5
 ───────
   22.25 mL
```

484

Multiplying and Dividing Decimals

When multiplying or dividing decimals, it is not necessary to line up the decimal points.

Multiply 0.5 N by 11.25 m to find the amount of work done in joules.

$W = F \times d$

$W = 0.5 \, N \times 11.25 \, m$

$W = 5.625 \, J$

Notice that the number of places to the right of the decimal point in the answer is equal to the sum of the places to the right of the decimal point in the numbers being multiplied.

Divide 4.05 m by 0.5 m to find the mechanical advantage of a lever.

MA = effort arm length/resistance arm length

MA = 4.05 m/0.5 m

MA = 8.1

When dividing a decimal by another decimal, you must first change the divisor to a whole number. For example, change 0.5 to 5 by moving the decimal point one place to the right. You must also change the dividend by moving the decimal point one place to the right. The result is $40.5 \div 5 = 8.1$.

Changing a Decimal to a Percent

To change a decimal to a percent, multiply the decimal by 100%.

Find the efficiency of a machine if the work output is 5 J and the work input is 10 J.

Efficiency = work output ÷ work input × 100%

Efficiency = 5 J ÷ 10 J × 100%

Efficiency = 0.5 × 100%

Efficiency = 50%

Notice that when you multiply 0.5 by 100%, the decimal point moves two places to the right.

Measuring Angles

Use a protractor to measure an angle. Place the center of the protractor's straight edge on the vertex. One ray must pass through 0°.

Angle ABC measures 75°.

Solving Word Problems

To solve distance problems, you can use $d = r \times t$ or $d = rt$.

The Smiths drove 220 miles at an average speed of 55 miles per hour. How long did the trip take?

PLAN

Substitute the values you know into the equation $d = r \times t$.

Then solve.

DO

$$220 = 55t$$

$$220 \div 55 = 55t \div 55$$

$$4 = t$$

SOLUTION

The trip took 4 hours.

Appendix F Formulas for Physical Science

MATTER

Density

Density is measured in grams per cubic centimeter (g/cm^3).

Density = mass ÷ volume

or

$D = m \div v$

or

$D = \dfrac{m}{v}$

Specific Gravity

Specific gravity has no units of measure.

To find the specific gravity of a sample of matter, divide the density of the sample by the density of water (1.0 g/cm^3).

Specific gravity = x g/cm^3 ÷ 1.0 g/cm^3

Area

1. The area of a rectangle is found by multiplying the length (l) by the width (w). Answers are given in square units (cm^2).

   $A = l \times w$

2. The area of a square is found by squaring the side.

   $A = s^2$

3. The area of a circle is found by multiplying pi by the radius squared (r^2).

   $(\pi \approx 3.14) \times r^2$
   $A = \pi r^2$

Volume of a Solid Shape

1. The volume of a cylinder is found by multiplying pi by the radius squared (r^2) by the height (h).

   $V = \pi \times r^2 \times h$

2. To find the volume of a rectangular prism or cube, multiply the length by the width by the height.

   $V = l \times w \times h$

3. The volume of a sphere is found by multiplying 4/3 by pi by the radius cubed (r^3).

   $V = 4/3 \times \pi \times r^3$

WORK

Mechanical Advantage

1. Mechanical Advantage = resistance force ÷ effort force

   or

   $MA = \dfrac{\text{resistance force}}{\text{effort force}} = \dfrac{F_r}{F_e}$

   or

   $MA = F_r \div F_e$

2. MA (of an inclined plane) = length × height

   $MA = l \times h$

   $MA = lh$

Efficiency

Efficiency is expressed as a percentage.

Efficiency = Work output ÷ Work input × 100%

or

$E = \dfrac{W_{out}}{W_{in}}$

or

$E = W_{out} \div W_{in} \times 100\%$

Work

Work is measured in joules (J). One joule equals one newton-meter (N-m).

W = force × distance

or

$W = F \times d$

Power

Power is measured in watts (W).

One watt is equal to one joule per second (J/s).

Power = Work ÷ time

or

$P = \dfrac{W}{t}$

or

$P = W \div t$

486

FORCE AND MOTION

Speed

Velocity is speed and direction.

1. Speed = distance ÷ time

   or

   $v = \dfrac{d}{t}$

   or

   $v = d \div t$

2. Change in velocity = final velocity − initial velocity

3. Acceleration = change in velocity ÷ time

Distance

Distance traveled is measured in miles or kilometers per hour (mph or km/h).

   Distance = rate × time

   or

   $d = r \times t$

   or

   $d = rt$

Momentum

   Momentum = mass × velocity

Force

   Force = mass × acceleration

   Force = pressure × area

Pressure

Pressure is expressed in pascals.

   $1\ Pa = 1\ \dfrac{N}{m^2}$

   Pressure = force ÷ area

   or

   $P = \dfrac{F}{a}$

   or

   $P = F \div a$

ENERGY

Energy

   Energy = mass × speed of light^2

   or

   $E = m \times c^2$

   or

   $E = mc^2$

Ohm's Law

Current is measured in amperes, or amps.

   Current = voltage ÷ resistance

   or

   $I = \dfrac{V}{R}$

   or

   $I = V \div R$

Gravitational Potential Energy

   PE = weight × height

   PE (N-m) = N × m

Speed of a Wave

   Velocity = frequency × wavelength

   $v = f \times D$

Glossary

Pronunciation and syllabication have been derived from *Webster's New World Dictionary*, Second College Edition, Revised School Printing (Prentice Hall, 1985). Syllables printed in capital letters are given primary stress. (Numbers in parentheses indicate the page number, or page numbers, on which the term is defined.)

PRONUNCIATION KEY					
Symbol	Example	Respelling	Symbol	Example	Respelling
a	transverse	(trans-VURS)	oh	coagulation	(koh-ag-yoo-LAY-shuhn)
ah	velocity	(vuh-LAHS-uh-tee)	oo	amplitude	(AM-pluh-tood)
aw	trough	(TRAWF)	oi	colloid	(KAHL-oid)
ay	radiation	(ray-dee-AY-shuhn)	s	solute	(SAHL-yoot)
eh	convection	(kuhn-VEHK-shuhn)	sh	suspension	(suh-SPEHN-shuhn)
ee	decomposition	(dee-kahm-puh-ZIH-shuhn)	u	fulcrum	(FOOL-kruhm)
f	coefficient	(koh-uh-FIHSH-uhnt)	uh	barometer	(buh-RAHM-uht-uhr)
ih	specialization	(spehsh-uhl-ih-ZAY-shuhn)	y, eye	binary, ion	(BY-nuh-ree), (EYE-uhn)
j	homogenization	(huh-mahj-uh-nih-ZAY-shuhn)	yoo	insoluble	(ihn-SAHL-yoo-buhl)
k	calorie	(KAL-uh-ree)	z	ionization	(eye-uh-nih-ZAY-shuhn)

A

absolute zero: lowest possible temperature; temperature at which particles of matter almost stop moving (p. 7)

acceleration (ak-sehl-uh-RAY-shuhn): rate of change in velocity over time (p. 274)

acid: substance that releases hydrogen ions (H^+) when dissolved in water (p. 190)

action force: force acting in one direction (p. 284)

air pressure: pressure caused by the force exerted by Earth's atmosphere (p. 262)

air resistance: force that opposes the movement of an object in air (p. 258)

alkali metals: metals in Group 1 of the periodic table (p. 218)

alkaline earth metals: metals in Group 2 of the periodic table (p. 218)

alloy: substance made of a mixture of two or more metals (p. 214)

alternating current: current in which electrons reverse direction at a regular rate (p. 436)

amino acids: building blocks of proteins (p. 96)

ampere: unit used to measure electric current (p. 442)

amplitude (AM-pluh-tood): height of a transverse wave (p. 362)

atom: smallest part of an element that can be identified as that element (p. 54)

atomic mass: total mass of the protons and neutrons in an atom, measured in atomic mass units (amu) (p. 60)

atomic number: number of protons in the nucleus of an atom (p. 58)

average speed: total distance traveled divided by the time it takes to travel that distance (p. 272)

B

balanced forces: forces that are equal in size but opposite in direction (p. 246)

barometer (buh-RAHM-uht-uhr): instrument used to measure air pressure (p. 262)

base: substance that releases hydroxyl ions (OH^-) when dissolved in water (p. 192)

battery: source of electricity that converts chemical energy into electrical energy (p. 432)

Bernoulli's principle: as the speed of a fluid increases, its pressure decreases (p. 262)

binary (BY-nuh-ree) **compound:** compound containing two elements (p. 152)

boiling point: temperature at which a liquid changes to a gas (pp. 116, 338)

488

boiling point elevation: increase in the boiling point of a liquid solvent because of the addition of a solute (p. 116)

buoyancy (BOI-uhn-see): tendency of an object to float in a fluid (p. 44)

C

calorie (KAL-uh-ree): unit of heat; amount of heat needed to raise the temperature of 1 g of water 1°C (p. 334)

carbohydrates (kahr-boh-HY-drayts): sugars and starches (p. 96)

chain reaction: uncontrolled series of fission reactions (p. 238)

chemical bond: force of attraction that holds atoms together (p. 82)

chemical change: change that produces new substances (p. 26)

chemical equation: statement in which chemical formulas are used to describe a chemical reaction (p. 172)

chemical formula: way of writing the name of a compound using chemical symbols (p. 148)

chemical reaction: process in which new substances with new chemical and physical properties are formed (p. 168)

chemical symbol: shortened way of writing the name of an element (p. 64)

chemistry (KEHM-ihs-tree): branch of science that deals with the study of the structure and the makeup of matter and the changes matter undergoes (p. 16)

chlorophyll (KLAWR-uh-fihl): substance in plants that absorbs the Sun's light and gives plants their green color (p. 408)

chloroplast: part of green plant cells where photosynthesis takes place (p. 408)

circuit breaker: switch that opens a circuit if too much current is flowing (p. 446)

coagulation (koh-ag-yoo-LAY-shuhn): use of chemicals to make the particles in a suspension clump together (p. 132)

cochlea (KAHK-lee-uh): organ that changes sound vibrations into nerve signals (p. 394)

coefficient (koh-uh-FIHSH-uhnt): number that shows how many molecules of a substance are involved in a chemical reaction (p. 172)

colloid (KAHL-oid): suspension in which the particles are permanently suspended (p. 136)

compound: substance made up of two or more elements that are chemically combined (p. 80)

compound machine: machine that combines two simple machines or more (p. 326)

compression (kuhm-PREHSH-uhn): part of a medium where the particles are close together (p. 360)

concave lens: lens that curves inward (p. 410)

concentrated solution: solution containing a large amount of solute compared with the amount of solvent present (p. 112)

condensation (kahn-duhn-SAY-shuhn): change from a gas to a liquid (pp. 22, 118)

conduction (kuhn-DUK-shuhn): process of heat transfer in solids (p. 340)

conductor: substance that conducts heat easily (p. 340); material that allows electric charges to flow through it easily (p. 434)

convection (kuhn-VEHK-shuhn): process of heat transfer in gases and liquids (p. 344)

convection current: movement of gases or liquids caused by differences in density (p. 344)

convex lens: lens that curves outward (p. 410)

corrosion: chemical change in a metal (p. 220)

covalent bond: bond formed when atoms share electrons (p. 92)

crest: high point of a transverse wave (p. 360)

D

data (DAYT-uh): information (p. 3)

decibel: unit used to measure the intensity or loudness of a sound (p. 384)

decomposition (dee-kahm-puh-ZIH-shuhn) **reaction:** reaction in which a complex substance is broken down into two or more simpler substances (p. 178)

degree Celsius (SEL-see-uhs): metric unit of temperature (p. 6)

density (DEHN-suh-tee): mass per unit volume (p. 34)

diatomic molecule: molecule made up of only two atoms (p. 158)

diffuse reflection: reflection that forms a fuzzy image (p. 416)

dilute solution: solution containing a small amount of solute compared with the amount of solvent present (p. 112)

direct current: current in which electrons always flow in the same direction (p. 436)

displacement (dihs-PLAYS-muhnt): the pushing aside of a volume of water, or any fluid, by an object (p. 40)

dissolve: go into solution (p. 104)

distillation (dihs-tuh-LAY-shuhn): process of evaporating a liquid and then condensing the gas back into a liquid (p. 118)

Doppler effect: apparent change in the frequency of waves (p. 392)

double-replacement reaction: reaction in which elements from two different compounds replace each other, forming two new compounds (p. 182)

ductile (DUK-tuhl): able to be drawn into thin wires (p. 68)

ear: sense organ that detects sound (p. 394)

eardrum: thin sheet of tissue that vibrates when sound waves strike it (p. 394)

echo: reflected sound waves (p. 380)

efficiency (eh-FIHSH-uhn-see): ratio of work output to work input (p. 314)

effort force: force applied to a machine (p. 312)

electric circuit: path that an electric current follows (p. 438)

electric current: flow of electric charge through a conductor (p. 436)

electric motor: device that changes electrical energy into mechanical energy (p. 468)

electrochemical cell: device that changes chemical energy into electrical energy (p. 432)

electrode: negative or positive pole of an electrochemical cell (p. 432)

electrolysis (ee-lehk-TRAHL-ih-sihs): process by which a substance is decomposed using an electric current (p. 178)

electrolyte (ee-LEHK-troh-lyt): substance that conducts an electric current when it is dissolved in water (p. 204, 432)

electromagnet: temporary magnet made by wrapping a current-carrying wire around a metal core (p. 464)

electromagnetic induction: process by which an electric current is produced by moving a wire in a magnetic field (p. 462)

electromagnetic (ee-lehk-troh-mag-NEHT-ihk) **spectrum:** range of electromagnetic waves (p. 400)

electromagnetic wave: wave that transfers energy through empty space (p. 358)

electromagnetism: relationship between electricity and magnetism (p. 462)

electromotive force (EMF): force that makes electrons move (p. 442)

electron: atomic particle with a negative charge (p. 56); atomic particle with a negative electrical charge (p. 428)

electroplating (ee-LEHK-troh-playt-ing): use of an electric current to plate one metal with another metal (p. 224)

element (EHL-uh-muhnt): substance that cannot be chemically broken down into simpler substances (pp. 52, 80)

emulsion (ee-MUL-shuhn): suspension of two liquids (p. 134)

energy: ability to make something happen (p. 292)

energy level: place in an electron cloud where an electron is most likely to be found (p. 62)

evaporation (ee-vap-uh-RAY-shuhn): change from a liquid to a gas at the surface of the liquid (pp. 22, 118, 338)

eye: sense organ that detects light (p. 412)

fiber optics: use of optical fibers (p. 420)

filtration: separation of particles in a suspension by passing the suspension through filter paper or some other porous material (p. 132)

force: a push or a pull (p. 246)

formula mass: sum of the mass numbers of all the atoms in a molecule or ions in an ionic compound (p. 160)

freezing: change from a liquid to a solid (p. 22)

freezing point: temperature at which a liquid changes to a solid (pp. 114, 336)

freezing point depression: lowering the freezing point of a liquid solvent by adding solute (p. 114)

frequency (FREE-kwuhn-see): number of complete waves passing a point in a given time (p. 362)

friction: force that opposes the motion of an object (p. 254)

fulcrum (FOOL-kruhm): fixed point around which a lever pivots or turns (p. 316)

fundamental (fun-duh-MEHN-tuhl) **tone:** lowest-pitched sound produced when a whole string vibrates (p. 390)

fuse: thin piece of metal that melts and breaks a circuit if too much current is flowing (p. 446)

G

gas: state of matter that has no definite shape or volume (p. 20)

generator: device that changes mechanical energy into electrical energy (p. 472)

gravity: force of attraction between all objects in the universe (p. 248)

group: vertical column of elements in the periodic table (p. 64)

H

halogens: elements that make up Group 17 in the periodic table (p. 70)

hearing: one of the five human senses (p. 394)

heat: total kinetic energy of all the particles in a sample of matter (p. 332)

hertz (HURTS): unit used to measure the frequency of a wave (p. 362)

homogenization (huh-mahj-uh-nih-ZAY-shuhn): formation of a permanent emulsion (p. 134)

hydrometer (hy-DRAHM-uht-uhr): device used to measure specific gravity (p. 38)

hydroxyl (hy-DRAHKS-ihl) **ion:** negative ion made up of one atom of hydrogen and one atom of oxygen (p. 192)

hypothesis (hy-PAHTH-uh-sis): suggested solution to a problem (p. 10)

I

ideal mechanical advantage: mechanical advantage a machine should have (p. 312)

illuminated (ih-LOO-muh-nayt-uhd) **object:** object that reflects light (p. 406)

image: picture formed by the eye (p. 412)

incident wave: wave that strikes a barrier (p. 366)

inclined plane: slanted surface, or ramp (p. 322)

indicator (IHN-dih-kayt-uhr): substance that changes color in an acid or a base (p. 194)

inertia (ihn-UR-shuh): tendency of an object to stay at rest or in motion (p. 280)

infrasonic (ihn-fruh-SAHN-ihk): sound below 20 Hz frequency (p. 386)

insoluble (ihn-SAHL-yoo-buhl): not able to dissolve (p. 106)

insulator: substance that does not conduct heat easily (p. 340); material that prevents electric charges from flowing through it easily (p. 434)

intensity: amount of energy in a sound wave (p. 384)

ion (EYE-uhn): atom with an electrical charge (p. 90)

ionic bond: bond formed between atoms that have gained or lost electrons (p. 90)

ionization (eye-uh-nih-ZAY-shuhn): formation of ions (p. 204)

isotope (EYE-suh-tohp): atom of an element with the same number of protons as the other atoms but a different number of neutrons (p. 72)

J

joule (JOOL): metric unit of work; equal to 1 N-m (newton-meter) (p. 302)

K

kinetic (kih-NEHT-ihk) **energy:** energy of motion (p. 292)

L

laser: device that produces a powerful beam of light (p. 420)

law of conservation of energy: energy cannot be made or destroyed but only changed in form (p. 296)

law of conservation of matter: matter cannot be created or destroyed by a chemical change (p. 168)

law of conservation of momentum: total momentum of any system always remains the same (p. 276)

lens: transparent material that bends light (p. 410)

lever (LEHV-uhr): bar that is free to turn around a fixed point (p. 316)

light: form of electromagnetic energy made up of streams of photons (p. 402)

lipids: fats and oils (p. 96)

liquid: state of matter with a definite volume but no definite shape (p. 20)

liter (LEE-tuhr): basic metric unit of volume (p. 4)

longitudinal (lahn-juh-TOOD-uhn-uhl) **wave:** wave in which the particles of the medium move back and forth in the direction of the wave motion (pp. 360, 380)

lubricants (LOO-brih-kuhnts): substances that reduce friction (p. 256)

luminous (LOO-muh-nuhs) **object:** object that gives off its own light (p. 406)

luster (LUS-tuhr): way a material reflects light (pp. 68, 230)

M

machine: device that makes work easier (p. 312)

magnetic domain: groups of atoms whose magnetic fields are all lined up in the same direction (p. 456)

magnetic field: area around a magnet where magnetic forces act (p. 456)

magnetic induction: process by which a material can be made into a magnet (p. 458)

magnetic lines of force: lines that show the shape of a magnetic field (p. 456)

magnetism: force of attraction or repulsion (p. 454)

magnetosphere (mag-NEET-oh-sfeer): region of Earth's magnetic field (p. 460)

malleable (MAL-ee-uh-buhl): able to be hammered into different shapes (p. 68)

mass: amount of matter in an object (p. 4)

mass number: number of protons and neutrons in the nucleus of an atom (p. 60)

matter: anything that has mass and takes up space (p. 18)

mechanical advantage: number of times a machine multiplies the effort force (p. 312)

mechanical wave: wave that transfers energy through matter (p. 358)

medium: material through which mechanical waves can travel (pp. 358, 380)

melting: change from a solid to a liquid (p. 22)

melting point: temperature at which a solid changes to a liquid (p. 336)

meniscus (muh-NIHS-kuhs): curved surface of a liquid in a graduated cylinder (p. 4)

metal: element that has the property of shiny luster, ductility, and malleability (p. 68)

metalloid: element that has properties of both metals and nonmetals (p. 232)

meter (MEET-uhr): basic SI and metric unit of length (p. 4)

mixture: two or more substances that have been physically combined (p. 80)

molecule: smallest part of a substance that has all the properties of that substance (p. 82)

momentum: property of all moving objects (p. 276)

motion: change in position relative to some fixed object or place (p. 272)

music: sounds combining a pleasing quality, melody, harmony, and rhythm (p. 390)

N

neutral: neither acidic nor basic (p. 196)

neutralization (noo-truh-lih-ZAY-shuhn): reaction between an acid and a base to produce a salt and water (p. 202)

neutron: particle that has no charge (pp. 56, 428)

newton: SI unit of force (pp. 44, 252, 282)

noble gases: elements that make up Group 18 in the periodic table (p. 70)

noise: unpleasant sounds with irregular patterns of vibration (p. 390)

nonelectrolyte: substance that will not conduct an electric current when it is dissolved in water (p. 204)

nonmetal: element that has the property of dull luster and is not ductile and not malleable (pp. 68, 230)

normal: line at right angles to a barrier (p. 366)

nuclear energy: energy stored in the nucleus of the atom and released during a nuclear reaction (p. 238)

nuclear fission: reaction in which a large nucleus is split into smaller nuclei and energy is released (p. 238)

nuclear fusion: reaction in which two smaller nuclei are joined to form a larger nucleus (p. 238)

492

nucleic acids: compounds made up of carbon, oxygen, hydrogen, nitrogen, and phosphorus (p. 96)

nucleus: center, or core, of an atom (p. 56)

O

ohm: unit used to measure resistance (p. 442)

Ohm's law: current in a wire is equal to the voltage divided by the resistance (p. 444)

opaque (oh-PAYK): material that blocks light (p. 406)

ore: rock or mineral from which a useful metal can be removed (p. 210)

organic chemistry: study of organic compounds (p. 94)

organic compound: compound containing carbon (p. 94)

overtone: sound that has a higher pitch than the fundamental tone (p. 390)

oxidation (ahk-sih-DAY-shuhn): chemical change in which electrons are lost (p. 174)

oxidation number: number of electrons an atom gains, loses, or shares when it forms a chemical bond (p. 150)

P

parallel circuit: circuit in which electric current can follow more than one path (p. 440)

period: horizontal row of elements in the periodic table (p. 64)

periodic (pihr-ee-AHD-ihk): repeating pattern (p. 64)

pH scale: measure of the concentration of hydrogen ions in a solution (p. 196)

photon (FOH-tahn): tiny bundle of energy (p. 402)

photosynthesis (foht-oh-SIHN-thuh-sihs): process by which plants use energy from the Sun to make food (p. 408)

physical change: change that does not produce new substances (p. 26)

physics: branch of science that deals with energy and matter and how they interact (p. 16)

pitch: how high or low a sound is (p. 386)

plane mirror: smooth surface that reflects light and forms images (p. 416)

plasma: state of matter that exists under the conditions of high temperature and pressure (p. 20)

polar molecule: molecule in which one end has a positive charge and the other end has a negative charge (p. 108)

pole: end of a magnet (p. 454)

pollution (puh-LOO-shuhn): release of harmful substances into the environment (p. 140)

polyatomic (pahl-ee-uh-TAHM-ihk) **ion:** group of atoms that acts as a charged atom, or ion, when combining with other atoms (p. 154)

polymers: large molecules that are formed by many smaller molecules (p. 94)

potable (POHT-uh-buhl) **water:** water that is safe to drink (p. 140)

potential (puh-TEHN-shuhl) **energy:** stored energy (p. 292)

power: amount of work done per unit of time (p. 304)

precipitate (pree-SIHP-uh-tayt): solid that settles to the bottom of a mixture (p. 182)

pressure: force per unit of area (p. 260)

prism (PRIZ-uhm): triangular and transparent piece of glass that breaks up white light into a band of colors (p. 418)

product: substance that is formed in a chemical reaction (p. 168)

properties (PRAHP-uhr-teez): characteristics used to describe an object (p. 18)

proteins: compounds used to build and repair body tissues (p. 96)

proton: atomic particle with a positive charge (pp. 56, 428)

pulley: rope wrapped around a wheel (p. 318)

R

radiation (ray-dee-AY-shuhn): energy and particles released from the nucleus of a radioactive element (p. 234); transfer of heat through space (p. 346)

radioactive element: unstable element whose nucleus breaks down (p. 234)

radioisotope: isotope that releases radiation (p. 234)

rarefaction (rer-uh-FAK-shuhn): part of a medium where the particles are far apart (p. 360)

ray: straight line that shows the direction of light (p. 402)

reactant: substance that is changed in a chemical reaction (p. 168)

reaction force: force acting in the opposite direction (p. 284)

real image: image that can be projected onto a screen (p. 410)

reduction (rih-DUK-shuhn): chemical change in which electrons are gained (p. 174); process of removing oxygen from an ore (p. 212)

reflected wave: wave that bounces off a barrier (p. 366)

reflection: bouncing back of a wave after striking a barrier (p. 366)

refraction: bending of a wave as it moves from one medium to another (p. 368); separation of white light into its component colors (p. 418)

regular reflection: reflection that forms a clear image (p. 416)

resistance: opposition to the flow of electric charges (p. 442)

resistance force: force that opposes the effort force (p. 312)

roasting: process in which an ore is heated in air to produce an oxide (p. 212)

S

salt: substance formed from the negative ion of an acid and the positive ion of a base (p. 202)

saturated solution: solution containing all the solute it can hold at a given temperature (p. 112)

scientific method: series of steps that can serve as a guide to solving problems or answering questions (p. 9)

series circuit: circuit in which electric current follows only one path (p. 438)

sight: one of the five human senses (p. 412)

single-replacement reaction: reaction in which one element replaces another element in a compound (p. 180)

solid: state of matter with a definite shape and volume (p. 20)

solubility: maximum amount of a substance that will dissolve in a given quantity of a solvent at a given temperature (p. 106)

soluble (SAHL-yoo-buhl): able to dissolve (p. 106)

solute (SAHL-yoot): substance that is dissolved in a solvent (p. 106)

solution: mixture in which the particles of one substance are evenly mixed with the particles of another substance (p. 104)

solvent: substance in which a solute dissolves (p. 106)

sonic boom: loud noise caused by breaking the sound barrier (p. 382)

sound: form of energy that travels as waves (p. 376)

specialization (spehsh-uh-lih-ZAY-shuhn): studying or working in one area of a subject (p. 16)

specific (spuh-SIF-ik) **gravity:** density of a substance compared with the density of water (p. 38)

specific heat: amount of heat needed to raise the temperature of 1 g of a substance 1°C (p. 348)

speed: distance traveled per unit of time (p. 272); distance a wave travels in one unit of time (p. 362)

state of matter: any of the four physical forms of matter (p. 20)

static electricity: buildup of electric charges on an object (p. 428)

structural formula: molecular model that uses straight lines to indicate bonds (p. 94)

sublimation: change from a solid directly to a gas (p. 22)

subscript: number written to the lower right of a chemical symbol in a chemical formula (p. 148)

substance: any element or compound (p. 80)

supersaturated solution: solution containing more solute than it can normally hold at a given temperature (p. 112)

supersonic: faster than the speed of sound for that medium (p. 382)

suspension (suh-SPEHN-shuhn): mixture of two materials or more that separate on standing (p. 130)

synthesis (SIHN-thuh-sihs) **reaction:** reaction in which substances combine to form a more complex substance (p. 176)

T

temperature: measure of the amount of heat energy something contains (p. 4); measure of the average kinetic energy of the particles in a sample of matter (p. 334)

terminal velocity: speed at which air resistance and gravity acting on a falling object are equal (p. 258)

theory: set of hypotheses that have been supported by testing over and over again (p. 10)

thermal (THUR-muhl) **expansion:** expansion of a substance caused by heating (p. 350)

thermal pollution: damage that occurs when waste heat enters the environment (p. 296)

timbre (TAM-buhr): sound quality (p. 390)

total internal reflection: occurs when light is repeatedly reflected within a given material (p. 420)

transformer: device in which alternating current in one coil of wire induces a current in a second coil of wire (p. 466)

translucent (trans-LOO-suhnt): material that transmits some light (p. 406)

transparent (trans-PEHR-uhnt): material that transmits light easily (p. 406)

transverse (trans-VURS) **wave:** wave in which the particles of the medium move up and down at right angles to the direction of the wave motion (pp. 360, 404)

trough (TRAWF): low point of a transverse wave (p. 360)

U

ultrasonic (uhl-truh-SAHN-ihk): sound above 20,000 Hz frequency (p. 386)

unbalanced forces: forces that cause a change in the motion of an object (p. 246)

unit (YOO-nit): amount used to measure something (p. 4)

unsaturated solution: solution containing less solute than it can hold at a given temperature (p. 112)

V

vacuum: space where no matter exists (pp. 258, 346)

valence electron: electron in the outermost energy level of an atom (pp. 90, 150)

velocity (vuh-LAHS-uh-tee): speed and direction (p. 274)

vibration: rapid back-and-forth movement (p. 376)

virtual image: image that cannot be projected onto a screen (p. 410)

visible spectrum: seven colors that make up white light (p. 400)

volt: unit used to measure voltage (p. 442)

voltage: energy available to move charges through a conductor (p. 442)

volume: amount of space something takes up (p. 4)

W

watt: SI unit of power; equal to 1 J/s (p. 304)

wavelength: distance between two neighboring crests or troughs or two compressions or rarefactions (p. 362)

wave: disturbance that transfers energy from place to place (p. 358)

weight: measure of the pull of gravity on a sample of matter (p. 5)

wheel and axle: two different-sized wheels that turn together around the same point (p. 312)

work: force exerted through a distance (p. 300)

work input: work done on a machine (p. 314)

work output: work done by a machine (p. 314)

Index

Photo Credits

Photography Credits: All photographs are by tne Pearson Learning Group (PLG), John Serafin for PLG, and David Mager for PLG, except as noted below.

Cover: Physical Science — Roller Coaster © Christian Michaels/Getty Images/FPG. Rocket Launch © StockTrek/Getty Images.

Table of contents: i Stock Trek/PhotoDisc, Inc.; v t Stock Trek/PhotoDisc, Inc.; v b Charles D. Winters/ Photo Researchers, Inc.; vi t Stock Trek/PhotoDisc, Inc.; vi b Traudel Sachs/Phototake; vii Stock Trek/ PhotoDisc, Inc.; viii t Stock Trek/PhotoDisc, Inc.; viii b Richard Megna/Fundamental Photographs; ix t Stock Trek/PhotoDisc, Inc.; x t Stock Trek/PhotoDisc, Inc.; x b Tom Twomey/Check Six; xi t Stock Trek/ PhotoDisc, Inc.; xi b Peter Hayman/British Museum/ Dorling Kindersley Limited; xii t Stock Trek/PhotoDisc, Inc.; xii b S. Dalton, OSF/Animals Animals/Earth Scenes; xiii t Stock Trek/PhotoDisc, Inc.; xiii b Philippe Plail/Photo Researchers, Inc.; xiv t Stock Trek/ PhotoDisc, Inc.; xiv b Scott Camazine/Photo Researchers, Inc.; xv Stock Trek/PhotoDisc, Inc.; xvi Stock Trek/PhotoDisc, Inc.; xvii Stock Trek/PhotoDisc, Inc.; xviii Stock Trek/PhotoDisc, Inc.

Frontmatter: P001 bl CityNet Telecom; P001 bm John Sohlden/Visuals Unlimited, Inc.; P001 tr Gregg Otto/Visuals Unlimited, Inc.; P001 br Stock Trek/ PhotoDisc, Inc.; P002 l Bernd Wittich/Visuals Unlimited, Inc.; P002 m Charles O'Rear/Corbis; P003 Stock Trek/ PhotoDisc, Inc.; P005 r Stock Trek/PhotoDisc, Inc.; P007 r Stock Trek/PhotoDisc, Inc.; P009 mr Larry Mulvehill/Photo Researchers, Inc.; P009 t Jay Freis/ Image Bank; P009 tr Ed Young/Corbis; P009 r Stock Trek/PhotoDisc, Inc.; P011 r Stock Trek/PhotoDisc, Inc.; P013 r Stock Trek/PhotoDisc, Inc.

Chapter 1: P015 Gerald & Buff Corsi/Visuals Unlimited, Inc.; P016 col. 1 Ed Young/Corbis; P016 col. 2 Science VU/Visuals Unlimited, Inc.; P016 col. 3 Gregg Otto/Visuals Unlimited, Inc.; P016 col. 4 John Sohlden/Visuals Unlimited, Inc.; P017 Bill Horsman/ Stock, Boston Inc.; P018 b Margaret Durrance/ Photo Researchers, Inc.; P019 Bettmann Archive/ Corbis; P022 Brian Leng/Corbis; P023 Charles D. Winters/Photo Researchers, Inc.; P026 Kit Kittle/Corbis; P030 Gerald & Buff Corsi/Visuals Unlimited, Inc.; P031 Gerald & Buff Corsi/Visuals Unlimited, Inc.; P032 Gerald & Buff Corsi/Visuals Unlimited, Inc.

Chapter 2: P033 David Wrobel/Visuals Unlimited, Inc.; P034 t Bill Webster/Visuals Unlimited, Inc.; P035 tl Bernd Wittich/Visuals Unlimited, Inc.; P035 tr Charles O'Rear/Corbis; P038 Becton Dickinson and Company; P039 Runk/Schoenberger/Grant Heilman Photography, Inc.; P040 b Smithsonian Institution; P048 David Wrobel/Visuals Unlimited, Inc.; P049 David Wrobel/Visuals Unlimited, Inc.; P050 David Wrobel/Visuals Unlimited, Inc.

Chapter 3: P051 Charles O'Rear/Corbis; P052 l Bill Beatty/Visuals Unlimited, Inc.; P052 m Runk/ Schoenberger/Grant Heilman Photography, Inc.; P052 r Charles D. Winters/Photo Researchers, Inc.; P053 Hulton/Getty Images; P054 The Granger Collection; P055 b Fermilab Visual Media Services; P055 t IBM/Phototake; P059 Bettmann Archive/Corbis; P061 Novosti/Science Photo Library/Photo Researchers, Inc.; P068 bl The Image Works; P068 br Barbara Stitzer/Photo Edit; P068 t A. J. Copley/Visuals Unlimited, Inc.; P071 b E. R. Degginger/Color Pic, Inc.; P071 t Esbin-Anderson/Omni-Photo Communications; P073 l Runk/Schoenberger/ Grant Heilman Photography, Inc.; P073 r Runk/Schoenberger/ Grant Heilman Photography, Inc.; P076 Charles O'Rear/Corbis; P077 Charles O'Rear/Corbis; P078 Charles O'Rear/Corbis

Chapter 4: P079 Jay Dorin/Omni-Photo Communications; P081 Art Resource; P082 l E. R. Degginger/Color Pic, Inc.; P082 r Charles D. Winters/ Photo Researchers, Inc.; P085 Ed Young/Corbis; P087 b Ken Lucas/Visuals Unlimited, Inc.; P087 t Grace Davies/Omni-Photo Communications; P091 l Traudel Sachs/Phototake; P091 r Science VU Kodak/ Visuals Unlimited, Inc.; P096 b Ken Karp/Omni-Photo Communications; P096 t Rachel Epstein/Stuart Kenter Associates; P098 E. F. Anderson/Visuals Unlimited, Inc.; P099 bl Joe McDonald/Corbis; P099 br Gregory G. Dimijian/Photo Researchers, Inc.; P099 t Ken Lucas/Visuals Unlimited, Inc.; P100 Jay Dorin/Omni-Photo Communications; P101 Jay Dorin/Omni-Photo Communications; P102 Jay Dorin/Omni-Photo Communications

Chapter 5: P103 Bob Barbour/Minden Pictures; P105 Courtesy of Dr. Sherman K. W. Fung; P106 l Martyn F. Chillmaid/Science Photo Library/Photo Researchers, Inc.; P106 r Martyn F. Chillmaid/Science Photo Library/Photo Researchers, Inc.; P107 b Martin Bond/Science Photo Library/Photo Researchers, Inc.; P107 t Bruce Gaylord/Visuals Unlimited, Inc.; P115 Flip Nicklin/Minden Pictures; P118 Mike Dunning/ Dorling Kindersley Limited; P122 b Dorling Kindersley Limited; P122 m Dorling Kindersley Limited; P122 t Dorling Kindersley Limited; P123 t Richard J. Green/ Photo Researchers, Inc.; P124 b E. R. Degginger/ Animals Animals/Earth Scenes; P124 b inset A. J. Copley/Visuals Unlimited, Inc.; P124 t Pawel Kumelowski/Omni-Photo Communications; P124 t inset Ross Frid/Visuals Unlimited, Inc.; P125 b John Gerlach/Visuals Unlimited, Inc.; P125 b inset George D. Lepp/Photo Researchers, Inc.; P125 t Deborah Davis/PhotoEdit, Inc.; P125 t inset Andrew Syred/ Science Photo Library/Photo Researchers, Inc.; P126 Bob Barbour/Minden Pictures; P127 Bob Barbour/ Minden Pictures; P128 Bob Barbour/Minden Pictures

Chapter 6: P129 Robert Garvey/Corbis; P131 t Bruce Davidson/Animals Animals/Earth Scenes; P133 Science VU/Visuals Unlimited, Inc.; P134 Grant Heilman/Grant Heilman Photography, Inc.; P136 col. 1 b Charles D. Winters/Photo Researchers, Inc.; P136 col. 1 t James L. Amos/Peter Arnold, Inc.; P136 col. 2 b Link/Visuals Unlimited, Inc.; P136 col. 2 t Barrie Fanton/Omni-Photo Communications; P136 col. 3 b P. Grecian/Visuals Unlimited, Inc.; P136 col. 3 t Leo Keeler/Animals Animals/Earth Scenes; P138 Photodisc, Inc.; P139 b inset Silver Burdett Ginn; P139 bl PhotoDisc, Inc.; P139 ml Phillip Hayson/ Photo Researchers, Inc.; P139 t John A. Rizzo/ Photodisc, Inc.; P139 tr inset Corbis Digital Stock; P141 t Francis Lepine/Animals Animals/Earth Scenes; P144 Robert Garvey/Corbis; P145 Robert Garvey/Corbis; P146 Robert Garvey/Corbis

Chapter 7: P147 Liba Taylor/Corbis; P152 Richard Megna/Fundamental Photographs; P153 Corbis; P155 Argus Fotoarchiv/Peter Arnold, Inc.; P159 Reuters NewMedia Inc./Corbis; P162 l Amos Zezmer/Omni-Photo Communications; P162 r PhotoDisc, Inc.; P163 l Bettmann/Corbis; P163 r Michael Andrews/Animals Animals/Earth Scenes; P164 Liba Taylor/Corbis; P165 Liba Taylor/Corbis; P166 Liba Taylor/Corbis

Chapter 8: P167 Bill Ross/Corbis; P174 John Carnemolla/Corbis; P175 Russell Thompson/Omni-Photo Communications; P177 Sovfoto/Eastfoto/ Picturequest; P178 Charles D. Winters/Photo Researchers, Inc.; P179 Richard Olivier/Corbis; P181 t Charles D. Winters/Photo Researchers, Inc.; P182 l Richard Megna/Fundamental Photographs; P182 r Richard Megna/Fundamental Photographs; P184 Christian Jeanthon; P185 b D. Foster, Woods Hole Oceanographic Institution/Science VU/Visuals Unlimited; P185 t Ken MacDonald/Science Photo Library/Photo Researchers, Inc.; P186 Bill Ross/ Corbis; P187 Bill Ross/Corbis; P188 b Charles D. Winters/Photo Researchers, Inc.; P188 t Bill Ross/Corbis

Chapter 9: P189 Richard Megna/Fundamental Photographs; P190 Jodi Jacobson/Peter Arnold, Inc.; P192 Corbis; P195 t Steven David Miller/Animals Animals/Earth Scenes; P200 Professors P.M. Motta & S. Correr/Science Photo Library/Photo Researchers, Inc.; P203 Paul A. Souders/Corbis; P206 Richard Megna/Fundamental Photographs; P207 Richard Megna/Fundamental Photographs; P208 Richard Megna/Fundamental Photographs

Chapter 10: P209 Jim Wark/Peter Arnold, Inc.; P210 col. 1 b Jodi Jacobson/Peter Arnold, Inc.; P210 col. 1 t E. R. Degginger/Animals Animals/Earth Scenes; P210 col. 2 b Breck P. Kent/Animals Animals/ Earth Scenes; P210 col. 2 t Breck P. Kent/Animals Animals/Earth Scenes; P210 col. 3 b Albert Copley/ Visuals Unlimited, Inc.; P210 col. 3 t John D. Cunningham/Visuals Unlimited, Inc.; P211 Richard A. Cooke/Corbis; P212 E. R. Degginger/Color Pic, Inc.; P213 Jim Wark/Peter Arnold, Inc.; P215 b Fritz Prenzel/Animals Animals/Earth Scenes; P215 inset Christopher Cormack/Corbis; P215 t George Hall/ Corbis; P216-17 Jodi Jacobson/Peter Arnold, Inc.; P219 Milepost 92 1/2/Corbis; P220 l Jana R. Jirak/ Visuals Unlimited, Inc.; P220 r Galen Rowell/Corbis; P224 br Stephen Frisch/Stock, Boston Inc.; P224 tl Dick Keen/Visuals Unlimited, Inc.; P224 tr Dorling Kindersley Limited; P226 Jim Wark/Peter Arnold, Inc.; P227 Jim Wark/Peter Arnold, Inc.; P228 t Jim Wark/ Peter Arnold, Inc.; P228 b Dorling Kindersley Limited

Chapter 11: P229 NASA; P233 Science/VU/TRW/ Visuals Unlimited, Inc.; P235 Larry Mulvehill/Photo Researchers, Inc.; P236 Bruce Coleman/Bruce Coleman, Inc.; P237 bl Renee Lynn/Photo Researchers, Inc.; P237 inset Mark Stouffer/Animals Animals/Earth Scenes; P237 tl Reuters NewMedia, Inc./Corbis; P237 tr Kenneth Garrett; P242 NASA; P243 NASA; P244 NASA

Chapter 12: P245 Grantpix/Photo Researchers, Inc.; P248 J-L Charmet/Science Photo Library/Photo Researchers, Inc.; P249 Tom Twomey/Check Six; P252 Larry Lefever/Grant Heilman Photography, Inc.; P254 Patrick Behar/Photo Researchers, Inc.; P257 b Bruce M. Wellman/Stock, Boston Inc.; P257 t Bob Daemmrich Photos/Stock, Boston Inc.; P259 John Elk, III/Bruce Coleman, Inc.; P264 Eric Neurath/Stock, Boston Inc.; P268 Grantpix/Photo Researchers, Inc.; P269 Grantpix/Photo Researchers, Inc.; P270 Grantpix/Photo Researchers, Inc.

Chapter 13: P271 E. R. Degginger/Animals Animals/Earth Scenes; P272 Leonard Lessin/Peter Arnold, Inc.; P274 Fotopic/Omni-Photo Communications; P276 Peter Sherrard/FPG; P277 Tim Fitzharris/Minden Pictures; P278 Johnny Cann Doubling for Chuck Norris on Walker Texas Ranger. Photo by Roy Empfield, property of Action P.A.C. Stunts, L.L.C./Action Pac; P279 b Insurance Institute for Highway Safety; P279 m Energy Absorption Systems, Inc.; P279 t Science VU/Visuals Unlimited, Inc.; P280 b Bettmann/Corbis; P281 George & Judy Manna/Photo Researchers, Inc.; P283 The Granger Collection, New York/The Granger Collection; P284 l PhotoDisc, Inc./Photodisc; P284 r Kevin Morris/Getty Images; P285 Mike Phillips/Peter Arnold, Inc.; P288 E. R. Degginger/Animals Animals/Earth Scenes; P289 E. R. Degginger/Animals Animals/Earth Scenes; P290 E. R. Degginger/Animals Animals/Earth Scenes

Chapter 14: P291 Neil Rabinowitz/Corbis; P292 inset Michael Matisse/PhotoDisc, Inc.; P292 l Walter H. Hodge/Peter Arnold, Inc.; P292 r Bill Ross/Corbis; P293 b C. C. Lockwood/Animals Animals/Earth Scenes; P293 t AP/Wide World Photos; P294 Johnny Johnson/Animals Animals/Earth Scenes; P295 Will & Deni McIntyre/Photo Researchers, Inc.; P296 Gary S. Settles/Photo Researchers, Inc.; P297 NOAO/Science Photo Library/Photo Researchers, Inc.; P297 inset LOC/Science Source/Photo Researchers, Inc.; P298 t Simon Fraser/Science Photo Library/Photo Researchers, Inc.; P298-299 b Amos Zezmer/ Omni-Photo Communications; P299 inset Billie Johnson/United States Corps. of Engineers, Washington; P299 tl Adam Jones/Photo Researchers, Inc.; P299 tr David R. Frazier Photolibrary/Photo Researchers, Inc.; P301 AFP/Corbis; P304 bl Richard Kolar/Animals Animals/Earth Scenes; P304 br Science VU/Visuals Unlimited, Inc.; P304 tl Michael Habicht/ Animals Animals/Earth Scenes; P308 Neil Rabinowitz/ Corbis; P309 Neil Rabinowitz/Corbis; P310 Neil Rabinowitz/Corbis

Chapter 15: P311 Paolo Koch/Photo Researchers, Inc.; P312 Geostock/Photodisc; P314 E. R. Degginger/Color Pic, Inc.; P315 AFP/Corbis; P322 b Esbin/Anderson/Omni-Photo Communications; P322 t Michael Thompson/Animals Animals/Earth Scenes; P324 bl Dorling Kindersley Limited; P324 inset Peter Hayman/British Museum/Dorling Kindersley Limited; P324 t British Museum/Dorling Kindersley Limited; P324-325 Geoff Brightling/Dorling Kindersley Limited; P325 t Daniel Moignot, P.L.J. Gallimard Jeunesse-Larousse/Dorling Kindersley Limited; P326 t Jodi Jacobson/Peter Arnold, Inc.; P327 b CityNet Telecom; P327 t Robin Smith/Getty Images; P328 Paolo Koch/Photo Researchers, Inc.; P329 Paolo Koch/Photo Researchers, Inc.; P330 Paolo Koch/Photo Researchers, Inc.

Chapter 16: P331 Michael Fairchild/Peter Arnold, Inc.; P333 l Science VU/Visuals Unlimited, Inc.; P333 r E. R. Degginger/Color Pic, Inc.; P334 Mark E. Gibson/Visuals Unlimited, Inc.; P335 The Granger Collection, New York; P337 b Jay Freis/Image Bank; P337 t Jerome Wexler/Visuals Unlimited, Inc.; P340 b Phil Degginger/Color Pic, Inc.; P341 b Phil Degginger/Color Pic, Inc.; P341 t Phil Degginger/ Color Pic, Inc.; P342 Johnny Johnson/DRK Photo; P346 Phil Degginger/Color Pic, Inc.; P347 t Pat Armstrong/Visuals Unlimited, Inc.; P350 l Richard Choy/Peter Arnold, Inc.; P350 r E. R. Degginger/ Color Pic, Inc.; P352 b Rod Planck/Photo Researchers, Inc.; P352 t Fritz Polking/Visuals Unlimited, Inc.; P353 bl A. & M. Shah/Animals Animals/Earth Scenes; P353 br Norbert Wu/Peter Arnold, Inc.; P353 t Dan Guravich/Photo Researchers, Inc.; P354 Michael Fairchild/Peter Arnold, Inc.; P355 Michael Fairchild/Peter Arnold, Inc.; P356 Michael Fairchild/Peter Arnold, Inc.

Chapter 17: P357 George Bernard/Animals Animals/Earth Scenes; P358 l Tony Arruza/Corbis; P358 r Nina Leen/Time Life Syndication; P363 Hulton-Deutsch Collection/Corbis; P366 Phil Degginger/Color Pic, Inc.; P370 inset Corbis; P370-371 bkgd Burstein Collection/Corbis; P371 inset l Ken M. Johns/Photo Researchers, Inc.; P371 inset m Courtesy Pacific Tsunami Museum; P371 inset r State of Hawaii, Department of Defense, Civil Defense Division; P372 George Bernard/Animals Animals/ Earth Scenes; P373 George Bernard/Animals Animals/ Earth Scenes; P374 George Bernard/Animals Animals/ Earth Scenes

Chapter 18: P375 E. R. Degginger/Color Pic, Inc.; P380 NASA/Omni-Photo Communications; P381 Robert Marien/Index Stock Imagery; P382 l Michael Fredericks, Jr./Animals Animals/Earth Scenes; P382 r Robert A. Hoover/NASA/Dryden Flight Center; P383 b Richard Neville/Check Six; P383 t Eric Risberg/AP Photo; P385 Robert Brenner/PhotoEdit, Inc.; P386 b Jack Parsons/Omni-Photo Communications; P386 t E. R. Degginger/Color Pic, Inc.; P387 Mark Newman/Photo Researchers, Inc.; P388 b Francois Gohier/Photo Researchers, Inc.; P388 t E. R. Degginger/Animals Animals/Earth Scenes; P389 bl William Lampas/Omni-Photo Communications; P389 br Bruna Stude/Omni-Photo Communications; P389 t S. Dalton, OSF/Animals Animals/Earth Scenes; P393 National Optical Astronomy Observatories/Coloured by Science Photo Library/Photo Researchers, Inc.; P395 AT&T Archives; P396 E. R. Degginger/Color Pic, Inc.; P397 E. R. Degginger/Color Pic, Inc.; P398 E. R. Degginger/Color Pic, Inc.

Chapter 19: P399 Tek Image/Science Photo Library/ Photo Researchers, Inc.; P405 Janis Christie/ PhotoDisc, Inc.; P409 David Julian/Phototake; P411 Robert Garvey/Corbis; P413 Alexander Tsiaras/ Science Course/Photo Researchers, Inc.; P416 l Jim Steinberg/Photo Researchers, Inc.; P416 r Jeremy Woodhouse/PhotoDisc, Inc.; P419 David M. Schleser/Nature's Images/Photo Researchers, Inc.; P420 Michael Rizza/Stock, Boston Inc.; P421 Philippe Plail/Photo Researchers, Inc.; P424 Tek Image/Science Photo Library/Photo Researchers, Inc.; P425 Tek Image/Science Photo Library/Photo Researchers, Inc.; P426 Tek Image/Science Photo Library/Photo Researchers, Inc.

Chapter 20: P427 Fotopic/Omni-Photo Communications; P433 Ecoscene/Corbis; P435 Bettmann/Corbis; P437 b Fritz Prenzel/Animals Animals/Earth Scenes; P437 t Richard T. Nowitz/ Photo Researchers, Inc.; P439 Science VU/ Honeywell/Visuals Unlimited, Inc.; P441 Rick Poley/ Visuals Unlimited, Inc.; P443 b Phil Degginger/ Color Pic, Inc.; P443 t E. R. Degginger/Color Pic, Inc.; P444 Richard Megna/Fundamental Photographs; P445 Grantpix/Photo Researchers, Inc.; P446 l Phil Degginger/Color Pic, Inc.; P446 m E. R. Degginger/ Color Pic, Inc.; P446 r Phil Degginger /Color Pic, Inc.; P447 GJLP/CNRI/Phototake; P448 inset b Bettmann/Corbis; P448 inset t Michael Freeman/ Corbis; P448-449 Getty Images/ Hulton Archive; P449 inset l Unknown/Con Edison of New York; P449 inset r Hulton-Deutsch Collection/Corbis; P450 Fotopic/Omni-Photo Communications; P451 Fotopic/Omni-Photo Communications; P452 Fotopic/Omni-Photo Communications

Chapter 21: P453 E. R. Degginger/Color Pic, Inc.; P454 Michael Newman/Photo Edit, Inc.; P455 Tony Craddock/Science Photo Library/Photo Researchers, Inc.; P456 b Biodisc/Visuals Unlimited, Inc.; P456 t Biodisc/Visuals Unlimited, Inc.; P457 Biodisc/Visuals Unlimited, Inc.; P458 E. R. Degginger/Color Pic, Inc.; P461 b Unknown/Hamblin Publishing Co., Inc.; P461 t NASA/Science Photo Library/Photo Researchers, Inc.; P463 National Portrait Gallery, Washington DC/ Art REsource; P465 Spencer Grant/Photoedit, Inc.; P467 Scott T. Smith/Corbis; P469 b Tony Freeman/ Photo Edit/Picturequest; P469 t Mark E. Gibson/ Visuals Unlimited, Inc.; P473 Jeff Greenberg/Omni-Photo Communications; P474 AP/Wide World Photos; P475 b Thomas Raupach/Woodfin Camp & Associates; P475 t Thomas Raupach/Woodfin Camp & Associates; P476 E. R. Degginger/Color Pic, Inc.; P477 E. R. Degginger/Color Pic, Inc.; P478 E. R. Degginger/Color Pic, Inc.; P479 Stock Trek/PhotoDisc, Inc.

Appendix: P479 Stock Trek/PhotoDisc, Inc.; P481 Stock Trek/PhotoDisc, Inc.; P483 Stock Trek/PhotoDisc, Inc.; P485 Stock Trek/PhotoDisc, Inc.; P487 Stock Trek/PhotoDisc, Inc.; P489 Stock Trek/PhotoDisc, Inc.

Index: P497 Stock Trek/PhotoDisc, Inc.